CAMBRIDGE BIOLOGICAL SERIES

FLOWERING PLANTS
AND
FERNS

A DICTIONARY
OF THE
FLOWERING PLANTS
AND
FERNS

BY

J. C. WILLIS

M.A., Sc.D., Hon. Sc.D. (Harvard), F.R.S.

EUROPEAN CORRESPONDENT, LATE DIRECTOR, BOTANIC GARDENS
RIO DE JANEIRO

SIXTH EDITION

REVISED

CAMBRIDGE:
AT THE UNIVERSITY PRESS
1951

PUBLISHED BY
THE SYNDICS OF THE CAMBRIDGE UNIVERSITY PRESS

London Office: Bentley House, N.W.1
American Branch: New York

Agents for Canada, India, and Pakistan: Macmillan

First Edition 1897
Second Edition 1904
Third Edition 1908
Reprinted 1914
Fourth Edition 1919
Fifth Edition 1925
Sixth Edition 1931
Reprinted 1948
1951

Printed in Great Britain at the University Press, Cambridge
(Brooke Crutchley, University Printer)

PREFACE

IN this edition the work is completely revised, and as far as possible brought up to date. The most noteworthy new feature is the incorporation of all the parts into one general dictionary, and the omission of Part I of previous editions. When first written this had certain advantages, as being one of the few presentations in English of the elementary facts and theories of ecology. But this advantage has long disappeared, and it seemed to me that the space would be better employed in increasing the number of genera dealt with. On consulting Sir David Prain and other botanists, I found that they agreed with this idea. By a slight addition to the total number of pages I have found it possible to include all the genera, and hope that in this way the usefulness of the work to botanists in general may be greatly increased. I have of course attempted no criticism of those included, but have tried to indicate, as far as space would permit, the genera from which they have been segregated in many cases, or to which they are united by the other of the two chief recent editors of the vegetable kingdom (Bentham-Hooker, Engler-Prantl). It is obviously impossible to do very much in this direction. As it stands, the book is convenient for use, but a very slight addition to the facts given for each genus would add a line to the entry and, as there are roughly some 20,000 entries, this would add 400 pages to the book, and make it unwieldy. The same remark applies to the geographical distribution, which could not in general be given in great detail.

Before criticising, again, the inclusion of many obsolete technical terms and synonyms, it must be remembered that some who use this book wish to use it in connection with floras now long published, and also that it is impossible to reset such a book all through for each edition, so that it is necessary to insert a little "padding" on practically every page.

* * * * * *

A book like this must obviously be a compilation, and I have to express my warmest thanks to Prof. A. Engler for permission to draw upon the vast mass of material contained in *Die Natürlichen Pflanzenfamilien.* Owing to the war I have had no opportunity of asking him to renew this permission, and I trust that he will understand as much. When an article, as is frequently the case with the grouping of the subfamilies within the family, is taken from the work mentioned, I have acknowledged the same by giving the name of the author. Otherwise I have in general drawn upon the book for the genera accepted by its authors, for the number of species (which has been brought roughly up to date by aid of the Supplements to the *Index Kewensis*), and for their geographical distribution.

The list of friends to whom I owe valuable suggestions, useful pieces of assistance, and the like, is very long, and I have no doubt that the following enumeration is incomplete, and must ask the pardon of those who do not figure in it, through some oversight on my part to note down their names at the moment the help was given. In the first place I wish to thank Sir David Prain and the staff at Kew, more especially Drs Hill, Stapf, and Rolfe, and Mr S. A. Skan, whose detailed knowledge of the library has been of the very greatest assistance in easing my labour. The writing of this edition has occupied very much time during the last five years, and I am particularly grateful to Prof. Seward, who placed at my disposal a table large enough to enable me to spread out 20 works of reference at once, and to Dr Moss and others of the Cambridge staff. The first two of the five years were spent in Rio de Janeiro and I am much indebted for help to my colleagues there, particularly the late Dr Alberto

Löfgren and Dr Achilles de Faria Lisbôa. I also owe many useful suggestions to my colleagues in other Botanic Gardens, *e.g.* Prof. O. Ames at Harvard, Prof. I. B. Balfour at Edinburgh, Prof. N. L. Britton at New York, Mr I. H. Burkill at Singapore, Prof. A. Engler at Berlin, Dr J. H. Maiden at Sydney, the late Dr H. H. W. Pearson at Cape Town, Dr Sargant at Jamaica Plain, and others. The late Dr E. A. N. Arber, and Mrs Arber, have laid me under very many obligations, and so have Sir Francis Darwin, Professors Bower, Farmer, Goebel, Goodale, Henry, Lang, Oliver, Scott, and Yapp, and Messrs Davie, Lock, Lynch, Riddle, Small, Smith, and many more. To my wife my obligations are unmeasured. Finally for the illustrations I have to thank Herr Engelmann for permission to copy some of the late Prof. Eichler's figures, and Dr Rendle for the use of some of those in his book on Classification.

J. C. WILLIS

CAMBRIDGE,
April 4, 1919.

PREFACE TO FIFTH EDITION

Pages 30, 31, 46, 51, 76, 80, 87, 94, 109, 117, 119, 147, 163, 176, 179, 205, 215, 217, 222, 243, 249, 250, 253, 255, 272, 284, 314, 335, 350, 360, 371, 374, 375, 377, 392, 404, 405, 417–20, 439–41, 457, 464, 480, 505, 535, 538, 615, 646 have been rewritten in a style that will gradually be adopted throughout.

J. C. W.

March 24, 1925.

PREFACE TO SIXTH EDITION

A considerable number of pages have been completely rewritten in this as in the Fifth Edition.

J. C. W.

January 1931.

INDEX

TO THE IMPORTANT GENERAL ARTICLES, UNDER WHICH LISTS OF EXAMPLES (DESCRIBED AT GREATER LENGTH) WILL BE FOUND.

GENERAL

Abbreviations, Collecting, Concrescence, Description, Dimorphism, Literature, Nomenclature.

VEGETATIVE ORGANS

Adnate, Adventitious, Aerenchyma, Aerial Root, Branch, Bud, Bulb, Bulbil, Cauli(flory), Concrescence, Corm, Iso-(bilateral, &c.), Leaf, Phyllo-(taxy, &c.), Poly-(morphism), Rhizome, Stem, Stipule, Sym-(podium), Thorn, Tuber, Vegetative Reproduction.

REPRODUCTIVE ORGANS

Aestivation, Aggregate fruit, Andro-(phore, &c.), Anemo-(philous), Aniso-(phylly), Apetalous, Apo-(gamy), Aril, Asymmetrical, Bee-flowers, Berry, Bract, Butterfly-flowers, Carrion-flowers, Cincinnus, Cleistogamy, Cyme, Dichasial cyme, Dichogamy, Dioecism, Dispersal, Endo-(sperm, &c.), Epi-(gynous, &c.), Floral, Flower, Fly-flowers, Fruit, Geo-(carpic), Gyno-(dioecism, &c.), Heter-(ostylism), Inflorescence, Loose-pollen mechanisms, Mixed inflorescence, Nectary, Nut, Ovary, Perianth, Pollination, Receptacle, Seed, Sex distribution, Stamen, Staminode, Zygo-(morphism).

CLASSIFICATION

Nomenclature; and *cf.* Key to Families at end of book.

FORMS OF VEGETATION; GEOGRAPHICAL DISTRIBUTION

Beach-jungle, Chaparral, Climbing Plants, Dispersal, Epiphytes, Floral regions, Halo-(phytes), Insectivorous Plants, Mangroves, Myrmecophilous Plants, Parasites, Pitcher Plants, Plant formations, Saprophytes, Water Plants, Xerophytes, Zones of Vegetation.

ECONOMIC BOTANY

Alcohol, Alkaloids, Arrowroot, Bamboo, Bark, Camphor, Cinnamon, Condiments, Cotton, Drugs, Dyes, Ebony, Economic Botany, Economic Products, Edible Products, Fibres, Fodder, Foliage Plants, Grass, Gum, Guttapercha, Lac, Latex, Mucilage, Oil, Ornamental Plants, Poison, Resins, Rubber, Sugar, Tan, Timber.

EXPLANATORY INTRODUCTION

The Index of English names, technical terms, &c., which formed Part III of former editions, is now incorporated with the list of genera, so that the work forms one dictionary from end to end, with the exception of the key to the families at the end of the book.

All the genera of Bentham-Hooker, Engler-Prantl, and Linnaeus are now included, as well as all given in the *Index Kewensis* and Supplements (except many synonyms), together with a large number published since the last Supplement, and which, by the kindness of the Director of Kew, I have been able to obtain from the MS lists kept at Kew. The most recent of these are given in a little Supplement at the end of the main dictionary, and I hope to bring this supplement up to date at intervals during the currency of the edition, adding the entries later to the body of the work so far as the padding will allow. Besides the genera, all families and higher divisions are also included.

The name of the genus is followed by the name of its author, often abbreviated, *e.g.* R.Br. (*cf.* Abbreviations), on the system explained under Nomenclature. The original description of the genus may be found by reference to the *Index Kewensis*. In the same way, the author is given after every species quoted, and the original description may be discovered from the same book.

Owing to the continual changes that go on in many families and genera, names are often reduced to synonyms; a great number of such are given in this book, chiefly those used in well-known floras; *e.g.* Abildgaardia Vahl = Fimbristylis Vahl. Under some of the best known genera, *e.g.* Abies, a few specific synonyms have also been given, especially names frequently met with in gardens, and opposite to each of these is given the name now generally used; thus *Abies alba* Michx. must be looked for under Picea, *Abies Douglasii* Lindl. under Pseudotsuga, and so on. It is very difficult to decide when divergence of two forms is sufficient to entitle them to rank as genera, and this difficulty is the cause of much synonymy. A genus *A* is established by one author, and then it is discovered not to differ sufficiently from another genus *B*, established by the same or another author, to remain as an independent genus. *A* is therefore merged in *B* and becomes a synonym. The species of *A* retain as far as possible their old specific names when placed in *B*. When an entry such as "Abildgaardia Vahl = Fimbristylis Vahl p.p." is found, it means that the genus Abildgaardia as established by Vahl is merged in his Fimbristylis. Many of the species change their names, but some retain their specific names, when the name is not already occupied. This latter case is often indicated by putting the name of the old genus in brackets after that of the new, thus, *F.* (*A.*) *fulvescens*. In many cases the names of some of the genera thus merged in other genera are indicated thus: *Axinandra* Thw. (*BH.* incl. *Naxiandra* Krasser); no attempt however has been made to give all such cases or a fraction of them, but only a few of the more important. In particular those have been given where the genus as here defined differs from the definition in Engler and Prantl's *Natürliche Pflanzenfamilien* or Bentham and Hooker's *Genera Plantarum* by the inclusion and exclusion of other genera.

The name of the genus is followed by that of the family to which it belongs, and after this is often a number (in brackets) indicating the section of the family, thus Acacia belongs to Subfamily 1 and Tribe 2 of Leguminosae. The general plan upon which the book has been constructed, and the necessity for condensation, render it essential, if the full advantage is to be derived from its use, that the student should refer to the family as well as the genus. There he will find the important general characters possessed by its members, and should examine the genus to see in what it agrees, and in what it disagrees, with these. A further reference to the classification given at the end of the article upon the family will point out the special characters to be looked for in the genus as a member of some particular sub-family or tribe. In this way a large amount of information about the particular plant in question may be obtained, and at the same time the student will get into the way of regarding plants not as so many independent and disconnected units, but as related members of one great whole. In this way too he will soon acquire an appreciation of the relative importance of the different characters in classification and will learn to recognise the approximate relationships of most plants after a brief inspection, or even at sight.

The families are those given by Engler in his *Syllabus* and in *Die natürlichen Pflanzenfamilien*, but sufficient reference is made to Bentham and Hooker's system of classification to enable any one who may prefer to use that system to do so.

The name of the family is followed by a statement of the number of species in the genus, and its geographical distribution. The number, unless very small, is always only an approximation; new research is always bringing new species to light, splitting up older ones, or combining two or more into one. This is all the information that is given about a very large number of the genera; only when a genus presents some character of interest which is not common to the order or group, is any particular mention made of it. The biological peculiarities of the most important genera are dealt with pretty fully, but much has been omitted. Thus in dealing with the pollination-methods of flowers a selection of important genera, illustrating the various methods, has been made for description; so too with epiphytes, xerophytes, the morphology of parts, and so on. General discussions of all these subjects will be found under the title of the subject itself, and numerous examples are there quoted; these examples are mostly dealt with more fully. Numerous cross-references to other articles, *e.g.* Buds, Dichogamy, Fruit, Leaf, Parasite, Xerophyte, &c. (*cf.* Index), are made, and should be looked up.

While in the morphology, &c. a selection has thus been made of genera for treatment, this is less the case with economic botany. This has been more fully treated, only a comparatively few genera being omitted. Space, however, has not permitted of a detailed description of economic products or the way in which they are obtained; for this reference must be made to other works (see Literature).

Turning now to the other articles upon the families, the same general principles apply to them. After the name of the family is given the order to which it belongs, marked *EP.* or *BH.* if necessary to distinguish between these systematists. This should be looked up in the key at the end; this will show the families which are most nearly related to the one under consideration, and the characters that distinguish one from the other can be made out by comparison of their descriptions. The student should always endeavour to make out why a given family is classified in the position assigned to it. When the family as defined by Engler differs from that defined by Bentham and Hooker, as is so often the case, an attempt should be made to discover the reasons for the difference.

After the position of the family in the system follows the number of its genera and species, the morphology and natural history of its vegetative and reproductive organs, its economic products, and finally, in the case of the more important families, its classification into sub-families and tribes, with the more important genera belonging to each. The student should work through this part and study as many of the genera as possible before leaving the family. This is easily managed in dealing with the outdoor collection in our botanic gardens.

No particular attempt is made in the book to avoid technical terms. When a term or abbreviation is used that the reader does not understand he should look it up in the Dictionary, or under Abbreviations.

To save space, in many cases in which there are several words in use beginning with the same prefix, *e.g.* aniso-, apo-, endo-, epi-, geo-, gyno-, halo-, heter-, iso-, phyllo-, poly-, sym-, xero-, &c., all are given under the heading of the prefix. If a word is looked up as a whole, therefore, and not found, reference should be made to the prefix before saying that it is omitted from the Dictionary.

Many genera are described by different authors under different spellings, and the most common and important of such cases are included; thus Prunella is also described under Brunella, Eleocharis also under Heleocharis, &c.

A (fl.-class), fls. with freely exposed honey; *Acer*, *Euphorbia*, *Galium*, *Hedera*, *Ilex*, *Rhamnus*, *Saxifraga*, *Umbelliferae*.

A-, **An-** (Gr. prefix), not.

Aaron's Beard, *Hypericum calycinum* L.

AB (fl.-class), fls. with partially concealed honey; *Caltha*, *Crataegus*, *Cruciferae*, *Fragaria*, *Potentilla*, *Ranunculus*, *Sedum*.

Ab- (Lat. prefix), from; **-axial** (side), away from axis; **-breviated**, shortened; **-errant**, differing from type; **-normal**, varying from the rule; **-original**, strictly native; **-ortion**, imperfect or arrested development; **-rupt**, terminating suddenly; **-sciss-layer**, separation-layer for dropping the l.; **-sorption**, taking up of fluids by r. or l.

Abaca, Manila hemp, *Musa textilis* Née.

Abasoloa La Llave. Compositae (5). 1 Mex.

Abatia Ruiz et Pav. Flacourtiaceae (7) (Samydaceae, *BH.*). 5 trop. S. Am. Fl. apet. L. opp.

Abauria Becc. (*Koompassia* Maingay, *EP.*). Legum. (II. 5). 2 Malaya.

Abbevillea Berg. = Campomanesia Ruiz et Pav. p.p. (Myrt.).

Abbottia F. Muell. Rubiaceae (II. 2). 1 N. Austr.

Abbreviations. Descriptions of floral morphology are largely given in the terms of Floral Formulae, explained under that heading. When the name of a genus or family is repeated in the article dealing with it, it is represented by the initial letter only, *e.g.* A. for Abies. The name of a family is sometimes abbreviated by the omission of the terminal *aceae*, &c.; *e.g.* Capparid., Compos. The term 'warm' is sometimes used instead of 'tropical and subtropical.' The expression *BH.* after a genus or family, &c., means "as defined by Bentham and Hooker in their *Genera Plantarum*"; *EP.* means "as defined by Engler and Prantl in the *Pflanzenfamilien* and *Pflanzenreich.*"

The following mathematical and other symbols are largely used:

☿, hermaphrodite
♂, male
♀, female
( ) enclosing P, K, C, A, or G, united or concrescent
$\underline{G}$ superior, $\overline{G}$ inferior, ovary
∞, indefinite, numerous
×, hybrid
§, section (of sp. or genus)

① or ⊙, annual
② or ⨀, biennial
♃, perennial
♄, tree or shrub
>, more than
<, less than
±, more or less than
⊥, at right angles to
||, parallel to

=, equal to, merged in
!, seen by author
μ, micromillimetre, $\frac{1}{1000}$ mm.
-⊕-, actinomorphic
·|·, zygomorphic
$\underline{\ast}$, N. hemisphere
$\overline{\ast}$, S. hemisphere
|*, Old World
*|, New World

The following abbreviations are largely employed in this and other botanical books:

A(ndroeceum)
Abyss(inia)
Achlam(ydeous)
Actinom(orphic)
Acum(inate)
Adv(entitious)
Afr(ica)
Aggr(egate)
Agr(icultural)
Alb(umen)
Alt(ernate)
Am(erica)
Amphitr(opous)
Anatr(opous)
Anemoph(ilous)
Ann(ual) (als, &c.)
Ant(arcti)c
Apet(alous)
Apoc(ar)p(ous)
Arch(ipelago)
Archichl(amydeae)
Arct(ic)
Arg(entina)
Art(icle)
As(ia)
Assim(ilation)
Asymm(etrical)
Atl(antic)
Austr(alia)
Axill(ary)
B(eatus), the late
Beitr(äge)
Ber(ichte)
Bot(any)
Br(act)
Braz(il)
Brit(ain)
Bull(etin)
C(entral) (orolla)
Cal(yx) (edonia)
Calif(ornia)
Campylotr(opous)
Cap(itate)
Caps(ule)
c.c., cubic centimetre
Cel(eberrimus)
Centr(al) (alblatt)
Char(acter)
Chi(na)
Cl(arissimus) (ements*)
Cleist(ogamic)
cm., centimetre
Col(ony)
Coll(ected by) (ection)
Concr(escence)
Consp(icuous)
Conv(olute)
Cor(olla)
Cosmop(olitan)
Cot(yledon)
C(om)p(oun)d
C(ar)p(e)l
Cult(ivated)
Dehisc(ent)
Dep(artment)
Descr(iption)
Dich(asial)
Dichlam(ydeous)
Dichot(omous)
Dicot(yledon)
Dim(inutive)
Dioec(ious)
Diplost(emonous)
Distr(ibution)
Dorsiv(entral)
Ed(ible) (ition)
Endosp(erm)
Engl(and)
Entomoph(ilous)
Epig(ynous)
Epipet(alous)
Epiph(yte)
Esp(ecially)
Ess(ential)
Eur(ope)
Evap(oration)
Evergr(een)
Exalb(uminous)
Exc(ept)
Excl(uding)
Exstip(ulate)
Extr(orse)
Extrafl(oral)
Fam(ily)
Fert(ilisation)
Fl(ower)(in)g
Fl(ore) pl(eno), double-flowered
Fol(ium, a leaf) (iage)
Fr(uit)
Fri(gid)
G(ynoeceum)
Gen(us)
Germin(ation)
Ges(ellschaft)
Gland(ular)
Gr(eek)
H(erbarium)
Hab(itat)
Hem(isphere)
Herb(arium)
Heterochlam(ydeous)
Heterost(yled)
Himal(aya)
Hind(ustani)
Homochlam(ydeous)
Horiz(ontal)
Hort(orum), of gardens

* *Research Methods in Ecology.*

Hybr(id)
Hypog(ynous)
I(sland)
Ic(on), figure
Imbr(icate)
Inc(ertae) sed(is), of unknown position
Incl(uding)
Inconspic(uous)
Ind(ia)
Indeh(iscent)
Indomal(aya)
Ined(itus), unpublished
Inf(erior)
Infl(orescence)
Interpet(iolar)
Intr(orse)
Invol(ucre)
Irreg(ular)
Isobil(ateral)
Jap(an)
Jard(in)
K, calyx
L(eaf)
Lat(in) (eral)
Laticif(erous)
L(oco) c(itato), in the place quoted
Linn(ean)
Loc(ulus)
Loculic(idal)
m(etre)
Madag(ascar)
Mag(azine)
Mal(aya)
Masc(arenes)
Mech(anism)
Medit(erranean)
Membr(anous)
Met(amorphosed)
Mex(ico)
mm., millimetre
Moluc(cas)
Monoch(asial)
Monochlam(ydeous)
Monocot(yledon)
Monoec(ious)
Mus(eum)
n(ovus), new
N(atural) O(rder)
Nat(ural) (uralised)
Nat(ürlichen) Pfl(anzenfamilien)
Nearct(ic)
Neotrop(ical)
Nom(en), a name
Nud(us), naked, without description
N(ew) Z(ealand)
Obdipl(ostemonous)
Off(icinal)
Opp(osite)
Orn(amental)
Orthotr(opous)
Ov(ule) (ary)
P(erianth)
Pac(ific)
Palaearct(ic)
Palaeotrop(ical)
Paras(ite)
Ped(icel) (uncle)
Pen(insula)
Pend(ulous)
Perenn(ial)
Perf(ume)
Perig(ynous)
Pet(al)
Pfl(anzen) R(eich)
Phil(ippines)
Pl(ant)
Plac(enta)
Poll(icaris), inch
Pollin(ation)
Polyg(amous)
Polyn(esia)
Post(erior)
p(ro) p(arte), in part
Pref(ix)
Prodr(omus)
Protandr(ous)
Protog(ynous)
P(oin)t
R(oot)
Rad(ix) (ical)
Recept(acle)
Reg(ular)
Repr(oduction)
Repres(ented)
Rev(iew)
Rhiz(ome)
Rudim(entary)
S(eu), or
Sandw(ich Is.)
Sci(ence)
Sem(en), a seed
Sep(al)
Septic(idal)
Septifr(agal)
Ser(ies)
Sicc(us), dry
Soc(iety)
Sol(itary)
Sp(ecies)
Sta(men)
St(amino)d(e)
Stip(ule)
Subm(erged)
Subtrop(ical)
Succul(ent)
Suff(ix)
Sup(erior)
Sympet(alous)
Syn(onym)
Sync(arpous)
T(abula), a figure
T(omus), a volume
Tab(ula), a figure
Tasm(ania)
Temp(erate)
Term(inal)
Trans(actions)
Transv(erse)
Trop(ical)
Undershr(ub)
Usu(ally)
Var(iety)
Varieg(ated)
Veg(etation)
V(idi) S(iccam), dry specimen seen
V(idi) V(ivam), living specimen seen
W(est) I(ndies)
Wiss(enschaft)
Xero(phyte)
Zygom(orphic)

Of course many of these abbreviations also signify the adjectival and other forms of the word, *e.g.* albumen, albuminous, &c.; character, characterised, characteristic, &c.

The following abbreviations of authors' names are in common use in giving the authority for genera or species:

Achar(ius)
Adans(on)
Afz(elius)
Ag(ardh)
Ait(on)
Alef(eld)
Allem(ao)
All(ioni)
Anders(on)
Andr(ews)
Ant(oine)
Arch(er)
Ard(uino)
Aresch(oug)
Arn(ott)
Aschers(on)
Aubl(et)
Auct(orum)
Bab(ington)
Bail(ey)
Baill(on)
Bak(er)
Bal(ansa)
Balb(is)
Balf(our)
Barb(osa) Rodr(igues)
Barnad(es)
Barn(eoud)
Barr(elier)
Bartl(ing)
Batem(an)
Bauh(in)*
Baumg(arten)
Beauv(ois)
Becc(ari)
Bedd(ome)
Benj(amin)
Benn(ett)
Benth(am)
B(entham and) H(ooker)†
Berg(ius)
Bernh(ardi)
Bert(ero)
Berth(elo)
Berthol(ini)
Bertol(oni)
Bess(er)
Bieb(erstein)
Bigel(ow)
Binn(endijk)
Bisch(off)
Bl(ume)
Boeck(eler)
Boerh(ave)
Boiss(ier)
Boj(er)
Bomm(er)
Bong(ard)
Bonpl(and)
Borck(hausen)
Br(aun, own)
Bref(eld)
Brongn(iart)
Brot(ero)
Brunf(els)
Buch(anan)-Ham(ilton)
Burch(eil)
Bur(eau)
Burm(ann)
Buxb(aum)
Camb(essedes)
Carr(iere)
Carr(uthers)
Casp(ary)
Cass(ini)
Cast(agne)
Cav(anilles)
C.DC., Casimir de Candolle
Cerv(antes)
Cham(isso)
Champ(ion)
Chapm(an)
Chav(annes)
Chois(y)
Cl(ements)
Clus(ius)
Cogn(iaux)
Colebr(ooke)
Col(enso)
Colm(eiro)
Comm(elin)
Comm(erson)
Corn(uti)
Coss(on)
Cram(er)
Cunn(ingham)
Curt(is)
Dalz(ell)
Dav(enport)
DC., A. P. de Candolle (1778–1841)
Dec(ais)ne
Deless(ert)
Del(ile)
Dennst(aedt)
De Not(aris)
Desf(ontaines)
Desr(ousseaux)
Desv(aux)
Dicks(on)
Didrichs(en)
Dietr(ich)
Dill(enius)
Dillw(yn)
Dodon(aeus)
Dougl(as)
Drumm(ond)
Dryand(er)
Duch(artre)
Dumort(ier)
Dun(al)
Eat(on)
Eckl(on)
Edgew(orth)
Ehrenb(erg)
Ehrh(art)
Eichl(er)
Ell(iott)
Endl(icher)‡
Engelm(ann)
Engl(er)§
Eschsch(oltz)
Eschw(eiler)
Ettingsh(ausen)
Fabr(icius)
Falc(oner)
Fing(erhuth)
Fisch(er)
Flac(ourt)
Forsk(ål)
Forst(er)
Fourn(ier)
Fourr(eau)
Franch(et)
Frem(ont)
Fres(enius)
Fr(ies)
Gaertn(er)
Gal(eotti)
Gardn(er)
Gasp(ari)
Gaudich(aud)
Gaud(in)
Gies(enhagen)
Gilb(ert)
Gilib(ert)
Gill(ies)
Gis(eke)
Gled(itsch)
Gmel(in)
Godr(on)
Goldm(ann)
Grah(am)
Gren(ier)
Grev(ille)
Griff(ith)
Griseb(ach)

* *Prodromus Theatri Botanici*, 1620.
† *Genera Plantarum*, 1862–83.
‡ *Ibid.* 1836–40.
§ *Natürlichen Pflanzenfamilien*, 1889–97; *Das Pflanzenreich*, 1900–(in progress).

Gronov(ius)
Guett(ard)
Guill(emin)
Guss(one)
Hack(el)
Hall(er)
Ham(ilton)
Hanst(ein)
Hartm(ann)
Hartw(eg)
Harv(ey)
Hassk(arl)
Haw(orth)
Hedw(ig)
Hegelm(aier)
Heist(er)
Hemsl(ey)
Henfr(ey)
Herb(ert)
Herm(ann)
Hern(andez)
Hieron(ymus)
Hildebr(and)
Hill(ebrand)
Hochst(etter)
Hoffm(ann)
Hoffm(an)s(eg)g
Honck(eney)
H(oo)k(er)
Hook(er)
Hook. f(ilius) *
Horan(inow)
Hort(orum), of gardens
Houst(on)
Houtt(uyn)
Huds(on)
Humb(oldt)
H(umboldt), B(onpland) & K(unth)
Isn(ard)
Jacks(on)
Jacq(uin)
Jenm(an)
Jord(an)
Jungh(uhn)
Juss(ieu) 1748–1836
Kaempf(er)
Karst(en)
Kaulf(uss)
Kell(ogg)
Kl(otzsch)
Knaut(ius)
Koel(er)
Koen(ig)
Koern(icke)
Kon(ig)
Korth(als)
Kostel(etzky)
K(un)tze, O.
K(un)ze
L(innaeus) † 1707–78
Labill(ardière)
Lag(asca)
Lam(arck)
Lamb(ert)
Langsd(orff)
Lapeyr(ouse)
Laxm(ann)
Leandr(o)
Leavenw(orth)
Ledeb(our)
Lehm(ann)
Lej(eune)
Lem(aire)
Lepr(ieur)
Lesch(enault)
Less(ing)
Lestib(oudois)
L. f(ilius)
L'Herit(ier)
Licht(enstein)
Liebm(ann)
Lindl(ey) 1799–1865
Lindm(ann)
Linn(aeus) †
Loefl(ing)
Loes(ener)
Loud(on)
Lour(eiro)
Ludw(ig)
Luerss(en)
Macfad(yen)
Maing(ay)
Mak(ino)
Marcgr(af)
Markh(am)
Mart(ius)
Mast(ers)
Maxim(owicz)
Medic(us)
Meissn(er)
Mert(ens)
Mett(enius)
Mey(er)
Mich(au)x
Mich(eli)
Mig(uel)
Mihi, of me
Mik(an)
Mill(er)
Miq(uel)
Mirb(el)
Mitch(ell)
Moc(ino)
Moehr(ing)
Mol(ina)
Monn(ier)
Moq(uin-Tandon)
Morr(en)
Muehlenb(erg)
Muell-Arg(au)
Muell(er)
Muell, F(erd. v.)
Murr(ay)
Naud(in)
Neck(er)
Newm(an)
Nied(en)z(u)
Nor(onha)
Nutt(all)
Nyland(er)
Nym(an)
Oerst(ed)
Oliv(er)
Ort(ega)
Parl(atore)
Parm(entier)
Pasq(uale)
Pav(on)
Perr(ottet)
Pers(oon)
Peterm(ann)
Peyr(itsch)
Pfeiff(er)
Pfitz(er)
Phil(ippi)
Planch(on)
Pluk(enet)
Plum(ier)
Poepp(ig)
Poir(et)
Poll(ich)
Ponted(era)
Pr(esl)
Putterl(ick)
Racib(orski)
Radlk(ofer)
Raf(inesque)
R(obert) Br(own)
Red(outé)
Reich(ardt)
R(ei)ch(en)b(ach)
Reinw(ardt)
Reiss(eck)
Retz(ius)
Reut(er)
Rich(ard)
Ridl(ey)
Riv(inus) ‡
Roem(er)
Rohrb(ach)
Roth(ert)
Rottb(oell)
Roxb(urgh)
Rudb(eck)
Rumph(ius)
Rupp(ius)
Rupr(echt)
Sadeb(eck)
Sald(anha)
Salisb(ury)
Sanguin(etti)
Sauv(ageau)

* See B. & H.

† The starting point of modern nomenclature is the publication in 1753 of his *Species Plantarum*.

‡ Bachmann, 1652—1723.

Sauv(alle)
Schau(er)
Scheff(er)
Scheidw(eiler)
Schlecht(en)d(al)
Schmid(el)
Schnizl(ein)
Schomb(urgk)
Schrad(er)
Schreb(er)
Schult(es)
Schum(acher)
Schum(ann)
Scop(oli)
Scortech(ini)
Seem(ann)
Sendtn(er)
Ser(inge)
Seub(ert)
Shuttl(eworth)
Sibth(orp)
Sieb(old)
Siegesb(eck)
Smirn(ow)
Sm(ith)
Sod(iro)
Soland(er)
Solms-Laub(ach)
Sond(er)
Sonn(erat)
Spegazz(ini)
Splitg(erber)
Spr(engel)
Steinh(eil)
Steph(ens)
Sternb(erg)
Steud(el)
St Hil(aire)
Sw(artz)
Tabern(aemontanus) 1520–90
Targ(ioni) Toz(zetti)
Taub(ert)
Teysm(ann)
Thoms(on)
Thonn(ing)
Thou(ars)
Thunb(erg)
Thw(aites)
Tod(aro)
Torr(ey)
Tourn(efort) 1656–1708
Tratt(inick)
Trautv(etter)
Tréc(ul)
Trev(isano)
Trin(ius)
Tul(asne)
Turcz(aninew)
Turp(in)
Tuss(ac)
Und(erwood)
Urb(an)
Vaill(ant)
Vand(elli)
Vell(ozo)
Vent(enat)
Vieill(ard)
Vill(ars)
Vis(iani)
Viv(iani)
Vog(el)
Wahlenb(erg)
Wall(ich)
Wallr(oth)
Walp(ers)
Walt(ers)
Warb(urg)
Warm(ing)
Wats(on)
Webb(er)
Wedd(ell)
Welw(itsch)
Wendl(and)
Wettst(ein)
Wigg(ers)
Wikstr(om)
Willd(enow)
Willem(et)
Willk(omm)
Wimm(er)
Wulf(enius)
Wydl(er)
Zahlbr(uckner)
Zenk(er)
Zeyh(er)
Zipp(el)
Zoll(inger)
Zucc(arini)

Abdominea J. J. Smith. Orchidaceae (II. 20). 1 Java.

Abdra Greene (*Draba* L. p.p.). Cruciferae (4). 1 N. Am.

Abele tree, *Populus alba* L.

Abelia R.Br. (*Linnaea* Gronov. p.p. *EP.*). Caprifoliaceae (3). 15 As., Mex. Sta. 4, didynamous.

Abelmoschus Medic. (*Hibiscus* L. p.p.). Malv. 50 trop., Austr.

Aberemoa Aubl. (*Duguetia* St. Hil.). Anon. (1). 30 trop. S. Am., W.I.

Aberia Hochst. (*Doryalis* E. Mey. p.p. *EP.*). Flacourtiaceae (4). (Bixineae, *BH.*). 12 Afr., Ceylon. *A. caffra* Harv. et Sond. (Kei apple), and others, ed. fr.

Abies (Tourn.) L. *Synonymy: A. alba* Michx. = Picea a.; *do.* Mill. = A. pectinata DC.; *A. americana* Mill. = Tsuga canadensis; *A. californica* Hort. = Pseudotsuga Douglasii; *A. canadensis* Michx. = Tsuga c.; *do.* Mill. = Picea alba; *A. Cedrus* Poir. = Cedrus Libani; *A. Deodara* Lindl. = C. D.; *A. Douglasii* Lindl. = Pseudotsuga D.; *A. excelsa* Link = A. pectinata; *do.* Poir. = Picea e.; *A. Kaempferi* Lindl. = Pseudolarix K.; *A. Larix* Poir. = Larix europaea; *A. montana* Nym. = Picea excelsa; *A. mucronata* Rafin. = Pseudotsuga Douglasii; *A. nigra* Desf. or Duroi = Picea n.; *A. Omorika* Nym. = Picea O.; *A. orientalis* Poir. = Picea o.; *A. pectinata* Poir. = Picea rubra; *A. Picea* Lindl. = A. pectinata DC.; *do.* Mill. = Picea excelsa; *A. rubra* Poir. = Picea r.; *A. vulgaris* Poir. = A. pectinata.

Coniferae (Pinaceae, 2; see C. for generic characters). 24 N. temp. The firs are evergreen trees with needle l. borne directly on the stems.

No short shoots. On the main stem the symmetry is radial, whilst on the horizontal branches the l. twist so as to get their surfaces all much in one plane. If the top bud or *leader* be destroyed, however, a branch bud below it takes up the vertical growth and radial symmetry. Cones large, arranged much like Pinus; ♀ often brightly coloured, though wind-fertilised. The carpel-scales are large and appear on the outside of the cone between the ovuliferous scales. The cone ripens in one year.

A. pectinata DC. (silver-fir, Mts. of S. Eur.) yields a valuable wood, 'Strasburg' turpentine, &c. *A. balsamea* Mill. (E. N. Am., balsam fir) yields the turpentine known as Canada balsam. Many others yield useful timbers and resins. Handsome trees; commonly cult. are *A. concolor* Lindl. et Gord. (N. W. Am.), *A. firma* Sieb. et Zucc. (Japan), *A. nobilis* Lindl. (N. W. Am.), *A. Nordmanniana* Spach (Caucasus), *A. Pinsapo* Boiss. (Spain), *A. Webbiana* Lindl. (Himal.).

Abietineae, a tribe of Coniferae Pinaceae.

Abildgaardia Vahl. = Fimbristylis Vahl p.p. (Cyper.).

Abiogenesis, spontaneous generation.

Abobra Naud. Cucurbitaceae (3). 1 temp. S. Am.

Abola Lindl. Orchidaceae (II. 19). 1 Colombia.

Abolboda Humb. et Bonpl. Xyridaceae. 10 S. Am.

Abortion, imperfect or arrested development.

Abroma Jacq. Sterculiaceae. 10 trop. As. to Austr. *A. augusta* L. (Indomal.) bark yields a good fibre.

Abronia Juss. Nyctaginaceae. 50 N. Am. Anthocarp winged.

Abrophyllum Hook. f. Saxifragaceae (V). 1 E. Austr.

Abrotanella Cass. Compositae (7). 15 Rodriguez, Tierra del Fuego, Austr., N.Z., Auckland Is.

Abrotanum (Tourn.) L. = Artemisia Tourn. p.p. (Compos.).

Abrus L. Leguminosae (III. 9). 6 trop. *A. precatorius* L. has hard red seeds with black tips (crab's eyes), strung into necklaces, rosaries, &c., and used as weights (rati) in India (*cf.* Adenanthera). See *Kew Bull.* 1890, p. 1 (Weather Plant). The roots are used in India as Indian liquorice.

Absinthe, *Artemisia*.

Absinthium Tourn. ex L. = Artemisia Tourn. p.p. (Compos.).

Absolmsia O. Ktze. (*Astrostemma* p.p. *BH.*). Asclepi. (II. 1). 1 Borneo.

Abundance (Cl.), the total number of individuals in an area.

Abuta (Barr.) Aubl. Menispermaceae. 10 trop. S. Am. *A. rufescens* Aubl. (Guiana) yields white Pareira root.

Abutilon Tourn. Malvaceae (2). 120 trop. and sub-trop. No epicalyx. Fl. mech. like *Malva silvestris*, but some are self-sterile; the sta. do not move down, and the styles emerge through the anther-mass. Many visited by humming-birds. *A. Avicennae* Gaertn. cult. in China for fibre China jute.

Abyssinian banana, *Musa Ensete* J. F. Gmel.; **primrose**, Primula.

Acacallis Lindl. (*Aganisia* Lindl. *EP.*). Orchid. (II. 13). 1 N. Brazil.

Acacia (Tourn.) L. Leguminosae (I. 2). 550 trop. and sub-trop., mostly trees (wattles); typical leaf-form bipinnate with ∞ leaflets and small scaly stips. About 300 sp., forming the § *Phyllodineae* (chiefly in Austr., where they are char., and Polynes.), have simple leaf-like *phyllodes*, *i.e.* petioles (or primary axes; *cf. Nature*, 5 Aug. 1920,

p. 724) flattened with their edges upwards, exposing less surface to radiation. Inspection shows the phyllode to be a leaf-structure with axillary bud, but not that it is not a l. turned edgewise, though it shows no twist. Occasionally there are *reversions to type* (*i.e.* to the ancestral form) on the plant, some phyllodes occurring with leaf-blades of the ordinary bipinnate type. This is still better seen in germinating seedlings. The first l. are typical bipinnate l., followed by others with slightly flattened stalks and less blade, and so on, until finally only phyllodes are produced. In *A. alata* R.Br. and others, the phyllodes are decurrent on the stem, like the l. of thistles. In many the stips. are repres. by large thorns, swollen at the base. In *A. sphaerocephala* Cham. et Schlecht. (Cent. Am.), the thorns are inhabited by colonies of ants, which bore into them and clear out the internal tissue. The ants live on the A. and are fed by it. Extrafl. nectaries occur on the petioles, and yellow sausage-shaped *food-bodies* on the tips of the leaflets. These consist of parenchymatous cells containing food-stuffs, and are eaten by the ants. If attempt be made to interfere with the tree the ants rush out. (*Cf.* Cecropia, and see *Nature*, Aug. 1893, for an account of the leaf-cutting ants: and *cf.* Schimper, *Plant Geogr.* p. 140. This was the first case of *myrmecophily* (symbiosis with ants) discovered; see Belt's *Naturalist in Nicaragua.*) Other sp. are myrmecophilous also.

A few are twiners, others hook-climbers. Most are xerophytes, often forming char. features in vegetation and scenery, *e.g.* the babul (*A. arabica* Willd.) with its low, spreading habit, is almost the only tree in many parts of the dry plains of India, and others are common in S. Afr. &c. In Austr. (esp. S. Austr.) the A. take a great part in the formation of the *scrub*, a concourse of shrubby plants of many genera, which covers the almost waterless country with a waste of veg. about 6—10 feet high, of a general bluish green effect, and with few herbs or grasses beneath.

The fl. (diagram, see order) has ∞ long sta., affording little protection to the pollen. In *A. homalophylla* A. Cunn. (S. E. Austr.; Myall) the seed hangs out on a long red funicle.

Many valuable products. *A. Senegal* Willd. (Soudan) yields the best gum-arabic; the gum exudes from the branches principally during the prevalence of the dry desert winds. Other sp. yield inferior qualities. *A. catechu* Willd. (E. Ind.) yields catechu or cutch (used in tanning), by digestion of the wood in hot water. With this the true khaki cloth is dyed and shrunk. *A. decurrens* Willd. (Austr.; black wattle), *A. pycnantha* Benth. (S. E. Austr.; golden wattle), *A. dealbata* Link (Austr.; silver wattle) &c. yield good tan-bark, cult. in Natal. That of *A. arabica* Willd. is largely used in India. The wood of many is valuable, esp. Australian black-wood, *A. melanoxylon* R.Br. Many have sweetly scented fls.; those of *A. Farnesiana* Willd. (trop.) are the Cassie flowers of perfumery. *A. armata* R.Br. (temp. Austr.; kangaroo thorn), *A. horrida* Willd. (S. Afr.) &c. form good hedges or sandbinders.

Acacia, false, *Robinia Pseud-acacia* L.

Acaena L. Rosaceae (III. 5). 120 $\overline{*}$, Mex., Calif., Polynes. Fr. hooked. Some sp. bud from junction of leaf and stalk.

Acajou (W. I.), *Guarea trichilioides* L.

Acaju, Cashew, *Anacardium occidentale* L.

Acalypha L. Euphorbiaceae (A. II. 2). 400 trop., S. Afr. Anther lobes twisted; stigmas branched. Several cult. for varieg. l.

Acampe Lindl. Orchidaceae (II. 16). 12 Indomal., China, (Afr. *BH.*).

Acamptocladus Nash (*Eragrostis* Host, p.p.). Gramin. (11). 1 S.W. U.S.

Acamptopappus A. Gray (*Aplopappus* Cass. *BH.*). Comp. (3). 2 N. Am.

Acanthaceae (*EP.*, *BH.*). Dicots. (Sympet. Tubiflorae). 240 gen., 2000 sp., esp. trop. but also Medit., U.S., Austr. 4 chief centres of distr.: Indomalaya, char. by Strobilanthes and Andrographidae, Afr. (Thunbergia and Barleria), Braz. (Mendoncia and Ruellia), and Centr. Am. (Aphelandreae and Odontonema). Many biological types—climbing plants, xerophytes, marsh plants, &c.—and much variety in habit. Very many in damp places in trop. forests. Trees are rare; most are shrubs or herbs with opp., usu. decussate and entire, exstip. l., usu. thin. Cystoliths, visible as streaks or protuberances, are usu. common on l. and stems. Infl. most commonly a dich. cyme, in its ultimate branchings tending to monoch., and frequently condensed in the leaf-axils as in Labiatae. Racemose infls. also occur, and sol. fl. are common. Bracts and bracteoles usu. present, often coloured; the latter frequently large, ± enclosing the fl.

Fl. ☿, hypog., zygom., usu. with nectariferous disc below ov. K (5—4), C (5—4), commonly two-lipped (upper lip sometimes not developed, *e.g.* in Acanthus). A rarely 5, usu. 4 or 2 epipet., usu. exserted; 1—3 stds. frequently present; anthers often with one lobe smaller than the other, or abortive; connective often long (*cf.* Salvia). The pollen exhibits great variety of patterns (see *Nat. Pfl.*); these are generally constant in the genus, and may be used in classification. $\underline{G}$ (2), 2-loc. with axile plac. each with 2—∞ usu. anatr. ov. in two rows. Style usu. long with two stigmas, the post. often smaller. The general arrangement of the fl. for visits of insects, protection of pollen, &c. is like Labiatae or Scrophulariaceae.

Fr. a bi-loc. caps. (with few exceptions), usu. ± stalked, loculic. to the very base. Seeds usu. exalb. Their modes of distribution are interesting (see *Nat. Pfl.*). The capsules of § IV explode and the seeds are thrown out, largely by the aid of peculiar hook-like outgrowths from their stalks (*retinacula* or *jaculators*). Many have superficial scales and hairs which on wetting become mucilaginous (*cf.* Linum, Collomia), *e.g.* Crossandra, Ruellia, Blepharis.

Classification and chief genera (after Lindau):

I. *NELSONIOIDEAE* (Ovules ∞; jaculators papilla-shaped): Ebermaiera, Nelsonia.

II. *MENDONCIOIDEAE* (Ov. 4, seeds not more than 2. Drupe; no jac.): Mendoncia.

III. *THUNBERGIOIDEAE* (Ov. 4. Capsule; jac. papilla-like): Thunbergia.

IV. *ACANTHIOIDEAE* (Ov. 2—∞. Capsule; jac. hook-shaped):

A. **Contortae** (cor. conv., or never ascendingly imbr.): Strobilanthes, Ruellia, Eranthemum, Barleria.

B. **Imbricatae** (cor. ascendingly imbr., or with no upper lip): Blepharis, Acanthus, Crossandra, Aphelandra, Andrographis, Dicliptera, Fittonia, Odontonema, Justicia, Beloperone.

Acanthella Hook. f. Melastomaceae (I). 1 Orinoco valley.

Acantho- (Gr. prefix), thorny; **-carpous**, spiny-fruited.

Acanthobotrya Eckl. et Zeyh. = Lebeckia Thunb. p.p. (Legum.).

Acanthocardamum Thell. (*Lepidium* p.p. *BH.*). Crucif. (2). 1 Persia.

Acanthocarpus Lehm. Liliaceae (III). 1 S.W. Austr. (Junc. *BH.*)

Acanthocephalus Kar. et Kir. Compositae (13). 2 W. As.

Acanthocereus Britton et Rose (*Cereus* p.p.). Cact. (III. 1). 7 S. Am.

Acanthochiton Torr. Amarantaceae (2). 1 Texas, Arizona.

Acanthocladus Kl. (*Polygala* L. p.p. *EP.*). Polygalaceae. 3 S. Am.

Acanthococos Barb. Rodr. (*Cocos* L. p.p.). Palmae (IV. 2). 1 Paraguay.

Acanthodium Delile = Blepharis Juss. (Acanth.).

Acantholepis Less. Compositae (11). 1 W. As.

Acantholimon Boiss. Plumbaginaceae. 80 E. Medit., desert pl.

Acanthomintha A. Gray. Labiatae (VI). 2 Calif.

Acanthonema Hook. f. Gesneriaceae (I). 1 W. Afr.

Acanthonychia Rohrb. (*Pentacaena* Bartl.). Caryophyll. (I. 4). 5 Pac. Am.

Acanthopale C. B. Clarke. Acanth. (IV. A). 7 trop. Afr. (Malaya?).

Acanthopanax Miq. Araliaceae. 25 Ind., Chi., Japan.

Acanthophippium Blume. Orchidaceae (II. 9). 10 Indomal. The axial outgrowth from the base of the column, common in O., is here very great and bends first downwards, then up, removing the insertion of the lateral sepals and labellum to a distance from the column.

Acanthophoenix H. Wendl. Palmae (IV. 1). 3 Mascarenes.

Acanthophyllum C. A. Mey. Caryophyllaceae (II. 2). 25 W. As., Siberia. Mostly desert xerophytes with prickly leaves.

Acanthopsis Harv. Acanthaceae (IV. B). 7 S. Afr.

Acanthorhiza H. Wendl. Palmae (I. 2). 4 trop. Am. The adv. roots from the lowest nodes grow normally downwards, but those from the nodes above develope into thorny branches.

Acanthoscyphus Small (*Oxytheca* Nutt. p.p.). Polygon. (I. 1). 1 N. Am.

Acanthosicyos Welw. Cucurbitaceae (3). 1 S.W. Afr., *A. horrida* Welw., the Narras, a remarkable plant growing on sand dunes (*cf.* Welwitschia). The thick root is very long (up to 40 ft.). Above ground is a thorny shrub, with long tendrils; the thorns are modified twigs. (See Welwitsch, *Trans. Linn. Soc.* 27, 1869.)

Acanthospermum Schrank. Compositae (5). 5 trop. Am., Galapagos.

Acanthosphaera Warb. Moraceae (II). 1 Amazon valley.

Acanthostachys Link, Klotzsch, et Otto (*Ananas* Tourn. p.p.). Bromeliaceae (4). 1 (*A. strobilacea* L. K. et O.) Brazil.

Acanthosyris Griseb. Santalaceae. 3 temp. S. Am. Furniture wood.

Acanthothamnus T. S. Brandegee. Celastraceae. 1 Mex.

Acanthotreculia Engl. Moraceae (II). 1 Cameroons.

Acanthura Lindau. Acanthaceae (IV. A). 1 Mattogrosso.

Acanthus Tourn. ex L. Acanthaceae (IV. B). 25 trop. and sub-trop., As., Afr., Eur., mostly xero. with thorny l. (those of *A. spinosus* L. furnished, it is supposed, the pattern for the decoration of the capitals of Corinthian columns). *A. ilicifolius* L. is part of the palaeotrop.

mangrove (*q.v.*) veg. Fl. a large bee-fl.; there is no upper lip to the C, and the protection of the pollen, &c. is undertaken by the K. The anthers form a box by fitting closely together at the sides, and shed their pollen sideways into it, where it is held by hairs till an insect probing for honey forces the filaments of the sta. apart and receives a shower of pollen on its head (*loose-pollen mechanism*, *cf.* many Scrophulariaceae, Ericaceae, &c.). In the young flr. the style is behind the anthers, later on it bends down so as to touch a visiting insect. The fr. explodes; large 'jaculators' on the seeds.

Acarna All. = Atractylis L. p.p. (Compos.).

Acarodomatia, cavities mite inhabited, *Anamirta*, *Fraxinus*, *Parameria*.

Acaulescent, almost stemless; **acaulis** (Lat.), without visible stem.

Accessory branch, bud, supernumerary in same axil, see *Buds*; **organs** of flower, the perianth.

Acclimatisation, adaptation to new climate.

Accrescent, enlarged and persistent.

Accumbent, see *Cruciferae*.

Aceituna, *Symplocos*.

Acentra Phil. (*Hybanthus* Jacq. p.p. *EP.*) Violaceae. 1 Chili.

Acer (Tourn.) L. Aceraceae (Sapind. *BH.*). 150 N. temp., esp. in hill districts (*A. pseudoplatanus* L., sycamore, and *A. campestris* L., maple, in Brit., the latter native) and trop. mts.; many in China and Japan. Trees and shrubs, with opp. exstip. l., deciduous or evergreen. L. often simple entire, more commonly 3- or 5-lobed, occasionally cpd. One may go through a collection of A. in an herbarium or elsewhere, comparing the l. as to degree of development of the *drip-tips* (acum. apices to easily wetted l., from which the water drips off rapidly after a shower, *cf.* Ficus) noting the kind of climate from which each has come. There is a correlation between length of tip and wetness of climate.

Large winter buds, covered by scale l. In many sp. transitional forms may be seen as the bud elongates in spring, between the scales and the green l., showing that the scale = not the whole l., but the leaf base. In the § Negundo there are no scales, but the bud is protected by the base of the petiole of the l. in whose axil it arises.

The l. commonly exhibit varnish-like smears, of sticky consistence, known as *honey-dew*, the excretion of aphides which live on the l.; the insect bores into the tissues, sucks their juices, and ejects a drop of honey-dew on an average once in half-an-hour. In passing under a tree infested with aphides one may sometimes feel the drops falling like a fine rain (see Pithecolobium). The fluid is rich in sugar. When the dew falls the hygroscopic honey-dew takes it up and spreads over the l.; then later in the day evap. reduces it to a varnish on the surface. Many other trees exhibit this phenomenon, *e.g.* lime, beech, oak (Büsgen, *Der Honigthau*, Jena).

Fls. in racemes, sometimes contracted to corymbs or umbels, reg., polyg., not conspic.; formula usu. K5, C5, A4+4, $\underline{G}$ (2). Apetaly in some. 3 cpls. are frequent, esp. in the end fl. of a raceme. ☿ fls. protandrous; honey freely exposed on the disc (fl.-class A), available to insects of all kinds. Fr. a samara. In germination, the long green cotyledons come above the soil almost at once.

A. saccharum Marshall (*A. saccharinum* Wangenh.) and others of the E.U.S. yield maple sugar (2—4 lb. a tree) obtained by boring holes in February and March and collecting and evaporating the juice. Many yield good timber and charcoal. A number of Japanese sp., with prettily shaped or varieg. l., cult. as orn. shrubs.

Aceraceae (*Sapind.* p.p. *BH.*). Dicots. (Archichl. Sapindales). 2 gen. (Acer, Dipteronia) with 150 sp. N. temp. and trop. mts. Trees and shrubs; l. opp., petiolate, exstip., simple entire or more often palmately or pinnately lobed or cpd. Infl. racemose, corymbose, or fasciculate. Fls. reg., andromonoec., androdioec., dioec., &c., 5-4-merous, usu. dichlam. Disc annular or lobed or reduced to teeth, rarely absent. A 4—10, usu. 8, hypog., perig., or on disc; ♂ flr. with rudimentary G. $\underline{G}$ (2), 2-loc., lat. compressed; styles 2, free or joined below; ov. 2 in each loc., orthotr. to anatr., with dorsal raphe. Fr. of 2 samaras, separating when ripe. Seeds usu. solitary, exalb., the cotyledons irreg. folded. Many yield good timber, sugar, &c. (*cf.* Acer). Largely represented in the Tertiary.

Aceranthus Morr. et Decne. (*Epimedium* Tourn. *EP.*). Berberidaceae. 3 Chi., Jap.

Aceras R.Br. Orchidaceae (II. 1). 1 Eur. (incl. Brit.), Medit., *A. anthropophora* R.Br., the man-orchis. Like Orchis.

Acerates Ell. = Gomphocarpus R. Br. p.p. (Asclepiad.).

Aceriphyllum Engl. Saxifragaceae (1). 1 N. China.

Acerose, needle-shaped.

Acetabuliform, like a shallow saucer.

Acetosa Tourn. ex Mill. = Rumex Linn. (Polygon.).

Acetosella Moehr. = Oxalis Linn. (Oxalid.).

-aceus (Lat. suffix), like.

Achaenipodium T. S. Brandegee. Compositae (5). 1 Mex.

Achaetogeron A. Gray. Compositae (3). 10 Mex., Calif.

Achantia A. Chevalier. Sterculiaceae. 1 trop. Afr.

Acharia Thunb. Achariaceae. 1 S. Afr.

Achariaceae (*Passifloraceae*, p.p. *BH.*). Dicot. (Archichl. Parietales). 3 gen., 3 sp. S. Afr. Herbs or undershrubs with reg. monoec. fl. K 3—5, C (3—5), A 3—5 epipet., $\underline{G}$ (3—5) with ∞ ov. on parietal plac. Caps. Endosp.

Acharitea Benth. Verbenaceae (3). 2 Madag.

Achatocarpus Triana. Phytolaccaceae (Amarant. *BH.*). 10 trop. Am.

Achene, a one-seeded small dry indehiscent fruit (*q.v.*) of 1 carpel.

Achetaria Cham. et Schlecht. = Beyrichia Cham. (Scrophular.).

Achillea L. Compositae (7). 115 N. temp. *A. Millefolium* L. (yarrow or milfoil) and *A. Ptarmica* L. (sneezewort) in Brit.

Achilus Hemsl. Zingiberaceae (1). 1 Siam. No stds. Unisex. fl.

Achimenes P.Br. Gesneraceae (II). 25 trop. Am., often cult.

Achlaena Griseb. Gramineae (6). 1 Cuba.

Achlamydeous, without a perianth (*q.v.*).

Achlamydosporeae (*BH.*). The sixth series of Monochlamydeae.

Achlys DC. Berberidaceae. 2 Japan and Pacif. N. Am. The perianth aborts early in development.

Achneria Munro. Gramineae (9). 8 S. and trop. Afr.

Achnophora F. Muell. Compositae (3). 1 Austr.

Achradotypus Baill. Sapotaceae (I). 4 New Cal.

Achras L. Sapotaceae (I). I W. Ind., trop. Am., *A. Sapota* L., cult. for ed. fr. (Sapodilla plum). The coagulated resinous latex (chicle gum) is used in U.S. for chewing-gum, statuettes, &c.

Achratinis O. Ktze. = Arachnitis Phil. (Burmann.).

Achroanthes Raf. (*Microstylis* Nutt. p.p. *BH.*). Orchid. (II. 4). 12 N. Am.

Achudemia Blume. Urticaceae (2). 2 Java, Japan (?).

Achyrachaena Schau. Compositae (5). I N.W. U.S. Pappus of broad, silvery scales; fruit-heads used as 'everlastings.'

Achyranthes L. Amarantaceae (2). 15 trop. and sub-trop.

Achyrocline Less. Compositae (4). 25 Madag., trop. Afr. and Am.

Achyronia Royen ex L. = Aspalathus L. (Legumin.).

Achyronychia Torr. et A. Gray. Caryophyll. (I. 4) (Illecebr. *BH.*). 3 S.W. U.S., Mex.

Achyropappus H. B. et K. = Schkuhria Roth. p.p. (Compos.).

Achyrophorus Adans. = Hypochaeris Linn. p.p. (Compos.).

Achyropsis Benth. et Hook. f. (*Achyranthes* L. p.p. *EP.*). Amarant. (2). 3 Afr.

Achyrospermum Blume. Labiatae (VI). 12 trop. Afr. to Malay Is.

Achyrostephus Kze. Compositae (inc. sed.). Nomen.

Achyrothalamus O. Hoffm. Compositae (12). 2 E. trop. Afr.

Aciachne Benth. Gramineae (8). I trop. S. Am.

Acianthus R.Br. Orchidaceae (II. 2). 12 Austr., N.Z., New Caled

Acicalyptus A. Gray. Myrtaceae (I). 3 Fiji (New Cal.?).

Acicarpha Juss. Calyceraceae. 5 S. Am.

Acicular, needle-shaped.

Acidanthera Hochst. Iridaceae (III). 25 trop. and S. Afr. Cult.

Acidocroton Griseb. Euphorbiaceae (A. II. 3). 2 Cuba, Jamaica.

Acidoton Sw. Euphorbiaceae (A. II. 2). 3 W. I.

Acies, the edge.

Acinaciform, scimitar-shaped.

Acineta Lindl. Orchidaceae (II. 13). 10 trop. Am., Mexico. An axial outgrowth carries out 2 sep. and the labellum (attached to the column).

Acinodendron O. Ktze. (**-drum** L. *BH.*) = Miconia Ruiz et Pav. (Melastom.).

Acinos Rupp., Moench. = Calamintha Lam. (Labiat.).

Acioa Aubl. (*Couepia BH.*). Ros. (VI. b). I N.E. S. Am. with ed. oily seed, 20 trop. Afr.

Aciotis D. Don. Melastomaceae (I). 30 trop. Am., W. Ind.

Aciphylla Forst. Umbelliferae (III. 5). 25 Austr., N.Z.

Acis Salisb. = Leucojum L. (Amaryllid.).

Acisanthera P.Br. Melastomaceae (I). 20 trop. Am., W.Ind.

Ackama A. Cunn. Cunoniaceae (Saxifrag. *BH.*). 2 N. Z., E. Austr., New Guinea.

Acleisanthes A. Gray. Nyctaginaceae. 8 Mex., Texas.

Aclisia E. Mey. (Pollia Thunb. p.p.). Commelin. 12 Indomal. Austr., [W. Afr.

Acmadenia Bartl. et Wendl. f. Rutaceae (I). 20 S. Afr.

Acmanthera Griseb. Malpighiaceae (II). 2 S. Am.

Acmella Rich. = Spilanthes Jacq. (Compos.).

Acmena DC. = Eugenia L. p.p. (*BH.*) = Syzygium Gaertn. p.p.

Acmopyle Pilger (*Dacrydium* Soland. p.p.). Taxaceae. I New Cal.

Acnida L. Amarantaceae (2). 3 U.S. Dioecious.

Acnistus Schott. Solanaceae (2). 20 trop. Am.

Acoelorrhaphe H. Wendl. Palmaceae (I. 2). Nomen.

Acokanthera G. Don. Apocynaceae (I. 1). 3 Abyss., S. Afr., *A. venenata* G. Don, root and wood supplies Zulu arrow-poison.

Acom (W.I.), *Dioscorea bulbifera* L.

Acomastylis Greene (*Potentilla* et *Geum* p.p.). Rosac. (III. 2). 5 N. Am.

Acomis F. Muell. Compositae (4). 3 Austr.

Acomosperma K. Schum. Asclepiadaceae (nomen). 1 Amazon valley.

Aconceveibum Miq. Euphorbiaceae (B. II). 1 Java.

Aconite, Aconitin, *Aconitum*; **winter-**, *Eranthis hyemalis* Salisb.

Aconitum Tourn. ex L. Ranunculaceae (2). 110 N. temp. *A. Napellus* L. (aconite, monkshood, wolf's bane) in Brit. Fls. in racemes (see order). The post. sepal forms a large hood, enclosing the two 'petals' which are repres. by nectaries on long stalks. Fl. protandrous, adapted, by its structure and its blue colour, to bees. The distribution of A. largely coincides with that of the humble-bee (Bombus). Humble-bees often rob the flr. of its honey by biting through the hood. Fr. of follicles which open so far as to expose the seeds, which only escape when shaken by wind or otherwise (*censer-mechanism*). All are poisonous; the tuberous roots contain alkaloids of the aconitin group (used in medicine). *A. ferox* Wall (root) furnishes the Bikh poison of Nepal.

Acontias Schott=Xanthosoma Schott, p.p. (Arac.).

Acophorum Gaudich. Gramineae. Nomen nudum.

Acorellus Palla ex Kneuck (*Cyperus* L. p.p.). Cyper. (I). 3 S. Eur., Medit.

Acoridium Nees et Meyen (*Ceratostylis* Blume, *Dendrochilum* Blume). Orchidaceae (II. 3). 45 Indomal.

Acorn, *Quercus*.

Acorus L. Araceae (I). 2 N. temp., S.E. As. *A. Calamus* L. (sweet flag) Brit. Rhiz. sympodial; l. isobil. Fl. ☿, protog., with P. Used in flavouring.

Acotyledones (Jussieu)=Cryptogamae.

Acourtia D. Don=Perezia Lag. (Compositae).

Acquired characters, non-hereditary, arising during life.

Acradenia Kipp. Rutaceae (I). 1 Tasm.

Acrandra Berg. (*Campomanesia* Ruiz et Pav. *BH.*). Myrtaceae (I. 1). 2 S. trop. Braz.

Acranthera Arn. Rubiaceae (I. 7). 20 Indomal.

Acranthous, cf. *Orchidaceae*.

Acridocarpus Guill. et Perr. Malpighiaceae (I). 20 Afr., Madag., Arabia.

Acriopsis Reinw. Orchidaceae (II. 16). 10 E. Indomal.

Acrista O. F. Cook. Palmae (IV. 1). 1 Porto Rico.

Acritochaete Pilger. Gramineae (5). 1 Kilimanjaro.

Acriulus Ridl. Cyperaceae (II). 2 Madag., Angola.

Acro- (Gr. pref.), apical; **-carpous**, with terminal fruit; **-gamae**= Porogamae; see Chalazogamae; **-gens**, ferns and mosses; **-nychius** (Lat.), curved like a claw; **-petal,** produced successively towards the apex; **-phytium** (Cl.), an alpine-plant-formation; **-scopic**, facing the apex; **-spire**, plumule; **-tonic**, cf. *Orchidaceae*.

Acrobotrys K. Schum. et Krause. Rubiaceae (I. 3). 1 Colombia.

Acrocarpidium Miq. = Peperomia Ruiz et Pav. (Piper.).

Acrocarpus Wight ex Arn. Leguminosae (II. 7). 3 Indomal.

Acrocephalus Benth. Labiatae (VII). 40 Malay Arch. to trop. Afr.

Acrochaene Lindl. Orchidaceae (II. 16). 1 Sikkim.

Acroclinium A. Gray = Helipterum DC. p.p. (Comp.).

Acrocoelium Baill. Icacinaceae (Olacineae, *BH.*). 1 Congo.

Acrocomia Mart. Palmae (IV. 2). 10 trop. Am., W. Ind.

Acrodiclidium Nees. Lauraceae (II). 20 trop. Am., W. I. *A. Puchury* Mez furnishes medic. puchurim nuts.

Acroglochin Schrad. Chenopodiaceae (A). 1 N. India, China. The fruit mass is prickly, many of the twigs not ending in fls.

Acrolasia Presl. (*Mentzelia* L.). Loasaceae. 25 N. Am.

Acrolophia Pfitz. (*Eulophia* R. Br. p.p.). Orchidaceae (II. 5). 9 S. Afr.

Acronychia Forst. Rutaceae (IV). 20 trop. As., Austr.

Acropera Lindl. = Gongora Ruiz et Pav. p.p. (Orchid.).

Acrophorus Presl. Polypodiaceae. 1 Indomal.

Acrophyllum Benth. Cunoniaceae (Saxifrag. *BH.*). 1 New S. Wales.

Acropogon Schlechter. Sterculiaceae. 3 New Cal.

Acrosanthes Eckl. et Zeyh. Aizoaceae (II). 5 S. Afr.

Acrosepalum Pierre (*Ancistrocarpus* Oliv. *EP.*). Tiliaceae. 1 trop. Afr.

Acrospira Welw. (*Debesia* O. Ktze. *EP.*). Liliaceae (III). 3 Angola.

Acrostemon Klotzsch (*Eremia* D. Don, p.p.). Ericaceae (IV. 2). 9 S. Afr.

Acrostichum L. Polypodiaceae. 4 trop. *A. aureum* L. is common on trop. coasts.

Acrostylia Frappier. Orchidaceae (II. 1). 1 Reunion.

Acrotome Benth. Labiatae (VI. 1). 5 S. and trop. Afr.

Acrotrema Jack. Dilleniaceae. 10 Indomal.

Acrotriche R. Br. Epacridaceae (3). 8 temp. Austr.

Acrymia Prain. Labiatae (I). 1 Malay Penin.

Actad (Cl.), plant of a rocky sea-shore.

Actaea (Tourn.) L. (*BH.* excl. *Cimicifuga* L.). Ranunculaceae (2). 15 N. temp. *A. spicata* L. (bane-berry or herb-christopher), in Brit. Fls. in racemes (*cf.* Aconitum). Cpl. 1. Berry.

Actephila Blume. Euphorbiaceae (A. I. 1). 10 Indomal., Austr.

Actinanthus Ehrenb. (*Oenanthe* Tourn. p.p. *EP.*). Umbellif. (III. 5). 1 W. As.

Actinea Juss. = Cephalophora Cav. *BH.* = Actinella Pers.

Actinella Nutt. Compositae (6). 20 Am. (dwarf sunflower).

Actinella Pers. = Actinella Nutt. *EP.*

Actinidia Lindl. Actinid., formerly Dillen.; *cf.* Suppl. 25 E. As.

Actiniopteris Link. Polypodiaceae. 1 trop. Afr., As. It has the habit of a small palm with fan leaves.

Actinocarya Benth. Boraginaceae (IV. 1). 1 Tibet.

Actinochloa Willd. = Bouteloua Lag. (Gramin.).

Actinodaphne Nees. Lauraceae (1). 50 E. Ind., Japan, N. Am.

Actinodium Schau. Myrtaceae (II. 3). 1 W. Austr.

Actinokentia Dammer. Palmae (IV. 1). 1 New Cal.

Actinolema Fenzl. (*Astrantia* Tourn. *BH.*). Umbellif. (II. 1). 2 E. Medit.

Actinolepis DC. (*Eriophyllum* Lag. p.p.). Compos. (6). 9 West U.S.
Actinomeris Nutt. Compositae (5). 3 Atl. U.S.
Actinomorphic (fl.), radially symmetrical, or symmetrical about any plane passing through the centre (includes cases like most Sympetalae, where there are only two carpels and more of other whorls).
Actinophloeus Becc. (*Drymophloeus* Zipp. p.p.). Palmae (IV. 1). 4 New Guinea.
Actinophora Wall. (*Schoutenia* Korth. *BH.*). Tiliaceae. 3 trop. As.
Actinophyllum Ruiz et Pav. = Sciadophyllum P. Br. *BH.* = Schefflera Forst. (Aral.).
Actinorhytis Wendl. et Drude. Palmae (IV. 1). 2 Malaya.
Actinoschoenus Benth. Cyperaceae (II). 3 China, Ceylon, Madag.
Actinostemma Griff. Cucurbitaceae (I). 6 Ind. to Japan.
Actinostemon Mart. ex Klotzsch. Euphorbiaceae (A. II. 7). 50 trop. Am., W.I.
Actinostrobus Miq. Coniferae (Pinaceae 4; see C. for generic characters). 2 S.W. Austr.
Actinotus Labill. Umbelliferae (I. 1). 15 Austr. (flannel flower).
Actium (Cl.), rocky sea-shore formation.
Actoplanes K. Schum. Marantaceae. 2 Malaya.
Aculeate, Aculeatus (Latin), prickly.
Acuminate, tapering to a point in hollow curves.
Acura Hill. Compositae. Nomen.
Acute, tapering to a sharp point in straight lines.
Acutifolius (Lat.), with acute leaf.
Acyclic, not in whorls.
Ad- (Lat. pref.), to; **-axial** (side), the side towards the axis; **-hesion**, concrescence (*q.v.*) of dissimilar organs, *e.g.* C and A; **-justment** (Cl.), functional response to stimuli; **-nascens** (Lat.), growing upon something; **-pressed**, appressed; **-verse**, facing the main axis.
-ad (Cl.), suffix denoting an ecad.
Ada Lindl. Orchidaceae (II. 19). 2 Colombia. Cult.
Adactylus Rolfe (*Apostasia* Blume p.p.). Orchidaceae (I. 1). 3 trop. As.
Adamia Wall. = Dichroa Lour. (Saxifrag.).
Adam's needle, *Yucca.*
Adansonia L. Bombacaceae (I). 10 palaeotrop. *A. digitata* L. is the baobab. Its height is not great, but the trunk may reach 30 feet in thickness. Fr. woody. (See *Gard. Chr.* 1900, 57.)
Adaphus Neck. Inc. sed. (= Laurus Tourn.?).
Adaptable (Cl.), able to originate ecads.
Adaptation, adjustment to conditions of life.
Adder's tongue, *Ophioglossum.*
Addisonia Rusby. Compositae (2). 1 Bolivia.
Adelia L. Euphorbiaceae (A. II. 2). 15 W.I., warm Am.
Adelia P. Br. = Forestiera Poir (Olea.).
Adeliopsis Benth. Menispermaceae. 1 N.E. Austr.
Adelmeria Ridl. (*Elmeria* Ridl.). Zingiberaceae. 4 Phil. Is.
Adelobotrys DC. Melastomaceae (I). 15 trop. Am., W.I.
Adelodypsis Becc. (*Dypsis* Nor. p.p.). Palmae (IV. 1). 2 Madag.
Adelonema Schott (*Homalonema* p.p. *BH.*). Araceae (V). 1 Amazon.
Adelonenga Becc. (*Nenga* p.p.). Palmae (IV. 1). 3 New Guinea.

Adelopetalum Fitzger. Orchidaceae (II. 3). 1 New S. Wales.
Adelosa Blume. Verbenaceae (4). 1 Madag.
Adelostemma Hook. f. Asclepiadaceae (II. 1). 1 Burma.
Adelostigma Steetz. Compositae (3). 2 trop. Afr.
Aden- (Gr. pref.), a gland; **-oid**, gland-like; **-ophore**, stalk supporting a gland.
Adenandra Willd. Rutaceae (I). 25 S. Afr. Cult. orn. fl.
Adenanthera Royen ex L. Leguminosae (I. 4). 5 trop. As., Austr. Seeds hard and bright red, or red and black (*cf.* Abrus).
Adenanthos Labill. Proteaceae (I). 20 W. and S. Austr.
Adenaria H. B. et K. Lythraceae. 1 Mex. to Arg.
Adeneleuthera O. Ktze. = Adeneleutherophora Barb. Rodr.
Adeneleutherophora Barb. Rodr. Orchidaceae (II. 6). 1 Brazil.
Adenia Forsk. (*Modecca* L. *BH.*). Passiflor. 80 palaeowarm. Dioec.
Adenimesa Nieuwland = Conophora Nieuwland (Compositae).
Adenium Roem. et Schult. Apocynaceae (II. 1). 10 Arabia, Afr. Xerophytes with thick stems, and rather fleshy l.
Adenocalymna Mart. Bignoniaceae (I). 55 trop. Am.
Adenocarpus DC. Leguminosae (III. 3). 10 Medit., trop. Afr.
Adenocaulon Hook. Compositae (4). 3 Ind., Japan, U.S., Chili.
Adenochilus Hook. f. Orchidaceae (II. 2). 2 Austr., N.Z.
Adenochlaena Boiss. ex Baill. Euphorb. (A. II. 4). 2 Madag., Indomal.
Adenocline Turcz. Euphorbiaceae (A. II. 6). 5 S. Afr.
Adenoderris J. Sm. Polypodiaceae. 2 W.I.
Adenodolichos Harms. Leguminosae (III. 10). 12 trop. Afr.
Adenogonum Welw. ex Hiern. (*Engleria* O. Hoffm. *EP.*). Compositae (3). 2 W. Afr.
Adenogramma Reichb. Phytolaccaceae (Ficoideae *BH.*). 7 S. Afr.
Adenogynum Reichb. f. et Zoll. (*Chloradenia* Baill. *BH.*). Euphorb. (A. II. 2). 1 Java, Timor.
Adenolinum Reichb. = Linum L. (Lin.).
Adenolisianthus Gilg. Gentianaceae (I). 2 Brazil.
Adenoncos Blume = Sarcochilus R. Br. (Orchid.).
Adenoon Dalz. Compositae (I). 1 Indomal.
Adenopappus Benth. Compositae (6). 1 Mex.
Adenopeltis Bert. Euphorbiaceae (A. II. 7). 1 Chili.
Adenopetalum Klotzsch et Garcke = Euphorbia L. p.p. (Euphorb.).
Adenophaedra Muell.-Arg. Euphorbiaceae (A. II. 2). 2 E. Brazil.
Adenophora Fisch. Campanulaceae (I). 35 temp. Eur., As.
Adenophyllum Pers. (*Dysodia* Cav. p.p. *EP.*). Compositae (6). 3 Mex.
Adenoplea Radlk. (*Buddleia* Houst. p.p. *EP.*). Loganiaceae. 2 Madag.
Adenoplusia Radlk. Loganiaceae. 2 Madag.
Adenoporces Small (*Tetrapteris* Cav. p.p.). Malpighiaceae (I). 1 San Domingo.
Adenopus Benth. Cucurbitaceae (3). 12 trop. Afr.
Adenoropium Pohl. = Jatropha L. p.p. (Euphorb.). 100 warm.
Adenosacme Wall. (*Mycetia* Reinw. *EP.*). Rubi. (I. 7). 10 Indomal.
Adenosma Nees = Cardanthera Buch.-Ham. (*BH.*) = Synnema Benth. (Acanth.).
Adenosma R. Br. Scrophular. (II. 6). 10 Indomal., Austr., China.
Adenostegia Benth. = Cordylanthus Nutt. (Scrophular.). 12 N. Am.

Adenostemma Forst. Compositae (2). 6 trop. Am., 1 cosmotrop. Pappus glandular and sticky; fr. carried by animals.
Adenostoma Blume. Scrophulariaceae. Nomen.
Adenostoma Hook. et Arn. Rosaceae (III. 3). 2 Calif. *A. fasciculatum* H. et A. is one of the shrubs forming the chaparral or chamisal.
Adenostyles Cass. Compositae (2). 6 alpine, Eur., As. Minor.
Adenostylis Blume = Zeuxine Lindl. (Orchid.).
Adesmia DC. (*Patagonium* Schrank). Leguminosae (III. 7). 100 S. Am. Leafstalks thorny, plants often with glandular hairs.
Adhatoda Tourn. ex Medic. (*Justicia* L. p.p. *EP.*) Acanth. (IV. B). 100 trop.
Adhunia Vell. Inc. sed. 1 Brazil.
Adiantopsis Fée. Polypodiaceae. 15 trop. Am. As.
Adiantum L. Polypodiaceae. 190 cosmop., esp. trop. Am. (maiden hair); *A. Capillus-veneris* L. in Brit. (rare). Hothouse favourites. Some are climbing epiphytes.
Adicea Raf. = Pilea Lindl. (Urtic.).
Adina Salisb. Rubiaceae (I. 6). 15 trop. As., Afr.
Adinandra Jack. Theaceae. 45 warm As., Afr.
Adinobotrys Dunn. Leguminosae (III. 6). 5 Indomal., China.
Adlumia Rafin. Papaveraceae (III). 1 E. N. Am. A leaf-climber.
Adnaria Raf. = Gaylussacia H. B. et K. (Eric.).
Adnate (**adnation**), concrescence of organs of different nature, *e.g.* axillary shoot to main shoot or leaf, stamens to petals, &c., *Anthurium*, *Apocynaceae*, *Araceae*, *Asclepiadaceae*, *Asclepias*, *Boraginaceae*, *Chailletia*, *Compositae*, *Cuphea*, *Cyperaceae*, *Erythrochiton*, *Juglans*, *Passiflora*, *Pontederiaceae*, *Samolus*, *Solanaceae* (figure), *Spathicarpa*, *Spathiphyllum*, *Tilia*, *Zostera*; **anther**, one joined to the filament by its whole length.
Adolia Lam. (*Scutia* Comm. *BH. EP.*). Rhamnaceae. 3 trop., and S. Afr.
Adolphia Meissn. Rhamnaceae. 2 Mex., Calif.
Adonis Dill. ex L. Ranunculaceae (3). 10 N. palaeotemp. *A. autumnalis* L., pheasant's eye, Brit.
Adoxa L. Adoxaceae. 1 N. temp., incl. Brit., *A. Moschatellina* L., (moschatel). Rhiz. creeping, monopodial, bearing a flg. shoot with a few rad. l., a pair of opp. cauline l., and a small head of greenish fls., usu. 5 (a condensed dich. cyme). The term. fl. is usu. 4-merous, the lat. 5-merous (cf. Ruta, &c.). Fl. ☿, reg., greenish, inconspic. P of 2 whorls; the outer usu. 3-merous, sometimes regarded as an invol. formed of bract and bracteoles, but quite probably a K. Sta. alt. with petals, divided almost to the base. G (3—5), rarely (2), semi-inf. with one pend. ov. in each loc. Drupe with several stones. Endosp. Chief visitors small flies, attracted by the musky smell.
Adoxaceae (*EP.*; *Caprifol.* p.p. *BH.*). Dicots. (Sympet. Rubiales). Only genus Adoxa (*q.v.*). Sometimes united to Saxifragaceae; no very close relationships (see Sprague, *Journ. Linn. Soc.* 47, p. 471).
Adrastaea DC. (*Hibbertia* Andr. p.p. *EP.*). Dilleniaceae. 1 E. Austr.
Adriana Gaudich. Euphorbiaceae (A. II. 4). 5 Austr.
Adromischus Lem. (*Cotyledon* Tourn. p.p. *BH.*). Crassul. 20 S. Afr.
Adrorhizon Hook. f. Orchidaceae (II. 16). 1 Ceylon.

Adruc (W. Ind.), *Cyperus articulatus* L.
Aduncate, bent like a hook.
Adventina Raf. Compositae (inc. sed.). 2 N. Am.
Adventitious (Cl.), invading from distant formations; **buds**, arising elsewhere than normally in an axil, *Begonia*, *Bryophyllum*, *Cardamine*, *Cystopteris*, *Linaria*, *Ophioglossum*, *Pteris*, *Pyrola*; **embryo**, one formed without fertilisation, *Alchornea*, *Citrus*, *Euonymus*, *Funkia*, *Nothoscordum*; **root**, one developed from stem or leaf, *Acanthorhiza*, *Araceae*, *Bromeliaceae*, *Gramineae*, *Orchidaceae*, *Palmae* and most Monocotyledons, *Peperomia*, *Podostemaceae*, *Ranunculaceae*, &c., and cf. Aerial roots; **shoot**, one arising from root or leaf, *Ailanthus*, *Anthurium*, *Podostemaceae*, *Rafflesiaceae*, *Testudinaria*.
Adventive (Cl.), established temporarily.
Adverse, facing main axis.
Adynamandry, self-sterility.
Adyseton Adans. = Alyssum L. (Crucifer.).
Aechmandra Arn. = Melothria L. p.p. (Cucurbit.).
Aechmanthera Nees. Acanthaceae (IV. A.). 2 Himalaya.
Aechmea Ruiz et Pav. Bromeliaceae (4). 150 epiph., W.I., S. Am.
Aechmolepis Decne. Asclepiadaceae (I). 1 Angola.
Aedesia O. Hoffm. Compositae (1). 2 W. trop. Afr.
Aegialitis R. Br. Plumbaginaceae. 1 trop. Austr. and As.
Aegiceras Gaertn. Myrsinaceae (II. 1). 2 palaeotrop. *A. majus* Gaertn. grows in mangrove swamps together with Rhizophora, &c., and exhibits a similar habit, vivipary, &c.
Aegilops L. = Triticum L. p.p. (Gramin.).
Aeginetia L. Orobanchaceae. 2 Ceylon to Japan and Phil. Is.
Aegiphila Jacq. Verbenaceae (4). 40 trop. Am., W.I.
Aegle Correa. Rutaceae (V). 3 Indo-mal. *A. Marmelos* Correa is the bael fruit, a valuable remedy for dysentery, &c.
Aeglopsis Swingle. Rutaceae (V). 1 Ivory Coast.
Aegopodium Knaut. ex L. Umbelliferae (III. 5). 5 Eur., As. *A. Podagraria* L. the goat, gout, or bishop's weed, in Brit.
Aegopogon Beauv. Gramineae (3). 3 Braz. to Calif.
Aeluropus Trin. Gramineae (10). 5 Medit. to Ind. Halophytes.
Aeneus (Lat.), brass-coloured.
Aeolanthus Mart. Labiatae (VII). 25 Afr.
Aeonia (*Oeonia*) Lindl. Orchidaceae (II. 20). 5 Masc.
Aeonium Webb et Berth. (*Sempervivum* L. p.p.). Crassul. 40 S. Medit.
Aequalis (Lat.), similar in size; **Aequi-** (Lat. pref.), equal.
Aerangis Reichb. f. (*Angraecum* Thou. p.p. *BH.*). Orchid. (II. 20). 50 palaeotrop.
Aeranthes Lindl. Orchidaceae (II. 20). 6 Madag., Masc.
Aeranthus Rchb. f. = Mystacidium Lindl. (*BH.*) = Macroplectrum Pfitz.
Aerating roots, roots with aerenchyma.
Aerenchyma, respiratory tissue formed by the phellogen; *Avicennia*, *Bruguiera*, *Herminiera*, *Jussieua*, *Neptunia*, *Rumex*, *Sesbania*, *Sonneratia*, *Taxodium*, *Terminalia*.
Aeria O. F. Cook. Palmae (IV. 1). 1 Porto Rico.
Aerial roots, adventitious roots arising above ground, often forming *buttresses* (Palmae, Pandanaceae), *pillars* (Araceae, Ficus), *clasping*

and climbing organs (Araceae, Hedera, Orchidaceae, Tecoma), *water-absorbing organs* (Orchidaceae, Velloziaceae), *assimilating organs* (Orchidaceae, Podostemaceae), *thorns* (Acanthorhiza), *parasitic suckers* (Cuscuta, Viscum), &c.

Aerides Lour. Orchidaceae (II. 20). 20 E. As. Leaves fleshy.

Aerophytes, epiphytes.

Aerotropism, influence of gases on growth and curvature.

Aeruginous, verdigris-coloured.

Aerva Forsk. Amarantaceae (2). 12 trop. As., Afr.

Aesandra Pierre (*Payena* A. DC. p.p. *EP.*). Sapotaceae (1). 1 trop. As.

Aeschynanthus Jack. (*Trichosporum* D. Don.) Gesneraceae (1). 75 Indomal., China. Many epiphytes with fleshy leaves. Extreme protandry with movement of sta. Seeds with long hairs.

Aeschynomene L. (incl. *Herminiera* Guill. et Perr. *EP.*). Legum. (III. 7). 90 warm. From the pith-like wood of *A. aspera* L. (shola, pith-plant) the solar helmets of trop. As. are made.

Aesculus L. (incl. *Pavia* Boerh.). Hippocastanaceae (Sapind. *BH.*). 25 N. temp., S. Am. *A. Hippocastanum* L. (horse-chestnut) and several of § Pavia orn. trees. *A. ohioensis* Michx. (*glabra* Willd.) buckeye (U.S.). Trees with large winter buds, covered with resinous scale l., containing next year's shoot and infl. very advanced. The bud expands rapidly in spring. In *A. parviflora* Walt. transitions from scale to perfect l. may be seen, showing the former to = leaf bases. L. opp., exstip., palmate; the blades when young are hairy and hang downwards. Owing to different lengths of stalk, &c., the l., looked at from above, form a very good *mosaic*, and are all equally exposed to light. Infl. mixed, the primary structure racemose, the lat. branches cymose (cincinni). Upper fls. ♂ with rudimentary ovary, and open first. ☿ fls. protog. The chief visitors are bees. On the C are yellow spots, which later on turn red (*cf.* Fumaria, Diervilla, &c.). K (5); C 5 or 4 zygomorphic; A 8—5 introrse; disc extrastaminal, often one-sided; $\underline{G}$ (3), 3-loc., with 2 ov. in each loc. Fr. a leathery caps., usu. 1-seeded, 3-valved; seed large, exalb. (*cf.* this fr. with Castanea).

Aestivalis (Lat.), of summer.

Aestivation, arrangement of perianth l. in the bud. L. or segments not even meeting at edges, the a. is *open* (C of Cruciferae, see floral diagrams), touching but not overlapping, *valvate* (C of Compositae), overlapping, *imbricate* (K of Leguminosae). Special cases of imbr. are *convolute* or *contorted* (each l. overlapping with the same right or left edge, so that the C looks twisted, as in Ericaceae) and *quincuncial* (two l. overlapping with both edges, two underlapping with both, one over- and under-lapping, as in K of Caryophyllaceae). Each l. overlapping the one post. to it, *ascending* (K of Vicia in Leguminosae), ant. to it, *descending* (C of Vicia). L. margins turned inwards, *induplicate* (C of many Compositae), outwards, *reduplicate*. L. rolled up inwards like watch springs, *circinate* (petals of Hamamelidaceae).

Aetaerio, Etaerio.

Aetanthus Engl. Loranthaceae (1). 10 N. Andes.

Aetheilema R. Br. = Phaylopsis Willd. (Acanth.)

Aethionema R.Br. (incl. *Eunomia* DC.). Cruciferae (2). 55 Medit. Fr. lomentose in some; in others, *e.g. A. heterocarpum* J. Gay, there are two kinds of fr., one many-seeded and dehiscent, the other one-seeded indehiscent. (Solms in *Bot. Zeit.* 1901, p. 61.)

Aethusa L. Umbelliferae (III. 5). 1 Eur. (incl. Brit.), *A. Cynapium* L. (fool's parsley), a poisonous weed resembling parsley.

Aextoxicon Ruiz et Pav. Euphorbiaceae (A. I. 1). 1 Chili.

Affinity, degree of resemblance and relationship.

Affixed, fixed upon.

Affonsea A. St. Hil. Leguminosae (I. 1). 3 Brazil.

Afrafzelia Pierre (*Afzelia* Sm. p.p. *EP.*). Leguminosae (II. 3). 5 trop. Afr.

Aframomum K. Schum. (*Amomum* L. p.p. Auct.). Zingiber. (I). 50 trop. Afr.

Afrardisia Mez. (*Ardisia* Sw. p.p.). Myrsinaceae (II. 2). 15 trop. Afr.

African corn-lily, *Ixia*; **lily,** *Agapanthus umbellatus* L'Hérit.; **marigold,** *Tagetes*; **oak,** *Lophira, Oldfieldia*; **rubber,** *Landolphia*; **violet,** *Saintpaulia ionantha* H. Wendl.

Afridia Duthie (*Nepeta* Riv. p.p.). Labiatae (VI). 1 Afghanistan.

Afrocalathea K. Schum. (*Calathea* G. F. W. Mey p.p.). Marant. 1 W. Afr.

Afrodaphne Stapf. (*Beilschmiedea* Nees p.p.). Lauraceae (II). 20 trop. Afr.

Afrofittonia Lindau. Acanthaceae (IV. B). 1 W. trop. Afr.

Afrohamelia Wernham. Rubiaceae (I. 7). 1 Nigeria.

Afromendoncia Gilg. Acanthaceae (II). 4 trop. Afr.

Afrorhaphidophora Engl. Araceae (II). 2 trop. W. Afr.

Afrormosia Harms (*Ormosia* Jacks. p.p.). Leguminosae (III. 1). 4 trop. Afr.

Afrosison H. Wolff. Umbelliferae (III. 4). 2 trop. Afr.

Afrostyrax Perkins et Gilg. Styraceae. 3 trop. Afr.

Afrothismia Schlechter (*Thismia* Griff. p.p.). Burmann. 1 trop. Afr.

Afzelia Sm. (*Intsia* Thou.). Legumin. (II. 3). 12 trop. As., Afr.

Afzeliella Gilg. (*Guyonia* Naud. p.p.). Melastomaceae (I). 1 Sierra Leone.

Agad (Cl.), a beach plant; **agium** a beach formation.

Agallis Phil. Cruciferae (inc. sed.). 1 Chili.

Agalma Miq. = Heptapleurum Gaertn. (*BH.*) = Schefflera Forst. (Aral.).

Agalmyla Blume. Gesneriaceae (I). 3 Java, Sumatra.

Agamogenesis, asexual reproduction by buds.

Aganippea Moç. et Sesse. Compositae (5). 2 Mex.

Aganisia Lindl. Orchidaceae (II. 13). 4 trop. Am. W.I. Cult.

Aganonerion Pierre. Apocynaceae (II. 2). 1 Indochina.

Aganosma G. Don (*Ichnocarpus* R. Br. *BH.*). Apocyn. (II. 1). 4 Ind. to Phil. Is.

Agapanthus L'Hérit. Liliaceae (IV). 5 S. Afr. *A. umbellatus* L'Hérit. (African lily) in gardens. Umbel cymose. Seeds winged.

Agapetes G. Don (incl. *Paphia* Seem. *BH.*). Ericaceae (III. 2) (Vaccin. *BH.*). 35 E. As., Austr., Fiji.

Agarista D. Don (*Leucothoe* Don p.p. *EP.*). Eric. (II. 4). 25 S. Am.

Agastache Clayt. ex Gronov., O. Ktze (*Lophanthus* Benth. p.p. *BH.*). Labiatae (VI). 8 N. Am.

Agastachys R. Br. Proteaceae (I). 1 Tasmania.
Agasyllis Spreng. (*Siler* Scop. p.p. *BH.*). Umbellif. (III. 6). 2 E. Medit.
Agatea A. Gray (*Agation* Brongn. *BH.*). Viol. 12 Fiji, New Guin.
Agathaea Cass. = Felicia Cass. p.p. (Compos.).
Agathelpis Choisy. Scrophulariaceae (II. 7). [Selagin. *BH.*] 6 S. Afr.
Agathis Salisb. (*Dammara* Lam.). Coniferae (Pinaceae 1; see C. for gen. char.). 20 Malaya to N.Z. Evergr. diœc. trees; the fr. takes two years to ripen. Several give copals or animes, used for varnish, &c. *A. Dammara* Rich. (*D. orientalis* Lamb., Malay and Phil. Is.), Manila copal. *A. australis* Steud. (Austr., N.Z., Kauri or Cowrie pine), kauri-copal; the best pieces are dug out of the soil, often far from trees now living. (Wiesner, *Die Rohstoffe*, 2nd ed. pp. 253, 264.)
Agathophora Bunge (*Halogeton* p.p. *BH.*). Chenopod. (B). 1 N. Afr., Arabia.
Agathophyllum Juss. = Ravensara Sonner. (Laurac.).
Agathosma Willd. Rutaceae (I). 140 S. Afr. Cult. orn. fl.
Agati Adans. = Sesbania Scop. p.p. (Legum.).
Agation Brongn. (*Agatea* A. Gray, *EP.*). Violaceae. 3 Fiji, New Cal.
Agauria Hook. f. Ericaceae (II). 5 trop. Afr., Madag.
Agave L. Amaryllidaceae (II). 275 trop. Am. and S.U.S., incl. *A. americana* Linn. (Century plant, Maguey, American aloe). The short stem grows in thickness like Yucca, bearing a rosette of large fleshy l. coated with wax; only 2 or 3 l. form in a year. During 5 to 60 or perhaps 100 years (hence the name), depending on climate, richness of soil, &c., the plant is veg., and stores up in the l. an enormous mass of reserves. At length it flowers, a gigantic term. infl. coming rapidly out, sometimes reaching 20 feet, and bearing many fls. When the fr. is ripe the pl. dies. Veg. repr. in two ways—by suckers from base of stem, and by formation of bulbils in place of many fls.

The rush of sap to so large and so rapidly developed an infl. is very great; the Mexicans cut off the young fl. head and collect the sap. As much as 1000 litres are said to be given by one plant. The fermented juice (pulque) is a national drink; from it they distil a spirit called mescal (*cf.* Cocos). Many yield useful fibres. The best are sisal hemp and henequen, given by *A. sisalana* Perrine, and *A. fourcroydes* Lem., cultivated in Yucatan, the Bahamas, India, &c. Others yield fibres variously known as pita, istle, ixtle, lechuguilla, keratto, &c. See *Rep. Miss. Bot. Gdn.* 1896, p. 47; *Kew Bull.* 1892, p. 21, *Tropenpfl.* 1899, p. 337; Dodge, *Useful Fiber Plants* (Bull. U.S. Dpt. Agr.), &c.
Agdestis Moç. et Sesse. Phytolaccaceae. 1 warm Am., W.I. A ∞.
Agelaea Soland. Connaraceae. 20 palaeotrop.
Agents, effecting seed-dispersal, see Dispersal; effecting pollination, see Pollination, &c.
Ageratella A. Gray. Compositae (2). 2 Mex. L. alt.
Ageratina O. Hoffm. Compositae (1). 2 trop. Afr.
Ageratum L. Compositae (2). 45 trop. all but one Amer. *A. conyzoides* L. (goatweed), a common weed in Ceylon. Scaly pappus.
Agglomerate, collected into a head.
Agglutinate, glued together.

Aggregatae (Warming). The 10th cohort of Sympetalae.
Aggregate (fruit), many similar fruits from one fl., *Anona*, *Fragaria*, *Illicium*, *Liriodendron*, *Magnolia*, *Phytolacca*, *Rosaceae*, *Rubus*, *Unona*.
Aggregation (Cl.), coming together of plants into groups.
Agiabampoa Rose. Compositae (5). 1 Mex.
Agialida O. Kuntze=Balanites Delile (Zygophyll.).
Agianthus Greene. Cruciferae (1). 2 N. Am.
Agiella Van Tiegh. Zygophyllaceae. 2 trop. Afr.
Aglaia Lour. Meliaceae (III). 125 Indomal., China.
Aglaodorum Schott (*Aglaonema* p.p. *BH.*). Araceae (V). 1 Sumatra, Borneo.
Aglaonema Schott. Araceae (V). 45 E. Ind. There are several infl. forming a sympodium. Fl. monœcious, naked.
Aglossorhyncha Schlecht. Orchidaceae (II. 5). 8 New Guinea.
Agonandra Miers. Opiliaceae [Olacin. *BH.*]. 1 E. trop. Brazil.
Agonis Lindl. Myrtaceae (II. 1). 13 Austr. (willow-myrtle).
Agoseris Raf.=Troximon Nutt. (Compos.). 40 Am.
Agrad (Cl.), a cultivated plant; **agrium**, a culture formation.
Agrestis (Lat.), **Agrestal**, growing in fields.
Agrianthus Mart. Compositae (2). 3 Brazil.
Agrimonia Tourn. ex L. Rosaceae (III. 5). 10 N. temp. *A. Eupatoria* Linn. and *A. odorata* Mill. (agrimony) in Brit. The receptacle encloses the two achenes in fr., and is covered with hooks.
Agrimony, *Agrimonia*; **hemp-**, *Eupatorium cannabinum* L.
Agriophyllum Bieb. Chenopodiaceae (A). 5 Centr. Asia.
Agronomy, agriculture of field crops and cultivation.
Agropyron J. Gaertn. Gramineae (12). 60 temp. *A. caninum* Beauv. (wheat-grass) and *A. repens* Beauv. (twitch or couch-grass) in Brit., the latter a troublesome weed. Its long rhizome roots at the nodes, and if broken up each node gives a new plant.
Agrostemma L. (*Lychnis* L. p.p. *BH.*). Caryophyll. (II. 1). 2 Medit.
Agrostis L. Gramineae (8). 125 cosmop., chiefly N. temp., 4 in Brit. incl. *A. alba* L., white Bent or fiorin grass (valuable pasture).
Agrostistachys Dalz. (incl. *Sarcoclinium* Wight). Euphorb. (A. II. 2). 11 Indomal.
Agrostocrinum F. Muell. Liliaceae (III). 1 SW. Austr.
Agrostology, study of grasses.
Agrostophyllum Blume. Orchidaceae (II and III). 20 Indomal.
Aguacate, avocado, *Persea gratissima* Gaertn. f.
Agyneia L. Euphorbiaceae (A. I. 1). 1 Madag. to Chi.
Ahernia Merrill. Flacourtiaceae (2). 1 Phil. Is.
Ai-camphor, *Blumea balsamifera* DC.
Aichryson Webb. et Berth. (*Sempervivum* L. p.p.). Crassul. 10 Macaronesia.
Aidia Lour. Inc. sed. 1 Cochinchina.
Ailanthus Desf. Simarubaceae. 8 As., Austr. *A. glandulosa* Desf. (tree of heaven) in parks. Absciss layers form at base of the leaflets as well as of the petiole; the leaflets usually drop first.
Aimorra Raf. Compositae (inc. sed.). 1 N. Am.
Ainsliaea DC. Compositae (12). 30 India to Japan.
Ainsworthia Boiss.=Tordylium L. p.p. (Umbell.).

Aiolotheca DC. Compositae (5). 1 Mex.
Aiouea Aubl. Lauraceae (11). 20 trop. Am., W.I.
Aiphanes Willd. = Martinezia Ruiz et Pav. (Palmae).
Aiphytium, an ultimate formation.
Aira L. p.p. Gramin. (9). 12 N. palaeotemp., 2 Brit. (hair-grass). *A. caespitosa* L. and *A. flexuosa* L. = Deschampsia; *A. canescens* L. = Corynephorus. *A. elegans* Gaudich., cult. orn.
Airopsis Desv. Gramineae (9). 1 S. Eur., NW. Afr.
Airosperma Lauterb. et K. Schum. Rubiaceae (II. 1). 3 New Guinea.
Air-plants, epiphytes.
Airspaces, intercellular spaces, or spaces enclosed in folded leaves.
Aitchisonia Hemsl. Rubiaceae (II. 6). 1 Afghanistan.
Aitonia Thunb. (*Nymania, EP.*). Meliac. (III) formerly Sapind. 1 S. Afr.
Aizoaceae (*EP.*; *Ficoideae BH*). Dicots. (Archichl. Centrospermae). 20 gen., 650 sp. chiefly S. Afr., but also in Calif., S. Am., trop. Afr. and As., Austr. Nearly allied to the other Centrospermae, but placed in various other relationships by different authors, *e.g.* near Cactaceae by B. and H., a relationship which is certainly very close and to which Engler agrees. Xero. herbs or undershrubs with opp. or alt. exstip. l., often fleshy, and with cymes of ☿ regular fls. Anatomy see *Nat. Pfl.* Formula P 4—5 or (4—5) (odd leaf, if 5, post.); A 5 or 3 or ∞; $\underline{G}$ or $\overline{G}$ (3) or (∞), 3-loc. with ∞ ov. in each loc. Dédoublement is very common in the androeceum, and in these cases, *e.g.* Mesembryanthemum, the outer sta. are frequently represented by petaloid stds. Ovary usu. sup. with axile plac., but in Mesembryanthemum inf., multiloc. with parietal plac., a very unusual feature brought about during development (see M.). Fr. usu. a caps.; seed with embryo curved round perisperm.

Classification and chief genera (after Pax):

I. *MOLLUGINOIDEAE* (perianth deeply 5-lobed: "petals" or not: ov. sup.): Mollugo.

II. *FICOIDEAE* (perianth tubular): ($\underline{G}$) Sesuvium, Trianthema, Aizoon; ($\overline{G}$) Tetragonia, Mesembryanthemum.

Aizoon L. Aizoac. (II). 3 Afr., Medit., Austr. A ∞ in bundles.
Ajax Salisb. = Narcissus L. p.p. (Amaryllid.).
Ajowan, *Carum copticum* Benth. et Hook. f.
Ajuga L. Labiatae (I. 1). 30 palaeotemp.; 3 in Brit., incl. *A. reptans* L. (bugle) and *A. Chamaepitys* Schreb. (yellow bugle, ground-pine). The corolla has no upper lip. Veg. repr. by runners.
Akania Hook. f. Akaniaceae. 1 E. Austr.
Akaniaceae (*EP.*, *Sapind.* p.p. *BH.*). Dicots. (Archichl. Sapindales). 1 gen. Akania (q.v.). Tree with alt. imparipinnate l. and paniculate infl.; fl. ☿ ⊕; K 5, C 5 contorted, no disc; A usu. 8, the 5 external opp. sepals, $\underline{G}$ 3-loc. with 2 anatr. pend. ov. in each. Loculic. caps.; fleshy endosp.; straight embryo.
Akebia Decne. Lardizabalaceae. 4 China, Japan. *A. quinata* Decne. often cult.; fls. monoecious, the lower usually ♀; the ♀ much larger than the ♂ (very unusual). The berries dehisce like follicles. Fr. ed.
Akee, *Blighia sapida* Kon.
Akene, achene.
Alabastrum (Lat.), flower-bud.

Alae, wings, *Leguminosae*, *Polygalaceae*.
Alafia Thou. Apocynaceae (II. I). 12 trop. Afr., Madag.
Alamania La Llave et Lex. (*Epidendrum* L. p.p. *EP.*). Orchid. (II. 6). 1 Mex.
Alangiaceae (*EP.*; *Cornaceae* p.p. *BH.*). Dicots. (Archichl. Myrtiflorae). Only genus Alangium (*q.v.*).
Alangium Lam. Alangiaceae. 22 palaeotrop. Trees or shrubs with cymose infl. of heterochlam., usu. ☿ fls. K and C 4—10, A 4—10 or 8—20, or more, $\overline{G}$ 1-2-3-loc. with 1 pend. ov. in each. 1-seeded drupe. Endosp.
Alania Endl. Liliaceae (III). 1 Austr., in Blue Mts.
Alaternus (Tourn.) Mill. = Rhamnus L. p.p. (Rhamn.).
Albersia Kunth. = Amaranthus L. p.p. (Amarant.).
Alberta E. Mey (*Ernestimeyera* O. Kuntze). Rubiac. (II. I). 3 Madag., S. Afr.
Albertia Regel et Schmalh. Umbelliferae (III. 4). 3 Turkestan.
Albertinia Spreng. Compositae (1). 1 Brazil.
Albertisia Becc. Menispermaceae. 1 New Guinea.
Albidus (Lat.), whitish.
Albinism, disease from absence of normal colour; **albino**, plant with a.
Albizzia Durazz. Leguminosae (I. I). 50 warm |✻ *A. Lebbek* Benth. (siris, E. Indian walnut) &c. good timber. *A. stipulata* Boiv. (sau), *A. moluccana* Miq. &c. as shade for tea cult. &c. (very rapid growth, about 10 ft. in height, and 1 ft. in girth, a year).
Albuca L. Liliaceae (V). 50 Afr. Outer sta. often stds. Cult. orn.
Albumen (**-inous**), the endosperm of a seed; **albuminoids**, proteids.
Alburnum, sap-wood, recently formed wood.
Albus (Lat.), white.
Alcamaspinosa Nor. Inc. sed. Nomen.
Alcantara Glaziou. Compositae. Nomen. 2 Brazil.
Alcea (Tourn.) L. = Althaea Tourn. (Malv.)
Alchemilla L. Rosaceae (III. 5). 75 temp., and trop. Mts. *A. arvensis* Scop. (parsley piert), *A. vulgaris* L. (lady's mantle), and *A. alpina* L. Brit. Fl. inconspic., apet., with epicalyx; A 2 or 4, G 1—4 each with 1 ov. Achenes enclosed in dry receptacle. Some are parthenogenetic; some show a kind of chalazogamy; some have an exudation of water from the l.
Alchornea Sw. Euphorbiaceae (A. II. 2). 50 trop. Only the ♀ of *A.* (*Coelebogyne*) *ilicifolia* Muell.-Arg. is cult., but produces good seed. Adv. embryos form by budding of the nucellus round the embryo-sac (cf. Funkia).
Alchorneopsis Muell.-Arg. Euphorbiaceae (A. II. 2). 2 S. Am.
Alciope DC. Compositae (8). 2 S. Afr.
Alcoceratothrix Niedenzu. Malpighiaceae (II). 2 Brazil, Guiana.
Alcoceria Fernald. Euphorbiaceae (A. II. 7). 1 Mex.
Alcohol (ethyl, the stimulant in drinks) is obtained usu. from sugar, either stored as such in the pl., or obtained by fermentation, whether natural as in the expansion of an infl., or artificial. The chief sources are the fr. of *Vitis* (grape), tubers of potato and beet, grain of barley, rye, maize, rice, &c., stem of sugarcane, and young infl. of *Agave*, *Arenga*, *Borassus*, *Caryota*, *Cocos*, &c. *Cf.* also *Bassia*, *Ceratonia*,

Eleusine, *Ipomoea*, *Manihot*, *Musa*, *Nipa*, *Phoenix*, *Sorghum*. Methyl or wood alcohol, for burning, is obtained from hard wood, esp. beech, oak, thorn, and wattle, by distillation. See Kew Bull. 1912, p. 113.

Aldenella Greene (*Polanisia* Raf. p.p. *EP.*). Capparid. (v). 1 N. Am.

Alder, *Alnus glutinosa* Medic.; **-buckthorn**, *Rhamnus Frangula* L.; **West Indian-**, *Conocarpus erectus* L.

Aldina Endl. Leguminosae (II. 9). 5 Guiana, N. Brazil.

Aldrovanda Monti. Drosera. 1 Eur. to Austr., *A. vesiculosa* L., a rootless swimming pl. with whorls of l. Each has a stalk portion, and a blade like Dionaea, working in the same way, capturing and digesting small animals. Winter buds form in cold climates.

Alectoroctonum Schlecht. = Euphorbia L. p.p. (Euphorb.).

Alectorolophus Hall. = Rhinanthus L. p.p. (Scrophular.).

Alectorurus Makino (*Anthericum* L. p.p.). Liliaceae (III). 1 Japan.

Alectra Thunb. (*Melasma* Berg. p.p.). Scrophular. (III. 2). 20 trop. exc. Austr.

Alectryon Gaertn. Sapindaceae (I). 15 Malaya, Polynesia.

Alehoof, *Nepeta Glechoma* Benth.

Alepidea La Roche. Umbelliferae (II. 1). 25 S. and trop. Afr.

Alepyrum Hieron. (*Gaimardia* Gaudich. *BH.*). 2 N.Z., Tasm. &c.

Alepyrum R. Br. = Centrolepis Labill. (Centrolepid.).

Aletes Coulter et Rose. Umbelliferae (III. 5). 5 N. Am.

Aletris L. Liliaceae (IX.) [Haemodor. *BH.*]. 8 E. As., N. Am.

Aleurites Forst. Euphorbiaceae (A. II. 3). 6 warm As. Extrafl. nectaries on petiole and at ends of large l.-veins. *A. triloba* Forst. and others cult. for oil from seeds (wood-oil).

Aleurone, proteid in seed, usually in form of crystalloids.

Alexa Moq. Leguminosae (III. 1). 1 Brit. Guiana.

Alexanders, *Smyrnium Olusatrum* L.

Alexandra Bunge. Chenopodiaceae (B). 1 Centr. As.

Alfa, esparto, *Stipa tenacissima* L.

Alfalfa, lucerne, *Medicago sativa* L.

Alfilaria, *Erodium cicutarium* L'Hérit.

Alfredia Cass. = Carduus L. p.p. (Compos.).

Algaroba, *Ceratonia Siliqua* L., *Prosopis alba* Griseb.

Algernonia Baill. Euphorbiaceae (A. II. 7). 8 Brazil.

Alguelaguen Feuill. = Sphacele Benth. (Labiat.).

Alhagi Tourn. ex Adans. Leguminosae (III. 7). 3 Medit., W. As. Thorny xero.; the rootstock blows about in the dry season. Honey-like sap exudes in hot weather, drying into brownish lumps (manna).

Alibertia A. Rich. Rubiaceae (I. 8). 25 trop. Am.

Aliciella Brand. (*Gilia* Ruiz et Pav. p.p.). Polemon. 1 N. Am.

Alien, an introduced plant which has become naturalised.

Aligera Suksdorf. Valerianaceae. 10 Pac. Am.

Alina Adans. Inc. sed. Nomen.

-alis (Lat. suff.), belonging to.

Alisma L. (excl. *Caldesia* Parl. *EP.*). Alismaceae. 1 N. temp., Austr. *A. Plantago* L., water-plantain, Brit. Sta. 6 (doubling of outer whorl), coherent at base, forming nectary. *A. natans* L. = Elisma n.

Alismaceae (*Alismataceae EP.*, *BH.* incl. *Butomaceae*). Monocots.

(Helobiae). 11 gen., 75 sp. cosmop. Water or marsh herbs with perenn. rhiz. L. rad., erect, floating or submerged, exhibiting corresponding structure (cf. Sagittaria). Small scales in axils. Latex. Infl. usu. much branched, primary branching racemose, secondary often cymose. Fl. ☿ or unisex., reg. K 3, C 3, A 6—∞, or 3, extrorse anthers, $\underline{G}$ 6—∞, with 1 (rarely 2 or more) anatr. ov. in each. Group of achenes. Exalb. Embryo horse-shoe shaped. *Chief genera*: Alisma, Elisma, Echinodorus, Sagittaria. [**BH. chars.** add: l. various, anthers also introrse, ovules also ∞ scattered over surface of cpls., embryo also straight.]

Alismorchis Thou. = Calanthe R. Br. p.p. (Orchid.).

Alizarin, the dye-stuff of madder, *Rubia tinctorum* L.

Alkali grass, *Distichlis*.

Alkaloids, compounds of C, H, N, with or without O, of alkaline reaction. Many here given are now classed under the more definite title of purine bases. The name often indicates the genus from which they are obtained, *e.g.* aconitin (*Aconitum*), atropin, brucin (*Strychnos*), caffein or thein (*Coffea*, *Thea*), cinchonidin, cinchonin (*Cinchona*), cocaine (*Erythroxylon*), codeine (in opium), digitalin, hyoscyamin, morphin (in opium, *Papaver*), nicotine, quinine (*Cinchona*), solanine, strophanthin, strychnine, thein (= caffein), theobromin.

Alkanet, alkannin, cf. next.

Alkanna Tausch. Boraginaceae (IV. 3). 35 Medit., S. Eur. The r. of *A. tinctoria* Tausch. gives the red dye alkanet or alkannin.

Allaeanthus Thw. Moraceae (I). 3 Indomal.

Allaeophania Thw. Rubiaceae (II. 5). 3 Indomal.

Allagopappus Cass. Compositae (4). 1 Canaries.

Allamanda L. Apocynaceae (I. 1). 12 trop. Am., W.I. Seeds hairy.

Allanblackia Oliv. Guttiferae (V). 5 trop. Afr. The seeds of *A. Stuhlmannii* Eng. yield a tallow-like fat.

Allantodia R. Br. = Athyrium Roth. (Filicin.)

Allantodioid, applied to ferns resembling Allantodia.

Allantoid, sausage-shaped.

Allantoma Miers. Lecythidaceae (Myrtaceae *BH.*). 12 Guiana, Brazil.

Allardia Decne. (*Waldheimia EP.*). Compositae (7). 8 C. As.

Allasia Lour. Inc. sed. (= Vitex Tourn.?). 1 E. Afr.

Allendea La Llave. Compositae (8). 1 Mex.

Allenia Ewart. Euphorbiaceae (B. 1). 1 Austr.

Allexis Pierre. Violaceae. 3 Cameroons.

Allgood, *Chenopodium*.

Allheal, *Valeriana officinalis* L.; **W. Indian-**, *Micromeria obovata* Benth.

Alliaceous, onion-like.

Alliaria Marsh, DC. (*Sisymbrium BH.*). Crucif. (2). 5 Eur. temp., As.

Alligator apple, *Anona palustris* L.; **-pear**, *Persea gratissima* Gaertn. f.; **-wood** (W. I.), *Guarea trichilioides* L.

Allionia L. Nyctaginaceae. 10 N. Am.; **do.** Loefl. (*Mirabilis* L. p.p. *EP.*). Nyctaginaceae. 20 Am. Anthocarp glandular (cf. Pisonia).

Allioniella Rydberg (*Mirabilis* L. p.p. *EP.*). Nyctagin. 1 N. Am.

Allium (Tourn.) L. Liliaceae (IV). 325 $\underline{*}$. *A. ursinum* L. (garlic), *A.*

Schoenoprasum L. (chives), and 6 others, in Brit. *A. Cepa* L. (Persia, &c.) is the onion, *A. Porrum* L. (Eur.) the leek, *A. ascalonicum* L. (Orient) the shallot, *A. sativum* L. (S. Eur.) the garlic. Bulbous herbs with linear (or hollow centric) l. and cymose umbels of fls. Many have collateral buds in the axils. In many the fls. are replaced by bulbils serving for veg. repr. (cf. Lilium). In *A. ursinum*, &c. honey is secreted by the septal glands of the ovary; fl. protandr.

Allmania R. Br. Amarantaceae (2). 3 trop. As.

Allocalyx Cordemoy. Scrophulariaceae (II. 6). 1 Reunion.

Allocarpus H. B. et K. = Calea L. p.p. (Compos.).

Allocarpy, fruiting from cross-fertilised fl.; **-gamy**, cross-fert.

Allocarya Greene (*Eritrichium BH.*). Boragin. (IV. 2). 35 Pac. Am.

Allochrusa Bunge (*Acanthophyllum* C. A. Mey, *BH.*). Caryophyll. (II. 2). 15 W. and S. As.

Allomorphia Blume. Melastomaceae (1). 25 Malaya, China, Polynesia.

Alloneuron Pilger. Melastomaceae (1). 1 Peru.

Allophylus L. Sapindaceae (1). 120 trop. and subtrop.

Allophyton T. S. Brandegee. Scrophulariaceae (III. 3). 1 Mex.

Alloplectus Mart. (*Crantzia* Scop.). Gesner (1). 40 trop. Am.

Alloschemone Schott (*Monstera* Adans. *BH.*). Araceae (II). 1 Braz.

Allosorus Bernh. = Cryptogramme, Cheilanthes, Pellaea, &c. (Filices.)

Allospondias Stapf. (*Spondias* L. p.p. *EP.*). Anacard. (2). 2 Indochina.

Alloteropsis C. Presl. (*Panicum* L. p.p. *EP.*). Gramin. (5). 1 Calif.

Allotropa A. Gray. Pyrolaceae. 1 W. U.S.

Allotropous (insects), short-tongued.

Allseed, *Polycarpon*, *Radiola*.

Allspice, *Pimenta officinalis*; **Carolina-**, *Calycanthus floridus*.

Alluandia Drake (*Didierea* Baill. p.p. *EP.*). Didieraceae. 4 Madag.

Almeidea St Hil. Rutaceae (1). 5 Brazil.

Almeloveenia Dennst. Inc. sed. 1 Indomal.

Almond, *Prunus Amygdalus* Stokes; **country-**, *Terminalia Catappa* L.; **Java-**, *Canarium commune*, L.; **-tree** (W.I.), *Terminalia Catappa* L.

Alniphyllum Matsumura. Styraceae. 2 Formosa, SW. China.

Alnus (Tourn.) L. Betulaceae (2). 25 N. temp. and Andes. *A. glutinosa* Medic. (alder), Brit. *Cf.* Betula. In the axil of each bract of the ♂ catkin are 3 fl. (see diagram of Betula, and *cf.* other genera) each with 4 sta. and 4 perianth l. The bracteoles α, β, β′, β′ are present. All these l. are united with one another. In the ♀ catkin only two, the lat., fl. occur, and the same bracts. After fert., the ov. gives a one-seeded nut, under which is found a 5-lobed scale, the product of subsequent growth of the 5 leaves. The fl. is chalazogamic.

Stem.
fl. fl. fl.
β′ β′
α β
bract.

Alocasia Neck. Araceae (VI). 65 E. Ind. Herbaceous; monoec. *A. macrorrhiza* Schott and others are cult. for ed. rhiz. (*cf.* Colocasia).

Alocasiophyllum Engl. (*Cercestis* p.p. *EP.*). Arac. (IV). 1 W. Afr.

Aloe Tourn. ex L. Liliaceae (III). 180 S. Afr., esp. the Karroo desert. Usu. shrubby or arborescent xero., growing in thickness and branching. L. in dense rosettes at ends of branches, very fleshy, with thick epidermis, often waxy, and stomata in pits. They are cut across and the juice evap. to obtain the drug aloes.

Aloes, *Aloe*; **aloe-wood**, Cordia Sebestena L.; **aloes-wood**, *Aquilaria Agallocha* Roxb.
Aloides Boerh. ex L. = Stratiotes L. (Hydrocharit.).
Aloitis Raf. (*Gentiana* Tourn. p.p.). Gentian. (I). 4 W. and C. N. Am.
Alomia H. B. et K. Compositae (2). 15 trop. Am., Chili.
Alona Lindl. Nolanaceae (Convolv. *BH.*). 15 Chili.
Alonsoa Ruiz et Pav. Scrophulariaceae (II. 2). 6 trop. Am.
Alopecurus L. Gramineae (8). 25 temp. Eurasia. 4 Brit. incl. *A. pratensis* L., foxtail, cult. for pasture. Fl. protog.
Alophia Herb. (*Herbertia BH.*). Irid. (II). 7 warm Am. Cult. orn. fl.
Aloysia Ort. et Palau ex L'Hérit. = Lippia L. p.p. (Verben.).
Alpestris (Lat.), growing at high levels, below the tree line.
Alphandia Baill. Euphorbiaceae (A. II. 5). 2 New Cal.
Alphitonia Reissek. Rhamnaceae. 6 Austr., Malaya, Polynesia.
Alphonsea Hook. f. et Thoms. Anonaceae (I). 12 trop. As.
Alphonseopsis E. G. Baker. Anonaceae (I). I Nigeria.
Alpine, at high levels, above the tree line; = **rose**, *Rhododendron*.
Alpinia L. Zingiberaceae (I). 225 warm As., Polynesia. K small tubular, C with short tube and 3 large teeth, big labellum; lat. stds. much reduced or absent; anther lobes divided by broad connective. *A. officinarum* Hance (China) gives rhizoma galangae.
Alsad (Cl.), a grove plant; **alsium**, a grove formation.
Alseis Schott. Rubiaceae (I. 5). 4 trop. Am.
Alseodaphne Nees (*Persea* p.p. *EP.*). Lauraceae (I). 10 Indomal.
Alseuosmia A. Cunn. Caprifoliaceae. 5 N.Z.
Alsike, *Trifolium hybridum* L.
Alsinastrum Schur. = Elatine L. (Elatin.).
Alsine Scop. (*Arenaria* L. *BH.*). Caryophyll. (I. I). 60 $\underline{*}$, Chili.
Alsinodendron H. Mann. Caryophyllaceae (I. I). I Sandwich Is.
Alsinopsis Small (*Arenaria* L. p.p.). Caryophyllaceae (I. I). 10 N. Am.
Alsocydia Mart. = Bignonia L., Lundia DC., &c. (Bignon.).
Alsodeia Thou. (*Rinorea* Aubl.). Violaceae. 80 trop., sub-trop.
Alsodeiidium Engl. = Alsodeiopsis Oliv.
Alsodeiopsis Oliv. Icacinaceae (Olacin. *BH.*). 7 trop. Afr.
Alsomitra M. Roem. Cucurbitaceae (I). 10 trop.
Alsophila R. Br. Cyatheaceae. 225 trop. Large tree ferns with naked sori (the only gen. of C. without indusium). The stems yield a sago.
Alstonia R. Br. Apocyn. (I. 3). 30 Indomal. L. whorled. Bark tonic.
Alstroemeria L. Amaryllidaceae (III). 50 S. Am. L. twisted at base so that true upper surface faces down (internal anatomy also reversed). Caps. splits explosively. Cult. orn. fl.
Altamiranoa Rose (*Cotyledon* Tourn. p.p. *EP.*). Crassul. 18 Mex.
Altensteinia H. B. et K. Orchidaceae (II. 3). 12 Andes. [to Peru.
Alternanthera Forsk. (excl. *Mogiphanes* Mart. *BH.*). Amarantaceae (3). 70 trop., sub-trop. Cult. orn. l.
Alternate (l.), one at a node.
Alternation of Generations, cf. Pteridophyta.
Althaea (Tourn.) L. Malvaceae (2). 15 temp. |*, 2 Brit. incl. *A. officinalis* L., marsh-mallow; *A. rosea* Cav., hollyhock, cult. orn. fl.
Althenia Petit. Potamogeton. (Naiad. *BH.*). 2 W. Medit., 3 Austr. (*Lepilaena* J. Drumm.).

Althoffia K. Schum. Tili. 3 New Guin., Timor. Dioec. K. A ∞.
Altingia Nor. Hamamel. 3 Chi. to Java. ♂ fl. of naked sta.; by comparison with related forms it can be shown that spike of sta. is really an infl., not a fl. Large trees; good timber.
Alum-root, *Geranium maculatum* L., *Heuchera* (Am.).
Alvaradoa Liebm. Simarub. 5 warm Am., W.I. Micropyle down.
Alveola, a surface cavity; **alveolate**, honey-combed.
Alvesia Welw. Labiat. (VII). 1 trop. Afr.
Alvisia Lindl. (*Eria* p.p. *BH.* non Hook. f.). Orchid. (II. 15). 1 Ceylon.
Alvordia T. S. Brandegee. Comp. (5). 2 Calif., Mex.
Alysicarpus Neck. (*Fabricia* Scop.). Legum. (III. 7). 10 warm |✱.
Alyssoides Adans., Druce, Miller = Vesicaria Lam. (Crucif.).
Alyssopsis Boiss. Crucif. (4). 2 Persia.
Alyssum Tourn. ex. L. (*BH.* incl. *Berteroa*, *Lobularia*, &c.). Cruc. (4). 120 Medit., Eur. Cult. perf. or orn. fl. [Madag., Indomal.
Alyxia Banks ex R. Br. (*Gynopogon* Forst.). Apocyn. (I. 3). 50
Alzatea Ruiz et Pav. Celastr. 1 Peru. L. opp. or whorled.
Amaioua Aubl. Rubi. (I. 8). 5 Braz. to Trinidad. Often dioecious.
Amalocalyx Pierre. Apocyn. (II. 1). 1 Cochinchina.
Amalophyllon T. S. Brandegee. Scroph. (III. 3). 1 Mex.
Amanoa Aubl. Euphorb. (A. I. 1). 7 trop. S. Am., W.I., Afr., Madag.
Amaraboya Linden ex Mast. (*Blakea* p.p. *EP.*). Melastom. (1).
Amaracarpus Blume. Rubi. (II. 5). 7 Malay Archip. [3 Colombia.
Amaracus Gled. (*Origanum* p.p. *BH.*). Labiat. (VI. 11). 15 E. Medit.
Amaralia Welw. (*Sherbournia* *BH.*). Rubi. (I. 8). 5 trop. Afr. K conv.
Amarantaceae (*EP.*, *BH.*). Dicots. (Archichl. Centrospermae; Curvembryae *BH.*; pp. xv, liii). 72/700 trop. and temp., usu. herbs or shrubs with opp. or alt. entire exstip. l. Fl. sol. or in axillary cymes (the whole infl. racemose), ☿, rarely unisexual, usu. reg. P usu. 4—5 or (4—5), usu. membranous; A 1—5 opp. P, free or ± united to P or disc, or to one another; $\underline{G}$ (2—3), free or united to P, 1-loc., with ∞—1 campylotr. ov. Berry or nut; usu. shiny testa; embryo curved; *Classification and chief genera* (after Engler): [endosp.
1. *Celosieae* (ov. > 1, anther 4-loc.): Celosia, Hermbstaedtia.
2. *Amaranteae* (ov. 1, anther 4-loc.): Amarantus, Sericocoma, Cyathula, Aerva, Ptilotus, Psilotrichum, Achyranthes.
3. *Gomphreneae* (anther 2-loc.): Froelichia, Pfaffia, Alternanthera, Gomphrena, Iresine.

Amarantellus Spegazz. Amarant. (2). 1 Arg.
Amarantus L. (incl. *Blitum* p.p.). Amarant. (2). 60 trop. and temp. Infl. of ∞ fl. *A. gangeticus* L., &c., are pot-herbs in India, &c.; *A. caudatus* L., *A. paniculatus* L., &c., give ed. grain, used as a cereal in trop. As. Cult. orn. fl. (love-lies-bleeding, prince's feather).
Amarella Griseb., Rafin. (*Gentiana* p.p.). Gentian. (1). 25 N. Am.
Amarenus C. Presl = Trifolium L. p.p. (Legum.).
Amaroria A. Gray. Simarub. 1 Fiji. 3-merous. G 1.
Amarus (Lat.), bitter.
Amaryllidaceae (*EP.*; *BH.* incl. *Velloz.*). Monocots. (Liliiflorae; Epigynae *BH.*; pp. ix, liv). 90/1050, usu. trop. or subtrop. Usu. xero., often bulbous, leafing only in spring or the rains; some (II) covered with wax. III have ordinary stems, many have rhiz.

Infl. usu. on a scape, with spathe, cymose, but often umbel- or head-like by condensation; solitary fls. in some. Fl. ☿, reg. or ·|· (transv. so in Anigozanthos). P or (P) 3 + 3 petaloid, A 3 + 3, sometimes some staminodial, usu. introrse; $\overline{G}$ (3), rarely ½-inf. or sup., 3-loc. or rarely 1-loc. with axile plac. and ∞ anatr. ov. In some (Narcissus, &c.) a conspic. *corona* looks like an extra whorl of P, between normal P and A (? combined ligules of P, or stips. of sta.), to be seen in stages in Caliphruria, Sprekelia, Eucharis, Narcissus. Loculic. caps., or berry; endosp., small straight embryo. Veg. repr. by bulbils common. (*BH.* chars. incl. ∞ sta. in bundles, and lamellate placentae, &c.)

Classification and chief genera (after Pax): near to Liliaceae. Anthers introrse.

I. *AMARYLLIDOIDEAE* (bulb, scape, spathe 2 or more l.):

1. *Amaryllideae* (no corona): Haemanthus, Clivia, Galanthus, Leucojum, Nerine, Amaryllis, Zephyranthes, Crinum.

2. *Narcisseae* (corona, sometimes reduced to scales or a ring): Hymenocallis, Eucharis, Narcissus, Pancratium, Sprekelia, Hippeastrum.

II. *AGAVOIDEAE* (rhiz.; l. fleshy, in rosettes): (fl. ·|·), Bravoa, Polianthes, (reg.), Agave, Furcraea, Doryanthes.

III. *HYPOXIDOIDEAE* (rhiz.; stem with small ordinary l.): Alstroemeria, Bomarea, Curculigo, Hypoxis, Anigozanthos.

Anthers extrorse.

IV. *CAMPYNEMATOIDEAE*: Campynema (only genus).

Amaryllis L. (*Belladonna* Sweet). Amaryllid. (I. 1). 1 Cape Col., *A. belladonna* L., cult. orn. fl. (A. of greenhouses = Hippeastrum).

Amasonia L. f. (*Taligalea EP.*). Verben. (1). 6 Brazil to Trinidad.

Amauria Benth. Comp. (6). 2 SW.U.S., Mex. Pappus o. [L. alt.

Amauriella Rendle. Arac. (V). 1 S. Nigeria.

Amauriopsis Rydberg (*Amauria* p.p.). Comp. (6). 1 S.W. U.S.

Ambelania Aubl. Apocyn. (I. 1). 6 trop. S. Am. Disc o.

Ambianella A. Chevalier (*Mimusops* p.p.) Sapot. (2). 1 Congo.

Ambiguous, of uncertain origin or doubtful position.

Amblogyna Rafin. = Amarantus L. p.p. (Amarant.).

Amblostoma Scheidw. Orchid. (II. 6). 7 trop. S. Am. Pollinia 4.

Amblyanthera Muell.-Arg. (*Mandevilla* Lindl.). Apocyn. (II. 1). 45 S. Am.

Amblyanthopsis Mez. (*Ardisia* p.p.). Myrsin. (II. 2). 3 E. Indomal.

Amblyanthus A. DC. Myrsin. (II. 2). 3 E. Indomal.

Amblygonocarpus Harms. Legum. (I. 4). 1 trop. Afr. [N. Am.

Amblynotopsis Macbride (*Antiphytum* p.p.). Borag. (IV. 4). 4 trop.

Amblyocalyx Benth. Apocyn. (I. 3). 1 Borneo. L. whorled.

Amblyocarpum Fisch. et Mey. Comp. (4). 1 near Caspian Sea.

Amblyopappus Hook. et Arn. Comp. (6). 2 Chile, Peru. Scaly pappus.

Amblystigma Benth. Asclep. (II. 1). 3 Arg., Bolivia. Corona o.

Ambora Juss. = Tambourissa Sonner. (Monim.).

Amborella Baill. Monim. 1 New Caled. Dioec. Ov. orthotr. L. alt.

Amboyna wood, *Pterocarpus indicus* Willd. (?).

Ambrosia L. Comp. (5). 15 Am., W.I., Afr. Head unisexual, ♀ one-fld. Fr. enclosed in invol. **Ambrosiaceae**, Compositae, p.p.

Ambrosinia L. Arac. (VII). 1 Medit.

Ambulia Lam. (*Limnophila* R. Br., *Terebinthina* Rumph. ex O. Ktze.). Scrophulariaceae (II. 6). 30 palaeotrop.
Amburana Schwacke et Taub. (*Torresea* Allem. *EP.*). Legum. (II. 3). 1 Minas Geraes, Brazil. Good timber.
Ameghinoa Spegazz. Compositae (12). 1 Patagonia.
Amelanchier Medic. Rosaceae (II). 15 N. temp.
Ameletia DC. = Ammannia Houst. (*BH.*) = Rotala L. (Lythr.).
Amellus L. Compositae (3). 10 S. Afr.
Amentaceae, the catkinate families, Salicaceae, Juglandaceae, Betulaceae, Fagaceae; **amentaceous**, catkin-bearing; **amentum**, a catkin.
American aloe, *Agave*; **-cowslip**, *Dodecatheon*; **-ebony**, *Brya Ebenus* DC.; **-elemi**, *Bursera gummifera* L.; **-fly-trap**, *Apocynum androsaemifolium* L.; **-laurel**, *Kalmia*; **-mastic**, *Schinus molle* L.; **-water-weed**, *Elodea canadensis* Michx.; **-witch-elder**, *Fothergilla*.
Amerimnon P. Br. = Dalbergia L. f. (Legum.).
Amethystea L. Labiatae (I. 1). 1 Siberia, E. Russia.
Amherstia Wall. Leguminosae (II. 3). 1 Burma, *A. nobilis*, Wall., a tree often cult. for its splendid fl. Stalk and br. as well as pets. are bright pink. Sta. united in a tube. The young l., covered with brownish spots, hang down "as if poured out"; later they stiffen, turn green and come to the horiz. position (Keeble, *Ann. Bot.* IX. 59).
Amianthium A. Gray (*Zygadenus* Michx.). Liliaceae (I). 1 Atl. Am.
Amicia H. B. et K. Leguminosae (III. 7), 5 Andes. In *A. Zygomeris* DC. the large stips. protect the bud.
Ammannia (Houst.) L. Lythraceae. 20 cosmop.
Ammi (Tourn.) L. Umbelliferae (III. 5). 7 Medit., trop. Afr.
Ammiopsis Boiss. Umbelliferae (III. 2). 2 NW. Afr.
Ammobium R. Br. Compositae (4). 2 New S. Wales. *A. alatum* R. Br. cult. for the fl. heads, dried to form "everlastings."
Ammobroma Torr. Lennoaceae. 1 New Mex., Calif.
Ammocallis Small = Vinca L. (*BH.*) = Lochnera Reichb. (Apocyn.).
Ammocharis Herb. Amaryllidaceae (I). 2 S. and trop. Afr.
Ammochloa Boiss. Gramineae (10). 2 Medit.
Ammochthad (Cl.), a sandbank pl.; **-thium**, a sandbank formation.
Ammodaucus Coss. et Dur. (*Daucus* p.p.). Umbellif. (III. 8). 1 Algeria.
Ammodendron Fisch. ex DC. Leguminosae (III. 1). 5 W. As.
Ammodenia Patrin = Arenaria L. p.p. (*BH.*) = Alsine Scop. p.p.
Ammoniacum, gum-, *Dorema ammoniacum* D. Don.
Ammophila Host. Gramineae (8). 4 N. temp. *A.* (*Psamma*) *arundinacea* Host. (marram) common on sandy coasts in Brit., and much used for sand-binding. After some years a light soil forms, in which other pl. take root. The l. curl inwards in dry air.
Ammoselinum Torr. et Gray. Umbelliferae (III. 5). 3 N. Am.
Ammosperma Hook. f. Cruciferae (2). 1 N. Afr.
Ammothamnus Bunge. Leguminosae (III. 1). 2 W. As.
Amoenus (Lat.), sweet, pleasant.
Amomum L. Zingiberaceae (2). 100 paleotrop. Fl. usu. on scapes from the rhiz.; wings and keel absent, standard folding round sta.-tube at base. Protog. with persistent stigma.
Amoora Roxb. Meliaceae (III). 20 Indomal.
Amoreuxia Moç. et Sesse. Cochlosperm. (Bixin. *BH.*). 3 Centr. Am.

Amoria C. Presl = Trifolium Tourn. p.p. (Legum.).
Amorpha L. Leguminosae (III. 6). 15 N. Am. Wings and keel 0; standard folds round base of sta.-tube. Protog. with persistent stigma.
Amorphocalyx Klotzsch = Sclerolobium Vog. p.p. (Legum.). 1 Guiana.
Amorphophallus Blume (incl. *Hydrosme*, *Synantherias*, *BH.*). Araceae (IV). 90 trop. | ※. Usu. corm-like rhiz., giving yearly a big l. (up to 10 ft.) and infl. (in *A. Titanum* Becc. 3 ft. high), with ♂ fl. above and ♀ below. Its dirty red colour and foetid smell attract carrion flies, which sometimes lay eggs on the spadix.
Amorphospermum F. Muell. (*Lucuma* p.p. *BH.*). Sapot. (I). 1 trop. E. Austr.
Amorphous, shapeless.
Ampacus Rumph. ex O. Ktze. = Evodia Forst. (Rutac.).
Ampalis Boj. Moraceae (I). 2 Madag.
Ampelanus Raf. = Enslenia Nutt. (Asclep.) 3 W. N. Am.
Ampelidaceae, **Ampelideae** (*BH.*) = Vitaceae.
Ampelocera Klotzsch. Ulmaceae. 3 trop. Am., W. I.
Ampelocissus Planch. (*Vitis* L. p.p. *BH.*). Vitaceae. 75 trop.
Ampelodaphne Meissn. Lauraceae (II). 5 Brazil, Guiana.
Ampelodesma Beauv. Gramineae (10). 1 Medit. When young used as fodder. The l. used like esparto (Stipa).
Ampelodonax Lojac. (*Arundo* Tourn. p.p.). Gramin. (10). 1 Sicily.
Ampelopsis (L. C. Rich. in) Michx. p.p. (*Vitis* L. p.p. *BH.*). Vitaceae. 24 temp. and subtrop. As. Am. For garden A. cf. *Parthenocissus*.
Ampelosicyos Thou. = Telfairia Hook. (?) Cucurbitac. 2 Madag.
Ampelothamnus Small (*Andromeda* p.p.). Ericaceae (II. 1). 1 Florida.
Amperea A. Juss. Euphorbiaceae (B. II). 6 Austr., Tasm.
Ampherephis H. B. et K. = Centratherum Cass. (Compos.).
Amphi- (Gr. pref.), both; **-bious** pl., pl. which can live in water or on land, *Peplis*, *Polygonum*; **-carpic**, with two kinds of fr., *Aethionema*, *Cardamine*, *Dichondra*, *Dimorphotheca*; **-mixis**, sexual repr.; **-tropous** (ovule), turning both ways on stalk.
Amphiachyris Nutt. (*Gutierrezia* Benth. p.p.). Comp. (3). 2 Calif.
Amphianthus Torr. Scrophulariaceae (II. 6). 1 Georgia.
Amphibecis Schrank = Centratherum Cass. (Comp.).
Amphiblemma Naud. Melastomaceae (I). 5 trop. W. Afr. Cult. orn.
Amphiblestra Presl. Polypodiaceae. 1 Venezuela.
Amphibolis C. Agardh. (*Cymodocea* Kon. p.p. *EP.*). Potamoget. 1 Austr.
Amphibromus Nees. Gramineae (9). 1 Austr.
Amphicarpaea Ell. Leguminosae (III. 10). 18 trop. and N. Am., E. As. Some have cleist. fl. below, which give subterranean fr. like Arachis.
Amphicarpum Kunth (**-on** Raf.). Gramineae (5). 2 S.E. U.S.
Amphicome Royle. Bignoniaceae (2). 2 Himal.
Amphicosmia Gardn. = Hemitelia R. Br. (Cyatheac.).
Amphidetes Fourn. Asclepiadaceae (II. 1). 2 Rio de Janeiro.
Amphidonax Nees = Arundo L. and Zenkeria Trin. (Gram.)
Amphidoxa DC. Compositae (4). 6 S. and trop. Afr., Madag.
Amphiestes Sp. Moore. Acanthaceae (IV. B). 1 Madag.
Amphigena Rolfe. Orchidaceae (II. 1). 2 Cape Colony.
Amphiglossa DC. Compositae (4). 4 S. Afr.
Amphilochia Mart. = Qualea Aubl. p.p. (Vochys.).

Amphilophis Nash (*Andropogon* L. p.p.). Gramineae (2). 10 U.S.
Amphilophium Kunth. Bignoniaceae (1). 10 warm Am.
Amphimas Pierre. Leguminosae (II. 8). 4 Gaboon.
Amphiodon Huber. Leguminosae (III. 6). 1 Amazon valley.
Amphipogon R. Br. Gramineae (8). 6 Austr.
Amphirhapis DC. = Inula L., Microglossa DC., Solidago L.
Amphirrhox Spreng. Violaceae. 3 trop. Am.
Amphistelma Griseb. = Vincetoxicum (*BH.*) = Metastelma (Ascl.).
Amphitecna Miers. Bignoniaceae (4). 2 Mex.
Amphithalea Eckl. et Zeyh. Leguminosae (III. 3). 10 S. Afr.
Amphoranthus Sp. Moore = Phaeoptilum Radlk. p.p. (Nyctag.).
Amphorchis Thou. = Cynorchis Thou. p.p. (Orchid.).
Amphorella T. S. Brandegee. Asclepiad. (II. 1). 1 Mex.
Amphoricarpus Vis. Compositae (11). 2 S.E. Eur.
Amphorocalyx Baker. Melastomaceae (1). 2 Madag.
Amphymenium H. B. et K. = Pterocarpus L. p.p. (Legum.). 15 trop. S. Am.
Amplectens (Lat.), embracing; **amplexicaul**, clasping the stem.
Amsinckia Lehm. Boraginaceae (IV. 2). 15 Pac. Am.
Amsonia Walt. Apocynaceae (I. 3). 10 N. Am., Japan.
Amydrium Schott (*Epipremnum NP.*). Arac. (11). 1 Malay Arch.
Amygdalopsis Carr. = Prunus Tourn. p.p. (Rosac.).
Amygdalus (Tourn.) L. = Prunus Tourn. p.p. (Rosac.).
Amylaceous, starchy; **amyloid**, starch-like.
Amylocarpus Barb. Rodr. (*Bactris* L. p.p.). Palmaceae (IV. 2). 20 Brazil.
Amyris P. Br. Rutaceae (IV) (Burseraceae *BH.*). 15 warm Am., W.I.
Anabasis L. Chenopodiaceae (B). 20 Medit., C. As.
Anabata Willd. = Faramea Aubl. (Logan.).
Anacampseros L. Portulacaceae. 15 S. Afr. Xero. with fleshy l., and buds protected by bundles of hair, representing stips.
Anacamptis Rich. (*Orchis* p.p. *BH.*). Orchid. (II. 1). 1 Eur. N. Afr.
Anacampt-orchis × G. Camus, hybrid with Orchis. 2 S.W. Eur.
Anacardiaceae (*EP.*; *BH.* incl. *Corynocarpaceae*, *Julianiaceae*). Dicots. (Archichl. Sapindales). 60 gen., 500 sp., chiefly trop., but also Medit., E. As., Am. Trees and shrubs with alt. exstip. l., and panicles of ∞ fl. Resin-passages occur, but the l. are not gland-dotted (hence they cannot be confounded with Rutaceae). Recept. convex, flat, or concave; gynophores, etc., occur. Fl. typically 5-merous, reg., hypog. to epig.; A 10–5 or other number; G (3–1) rarely 5, each with 1 anatr. ov., often only one fertile. Usually drupe with resinous mesocarp; embryo curved; no endosperm. The fr. of Mangifera, Anacardium, Spondias, Pistacia, &c., are important. Rhus furnishes various useful products. [**BH. chars.** include chars. of Corynocarpus and Julianiaceae, both rare; fam. in Sapindales.]

Classification and chief genera (after Engler):

A. 5 free cpls., or 1. L. simple, entire:
1. *Mangifereae*: Mangifera, Anacardium.

B. Cpls. united. L. rarely simple:
2. *Spondieae* (ovules in each cpl.): Spondias.
3. *Rhoideae* (1 ovule only, ovary free): Pistacia, Rhus.
4. *Semecarpeae* (do., ovary sunk in axis): Semecarpus.

C. Cpl. 1. ♀ fl. naked. L. simple, toothed:
5. *Dobineae*: Dobinea (only genus).

Anacardium L. Anacardiaceae (1). 8 trop. Am.; *A. occidentale* L. (cashew-nut) largely cult. Fl. polygamous. Each has 1 cpl. yielding a kidney-shaped nut with hard acrid coat. The nut (promotion nut, coffin-nail) is ed. Under it the axis swells up into a pear-like body, fleshy and ed. The stem yields a gum like arabic.
Anacharis Rich. = Elodea Michx. (Hydrochar.).
Anacolosa Blume. Olacaceae (Olacin. *BH.*). 10 Indomal.
Anacyclus L. Compositae (7). 15 Medit. Some offic. (radix pyrethri).
Anadendrum Schott. Araceae (1). 6 Indomal.
Anadenia R. Br. = Grevillea R. Br. p.p. (Proteac.).
Anaectocalyx Triana. Melastomaceae (1). 2 Venezuela.
Anagallis (Tourn.) L. Primulaceae. 25 Eur., As., Afr., S. Am., 2 Brit. (pimpernel). The fl. of *A. arvensis* L. (poor man's weather glass) closes in dull or cold weather.
Anaglypha DC. Compositae (4). 2 S. Afr.
Anagosperma Wettst. Scrophulariaceae (III. 3). 1 N. Zealand.
Anagyris L. Legum. (III. 2). 2 Medit. **A.** Lour. = Ormosia Jacks.
Analogous (organs), agreeing in function, but not in descent, mode of origin, nor position; *e.g.* the r.-like l. of Salvinia are analogous to r.
Anamirta Colebr. Menispermaceae. 1 Indomal. The achenes of *A. Cocculus* Wight et Arn. (Cocculus indicus) are used to adulterate porter. In the angles between the big veins of the l. are little cavities covered by hairs and inhabited by mites (acaro-domatia).
Anamomis Griseb. = Eugenia L. p.p. (Myrt.). 8 W.I., Fla.
Ananas Tourn. ex L. (*Ananassa* Lindl.). Bromeliaceae (4). 5 trop. Am., incl. *A. sativus* Schult., the pine-apple, largely cult. in Sandw. Is., Singapore, &c. Stem short and leafy, terrestrial, bearing a term. infl., which after fert. forms a common mass, fr. bracts, and axis, while the main axis grows beyond and forms a tuft of l.—the crown of the pineapple. Some vars. cult. orn. l.
Anandrous, without sta.
Ananthacorus Underw. et Moxon (*Taenitis* p.p.) Polypod. 1 trop. Am.
Anantherix Nutt. = Asclepiodora A. Gray (*BH.*) = Asclepias L. p.p.
Anapeltis J. Sm. = Polypodium L. (Filic.).
Anaphalis DC. Compositae (4). 50 As., Eur., Am. Hairy.
Anaphrenium E. Mey. (*Heeria* Meissn. *EP.*). Anacard. (3). 12 Afr.
Anaphyllum Schott. Araceae (IV). 2 S. India.
Anarrhinum Desf. (*Simbuleta EP.*). Scroph. (II. 3). 12 Medit.
Anarthria R. Br. Restionaceae. 6 S.W. Austr.
Anarthrophyllum Benth. Leguminosae (III. 3). 12 Andes.
Anartia Miers (*Tabernaemontana* L. p.p.). Apocyn. (I. 3). 7 trop. Am.
Anastatica L. Cruciferae (4). 1 E. Medit., *A. hierochuntina* L. (rose of Jericho). While the seeds are ripening in the dry season the l. fall off and the branches fold inwards, reducing the pl. to a ball of wickerwork, which rolls about with the pods closed until it reaches a wet spot, or the rainy season begins.
Anastomosis, reunion of branches.
Anastrabe E. Mey. Scrophulariaceae (II. 4). 1 S. Afr.
Anastraphia D. Don. Compositae (12). 20 W. Ind.
Anastrophus Schlecht. = Paspalum L. p.p. (Gram.). 8 U.S.

Anatherum Beauv. = Andropogon L. p.p. (Gram.).
Anatropanthus Schlecht. Asclepiadaceae (II. 3). 1 Borneo.
Anatropous (ovule), reversed on stalk.
Anaxagorea St. Hil. Anonaceae (1). 15 trop. As., Am.
Anaxeton Gaertn. Compositae (4). 7 S.W. S.Afr.
Ancad, a cañon plant.
Anceps (Lat.), **ancipitous**, two-edged.
Anchietea A. St. Hil. Violaceae. 8 trop. S. Am.
Anchomanes Schott. Araceae (IV). 7 trop. Afr.
Anchonium DC. Cruciferae (4). 3 W. As.
Anchovy pear, *Grias cauliflora* L.
Anchusa L. Boragin. (IV. 3). 45 Eur., N. Afr., W. As. *A. officinalis* L. was formerly offic., and is widely scattered (escape in Brit.).
Ancistranthus Lindau. Acanthaceae (IV. B). 1 Cuba.
Ancistrocarpus Oliv. Tiliaceae. 2 trop. W. Afr.
Ancistrocarya Maxim. Boraginaceae (IV. 4). 1 Japan.
Ancistrochilus Rolfe. Orchidaceae (II. 9). 2 trop. Afr.
Ancistrocladaceae (*EP. Dipterocarpaceae*, p.p. *BH.*). Dicots. (Archichl. Parietales.) Only gen. Ancistrocladus (*q.v.*).
Ancistrocladus Wall. Ancistrocladaceae. 12 palaeotrop. Sympodial lianes, each member ending in a watch-spring tendril. L. alt., lanceolate, entire, with minute stips. Racemose infl. of ☿ reg. fl. K 5, teeth unequal; C (5) slightly united, convolute; A 5 or 10; $\overline{G}$ 1-loc. with 1 basal erect semi-anatr. ov. Nut. Endosperm.
Ancistrophyllum G. Mann et H. Wendl. Palmae (III). 4 W. Afr.
Ancistrorhynchus Finet. Orchidaceae (II. 20). 2 trop. Afr.
Ancistrum Forst. = Acaena L. (Rosac.).
Ancrumia Harv. Liliaceae (IV). 1 Chili.
Ancylacanthus Lindau. Acanthaceae (IV. A). 1 New Guinea.
Ancylanthos Desf. Rubiaceae (II. 1). 4 trop. Afr.
Ancylobothrys Pierre (*Landolphia* p.p.). Apocyn. (I. 1). 6 trop. Afr.
Ancylocladus Wall. = Willughbeia Roxb. (Apocyn.).
Ancylogyne Nees = Sanchezia Ruiz et Pav. (Acanth.).
Andersonia R. Br. (*Sprengelia* p.p. *EP.*). Epacrid. (2). 20 W. Austr.
Andes rose, *Befaria racemosa* Vent. and other spp.
Andira Lam. (*Vouacapoua* Aubl.). Legum. (III. 8). 25 trop. Am., Afr. *A. inermis* H.B. et K. (angelin) is a rain-tree (cf. Pithecolobium); its wood (partridge-wood) is useful.
Andiroba, *Carapa spp.*
Andrachne L. Euphorbiaceae (A. I. 1). 15 trop. and subtrop.
Andradaea Allem. Nyctaginaceae (? Phytolac.). 1 Rio de Janeiro.
Andradia T. R. Sim. Leguminosae (II. 9). 1 trop. Afr.
Andrea Mez. Bromeliaceae (4). 1 C. Brazil.
Andreoskia (*Andrzeiowskya*) Reichb. Crucif. (2). 1 E. Medit.
Andriapetalum Pohl = Panopsis Salisb. (Proteac.).
Andro- (Gr. pref.), male; **-dioecious**, ☿ and ♂ on separate pl., *Acer*, *Dryas*; **-eceum**, the stamens (*q.v.*); **-gynous**, monoecious in one infl.; **-monoecious**, ☿ and ♂ on same pl., *Acer*, *Veratrum*; **-phore**, an elongation of the axis between C and A, *Capparidaceae*, *Caryophyllaceae*, *Elaeocarpaceae*, *Passiflora*.
Androcentrum Lem. Acanthaceae (IV. A). 1 Mex.

Androcephalium Warb. (*Lunasia* Blanco). Euph. (A. II. 2). 1 N. Guinea.
Androcera Nutt. (*Solanum* L. p.p.). Solanaceae (2). 4 N. Am.
Androchilus Liebm. (*Liparis* Rich. p.p.). Orchid. (II. 4). 1 Mex.
Androcymbium Willd. Liliaceae (I). 35 Medit., Afr. Fls. in heads.
Andrographis Wall. Acanthaceae (IV. B). 20 trop. As. (char.).
Androlepis Brongn. (*Aechmea* p.p. *BH.*). Bromel. (4). 2 Guatemala.
Andromachia Humb. et Bonpl. = Liabum Adans. p.p. (Compos.).
Andromeda L. Eric. (II. 1). 6 N. temp. and cold, 1 Brit. Cult. orn. fl.
Andromycia A. Rich. (*Xanthosoma* Schott p.p.). Arac. (VI). 1 Cuba.
Andropogon L. (excl. *Cymbopogon* Spreng., *Vetiveria* Thou., etc.). Gramineae (2). 180 cosmop. The sp. yielding aromatic oils are now chiefly placed in the excluded genera (*q.v.*). *A. odoratus* Lieb. is the ginger grass, from which an oil is prepared. Cf. Stapf in Kew Bull. 1906, p. 297.
Andropus Brand. Hydrophyllaceae. 1 New Mexico.
Androsace (Tourn.) L. Primulaceae. 80 N. temp. Tufted xerophytes. Often heterostyled like Primula. Cult. orn. fl.
Androsaemum Tourn. ex Adans. = Hypericum L. (Guttif.).
Androsiphonia Stapf. Flacourt. (6). (Passifl. *BH.*) 1 trop. Afr.
Androstachys Prain. Euphorbiaceae (A. I. 1). 5 trop. Afr.
Androstephium Torr. (*Bessera EP.*). Liliac. (IV). 3 Mex. — Calif.
Androtium Stapf. Anacardiaceae (1). 1 Borneo.
Androtrichum Brongn. Cyperaceae (I). 1 E. temp. S. Am.
Andruris Schlechter. Triuridaceae. 6 Indomal.
Andryala L. Compositae (13). 15 Medit.
Andrzeiowskya Reichb. Cruciferae (2). 1 As. Minor.
Anechites Griseb. Apocynaceae (I. 3). 1 Cuba.
Aneilema R. Br. Commelinaceae. 100 warm esp. |※.
Aneimia Sw. Schizaeaceae. 80 trop. and subtrop. The l. divides at the base (cf. fronds of Ophioglossaceae) into sterile and fertile portions. The two lowest pinnae form a pair of panicles bearing sori (cf. Osmunda), resembling the infl. of many fl. plants.
Anelasma Miers = Abuta Aubl. p.p. (Menisp.). 5 W. I., S. Am.
Anelytrum Hackel. Gramineae (9). 1 Italy.
Anemarrhena Bunge. Liliaceae (III). 1 N. China.
Anemo- (Gr. pref.), wind-; **-philous** (fl.), pollinated by wind, usu. showing dry incoherent pollen, freely accessible to wind, large stigmas, and lack of conspicuousness, *Artemisia*, *Betulaceae*, *Calluna*, *Carex*, *Casuarina*, *Coniferae*, *Corylus*, *Cycadaceae*, *Cyperaceae*, *Elaeagnaceae*, *Empetrum*, *Fraxinus*, *Gramineae*, *Humulus*, *Juglandaceae*, *Juncaceae*, *Littorella*, *Mercurialis*, *Myrothamnaceae*, *Platanus*, *Potamogeton*, *Quercus*, *Rumex*, *Sparganium*, *Spinacia*, *Thalictrum*, *Triglochin*, *Typhaceae*, *Ulmaceae*, *Urticaceae*, *Zea*, &c.
Anemoisandra Pohl. Inc. sed. 1 Brazil.
Anemone L. Ranunculaceae (3). 120 cosmop. *A. nemorosa* (wood anemone) and *A. Pulsatilla* L. (pasque fl.) Brit. Herbs with rhiz. and radical l. Fl. sol. or in cymes, apet.; the invol. of green l. in the hepatica (*A. Hepatica* L.) is so close to the fl. as to resemble a K. The fl. of the first named contains no honey, is white, and visited for pollen (class Po.); that of the third is blue and bee-visited, while in

the second there is honey secreted by stds., and the long-tubed blue fl. is visited mainly by bees. The achenes of many spp. have hairs aiding wind-dispersal. Cult. orn. fl.

Anemonopsis Sieb. et Zucc. Ranunculaceae (2). 1 Japan.

Anemonospermos Böhm. Menispermaceae (inc. sed.). Nomen.

Anemopaegma Mart. Bignoniaceae (1). 40 trop. S. Am.

Anemopsis Hook. et Arn. (*Houttuynia BH.*). Saurur. 1 California.

Anepsias Schott. (*Rhodospatha* Poepp. *BH.*). Arac. (II). 1 Venezuela.

Anerincleistus Korth. Melastomaceae (1). 20 Malaya.

Anetanthus Hiern. Gesneriaceae (1). 5 trop. Am.

Anethum Tourn. ex L. (*Peucedanum BH.*). Umbel. (III. 5). 2 W. As.

Anetium (Kunze) Splitg. Polypod. 1 trop. Am.

Aneulophus Benth. Erythroxyl. (Linac. *BH.*). 1 Guinea. L. opp.

Anfractuosus (Lat.), sinuous.

Angadenia Miers. Apocynaceae (inc. sed.). 30 Mex., S. Am.

Angeia Tidestrom. Myricaceae. 1 N. temp.

Angeja Vand. Inc. sed. 1 Brazil.

Angelesia Korth. (*Trichocarya* Miq. *BH.*). Rosaceae (VI. b). 2 Sundas.

Angelica (Riv.) L. (incl. *Archangelica* Hoffm.). Umbel. (III. 6). 70 ⁎ and N. Z. The petioles of *A.* (*Arch.*) *officinalis* are offic., and are used in confectionery.

Angelin tree (W. I.), *Andira inermis* H.B. et K.

Angelocarpa Rupr. (*Coelopleurum* Ledeb.). Umbel. (III. 5). 1 C. As.

Angelonia Humb. et Bonpl. Scrophul. (II. 2). 30 trop. Am., W. Ind.

Angianthus Wendl. Compositae (4). 25 temp. Austr. Heads cpd.

Angico gum, *Piptadenia rigida* Benth.

Angiopetalum Reinw. Myrsinaceae (inc. sed.). 1 Java.

Angiopteris Hoffm. Marattiaceae (1). 65 Madag., Indomal., *A. evecta* Hoffm. Large ferns with the sori not united into synangia as in most M. Annulus like that of Osmundaceae at apex of sporangium. The r. arise close to apex, and burrow down and outwards through the stem and leaf-bases, emerging some distance down.

Angiospermae. One of the two great divisions of Spermaphyta, distinguished from Gymnosperms by the fact that the cpls. are so infolded or arranged as to form an ovary in which the ovules are borne. Endosperm formed after, instead of before fert.

All A. possess true fl., the essential parts of which are sta. and cpls. The former bear pollen-sacs (= microsporangia of Pteridophyta), the latter ovules (megasporangia). The ovule is always enclosed in the cpl.; it has two (or one) integuments, and usually one embryo-sac (more in some chalazogamic forms, Loranthaceae, &c.). The pollen-tube may enter by the micropyle or by the chalaza (cf. Chalazogamae). Parthenogenesis, or development of the ovum into an embryo without fert., occurs in *Antennaria*, *Alchemilla*, *Hieracium*, *Houttuynia*, *Thalictrum*, *Wikstroemia*, &c., embryo formation by adv. budding in *Alchornea*, *Citrus*, *Euonymus*, *Funkia*, *Nothoscordum*, &c., apogamy (*cf.* Filicineae) in *Balanophora*.

A. are divided into Mono- and Di-cotyledons (*cf.* classification at end of the book).

Angkalanthus Balf. f. Acanthaceae (IV. B). 1 Socotra.

Angolaea Wedd. Podostemaceae. 1 Angola.

Angophora Cav. Myrtaceae (II. 1). 7 E. Austr.
Angorchis Thou. = Angraecum Bory (Orchid.).
Angostura bark, *Cusparia febrifuga* Humb.
Angostyles Benth. Euphorbiaceae (A. II. 2). 1 N. Brazil.
Angraecopsis Krzl. Orchidaceae (II. 20). 5 trop. E. Afr.
Angraecum Bory. Orchidaceae (II. 20). 120 trop. Afr., Madag., Masc. Monopodial epiphytes, often cult. *A. sesquipedale* Thou. (wax-fl.) has an enormous spur a foot long, secreting honey at the bottom and is probably fert. by a moth with equal proboscis (cf. *Yucca, Ficus*). See Darwin's *Orchids*, p. 162. Some are leafless.
Anguillaria R. Br. Lili. (1). 2 Austr., Tasm. **A.** Gaertn. = Ardisia.
Anguillicarpus Burkill. Cruciferae (2). 1 Beluchistan.
Anguloa Ruiz et Pav. Orchid. (II. 12). 5 Peru, Colombia.
Anguria (Tourn.) L. Cucurbit. (2). 45 trop. Am.
Anguriopsis J. R. Johnston. Cucurbit. (2). 1 Venezuela.
Angusti- (Lat. pref.), narrow-; **-folius** (Lat.), -leaved.
Angylocalyx Taub. Leguminosae (III. 1). 6 trop. Afr.
Anhalonium Lem. = Mammillaria Haw. (*BH.*) = Ariocarpus Scheidw.
Aniba Aubl. (*Aydendron* Nees, *Ocotea BH*). Lauraceae (II). 55 trop. Am.
Anigozanthos Labill. Amaryll. (III) (Haemod. *BH.*). 8 S.W. Austr. Fl. transversely ·|·.
Anil Ludw. ex O. Ktze. = Indigofera L. (Legum.).
Animals, seed-dispersal by, *cf.* Dispersal.
Anime (resin), copal.
Anisacantha R. Br. (*Bassia* All. p.p. *EP.*). Chenopodiaceae (A). 6 Austr.
Anisacanthus Nees. Acanthaceae (IV. B). 10 Am.
Anisadenia Wall. Linaceae. 2 Himalaya.
Anise, aniseed, *Pimpinella Anisum* L.; **star-, -tree,** *Illicium verum* Hook. f.
Aniseia Choisy (*Ipomoea* L. p.p. *BH.*). Convolv. (1). 15 trop.
Aniselytron Merrill. Gramineae (8). 1 Phil. Is.
Aniserica N. E. Br. Ericaceae (IV. 2). 1 S. Afr.
Aniso- (Gr. pref.), unequal-; **-merous,** with — numbers in the whorls; **-phylly,** with — l. at same node, *Anisophyllea, Centradenia, Columnea, Gardenia, Gesneriaceae, Klugia, Melastomaceae, Nyctaginaceae, Philadelphus, Randia, Sambucus, Scrophularia, Strobilanthes, Tabernaemontana.*
Anisocarpus Nutt. (*Madia* Molina). Compositae (5). 5 W. U.S.
Anisochaeta DC. Compositae (4). 1 S. Afr.
Anisochilus Wall. Labiatae (VII). 20 trop. As., Afr.
Anisocoma Torr. et Gray. Compositae (13). 1 W. U.S.
Anisocycla Baill. Menispermaceae. 6 S. and trop. Afr., Madag.
Anisodus Link et Otto = Scopola Jacq. p.p. (Solan.).
Anisolobus A. DC. = Odontadenia Benth. (Apocyn.).
Anisolotus Bernh. = Hosackia Dougl. (Legum.). 5 U.S.
Anisomallon Baill. Icacin. (Olacin. *BH.*). 1 New Caled.
Anisomeles R. Br. Labiatae (VI). 6 Indomal.
Anisomeria D. Don. Phytolaccaceae. 3 Chili.
Anisomeris Presl (*Chomelia* Jacq.). Rubi. (II. 2). 17 trop. S. Am.

Anisonema A. Juss. = Phyllanthus L. p.p. (Euphorb.).
Anisopappus Hook. et Arn. Compos. (4). 8 S. China to S. Afr.
Anisophyllea R. Br. Rhizophoraceae. 15 palaeotrop. It differs from other R. in its drupe fr., exalb. seed, and alt. exstip. sometimes anisophyllous l.
Anisophyllum Haw. = Euphorbia L. p.p. **do.** Jacq. Inc. sed. 1 Baru.
Anisopoda Baker. Umbell. (III. 5). 1 Madag.
Anisopogon R. Br. Gramineae (9). 1 Austr.
Anisoptera Korth. Dipterocarpaceae. 20 E. Indomal.
Anisopus N. E. Br. Asclepiadaceae (II. 3). 2 trop. W. Afr.
Anisosciadium DC. (*Echinophora* L. *BH.*). Umbell. (III. 1). 2 W. As.
Anisosperma Manso. Cucurb. (1). 1 Brazil. Seeds medicinal.
Anisostachya Nees (*Justicia BH.*). Acanth. (IV. B). 5 trop. Afr., Madag.
Anisostigma Schinz. Aizoaceae (II). 1 Namaland.
Anisotes Nees. Acanthaceae (IV. B). 8 trop. Afr., Arabia.
Anisothrix O. Hoffm. Compositae (4). 1 S. Afr.
Anisotoma Fenzl. Asclepiadaceae (II. 3). 1 S. Afr.
Anisotome Hook. f. = Aciphylla Forst. (Umbell.).
Annatto, *Bixa Orellana* L.
Anneslea Wall. (*Mountnorrisia* Szysz.). Theac. 2 Indomal.
Annesorrhiza Cham. et Schlechtd. Umbelliferae (III. 5). 10 S. Afr. *A. capensis* C. et S. has ed. roots.
Annexed, adnate.
Annona L. = Anona L.
Annotinus (Lat.), applied to branches of last year's growth.
Annual, annuus (Lat.), living one year only.
Annulate, marked with rings.
Annulus, *Filicineae Leptosp.*
Anochilus Rolfe. Orchidaceae (II. 1). 2 S. Afr.
Anoda Cav. Malvaceae (2). 10 trop. Am. Cult. orn.
Anodal, in the upward direction on the genetic spiral.
Anodendron A. DC. Apocynaceae (II. 1). 10 Ceylon to China.
Anodiscus Benth. Gesneriaceae (II). 1 Peru.
Anodopetalum A. Cunn. Cunoniaceae. 1 Tasmania.
Anoectochilus Blume. Orchidaceae (II. 2). 25 Indomal. Cult. orn. l.
Anoectomaria × Rolfe. Hybrid of last with Haemaria.
Anogeissus Wall. Combretaceae. 5 trop. Afr., As.
Anogra Spach (*Oenothera* L. p.p.). Onagrac. (2). 20 N. Am.
Anogramma Link. Polypodiaceae. 10 trop. Am., Japan.
Anoiganthus Baker. Amaryllidaceae (I). 2 Natal and trop. Afr.
Anomalanthus Klotzsch = Simochilus Klotzsch (Eric.).
Anomanthodia Hook. f. (*Randia* p.p. *EP.*). Rubiac. (I. 8). 1 trop. As.
Anomatheca Ker-Gawl. = Lapeirousia Pourr. (Irid.).
Anomianthus Zoll. Anonaceae (1). 1 trop. As.
Anomochloa Brongn. Gramineae (6). 1 Brazil.
Anomopanax Harms. Araliaceae (3). 5 Malay Arch.
Anomospermum Miers. Menispermaceae. 8 Brazil, Guiana.
Anomostephium DC. = Aspilia Thou. (Compos.).
Anomotassa K. Schum. Asclepiadaceae (II. 3). 1 Ecuador.
Anona L. Anonaceae (4). 90 warm esp. Am. Fr. aggregate, often

very large, made up of the individual berries derived from the separate cpls., sunk in, and united with, the fleshy recept. That of some cult. sp. is ed., *e.g.* of *A. Cherimolia* Mill. (cherimoyer; trop. Am.), *A. squamosa* L. (sweet sop, custard or sugar apple; E. Ind.), *A. muricata* L. (sour sop; trop. Am.) and *A. reticulata* L. (custard-apple or bullock's heart; trop. Am.).

A. (*Geanthemum*) *rhizantha* Eichl. (Braz.) has rhizomes below the soil, bearing scale leaves only. The fls. are borne on branches of these above the ground.

Anonaceae (*EP.*; *BH. incl. Eupomatiaceae*). Dicots. (Archichl. Ranales). 80 gen. 820 sp. chiefly trop. (esp. Old World). Trees and shrubs (exc. one) with usu. two-ranked undivided exstip. l. Stem sometimes sympodial, at least in infl. Oil passages present.

Fls. reg. ☿ (rarely unisex.), solitary or in infl. of various types. Usu. formula P 3+3+3 (one or two outer whorls sepaloid); A ∞ (rarely few), spiral, hypog.; $\underline{G}$ ∞ (Monodora is syncp.). Ovules usu. ∞, ventral or basal, anatr. Fr. commonly an aggregate of berries, when many-seeded frequently constricted between the seeds. In Anona, &c. the berries coalesce with the receptacle. Ruminate endosperm (the chief character that separates A. from Magnoliaceae). Many yield ed. fr., *e.g.* Anona, Artabotrys. [**BH. chars.** incl. P o and fl. perig.]

Classification and chief genera (after Prantl):

a. Apocarpous.
1. *Uvarieae* (P unjointed or clawed with claws against sta.): Uvaria, Asimina, Guatteria, Unona, Cananga.
2. *Miliuseae* (P valvate, usu. unequal, if clawed the claws away from sta.): Miliusa.
3. *Hexalobeae* (P equal, with crossfolds in bud): Hexalobus.
4. *Xylopieae* (P hollow at base, ± constricted above it and again spread out or laterally compressed): Xylopia, Artabotrys, Anona.

b. Syncarpous; ov. uniloc. with parietal plac.
5. *Monodoreae:* Monodora (only genus).

[Placed in Ranales by *BH.*]

Anonidium Engl. et Diels. Anonaceae (I). 3 W. trop. Afr.

Anonymus Walt. Inc. sed. (pro omnibus dubiis).

Anoplophytum Beer=Tillandsia L. (Bromel.).

Anopteris (Prantl) Diels. Polypodiaceae. 1 trop. Am.

Anopterus Labill. Saxifragaceae (V). 2 E. Austr., Tasm.

Anopyxis Pierre. Rhizophoraceae. 1 trop. Afr.

Anotis DC. Rubiaceae (I. 2). 25 Indo-mal., 1 S. Am.

Anotites Greene. Caryophyllaceae (II. 1). 20 N. Am.

Anoumabia A. Chevalier. Sapindaceae. 1 Ivory Coast.

Anplectrum A. Gray (*Diplectria* Rchb.). Melastom. (I). 20 Malaya.

Anredera Juss. Basellaceae. 1 trop. Am.

Ansellia Lindl. Orchidaceae (II. 5). 4 trop. Afr., Natal.

Ante- (Lat. pref.), before; **-petalous** (sta.), opp. petals; **-posed**, opp. and not alt. with.

Antelaea Gaertn. Inc. sed. 2 Java.

Antennaria Gaertn. Compositae (4). 75 extra-trop., exc. Afr. *A.*

dioica Gaertn. (mountain everlasting, cat's foot) in Brit. is a small creeping dioec. perenn., hairy and semi-xero., occurring chiefly on hills and at the sea-shore, but not common in intermediate places. In *A. alpina* (L.) R. Br. only ♀ plants usu. occur, and show true *parthenogenesis*, the ovum developing into an embryo without fert. (not to be confused with the veg. budding of Alchornea).

Anterior (side of fl.), facing the bract; **antero-posterior**, median.

Anthacanthus Nees. Acanthaceae (IV. B). 6 W. Ind.

Anthaenantia Beauv. Gramineae (5). 8 warm Am.

Anthagathis Harms. = Jollydora Pierre (Legum.). 1 trop. Afr.

Anthelia Schott. Araceae (inc. sed.). 1 Celebes.

Anthemis Mich. ex L. Compositae (7). 120 Eur., Medit. (4 Brit., chamomile). The fr. of *A. arvensis* L. has papillae on its upper surface which become sticky when wet (*cf.* Linum). Shows suborder chars. well. *A. nobilis* L. (chamomile) fl. offic.

Anthephora Schreb. Gramineae (3). 10 trop. Am., trop. and S. Afr.

Anther, *cf.* Stamen; **-idium,** *Filicineae Lepto*, *Pteridophyta*; **-ozoid,** spermatozoid, *Pteridophyta*.

Anthericopsis Engl. Commelinac. (Liliac. *BH.*). 1 E. trop. Afr.

Anthericum L. Liliaceae (III). 100 Afr., Eur., Am., E. As.

Antheropeas Rydberg. Compos. (6). 5 N. Am.

Antherothamnus N. E. Br. Scrophular. (II. 4). 1 S. Afr.

Antherotoma Hook. f. Melastom. (I). 2 trop. Afr., Madag.

Antherura Lour. Rubiaceae (inc. sed.). 1 S.E. As., Malay Arch.

Antherylium Rohr. et Vahl (*Ginoria* Jacq. p.p. *EP.*). Lythr. 2 Mex., W. Ind.

Anthesis, flower-opening.

Anthistiria L. f. (*Themeda*). Gramineae (2). 15 palaeotrop. *A. vulgaris* Hack. (kangaroo grass) covers large areas in Austr. and S. Afr.

Antho- (Gr. pref.), flower-; **-carp,** *Nyctaginaceae*; **-lysis,** retrograde metamorphosis of fl.; **-philous,** fl.-visiting; **-phore,** stalk between K and C; **-taxy,** arrangement of fl.

Anthobembix Perkins. Monimiaceae. 3 New Guinea.

Anthobolus R. Br. Santalaceae. 5 Austr. Hypogynous.

Anthobryum Phil. Frankeniac. (? Primul.). 2 Bolivia.

Anthocarapa Pierre (*Amoora* p.p.). Meliac. (III). 2 Cochin China.

Anthocephalus A. Rich. Rubiaceae (I. 6). 3 Malaya.

Anthocercis Labill. Solanaceae (5). 20 Austr.

Anthochlamys Fenzl. Chenopodiaceae (A). 1 W. Centr. As.

Anthochloa Nees et Meyen. Gramineae (10). 3 Am.

Anthocleista Afzel. Loganiaceae. 25 trop. Afr.

Anthodiscus G. F. W. Mey. Caryocarac. (Ternstr. *BH.*). 4 trop. S. Am.

Anthodon Ruiz et Pav. = Salacia L. (Hippocrat.).

Anthogonium Wall. ex Lindl. Orchid. (II. 9). 1 Himalaya, Burma.

Antholoma Labill. Elaeocarp. 3 New Caled., New Guinea.

Antholyza L. Iridaceae (III). 25 Afr. Cult. orn. fl.

Anthopogon Neck. (*Gentiana* L. p.p.) Gentian. 5 N. Am.

Anthopterus Hook. Ericac. (III. 2) (Vaccin. *BH.*). 10 Andes.

Anthospermum L. Rubiaceae (II. 7). 35 Afr., Madag.

Anthostema A. Juss. Euphorb. (A. II. 8). 3 trop. Afr., Madag. Fls.

in a cyathium like Euphorbia, but the ♂, reduced as in E. to 1 sta., has a P where in E. there is a joint. The ♀ also has a P.

Anthostyrax Pierre (*Styrax* p.p.). Styracaceae. 1 Tonquin.

Anthotium R. Br. Goodeniaceae. 2 S.W. Austr.

Anthotroche Endl. Solanaceae (5). 4 Austr.

Anthoxanthum L. Gramineae (7). 14 N. temp. and Ind.; *A. odoratum* L. (sweet vernal grass) Brit. The stems contain large quantities of coumarin, to which the smell char. of newly mown hay is due; it may be recognized by chewing a stalk. Fl. with 2 sta. only, protog. Awns of fr. hygroscopic.

Anthriscus Bernh. Umbelliferae (III. 2). 10 Eur., As., Afr., 2 Brit., incl. *A. sylvestris* Hoffm. (chervil). *A. Cerefolium* Hoffm. is the cult. chervil of France &c.

Anthurium Schott. Arac. (1). 500 trop. Am., W.I. Most are sympodial herbs, with an accessory bud beside the 'continuation' bud of the sympodium. Axillary shoot often 'adnate' to the main one (*cf.* Solanaceae &c.). Aerial roots frequent at the base of the l. Some epiphytes. Fls. ☿, with P, protog., arranged in a dense mass upon a spadix, at whose base is a flat usu. brightly coloured spathe. Fr. a berry; when ripe it is forced out of the spadix and hangs by two threads formed from the P. In *A. longifolium* G. Don the root apex has been observed to develop into a shoot.

-anthus (Gr. suff.), -flowered.

Anthyllis Riv. Leguminosae (III. 5). 30 Eur., N. Afr., W. As. (*A. vulneraria* L., lady's fingers, kidney-vetch, Brit.). Fl. mech. resembles Lotus; stigma only receptive when rubbed.

Anti- (Lat. pref.), against, opp.; **-dromous**, r. and l. handed; **-petalous**, **-sepalous**, opp. pet. or sep.; **-thetic**, not homologous.

Antiaris Lesch. Moraceae (II). 6 Indomal. incl. *A. toxicaria* Lesch. (Upas-tree). The latex is poisonous. Extraordinary stories of its effects were spread abroad about a century ago. The surroundings were said to be a desert, the poisonous influence emanating from the tree being fatal to life (see *Treas. of Bot.*).

Antiaropsis K. Schum. Moraceae (II). 1 New Guinea.

Anticharis Endl. Scrophulariaceae (I. 2). 10 Afr., Arabia.

Anticlea Kunth = Zygadenus Michx. p.p. (Lili.).

Anticoryne Turcz. = Baeckea L. (Myrtac.).

Anticous, on anterior side.

Antidaphne Poepp. et Endl. Loranthac. (II). 2 Peru to Venezuela.

Antidesma Burm. ex L. Euphorbiaceae (A. I. 1). 150 palaeowarm. G. 1.

Antidote-cocoon (W.I.), *Fevillea cordifolia* L.

Antigonon Endl. Polygonaceae (III. 1). 4 trop. Am. *A. Leptopus* Hook. et Arn. is a (stem) tendril climber, cult. orn. fl.

Antinoria Parl. (*Aira* L. p.p. *BH.*) Gramin. (9). 2 S. Eur.

Antiphylla Haw. = Saxifraga L. p.p. (Saxifr.). 15 Eur.

Antiphytum DC. Boraginaceae (IV. 4). 6 S. trop. Am.

Antirrhinum Tourn. Scrophulariaceae (II. 3). 36 $\underline{*}$. *A. majus* L. (snapdragon) in Brit., but probably an escape. The mouth of the fl. is closed and the honey thus preserved for bees, which alone are strong enough to force an entrance.

Antirrhoea Comm. Rubiaceae (II. 2). 25 E. As. to Madag., W. Ind.

Antistrophe A. DC. Myrsinaceae (II). 2 Indomal.
Antitaxis Miers (*Pycnarrhena* Miers *EP.*). Menisp. 4 Malaya.
Antithrixia DC. Compositae (4). 3 S. Afr. to Abyss.
Antizoma Miers (*Cissampelos* L. p.p. *BH.*). Menisp. 5 S. warm Afr.
Antochortus Nees (*Willdenowia* Thunb.). Restion. 10 S. Afr.
Antonia Pohl. Loganiaceae. 1 Brazil, Guiana.
Antrocaryon Pierre. Anacardiaceae (2). 3 Gaboon.
Antrophyum Kaulf. Polypodiaceae. 30 trop. and subtrop.
Ants and plants, *cf.* Myrmecophily.
Anubias Schott. Araceae (V). 13 W. Afr.
Anulocaulis Standley (*Boerhaavia* L. p.p.). Nyctag. 3 N. Am.
Anvillea DC. Compositae (4). 4 Medit.
Anychia Michx. Caryophyllaceae (I. 4). (Illecebr. *BH.*) 2 N. Am.
Anychiastrum Small (*Paronychia* L. p.p.). Caryophyll. (I. 4). 3 N. Am.
Aonikena Spegazz. Euphorbiaceae (A. II. 2). 1 Patagonia.
Aostea Buscalioni et Muschler. Compos. (4). 2 Centr. Afr.
Aotus Sm. Leguminosae (III. 2). 11 Austr., Tasm.
Apabuta Griseb. Menispermaceae. Nomen.
Apalatoa Aubl. (*Crudia* Schreb.). Leguminosae (II. 3). 11 trop.
Apaloxylon Drake del Castillo. Leguminosae (II. 2). 1 Madag.
Apama Lam. (*Bragantia* Lour. *BH.*). Aristoloch. 5 Indomal.
Apargia Scop. = Leontodon L. (Compos.).
Apargidium Torr. et Gray. Compositae (13). 1 Calif. — Alaska.
Aparine Tourn. ex Mill. = Galium Tourn. (Rubiac.).
Apatemone Schott (*Schismatoglottis* Z. et M.). Arac. (V). 1 Borneo.
Apeiba Aubl. Tiliaceae. 7 warm Am. Some have good wood.
Apera Adans. Gramineae (8). 4 Eur., W. As. *A.* (*Agrostis*) *Spica-Venti*, Beauv. (silky bent-grass), Brit.
Apetahia Baill. Campanulaceae (III). 1 Tahiti and Raiatea.
Apetalae = Monochlamydeae or Incompletae.
Apetalous, petal-less, when one would expect a C; *Abatia*, *Acer*, *Achlys*, *Alchemilla*, *Anemone*, *Azara*, *Bocconia*, *Datiscaceae*, *Heuchera*, *Lespedeza*, *Liquidambar*, *Fraxinus*, *Oleaceae*, *Parrotia*, *Pringlea*, *Sagina*, *Thalictrum*, and *cf.* Cleistogamy.
Apetlorhamnus Nieuwland (*Rhamnus* p.p.). Rhamn. 1 N. Am.
Aphaenandra Miq. Rubiaceae (inc. sed.). 1 Sumatra.
Aphaerema Miers. Flacourt. (8) (Samyd. *BH.*). 1 S. Paulo.
Aphanactis Wedd. Compositae (5). 2 Andes.
Aphanamixis Blume (*Amoora* pp. *BH.*). Meliac. (III). 8 Malaya.
Aphanandrium Lindau (*Neriacanthus*). Acanth. (IV. B). 1 Columbia.
Aphananthe Planch. Ulmaceae. 5 Austr., E. As.
Aphanelytrum Hackel. Gramineae (8). 1 Ecuador.
Aphanes L. = Alchemilla L. (Ros.).
Aphania Blume (*Sapindus* L. p.p. *BH.*). Sapind. (I). 12 trop. As., Afr.
Aphanisma Nutt. Chenopodiaceae (A). 1 California.
Aphanocalyx Oliv. Leguminosae (II. 2). 1 Guinea.
Aphanococcus Radlk. Sapindaceae (I). 1 Celebes.
Aphanomyrtus Miq. Lauraceae (I). 4 Malaya.
Aphanopetalum Endl. Cunoniaceae. 2 S.E. and S.W. Austr.
Aphanopleura Boiss. Umbell. (III. 5). 4 Armenia.

Aphanostephus DC. Compositae (3). 5 Mex., U.S.
Aphanostylis Pierre (*Clitandra* p.p.). Apocyn. (I. 1). 5 trop. Afr.
Aphantochaeta A. Gray (*Pentachaeta* p.p. *EP.*). Compos. (3). 2 Calif.
Aphelandra R. Br. Acanth. (IV. B). 80 warm Am. Cult. orn. fl.
Aphelexis D. Don (*Helichrysum* p.p. *EP.*). Compos. (4). 10 Madag.
Aphelia R. Br. Centrolepidaceae. 1 S. Austr., Tasm.
Apheliotropism, negative heliotropism.
Aphloia Benn. (*Neumannia* A. Rich.). Flacourt. (4) (Bix. *BH.*). 4 S. Afr., Madag., Masc.
Aphora Nutt. = Argithamnia P. Br. (*BH.*) = Ditaxis Vahl p.p.
Aphotic, dark.
Aphragmus Andrz. (*Braya* p.p. *BH.*). Crucif. (2). 3 Alaska to C. As.
Aphyllanthes Tourn. ex L. Liliaceae (III). 1. W. Medit., *A. monspeliensis* L. The sol. fl. is surrounded by an invol. of br., and is regarded as the only remaining fl. of a head; the other fl. are only repres. by their bracts.
Aphyllarum Sp. Moore. Araceae (VI). 1 Matto Grosso.
Aphyllon Mitch. (*Orobanche* p.p. *EP.*). Orobanchaceae. 10 N. Am.
Aphyllorchis Blume. Orchidaceae (II. 2). 18 Indomal.
Aphylly, absence of l.
Apiastrum Nutt. Umbelliferae (III. 4). 2 N. Am.
Apical (plac.), at upper end of ovary.
Apicra Willd. Liliaceae (III). 10 S. Afr. Some, *e.g. A. foliolosa* Willd., show extreme superposition of l., forming almost solid masses of tissue. Many cult. orn. fl.
Apiculate, with small sharp point.
Apinagia Tul. Podostemaceae. 25 Guiana, Brazil.
Apio, *Arracacia xanthorhiza* Bauer &c.
Apiocarpus Montr. Staphyleaceae. 1 New Caled.
Apiopetalum Baill. Araliaceae (3). 3 New Caled.
Apios Moench. Leguminosae (III. 10). 8 N. Am., E. As. *A. tuberosa* Moench is a climber with tuberous base. The keel of the fl. forms a tube which bends up and rests against a depression in the standard. When liberated by insects the tension of the keel makes it spring downwards, coiling up more closely, and causing the essential organs to emerge at the apex. Cult. orn. fl.
Apium (Tourn.) L. Umbelliferae (III. 5). 40 cosmop., 3 Brit. *A. graveolens* L. is the celery. Cult., and the etiolation of the leaf-stalks by heaping earth over them, render the garden form ed. A var. is the turnip-rooted celery or celeriac.
Aplectrum Torr., Nutt. Orchidaceae (II. 9). 2 N. Am.
Apleura Phil. Umbelliferae (I. 2). 1 Chili.
Aplolophium Cham. (*Haplolophium*). Bignoniaceae (1). 3 Brazil.
Aplopappus Cass. (*Haplopappus* Endl.). Compos. (3). 125 W. Am.
Aplophyllum A. Juss. = Ruta L. (Rutaceae).
Aplotaxis DC. = Saussurea DC. (Compos.).
Apluda L. Gramineae (2). 1 Indomal., Madag.
Apo- (Gr. pref.), from; **-carpous**, with free cpls., *Ranunculaceae*, *Rosaceae*, &c.; **-gamy**, omission of sexual process, *Angiospermae*, *Asplenium*, *Balanophora*, *Elatostema*, *Filicineae Leptosp.*, *Pteris*, *Todea*; **-geotropic**, **-heliotropic**, negatively g. or h., *Bowenia*;

-petalous, polypetalous; **-spory**, *Filicineae Leptosp.*, *Dryopteris*; **-tropous**, anatr. with ventral raphe.

Apocarpae (*BH.*). 6th series of Monocots. (p. liv).

Apochoris Duby (*Lysimachia* p.p.). Primul. (III). 1 N. China.

Apocopis Nees. Gramin. (2). 8 Indomal., Chi. Racemes paired.

Apocynaceae (*EP.*, *BH.*). Dicots. (Sympet., Contortae; Gentianales *BH.*; pp. xliii, liii). 180/1400, mostly trop., a few temp. Usu. twining shrubs, rarely erect; many large trop. lianes. Latex present; bundles bi-collateral. L. simple, opp. or alt. or in whorls of 3, entire, usu. with close || lat. veins, rarely with small interpetiolar stip. Primary type of infl. a panicle, often going over into dich. cyme or cincinnus; br. and bracteoles present. Fl. ☿, reg., usu. 5—4-merous. K (5), deeply lobed, quincuncial with odd sep. post., often with glands at base; C (5), usu. salver- or funnel-shaped, often hairy within, conv. or rarely valv., tips often conv. the opp. way, pets. sometimes asymmetric; A 5, alt. with C, epipet., with short incl. filaments; anther lobes full of pollen to base, or empty below and prolonged into rigid spines, usu. united to stylar head; disc usu. present. $\underline{G}$ or ½-inf. (2), or 2 (united by style), or more, 1—2-loc. with ∞—2—4—6 ov. in each loc., anatr., pend.; style usu. simple with thickened head, and ring of hairs below it. Fr. 2 follicles, berry, caps., or 2 indeh. fr.; seeds usu. flat, often with crown of hairs. Embryo straight, with endosp. or none. When the stylar head is large the stigma is at its edge or under surface, and self-fert. is almost impossible. Cf. Apocynum. Many are showy ornamentals. Landolphia, Carpodinus, Hancornia, Funtumia, Mascarenhasia, &c. yield rubber, and several give useful drugs, alkaloids, &c.

Classification and chief genera (after Schumann): cf. Asclep.

I. *PLUMIEROIDEAE* (sta. free or loosely joined to stylar head; thecae full of pollen, rarely with spines; seeds usu. hairless):

1. *Arduineae* (syncp.; style not split at base); Arduina, Allamanda, Landolphia, Carpodinus, Hancornia.
2. *Pleiocarpeae* (apocp.; style split at base; > 2 cpls.): Pleiocarpa.
3. *Plumiereae* (do.; 2 cpls.): Plumiera, Alstonia, Aspidosperma, Amsonia, Lochnera, Vinca, Tabernaemontana, Voacanga, Alyxia, Rauwolfia, Ochrosia, Cerbera.

II. *ECHITOIDEAE* (sta. firmly joined to stylar head; thecae empty at base, and with spines; seeds hairy):

1. *Echitideae* (anthers included): Echites, Dipladenia, Odontadenia, Mandevilla, Baissea, Funtumia, Mascarenhasia, Apocynum, Nerium, Strophanthus.
2. *Parsonsieae* (anthers exserted): Wrightia, Parsonsia, Lyonsia, Malouetia, Forsteronia, Prestonia.

Apocynum (Tourn.) L. Apocyn. (II. 1). 25 N. temp. Some cult., incl. *A. androsaemifolium* L. (American fly-trap), with fl. mech. like Asclep. Stylar disc stigmatic below, surrounded by rigid lignified sta. An insect withdrawing proboscis usu. brings it up the narrow slit between sta., at whose base is a drop of cement. Higher up the anthers open lat. and thus pollen is attached to proboscis, but strength is needed, and small insects are usu. caught, as may be seen in gardens. Seeds hairy (wind carriage).

Apodanthera Arn. Cucurbitaceae (2). 20 warm Am.

Apodanthes Poit. Rafflesiac. (Cytinac. *BH.*). 5 trop. S. Am.

Apodiscus Hutch. Euphorb. (A. I. 1). 1 French Guinea.

Apodocephala Baker. Compositae (2). 2 Madag.

Apodolirion Baker. Amaryllidaceae (1). 6 S. Afr.

Apodytes E. Mey. Icacinaceae. 14 S. Afr. to Malaya. *A. dimidiata* E. Mey. (S. Afr., white pear), good timber.

Apogon Ell. (*Serinia* Raf.). Compositae (13). 3 N. Am.

Apollonias Nees. Lauraceae (II). 2 Canaries, Madeira.

Aponogeton L. f. Aponogetonaceae (Naiad. *BH.*). 25 palaeotrop., and S. Afr. Water pl. with sympodial tuberous rhiz. and basal l., usu. floating. Submerged l. occur in some, *e.g.* *A.* (*Ouvirandra*) *fenestrale* Hook. f. The whole tissue between the veins breaks up as the l. grows, leaving a network of veins with holes between. The interior does not contain the usual intercellular spaces.

The ☿ reg. fl. project above the water in spikes, sometimes divided longitudinally into 2 or 3; spathe early thrown off. P usu. 2, sometimes 3 or even 1, as in the much cult. *A. distachyum* Thunb. (Cape pondweed), where it is attached by a broad base, and looks like a br. In this sp. A ∞, $\underline{G}$ 3—6, but usu. A 3+3, $\underline{G}$ 3, with 2 or ∞ ov. in each, anatr., erect. Fr. leathery. Embryo straight. Exalb.

Aponogetonaceae (*EP.*; *Naiadeae* p.p. *BH.*). Monocots. (Helobieae). Only genus Aponogeton (*q.v.*). Distinguished from Potamogetonaceae by coloured P and straight embryo, from Scheuchzeriaceae by P and sympodial structure.

Apopetalum Pax. Rosaceae (I. 1). 1 Bolivia.

Apophyllum F. Muell. Capparidaceae (II). 1 N.E. Austr.

Apoplanesia C. Presl. Leguminosae (III. 6). 1 Mex.

Aporocactus Lem. (*Cereus* Mill. p.p.). Cactaceae (III. 1). 2 N. Am.

Aporosa Blume. Euphorb. (A. I. 1). 75 Indomal.

Aporosella Chodat. Euphorb. (A. I. 1). 1 Paraguay.

Aporrhiza Radlk. Sapindaceae (I). 3 Centr. Afr.

Aporuellia C. B. Clarke. Acanth. (IV. A). 4 Malay Pen., Sumatra.

Aporum Blume (*Dendrobium* Sw. p.p. *BH.*). Orchid. (II. 15). 12 trop. As.

Aposeris Neck. (*Hyoseris* L. p.p. *BH.*). Compos. (13). 1 C. Eur. Mts.

Apostasia Blume. Orchidaceae (I. 1). 8 Indomal. Fl. almost reg. with 2 sta.; ovary 3-loc.

Appendicula Blume. Orchidaceae (II *a.* III.). 40 Malaya, Polynesia.

Appendiculana O. Ktze. = next.

Appendiculate, with appendages.

Appendicularia DC. Melastomaceae (I). 1 Guiana.

Apple, *Pyrus Malus* L.; **alligator-**, *Anona palustris* L.; **balsam-**, *Momordica balsamina* L.; **custard-**, *Anona squamosa* L., *reticulata* L.; **elephant-**, *Feronia Elephantum* Correa; **kangaroo-**, *Solanum aviculare* Forst.; **Kei-**, *Aberia caffra* Harv. et Sond.; **love-**, *Lycopersicum esculentum* Mill.; **Malay-**, *Eugenia malaccensis* L.; **mammee-**, *Mammea americana* L.; **May-**, *Podophyllum peltatum* L.; **pine-**, *Ananas sativus* Schult. f.; **rose-**, Malay; **star-**, *Chrysophyllum*

Cainito L.; **sugar-**, *Anona squamosa* L.; **thorn-**, *Datur Stramonium* L.; **wood-**, elephant-.

Appressed, flattened down.

Approximate, close together.

Appunia Hook. f. Rubiaceae (II. 9). 3 trop. S. Am.

Aprevalia Baill. Leguminosae (II. 7). 1 Madag.

Apricot, *Prunus Armeniaca* L.; **San Domingo-**, *Mammea americana* L.

Aptandra Miers. Olacaceae. 5 trop. S. Am., Afr.

Apteria Nutt. Burmanniaceae. 5 warm Am.

Apteron Kurz. Rhamnaceae. 1 Tenasserim.

Apterous, wingless.

Aptosimum Burchell. Scrophular. (I. 2). 40 S. and trop. Afr.

Aptotheca Miers (*Forsteronia*). Apocyn. (inc. sed.). 1 Cuba.

Apuleia Mart. Legum. (II. 5). 2 Brazil. *A. praecox* Mart. excellent timber.

Aquaticus (Lat.), living in water.

Aquifoliaceae (*EP.*; *Ilicineae BH.*). Dicots. (Archichl. Sapindales; Olacales *BH.*). 5 gen., 300 sp. temp. and trop. Shrubs and trees with leathery alt., l. with minute or no stips. and cymose infl. Fl. reg. unisexual, 3—6-merous; no disc. Usu. K 4, C 4, A 4, $\underline{G}$ usu. (4), 4-loc., each with 1 or 2 pend. anatr. ovules. Drupe. Endosp. *Chief genus*: Ilex.

Aquifolium Tourn. ex Hall. = Ilex L. (Aquifol.).

Aquilaria Lam. Thymelaeaceae. 8 Indomal., China. The wood of *A. Agallocha* Roxb. (Calambac, aloe-wood, eagle-wood), in about 8 °/₀ of the trees, is saturated with resin (agar), used in India as a drug and perfume.

Aquilegia (Tourn.) L. Ranunculaceae (2). 75 N. temp. *A. vulgaris* L. (columbine), Brit., cult. orn. fl., with many others and many hybrids. Pets. with long spurs secreting honey (*cf.* Delphinium). Fl. of class H, protandrous, visited by humble-bees. Sta. often 50 or more, in whorls of 5.

Arabian coffee, *Coffea arabica* L.

Arabidopsis Schur. (*Sisymbrium* L. *BH.*, *Stenophragma EP.*). Cruc. (2). 12 $\underline{*}$.

Arabis Linn. Cruciferae (4). 220 N. temp., S Am., 5 Brit. (rock-cress). Cult. orn. fl.

Araceae (*EP.*; *Aroideae BH.*). Monocots. (Spathiflorae). 107 gen., 1900 sp., trop. and temp. (92 °/₀ trop.). Many types of veg. habit—herbs large and small, with aerial stems, tubers or rhiz., climbing shrubs, climbing epiph., marsh pl., one water pl. (Pistia) &c. In a few Pothoideae the stem is monopodial, but in most A. it is sympodial. Each joint of the sympodium begins as a rule with one or more scale l. before bearing fol. l. Accessory (collateral) buds often found in the leaf axils. Sometimes, as in Anthurium, Philodendron &c., the axillary shoot is 'adnate' to the main axis for some distance (*cf.* Solanaceae, Zostera &c.). The buds usually appear in the l. axils, but often get pushed to one side, and sometimes (*e.g.* Pothos) break through the leaf-bases as in Equisetum.

L. of many types. Pinnately and palmately divided l. are frequent, but development not like that of such leaves in Dicots. Holes are present in the l. of Monstera. See Monstera, Rhaphidophora, Philodendron, Helicodiceros, Dracontium, Zamioculcas, &c.

Roots adv. and mostly formed above ground in the larger forms. Two types of aerial r.—climbing and absorbent. The former, like ivy, insensitive to gravity, show great negative heliotropism; they cling closely to the support and force their way into the crevices. The latter, insensitive to light, respond markedly to gravity; they grow down to the soil and enter it, branching out and taking up nourishment.

The larger trop. A. show interesting stages in the development of epiphytism. The climbing forms grow to considerable size and form longer and longer aerial r. as they grow upwards. The original r. at the base thus become of less and less importance and they often die away together with the lower end of the stem, so that the plant thus becomes an epiph. Of course, as it still obtains its water &c. from the soil, it is not an epiph. in the sense that *e.g.* many Orchids or Bromeliaceae are such, and it is evident that if this method of becoming epiph. were the only one found in the order, these plants could with no more justice be classed as true epiph. than the ivy which may often be seen in the 'bowls' of pollard willows in Europe, and which has come there by climbing up the trunk and dying away below. It is found however that some sp. of Philodendron, Pothos, &c. are able to commence life as epiphytes. The fleshy fr. is eaten by birds and the seed dropped on a lofty branch. The seedling forms clasping r. and dangling aerial r. which grow steadily down to the soil, even if it be 100 feet or more away. It is hardly possible to suppose that these true epiph. sp. have been evolved in any other way than from former climbing sp. Lastly, some sp. of Anthurium &c. are true epiph. without connection with the soil (*e.g. A. Hügelii* Schott =*A. Hookeri* Kunth.); they have clasping r. and also absorbent r. which ramify amongst the humus collected by the pl. itself. The aerial r. of some A. possess a velamen like Orchids. The l. of *Philodendron cannifolium* Schott have swollen petioles full of large intercellular spaces lined with mucilage. When rain falls these fill with water and act as reservoirs. [Cf. Schimper's *Epiph. Veg. Amerikas.*]

Fls. without br., usu. massed together on a cylindrical spadix enclosed in a large spathe; the spadix usu. terminates a joint of the sympodium (the 'continuation' bud is generally in the axil of the l. next but one before the spathe), so that there is only one formed each year. Fl. ☿ or monoec. (dioec. in Arisaema), with or without P. Sta. typically 6 but usually fewer (down to 1), often united into a *synandrium* (*e.g.* Colocasia, Spathicarpa); in Ariopsis the synandria again united to one another. Stds. often present, and these also may be fused into a synandrodium as in Colocasia. G with much variety of structure; frequently reduced to 1 cpl. Berry. Outer integument of seed often fleshy. Endosperm or none.

Fls. usu. protog. (even when monoec.). In many gen. (incl. most Eur.) the smell is disagreeable and attracts carrion flies as pollen carriers (see Arum, Dracunculus, Helicodiceros, &c.).

Many A. contain latex, which is usually poisonous but is dispelled by heat. The rhizomes of many sp. contain much starch and are used as food (Caladium, Colocasia, Arum, &c.).

Classification and chief genera (after Engler): *Cf. Pfl. R.*

The grouping of the A. is very difficult and account has to be taken of histological as well as external characters.

I. *POTHOIDEAE* (land pl.; no latex or raphides; l. 2-ranked or spiral; lat. veins of 2nd and 3rd order netted; fls. usu. ☿; ov. anatr. or amphitr.): Pothos, Anthurium, Acorus.

II. *MONSTEROIDEAE* (land pl.; no latex; raphides; lat. veins of 3rd, 4th, and sometimes 2nd orders netted; fl. ☿, usu. naked; ov. anatr. or amphitr.): Rhaphidophora, Monstera, Spathiphyllum, Epipremnum.

III. *CALLOIDEAE* (land or marsh pl.; latex; fl. usu. ☿; ov. anatr. or orthotr.; l. never sagittate, usu. net-veined): Symplocarpus, Calla.

IV. *LASIOIDEAE* (land or marsh pl.; latex; fl. ☿ or ♂ ♀; ov. anatr. or amphitr.; seed usu. exalbum.; l. sagittate, often much lobed, net-veined): Dracontium, Amorphophallus.

V. *PHILODENDROIDEAE* (land or marsh pl.; latex; fl. naked, unisex.; ov. anatr. or orthotr.; seed usu. album.; l. usu. ||-veined): Philodendron, Zantedeschia.

VI. *COLOCASIOIDEAE* (land or marsh pl.; latex; fl. naked unisex.; sta. in synandria; ov. orthotr. or anatr.; seed album. or not; l. net-veined): Remusatia, Colocasia, Alocasia, Xanthosoma.

VII. *AROIDEAE* (land or marsh pl.; latex; l. various, net-veined; stems mostly tuberous; fl. unisex., usually naked; sta. free or in synandria; ov. anatr. or orthotr.; seed album.): Spathicarpa, Arum, Dracunculus, Helicodiceros, Arisaema.

VIII. *PISTIOIDEAE* (swimming pl.; no latex; fl. unisex., naked; ♂ fls. in a whorl, ♀ sol.): Pistia (only genus).

For further details of this most interesting order, see Engler in *Nat. Pfl.* and *Pfl. R.*, from which much of the above is abridged.

[Placed in Nudiflorae by *BH.*]

Arachis Linn. Leguminosae (III. 7). 10 Brazil, Paraguay. *A. hypogaea* L. (ground-, earth-, or pea-nut), largely cult. in warm regions for its seeds, which are ed. and when pressed yield one of the many oils used in place of olive oil. The fl. after fert. bends down (cf. Linaria) and the elongation of its stalk forces the young pod under ground, where it ripens.

Arachnanthe Blume (*Renanthera* p.p. *EP.*). Orchid. (II. 20). 10 S.E. As., Malaya.

Arachnites F. W. Schmidt = Ophrys L. (Orchid.).

Arachnitis Phil. Burmanniaceae. 1 Chili.

Arachnoid, cobweb-like.

Arachnopogon Berg. Inc. sed. Nomen.

Aracium Neck. = Crepis L. (Compos.).

Araeococcus Brongn. Bromeliaceae (4). 2 Guiana, E. Brazil.

Aragallus Neck. = Astragalus Tourn. (Legum.).

Aragoa H.B. et K. Scroph. (III. 1). 3 Andes.

Aralia Tourn. Aral. (2). 35 ✻. *A. Ginseng* Baill. *cf.* Panax.

Araliaceae (*EP.*, *BH.*). Dicots. (Archichl. Umbelliflorae; Umbellales *BH.*; pp. xxxix, lii). 55/700, chiefly trop., esp. Indomal., trop. Am. Usu. trees and shrubs, sometimes palm-like; some twine, some, *e.g.* ivy, root-climbers. Resin-passages. L. alt., rarely opp. or whorled, often large and cpd., with small stips.; mature l. often simpler than those of seedlings. Fl. small, in umbels or heads often massed into cpd. infls., ☿, reg., usu. epig., usu. 5 (3—∞)-merous. K usu. 5, very small; C 5, rarely (5), often valv.; A 5 (3—∞); $\overline{G}$ (5) (1—∞), rarely ½-inf. or $\underline{G}$, 5-loc. with 1 anatr. pend. ov. in each, micropyle facing outwards; styles free or united in great variety. Usu. drupe with as many stones as cpls. Embryo small in rich endosperm. Tetrapanax, Panax, and others are economically important.

Classification and chief genera (after Engler):

1. *Scheffleraeae* (C valv.): Fatsia, Tetrapanax, Hedera.
2. *Aralieae* (C ± imbr., sessile with broad base): Aralia, Panax.
3. *Mackinlayeae* (C valv., shortly clawed): Mackinlaya.

Aralidium Miq. Aral. (2). 2 Malaya. Dioec. Fr. 1-seeded. Endosp. ruminate. (Cornac., Ridley.)

Araliopsis Engl. Rut. (IV). 1 Gaboon. Drupe 4-stoned.

Aranella Barnhart in Small (*Utricularia* p.p.). Lentibul. 1 Fla., Cuba.

Ararocarpus Scheff. Anon. (4). 1 Java.

Arar wood, *Tetraclinis articulata* Masters (N.W. Afr.).

Araucaria Juss. Conif. (Pinac., 12; *cf.* C. for gen. chars.). 15 S. Am., N.Z., Austr., New Caled., New Guin., &c. In § 1 (Colymbea, l. broad, fr. cpls. not winged) *A. imbricata* Pav. (monkey-puzzle, Chile), with ed. seed, *A. brasiliana* A. Rich. (Brazilian pine, abundant in S. Braz.), *A. Bidwilli* Hook. (bunya-bunya pine, Queensland), and others. In § 2 (Eutacta, needle l., scales winged) *A. excelsa* R. Br. (Norfolk I. pine), *A. Cunninghamii* Ait. (hoop pine, E. Austr.), &c. All have useful timber. Many cult. orn. trees.

Araucariaceae = Pinaceae.

Araujia Brot. (incl. *Lagenia* Fourn.). Asclep. (II. 1). 6 Braz., Paraguay, Arg. Follicle leathery.

Arborescens, arboreus (Lat.), tree-like; **arboretum**, collection of trees.

Arbor-judae, *Cercis*; **-vitae**, *Thuja*; **arbour-vine, Spanish** (W.I.), *Ipomoea tuberosa* L.; **arbustum** (Lat.), a shrub.

Arbutus (Tourn.) L., Adans. Eric. (II. 3). 20 Medit., W. Eur., W. As., N. and C. Am. Small trees or shrubs. Fr. a dry berry. *A. Menziesii* Pursh. (Madrona laurel, N. Am.), useful wood. *A. Unedo* L. (strawberry tree) at Killarney.

Arbutus, trailing (Am.), *Epigaea repens* L.

Arcangelisia Becc. Menisperm. 3 Malaya, Phil. Is. P 9, A (9—12).

Arceuthobium Bieb. Loranth. (II). 12 ✻. *Ann. Bot.* II. 137.

Archaeocarex Börner. Cyper. (III). 1 S. Afr.

Archangel, see next; **yellow-**, *Lamium Galeobdolon* Crantz.

Archangelica Hoffm. (*Angelica* p.p. *EP.*). Umbell. (III. 6). 10 N. temp. The petiole of *A. officinalis* Hoffm. is ed., and offic.

Archangiopteris Christ et Giesenh. Maratt. (I). 2 S.W. China, Formosa. L. once pinnate; sori linear, of 80—160 sporangia.

Archemora DC. = Peucedanum L. (*BH.*) = Tiedemannia DC. (Umbell.).

Archegoniatae, plants with ♀ cell in an *archegonium*, a flask-shaped organ with neck of one layer of cells thick; Bryo- and Pteridophyta.
Archegonium, see last, and *Filicineae*, &c.
Archeria Hook f. Epacridaceae (2). 5 Tasmania, N.Z.
Archesporium, *Pteridophyta*.
Archibaccharis Heering. Compositae (3). 2 Mex.
Archichlamydeae. A division of Dicots. (*cf.* classification at end).
Archidendron F. Muell. Leguminosae (I. 1). 10 trop. Austr., New Guin. G to 15-loc.
Archiphyllum Van Tiegh. (*Myzodendron* p.p. *EP.*). Santal. 3 temp. S. Am.
Archontophoenix H. Wendl. et Drude. Palmae (IV. 1). 3 E. Austr.
Archytaea Mart. Theaceae. 2 Brazil, Guiana.
Arctagrostis Griseb. Gramineae (8). 2 arctic.
Arcteranthis Greene (*Oxygraphis* p.p. *EP.*; *Ranunculus* p.p. *BH.*). Ranunculaceae (3). 1 N. Am.
Arcterica Coville (*Cassiope* p.p. *EP.*; *Andromeda* p.p. *BH.*). Ericac. (II. 1). 1 Behring Str.
Arctic plants, *cf.* Zones of Veg.; **zone**, above cult. limit.
Arctium L. Compositae (11). 4 palaeotemp. *A. Lappa* L. (burdock) Brit. The invol. br. become hooked and woody after the fl. wither, and by clinging to fur &c. aid in jerking out the fr.
Arctocrania Nakai (*Cornus* p.p.). Cornaceae. 2 N. temp.
Arctomecon Torr. et Frem. Papaveraceae (II). 3 S.W. U.S.
Arctophila Rupr. = Poa L. and Colpodium Trin. (Gramin.).
Arctopus L. Umbelliferae (II. 2). 3 S. Afr.
Arctostaphylos Adans. Ericaceae (II. 3). 30 N. temp. and arctic; 2 Brit. (bearberry); the fl. appear as soon as the snow melts. *A. pungens* H.B. et K. (manzanita, Calif.), orn. wood.
Arctotheca Wendl. (*Arctotis* p.p. *EP.*). Compositae (10). 2 S. Afr.
Arctotis L. Compositae (10). 65 trop. and S. Afr., Austr. Shows chars. of § 10 well.
Arctous Niedz. (*Arctostaphylos* p.p.). Eric. (II. 3). 1 N. circumpolar.
Arcuate, bow-like.
Arcynospermum Turcz. Malvaceae (inc. sed.). 1 Mex.
Arcythophyllum Willd. (*Mallostoma BH.*). Rubi. (I. 2). 15 trop. Am. Mts.
Ardisia Sw. Myrsinaceae (II). 260 warm countries. Fl. usu. ☿.
Ardisiandra Hook. f. Primulaceae. 1 trop. Afr. Mts.
Arduina Mill. (*Carissa* L.). Apocynaceae (I. 1). 20 palaeotrop.
Areca L. Palmae (IV). 20 Indomal. *A. Catechu* L. largely cult. in trop. As. for its seeds (Areca or Betel nuts). The infl. is below the oldest living l., monoec., with the ♀ fls. at the bases of the twigs, the ♂ above. The seed, about as big as a damson, is cut into slices and rolled up in a leaf of Betel pepper (*Piper Betle*) with a little lime. When chewed, it turns the saliva bright red; it acts as a stimulus upon the digestive organs, and is supposed by the natives (who use it habitually) to be a preventive of dysentery. *A. oleracea* Jacq. = Oreodoxa o.
Areca-nut, *Areca Catechu* L.
Arechavaletaia Spegazz. Flacourt. (7) (Samyd. *BH.*). 1 Uruguay.

Aregelia O. Ktze. (*Nidularium* Lem. p.p.). Bromel. (4). 30 trop. Am.
Aremonia Neck. (*Agrimonia* L. p.p *BH.*). Ros. (III. 5). 1 S.E. Eur.
Arenaceous, arenarius (Lat.), growing in sandy places.
Arenaria Rupp. ex L. Caryophyllaceae (I. 1). 100 N. temp.; 8 Brit., incl. *A.* (*Honckenya*) *peploides* L. (sea-purslane), common on sandy coast, with long creeping underground stems with scale l., the green l. fleshy with water tissue. *A. Cherleria* Hook. (*Cherleria sedoides* L.) is a tufted alpine pl. of Scotland.
Arenga Labill. Palmae (IV. 1). 15 E. As. Like Caryota, but spadix unisexual; sta. ∞, cpls. 3. *A. saccharifera* Labill. (gomuti palm) cult. for sugar (jaggery), obtained by wounding the young infl. and evaporating the sap. A var. of sago is obtained from the pith by washing and granulating. The tree flowers when mature, infls. appearing in descending order till it dies. An excellent fibre is obtained from the leaf-sheaths.
Areole, *Cactaceae.*
Arethusa Gronov. Orchidaceae (II. 2). 4 Japan, Atl. N. Am.
Arethusantha Finet. Orchidaceae (II. 5). 1 trop. As.
Aretia Hall., L. (*Androsace* L. p.p.). Primul. 30 N. palaeotemp.
Aretiastrum DC. = Valeriana L. p.p. (Valer.).
Arfeuillea Pierre. Sapindaceae (II). 1 Siam.
Argan oil, *cf.* next.
Argania Roem. et Schult. Sapotaceae (I). 1 Morocco, *A. Sideroxylon* R. et S. The pressed seeds yield argan oil, used like olive oil; the timber is hard and durable; the fr. eaten by cattle.
Argemone Tourn. ex L. Papaveraceae (II). 12 warm Am.
Argentate, argenteus (Lat.), silvery.
Argentina Lam. (*Potentilla* L. p.p.). Rosaceae (III. 2). 5 N. Am.
Argillaceus (Lat.), growing on clay.
Argithamnia Sw. Euphorbiaceae (A. II. 2). 8 S. Am., W. Ind.
Argomuellera Pax. Euphorbiaceae (A. II. 2). 1 trop. Afr.
Argophyllum Forst. Saxifragaceae (V). 10 trop. Austr., New Cal.
Argostemma Wall. Rubiaceae (I. 2). 85 trop. As., Afr.
Argylia D. Don. Bignoniaceae (2). 12 Chili.
Argyranthemum Webb. = Chrysanthemum L. (Compos.).
Argyreia Lour. Convolvulaceae (I). 40 trop. As., Afr.
Argyrocalymma K. Schum. et Lauterb. Saxifragac. (V). 1 New Guinea.
Argyrocome Gaertn. = Helipterum DC. (Compos.).
Argyrolobium Eckl. et Zeyh. Leguminosae (III. 3). 60 Afr., Medit. to India. Mostly xero. Some have cleist. fl.
Argyrorchis Blume (*Macodes* Lindl. *EP.*). Orchid. (II. 2). 1 Java.
Argyrostachys Lopriore. Amarantaceae (3). 1 E. trop. Afr.
Argyroxiphium DC. Compositae (5). 2 Sandwich Is. Small trees.
Argythamnia P. Br. = Argithamnia Sw. (Euphorb.).
Aria Jacq. f. = Pyrus L. (Rosac.).
Aridarum Ridl. Araceae (V). 1 N. Borneo.
Arikuryroba Barb. Rodr. Palmae (IV. 2). 1 Brazil.
Aril, an extra coat to the seed, *Biophytum*, *Dillenia*, *Durio*, *Euonymus*, *Marantaceae*, *Myristica*, *Oxalis*, *Phyllocladus*, *Podocarpus*, *Taxus*,

Turneraceae; **-late**, with an aril; **-lode**, a false aril, not arising from the placenta.

Arillaria S. Kurz (*Ormosia* Jack, *BH.*). Legumin. (III. 1). 1 Burma.

Ariocarpus Scheidw. (*Mammillaria* p.p. *BH.*). Cact. (III. 2). 4 Mex.

Ariopsis J. Grah. Araceae (VI). 1 Indomal., *A. peltata* J. G., a small tuberous herb. The few ♀ fls. are at the base of the spadix, the ♂ above. This part is full of round holes leading into pear-shaped cavities surrounded each by a synandrium of 6-8 sta. The synandria are fused to each other so that the surface of the spadix is continuous from the opening of one fl. to that of the next.

Arisacontis Schott. Araceae (inc. sed.). 1 New Guinea, Polyn.

Arisaema Mart. Araceae (VII). 105 As., Abyss., N. Am. Like Arum, but dioec., said to be fert. by snails. The corm is known as Indian turnip.

Arisarum (Tourn.) Targ. Tozz. Araceae (VII). 3 Medit.

Aristate (dimin. **aristulate**), awned.

Aristea Soland. ex Ait. Iridaceae (II). 40 S. and trop. Afr., Madag.

Aristega Miers. (*Tiliacora* p.p.). Menispermaceae. 1 Andamans.

Aristida Linn. Gramineae (8). 160 temp. and sub-trop.

Aristobulia Mart. = Andira Lam. p.p. (Legum.).

Aristogeitonia Prain. Euphorbiaceae (A. I. 1). 1 W. trop. Afr.

Aristolochia Tourn. Aristolochiaceae. 300 trop. and temp.; herbs with rhiz. or twining lianes. *A. Gigas* Lindl. (pelican flower) and others often cult. orn. fl. Many trop. sp. have a small l. surrounding the stem at the base of each ordinary l., and looking like a stip., but really the first l. of the axillary shoot, which grows very rapidly at first. In other cases this l. remains small and its shoot does not develope, so that it looks like an interpet. stip. In most several buds form in each axil; the fls. usu. come from the upper ones.

A. Clematitis L. (birthwort) an escape in Brit. P tubular, hooded at top, and enlarged below round the gynostemium; this has 6 sessile extr. anthers below and as many stigmatic lobes above (really not the true stigmas, but the connectives of the anthers, which have assumed stigmatic functions). The young fl. stands erect and its tube contains numerous hairs, jointed at the base so that they can easily be bent down but not up. No honey. Small flies enter the fl. at this stage and find the stigmas ripe, so that if they bear pollen from other fls. fert. takes place. They are unable to escape until in a day or two the pollen is shed, and the hairs wither, the fl. at the same time bending down (*cf.* Arum). In *A. Sipho* L'Hérit. (Dutchman's pipe) the P is bent like a siphon and has a polished interior surface.

Aristolochiaceae (*EP. BH.*). Dicots. (Archichl. Aristolochiales). 5 gen., 300 sp., trop. and warm temp., except Austr. Herbs or shrubs, the latter usu. twining lianes. L. alt., stalked, often cordate, usu. simple, exstip. Fl. ☿, epig., reg. or ·|·. P usu. (3), petaloid; A 6—36, free, or united with the style into a gynostemium (cf. Asclepiads, Orchids, &c.). $\overline{G}$ 4—6-loc.; ov. ∞ in each loc., anatr., horiz. or pend. Caps. Embryo small in rich endosp. The A. are difficult to place in the system. They have been put near Dioscoreaceae, though not monocot. *BH.* place them in Multiovulatae Terrestres. *Chief genera:* Asarum, Aristolochia.

Aristolochiales. The 15th order of Dicot. Archichl. *Cf.* p. xiv.
Aristotelia L'Hérit. Elaeocarpaceae. 10 S. temp.
Arjona Comm. ex Cav. Santalaceae. 9 temp. S. Am.
Armed, thorny.
Armeniaca Tourn. ex Mill. = Prunus Tourn. (Rosac.).
Armeria Linn. Plumbaginaceae. 60 N. temp. and andine. *A. vulgaris* Willd. (thrift, sea pink) common on the coast of Brit. and in high mountain regions of Scotland, a fairly frequent phenomenon, due perhaps to similarity of conditions. Primary root perennial; each year's shoot dies down all but a short piece, on which the following year's shoot arises as an axillary branch. Infl. a capitulum of cincinni, surrounded by a whorl of bracts, the outer forming a sheath round the top of the peduncle. After fert. the K becomes a membranous funnel-like organ aiding seed-distribution by wind.
Armoracia Gaertn. = Cochlearia L. and Nasturtium R. Br. (Cruc.).
Arnatto, arnotto, *Bixa Orellana* L.
Arnebia Forsk. Boraginaceae (IV 4). 18 Medit., trop. Afr., Himal. Some have black spots on the C, which fade as it grows older (see fam., and cf. Diervilla, Fumaria, &c.).
Arnica Rupp. ex L. Compositae (8). 50 N. temp. and arctic. Tincture of arnica is prepared from all parts of the pl.
Arnicastrum Greenman. Compositae (6). 1 Mex.
Arnocrinum Endl. et Lehm. Liliaceae (III). 3 S.W. Austr.
Arnoseris Gaertn. Compositae (13). 1, *A. pusilla* Gaertn., Eur. (incl. Brit.). The bases of the invol. brs. enclose the ripe fr. (cf. Rhagadiolus).
Arnottia A. Rich. Orchidaceae (II. 1). 2 Mauritius.
Aroideae (*BH.*) = Araceae.
Arodendron Werth. (*Typhonodorum* p.p.). Araceae (V). 1 Zanzibar.
Aronia Pers. = Amelanchier Lindl. (Rosac.).
Aronicum Neck. = Doronicum L. p.p. (Compos.).
Arpophyllum Llave et Lex. Orchidaceae (II. 6). 6 C. Am., W.I.
Arrabidaea DC. Bignoniaceae (I). 100 S. Am.
Arracacia Bancroft. Umbelliferae (III. 4). 45 Peru to Mex. *A. xanthorhiza* Bauer and others cult. ed. tuberous r.
Arrack, cf. Borassus, Cocos, &c.
Arrhenatherum Beauv. Gramineae (9). 6 Eur., Medit. *A. avenaceum* Beauv. (false oat-grass, French rye-grass), Brit.
Arrhostoxylum Mart. = Ruellia L. p.p. (Acanth.).
Arrow-grass, *Triglochin*; **-head,** *Sagittaria sagittifolia* L.
Arrowroot, a pure starch obtained from various pl.; **Bermuda-, W. Indian-,** *Maranta arundinacea* L.; **Brazilian-,** *Manihot utilissima* Pohl.; **E. Indian-,** *Curcuma angustifolia* Roxb., *Tacca pinnatifida* Forst. &c.; **Portland-,** *Arum maculatum* L. Cf. Canna, Zea, &c.
Arrowsmithia DC. Compositae (4). 1 S. Afr.
Arsenococcus Small (*Vaccinium* p.p.). Eric. (III. 1). 1 Atl. U.S.
Artabotrys R. Br. Anonaceae (4). 30 palaeotrop. Some cult. for sweetly scented fl. and ed. fr. They usually climb by aid of recurved hooks, which are modified infl. axes, and thicken and lignify when they clasp.
Artanema D. Don. Scrophulariaceae (II. 6). 4 Indomal.

Artanthe Miq. = Piper L. (Piper.).
Artedia L. Umbelliferae (III. 8). 1 W. As.
Artemisia L. Comp. (7). 280 ✻, S. Afr., S. Am., common on arid soil of the western U.S., the Steppes, &c. 4 Brit. (wormwood). *A. tridentata* Nutt. and others form the ± halophytic 'sage-brush' of the S.W. U.S. Fl.-heads small, inconspic., and *wind* fert. (cf. Poterium, Rheum and Rumex, Plantago, Thalictrum, &c.). In *A. vulgaris* L. the marginal florets ♀, the rest ☿. Head pend.; the anther-tube projects beyond the C so that the dry powdery pollen is exposed to the wind. On the tips of the anthers are long bristles which together form a temporary pollen-holder. Afterwards the style emerges and the large hairy stigmas spread out. An interesting case of reacquisition of a character not found in most higher flowering pl. *A. Abrotanum* L. (old man, southernwood), and others, cult. orn. fl. The flavouring matter of absinthe is derived from wormwood.
Artemisiopsis Sp. Moore. Compositae (4). 1 Nyassaland.
Arthraerua Schinz. Amarantaceae (2). 1 S.W. Afr.
Arthratherum Beauv. = Aristida L. p.p. (Gramin.).
Arthraxon Beauv. Gramineae (2). 15 palaeotrop., E. As.
Arthrocarpum Balf. f. (*Ormocarpum EP.*). Legumin. (III. 7). 1 Socotra.
Arthroclianthus Baill. Leguminosae (III. 7). 6 New Cal.
Arthrocnemum Moq. Chenopodiaceae (A). 8 coasts |✻.
Arthrolobium Reichb. = Ornithopus L. and Scorpiurus L.
Arthrophyllum Blume. Araliaceae (1). 10 Indomal.
Arthrophytum Schrenk. Chenopodiaceae (B). 3 W. As.
Arthropodium R. Br. Lili. (III). 8 Austr., N.Z., New Cal. Cult. orn. fl.
Arthropogon Nees. Gramineae (4). 2 Brazil, Cuba.
Arthropteris J. Sm. Polypodiaceae. 4 trop. and subtrop.
Arthrosolen C. A. Mey. (*Gnidia* L. p.p. *EP.*). Thymel. 12 trop. and S. Afr.
Arthrostema Ruiz et Pav. Melastomac. (1). 12 Cuba, W. trop. Am.
Arthrostylidium Rupr. Gramin. (13). 16 trop. Am., W.I. Climbing.
Arthrostylis R. Br. Cyperaceae (II). 2 Austr.
Arthrotaxis Endl. = Athrotaxis D. Don (Conif.).
Arthrothamnus Klotzsch et Garke = Euphorbia L. p.p. (Euph.).
Artichoke, *Cynara Scolymus* L.; **Jerusalem-**, *Helianthus tuberosus*.
Articulate (l.), cut off by an absciss layer.
Articulated, jointed.
Artillery plant, *Pilea*.
Artocarpus Forst. Moraceae (II). 60 Indomal., China. Many show good bud-protection by stips. *A. laciniata* Hort. has large drip-tips (*Acer*, *Ficus*). Fls. monoec., the ♂ in pseudo-catkins, the ♀ in pseudo-heads. A multiple fr. is formed, the achenes being surrounded by the fleshy P and the common receptacle also becoming fleshy. The fr. contains much starch &c. and is a valuable food-stuff. Several sp. are cult. all over the trop., *e.g. A. incisa* L. (bread-fruit) and *A. integrifolia* L. (jak). The flesh has somewhat the texture of bread and is often roasted. The best cult. forms (*cf.* pear, banana, &c.) produce no seeds. The jak and others are caulifloral. Timber useful.

Artrolobium Desv. = Coronilla L., Ornithopus L., &c. (Legum.).

Arum (Tourn.) Linn. Araceae (VII). 12 Eur., Medit. *A. maculatum* L. (cuckoo-pint, wake-robin, lords and ladies, Brit.) is a perenn. tuberous pl. with monoec. fls.; ♀ fls. at base of spadix (each of 1 cpl., naked) and ♂ above (each of 2—4 sta.), and above these again rudimentary ♂ fls. repres. by hairs which project and close the mouth of the spathe. The foetid smell attracts flies, which enter the spathe, find the stigmas ripe, and are kept prisoners till the pollen is shed; then the hairs wither and escape is possible (cf. Aristolochia). Fr. a berry. The starch of the tubers was formerly used as food under the name Portland arrowroot, but it is difficult to get rid of the poisonous juices accompanying it. Other sp. are similarly used in Eur.

Arum lily, *Zantedeschia aethiopica* (L.) Spreng.

Aruncus Adans. Rosaceae (I. 1). 6 N. temp. Sta. on inner side of axis.

Arundina Blume. Orchidaceae (II. 4). 8 S.E. As., Malay Arch.

Arundinaceous, reed-like.

Arundinaria Michx. Gramineae (13). 80 warm. Bamboos (*q.v.*).

Arundinella Raddi. Gramineae (4). 45 warm. Inf. palea awned.

Arundo Tourn. Gramineae (10). 12 trop. and temp. *A. Phragmites* L. (Brit.) = P. communis. The stems of *A. Donax* L. are used for sticks, fishing-rods, &c.

Arvensis (Lat.), of arable land.

Arytera Blume (*Ratonia* DC. p.p. *BH.*). Sapind. (I). 20 E. As., Austr.

Asaemia Harv. Compositae (7). 1 S. Afr.

Asafoetida, *Ferula Narthex* Boiss., *F. Assafoetida* L., &c.

Asagraea Baill. (*Dalea* L. p.p. *BH.*). Leguminosae (III. 6). 2 N. Am.

Asarabacca, *Asarum europaeum* L.

Asarca Poepp. ex Lindl. = Chloraea Lindl. (Orchid.).

Asarum (Tourn.) L. Aristolochiaceae. 30 N. temp. *A. europaeum* L. (asarabacca), an escape in Brit. (formerly medic.). Rhiz. below ground and creeping shoots above; the latter are sympodial, each annual joint bearing several scale l. below, then two green l. and a terminal fl. Fl. reg.; P (3), sometimes with 3 small teeth between the segments (perhaps remnants of a former inner whorl); A 12; G (6). The dark-brown, resinously scented fl. is visited by flies, and is very protog.; when the stigmas are ripe the sta. are all bent away, but later on they move up to the centre and dehisce extr. The P lobes are bent in at first towards the centre of the fl. and form a sort of prison of it, but afterwards gradually straighten.

Ascarina Forst. Chloranthaceae. 6 Polynesia.

Ascending (aestivation), cf. Aest.; (ovule), sloping upwards; (stem), *do.*

-ascens (Lat. suffix), tending towards.

Aschamia Salisb. = Hippeastrum Herb. p.p. (Amaryllid.).

Aschenbornia Schauer. Compositae (2). 1 Mex.

Aschersoniodoxa Gilg et Muschler (*Draba* p.p.). Cruc. (4). 1 Ecuador.

Asciadium Griseb. Umbelliferae (inc. sed.). 1 Cuba.

Ascidium, a pitcher.

Asclepiadaceae (*EP. BH.*). Dicots. (Sympet. Contortae). 320 gen., 1700 sp., mostly trop. (esp. Afr.), but a few temp. In veg. habit like Apocynaceae; some perenn. herbs, but most are climbing shrubs or lianes, with simple, entire, opp., exstip. l. Latex is present. Many, esp. S. Afr. sp., xero.; some, *e.g.* Periploca, with much reduced l., others, *e.g.* Hoya, and still more, Stapelia, with fleshy stems. Epiphytes also occur; *cf.* esp. Dischidia.

Infl. usu. of many fls. and cymose or racemose (raceme or umbel). In the former case it is dich., but as in Caryophyll. the one branch tends to outgrow the other, and a monoch. (cincinnus) may arise in later branchings. When infl. axillary, there is usu. only one at each node; in the axil of the other l. there is a veg. shoot, or nothing. In some gen. (*cf.* Asclepias) the infl. is extra-axillary.

Fl. ☿, reg., 5-merous, usu. small. K 5, quincuncial, the odd sep. post.; C (5) usu. rotate or campanulate, with conv. or valvate aestivation. The essential organs (5 sta., 2 cpls.) are complex. The sta. and style are usu. united to form a *gynostegium*. The cpls. are free below as in Apocyn., but united at the tip with a common style; ov. sup. The head of the style is large and variously shaped, and the stigmatic surface is usually upon the edge or under side of it. To its margin are united the anthers of the 5 epipet. sta.; the filaments of these are short or non-existent. The pollen in § 1 is united merely in tetrads, in the higher group, comprising the bulk of the fam., into pollinia, as in Orchids. Usu. each anther contains two. In this group also there are curtain-like projections at the sides of the anthers, leaving a narrow slit between each pair of anthers.

The pollen is removed from the anthers by a curious mechanism—the *translator*. This differs in the two suborders and so also does the fert. method. The translator always stands between two anthers and serves to carry away half the pollen from each of them. In the *Periplocoideae* it is a spoon- or funnel-like body with a sticky disc at the narrow end. Into it is shed the pollen from the two half anthers next to it, and as the sticky disc projects outwards in the male stage of the flower an insect will be likely to get it attached to its head, and carry it about like the pollinia of an orchid. In visiting a second flower the pollen may be placed on the stigmatic surface. In the *Cynanchoideae*, on the other hand, there are pollinia, and the translator has a different structure. It forms an inverted Y-shaped organ, the foot of the Y being formed by the adhesive body (*corpusculum*); from this diverge the threads (*retinacula*) which are attached to the pollinia, one in each anther. An insect in obtaining honey catches its leg in the slit between the anthers, and in drawing it up removes the pair of pollinia. The threads as they dry contract on the inner side till the pollinia meet, thus closely clasping the insect's leg. In drawing the leg through a similar slit in another fl. the pollinia catch on the stigmatic under-surface of the stylar head. (Cf. Apocynum, which shows an approach to this mech.)

The backs of the anthers as a rule bear appendages (*cuculli*) forming a *corona*. In some cases it springs from the C. It may consist of small teeth, or be more complex, as in Asclepias and Ceropegia, and often takes up the functions of secreting and storing the honey.

$\underline{G}$ (2), 2-loc., with ∞ anatr. ov. pend. from the ventral plac. Fr. a pair of follicles; seeds usu. crowned by a tuft of hairs for wind-carriage. Endosperm slight, cartilaginous. Some give useful fibres.

Closely related to Apocyn., the only absolute distinction being the presence of translators in Ascl.; otherwise the two sub-orders of each form a corresponding series, and the lower one in each is almost as nearly related to the corresponding one in the other order as to the higher group in its own order. Placed in Gentianales by *BH.*

Classification and chief genera (after K. Schumann):

I. *PERIPLOCOIDEAE* (pollen in tetrads; translator spoon-like).

1. *Periploceae:* Streptocaulon, Periploca.

II. *CYNANCHOIDEAE* (pollinia; corpusculum, &c.).

1. *Asclepiadeae* (pollinia pendulous on threads): Asclepias, Calotropis, Cynanchum.
2. *Secamoneae* (pollinia erect or horizontal, 4 in each anther): Secamone (only genus).
3. *Tylophoreae* (do. but 2 in each, erect): Ceropegia, Stapelia, Stephanotis, Hoya.
4. *Gonolobeae* (do. but 2 in each, horiz.): Gonolobus.

Asclepias L. Asclepiad. (II. 1). 160 Am., Afr., esp. U.S. (silk-weeds). Herbs with umbellate infls. which spring from the stem between the petioles of the opp. l. (*cf.* Cuphea), or above or below this. Two explanations exist, but which is right the evidence available does not show. Either the infl. is axillary to the l. below it and is 'adnate' to the stem (*cf.* Cuphea), or it is the termination of a shoot, and the stem is really a sympodium.

The cuculli of the anthers form little pockets, into which honey is poured by the horn-like nectaries that project from them. Insects walking over the fl. and sipping honey frequently slip their legs down the sides of the gynostegium, and in drawing them up catch in the slit between two anthers and remove the pollinia (*cf.* family). The process may be watched on *A. Cornuti* Decne. in gardens.

Asclepiodora A. Gray (*Asclepias* p.p. *EP.*). Asclep. (II. 1). 2 N. Am.

Ascocentrum Schlechter. Orchidaceae (II. 20). 4 New Guinea.

Ascochilus Ridl. Orchidaceae (II. 20). 4 Malay Penins.

Ascoglossum Schlechter. Orchidaceae (II. 17). 2 New Guinea.

Ascolepis Nees. Cyperaceae (I). 10 warm Afr., Am.

Ascotainia Ridl. (*Tainia* p.p.). Orchid. (II. 7). 4 Malay Penins.

Ascyrum L. Guttiferae (II). 5 N. Am., W.I., Himalaya.

Asemnantha Hook. f. Rubiaceae (II. 3). 1 Yucatan.

Aseptate, without partitions.

Asexual, sexless; **-generation,** *Pteridophyta.*

Ash, *Fraxinus excelsior* L.; **mountain-,** *Pyrus Aucuparia* Ehrh.; **prickly-,** *Zanthoxylum fraxineum* Willd.; **-pumpkin,** *Benincasa cerifera* Savi.

Asimina Adans. Anonaceae (2). 10 E. U.S. *A. triloba* Dun. (papaw) has ed. fr.

Askidiosperma Steud. Restionaceae. 1 S. Afr.

Aspalathus L. Leguminosae (III. 3). 160 S. Afr Many are xero. with a heath-like habit.

Asparagopsis Kunth = Asparagus Tourn. p.p. (Lili.).

Asparagus Tourn. (incl. *Myrsiphyllum* Willd.). Liliaceae (VII). 300 |⁂, mostly in dry places. Rhiz. with aerial shoots; l. reduced to scales with linear green shoots in axils, usu. in tufts. These are small condensed cymes, of the type shown in the diagram (figs. represent the branches of successive orders). The number of shoots that develope varies. In the infl. the same construction holds, the shoots 2, 2 bearing the fls. In the sub-genus M. there are flat phylloclades (*cf.* Ruscus). Fr. a berry. *A. officinalis* L. cult., the young shoots being eaten.

stem
1
2 2
3 3
4 4
leaf

Aspasia Lindl. Orchidaceae (II. 19). 8 trop. Am.

Aspen, *Populus tremula* L.

Asper (Lat.), rough; **-ifolius** (Lat.), rough-leaved.

Asperella Humb. Gramineae (12). 2 As. (*BH.*), 4 N. Am., N. As., N.Z. (*EP.*).

Asperifoliae = Boraginaceae.

Aspermous, seedless.

Asperugo (Tourn.) L. Boraginaceae (IV. 2). 1 Eur., As.

Asperula L. Rubiaceae (II. 11). 80 Eur., As., Austr., esp. Medit. *A. odorata* L. (woodruff) and *A. cynanchica* L. (squinancy-wort), Brit. Fls. homogamous; fr. of woodruff hooked.

Asphodel, *Asphodelus*; **bog-,** *Narthecium ossifragum* Huds.; **Scottish-,** *Tofieldia palustris* Huds.

Asphodeline Rchb. Liliaceae (III). 15 Medit.

Asphodelus (Tourn.) L. Liliaceae (III). 12 Medit. (asphodel). L. isobil.; fls. protog.

Aspicarpa Rich. Malpighiaceae (I). 12 Texas to Argentina.

Aspidandra Hassk. Euphorbiaceae (inc. sed.). 1 Java.

Aspidistra Ker-Gawl. Liliaceae (VII). 5 E. As. The large flat style forms a lid to the cavity made by the 8 P-leaves. Cult. orn. fl.

Aspidium Sw. *Synonymy: A. aemulum* Sw., *cristatum* Sw., *dilatatum* Willd., *Filix-mas* Sw., *Oreopteris* Sw., *rigidum* Sw., *spinulosum* Sw., *Thelypteris* Sw. = Dryopteris (same spec. names); *A. Filix-foemina* Sw. = Athyrium F.-f.

Polypodiaceae, 200 cosmop. *A. aculeatum* Sw. (prickly shield-fern) and *A. Lonchitis* Sw. (holly-fern) in Brit.

Aspidixia Van Tieghem (*Viscum* p.p.). Loranthac. (II). 10 palaeotrop.

Aspidocarya Hook. f. et Thoms. Menispermaceae. 1 E. As. K 12 (A).

Aspidopterys A. Juss. Malpighiaceae (I). 20 trop. As.

Aspidosperma Mart. et Zucc. Apocynac. (I. 3). 50 trop. and S. Am., W.I. Wood useful; bark (quebracha) used for tanning.

Aspilia Thou. Compositae (5). 90 Brazil to Madagascar.

Aspiliopsis Greenman. Compositae (5). 1 Mex.

Aspleniopsis Mett. Polypodiaceae. 1 Melanesia.

Asplenium L. Polypodiaceae. 540 cosmop.; 11 in Brit., including *A. Filix-foemina* Bernh. (lady-fern), *A. Ruta-muraria* L. (wall-spleenwort), *A. Trichomanes* L. (spleenwort) and *A. Adiantum-nigrum* (black spleenwort). The var. *clarissima* of the lady-fern shows apogamy (see Filicineae, Lepto.). *A. bulbiferum* Forst. and other sp. are 'viviparous,' producing young plants on their leaves by vegetative budding (not to be confounded with apospory). *A. Nidus*

L. (the bird's nest fern) is an interesting epiphyte of the Old World tropics. It bears a rosette of leaves forming a nest in which humus collects; the roots ramify in this and obtain food and water. *A. rhizophyllum* Kunze is the walking fern, so called because the leaf-tips when they touch the soil bud into new individuals, and thus the plant spreads to some distance.

Asprella Schreb. = Leersia Sw. (Gramin.).

Assai palm, *Euterpe edulis* Mart.

Assegai wood, *Curtisia faginea* Ait.

Associations, plant, the grouping of pl. which occupies any definite uniform area and kind of land.

Assurgent, ascending.

Astartea DC. (*Baeckea* L. p.p.). Myrtaceae (II. 1). 5 Austr.

Astelia Banks et Soland. Liliaceae (VI). 15 Polynes. Dioec. Cult. orn. fl.

Astelma R. Br. = Helichrysum, Helipterum (Compos.).

Astelma Schlecht. Asclepiadaceae (II. 3). 1 New Guinea.

Astemma Less. Compositae (5). 1 Ecuador.

Astemon Regel. Labiatae (inc. sed.). 1 S. Am.

Astephania Oliv. Compositae (4). 2 E. Afr.

Astephanocarpa Baker. Compositae (4). 1 Madag.

Astephanus R. Br. Asclepiad. (II. 1). 12 Madag., trop. Afr., warm Am.

Aster Tourn. ex L. Compositae (3). 500 Am., As., Afr., Eur.; 2 on Brit. coast (Michaelmas daisy), somewhat fleshy halophytes. Style sta. typical of § 3. The China aster of gardens (*A. chinensis* L.) is a Callistephus. Many cult. orn. fl.

Aster, China, *Callistephus hortensis* Cass.

Asteracantha Nees (*Hygrophila BH.*). Acanth. (IV. A). 1 palaeotrop.

Asteraceae = Compositae.

Asterales (*BH.*). The 2nd cohort of Dicotyledons (Gamopet.).

Asteranthe Engl. et Diels (*Asteranthopsis*). Anon. (1). 1 Zanzibar.

Asteranthera Hanst. Gesneriaceae (1). 1 Chili.

Asteranthopsis O. Ktze. Anonaceae (1). 1 Zanzibar.

Asteranthus Desf. Lecythidaceae. 1 Venezuela, N. Brazil.

Asteriastigma Bedd. (*Hydnocarpus* p.p. *EP.*). Flacourt. (3). 1 India.

Asteriscium Cham. et Schlecht. Umbelliferae (I. 2). 27 Mex., S. Am.

Asteriscus Moench = Odontospermum Neck. (Comp.).

Asterocephalus (Vaill.) Adans. = Scabiosa L. p.p. (Dipsac.).

Asterochaete Nees. Cyperaceae (II). 4 Masc., S. Afr.

Asterochlaena Garcke = Pavonia Cav. (Malv.).

Asterogyne H. Wendl. Palmaceae (IV. 1). 2 C. Am.

Asteroid, star-shaped.

Asterolasia F. Muell. Rutaceae (1). 7 Austr.

Asterolinon Hoffmannsegg et Link. Primulaceae. 2 Medit., Abyss.

Asteromaea Blume (*Bottonia BH.*). Compositae (3). 3 E. As.

Asteropeia Thou. Theaceae (Samyd. *BH.*). 5 Madag.

Asterophorum Sprague. Tiliaceae. 1 Ecuador.

Asteropsis Less. (*Podocoma* Cass. *BH.*). Compositae (3). 1 S. Brazil.

Asterostemma Decne. Asclepiadaceae (II. 3). 1 Java.

Asterostigma Fisch. et Mey. (*Staurostigma BH.*). Arac. (VII). 5 Brazil.

Asthenochloa Buese. Gramineae (inc. sed.). 1 Java.

Astianthus D. Don (*Tecoma* Juss. p.p. *BH.*). Bignon. (2). 1 C. Am., Mex.

Astichous, not in rows.

Astilbe Buch.-Ham. Saxifragaceae (I). 20 As., N. Am.

Astiria Lindl. Sterculiaceae. 1 Masc.

Astoma DC. Umbelliferae (III. 4). 1 Palestine.

Astragalus Tourn. ex L. Leguminosae (III. 6). 1600 cosmop. exc. Austr.; 3 Brit. (milk-vetch). Usu. on steppes, prairies, &c. and ± xero. often thorny; the thorns commonly form by the stiffening of the petiole or midrib of the l. when the blade falls off. *A. gummifer* Labill. and others yield gum-tragacanth, obtained by wounding the stem; the gum exudes and hardens.

Astrantia (Tourn.) L. Umbelliferae (II. 1). 10 Eur., As.

Astrebla F. Muell. Gramineae (11). 3 Austr.

Astrephia Dufresne. Valerianaceae. 4 Chili.

Astrocalyx Merrill. Melastomaceae (II). 2 Phil. Is.

Astrocarpus Neck. Resedaceae. 2 S.W. Eur.

Astrocaryum G. F. W. Mey. Palmae (IV. 2). 40 trop. Am. Several yield fibre and oil, or are cult. as decorative.

Astrocasia Robinson et Millspaugh. Euphorb. (A. I. 1). 1 C. Am.

Astrochlaena Hallier f. Convolvulaceae (I). 20 Afr.

Astrococcus Benth. Euphorbiaceae (A. II. 2). 2 Brazil.

Astrodaucus Drude (*Daucus* p.p.). Umbelliferae (III. 2). 4 Medit.

Astroloma R. Br. (*Styphelia* p.p. *EP.*). Epacridaceae. 25 Austr.

Astronia Noronha. Melastomaceae (II). 50 Malay Arch., Polynes.

Astronium Jacq. Anacardiaceae (3). 10 S. Am. Hard wood.

Astrophiolate, with no strophiole.

Astrophyllum Torr. et Gray. Rutaceae (I). 1 Mex., S.W. U.S.

Astrostemma Benth. Asclepiadaceae (II. 1). 1 Borneo.

Astrothalamus C. B. Robinson. Urticaceae (3). 1 Phil. Is.

Astrotheca Miers (*Clusia* L. p.p. *BH.*). Guttiferae (V). 1 Brazil.

Astrotricha DC. Araliaceae (I). 6 Austr.

Astydamia DC. Umbelliferae (III. 6). 1 Canaries.

Asymmetrical (fl.), with no plane of symmetry, *Canna*, *Marantaceae*, *Valerianaceae*; (l.), divided into unequal parts by midrib, *Begonia*, *Ulmaceae*.

Asystasia Blume. Acanthaceae (IV. B). 30 palaeotrop.

Asystasiella Lindau. Acanthaceae (IV. B). 3 trop. As., Afr.

Ataenidia Gagnep. Marantaceae. 1 Gaboon.

Atalantia Correa. Rutaceae (V). 18 trop. As., China, Austr.

Atalaya Blume. Sapindaceae (I). 5 Austr., Malay Arch.

Atamasco Raf. = Zephyranthes Herb. (*BH.*) = Amaryllis L.

Atamisquea Miers. Capparidaceae (II). 1 Chili, Arg.

Atamosco, *Zephyranthes texana* Herb.

Atavism, a reversion to type.

Atelandra Bello (*Meliosma* Blume *EP.*). Sabiaceae [Myrsinaceae (*BH.*)]. 2 Porto Rico.

Atelanthera Hook. f. et Thoms. Cruciferae (4). 1 W. Tibet.

Ateleia Moc. et Sesse. Leguminosae (III. 1). 4 trop. Am., W.I.

Atelophragma Rydb. (*Astragalus* p.p.). Legumin. (III. 6). 6 N. Am.

Ater (Lat.), black.

Ateramnus P. Br. = Gymnanthes Sw. (Euphorb.).
Athamanta L. Umbelliferae (III. 5). 10 Medit.
Athanasia L. Compositae (7). 50 S. and trop. Afr., Madag.
Athenaea Sendtn. Solanaceae (2). 15 trop. Am.
Atherandra Decne. Asclepiadaceae (I). 3 Malaya.
Atheranthera Mast. Passifloraceae. 1 Angola.
Atherolepsis Hook. f. Asclepiadaceae (I). 2 Burma.
Atheropogon Muhl. ex Willd. = Bouteloua Lag. p.p. (Gramin.).
Atherosperma Labill. Monimiaceae. 2 Victoria, Tasmania. The strongly scented bark is sometimes used as a tea.
Atherostemon Blume. Asclepiadaceae (I). 1 Burma, Malaya.
Athrixia Ker-Gawl. Compositae (4). 20 Austr., Afr.
Athroisma DC. Compositae (4). 1 E. Indomal.
Athroostachys Benth. Gramineae (13). 1 Brazil. Climbing.
Athrotaxis D. Don. Coniferae (Pinaceae; see C. for gen. char.). 4 Tasmania, Austr.
Athyana Radlk. Sapindaceae (I). 1 Arg., Paraguay.
Athyrium Roth. Polypodiaceae. 120 cosmop. *A. Filix-femina* Roth. (lady fern) Brit.
Athyrocarpus Schlecht. (*Phaeospherion EP.*). Commel. 3 trop. Am.
Athysanus Greene. Cruciferae (4). 2 Calif.
Atlantic cedar, *Cedrus atlantica* Manetti.
Atomostigma O. Ktze. Rosaceae (VI). 1 Matto Grosso.
Atractocarpa Franchet. Gramineae (13). 1 Congo.
Atractocarpus Schlechter et Krause. Rubiaceae (I. 8). 1 New Cal.
Atractogyne Pierre. Rubiaceae (I. 8). 1 trop. Afr.
Atractylis L. Compositae (11). 20 Medit. to Japan.
Atragene L. = Clematis L. (Ranunc.).
Atraphaxis L. Polygonaceae (II. 1). 18 C. As., N. Afr., Greece.
Atratus (Lat.), blackened.
Atrichoseris A. Gray. Compositae (13). 1 Calif.
Atriplex (Tourn.) L. Chenopodiaceae (A). 180 temp. and subtrop.; 6 Brit. (orache). Fls. unisexual or polyg., naked or with P.
Atro- (Lat. pref.), black; **-purpureus,** dark purple; **-virens,** dark green.
Atropa L. Solanaceae (2). 4 Eur., Medit., As. *A. Belladonna* L. (deadly nightshade) contains the alkaloid atropin, the basis of the drug belladonna used in medicine.
Atropanthe Pascher (*Scopolia* p.p.). Solanaceae (2). 1 China.
Atropin, *Atropa Belladonna* L.
Atropis Rupr. (*Glyceria* R.Br. *BH*). Gramineae (10). 30 temp.
Atropous (ovule), in a line with funicle.
Atroxima Stapf. Polygalaceae. 4 trop. Afr.
Atrutegia Bedd. (*Goniothalamus* Bl. *EP.*). Anonac. (2). 1 S. India.
Attalea H. B. et K. Palmae (IV. 2). 30 S. Am., W. I., trop. Afr. *A. funifera* Mart. (Brazil) yields Bahia Piassaba fibre (*Kew Bull.* 1889, p. 237). *A. Cohune* Mart. (Honduras) yields the ivory-like Cohune nuts.
Attar of roses, Rosa, Pelargonium.
Attenuate, tapering.
-atus (Lat. suffix), provided with.

Atylosia Wight et Arn. (*Cantharospermum* W. et A. pp. *EP.*). Leguminosae (III. 10). 20 trop. As., Austr., Madag., Mascarenes.
Aubergine, *Solanum Melongena* L.
Aubletella Pierre (*Chrysophyllum* L. p.p.). Sapotac. (1). 1 Guiana.
Aubrietia Adans. Cruciferae (4). 15 Medit. Mts.
Aubrya Baill. (*Saccoglottis EP.*). Humiriac. 10 S. Am., trop. Afr.
Aucoumea Pierre. Burseraceae. 1 Gaboon. Yields resin.
Aucuba Thunb. Cornaceae. 3 Himal. to Japan. *A. japonica* Thunb. (Japan laurel) cult. orn. shrub; it is dioecious.
Aucubaephyllum Ahlburg (*Grumilea* p.p. *EP.*). Cornaceae. 1 Japan.
Audibertia Benth. (*Ramona* Greene). Labiat. (VI). 10 N. Am.
Audibertiella Briq. Labiatae (VI). 10 Calif.
Audouinia Brongn. Bruniaceae. 1 S. Afr.
Augea Thunb. Zygophyllaceae. 1 S. Afr. Exalb.
Augia Lour. Inc. sed. 1 China.
Augusta Leandr. = Stifftia Mikan. (Compos.).
Augusta Pohl (*Ucriana* Spreng.). Rubiaceae (I. 3). 1 E. Brazil.
Aulacocalyx Hook. f. Rubiaceae (II. 1). 4 trop. Afr.
Aulacocarpus Berg. Myrtaceae (I). 2 Brazil.
Aulacodiscus Hook. f. (*Pleiocarpidia*). Rubiaceae (I. 7). 1 Malay Pen.
Aulacolepis Hackel. Gramineae (8). 1 Japan.
Aulacorhynchus Nees. Cyperaceae (inc. sed.). 1 S. Afr.
Aulax Berg. Proteaceae (I). 3 Mts. S. Afr.
Aulaya Harv. = Harveya Hook. (Scrophular.).
Aulisconema Hua (*Disporopsis* p.p.). Liliaceae (VII). 2 China.
Aulojusticia Lindau. Acanthaceae (IV B.). 1 S. Afr.
Aulomyrcia Berg. = Myrcia DC. p.p. (Myrtac.).
Aulospermum Coulter et Rose (*Cymopterus* p.p.). Umb. (III. 6). 12 N. Am.
Aulostephanus Schlechter. Asclepiad. (II. 3). 1 Natal.
Aulostylis Schlechter. Orchidaceae (II. 9). 1 New Guinea.
Aulotandra Gagnep. Zingiber. (1). 2 Madag., trop. Afr.
Aurantium Tourn. ex Mill. = Citrus L. (Rutac.).
Aureus (Lat.), golden.
Auricled (l.), with two lobes overlapping stem.
Auricula, *Primula Auricula* L.
Auricula Tourn. ex Spach = Primula Tourn.
Aurila Noronha. Inc. sed. Nomen.
Austere, astringent.
Australian blackwood, *Acacia melanoxylon* R. Br.; **chestnut**, *Castanospermum australe* A. Cunn.; **-currant**, *Leucopogon*; **-daisy**, *Vittadinia*; **-fuchsia**, *Correa*; **-heath**, *Epacris*; **-honeysuckle**, *Banksia*; **red cedar**, *Cedrela australis* F. Muell.
Australina Gaudich. Urticaceae (5). 5 Austr., N.Z., S. Afr.
Australis (Lat.), southern.
Autochthonous, native.
Autogamy, self-pollination, *Capsella*, *Senecio*, &c.
Autrandra Pierre ex Prain (*Erythrococca* p.p.). Euph. (A. II. 2). 1 trop. Afr.
Autrania C. Winckler et Barbey (*Centaurea* p.p. *EP.*). Comp. (11). 1 Syria.

Autumn crocus, *Colchicum*.
Autunesia O. Hoffm. Compositae (1). 1 Angola.
Auxemma Miers. Boraginaceae (1). 2 Brazil. Useful firewood.
Auxopus Schlechter. Orchidaceae (II. 2). 1 Cameroons.
Avellanita Phil. Euphorbiaceae (A. II. 3). 1 Chili.
Avellinia Parl. Gramineae (10). 2 Medit.
Avena L. Gramineae (9). 70 temp. and Mts. of trop.; 2 Brit. (oat-grass). *A. sativa* L., the cult. oat, is perhaps derived from *A. fatua* L. It is cult. in Eur. to 69½° N. and forms the staple of the food of a large population. It occurs in two chief forms, the common oat with open spreading panicles, and the Tartarian oat with contracted one-sided panicles. [See De Candolle's *Orig. of Cult. Plts.* p. 373.] The 2–6-flowered spikelets form a loose panicle. The paleae are awned, the awn of the inf. palea being usually twisted and hygroscopic. In *A. sterilis* L. the awns cross, and when wetted try to uncurl and thus press on one another till a sort of explosion occurs jerking away the fruits. [*Cf.* Bews, *Grasses of the World.*]
Avenastrum Jessm. (*Avena* L. p.p.). Gramineae (9). 10 S. Afr.
Avens, *Geum*.
Averrhoa, L. Oxalidaceae. 2 trop. As. (?; long cult.; origin uncertain). *A. Bilimbi* L. (blimbing) and *A. Carambola* L. (carambola) cult. for fr., which is borne on the older stems (cauliflory).
Averrhoidium Baill. Sapindaceae (II). 2 Brazil, Paraguay.
Averse, turned back.
Avicennia L. Verbenaceae (7). 4 warm, a constituent of the mangrove veg. (*q.v.*). The seeds germinate in the fr., and they have aerial r. projecting out of the mud like Sonneratia.
Avocado, *Persea gratissima* Gaertn. f.
Awl-wort, *Subularia aquatica* L.
Awn, a thread-like organ on a fr., *Anthoxanthum*, *Erodium*, *Geraniaceae*, *Gramineae*.
Axanthes Blume = Urophyllum Wall. (Rubiac.).
Axia Lour. (*Boerhaavia* L. p.p. *EP.*). Nyctaginaceae (Valerianaceae? *BH.*). 1 Cochinchina.
Axial, axile, belonging to the axis; **-placentation**, on the axis, *cf.* diagram of *Guttiferae*, *Liliaceae*.
Axil, the upper angle between a l. and the stem on which it is borne; **-lary**, in the axil. *Cf.* Buds, Concrescence, &c.
Axinaea Ruiz et Pav. Melastomaceae (I). 25 trop. Am.
Axinandra Thw. (*BH.* incl. *Naxiandra* Krasser). Melastomaceae (III). (Lythraceae *BH.*) 1 Ceylon.
Axiniphyllum Benth. Compositae (5). 2 Mex.
Axis, the stem.
Axonopus Beauv. = Paspalum L. (Gramin.). 12 warm.
Axyris L. Chenopodiaceae (A). 6 Mid. and N. As.
Ayapana, *Eupatorium Ayapana* Vent.
Aydendron Nees. Lauraceae (II). 45 trop. Am.
Ayenia Loefl. (*Aniba* Aubl.). Sterculiaceae. 25 trop. and subtrop. Am.
Azadirachta A. Juss. (*Melia* L. *BH.*) 1 Indomal. *A. indica* A. Juss. (nim) has astringent medicinal bark, and yields good timber.
Azalea Gaertn. = Loiseleuria Desv.; **Azalea** L. = Rhododendron L. p.p.

Azaleastrum Rydb. (*Rhododendron* p.p.). Ericaceae (I. 2). 1 N. Am.

Azara Ruiz et Pav. Flacourtiaceae. 20 Mex., S. Am. Shrubs with alt. l.; one stip. is frequently almost as large as the l. to which it belongs, giving the appearance of a pair of l., not opp. Fl. apetalous; outer sta. often without anthers.

Azedarach Tourn. ex L. = Melia L. (Meliac.).

Azeredia Arruda (*Cochlospermum* p.p. *EP.*). Cochlosperm. 1 Brazil.

Azima Lam. Salvadoraceae. 3 S. Afr. to Phil. Is. In the axils are thorns (the l. of an undeveloped shoot, *cf.* Cactaceae). Polypet.

Azolla Lam. Salviniaceae. 5 trop. and subtrop. General structure like Salvinia. Two l. are formed at each node, from the dorsal half of a segment of the apical cell; from the ventral half are formed roots and branches, but not at every node. The l. are all alike; each is bilobed and has a small cavity near the base, opening by a small pore, and inhabited by the Alga *Anabaena*. The r. hang freely down in the water; usually the root cap is thrown off after a time and the r. comes almost exactly to resemble the submerged l. of Salvinia. The sporocarps are formed in pairs (4 in *A. nilotica*) on the ventral lobes of the first l. of the branches. Each contains one sorus. The microspores are joined together into several masses in each sporangium by the hardened frothy mucilage (epispore, *cf.* Salvinia). Each of these *massulae* has its outer surface provided with curious barbed hairs (*glochidia*), and escapes on its own account. The megasporangium contains one spore. It sinks to the bottom; decay of the indusium frees the spore and it germinates, giving rise to a ♀ prothallus which floats about on the water and may be anchored to a floating massula by the barbs.

Azorella Lam. Umbelliferae (I. 2). 70 Andes to N.Z. Densely tufted xero. *A. caespitosa* Vahl. (balsam-bog, Falklands) forms tufts like Raoulia.

Azureus (Lat.), sky-blue.

B (fl.-class), fls. with fully concealed honey, *Calluna*, many *Caryophyllaceae*, *Geranium*, *Gypsophila*, *Polemonium*, *Rubus*, *Thymus*.

B' (fl.-class), like B, but aggregated into dense heads, *Armeria*, *Compositae*, *Dipsaceae*, *Scabiosa*.

Babbagia F. Muell. (*Osteocarpum EP.*). Chenopodiac. 4 Austr.

Babiana Ker-Gawl. Iridaceae (III). 40 S. and trop. Afr., Socotra

Babingtonia Lindl. = Baeckea L. p.p. (Myrt.).

Babul, *Acacia arabica* Willd.

Bacca (Lat.), a berry; **-cate**, with berry; **-iform**, berry-like.

Baccaurea Lour. Euphorbiaceae (A. I. 1). 60 trop. Afr., As., Polynesia.

Baccaureopsis Pax. Euphorbiac. (A. I. 1). 1 trop. Afr.

Baccharis L. Compositae (3). 380 Am., esp. campos. Many are leafless xero. with winged or cylindrical green stems (*Bot. Jb.* 27, 446).

Bachelor's button, double fld. *Centaurea*, *Lychnis*, *Ranunculus*, &c.; also *Jasione*, &c.; **do.** (W.I.), *Gomphrena*.

Bachmannia Pax. Capparidaceae (II). 2 Pondoland.

Bacillar, rod-shaped.

Backhousia Hook. et Harv. Myrtaceae (II. 1). 5 E. Austr. *B. citriodora* F. Muell. gives an essential oil almost entirely citral.

Baconia DC. = Pavetta L. (Rubi.).
Bacopa Aubl. (*Herpestis* Gaertn. f.). Scroph. (II. 6). 65 warm.
Bacterial colonies, *Pavetta.*
Bacteroids, *Leguminosae.*
Bactris Jacq. Palmae (IV. 2). 100 trop. Am., W.I. Fls. in groups of 3, one ♀ between two ♂. *B. minor* Jacq. (pupunha or peach palm, Brazil), ed. fr.
Bacularia F. Muell (*Linospadix* p.p. *EP.*). Palm. (IV. 1). 5 Austr., Malaya.
Badiera DC. (*Polygala* p.p. *EP.*). Polygalaceae. 15 W.I.
Badinjan (W.I.), *Solanum Melongena* L.
Badius (Lat.), chestnut brown.
Badula Juss. (*Ardisia* Sw. p.p. *BH.*). Myrsin. (II). 12 E. Afr. Is.
Badusa A. Gray. Rubiaceae (I. 5). 1 Fiji, Society Is.
Baeckia L. Myrtaceae (II. 1). 60 Austr. to China.
Bael, *Aegle Marmelos* Correa.
Baeobotrys Forst. = Maesa Forsk. (Myrsin.).
Baeometra Salisb. Liliaceae (1). 1 S. Afr.
Baeria Fisch. et Mey. Compositae (6). 20 Calif.
Bagassa Aubl. Moraceae (1). 3 Guiana, N. Brazil.
Bagnisia Becc. Burmanniaceae. 3 Malay Arch.
Bahamas hemp, *Agave rigida* Mill. var.; **-grass**, *Cynodon Dactylon.*
Bahia Lag. Compositae (6). 15 N. Am., Chile.
Bahia piassaba, *Attalea funifera* Mart.
Baikiea Benth. Leguminosae (II. 3). 6 trop. Afr.
Baileya Harv. et A. Gray. Compositae (6). 3 Utah-Mexico.
Baillonacanthus O. Ktze. = Solenoruellia Baill. (Acanth.).
Baillonella Pierre (*Mimusops* L. p.p. *EP.*). Sapot. (2). 1 Gaboon.
Baillonia Bocquillon. Verbenaceae (1). 2 S. Am.
Baissea A. DC. Apocynaceae (II. 1). 12 trop. Afr., As.
Bajri, *Pennisetum typhoideum* Rich.
Bakeria André. Bromeliaceae (3). 1 Colombia. Cult. orn. infl.
Bakeridesia Hochreut. Malvaceae (2). 1 Mex.
Bakeriella Dubard. Sapotaceae (1). 11 Afr.
Bakerisideroxylon Engl. (*Sideroxylon* p.p.). Sapot. (1). 3 trop. Afr.
Balaka Becc. (*Ptychosperma* p.p. *EP.*). Palmae (IV. 1). 2 Fiji.
Balangue Gaertn. Oleaceae. 1 Madag.
Balania Nor. Inc. sed. Spp. 0.
Balania Van Tiegh. (*Balanophora* p.p. *EP.*). Balan. 2 E. As.
Balaniella Van Tiegh. (*Balanophora* p.p.). Balan. 10 E. As.
Balanites Delile. Zygophyllaceae. 2 Egypt, trop. Afr., Abyss. Oil.
Balanocarpus Bedd. Dipterocarpaceae. 16 Indomal.
Balanophora Forst. Balanophoraceae. 20 Indomal. Some apogamous (*cf.* Filicineae, Angiospermae; Treub in *Ann. Buitenz.* XV).
Balanophoraceae (*EP.*; *BH.*). Dicots. (Archichl. Santalales). 15 gen., 40 sp., all but one trop. Parasites (no chlorophyll) on tree roots, to which the tuberous rhiz. is attached by suckers. From it springs the infl. (sometimes developed within the rhiz. and breaking through it), which comes above ground as a spike or head with scaly l. and small unisexual fls. ♂ usu. P 3—4 or (3—4), A 3—4 or more or less. ♀ usu. P 0 $\overline{G}$ (1—2, rarely 3); ovule without an integument. Nut- or drupe-

like fr. Endosperm. For details and figures see *Nat. Pfl.*, or Kerner's *Nat. Hist. of Pl. Chief genera:* Scybalium, Balanophora, Langsdorffia. [Placed in Achlamydosporeae by *BH.*]

Balanops Baill. Balanopsidaceae. 7 New Cal.

Balanopsidaceae (*EP. Balanopseae* BH.). Dicots. (Archichl. Balanopsidales). An anomalous order placed in Monochlam. Unisexuales by *BH.* Trees with simple l., ♂ fl. in spikes, ♀ sol. Dioec.; ♂ with one whorl of P, ♀ with ∞ scaly bracts. G (2), each with 2 ascending ov. with 1 integument. Drupe. 2/10 New Caled.

Balanopsidales (Engler). The 6th order of Archichlamydeae. *Cf.* p. x.

Balanostreblus Kurz. Moraceae (II). 1 Burma.

Balansaephytum Drake del Castillo. Morac. (II). 1 Tonquin.

Balansochloa O. Ktze. = Germainia Bal. et Poitr. (Gramin.).

Balantium Kaulf. Cyatheaceae. 7 Am., Polynesia, Afr.

Balata, a guttapercha-like body; *Mimusops Balata* Crueg.; **-tree** (W.I.), *Bumelia.*

Balaustion Hook. Myrtaceae (II. 1). 1 W. Austr.

Balbisia Cav. Geraniaceae. 6 S. Am. undershrubs. Ov. ∞ per cpl.

Balboa Planch. et Triana. Guttiferae (V). 1 Colombia.

Bald-money, *Meum athamanticum* Jacq.

Balduina Nutt. (*Baldwinia*). Compositae (5). 3 S. U.S.

Baldwinia Nutt. (*Balduina*). Compositae (5). 3 S. U.S.

Balfourodendron Mello. Rutaceae (IV). 1 Rio de Janeiro.

Baliospermum Blume. Euphorbiaceae (A. II. 6). 10 Indomal.

Balisaea Taub. Leguminosae (III. 7). 1 Brazil.

Ball moss (Am.), *Tillandsia recurvata* L.

Ballochia Balf. f. Acanthaceae (IV. B). 3 Socotra.

Ballota L. Labiatae (VI). 30 Eur., Medit., W. As. *B. nigra* L. (foetid horehound), Brit.

Balls-Headleya F. Muell. Saxifragaceae (inc. sed.). Undescribed.

Balm, *Melissa officinalis* L.; **bastard-**, *Melittis Melissophyllum* L.; **of Gilead,** *Commiphora opobalsamum* Engl.

Baloghia Endl. Euphorbiaceae (A. II. 5). 15 E. Indomal., New Cal.

Balsa, *Ochroma Lagopus* Sw.

Balsam, *Impatiens spp.*; fluid resins; **-apple** (W.I.), *Momordica Balsamina* L.; **-bog**, *Azorella*; **broad-leaved-** (W.I.), *Oreopanax capitatum* Decne. et Planch.; **Canada-**, *Abies balsamea* Mill.; **-fig** (W.I.), *Clusia rosea* Jacq.; **-fir**, *Abies balsamea* Mill.; **Gurjun-**, *Dipterocarpus*; **of Copaiba,** *Copaifera spp.*; **of Peru,** *Myroxylon Pereirae*; **of Tolu,** *M. punctatum*; **pig's-**, *Hedwigia balsamifera* Sw.; **-poplar,** *Populus balsamifera* L.; **-tree,** *Commiphora*; **yellow-** (W.I.), *Croton flavens* L.

Balsamea Gled. = Commiphora Jacq. (Burser.).

Balsamina Tourn. ex Scop. = Impatiens Linn. (Balsam.).

Balsaminaceae (*EP.*; *Geraniaceae* p.p. *BH.*). Dicots. (Archichl. Sapindales). 2 gen., 430 sp., As., Afr., Eur., N. Am. Herbs with watery translucent stems and alt. l., usu. exstip. Fl. ☿, ·|·. K 5 (the 2 ant. small or aborted, the post. one spurred), petaloid; C 5 (the lat. petals united in pairs); A 5, anthers adhering to one another and forming a cap over the ovary, whose growth ultimately breaks the sta. at their bases; $\underline{G}$ (5), 5-loc., with ∞ ovules, anatr., pend. with dorsal raphe. Explosive capsule. Seed exalb. *Chief genus:* Impatiens. *BH.* unite B. with Geraniaceae (*q.v.*), but the arrangement of the ovule is that of Sapindales.

Balsamita Desf. = Chrysanthemum L. p.p. (Compos.).

Balsamocitrus Stapf. Rutaceae (v). 2 trop. Afr.

Balsamodendrum Kunth = Commiphora Jacq. (Burser.).

Balsamorhiza Hook. Compositae (5). 10 W. N. Am.

Baltimora L. Compositae (5). 3 Am.

Bambarra groundnut, *Voandzeia subterranea* Thou.

Bamboo, a member of the 13th group of Gramineae, char. by stems that become woody below and often grow to great size. The trop. forms usu. grow in clumps, which continually expand, the new shoots appearing at the outer side; the subtrop. and temp. forms are usu. continuous in their growth. There is a big rhiz. below ground and erect perenn. woody stems above, which appear in the rains (or spring) and grow rapidly to the full height, when the scale l. fall and the leafy branches spread out. Growth is very rapid in *Dendrocalamus giganteus* Munro, reaching as much as 41 cm. a day (cf. Lock, *Ann. Perad.* II. 211). Some climb. The height is often great, reaching to 120 feet in some forms.

Some fl. annually, others at longer intervals, and some are like Agave and Corypha, flowering only once, all together, and then dying down. They fl. only when in full leaf, and as the infl. grows the l. usu. fall. The seedlings grow for several years without forming tall shoots, producing large well-stored rhiz. They then send up shoots increasing in length from year to year.

Spikelets 2–∞-flowered in racemes or panicles. Sta. usu. 6.

The economic uses of bamboos are very numerous, esp. in Asia. The stems are hollow, with cross partitions at the nodes, and the wood is elastic and very hard, owing to the deposition of silica in the cell walls. The stems are consequently very light and strong, and are also easily split. They are largely used in building, entire as posts, and split as roofing tiles, while the houses in Assam, Burma, and Malaya are often made of bamboo split finely, and woven into a kind of mat which is fastened upon bamboo posts. Bridges are often made of them, and they furnish water-pipes, water-vessels, gutters, floats, beehives, walking-sticks, pipes, flutes, masts, furniture, household utensils, agricultural tools, &c. The distichous bamboo shoot, with the side branches cut down to about 6 inches, is used as a ladder. Split bamboos, with the edges trimmed sharp, are used as grass cutters, and will keep lawns in good order. Finely split bamboos are made into mats, blinds, rigging, baskets, fans, hats, coarse clothing, umbrellas, ropes, brushes, &c., esp. in Japan, where fine work is done in bamboo. Paper is made from bamboos in China and elsewhere. The stout stems of the male bamboo (*Dendrocalamus strictus* Nees) are used for the handles of lances. The stems cut into lengths form very useful flower pots, largely employed in tropical gardens. The young shoots are eaten like asparagus, and the poorer natives also use the seeds as food. In the stems of *B. arundinacea* Willd. curious concretions of silica are found, known as tabashir or bamboo manna, used in the East as a medicine in many diseases.

(See Kurz, Bamboo and its uses, *Ind. Forester*, 1876, and art. in *Nat. Pfl.* by Sir D. Brandis; Lock, on growth, in *Ann. Perad.* II. 211; Freeman-Mitford, *The Bamboo Garden.*)

Bamburanta L. Linden. Marantaceae. 1 trop. Afr.

Bambusa Schreb. Gramineae (13). 70 trop. and subtrop. As., Afr., Am. The typical genus of bamboos (*q.v.*).

Bamia (L.) R. Br. ex Wall. = Hibiscus Tourn. (Malv.).

Bamlera K. Schum. et Lauterb. Melastomaceae (II). 1 New Guinea.

Banalia Moq. Amarantaceae (2). 1 Indomal.

Banana, *Musa Sapientum* L.

Banara Aubl. Flacourt. (5) (Samyd. *BH.*). 24 W.I., trop. Am.

Bandakai, *Hibiscus esculentus* L.

Bandeiraea Welw. (*Griffonia EP.*). Legumin. (II. 4). 3 W. trop. Afr.

Baneberry, *Actaea spicata* L.

Bania Becc. Menispermaceae. 1 New Guinea.

Banisteria L. Malpighiaceae (1). 90 warm Am., W.I. Fr. like Acer.

Banisteriopsis C. B. Robinson. Malpigh. 9 trop. Am.

Banjolea Bowdich. Acanthaceae (inc. sed.). 1 Madeira.

Banksia L. f. Proteaceae (II). 50 Austr. (Austr. honeysuckle). Shrubs and trees with xero. habit. Fls. in dense spikes. Hard woody follicle enclosed in woody twigs derived from bract and bracteoles. Seeds winged.

Ban rhea, *Villebrunia integrifolia* Gaudich.

Banyan, *Ficus benghalensis* L.

Baobab, *Adansonia digitata* L.

Baoulia A. Chevalier. Commelinaceae. 1 Ivory Coast.

Baphia Afzel. Leguminosae (III. 1). 60 warm Afr., Madag. *B. nitida* Afzel, cam-wood, used for red dye; the wood when first cut is white, but turns red in the air.

Baphiastrum Harms. Leguminosae (III. 1). 1 Cameroons.

Baphiopsis Benth. Leguminosae (II. 9). 2 trop. Afr.

Baptisia Vent. Leguminosae (III. 2). 25 N. Am. In *B. perfoliata* R. Br. there are perfoliate l., really in two vertical ranks, but becoming one-ranked by twisting of internodes alt. right and left.

Baptistonia Barb. Rodr. Orchidaceae (II. 19). 1 Brazil. [Madag.

Barbacenia Vand. Velloz. (Amaryll. *BH.*). 100 S. Am., trop. Afr.,

Barbadoes gooseberry, *Pereskia aculeata* Mill.; **-pride,** *Caesalpinia pulcherrima* Sw., *Adenanthera pavonina* L.

Barbarea R. Br. Cruciferae (2). 15 N. temp.; 2 Brit. (yellow rocket, winter-cress).

Barbatus (Lat.), bearded.

Barberetta Harv. Haemodoraceae. 1 S. Afr. G.

Barberina Vell. = Symplocos L. p.p. (Symploc.)

Barberry, *Berberis.*

Barbeuia Thou. Phytolaccaceae. 1 Madag.

Barbeya Schweinf. Ulmaceae. 1 Arabia, Abyssinia.

Barbeyastrum Cogn. Melastomaceae (1). 1 Congo.

Barbiera DC. Leguminosae (III. 6). 1 trop. Am., W.I.

Barbosa Becc. Palmaceae (IV. 2). 1 E. Brazil.

Barcella Drude (*Elaeis* Jacq. p.p. *BH.*). Palmae (IV 2). 1 Amazonas.

Barcena Dugès. Rhamnaceae. 1 Mex.

Barclaya Wall. Nymphaeaceae (III). 4 Indomal. K 5 hypog.; C up to (21), epig., tubular; A ∞; G (10—12) with projections forming a tube above the stigmatic disc.

Bargemontia Gaudich. (*Dolia* Lindl. *EP.*). Nolan. 1 Peru.

Barilla, *Halogeton sativus* Moq.; - (W.I.), *Batis.*

Barjonia Decne. Asclepiadaceae (II. 3). 8 Brazil.

Bark, the outer coat of a tree, applied esp. to that of Cinchona; **Angostura-**, *Cusparia febrifuga* Humb.; **Cartagena, crown, Jesuit's, Peruvian, brown** and **red Peru, yellow,** &c. *cf. Cinchona*; **Canella-**, *Canella*; **Cascarilla-**, *Croton Cascarilla* Benn.; **Cassia-**, *Cinnamomum Cassia* Blume; **iron-**, *Eucalyptus*; **quercitron,** *Quercus tinctoria* Bartr.; **stringy-**, *Eucalyptus*; **West Indian-**, *Exostemma*; **Winter's-**, *Drimys Winteri* Forst.

Barkerwebbia Becc. Palmae (IV. 1). 1 New Guinea.

Barkhausia Moench = Crepis L. (Compos.).

Barklya F. Muell. Legum. (III. 1). 1 Queensland. Thin endosp.

Barlaea Reichb. f. (*Habenaria* p.p.). Orchid. (II. 1). 1 trop. Afr.

Barleria L. Acanthaceae (IV. A). 180 trop. largely xero. on steppes. Bracteoles frequently repres. by thorns. The seeds have surface hairs which swell when wetted. Many cult. orn. fl.

Barleriola Oerst. Acanthaceae (IV. A). 2 W. Ind.

Barley, *Hordeum vulgare* L.; **-grass,** *Hordeum.*

Barnadesia Mutis. Compositae (12). 18 S. Am. Shrubs.

Barnyard grass (Am.), *Panicum Crus-galli* L.

Baronia Baker. Anacardiaceae (3). 1 Madag.

Baroniella Costantin et Galland. Asclepiadaceae (I). 1 Madag.

Barosma Willd. Rutaceae (I). 15 S. Afr. The l. of 3 spp., esp. *B. betulina* Bartl. et Wendl. f. (buchu l.) are offic.

Barren (fl.), male.

Barreria, L. Inc. sed. 1 S. Afr.

Barrettia T. R. Sim. Euphorbiaceae (inc. sed.). 1 E. trop. Afr.

Barringtonia Forst. Lecythidaceae. 45 palaeotrop. Char. of beach-jungle. Wood of some useful; the seeds yield oil.

Barroetia A. Gray. Compositae (2). 5 Mex.

Barrotia Gaudich. = Pandanus L. (Pandan.).

Barrowia Decne. (*Orthanthera* p.p. *EP.*). Asclep. (II. 3). 2 S. and trop. Afr.

Barteria Hook. f. Flacourt. (6) (Passifl. *BH.*). 5 W. Afr.

Barthea Hook. f. Melastomaceae (I). 3 China.

Bartholina R. Br. Orchidaceae (II. 1). 1 S. Afr.

Bartlettia A. Gray. Compositae (8). 1 Mex.

Bartlingia F. Muell (*Laxmannia* R. Br.). Liliac. (III). 8 Austr.

Bartonia Muhl. Gentianaceae (I). 5 N. Am. Saprophytes with a little chlorophyll and leaves reduced to scales.

Bartonia Sims. = Mentzelia L. (Loasac.).

Bartramia L. = Triumfetta L.

Bartsia L. Scrophulariaceae (III. 3). 30 N. temp., trop. Mts.; 2 Brit. Mostly herbs, semi-parasitic on grass-roots (see fam.). Fl. with loose-pollen mech. (see fam.).

Barus camphor, *Dryobalanops aromatica* Gaertn.

Barwood, *Baphia nitida* Afzel.
Baryxylum Lour. (*Peltophorum* Walp. *EP.*). Legum. (II. 7). 1 China.
Basal (plac.), at base of ovary.
Basanacantha Hook. f. Rubiaceae (I. 8). 15 trop. Am.
Basananthe Peyr. (*Tryphostemma EP.*). Passifl. 3 trop. Afr.
Basella (Rheede) L. Basellaceae. 1 trop. As., a climbing herb whose fls. remain closed. Fr. enclosed in the P. Cult. as spinach.
Basellaceae (*EP.*; *Chenopodiaceae* p.p. *BH.*). Dicots. (Archichl. Centrospermae). 4 gen. 15 sp. Am., As., Afr. Rhiz. or tuber, giving annually a climbing shoot, often with fleshy l., and racemes or panicles of fls., stalked and often conspic. coloured, each with 2 bracteoles. K 2, C 5, A 5 opp. pets.; $\underline{G}$ (3) with terminal style and 3 stigmas, 1-loc.; ovule 1, basal, campylotropous. Usu. berry. *Chief genera:* Basella, Ullucus, Boussingaultia.
Baseonema Schlechter et Rendle. Asclep. (1). 6 trop. Afr., Madag.
Basi- (Lat. pref.), basal; **-fixed** (anther), joined to filament at base; **-fugal**, from base upwards; **-lar**, basal; **-petal**, towards base downwards; **-scopic**, facing the base; **-tonic**, *Orchidaceae.*
Basil, *Calamintha*, *Ocimum Basilicum* L.
Basiloxylon K. Schum. Sterculiaceae. 1 Brazil. Good timber.
Basistelma Bartlett. Asclepiad. (II. 1). 2 Mex., C. Am.
Basistemon Turcz. Scrophulariaceae (II. 4). 2 Colombia, Peru.
Baskervilla Lindl. Orchidaceae (II. 2). 1 Peru.
Basket-hoop (W.I.), *Croton lucidus* L.; **-withe** (W.I.), *Tournefortia.*
Baskets, *cf. Andropogon*, *Bamboos*, *Borassus*, *Cocos*, *Juncus*, &c.
Bass, inner fibrous bark, esp. of Tilia; **-wood**, *Tilia americana* L.
Bassellinia Vieill. Palmaceae (inc. sed.). 5 New Cal.
Bassia All. (*Anisacantha* R. Br. *BH.*) Chenopodiaceae (A). 30 N. palaeotemp., Austr.
Bassia Koenig ex L. (*Illipe* F. Muell. *EP.*). Sapotaceae (1). 50 Indomal., Austr. *B. pallida* Burck yields a gutta-percha. The seeds of *B. butyracea* Roxb. (Indian butter tree) yield a butter-like substance, used for soap-making, &c. The fls. of *B. latifolia* Roxb. (mahua, mahwa, or mowa) are ed., and the wood useful.
Bassora gum, a mixture of Indian bassorin gums.
Bassorin, *cf.* Gums.
Bassovia Aubl. Solanaceae (2). 15 Cent. and S. Am.
Bast, the outer part of a vascular bundle; also piassaba fibre, &c.
Bastard-balm, *Melittis Melissophyllum* L.; **-cedar**, *Chickrassia tabularis* A. Juss.; **-teak**, *Butea frondosa* Roxb.; **-toadflax**, *Thesium humifusum* DC.
Bastardia H. B. et K. Malvaceae (2). 6 W. Ind. and warm Am.
Bastardiopsis Hassler. Malvaceae (2). 1 S. Am.
Bat pollination, *Freycinetia.*
Batanthes Raf. (*Gilia* Ruiz et Pav. p.p. *BH.*). Polemon. 10 N. Am.
Bataprine Nieuwland (*Galium* L. p.p.). Rubiac. (II. 11). 2 N. Am.
Batatas Choisy = Ipomoea L. p.p. (*B. edulis* Choisy = I. Batatas).
Batemannia Lindl. Orchidaceae (II. 12). 1 Brit. Guiana.
Batesanthus N. E. Br. Asclepiadaceae (1). 1 Cameroons.
Batesia Spruce. Leguminosae (II. 8). 1 Amazon valley.
Bathieaea Drake del Castillo. Leguminosae (II. 2). 1 Madag.

Bath-sponge, *Luffa cylindrica* M. Roem.
Bathyphytium (Cl.), a lowland plant formation.
Bathysa C. Presl. Rubiaceae (I. 3). 7 Brazil, Peru.
Bathysograya O. Ktze. (*Badusa* A. Gray). Rubiaceae (I. 5). 1 Fiji, Soc. Is.
Batidaceae (*EP.*; *Batideae*, *BH.*). Dicots. (Archichl. Centrospermae). Only genus Batis (*q.v.*). Placed in Curvembryae by *BH.*
Batidaea Greene. Rosaceae (III. 2). 16 N. Am.
Batidales. The 9th cohort of Dicots. Archichl. *Cf.* p. xii.
Batis L. Batidaceae. 1 Am., Sandw. Is. Coast shrub with opp. fleshy linear l. and spikes of dioec. fl. ♂ in axils of 4-ranked br., with cup-like P, A 4. ♀ naked, G̲ (2), 4-loc., with 1 anatr. ov. in each. No endosp.
Batocarpus Karst. Moraceae (II). 1 Colombia.
Batodendron Nutt. (*Vaccinium* L. p.p.). Eric. (III. 1). 3 N. Am.
Batrachium S. F. Gray = Ranunculus Tourn. (the aquatic sp.).
Batratherum Nees = Arthraxon Beauv. (Gramin.).
Batschia Vahl. (*Humboldtia* Vahl. *BH.*). Legum. (II. 3). 4 Ceyl., S. Ind.
Bauchea Fourn. (*Epicampes* J. Presl *EP.*). Gramineae (8). 1 Mex.
Baucis Phil. Compositae (12). 1 Chili.
Baudouinia Baill. Leguminosae (II. 5). 2 Madag.
Bauera Banks. Saxifragaceae (VII). 4 temp. E. Austr. Shrubs. Fls. solitary, axillary, 4—10-merous. Sta. = pet. or ∞.
Bauerella Borzi. Rutaceae (V). 1 Austr.
Bauhinia L. Leguminosae (II. 4). 250 warm. Many lianes with stems curiously shaped, flattened or corrugated and twisted owing to a peculiar mode of growth in thickness (*cf.* other lianes). Some sp. have tendrils (branches). In some the young l. droop. In the axils of the stips. are usu. found small linear trichome structures; in some they form stout interstipular thorns. Great variety in floral structure, &c. (see *Nat. Pfl.* III. 3, p. 151).
Baukea Vatke. Leguminosae (III. 10). 1 Madag.
Baumannia K. Schum. Rubiaceae (II. 1). 1 trop. E. Afr.
Baumea Gaudich. = Cladium P. Br. p.p. (Cyper.).
Baumia Engl. et Gilg. Scrophulariaceae (III. 2). 1 trop. Afr.
Bawchan seed, *Psoralea corylifolia* L.
Baxteria R. Br. Liliaceae (III) (Junc. *BH.*). 1 W. Austr.
Bay, *Laurus nobilis* L.; **-bean** (Bermuda), *Canavalia obtusifolia* DC.; **-berry** *Myrica cerifera* L.; **loblolly-**, *Gordonia Lasianthus* L.; **-rum**, *Pimenta officinalis* Lindl.; **sweet-**, *Magnolia*, *Laurus*.
Bdallophyton Eichl. (*Cytinus* L. *BH.*). Rafflesiaceae. 2 Mex.
Bdellium, *Commiphora*.
Beach-grass (Am.), *Ammophila*; **-jungle**, a palaeotrop. shore formation, char. by *Barringtonia* and other woody pl., *e.g.* *Pandanus*, *Pemphis*, *Premna*, *Scaevola*, *Sophora*, *Thespesia*, &c.; **-pea** (Am.), *Lathyrus maritimus* Bigelow.
Beadlea Small (*Spiranthes* Rich. p.p.). Orchid. (II. 2). 1 N. Am.
Bead-tree, *Melia Azedarach* L.; **do.** (W.I.), *Ormosia dasycarpa* Jacks.; **-vine** (W.I.), *Rhynchosia*.
Beads, *Abrus*, *Adenanthera*, *Coix*, &c.

Beak, a pointed outgrowth; **-rush**, *Rhynchospora*.
Beam tree, *Pyrus Aria* Ehrh.
Bean, *Vicia Faba* L.; **asparagus-** (W.I.), *Dolichos sesquipedalis* L.; **bog-**, *Menyanthes trifoliata* L.; **Bengal-**, *Mucuna* (*Stizolobium*) *sp.*; **broad-**, *Vicia Faba* L.; **black-**, *Castanospermum australe* A. Cunn.; **Calabar-**, *Physostigma venenosum* Balf.; **cherry-**, *Vigna sinensis* Endl.; **cluster-**, *Cyamopsis psoraloides* DC.; **duffin-**, *Phaseolus lunatus* L.; **French** or **haricot-**, *P. vulgaris* L.; **Hibbert-** (W.I.), *P. lunatus* L.; **Florida velvet-**, *Mucuna pruriens* DC. var.; **horse-** (W.I.), *Canavalia ensiformis* DC.; **horse-eye-** (W.I.), *Mucuna urens* Medic.; **kidney-**, *Phaseolus vulgaris* L.; **Lima-**, *P. lunatus* L.; **nickar-**, *Caesalpinia bonducella* Fleming, *Entada scandens* Benth.; **ordeal-**, *Physostigma venenosum* Balf.; **red-** (W.I.), *Vigna Catjang* Walp.; **sabre-**, *Canavalia*; **sacred-**, *Nelumbium speciosum* Willd.; **seaside-** (W.I.), *Canavalia obtusifolia* DC., *Vigna glabra* Savi; **soja** or **soy-**, *Glycine Soja* Sieb. et Zucc.; **sugar-** (W.I.), *Phaseolus lunatus* L.; **St Ignatius'-**, *Strychnos Ignatii* Berg.; **sword-** (W.I.), *Canavalia ensiformis* DC.; **Tonka** or **Tonquin-**, *Dipteryx odorata* Willd.; **-tree**, *Castanospermum australe* A. Cunn.; **do.** (W.I.), *Erythrina*; **white-**, Lima-; **yam-**, *Pachyrhizus tuberosus* Spr., *Dolichos Lablab* L.; **year-** (W.I.), *Phaseolus vulgaris* L.
Bearberry, *Arctostaphylos*, (Am.) *Rhamnus Purshiana* DC.; **-grass** (Am.), *Yucca*; **-'s foot**, *Helleborus foetidus* L.
Beard grass, *Polypogon*.
Beatsonia Roxb. (*Frankenia* L. p.p. *BH.*). Franken. 1 St Helena.
Beaucarnea Lem. (*Nolina* Michx.). Liliaceae (VI). 15 N. Am.
Beaufortia R. Br. Myrtac. (II. 1). 15 W. Austr. Some cult. orn. fl.
Beaumontia Wall. Apocynaceae (II. 1). 8 Indomal.
Beauprea Brongn. et Gris. Proteaceae (I). 7 New Cal.
Beauvisagea Pierre = Lucuma (*BH.*) = Sideroxylon (Dill.) L.
Beaver poison (Am.), *Cicuta maculata* L.
Bebbia Greene. Compositae (5). 3 S.W. U.S.
Beccarianthus Cogn. Melastomaceae (II). 1 Borneo.
Beccariodendron Warb. (*Mitrephora EP.*). Anonac. (2). 1 Oceania.
Becium Lindl. = Ocimum Tourn. (Labiat.).
Beckera Fresen. Gramineae (4). 3 Abyss.
Becheria Ridl. Rubiaceae (I. 7). 1 Malaya.
Beckmannia Host. Gramineae (11). 1 N. temp.
Beckwithia Jepson (*Ranunculus* p.p.). Ranunc. (3). 1 Calif.
Becquerelia Brongn. Cyperaceae (II). 3 trop. S. Am.
Beda nut, *Terminalia belerica* Roxb.
Beddomea Hook. f. (*Aglaia* p.p. *EP.*). Meliaceae (III). 3 Indomal.
Bedfordia DC. Compositae (8). 2 temp. Austr., Tasm.
Bed-straw, *Galium*.
Bee-flowers, fl. esp. of class H, chiefly visited by bees; *Antirrhinum, Aquilegia, Boraginaceae, Borago, Calluna, Campanulaceae, Cobaea, Compositae, Digitalis, Gentiana, Labiatae, Lamium, Lavandula, Leguminosae, Lotus, Lychnis, Monarda, Onagraceae, Pedicularis, Phacelia, Pyrus, Rhododendron, Symphytum, Tilia, Trifolium, Vaccinium.*

Beech, *Fagus sylvatica* L.; **-fern**, *Dryopteris Phegopteris* L.; **-mast**, the capsules of fr.; **seaside-** (W.I.), *Exostemma*.

Beef-apple (W.I.), *Sapota*; **-wood**, *Stenocarpus*, *Casuarina*, &c.

Beesha Kunth = Melocanna Trin. (Gramin.); **do.** Munro = Ochlandra.

Beetroot, *Beta vulgaris* L.; **sugar-**, a var.

Befaria Mutis (*Bejaria*). Ericaceae (I. 1). 20 trop. and subtrop. Am. *B. racemosa* Vent. and others (Andes rose) form a consp. feature in the veg., taking the place of Rhododendrons.

Begonia (Tourn.) L. Begoniaceae. 750 trop. and subtrop., esp. Am. Many cult. for handsome fls. and foliage. Most are perenn. herbs with thick rhiz. or tubers. Several climb by aid of roots like ivy. L. rad. or alt., in two ranks, with large stips. One side of the l. is larger than the other, whence the name 'elephant's ear,' by which they are sometimes known. The surface of the l. is easily wetted, and drip-tips are frequent (*cf. Ficus*). In the axils groups of little tubers are frequently found; these are not axillary branches, but are borne upon the true axillary branch, which does not lengthen. They also repr. easily by adv. buds which readily form on pieces of l. cut off and placed on the soil under suitable conditions of moisture &c. (the common mode used in horticulture). A callus forms over the wound, and in it there develops a meristem which gives rise to one or more buds.

Infl. axillary, dich. with a bostryx tendency. The first axes usually end in ♂, the last and sometimes the last but one in ♀, fls. In the ♂, P 2, valvate, or 4, decussate, corolline; A ∞, free or not, the connective often elongated and the anthers variously shaped. In the ♀, P 2—5; $\overline{G}$ usu. (2—3), with 2—3 loc., and axile plac. often projecting far into them; ovules ∞, anatr.; styles ± free. Ovary usu. winged; the wings persistent upon the capsular fr. No endosperm.

Begoniaceae. Dicotyledons (Archichl. Parietales). 4 gen. with the characters of Begonia (*q.v.*). Placed in Passiflorales by *BH.*

Begoniella Oliv. Begoniaceae. 3 Colombia.

Behaimia Griseb. Leguminosae (III. 8). 1 Cuba.

Behen-oil, *Moringa pterygosperma* Gaertn.

Behnia Didrichsen. Liliaceae (X). 1 S. Afr.

Behria Greene. Liliaceae (IV). 1 S. Calif.

Behuria Cham. Melastomaceae (I). 7 S. Brazil.

Beilschmiedia Nees. Lauraceae (II). 40 trop., and Austr., N.Z.

Bejaria Zea (*Befaria* Mutis, *q.v.*). Ericac. (I. 1). 15 warm Am.

Belairia A. Rich. Leguminosae (III. 1). 2 Cuba.

Belamcanda Adans. Iridaceae (II). 1 E. As. Cult. orn. fl.

Belangera Cambess. Cunoniaceae. 10 S. Brazil, Paraguay.

Belencita Karst. Capparidaceae (II). 1 Colombia.

Belladonna, *Atropa Belladonna* L.

Belladonna Sweet = Amaryllis L. (Amaryll.).

Bell apple (W.I.), *Passiflora laurifolia* L.; **-flower**, *Campanula*, *Wahlenbergia*.

Bellardia All. (*Bartsia* L. p.p. *BH.*). Scroph. (III. 3). 2 Medit.

Bellendena R. Br. Proteaceae (I). 1 Tasmania.

Bellevalia Lapeyr. = Hyacinthus Tourn. p.p. (Liliac.).

Bellida Ewart. Compositae (3). 1 Austr.

Bellis (Tourn.) L. Comp. (3). 15 Eur., Medit. *B. perennis* L. (daisy, Brit.) multiplies and hibernates by short rhiz. Ray ♀. Pappus usu. o. Head closes at night and when it is wet. Cult. orn. fl.
Bellium L. Comp. (3). 6 Medit. Usu. tufted herbs.
Bellonia (Plum.) L. Gesner. (II). 2 W.I. Often axillary thorns.
Bellucia Neck. Melast. (I). 15 trop. Am. G 8—15-loc. Trees. Fr. ed.
Belly-ache bush (W.I.), *Jatropha gossypifolia* L.
Bellynkxia Muell.-Arg. = Appunia Hook f. (Rubi.).
Belmontia E. Mey. Gentian. (I). 20 S. and trop. Afr., Madag. G
Beloanthera Hassk. Inc. sed. 1 Java. ⌊2-loc., each with 1 or 2 plac.
Belonanthus Graebn. Valerian. 2 Peru, Bolivia.
Belonophora Hook. f. Rubi. (II. 1). 1 St Thomas (W. Afr.).
Beloperone Nees. Acanth. (IV. B). 45 warm Am., W.I. Cult. orn. fl.
Belotia A. Rich. Tili. 4 W.I., C. Am. K. Androphore. Fr. 2-
Belou Adans. = Aegle Correa, Limonia L., &c. ⌊valved, winged.
Bembicia Oliv. (*Bembicina* O. Ktze.). Flacourt. (7) (Samyd. *BH.*). 1 Madag. $\overline{G}$. Infl. axillary, sessile, surrounded by scales.
Bembix Lour. Malpigh. (inc. sed.). 1 Cochinchina.
Bencomia Webb. et Berth. Ros. (III. 5). 3 Canaries, Madeira. Hollow axis only in ♀. ⌈glabrous.
Benevidesia Saldanha et Cogn. Melast. (I). 1 Rio de Janeiro. G
Bengal beans, *Stizolobium* (*Mucuna*) *sp.*; **-kino**, *Butea frondosa* Roxb.;
Beni seed (W. Afr.), *Polygala butyracea* Heckel. ⌊**-quince** = bael.
Benincasa Savi. Cucurb. (3). 2 trop. As. Fr. of *B. cerifera* Savi coated with wax; it is eaten in curries. ⌈*zoin* Meissn.
Benjamin, gum-, *Styrax Benzoin* Dryand.; **-bush** (Am.), *Lindera Ben-*
Bennettia Miq. Flacourt. (4). 2 Malay Arch.; **do.** R. Br. = Galearia
Ben nut, -oil, *Moringa pterygosperma* Gaertn. ⌊Zoll. et Mor. (Euphorb.).
Benny-seed, *Sesamum orientale* L.
Bent-grass, *Agrostis*, *Apera*; **silky-**, *Cynosurus*.
Benthamantha Alef. = Cracca Benth. (Legum.). 10 trop. Am.
Benthamia Lindl. (1830) = Amsinckia Lehm.; (1833) = Cornus Tourn.
Benthamiella Spegazz. Solan. (inc. sed.). 1 Patagonia.
Bentia Rolfe. Acanth. (IV. B). 1 S. Arabia. ⌈Sheaths 2—4.
Bentinckia Berry. Palm. (IV. 1). 2 India. G 3-loc. Berry 1-seeded.
Benzoin Hayne = Styrax L.; **do.** Nees, Ludw. = Lindera Thunb. p.p.
Benzoin, gum-, *Styrax Benzoin* Dryand.
Benzonia Schum. Rubi. (inc. sed.). 1 W. Afr.
Berardia Brongn. = Nebelia Neck. (*BH.*) = Diberara Baill. (Bruni.).
Berardia Vill. Comp. (12). 1 Alps. Head sessile or short-stalked.
Berberidaceae (*EP.*; *BH.* incl. *Lardizabal.*). Dicots. (Archichl. Ranales, pp. xvii, 1). 12/200 N. temp., trop. Mts., S. Am. Perennial herbs or shrubs, the former usu. with sympodial rhiz. Fls. usu. in racemes, ☿, reg. Typical formula P 3+3+3+3, A 3+3, $\underline{G}$ 1; sometimes 2-merous. Of the outer whorls, the 2 outer are P proper, the two inner "honey-l.," usu. with nectaries at base (*cf.* Ranunculac.), the former often termed K, the latter C. Anthers intr., but usu. opening by two post. valves (*cf.* Laurac.); the valve with the pollen upon it moves upward and turns round so that pollen faces centre of fl. Cpl. always 1, with 1 usu. basal or many ventral ov. Berry, or dry fr. opening in various ways. Embryo straight in rich endo-

sperm. *Chief genera:* Podophyllum, Epimedium, Leontice, Berberis. [Placed in Ranales by **BH.**; their **chars.** include unisexual fl., extrorse anthers.]

Berberideae (*BH.*) includes preceding and Lardizabalaceae.

Berberidopsis Hook. f. Flacourt. (1). (Berber., Lardizabal. auct.) 1 Chili. *Bot. Mag.* t. 5343.

Berberis (Tourn.) L. Berberidaceae. 190 * S. Am. *B. vulgaris* L. (barberry) Brit. Shrubs. Two sections. In § 1, *Mahonia* (Nutt.), the l. are pinnate; many cult. shrubs. In § 2, *Euberberis*, the l. are simple, but usu. show a joint where the blade meets the petiole, seeming to indicate a derivation from a cpd. l. There are also 'short' and 'long' shoots (*cf.* Coniferae) in this §, to which *B. vulgaris* belongs. The latter have their l. met. into spines (usu. tripartite); transitions may often be seen. The former stand in the axils of the spines and bear green l. and racemes of fls. (afterwards sometimes elongating to 'long' shoots). The pollination mechanism is interesting. The upper surface of the base of each sta. is sensitive to contact, and when it is touched by an insect in search of honey (secreted by the nectaries upon the bases of the inner P l.) the sta. springs violently upwards, covering the side of the visitor's head with pollen, which it may place on the stigma in the next flr. visited. The fr. is sometimes made into preserves.

An interesting point about the common barberry is its connection with the disease known as *black rust*, which occurs on wheat and other Gramineae. The fungus (*Puccinia graminis* or *Aecidium berberidis*) passes through two alt. stages in its life history, one on the grass, the other on the barberry, so that if there are no barberry plants in a district, it is to a large extent, though by no means absolutely, insured against black rust.

Berberry, *Berberis*.

Berchemia Neck. Rhamnaceae. 15 palaeotrop., Atl. N.Am.

Bere, *Hordeum vulgare* L.

Berendtia A. Gray. Scrophulariaceae (II. 4). 4 Mex., C. Am.

Berendtiella Wettst. et Harms = Berendtia A. Gray.

Berenice Tul. Saxifragaceae (V). 1 Bourbon.

Bergamot, *Mentha citrata* Ehrh. = *aquatica* L.; **-orange**, *Citrus Aurantium* L., var. *Bergamia* Wight et Arn.

Bergenia Moench (*Saxifraga* p.p. *BH.*). Saxifr. (I). 10 E. As.

Bergera Koen. ex L. = Murraya L. (Rutac.).

Bergerocactus Britton et Rose (*Cereus* p.p.). Cact. (III). 1 Calif.

Bergeronia M. Micheli. Leguminosae (III. 8). 1 Paraguay.

Berghesia Nees. Rubiaceae (inc. sed.). 1 Mex.

Bergia L. Elatinaceae. 25 trop. and temp.

Berginia Harv. Acanthaceae (IV. B). 1 Calif.

Bergsmia Blume (*Ryparosa* Blume). Flacourt. (3) (Bix. *BH.*). 8 S.E. As.

Beringeria Neck. = Ballota L. p.p. (Labiat.).

Berinia Brignol. = Crepis Vaill. p.p. (Compos.).

Berkheya Ehrh. Compositae (6). 80 Afr.

Berkheyopsis O. Hoffm. Compositae (10). 5 S. and trop. Afr.

Berlandiera DC. Compositae (5). 5 sp. S. and E. U.S.

Berlinia Soland. Leguminosae (II. 3). 18 trop. Afr.
Bermuda arrowroot, *cf.* A.; **-grass**, *Cynodon Dactylon* Pers.
Bermudiana (Tourn.) L. = Sisyrinchium L. p.p. (Crucif.).
Bernardia Houst. ex P. Br. Euphorb. (A. II. 2). 40 warm Am., W.I.
Bernardinia Planch. Connaraceae. 2 S. Brazil.
Berneuxia Decne. Diapensiaceae. 1 E. Tibet.
Bernieria Baill. Lauraceae (II). 1 Madag.
Bernoullia Oliv. Bombacaceae (2) (Stercul. *BH.*). 1 C. Am.
Berria Roxb. (*Berrya*). Tiliaceae. 4 Indomal., Polynesia. *B. Ammonilla* Roxb. gives a valuable timber (Trincomali wood, Ceylon, India).
Berries, yellow, *Rhamnus infectoria* L.
Berroa Beauverd (*Lucilia* p.p.). Compositae (4). 1 S. Am.
Berry, a fleshy fr. containing no hard part but the seeds, *Actaea*, *Berberis*, *Ribes*, *Solanum*, *Vaccinium*, *Vitis;* dehiscent in *Akebia*, *Myristica*, constricted between seeds in *Maerua*, *Unona*, &c.; **bay-**, *Myrica cerifera* L.; **bil-**, *Vaccinium Myrtillus* L.; **black-**, *Rubus;* **blae-**, = bil-; **buffalo-**, *Shepherdia argentea* Nutt.; **checker-**, *Gaultheria procumbens* L.; **cloud-**, *Rubus Chamaemorus* L.; **cow-**, *Vaccinium Vitis-Idaea* L.; **cran-**, *Vaccinium Oxycoccus* L.; **crow-**, *Empetrum nigrum* L.; **dew-**, *Rubus caesius* L.; **goose-**, *Ribes Grossularia* L.; **huckle-**, *Gaylussacia*; **partridge-**, = checker; **rasp-**, *Rubus Idaeus* L.; **straw-**, *Fragaria vesca* L.; **trimble-**, *Rubus occidentalis* L.; **whortle-**, = bil-.
Berrya Roxb. (*Berria*, *q.v.*). Tiliaceae. 4 Indomal., Polynesia.
Bersama Fres. Melianthaceae (Sapind. *BH.*). 20 trop. and S. Afr.
Bersim, *Trifolium alexandrinum* L.
Berteroa DC. (*Alyssum* p.p. *BH.*). Cruciferae (4). 5 N. palaeotemp.
Bertholletia Humb. et Bonpl. Lecythidaceae. 2 trop. S. Am., W. I. Fr. a large woody capsule, containing seeds with hard woody testa and oily endosperm (Brazil nuts). The fr. is indehiscent and the seeds are procured by opening it with an axe. It is closed by a plug formed of the hardened calyx, and in germination the seedlings escape here (Watson, *Ann. Bot.* XV. 1901, p. 99).
Bertiera Aubl. Rubiaceae (I. 8). 25 trop. Am., Afr.
Bertiera Blume = Adenosacme Wall. (*BH.*). = Mycetia Reinw.
Bertolonia Raddi. Melastomaceae (I). 10 Brazil, cult. orn. Young plants form at cuts across the midrib of a l. placed on damp soil.
Bertya Planch. Euphorbiaceae (B. II). 20 Austr., Tasm.
Berula Hoffm. ex Bess. = Sium Tourn. p.p. (Umbell.).
Berzelia Brongn. Bruniaceae. 7 S. Afr.
Beschorneria Kunth. Amaryllidaceae (II). 10 Mex. Cult. orn. fl. and l.
Besleria Plum. ex L. Gesneriaceae (I). 70 warm Am., W.I.
Bessera Schult. f. (*BH.* excl. *Androstephium*). Liliac. (IV). 3 Mex., Calif.
Besseya Rydb. (*Synthyris* Benth. *EP.*). Scroph. (III. 1). 7 N.W. Am.
Beta (Tourn.) Linn. Chenopodiaceae (A). 6 sp. Eur., Medit.; 1 in Brit., *B. vulgaris* L. or *B. maritima* L. the sea-beet, from which are derived the garden beetroot, the sugar-beet (var. *Rapa* Dumort.),

and the mangold-wurzel. The plant is a biennial and stores reserves in the root, the non-nitrogenous materials taking the form of sugar.

The sugar-beet is largely cult. in W. Eur. for its sugar, a formidable rival to the older industry of cane sugar. The sugar-contents of the roots have been continually improved by selection, and now frequently represent over 20 °/₀ of the weight. Germany grows 1½ million tons of beet sugar annually, and other countries about another 3 millions. [Herzog, *Monographie der Zucker-rübe*, Hamburg, 1899; v. Lippman, *Geschichte der Rübe*, Berlin, 1925.]

The garden beet is a favourite vegetable; the mangold is valuable for feeding cattle, &c. The l. are sometimes eaten like spinach.

Betckea DC. = Plectritis DC. (Valerian.).

Betel-nut, *Areca Catechu* L.; **-pepper**, *Piper Betle* L.

Betonica (Tourn.) Linn. = Stachys Tourn. (Labiat.).

Betony, *Stachys*.

Betula (Tourn.) L. Betulaceae (2). 38 N. temp., arct. *B. alba* L., the birch, is common in Brit. and reaches to the N. limit of trees, which is occupied by *B. nana* L., a creeping shrubby form, in much of the N. temp. zone. The winter buds are scaly, the scales representing stips.: the outer two or three pairs of them have no l. Witches' brooms are very commonly to be seen as dense tufts of twigs.

Trees with catkins of fls. The ♂ catkins are laid down in autumn as large buds at the end of the year's growth, the ♀ further back, on

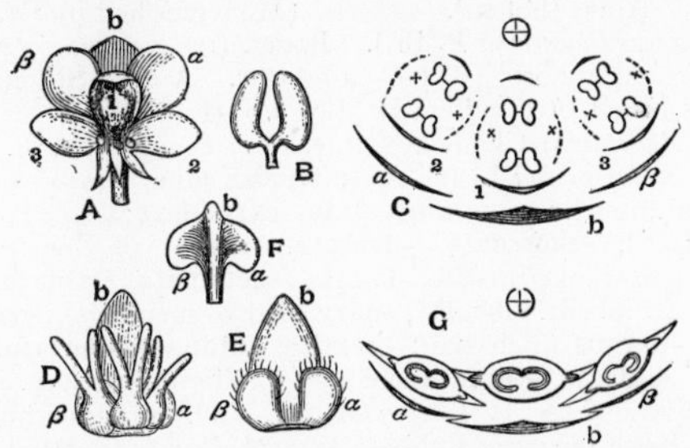

B. alba. *A*, bract, bracteoles, and perianth, of ♂, from within, with sta. removed; *B*, a stamen; *C*, floral diagram of *A*; *D*, bract, bracteoles and fls. of ♀ from within; *E*, the same with fls. removed; *F*, the same at ripeness of seed; *G*, floral diagram of *D*. *b* = bract; *α*, *β* = bracteoles of fl. 1, or bracts of fls. 2, 3. After Eichler.

leafy branches. In the axil of each l. of the catkin there are 3 fls. (*cf.* other genera of B.). The bracts of the lateral fls. occur (*α*, *β*) but no bracteoles. In the ♂ the bracteoles *α* *β* are joined to the bract itself. Each fl. has two sta. and a perianth, often reduced from the typical 4 l. to the 2 median l., or even to the single anterior l. The sta. are divided into halves nearly to the base; the lat. ones are absent. In the ♀ the bracteoles *α* *β* are free from the bract at the time of fertilisation, but afterwards they unite with it to form the 3-lobed woody scale (*F* in figure) under the fruit (or rather the tissue beneath them grows up, carrying up all together). The 2-loc. ovary gives rise to a 1-seeded nut, attached to the scale. No P. Tough wood, used for shoes, charcoal, &c. The oil from bark used in tanning Russia leather, to which it gives its fragrance. The bark of *B. papyracea* Ait. (N. Am.) used for making canoes.

Betulaceae (*EP.*; *Cupuliferae* p.p. *BH.*). Dicots. (Archichl. Fagales; pp. xiii, liv). 6/105, N. temp., trop. Mts., Andes, Arg. ♄ with alt. undivided l. and membranous deciduous stips. Seedling stems radial in symmetry, but in old branches l. usu. 2-ranked, and facing upwards.

Fls. monoec., anemoph., in term. catkins (or ♀ in heads); stem thus sympodial. In axils of catkin-l. are small dich. cymes, typically of 3 fls. (*cf.* Betula, &c.). Central fl. often absent, or some of the (typically) 6 bracteoles. ♂ fl. united to br., P or o, A 2—12; ♀ with epig. P or o, $\overline{G}$ (2), 2-loc. at base, each with 1 pend. anatr. ov. with one integument; 2 free styles. Some chalazogamic. 1-seeded nut; endosp. o. After fert. br. and bracteoles grow into a scale- or cup-like organ which may remain attached to fr.

Classification and genera (after Winkler):

1. *Coryleae* (♂ fl. sol., naked, on br.; A 3—∞): Ostryopsis (♂ with no bracteoles; fr. in heads), Carpinus (do.; fr. in spikes, invol. flat), Ostrya (do.; invol. incl. fr.), Corylus (♂ with 2 bracteoles).
2. *Betuleae* (♂ fl. with P, in dich.; A 2—4): Betula (sta. bifid), Alnus (not so). (Monographed in *Pfl. R.* 1904.)

Beureria Jacq. (*Bourreria* P. Br.). Borag. (II). 35 warm Am., W.I.

Beyeria Miq. Euphorb. (B. II). 12 Austr. A ∞. Stigma peltate.

Beyeriopsis Muell.-Arg. = Beyeria Miq. p.p. (Euphorb.).

Beyrichia (*Achetaria*) Cham. et Schlechtd. Scroph. (II. 6). 3 Braz., W.I.

Bhang, *Cannabis sativa* L. (C. As.); **Bhotan pine**, *Pinus excelsa* Wall.

Bi-, Bis- (Lat. pref.), two-; **-auriculate, -carpellary, -ceps** (Lat. heads), **-color** (Lat.), **-cuspidate, -dentate, -ennial** (lasting two years), **-farious** (two-ranked), **-fid, -foliate, -geminate, -labiate, -lateral, -lobus** (Lat. lobed), **-locular, -nary** (of two members), **-nate** (of two leaflets), **-parous** (dichasial), **-partite, -pinnate, -seriate, -serrate, -spinose, -sulcate, -ternate**, &c., are intelligible enough.

Biarum Schott. Arac. (VII). 12 Medit. Infl. appears when leafless.

Biasolettia Koch (*Freyera* Rchb., *Chaerophyllum* p.p. *BH.*). Umbell. (III. 2). 10 Medit. Cot. 1.

Biaurella Lindl. = Thelymitra Forst. p.p. (Orch.).

Bicarpellatae (*BH.*). The 3rd series of Gamopetalae; p. lii.

Bicchia Parl. = Habenaria Willd. (*BH.*) = Gymnadenia R. Br. (Orch.).

Bicornella Lindl. Orchid. (II. 1). 2 Madag. Spur funnel-shaped.

Bicornes (Warming). The 1st order of Sympetalae.

Bicuculla Adans., Borckh. = Adlumia and Dicentra p.p. (Papav.).

Bicuspidaria Rydb. (*Mentzelia* L. p.p.). Loas. 3 Calif.

Bidens (Tourn.) L. Comp. (5). 150 cosmop. (Spanish needle); 2 Brit. (bur-marigold). Fr. distr. by the 2—6 barbed bristles of the pappus. *B. Beckii* Torr. (N. Am.) a heterophyllous water pl.

Bidwillia Herb. Lili. Nomen.

Biebersteinia Steph. Geran. 5 Peloponnesus, W. and C. As. Ovules 1 per loc.

Bieneria Rchb. f. (*Chloraea* p.p. *BH.*). Orchid. (II. 2). 1 Bolivia.

Bienertia Bunge. Chenopodiaceae (B). 1 W. As.
Biermannia King et Pantl. Orchid. (II. 20). 2 E. Indies.
Bifaria O. Ktze. (*Panicum* L. p.p.). Gramin. (5). 3 Brazil.
Bifaria Van Tiegh. Loranthaceae (1). 50 warm | ✲.
Bifora Hoffm. Umbelliferae (III. 3). 4 N. subtrop.
Bifrenaria Lindl. Orchidac. (II. 12). 14 trop. S. Am. Cult.
Big, 4-rowed barley.
Big tree, *Sequoia gigantea* Lindl. et Gord., *Eucalyptus*.
Bigelovia Spreng. = Spermacoce L. (*BH.*) = Borreria G. F. W. Mey.
Bigelowia DC. Compositae (3). 40 N. Am. to Ecuador.
Biglandularia Karst. (*Leiphaimos* p.p. *EP.*). Gentian. (1). 1 Venezuela.
Bignonia (Tourn.) L. (*BH.* incl. *Cremastus*, *Cydista*, *Doxantha*, *Phaedranthus*, *Pleonotoma*, *Stizophyllum*, of Miers, and *Paragonia* Bur., *Pyrostegia* Presl, making 150 spp. in all). Bignon. (1). 2 W. I. to Argentina, incl. *B. Unguis-cati* L. cult. for its masses of fl., which appear simultaneously. Tendrils grapnel-like with three claws (modified l.), thickening after clasping. Fl. protandr.
Bignoniaceae (*BH. EP.*). Dicots. (Sympet. Tubiflorae; Personales, *BH.*). 100 gen., 800 sp. trop. One genus (Catalpa) common to old and new worlds. Most in Brazil; a few temp. Trees and shrubs, most commonly lianes, with opp. usu. cpd. exstip. l. Many xero. shrubs with condensed stems, but the chief interest centres in the climbers, a very important feature in the forest veg. of S. Am. Twiners (*e.g.* Tecomaria, Pandorea), root-climbers (*Tecoma radicans*), and tendril climbers (most B.). In Eccremocarpus &c. the internodes and petioles are sensitive, but in most B. the tendrils are at the ends of the l. (in place of leaflets, as in Vicia). The tendrils are frequently branched; in some cases the branched tendril occupies the place of one leaflet. Three types of tendril are found—simple twiners, tendrils provided with adhesive discs (as in Virginia creeper), and hooked tendrils. See Glaziovia, Bignonia &c. The climbing stems exhibit many features of anatomical interest, owing to the peculiar growth in thickness.

Infl. usu. dich. with cincinnal tendency; bracts and bracteoles present. Flr. ☿, ·|·, hypog. K (5): C (5), usu. bell- or funnel-shaped, descendingly imbr.; A 4, epipet., didynamous, the anther-lobes usu. one above the other, the post. std. always present; $\underline{G}$ (2) on hypog. disc, 2- (or rarely 1-) loc., with ∞ erect anatr. ov. on axile plac. Caps. septifr. or loculic.: seed usu. flattened and with large membranous wing, exalb.

Classification and chief genera (after Schumann):

I. *Bignonieae* (ovary completely 2-loc., compressed || septum, or cylindrical; caps. septifr. with winged seeds; usu. tendrillate): Glaziovia, Bignonia, Oroxylum.

II. *Tecomeae* (ovary 2-loc., compressed ⊥ septum or cylindrical; caps. loculic. with winged seeds; rarely tendrillate): Incarvillea, Jacaranda, Catalpa, Tecoma, Spathodea.

III. *Eccremocarpeae* (ovary 1-loc.; caps. splits from below up.; seeds winged; tendrils): Eccremocarpus (only gen.).

IV. *Crescentieae* (ovary 1- or 2-loc.; fr. berry or dry indehiscent; seed not winged; usu. erect pl.): Parmentiera, Crescentia, Phyllarthron, Kigelia.

Bihai Adans. = Heliconia L. (Musac.).
Bikh poison, *Aconitum ferox* Wall.
Bikkia Reinw. Rubiaceae (I. 1). 15 E. Malay Arch., Polynesia. (A).
Bilabium Miq. = Didymocarpus Wall. p.p. (Gesner.).
Bilberry, *Vaccinium Myrtillus* L.
Bilegnum Brand (*Rindera* Pall.). Boragin. (IV. 1). 1 Persia.
Bileveillea Vaniot (*Blumea* p.p. *EP.*). Compos. (4). 5 Nepal, China.
Bilimbi, *Averrhoa Bilimbi* L.
Bilitalium Buch.-Ham. Inc. sed. 1 India.
Billardiera Sm. Pittosporaceae. 9 Austr.
Billbergia Thunb. Bromel. (4). 60 warm Am. Epiph. Cult. orn. infl.
Billia Peyr. (*Aesculus* p.p. *BH.*). Hippocast. 2 trop. Am.
Billiard balls, *Phytelephas.*
Billiottia DC. (*Melanopsidium EP.*). Rubi. (I. 8). 1 Brazil.
Billottia R. Br. = Agonis DC. (Myrt.).
Biltia Small (*Rhododendron* p.p.). Eric. (I. 2). 1 N. Am.
Bima Nor. Inc. sed. Nomen.
Bindweed, *Convolvulus spp.*; **black-,** *Polygonum.*
Bingeria A. Chevalier (*Guarea* p.p.). Meliaceae (III) 1 Afr.
Binotia Rolfe. Orchidaceae (II. 19). 1 Brazil.
Biogenesis, life from life.
Biolettia Greene (*Trichocoronis* p.p.). Compos. (6). 1 Calif.
Biology, in narrower sense, ecology.
Biometry, statistical measurement of living beings.
Bion, an independent individual.
Biondia Schlechter. Asclepiadaceae (II. 3). 1 China.
Biophytum DC. Oxalid. 60 trop. Many have sensitive pinnate l.; the leaflets bend down when touched (*cf.* Mimosa). Explosive aril on the seeds (*cf.* Oxalis).
Biota D. Don = Thuja L. p.p. (Conif.).
Biotia DC. = Aster Tourn. p.p. (Compos.).
Biovularia Kamienski. Lentibul. 2 W. Ind., N. Brazil.
Bipinnula Comm. ex Juss. Orchidaceae (II. 2). 8 temp. S. Am.
Birch, *Betula*; (W.I.) *Bursera.*
Bird-cherry, *Prunus Padus* L.; **-pepper,** *Capsicum minimum.*
Birds as agents in pl. dispersal, *cf.* Dispersal.
Bird's foot, *Ornithopus perpusillus* L.; **--trefoil,** *Lotus*; **-nest fern,** *Asplenium Nidus* L.; **--orchis,** *Neottia Nidus-avis* Rich.; **yellow -nest,** *Monotropa Hypopitys* Walt.
Birthwort, *Aristolochia Clematitis* L.
Bisboeckelera O. Ktze. (*Hoppia* Nees). Cyper. (II). 4 S. Am.
Bischofia Blume. Euphorb. (A. I. 1). 1 Indomal., Polyn. Bark medic.
Biscutella L. Cruciferae (2). 20 S. and mid. Eur.
Biserrula L. Leguminosae (III. 6). 1 Medit.
Bisglaziovia Cogn. Melastomaceae (1). 1 Brazil.
Bisgoeppertia O. Ktze. (*Goeppertia* p.p.). Gent. (1). 2 Cuba.
Bishop's cap (Am.), *Mitella*; **-weed,** *Aegopodium.*
Bisluederitzia O. Ktze. (*Neoluederitzia*). Zygophyll. 1 S. Afr.
Bismarckia Hildebr. et H. Wendl. (*Medemia* Princ. Guil. de Wurtt.). Palmae (II). 1 Madagascar.
Bisphaeria Nor. Inc. sed. Nomen.

Bisrautanenia O. Ktze. (*Neorautanenia*). Legum. (III. 10). 1 S. Afr.
Bissy nuts, Cola nuts, *Cola*.
Bistania Nor. Inc. sed. Nomen.
Bistella Adans. Inc. sed. Nomen.
Bistort, *Polygonum*.
Bistorta Tourn. = Polygonum L. p.p. (Polyg.).
Biswarea Cogn. Cucurbitaceae (3). 1 Himal.
Bitchwood (W.I.), *Lonchocarpus*.
Bitter ash (W.I.), *Picraena*; **cress**, *Cardamine*; **-nut**, *Carya*; **-orange**, *Citrus Aurantium* L. var. *Bigaradia*; **-root**, *Lewisia*; **-sweet**, *Solanum Dulcamara* L.; **-wood**, *Picraena*, *Picramna*, &c.
Bitteria Börner (*Carex* p.p.). Cyperaceae (III). 5 N. temp.
Bivinia Tul. (*Calantica* p.p. *EP.*). Flac. (9) (Samyd. *BH.*). 1 Madag.
Bivolva Van Tiegh. (*Balanophora* p.p.). Balan. 5 India, China.
Bivonaea DC. Cruciferae (2). 4 W. Medit.
Bixa L. Bix. 2 trop. Am. W.I. *B. Orellana* L. cult. for the seed; the orange colouring matter of the outer layer of the testa (annatto, arnotto, roucou) is used in dyeing sweetmeats &c.
Bixaceae (*EP.*; *Bixineae BH.* incl. *Flacourtiaceae* and *Cochlospermaceae*). Dicots. (Archichl. Parietales *EP. BH.*). 3 gen. 6 sp. trop. Small trees or shrubs; l. alt. stip. entire. Fl. in panicles, ☿, reg. K 5, C 5, A ∞, G̲ (2), 1-loc. with parietal plac. and ∞ anatr. ov. Style simple. Capsule splitting between plac. Seeds with red fleshy papillae. Endosp. starchy. *Chief genus* Bixa.
Bixineae (*BH.*). Bixaceae, in wide sense. See above.
Blachia Baill. Euphorbiaceae (A. II. 5). 8 Indomal.
Black bead shrub (W.I.), *Pithecolobium Unguis-cati* Benth.; **-berry**, *Rubus fruticosus*, &c.; **-bindweed**, *Polygonum Convolvulus* L.; **-boy**, *Xanthorrhoea hastilis* R. Br.; **-bryony**, *Tamus communis* L.; **-butt**, *Eucalyptus pilularis* Sm. &c.; **-cap raspberry**, *Rubus occidentalis* L.; **-dammar**, *Canarium*; **-gram**, *Phaseolus Mungo* L., var. *radiatus*; **-grass** (Am.), *Juncus Gerardi* Loisel.; **-gum tree** (Am.), *Nyssa*; **-jack** (Am.), *Quercus nigra* L.; **-moss** (Am.), *Tillandsia usneoides* L.; **-mustard**, *Brassica nigra* Koch; **-oil**, *Celastrus*; **-snake-root**, *Cimicifuga* (*Actaea*) *racemosa* Nutt.; **-spleenwort**, *Asplenium Adiantum-nigrum* L.; **-thorn**, *Prunus spinosa* L.; **-wattle**, *Acacia decurrens* Willd.; **-wood**, *Acacia melanoxylon* R.Br., *Dalbergia latifolia* Roxb., &c.
Blackstonia Huds. = Chlora Ren. (Gentian.).
Blackwellia Comm. ex Juss. = Homalium Jacq. p.p. (Flacourt.).
Blackwellia Gaertn. Inc. sed. 1 sp. Habitat?
Bladder-campion, *Silene inflata* Sm.; **-fern**, *Cystopteris fragilis* Bernh.; **-nut**, *Staphylea pinnata* L.; **-seed**, *Physospermum*; **-senna**, *Colutea arborescens* L.; **-wort**, *Utricularia*.
Blaeberry, *Vaccinium Myrtillus* L.
Blaeria L. Ericaceae (IV. 1). 25 S. and trop. Afr.
Blainvillea Cass. Compositae (5). 10 cosmotrop.
Blairia Houst. ex L. = Priva Adans. (Verben.).
Blakea P. Br. Melastomaceae (1). 35 S. Am., W.I. Ed. fr.
Blanchetia DC. Compositae (1). 1 Bahia. Raises perspiration.
Blanchetiastrum Hassler. Malvaceae (3). 1 Brazil.

Blancoa Lindl. Amaryllid. (III). 1 S.W. Austr. (Haemodor. *BH.*)
Blandfordia Sm. Liliaceae (III). 4 E. Austr. Cult. orn. fl.
Blanket flower, *Gaillardia*.
Blastania Kotschy et Peyr. Cucurbit. (2). 3 trop. Afr. and As.
Blastemanthus Planch. Ochnaceae. 4 N. Brazil, Guiana. K 5+5.
Blastocaulon Ruhland (*Paepalanthus* p.p.). Eriocaul. 3 Brazil.
Blastochore (Cl.), a plant distr. by offshoots.
Blastus Lour. Melastomaceae (I). 4 E. As.
Blatti Adans. (*Sonneratia* L. f. *q.v.*). Sonnerat. 6 Indomal.
Blattiaceae = Sonneratiaceae.
Blazing star, *Liatris squarrosa* Willd.
Blechnum L. Polypodiaceae. 220 cosmop. *B. boreale* Sw. (*B. Spicant* Roth.) in Brit. has fertile and barren l., the latter larger. Cf. Bower, Studies, *Ann. Bot.* 28, 1914, p. 363.
Blechum P. Br. Acanthaceae (IV. A). 4 trop. Am., W.I.
Bleeding heart, *Dicentra*; (W.I.), *Colocasia antiquorum*.
Bleekrodea Blume. Moraceae (I). 3 Madag., Borneo, Indochina.
Blennodia R. Br. Cruciferae (4). 11 Austr.
Blennosperma Less. Compositae (6). 2 Chili, California.
Blepharacanthus Nees = Blepharis Juss. (Acanth.).
Blepharandra Griseb. Malpighiaceae (II). 1 Guiana.
Blepharanthera Schlechter. Asclep. (II. 3). 2 Damaraland.
Blepharidachne Hackel (*Eremochloe* Wats.). Gramin. (10). 2 W.N. Am.
Blephariglottis Rafin. = Habenaria Willd. (Orchid.).
Blepharipappus Hook. Compositae (5). 1 W. U.S. Many = Layia.
Blepharis Juss. Acanthaceae (IV. B). 80 palaeotrop., Medit., S. Afr. The seeds have hairs which swell up when wetted.
Blepharispermum Wight ex DC. Compos. (4). 10 trop. As. and Afr.
Blepharistemma Benth. in Wall. Rhizophoraceae. 1 India.
Blepharizonia Greene. Compositae (5). 2 California.
Blepharocalyx Berg. (*Myrtus* p.p. *BH.*). Myrtac. (I). 3 warm S. Am.
Blepharocarya F. Muell. Anacard. (3). (Sapind. *BH.*) 1 E. trop. Austr.
Blepharodon Decne. Asclepiadaceae (II. 1). 25 Mex. to Chili.
Blepharoneuron Nash (*Vilfa* p.p.). Gramin. (8). 1 S.W. U.S., Mex.
Blephilia Rafin. Labiatae (VI). 2 N. Am.
Bletia Ruiz et Pav. Orchid. (II. 9). 45 trop. Am., W.I. Cult.
Bletilla Reichb. f. Orchidaceae (II *a*. II). 6 E. As.
Blighia Kon. Sapindaceae (I). 3 trop. Afr. *B. sapida* Kon (akee, vegetable marrow) cult. for ed. fr. (fleshy arillate seed stalk).
Blimbing, *Averrhoa Bilimbi* L.
Blinding tree (Ceylon), *Excoecaria Agallocha* L.
Blinks, *Montia fontana* L.
Blinkworthia Choisy. Convolvulaceae (I). 2 Burma.
Blitum (Tourn.) L. = Chenopodium L. p.p. (Chenopod.).
Blood-flower, *Haemanthus*, (W.I.) *Asclepias curassavica* L.; **-leaf**, *Iresine*; **-lily**, *Haemanthus*; **-root**, *Sanguinaria canadensis* L.; **-wood**, *Eucalyptus*, (W.I.) *Laplacea*.
Bloomeria Kellogg. Liliaceae (IV). 2 S. California.

Blue-bell, *Campanula rotundifolia* L., *Scilla festalis* Salisb.; **-berry** (Am.), *Vaccinium spp.*; **-bottle,** *Centaurea Cyanus* L.; **-flag** (Am.), *Iris*; **-grass** (Am.), *Poa pratensis* L.; **-gum,** *Eucalyptus Globulus* Labill.; **-lettuce** (Am.), *Mulgedium*; **-tangle** (Am.), *Gaylussacia frondosa* Torr. et Gray; **-weed** (Am.), *Echium*.

Bluet, *Vaccinium pennsylvanicum* Lam., *Houstonia*.

Blumea DC. Comp. (4). 80 palaeotrop., S. Afr. Ai or ngai camphor is distilled from *B. balsamifera* DC. (S.W. China).

Blumenbachia Schrad. Loasaceae. 6 temp. S. Am. Fr. very light, twisted, covered with grapnel hairs.

Blumeodendron Muell.-Arg. = Mallotus Lour. p.p. (Euphorb.).

Blunt, with rounded end.

Blysmus Panz. = Scirpus Tourn. p.p. (Cyper.).

Blyxa Noronha. Hydrocharidaceae. 12 |※ warm.

Blyxopsis O. Ktze. (*Enhydrias* Ridl.). Hydrocharid. 1 Malay Penin.

Bo (Ceylon), *Ficus religiosa* L.

Bobartia L. Iridaceae (II). 10 S. Afr. L. sword-like or centric.

Bobea Gaudich. Rubiaceae (II. 2). 5 Sandwich Is.

Bobua DC. = Symplocos L. p.p. (Symploc.).

Bocagea St. Hil. Anonaceae (1). 10 trop. Am. and As.

Bocconia Plum. ex L. (*BH.* incl. *Macleya* Reichb.). Papaveraceae (II). 5 warm Am., W.I. Apetalous.

Bocoa Aubl. (*Inocarpus* Forst. *BH.*). Leguminosae (III. 8). 1 Guiana. The seeds are ed.

Bocquillonia Baill. Euphorbiaceae (A. II. 2). 6 New Caled.

Bodinieria Leveillé et Vaniot. Ranunc. (2). 1 China.

Bodinieriella Leveillé. Ericaceae (II. 1). 1 China.

Boea Comm. ex Lam. Gesneriaceae (I). 25 trop. As. and Austr.

Boebera Willd. = Dyssodia Cav. p.p. (Compos.).

Boeberastrum Rydberg (*Dyssodia* p.p.). Compos. (10). 3 S.W. U.S.

Boeckeleria T. Durand (*Decalepis* Boeck.). Cyper. (II). 1 S. Afr.

Boehmeria Jacq. Urticaceae (3). 75 trop. and N. subtrop. *B. nivea* Gaudich. has good drip-tips (*cf.* Acer). It is cult. in China for the fibre (China grass, rhea) obtained from the inner bark (*cf.* Linum), perhaps the longest, toughest, and most silky of all veg. fibres, but most difficult to prepare. In the trop. the var. *tenacissima* (ramie) is cult.

Boehmeriopsis Komarow. Urticaceae (3). 1 Corea.

Boeica C. B. Clarke. Gesneriaceae (I). 6 S.E. As.

Boenninghausenia Reichb. Rutaceae (I. 2). 1 Khasias to Japan.

Boerhaavia Vaill. ex L. Nyctaginaceae. 50 cosmop. Anthocarp often glandular, aiding in seed-dispersal.

Boerlagea Cogn. Melastomaceae (I). 1 Borneo.

Boerlagella Pierre. Sapotaceae (II). 1 Sumatra.

Boerlagiodendron Harms. Araliaceae (1). 20 Malaya.

Bog-asphodel, *Narthecium ossifragum* Huds.; **-bean,** *Menyanthes trifoliata* L.; **-myrtle,** *Myrica Gale* L.; **-rush** (Am.), *Juncus*.

Bogoria J. J. Sm. Orchidaceae (II. 20). 2 Java, New Guin.

Bois fidèle, *Citharexylum*; **-immortelle,** *Erythrina umbrosa*.

Boisduvalia Spach (*Oenothera* p.p. *BH.*). Onagr. (2). 8 W. coast Am.

Boissiera Hochst. et Steud. Gramineae (10). 1 W. As.
Bojeria DC. (*Inula* p.p. *EP.*). Compositae (4). 3 Madag., S. Afr.
Bolandra A. Gray. Saxifragaceae (1). 2 Pac. N. Am.
Bolanosa A. Gray. Compositae (1). 1 Mex.
Bolax Comm. ex Juss. = Azorella Lam. (Umbell.).
Bolbophyllaria Reichb. f. Orchidaceae (II. 16). 6 trop.
Bolbophyllum Spreng. = Bulbophyllum Thou. (Orchid.).
Bolboschoenus Palla (*Scirpus* p.p.). Cyper. (1). 1 cosmop.
Bolboxalis Small (*Oxalis* p.p.). Oxalidaceae. 1 S. Afr.
Boldo, *Peumus Boldus* Molina.
Boldoa Cav. Nyctaginaceae. 2 Mex., W.I.
Boldoa Endl. = Peumus Molina. (Monim.)
Bole, straight main trunk.
Boleum Desv. Cruciferae (2). 1 Spain.
Bolivaria Cham. et Schlecht. = Menodora Humb. et Bonpl. p.p.
Boll, a capsule, especially of cotton.
Bollea Reichb. f. (*Zygopetalum* p.p. *BH.*). Orchid. (II. 14). 3 W. trop. Am.
Bollwilleria Zabel (*Pyrus* p.p.). Rosaceae (II). 2 Eur., Medit.
Boltonia L'Herit. Compositae (3). 4 U.S.
Bolusanthus Harms (*Lonchocarpus* p.p.). Legum. (III. 1). 1 S. Afr.
Bolusia Benth. Leguminosae (III. 6). 1 S. Afr.
Bomarea Mirb. Amaryllidaceae (III). 120 Mex., W.I., trop. Am. L. like Alstroemeria. Often climbing. Umbels cymose. Cult. orn. fl.
Bombacaceae (*EP.*; *Malvaceae* p.p. *BH.*). Dicots. (Archichl. Malvales). 20 gen., 140 sp., trop., esp. Am. Trees, often very large, with thick stems, sometimes egg-shaped owing to formation of water storage tissue; l. entire or palmate, with deciduous stips. Fl. ☿, often large, usu. reg. K (5), valvate, often with epicalyx; C 5, conv., pets. asymmetric; A 5—∞, free or united into a tube, pollen smooth; G̲ (2—5), in the latter case the cpls. opp. the pets., multiloc.; style simple, lobed or capitate; ovules 2—∞ in each loc., erect. anatr. Capsule; seeds smooth, often embedded in hairs springing from wall; endosp. little or 0. The Adansonieae are ± myrmecophilous (*cf.* Acacia), with extrafloral nectaries on l., K, or fl. stalk. *Chief genera* Adansonia, Bombax, Chorisia, Durio, Eriodendron.
Bombax L. (incl. *Pachira* Aubl. *EP.*). Bombacaceae. 60 trop. *B. malabaricum* DC. (cotton-tree, Ind., Ceylon) drops its l. in Dec. and remains leafless till Apr., but fls. in Jan. The cotton is used for cushions, &c. Dug-out canoes are made of the soft wood.
Bombay aloe, *Agave*; **-hemp,** *Crotalaria, Agave.*
Bombycidendron Zoll. et Morr. (*Hibiscus* p.p.). Malv. (4). 4 Phil. Is.
Bombycinus (Lat.), silky.
Bombynia Nor. Inc. sed. Nomen.
Bonace (W.I.), *Daphnopsis.*
Bonamia Thou. Convolvulaceae (1). 3 Sandwich Is., Madag.
Bonania A. Rich. Euphorbiaceae (A. II. 7). 3 Cuba, Bahamas.
Bonannia Guss. Umbelliferae (III. 6). 2 S. Eur.
Bonapartea Haw. = Agave L. (Amaryll.).
Bonatea Willd. (*Habenaria* p.p.). Orchid. (II. 1). 5 trop. and S. Afr.
Bonatia Schlechter et Krause. Rubiaceae (I. 8). 1 New Caled.

Bonaveria Scop. = Securigera DC. (Legum.). 1 Medit.
Bonavist (W.I.), *Dolichos Lablab* L.; **Boneset** (Am.), *Eupatorium*.
Bonduc Adans. = Caesalpinia L. (Legum.).
Bongardia C. A. Mey (*Leontice* p.p. *EP.*). Berberid. 1 E. Medit. L. and rhiz. ed.
Bonia Bal. Gramin. (13). 1 Tonquin.
Boninia Planch. Rut. (I. 1). 2 Bonin Is. 4-merous.
Bonjeania Rchb. = Dorycnium L. p.p. (Legum.).
Bonnaya Link et Otto (*Ilysanthes* p.p. *EP.*). Scroph. (II. 6). 5 warm.
Bonnetia Mart. et Zucc. Theac. 7 trop. Am. G (3). Caps. septic.
Bonniera Cordemoy. Orchid. (II. 20). 2 Réunion.
Bonnierella Viguier (*Polyscias* p.p. *EP.*) Aral. (1). 1 Tahiti.
Bonplandia Cav. Polemon. 2 Mex. Fl. ± ·|·.
Bontia L. Myopor. 1 W.I.
Bonyunia Schomb. Logan. 3 Guiana, Braz.
Boopis Juss. Calycer. 25 Andes, Arg., S. Braz. Fr. free, all alike.
Bootia Wall. Hydrocharid. (1). 20 palaeotrop., Chi. L. stalked, erect or submerged. Dioec.
Boquila Decne. Lardizabal. 1 Chile. Dioec. 6 honey-l.
Borage, *Borago officinalis* L. (S. Eur., As. Minor.).
Boraginaceae (*EP.*, *BH.*). Dicots. (Sympet. Tubiflorae; Polemoniales *BH.*, pp. xlv, liii). 100/1800, trop. and temp., esp. Medit. Mostly herbs, often perenn. by fleshy r., rhiz., &c., a few ♄; sometimes climbing. L. usu. alt., exstip., usu., like rest of pl., covered with stout hairs (hence name Asperifolieae, by which B. sometimes known). Infl. usu. a coiled cincinnus, sometimes double, with marked dorsiventrality, uncoiling as fls. open, so that newly opened fls. face always in same direction. The morphology of this infl. is not fully clear; adnation or concrescence occurs, and possibly dichotomy at apex. General agreement favours the view that the "boragoid," as it is sometimes called, is composed of dorsiventral monopodia. Cf. *Nat. Pfl.*, Müller in *Flora*, 94, Schuman, *Morphol. Studien*, II.

Fl. ☿, usu. reg., hypog., usu. 5-merous; K (5), imbr. or open, rarely valv., odd sep. post.; C (5), imbr. or conv., funnel-shaped or tubular, limb usu. flat; A 5, epipet., alt. to pets., intr.; G̲ (2), on hypog. disc, usu. 4-loc. (rarely 2- or 10-loc.) with "false" septum (cf. Labiatae), usu. with gynobasic entire or lobed style from base of ovary; ov. 1 in each loc., erect, ascending or horiz., anatr. Fr. of 4 achenes (nutlets), or drupe; seed with straight or curved embryo in usu. slight endosp.; radicle directed upwards (cf. § V).

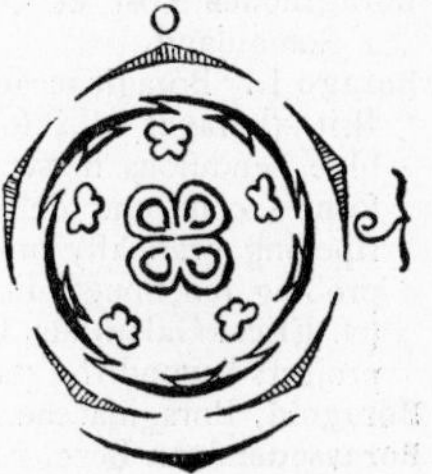
Floral diagram of Anchusa; after Eichler.

Most have a short tube, partly concealing the honey: many (esp. IV. 1 and 3) have scales projecting inwards from the throat of the C, concealing and protecting the honey, and narrowing the entrance, so that visiting insects must take a definite track. "Many sp. in the course of their individual development, seem to recapitulate to us the evolution of their colours—white, rosy, blue in several sp. of Myosotis; yellow, bluish, violet in *M. versicolor*; and red, violet, blue in Pulmonaria, Echium, &c. Here, white and yellow seem to have been the primitive colours." (Müller.) Many B. are heterostyled, *e.g.* Pulmonaria. The fls. of many sp. are pendulous (and thus bee-flowers), *e.g.* Borago, Symphytum. Echium is gynodioecious.

Classification and chief genera (after Gürke):

I. *CORDIOIDEAE* (drupe; style terminal: twice bi-lobed): Cordia.

II. *EHRETIOIDEAE* (do.; style simple or bi-lobed or double; no ring of hairs): Ehretia.

III. *HELIOTROPIOIDEAE* (do., do., but ring of hairs near tip of style): Tournefortia, Heliotropium.

IV. *BORAGINOIDEAE* (style gynobasic: achenes).

1. *Cynoglosseae* (fl. reg.; base of style more or less conical; tips of achenes not projecting above pt. of attachment): Omphalodes, Cynoglossum, Rindera.
2. *Eritrichieae* (do., but tips projecting above pt. of attachment): Echinospermum, Eritrichium, Cryptanthe.
3. *Anchuseae* (fl. reg.; base of style flat or slightly convex; achenes with concave attachment surface): Symphytum, Borago, Anchusa, Alkanna, Pulmonaria.
4. *Lithospermeae* (do., but surface of attachment flat): Myo sotis, Lithospermum, Arnebia, Cerinthe.
5. *Echieae* (fl. zygomorphic): Echium.

V. *WELLSTEDIOIDEAE* (4-merous; ov. compressed, 2-loc. with one pend. ov. in each; caps.): Wellstedia.

Boragineae (*BH.*) = Boraginaceae.

Boraginodes Post et O. Ktze. (*Trichodesma* p.p.). Borag. (IV. 1). 1 Somaliland.

Borago L. Boraginaceae (IV. 3). 3 Medit., Eur., As. *B. officinalis* L. Brit. (borage) cult. for bee feeding. It has a typical bee-fl. The blue pendulous fl. secretes honey below the ovary; the elastic sta. form a cone and dehisce introrsely from apex to base, the pollen ripening gradually and trickling into the tip of the cone. Insects probing for honey dislocate the sta., receiving a shower of pollen (cf. Erica, Galanthus, Cyclamen). In older fls. the stigma, now ripe, projects beyond the sta. so as to be touched first.

Boragoid, Boraginaceae.

Borassodendron Becc. Palmae (II). 1 Perak.

Borassus L. Palmae (II). 4 palaeotrop. *B. flabellifer* L. (Palmyra palm) cult. in Ceylon, India, &c. Dioecious. Its uses are legion; an old Tamil song enumerates 801. The wood of the trunk is very hard and durable, and resists salt water; it is also used for rafters, well-sweeps, &c. The large fanshaped l. are used as thatch, and made into olas or writing "paper" sheets, the writing being done upon them with a stylus. From the base of the l. Palmyra fibre is collected, and used for making brushes, &c. The split l. are woven into mats, baskets, &c. The fr. is eaten roasted, and the infl. is tapped for toddy (cf. Cocos, Agave) from which sugar or jaggery is

made, as well as vinegar, &c. The young seedlings are also eaten and yield a good flour when ground, and there are many other uses.
Borbonia L. Leguminosae (III. 3). 15 S. Afr.
Borderea Miègeville (*Dioscorea* p.p. *BH.*). Dioscor. 1 Pyrenees, 1 Chili.
Borea Zipp. Inc. sed. Nomen.
Boreava Jaub. et Spach. Cruciferae (2). 2 E. Medit.
Borecole, *Brassica oleracea* L. var.
Boree (Austr.), *Acacia pendula* A. Cunn.
Boretta Neck. = Daboecia D. Don (Eric.).
Borneo camphor, *Dryobalanops aromatica* Gaertn.; **-rubber**, *Willughbeia edulis* Roxb., &c.
Bornmuellera Hausskn. Cruciferae (4). 1 E. Medit.
Boronella Baill. Rutaceae (I. 3). 2 New Caled.
Boronia Sm. Rutaceae (I). 65 Austr.
Borreria G. F. W. Mey. (*Spermacoce* L.). Rubi. (II. 10). 100 warm.
Borrichia Adans. Compositae (5). 6 warm Am., W. I.
Borsczowia Bunge. Chenopodiaceae (B). 1 Aral plain.
Borthwickia W. W. Smith. Capparidaceae (II). 1 Burma.
Borya Labill. Liliaceae (III). 2 Queensland, W. Austr.
Borzicactus Riccobono (*Cereus* p.p.). Cactac. (III. 1). 8 Andes.
Boschia Korth. Bombacaceae. 4 Malaya.
Boschniakia C. A. Mey. Orobanchaceae. 1 N.E. As., N.W. N. Am.
Boscia Lam. Capparidaceae (II). 30 trop. and S. Afr. C o.
Bosea L. Amarantaceae (2). 3 Medit., India.
Bosistoa F. Muell. Rutaceae (I). 2 E. Austr.
Bosleria Aven Nelson. Solanaceae (2). 1 Nevada.
Bosqueiopsis de Wild. et Durand. Morac. (II). 4 trop. Afr.
Bosquiea Thou. Moraceae (II). 4 Madag., trop. Afr.
Boss, a protuberance.
Bossekia Necker (*Rubus* p.p.). Rosaceae (III. 2). 2 N. Am.
Bossiaea Vent. Leguminosae (III. 3). 35 Austr. Several xero. sp. have flattened green stems (phylloclades) with minute scaly l. As in Acacia, &c., seedlings show transitions from l.
Bostrychanthera Benth. Labiatae (III). 1 China.
Bostryx, a monoch. cyme where each lat. branch falls upon the same side of relatively main axis, *Begonia*, *Butomus*, *Hemerocallis*, *Hypericum*, *Liliaceae*.
Boswellia Roxb. ex Colebr. Burseraceae. 10 trop. As. and Afr. *B. Carteri* Birdw. (Somaliland, &c.) and other sp. yield the resin frankincense or gum-olibanum, formerly offic., now used in incense. Other sp. also yield fragrant resins. *B. serrata* Roxb., an important tree on dry hills in India.
Bothriochloa O. Ktze. (*Andropogon* p.p.). Gramin. (2). 1 Annam.
Bothriocline Oliv. Compositae (1). 10 trop. Afr.
Bothriospermum Bunge. Boragin. (IV. 2). 5 trop. and N.E. As.
Bothriospora Hook. f. Rubiaceae (I. 8). 1 Guiana.
Botryanthus Kunth = Muscari Mill. p.p. (Liliaceae).
Botryceras Willd. (*Laurophyllus EP.*). Anacard. (3). 1 S. Afr.
Botrychium Sw. Ophioglossaceae. 40 cosmop. *B. Lunaria* Sw. (moonwort) in Brit. Habit like Ophioglossum, but the sterile as

well as the fertile part of the l. is usu. branched. The r. appear one at the base of each l., and branch monopodially. The spike is usu. much branched, the ultimate twigs being the sporangia.

B. Lunaria has no veg. repr. like Ophioglossum, and each new pl. comes from a prothallus, which is small, not > 1 or 2 mm. long, oval, saprophytic, buried to a depth of 1–10 cm. In *B. virginianum* Sw. it is as much as 20 mm. long, and seems to remain attached to the sporophyte for 5 or 6 years. The prothallus has a mycorhiza. (Jeffrey, *Univ. of Toronto Studies*, 1898; Bruchmann in *Flora*, 96, 1906, p. 203.)

Botrymorus Miq. (*Pipturus* Wedd. *EP.*). Urtic. (3). 1 Malaya.

Botryophora Hook. f. Euphorbiaceae (B. II). 1 Perak.

Botryopleuron Hemsl. Scrophulariaceae (III. 1). 5 China.

Botryose, racemose.

Bottionea Colla. Liliaceae (III). 1 Chili.

Bottle-brush, *Callistemon*; **-cod-root** (W.I.), *Capparis*; **-gourd**, *Lagenaria*; **-grass** (Am.), *Setaria viridis* Beauv.

Boucerosia Wight et Arn. (*Caralluma* p.p. *EP.*). Asclepiad. (II. 3). 30 trop. Afr. and As.

Bouchardatia Baill. (*Melicope BH.*). Rutac. (I). 1 E. Austr.

Bouchea Cham. Verbenaceae (2). 20 warm.

Bouchetia DC. Solanaceae (4). 3 Texas to Brazil.

Bouea Meissn. Anacardiaceae (1). 4 Malaya.

Bouetia A. Chevalier. Labiatae (VII). 1 Dahomey.

Bougainvillaea Comm. ex Juss. Nyctaginaceae. 12 S. Am. The group of 3 fls. is surrounded by 3 lilac or red persistent bracts. *B. spectabilis* Willd. is a splendid flowering creeper often cult.

Bougueria Decne. Plantaginaceae. 1 Andes.

Bourgeon, to bud or sprout.

Bourgia Scop. Boraginaceae (inc. sed.). Nomen.

Bournea Oliv. Gesneriaceae (I). 1 China.

Bourreria P. Br. (*Beureria* Jacq.). Boragin. (II). 35 warm Am., W. Ind.

Bousigonia Pierre. Apocynaceae (I. 1). 3 Cochinchina.

Boussingaultia H. B. et K. Basellaceae. 10 trop. Am. Tubers ed.

Bouteloua Lag. Gramineae (II). 40 Canada to S. Am., mainly in SW. U.S. (mesquit grasses, grama, side-oats). They form a large proportion of the herbage of the prairie, and are valuable as fodder.

Boutonia DC. (*Periblema* DC. *BH.*). Acanth. (IV. A). 1 Madag.

Bouvardia Salisb. Rubiaceae (I. 5). 30 trop. Am. Some heterostyled like Primula. Cult. orn. perf. fls.

Bouzetia Montr. Rutaceae (inc. sed.). 1 New Caled.

Bowdichia H. B. et K. Legumin. (III. 1). 2 trop. S. Am. Good wood.

Bowenia Hook. Cycad. 1 Queensland, *B. spectabilis* Hook., easily recognized by the bipinnate l. The upper part of the main r. gives rise to curiously branched apogeotropic r., which contain Anabaena (an alga) living in symbiosis, and branch exogenously (*Ann. Bot.*, 1898).

Bowiea Harv. Liliaceae (III). 1 S. Afr., *B. volubilis* Harv., a xero. like Testudinaria, with a large partly underground stock (corm), giving off each year a much-branched climbing stem. This bears small l., but they soon drop, and assim. is carried on by the green stem.

Bowkeria Harv. Scrophulariaceae (II. 4). 7 S. Afr.

Bowlesia Ruiz. et Pav. Umbelliferae (I. 2). 20 Am.

Bowringia Champ. Leguminosae (III. 1). 1 Hongkong.

Bowstring hemp, *Sansevieria zeylanica* Willd.

Bow-wood, *Maclura aurantiaca* Nutt.

Box, *Buxus*; (Austr.) *Eucalyptus*; **jasmine-**, *Phillyrea*; **Maracaibo** or **W. Indian-**, *Casearia praecox* Griseb., (W.I.), *Vitex umbrosa* Sw.

Boxwoods of Commerce. Record in *Bull. Torr. Bot. Cl.* 1921, p. 297.

Boykinia Nutt. Saxifragaceae (I). 8 N. Am., Japan.

Brabejaria Burm. f. Inc. sed. 1 S. Afr.

Brabejum L. Proteaceae (I). 1 S. Afr., *B. stellatifolium* L. (wilde castanjes), whose seeds are eaten roasted.

Bracea Britton. Apocynaceae (inc. sed.). 1 Bahamas.

Bracea King = Sarcosperma Hook. f. (Sapot.).

Brachialis (Lat.), a cubit long; **brachiate**, with spreading branches.

Brachiaria Griseb. = Panicum L. p.p. (Gram.).

Brachiolobos All. = Nasturtium R. Br. (Crucif.).

Brachionidium Lindl. Orchidaceae (II. 8). 6 W.I., trop. S. Am.

Brachistus Miers. Solanaceae (2). 20 Cent. and S. Am.

Brachtia Reichb. f. Orchid. (II. 19). 3 Colombia.

Brachy- (Gr. pref.), short.

Brachyachaenium Baker (*Dicome* p.p.). Compos. (12). 1 Madag.

Brachyactis Ledeb. (*Aster* p.p. *EP.*). Compos. (3). 6 N. As., N. Am.

Brachyandra Phil. Compositae (2). 2 Chili.

Brachybotrys Maxim. Boraginaceae (IV. 1). 1 China.

Brachycarpaea DC. Cruciferae (1). 1 S. Afr.

Brachychaeta Torr. et A. Gray. Compos. (3). 1 S. U.S.

Brachychilum Petersen. Zingiberaceae (I). 1 Java.

Brachychiton Schott et Endl. (*Sterculia* L. p.p. *BH.*). Sterculiaceae. 11 Austr. *B. rupestris* K. Schum. (bottle tree) has swollen stems, *B. acerifolius* N. Muell. (flame tree) very fine fl.

Brachyclados D. Don. Compositae (12). 1 S. Andes.

Brachycome Cass. Compositae (3). 50 Austr., N.Z., N. Am., Afr.

Brachycorythis Lindl. Orchidaceae (II. 1). 12 W. and S. Afr.

Brachyelytrum Beauv. Gramineae (8). 4 warm Am., Afr.

Brachyglottis Forst. Compositae (8). 1 N.Z.

Brachygyne Small (*Seymeria* p.p.). Scroph. (III. 2). 1 N. Am.

Brachylaena R. Br. Compositae (4). 10 S. and trop. Afr. Shrubs.

Brachylepis C. A. Mey. = Anabasis L. p.p. (Chenopod.).

Brachylepis Wight et Arn. Asclepiadaceae (I). 1 Nilgiris.

Brachyloma Sond. Epacridaceae. 7 Austr.

Brachylophon Oliv. Malpighiaceae (I). 2 Malay Penins., E. Afr.

Brachynema Benth. Ebenaceae. 1 N. Brazil.

Brachyotum Triana. Melastomaceae (I). 35 S. Am.

Brachypodium Beauv. Gramineae (10). 10 temp., and Mts. of trop. 2 Brit. (false brome grass). Leaf reversed (cf. Alstroemeria).

Brachypterys A. Juss. Malpighiaceae (I). 3 trop. S. Am., W.I.

Brachyris Nutt. = Gutierrezia Lag. p.p. (Compos.).

Brachysema R. Br. Leguminosae (III. 2). 15 Austr.
Brachysiphon A. Juss. Penaeaceae. 5 S. Afr.
Brachystegia Benth. Leguminosae (II. 3). 20 trop. Afr.
Brachystelma R. Br. Asclepiadaceae (II. 3). 50 warm Afr. *B. Bingeri* A. Chev. has an ed. tuber.
Brachystelmaria Schlechter. Asclepiad. (II. 3). 6 S. Afr.
Brachystemma D. Don (*Arenaria* p.p. *BH.*). Caryoph. (I. 1). 1 Himal.
Brachystephanus Nees. Acanthaceae (IV. B). 10 trop. Afr., Madag.
Brachythalamus Gilg. Thymelaeaceae. 2 New Guinea.
Brachytome Hook. f. (*Randia* p.p. *EP.*). Rubiaceae (I. 8). 2 Indomal.
Bracken, *Pteridium aquilinum* (L.) Kuhn.
Brackenridgea A. Gray. Ochnaceae. 10 palaeotrop.
Bract, the l. in whose axil a fl. arises; **coloured-**, *Amherstia*, *Bougainvillaea*, *Castilleja*, *Euphorbia*, *Salvia*, &c.; **persistent-**, forming wings to fr., *Bougainvillaea*, *Carpinus*, *Mirabilis*, *Spinacia*; **bracteate**, bearing bracts; **bracteole**, a bractlet, borne on same axis as the fl.
Bradburia Torr. et Gray. Compositae (3). 2 Texas, Mexico.
Bradburya Rafin. (*Centrosema* Benth. *BH.*). Legu. (III. 10). 30 Am.
Bradleia Banks = Glochidion Forst. (Euph.).
Bragantia Lour. (*Apama* Lam. p.p.). Aristoloch. 5 Indomal.
Brahea Mart. Palmae (I. 2). 4 Mexico, Texas. Decorative.
Brainea J. Sm. Polypodiaceae. 1 E. As., *B. insignis* Sm., a dwarf tree-fern. The primary veins branch and rejoin repeatedly, forming small areas in the leaf; the veinlets run parallel and distinct.
Brake, *Pteridium aquilinum* (L.) Kuhn; **curled rock-**, *Cryptogramme crispa* R. Br.
Bramble, *Rubus*.
Branch, an outgrowth of r. or shoot which repeats its structure; usu. lat. (not dichotomous), exogenous in case of shoot, endogenous in r. In many ferns the branches are on the l. bases, but in *Equisetum* and fl. plants are usu. axillary. Usu. only one in each axil; if more than one, the others are **accessory**; if side by side, **collateral**, *Allium*, *Araceae*, *Crataegus*, *Liliaceae*, *Muscari*, *Quercus*, *Salix*; if one above the other, **serial**, *Aristolochia*, *Calycanthus*, *Cercis*, *Colletia*, *Fuchsia*, *Gleditschia*, *Robinia*, *Syringa*. Branches of two kinds—long and short shoots, or shoots of unlimited and limited growth—occur in *Pinus* and other *Coniferae*, *Berberis*, *Cactaceae*, *Ginkgo*, *Spergula*.

Branching may be of two types—**monopodial**, *Pinus* and other *Coniferae*, *Orchidaceae*, *Paris*, *Pothos*, or **sympodial**, *Acorus*, *Aglaonema*, *Ancistrocladus*, *Anonaceae*, *Anthurium*, *Araceae*, *Asarum*, *Eichhornia*, *Fagus*, *Iridaceae*, *Iris*, *Juncus*, *Liliaceae*, *Narthecium*, *Orchidaceae*, *Peperomia*, *Pistia*, *Polygonatum*, *Pontederiaceae*, *Potamogeton*, *Ranunculus*, *Rhaphidophora*, *Ulmaceae*, *Vitis*, *Zostera*.

And *cf.* Buds, Concrescence, &c.
Branda (W. I.), *Chione glabra* DC.
Brandegea Cogn. Cucurbitaceae (4). 2 California.
Brandesia Mart. = Telanthera R. Br. (*BH.*) = Alternanthera Forsk.
Brandisia Hook. f. et Thoms. Scrophular. (II. 4). 3 Burma, China.

Brandy-bottle, *Nuphar luteum* Sibth. et Sm.
Brandzeia Baill. Leguminosae (II. 1). 1 Seychelles, Madagascar.
Brasenia Schreb. Nymphaeaceae (II). 1 cosmop., exc. Eur. A 12 or more.
Brassaia Endl. (*Schefflera EP.*). Araliaceae (I). 3 Malaya.
Brassaiopsis Dcne. et Planch. Araliaceae (I). 10 Indomal.
Brassavola R. Br. Orchidaceae (II. 6). 24 trop. Am.
Brassia R. Br. Orchidaceae (II. 19). 30 trop. Am.
Brassica (Tourn.) L. (*BH.* incl. *Erucastrum* Presl and *Sinapis* L.). Cruciferae (2). 35 Eur., Medit., As. 7 in Brit. Many forms are cult., some for the flr., others for the stem, root, leaf, or seed. *B. nigra* Koch is the black mustard, whose seeds yield the condiment. *B. oleracea* L. is the cabbage, with the various races derived from it, such as cauliflower and broccoli (fleshy infl.), kale or curly greens or borecole, brussels-sprouts (a form in which miniature cabbages are produced in all the leaf-axils on the main stem), kohl-rabi or knol-kohl (trop.) (a thickened stem, or corm, showing leaf scars on its surface), &c. *B. campestris* L. is the turnip, a biennial with thickened root, and a var. of it—*B. Napus* L.—is the rape, used in salads and in the preparation of rape- or colza-oil, expressed from the seeds. [See De Candolle's *Orig. of Cultiv. Plts.*] It is of interest to notice the great variety of morphology in the veg. organs, correlated with the different ways in which storage of reserve materials is effected, in the root, stem, leaf, flowerstalk, &c.

Sauer-kraut, or salted cabbage, made by packing cabbage shreds in barrels with salt and pepper, and slightly fermenting, is a favourite food in Germany, esp. for winter use.

The outer coat of the seed has mucilaginous cell-walls which swell when wetted (cf. Linum).
Brassocattleya × Rolfe. Hybrid, *Brassavola* × *Cattleya*; others are *Brassolaelia*, *Brassoepidendrum*, *Brassocattlaelia* (triple).
Brathys Mutis ex L. f. = Hypericum Tourn. p.p. (Guttif.).
Brauna, *Melanoxylon Brauna* Schott.
Bravaisia DC. Acanthaceae (IV. A). 2 trop. Am., W. I.
Bravoa Lex. Amaryllidaceae (II). 5 Mexico. Rhizome with tuberous roots. Fl. zygomorphic by bending.
Braya Sternb. et Hoppe. Cruciferae (4). 12 Eur., As., S. Am.
Brayera Kunth. (*Hagenia* Willd.) Rosaceae (III. 5). 1 Abyssinia. The dried ♀ fls. (Koso) are used as a remedy for tapeworm.
Brayodendron Small (*Diospyros* p.p.). Ebenaceae. 1 Texas, Mex.
Brayopsis Gilg et Muschler (incl. *Draba* p.p.). Cruc. (2). 4 Andes.
Brayulinea Small (*Guilleminea* p.p.). Amarant (3). 1 Ecuador.
Brazil-cherry, *Eugenia* spp.; **-nut**, *Bertholletia excelsa* H. et B.; **-wood**, *Caesalpinia Sappan* L. &c.; **-ian arrowroot**, *Manihot utilissima* Pohl, *M. Aipi* Pohl; **-nutmeg**, *Cryptocarya moschata* Nees & M.
Braziletto (W. I.), *Caesalpinia*, *Peltophorum*, *Sciadophyllum*, *Weinmannia*.
Brazoria Engelm. et Gray. Labiatae (VI). 2 Texas.
Brazzeia Baill. Tiliaceae. 2 W. trop. Afr.
Bread-fruit, *Artocarpus incisa* L; **Nicobar-**, *Pandanus*; **-nut**, *Brosimum*, (Barbados) *Artocarpus*.

Bredemeyera Willd. (incl. *Comesperma*). Polygal. 60 Austr., Tasm., S. Am., W.I. Seed hairy.
Bredia Blume. Melastom. (I). 4 Jap., Chi. A dimorphic.
Bremontiera DC. (*Indigofera* p.p. *EP.*). Legum. (III. 6). I Masc.
Breonia A. Rich. Rubi. (I. 6). 10 Madag., Mauritius.
Bretschneidera Hemsl. Hippocast. I China.
Brevi- (Lat. pref.), short-: **-lobus**, -lobed, &c. [Stds. petaloid.
Brevoortia Wood. Lili. (IV). I Calif. (P). A 3, anthers nearly sessile.
Breweria R. Br. (*Bonamia* Thou.) Convolv. (I. 2). 35 warm | ✻
Brexia Nor. ex Thou. Saxifrag. (V). I Madag., Seychelles. G iso-
Breynia Forst. Euphorb. (A. I. I). 25 Indomal. A (3). [merous.
Breynia (Plum.) L. = Capparis Tourn. (Capparid.).
Briar, *Rosa*; **-wood**, *Erica scoparia* L. (S. France).
Bricchettia Pax = Cocculus DC. p.p. (Menisp.). I Somaliland.
Brickellia Ell. Comp. (2). 80 warm Am., W.I. [2-loc.
Bridelia Willd. Euphorb. (A. I. 2). 60 palaeotrop. and subtrop. G.
Bridgesia Bert. ex Cambess. Sapind. (I). I Chile.
Bridgesia Hook. et Arn. = Ercilla A. Juss. (*BH.*) = Phytolacca L. p.p.
Brieya de Wild. Anon. (2). I Belgian Congo.
Brighamia A. Gray. Campanul. (III). I Sandwich Is. Arborescent.
Brillantaisia Beauv. Acanth. (IV. A). 35 trop. Afr., Madag. 2 post.
Brinjal, *Solanum Melongena* L. [sta. perfect (only case in fam.).
Briquetia Hochreutiner. Malv. (2). I Paraguay.
Bristle-fern, *Trichomanes*. [Testa membranous. (K) breaking irreg.
Britoa Berg. (*Campomanesia BH.*). Myrt. (I). 10 Braz. Ed. fr.
Brittenia Cogn. Melastom. (I). I Borneo. 5-merous. Sta. equal.
Brittonastrum Briq. (*Cedronella* p.p. *BH.*). Labiat. (VI. 3). 15 Mex. SW.U.S.
Brittonella Rusby (*Mionandra* p.p. *EP.*). Malpigh. (I). I Bolivia.
Briza L. Gramin. (10). 18 N. temp., S. Am. 2 Brit. (quake-grass).
Brizopyrum L. = Demazeria Dum.; **do.** Nees. Gramin. (10). 7 S. Afr.; **do.** J. Presl. = Distichlis Rafin. (Gramin.).
Brizula Hieron. (*Aphelia BH.*). Centrolepid. 5 S. Austr., Tasm.
Broad bean, *Vicia Faba* L.; **-leaf tree** (W.I.), *Terminalia latifolia* Sw.
Brocchinia Schult. f. Bromel. (3). 4 trop. S. Am. L. rosetted.
Broccoli, *Brassica oleracea* L., var.
Brochoneura Warb. (*Myristica* p.p.) Myristic. 5 Madag., trop. Afr.
Brockmania W. V. Fitzger. Malv. (4). I W. Austr.
Brodiaea Sm. Lili. (IV). 50 W. N. Am., temp. S. Am. Cymose umbels. Sta. with projecting appendages. (P). Cult. orn. fl.
Brombya F. Muell. (*Melicope* p.p. *EP.*). Rut. (I). I Austr.
Brome grass, *Bromus*: **false-**, *Brachypodium*. [ed. fr.
Bromelia Plum. ex L. Bromel. (4). 12 trop. Am., W.I. Some with
Bromeliaceae (*EP.*, *BH.*). Monocots. (Farinosae; Epigynae *BH.*; pp. vii, liv). 65/850, trop. Am., W.I. Many terrestrial (xero., on rocks, &c.), but most epiph. by virtue of seed distr. and xero. habit, and more char. of trop. Am. than the orchids. Stem usu. reduced, with rosette of fleshy l. channelled above, fitting closely at base, so that the whole pl. forms a kind of funnel, usu. full of water. In this are dead l., decaying animal matter, and other debris (certain Utricularias live only in these pitchers). There are many adv. r.

which fasten the plant to its support, but which do not aid in its nutrition, or very little. The bases of the l. are covered with scaly hairs by which the water in the pitcher is absorbed. Water is stored in the l., which consist largely of water-tissue. They have a thick cuticle and often bear scaly hairs that reduce transpiration. Some show a totally different habit to this, *e.g. Tillandsia usneoides* (*q.v.*). [See Schimper, *Epiph. Veg. Amerikas.*]

Infl. usu. out of the centre of the pitcher; bracts coloured. Fl. usu. ☿, reg., 3-merous. P 3 + 3 or (3) + (3), the outer whorl sepaloid, persistent, the inner petaloid; A 6, introrse, often epipet.; G (3), inf., semi-inf., or sup., 3-loc., with ∞ anatr. ov. on the axile plac. in each. Style 1, stigmas 3. Berry or caps.; seeds in the latter case very light, or winged. Embryo small, in mealy endosp.

Classification and chief genera (after Wittmack):

1. *Tillandsieae* (caps.; ov. sup.; l. entire; seed hairy): Tillandsia.
2. *Puyeae* (caps.; ov. sup.; l. thorny; usu. large stem): Puya, Dyckia.
3. *Pitcairnieae* (caps.; ov. semi-inf. or almost sup.; l. entire, or toothed at base, rarely at top); Pitcairnia.
4. *Bromelieae* (berry; ovary inf.; l. with thorny teeth): Bromelia, Ananas, Billbergia, Aechmea.

Bromheadia Lindl. Orchidaceae (II. 5). 6 Malaya.

Bromus Dill. ex L. Gramineae (10). 100 temp., and trop. Mts. 7 Brit. (brome-grass). Of little value as pasture.

Brongniartia H. B. et K. Leguminosae (III. 6). 30 trop. Am.

Brookea Benth. Scrophulariaceae (II. 4). 2 Borneo.

Brook-lime, *Veronica Beccabunga*; **-weed,** *Samolus Valerandi.*

Broom, *Cytisus* (*Sarothamnus*) *scoparius* Link.; **-bush** (W.I.), *Parthenium*; **-corn,** *Sorghum vulgare* Pers.; **butcher's-,** *Ruscus aculeatus* L.; **-rape,** *Orobanche*; **Spanish-,** *Spartium junceum* L.; **-root,** *Epicampes*; **-tree** (W.I.), *Baccharis*; **-weed** (W.I.), *Corchorus*, *Scoparia.*

Brosimopsis Sp. Moore. Moraceae (II). 1 Matto Grosso.

Brosimum Sw. Moraceae (II). 10 trop. and S. temp. Am. Infl. remarkable, a spherical pseudo-head composed of one ♀ fl. and many ♂ fls. The former is sunk into the centre of the common recept. and its style projects at the top, whilst the latter occupy the whole of the outer surface. Each ♂ fl. has a rudim. P. and one sta., whose versatile anther in dehiscing passes from a shape somewhat like ⫧ to one like ⫪. Achene embedded in the fleshy recept.

The achene of *B. Alicastrum* Sw. is the bread-nut (not to be confused with Artocarpus, the bread-fruit), which is cooked and eaten in the W.I., &c. [The bread-nut of Barbados is, however, a seeded var. of the bread-fruit.] *B. Galactodendron* D. Don is the cow-tree or milk-tree of Venezuela. The milky latex flows in considerable quantities, tastes very like ordinary milk, and is used for the same purposes. The wood of several sp. is useful (snake-wood).

Brossardia Boiss. Cruciferae (2). 2 Persia.

Brotera Willd. (*Cardopatium* Juss.). Compos. (11). 4 Medit.

Broughtonia R. Br. (*Epidendrum EP.*). Orchid. (II. 6). 2 W. Ind.

Brousemichea Bal. Gramineae (8). 1 Tonquin.
Broussa tea, *Vaccinium Arctostaphylos* L.
Broussaisia Gaudich. Saxifragaceae (III). 2 Sandwich Is.
Broussonetia L'Hérit. Moraceae (I). 3 E. As., Polynes. Dioecious; ♂ fls. in pseudo-racemes with explosive sta. like Urtica (unus. in M.); ♀ fls. in pseudo-heads. Multiple fr. (cf. Morus, &c.). A good fibre, used for paper, &c., is obtained from the inner bark of *B. papyrifera* Vent. (paper-mulberry, Japan); in Polynes. the natives make tapa or kapa cloth from it. The l. double upwards during the heat of the day.
Browallia L. Solanaceae (5). 6 trop. Am., W.I. A 4. Caps.
Brown Peru bark, *Cinchona officinalis* L
Brownea Jacq. (*Hermesias* Loefl.). Leguminosae (II. 3). 10 trop. Am., W. Ind. The young shoots emerge very rapidly from the bud and hang downwards on flaccid stalks, the leaflets at first rolled up, and later spread out, and pink or red speckled with white. After a time they turn green and stiffen up and spread out normally. *Cf.* Amherstia. *B. grandiceps* Jacq. and others have fine bunches of fl.
Browneopsis Huber. Leguminosae (II. 3). 2 Brazil.
Brownleea Harv. ex Lindl. Orchid. (II. 1). 8 S. and trop. Afr.
Brownlowia Roxb. Tiliaceae. 10 Indomal.
Brucea J. S. Mill. Simarubaceae. 6 paleotrop. Very astringent. The seeds of *B. sumatrana* Roxb. &c. are remedies in dysentery.
Bruckenthalia Reichb. Ericaceae (IV. 1). 1 S.E. Eur.
Bruea Gaudich. Moraceae (inc. sed.). 1 E. Ind.
Brugmansia Blume. Rafflesiaceae. 3 Malay Arch.
Brugmansia Pers. = Datura L. p.p. (Solan.).
Bruguiera Lam. Rhizophoraceae. 6 palaeotrop. One of the mangroves (*q.v.*). Like Rhizophora, but without the aerial r. from higher branches. The r. in the mud give off erect aerating branches, as in Sonneratia.
Bruinsmea Boerlage et Koorders. Styraceae. 2 Java, Celebes.
Brumalis (Lat.), winter.
Brunella Tourn. ex L. (*Prunella*). Labiat. (VI). 5 ± cosmop. 1 Brit.
Brunellia Ruiz et Pav. Brunelliaceae. 8 Peru to Mexico.
Brunelliaceae (*EP.*; *Simarubaceae* p.p. *BH.*). Dicots. (Archichl. Rosales). Only genus Brunellia. Trees and shrubs; l. opp. or in whorls. Fl. monochlam., unisex., 4-5-7-merous, diplost. Cpls. 5-2, each with 2 pend. ov. Caps. Endosp.
Brunfelsia Plum. ex L. Solan. (5). 25 trop. Am., W.I. Several cult. The fl. change colour as they grow older (*cf.* Ribes, Fumaria).
Brunia L. Bruniaceae. 5 S. Afr.
Bruniaceae (*EP. BH.*). Dicots. (Archichl. Rosales *EP. BH.*). 12 gen., 75 sp. S. Afr. Heath-like shrubs, with alt. exstip. l., and racemose infl. Fl. ☿ usu. reg., 5-merous, generally perig. Sta. in one whorl. Cpls. (3—2) each with 3 or 4 ov., or 1 with 1 ov. Caps. with 2, or nut with 1, seeds. Aril. Endosp. *Chief genera:* Brunia, Berzelia.
Brunneus (Lat.), brown.
Brunnichia Banks. Polygonaceae (III. 1). 3 N. Am., W. Afr.

Brunonia Sm. Brunoniaceae. 1 Austr., Tasm. Herb with rad. entire exstip. l. Blue fl. in heads, ☿. K (5), C (5), A 5, G 1-loc. 1-ovuled. Achene. Exalb. Pollen-cup like Goodeniaceae.

Brunoniaceae (*EP.*; *Goodeniaceae* p.p. *BH.*). Dicots. (Sympet. Campanulatae). Only genus Brunonia, *q.v.*

Brunsvigia Heist. Amaryllidaceae (1). 10 Afr. Cult. orn. fl.

Brush (N.S. Wales, Queensland), forest; **-box**, *Tristania.*

Brussels sprouts, *Brassica oleracea* L. var.

Bruxanelia Dennst. Rubiaceae (inc. sed.). 1 E. Ind.

Bruyere, *Erica scoparia* L.

Brya P. Br. Leguminosae (III. 7). 5 Cent. Am., W. Ind. *B. Ebenus* DC. yields the wood Jamaica or American ebony, cocus or cocos wood, the heart wood turning black with age (*cf.* Diospyros).

Bryanthus S. G. Gmel. Ericaceae (I. 3). 1 E. Siberia.

Brylkinia F. Schmidt. Gramineae (10). 1 Japan, Saghalien.

Bryo- (Gr. pref.), moss.

Bryocarpum Hook. f. et Thoms. Primulaceae. 1 Sikkim.

Bryodes Benth. Scrophulariaceae (II. 6). 1 Mauritius.

Bryomorphe Harv. Compositae (4). 1 Cape Colony.

Bryonia L. Cucurbitaceae (3). 10 Eur., As., Afr. *B. dioica* Jacq. (Brit., white bryony) marks the N. limit of the family in Eur. ♂ fl. larger. Honey secreted at the base of the P.

Bryonopsis Arn. Cucurbitaceae (3). 2 trop. Afr. and As.

Bryony, bastard (W.I.), *Cissus*; **black-**, *Tamus communis* L.; **white-**, *Bryonia dioica* Jacq.

Bryophyllum Salisb. Crassul. 20 warm. In the notches on the l. of *B. calycinum* Salisb. adv. buds develope, giving rise to new pl. In *B. proliferum* Bowie there are simple and cpd. l. on the same pl. K and C both gamophyllous. Cult. orn.

Bryopsis Reiche (*Lyallia*, *Reicheella* p.p.). Caryo. (I. 3). 1 Chili.

Buaze fibre, *Securidaca longipedunculata* Fres. (trop. Afr.).

Bubon L. = Seseli L. (Umbel.).

Bucco Wendl. = Agathosma Willd. (Rutac.).

Bucephalandra Schott. Araceae (V). 1 Borneo.

Bucephalon L. = Trophis P. Br. (Morac.).

Buceragenia Greenman. Acanthaceae (IV. B). 1 Mexico.

Buceras Hall. ex All. = Trigonella L. p.p. (Legum.).

Buchanania Spreng. Anacard. (1). 20 Indomal G 4—6, one fertile.

Buchenavia Eichl. (*Terminalia* p.p. *BH.*). Combret. 8 Brazil., W.I.

Buchenroedera Eckl. et Zeyh. Leguminosae (III. 3). 15 S. Afr.

Buchholzia Engl. Capparidaceae (II). 3 trop. Afr.

Buchingera Boiss. et Hohen. Cruciferae (4). 1 Persia.

Buchloe Engelm. (*Bulbilis* Rafin.). Gramineae (11). 1 (*B. dactyloides* Engelm.) the buffalo-grass of the western prairies of the U.S., a good fodder. It is a small creeping grass.

Buchnera L. Scrophulariaceae (III. 2). 60 trop. and subtrop.

Buchnerodendron Gürke. Flacourtiaceae (2). 6 trop. Afr.

Bucholzia Mart. = Telanthera R. Br. (*BH.*) = Alternanthera Forsk.

Buchu, *Barosma betulina* Bartl. et Wendl. f. and others.

Bucida L. (*Terminalia* p.p. *BH.*). Combret. 2 Cent. Am., W.I.

Buck-bean, *Menyanthes trifoliata* L.; **-eye** (Am.), *Aesculus ohioensis*

Michx.; **-'s horn plantain,** *Plantago Coronopus* L.; **-thorn,** *Rhamnus* (W.I.), *Rosa laevigata* Michx., **sea -thorn,** *Hippophaë rhamnoides* L.; **-wheat,** *Fagopyrum esculentum* Moench.

Buckinghamia F. Muell. Proteaceae (II). 1 Queensland.

Bucklandia R. Br. Hamamelidaceae. 1 Himal. to Java, *B. populnea* R. Br. The large stips. are folded against one another, enclosing and protecting the young axillary bud or infl. Fls. in heads in groups of 4, polyg. or monoec., sunk in the axis. The "calyx-tube" becomes visible as a ring after flowering. Wood valued.

Buckleya Torr. Santalaceae. 5 N. Am., China, Japan.

Bucquetia DC. Melastomaceae (I). 2 Colombia, Ecuador.

Bud, the much condensed undeveloped shoot end of the axis, composed of closely crowded young l. with very short internodes, well seen in Brussels sprouts, Cabbage, Lettuce, *Acer*, *Aesculus*, *Hippuris*, *Pinus*, *Syringa*, *Ulmus*; usu. axillary or terminal; **abortion,** *Syringa*; **accessory,** extra buds in an axil, which may be collateral (side by side), *Araceae*, *Crataegus*, *Muscari*, *Quercus*, or serial (one above another), *Aristolochia*, *Chrysophyllum*, *Colletia*, *Fraxinus*, *Fuchsia*, *Gleditschia*, *Goethea*, *Gymnocladus*, *Juglandaceae*, *Lonicera*, *Menispermaceae*, *Oleaceae*, *Rhamnaceae*, *Sambucus*, *Theophrasta*; **adventitious,** arising elsewhere than normally in an axil, *Begonia*, *Bryophyllum*, *Cardamine*, *Cystopteris*, *Linaria*, *Ophioglossum*, *Pteris*, *Pyrola*; **dormant,** branch buds which do not develope at once; **extra-axillary,** *Fagus*, *Monstera*, *Juglans*; **-scales,** the altered l. which protect the (usu. winter) bud, *Acer*, *Aesculus*, *Betula*, &c.; **sub-petiolar-,** *Cladrastis*, *Gleditschia*, *Platanus*, *Rhus*, *Robinia*, *Wormia*; **winter-,** *Acer*, *Aesculus*, *Betula*, *Hottonia*, *Hydrocharis*, *Juglandaceae*, *Myriophyllum*, *Quercus*, *Rhododendron*, *Sophora*, *Utricularia*, *Viburnum*. And *cf.* Aestivation, Flower bud, Vegetative Repr., Vernation, and next art. **-protection** against cold, heat, radiation, &c. is obtained in many ways; by stipules in *Artocarpus*, *Bucklandia*, *Cosmibuena*, *Cunonia*, *Dipterocarpus*, *Ficus*, *Magnoliaceae*; the young l. are pendulous in *Aesculus*, *Amherstia*, *Bauhinia*, *Brownea*, *Cinnamomum*, *Dryobalanops*, *Maniltoa*, *Saraca*, *Theobroma*; the young l. red in *Cinnamomum*, *Dryobalanops*, *Haematoxylon*, *Mesua*, &c.; the buds sub-petiolar in *Cladrastis*, *Gleditschia*, *Platanus*, *Rhus*, *Robinia*, *Wormia*; other ways occur in *Iochroma*, *Manihot*, *Philadelphus*, *Pothos*, *Spathodea*, *Tabernaemontana*, &c.

Buda Adans. = Spergularia Presl (Caryoph.).

Buddleia Houst. Loganiaceae. 90 trop. and subtrop. Sometimes placed in Scrophul., but possesses stips. (sometimes reduced to interpetiolar lines).

Buena Pohl = Cosmibuena Ruiz et Pav. and Cascarilla Wedd.

Buergersiochloa Pilger. Gramineae (5). 1 New Guinea.

Buettneria Loefl. Sterculiaceae. 60 trop.

Buffalo-berry, *Shepherdia argentea* Nutt.; **-wood,** *Burchellia*.

Bufonia Sauv. ex L. (*Buffonia*). Caryophyllaceae (I. 1). 20 Medit., Eur. Not unlike *Juncus bufonius* in habit. 4-merous.

Buforrestia C. B. Clarke. Commelinaceae. 5 trop. W. Afr.

Bugbane, *Cimicifuga*.

Bugle, *Ajuga reptans* L.

Bugloss, *Lycopsis arvensis* L.; **viper's-**, *Echium vulgare* L.

Buglossum (Tourn.) Adans. = Anchusa L. p.p. (Borag.).

Bugula Tourn. ex Mill. = Ajuga L. p.p. (Labiat.).

Bulb, a modified stem, bearing a ± spherical mass of swollen l. closely folded over one another, *Allium*, *Galanthus*, *Liliaceae*, *Lilium*, *Oxalis*. Common in dry climates.

Bulbil, a little bulb, usu. in place of a fl. in the infl., *Agave*, *Allium*, *Cardamine*, *Gagea*, *Globba*, *Lilium*, *Lycopodium*, *Oxalis*, *Remusatia*, *Saxifraga*, *Scilla*, and *cf.* Vegetative Repr.

Bulbilis Rafin. = Buchloe Engelm. (Gram.).

Bulbine L. Liliaceae (III). 30 Afr., E. Austr.

Bulbinella Kunth. Liliaceae (III). 15 S. Afr., N.Z., &c.

Bulbinopsis Borzi. Liliaceae (III). 2 Austr.

Bulbocodium L. Liliaceae (I). 1 Eur.

Bulbophyllum Thou. Orchidaceae (II. 16). 450 trop., and S. temp. Epiph. with great reduction of l. The l. are often mere scales and assim. is performed by the tubers. In *B. minutissimum* F. Muell., &c., the tubers are hollow with stomata on inner surface (*cf.* l. of Empetrum). For the fl. see Darwin's *Orchids*, p. 137. Cult. orn. fl.

Bulbostylis DC. = Brickellia Ell. (Comp.).

Bulbostylis Kunth (*Fimbristylis* p.p.). Cyper. (I). 60 S. Am., Afr.

Bull apple tree (W.I.), *Sapota rugosa* Griseb.; **-hoof** (W.I.), *Passiflora Murucuja* L.; **-ock's heart**, *Anona reticulata* L.; **-pine**, *Pinus*; **-'s horn thorn**, *Acacia sphaerocephala*.

Bullace, *Prunus insititia* L.

Bullate, puckered.

Bulleyia Schlechter. Orchidaceae (II. 3). 1 Yunnan.

Bulliarda DC. = Tillaea Michx. (*BH.*) = Crassula L. p.p.

Bully-tree (W.I.), *Dipholis*, *Myrsine*, *Sapota*, &c.

Bulnesia C. Gay. Zygophyll. 6 Argentina, Chili. Timber.

Bulrush, *Typha*, *Scirpus*; **-millet**, *Pennisetum typhoideum*.

Bumelia Sw. Sapotaceae (I). 35 warm Am., W.I. Exalb.

Bunch-berry (Am.), *Cornus canadensis* L.

Bunchosia Rich. ex Juss. Malpighiaceae (II). 40 trop. Am., W.I.

Bungea C. A. Mey. Scrophulariaceae (III. 3). 3 As.

Bunias (Tourn.) L. Cruciferae (4). 5 Medit., As.

Bunioseris Jord. (*Lactuca* p.p.). Compositae (13). 2 France.

Buniotrinia Stapf. et Wettst. Umbelliferae (III. 5). 1 Persia.

Bunium L. (*Carum* L. p.p. *BH.*). Umbell. (III. 5). 30 N. palaeotemp.

Bunophila Willd. = Machaonia Humb. et Bonpl. (Rub.).

Bunya-bunya pine, *Araucaria Bidwillii* Hook.

Buphane Herb. Amaryllidaceae (I). 3 S. and trop. Afr. Cult. orn. fl.

Buphthalmum L. Compositae (4). 4 Eur., As. minor. *B. salicifolium* L. is a char. pl. of the chalky Alps.

Bupleurum (Tourn.) L. Umbelliferae (III. 5). 100 Eur., As., Afr., N. Am. 4 Brit. (buplever or hare's ear). *B. rotundifolium* L. has perfoliate l., whence the name throw-wax (thorow-wax) by which it is known. All sp. have entire l., unusu. in this family.

Buplever, *Bupleurum*.

Buprestis Spreng. = Bupleurum Tourn. (Umbel.).

Bur or **burr**, a hooked fr.; **-bark** (W.I.), *Triumfetta*; **Bathurst** or **Noogoora**, *Xanthium*; **-dock**, *Arctium Lappa* L.; **-grass** (Am.), *Cenchrus*; **-marigold**, *Bidens*; **-reed** (Am.), *Sparganium*; **-weed**, *Medicago*, *Sparganium*.

Buraeavia Baill. Euphorbiaceae (A. I. 1). 2 New Caled.

Burasaia Thou. Menispermaceae. 4 Madag.

Burbidgea Hook. f. Zingiberaceae (I). 3 Borneo. C-segments large, lat. stds. absent. The small labellum and petaloid sta. stand up in the centre of the fl.

Burchardia R. Br. (*Reya* O. Ktze.). Liliaceae (I). 2 Austr., Tasm.

Burchellia R. Br. Rubiaceae (I. 8). 1 S. Afr. Buffalo wood, very hard.

Burdachia Mart. Malpighiaceae (II). 2 N. Brazil.

Bureavella Pierre. Sapotaceae (II). 1 Indomal.

Burkea Benth. Leguminosae (II. 1). 2 W. and S. Afr.

Burlingtonia Lindl. = Rodriguezia Ruiz et Pav. (Orch.).

Burmannia L. Burmanniaceae. 40 trop. and subtrop.

Burmanniaceae (*EP.*, *BH.*). Monocots. (Microspermae). 5 gen., 60 sp., trop. forest herbs, chiefly 'colourless' saprophytes. P (3 + 3), A 6 or 3, $\overline{G}$ (3), with parietal plac., or 3-loc. Caps. Seeds ∞. Endosp. *Chief genera:* Burmannia, Thismia. (See *Nat. Pfl.*, and *Ann. of Bot.* 1895.)

Burmeistera Karst. et Triana. Campanulac. (III). 10 trop. S. Am.

Burnatastrum Briq. Labiatae (VII). 3 S. Afr., Madag.

Burnatia M. Mich. Alismaceae. 1 trop. Afr.

Burnet, *Poterium*; **-saxifrage**, *Pimpinella Saxifraga* L.

Burnettia Lindl. Orchidaceae (II. 2). 1 Tasmania.

Burning bush (Am.), *Euonymus atropurpureus* Jacq.

Burn-nose (W.I.), *Daphnopsis*.

Burragea Donn. Smith et Rose (*Gaura* p.p.). Onagr. (2). 2 Lower Calif.

Burrielia DC. Compositae (6). 1 Calif.

Bursa Weber in Wigg. = Capsella Medic. (Crucif.).

Bursaria Cav. Pittosporaceae. 3 Austr. Seeds few in fr.

Bursera 'Jacq.' ex L. Burseraceae. 45 trop. Am. *B. gummifera* L. (birch tree, gommier, turpentine tree) furnishes the balsam resin known as American elemi, chibou, cachibou, or gomart.

Burseraceae (*EP.*, *BH.*). Dicots. (Archichl. Geraniales *EP.*, *BH.*). 13 gen., 350 sp., trop. Shrubs and trees with alt., usu. cpd., dotted l. Balsams and resins occur, in lysigenous or schizogenous passages. Fls. small, generally unisex., with disc like Rutaceae, 5- or 4-merous, obdiplost. when both whorls of sta. are present. Cpls. (5—3), ov. usu. 2 in each. Ovary multiloc. with one style. Drupe or caps. Seed exalb. Many of the order are useful on account of their resins, &c. *Chief genera:* Commiphora, Boswellia, Bursera, Canarium.

Burtonia R. Br. Leguminosae (III. 2). 10 Austr.

Buseria Th. Dur. (*Leiochilus EP.*). Rubiaceae (II. 4). 1 Madag.

Bush (Austr.), scrub, *cf.* Acacia; **-clover**, Lespedeza.

Bush-wood, a forest in which the shrubs are so abundant as to keep the crowns of the trees from touching.

Bushiola Nieuwland (*Kochia* p.p.). Chenopod. (A). 1 N. Am.
Bussea Harms. Leguminosae (II. 7). 1 E. trop. Afr.
Bustelma Fourn. Asclepiadaceae (II. 1). 1 Brazil.
Butayea Wildem. (*Pseudoblepharis EP.*). Acanth. (IV. B). 1 Congo.
Butcher's broom, *Ruscus aculeatus* L.
Butea Koen. ex Roxb. Leguminosae (III. 10). 4 Ind., China. *B. frondosa* Roxb. (dhak or palas tree, or bastard teak), one of the handsomest of flg. trees. A red juice flows from incisions in the bark; when dried it is known as Bengal kino and used as an astringent. The fls. yield a fugitive orange-red dye. The tree also yields lac (see *Ficus*), and is very important for lac cult.
Butomaceae (*EP.*; *Alismaceae* p.p. *BH.*). Monocots. (Helobieae). 4 gen., 7 sp., trop. and temp. Water and marsh herbs with l. of various types. Infl. usu. a cymose umbel. Flr. ☿, reg., 2- or 3-merous, hypog. P 6, in two whorls, the outer sepaloid, the inner petaloid (exc. Butomus). Sta. 9 – ∞, with introrse anthers. Cpls. 6 – ∞, apocp., with ∞ anatr. ov. scattered over their inner walls (*cf.* Nymphaea), except on midrib and edges. Follicles; seed ex-alb.; embryo straight or horse-shoe shaped. *Chief genera:* Butomus, Hydrocleis.
Butomopsis Kunth (*Tenagocharis EP.*). Butomaceae. 1 Austr.
Butomus L. Butom. 1 temp. As., Eur. (incl. Brit.), *B. umbellatus* L. (flowering rush). Infl. a term. fl. surrounded by 3 bostryx-cymes.
Butonica Lam. = Barringtonia Forst. p.p. (Lecyth.).
Butter, *cf.* oils; **-bean,** *Phaseolus vulgaris* L.; **-bur,** *Petasites officinalis* Moench.; **-and eggs** (Am.), *Linaria*; **-cup,** *Ranunculus*; **-nut,** *Caryocar*, (Am.) *Juglans*; **shea-,** *Butyrospermum*; **-tree,** *Pentadesma*, *Bassia*; **-wort,** *Pinguicula*.
Butterfly flowers (class F), *Cuphea*, *Daphne*, *Eupatorium*, *Gentiana*. *Lonicera*, *Lychnis*, *Onagraceae*, *Rubiaceae*, &c.; **-orchis,** *Habenaria*, *Oncidium*.
Button-bush (Am.), *Cephalanthus*; **-tree,** (W.I.), *Conocarpus*; **-weed** (W.I.), *Spermacoce*, *Borreria*; **-wood,** *Platanus occidentalis*.
Buttonia MacKen. Scrophulariaceae (III. 2). 2 S. and trop. Afr.
Butua Eichl. = Abuta Aubl. p.p. (Menisperm.).
Butyrospermum Kotschy. Sapotaceae (I). 2 trop. Afr. The oily seeds of *B. Parkii* Kotschy when pressed yield shea butter.
Buxaceae (*EP.*; *Euphorbiaceae* p.p. *BH.*). Dicots. (Archichl. Sapindales). 6 gen., 30 sp. temp. and trop. Evergreen shrubs with exstip. leathery l., and no latex. Fls. in heads or spikes, unisex., reg., apet. or naked. Sta. 4—∞. $\underline{G}$ usu. (3), 3-loc., with 3 styles which are persistent on the fr. Ov. 2—1 in each loc., pend., anat., with dorsal raphe. Loculic. caps., or drupe. Seed with caruncle or none. Endosp. *Chief genera:* Buxus, Pachysandra.
Buxanthus Van Tieghem (*Buxus* p.p.). Buxaceae. 2 trop. Afr.
Buxella Van Tieghem (*Buxus* p.p.). Buxaceae. 2 S. Afr., Madag.
Buxus L. Buxaceae. 25 palaeotemp., W.I. *B. Sempervirens* L. (box) often cult. Fls. in heads, a term. ♀ flr. surrounded by a number of ♂ fls. The fr. dehisces explosively, the inner layer of the pericarp separating from the outer and shooting out the seeds by folding into

a U-shape (*cf.* Viola). The wood of box (*q.v.*) is exceedingly firm and close-grained, and is largely used in turning, wood-engraving, &c.

Byblis Salisb. Lentibulariaceae (usually in Droseraceae, but *cf.* Lang in *Flora* 88, p. 179). 2 Austr. Insectivorous undershrubs, with stalked and sessile glands like Pinguicula.

Byronia Endl. (*Ilex* p.p.). Aquifol. 3 Austr., Polynesia.

Byrsa Nor. Inc. sed. Nomen.

Byrsanthus Guillem. Flacourt. (9) (Samyd. *BH.*). 2 W. Afr.

Byrsocarpus Schumach. et Thonn. Connar. 5 trop. Afr., Madag.

Byrsonima Rich. ex Juss. Malpighiaceae (II). 120 Cent. and S. Am., W. Ind. Fr. a drupe, ed. The bark of some sp. is used in tanning.

Byrsophyllum Hook. f. Rubiaceae (I. 8). 2 India, Ceylon.

Bystropogon L'Hérit. Labiatae (VI). 20 Andes, Canary Is.

Bythophyton Hook. f. Scroph. (II. 6). 1 Indomal. Submerged.

Caatinga forests (Brazil), forests in which the l. fall in dry season.

Cabbage, *Brassica oleracea* L.; **-bark tree** (W.I.), *Andira inermis* H. B. et K.; **Kerguelen-,** *Pringlea antiscorbutica* R. Br.; **-palm,** *Oreodoxa oleracea* Mart., *Euterpe*, *Sabal*, &c.; **-rose,** *Rosa centifolia* L.; **skunk-,** *Symplocarpus foetidus* Nutt.; **-tree,** *Sabal* (W.I.), *Oreodoxa*, *Andira*.

Cabomba Aubl. Nymphaeaceae (II). 4 warm Am. Water pl. with peltate floating l. and much-divided submerged l. (*cf.* Ranunculus, Trapa). Fl. 3-merous (P 3 + 3, A 3—6, G. usu. 3) and fully apocp. (thus forming a link to the other Ranales, with which the gynaeceum of most N. does not agree). Closed follicles. No aril; endo- and peri-sperm. Ovules sometimes attached to the cpl. *midrib*.

Cabralea A. Juss. Meliaceae (III). 35 trop. Am.

Cacabus Bernh. Solanaceae (2). 4 W. trop. S. Am.

Cacalia L. (*Senecio* p.p. *Bil.*). Compositae (8). 40 N.E. As., Am.

Cacaliopsis A. Gray. Compositae (8). 1 Pac. U.S.

Cacao, *Theobroma*; **do.** Tourn. ex Mill. = Theobroma L.

Cacara Thou. = Pachyrhizus Rich. p.p. (Legum.).

Caccinia Savi. Boraginaceae (IV. 1). 7 W. and Cent. As.

Cachibou, *Bursera gummifera* L.

Cachrys L. Umbelliferae (III. 4). 8 Medit., W. and Cent. As.

Cacoon (W.I.), *Entada scandens* Benth.

Cacosmia H. B. et K. Compositae (6). 1 Peru.

Cacoucia Aubl. (*Combretum* p.p. *EP.*). Combret. 5 W. trop. Afr.

Cactaceae (*EP.*, *BH.*). Dicots. (Archichl. Opuntiales; Ficoidales *BH.*). 25 gen., 1500 sp., chiefly localised in the dry regions of trop. Am., but spreading to a distance N. and S. (*Opuntia missouriensis* as far as 59° N.), and far up the mountains (to 12,000 ft. and even higher). Even in the damp forest regions some sp. appear as epiphytes. The only representative of the order in the Old World is Rhipsalis, found in Afr., Mauritius, &c., but several sp. of Opuntia, &c. are now nat. in S. Afr., Austr., &c. and becoming troublesome.

Xero. of the most pronounced type, exhibiting reduction of the transpiring surface, and also storage of water, often in great quantity. The veg. organs show great var. of type; the classification is perhaps better based upon them than upon the repr. organs. R. generally long and well-developed (in cultivation liable to decay). Stem fleshy, of various shapes, rarely bearing green l., and usu. provided with sharp barbed thorns, which give protection against animals. We may consider briefly some of the more important types of shoot found in C. (refer to genera for further details). The nearest approach to the ordinary plant-type is perhaps Pereskia, which has large green l., somewhat fleshy, in whose axils are groups of thorns mixed with hairs; the space occupied by these is termed the *areole*. About the morphology of the spines there has been much dispute; most authors regard them as repres. the l. of the axillary shoot, whose stem is undeveloped, but there is also good evidence in favour of the view that they are "emergences." In some gen. they are provided with barbs. The next stage is found in Opuntia, where the stem has taken over the water-storing and assim. functions, but still bears l.; in some sp. these aid the stem functions throughout life, but in most they fall off very early, and the stem is usually flattened to expose more surface to air and light. Then we come to Leuchtenbergia, which has an aloe-like habit with the areoles on the tips of the apparent l.; the fl. arises either in the axil of the "leaf" or on the areole. Development shows that the apparent l. is really a cpd. structure. The bud stands, not exactly in the axil, but on the base of the l., and the two grow out together to form a *leaf-cushion* or *mammilla*, at the outer end of which is the growing point and the rest of the l. itself; the latter is represented by a small scale (often microscopic) and the former gives rise to the thorns, &c. on the areole. The same phenomenon is seen in Mammillaria, Cereus sp., &c. In some cases the growing point divides, during the growth of the mammilla, into two, one on the tip, the other in the axil, of the cushion. The latter gives rise to the fl. In Cereus, Echinocactus, &c. the stem is ± cylindrical, bearing ribs on which are the areoles at regular intervals; the rib is formed by the "fusion" of mammillae, *i.e.* by the growth of the tissue under them during their development (*cf.* formation of sympetalous corolla). In Phyllocactus, Epiphyllum, and sp. of Rhipsalis some or all of the shoots exhibit a flattened leafy form with areoles in notches on their edges. This form appears to be derived from the preceding by abortion of some of the ridges, and reversions are often seen (they appear if access of light be prevented). Lastly, other sp. of Rhipsalis show perfectly cylindrical stems.

The bulk of the internal tissue consists of parenchyma in which water is stored; the cell-sap is commonly mucilaginous, thus further obstructing evaporation. The cuticle is thick, and the ridges of the stem are usu. occupied by mechanical tissue, whilst the stomata are in the furrows. Everything thus goes to check transpiration to the utmost extent; it is very difficult to dry a cactus for the herbarium, and its vitality is very great. Its growth is slow, but sp. of Cereus, &c. reach a great size. Veg. repr. is frequent in the mammillate forms, and occurs to some extent in others. In garden practice, cacti are often multiplied by cuttings, for a piece cut off and stuck into the soil will usually grow. Grafting is also largely resorted to.

Fls. usu. solitary (exc. Pereskia), borne upon or near the areoles or in the axils of mammillae, large, brightly coloured, ☿, reg. or ·|·. P (∞), showing gradual transition from sepaloid to petaloid l., spirally arranged, often up the side of the ovary (cf. Nymphaea). Sta. ∞, epipet. $\overline{G}$ (4 – ∞), uniloc. with parietal plac. and ∞ anatr. ov.; style simple. Berry, the flesh derived from the funicles. Endosp. or none.

The fr. of many sp. is edible (*e.g.* Opuntia, &c.). Several are used in making hedges. Cochineal is cultivated on Nopalea, Opuntia, &c.

Classification and chief genera (after K. Schumann):

I. *PERESKIOIDEAE* (habit of ordinary pl., with flat l. and panicles; no barbed thorns): Pereskia (only genus).

II. *OPUNTIOIDEAE* (succulents with round or flat leaf-like joints; l. cylindrical, usu. falling very early; barbed thorns; fl. rotate): Opuntia, Nopalea (only genera).

III. *CEREOIDEAE* (succulents; l. reduced to scales, often very minute; no barbed thorns):

1. *Echinocacteae* (fl. funnel- or salver-shaped, in or near the areole): Cereus, Phyllocactus, Epiphyllum, Echinocactus, Melocactus, Leuchtenbergia.
2. *Mammillarieae* (do., but in axil of mammilla): Mammillaria, Pelecyphora.
3. *Rhipsalideae* (fl. rotate): Rhipsalis.

Cf. genera. Also Britton and Rose, *Cactaceae*, *Nat. Pfl.*, 2nd ed., Goebel, *Pflanzenb. Sch.* and in *Flora* 1895, Ganong in *Ann. Bot.* 1898, Schumann in *Nat. Pfl.* and *Gesammtbeschreibung der Kakteen*, 1897–99, and Vöchting in *Pringsh. Jahrb.* 1894. *Cf.* also Euphorbia and Stapelia.

Cacteae (*BH.*) = Cactaceae.

Cactiflorae (Warming), the 7th order of Choripetalae.

Cactus L. = Cactaceae, esp. Mammillaria.

Cactus, night-flowering, *Cereus*; **old man-,** *Cereus senilis*.

Cadaba Forsk. Capparidaceae (II). 20 palaeotrop. Disc prolonged post. into a tube; both androphore and gynophore present.

Cadalvena Fenzl. Zingiberaceae (II). 1 trop. Afr.

Cadellia F. Muell. Simarubaceae. 2 subtrop. Austr.

Cadetia Gaudich. = Dendrobium Sw. (Orchid).

Cadia Forsk. Leguminosae (III. 1). 5 E. Afr., Madag., Arabia. Fl. almost reg. with free sta.

Cadiscus E. Mey. Compositae (6). 1 S.W. Cape Colony. Water pl.

Cadjans, *Cocos*, *Nipa*, &c.

Caducous, dropping early.

Caecum, a prolongation of the embryo-sac, *Casuarina*, &c.

Caelestina Cass. = Ageratum L. (Compos.).

Caeruleus (Lat.), pale sky blue.

Caesalpinia L. Leguminosae (II. 7). 60 trop. and subtrop., often hook climbers. The pods of *C. bonducella* Fleming (nickar bean) are brought to Eur. by the Gulf Stream. Those of *C. coriaria* Willd. (divi-divi) are imported from Venezuela and W.I. for tanning. *C. sappan* L. (Indomal., cult.) and several Brazilian sp. yield a red dye from the wood (sappan, Brazil, or peach wood). *C. pulcherrima* Sw. (peacock fl., Barbados pride) is cult. orn. fl.

Caesarea Cambess. = Viviania Cav. p.p. (Geran.).

Caesia R. Br. Liliaceae (III). 10 Austr., S. Afr.

Caesius (Lat.), lavender-coloured, or pale green and grey.
Caespitose, in tufts.
Caesulia Roxb. Compositae (4). 1 N.E. India.
Caffein, *Coffea*, *Cola*, *Ilex*.
Cafta, *Catha edulis* Forsk.
Caiophora Presl (*Blumenbachia* p.p. *BH.*). Loasaceae. 50 S. Am.
Cajanus DC. Legum. (III. 10). 1 trop. Afr., As., *C. indicus* Spreng. (dhal, pigeon pea, or Congo pea) cult. in India, &c. for its ed. seeds.
Cajeput oil, *Melaleuca Leucadendron* L.
Cakile L. Cruciferae (2). 4 ✻. *C. maritima* Scop. (sea-rocket, Brit.) has fleshy leaves, and long tap root.
Calabar bean, *Physostigma venenosum* Balf.
Calabash, *Crescentia*; **-cucumber**, *Lagenaria*; **-nutmeg** (W. Afr.), *Monodora grandiflora* Benth., (W.I.) *M. myristica* Dun.; **sweet-**, *Passiflora maliformis* L.
Calacanthus T. Anders. Acanthaceae (IV. A). 1 Indomal.
Caladenia R. Br. Orchidaceae (II. 2). 70 Austr., N.Z. Labellum in some irritable (*cf.* Pterostylis; Darwin, *Orchids*, p. 90).
Caladiopsis Engl. Araceae (VI). 1 Colombia.
Caladium Vent. Araceae (VI). 15 trop. S. Am. Cult. orn. l. (∞ vars.).
Calais DC. = Microseris D. Don, p.p. (Compos.).
Calalu (W.I.), *Phytolacca*.
Calamagrostis Adans. (incl. *Deyeuxia* Beauv. *EP.*). Gramineae (8). 200 temp., 3 Brit.
Calamander, *Diospyros quaesita* Thw.
Calamiferous, with hollow stem.
Calamint, *Calamintha*.
Calamintha (Tourn.) Lam. (*Satureia* p.p. *EP.*). Labiatae (VI). 60 N. temp., trop. Mts.; 3 Brit. (basil, calamint). Often gynodioec.
Calamochloa Fourn. Gramineae (10). 1 Mexico.
Calamovilfa Hack. (*Ammophila* p.p. *BH.*). Gramineae (8). 2 N. Am.
Calamus L. Palmae (III). 325 palaeotrop., mostly leaf-climbers with thin reedy stems. In some there are hooks on the back of the mid-rib, but the more common type of l. is one in which the pinnae at the outer end are repres. by stout spines pointing backwards (*cf.* Desmoncus). The l. shoots almost vertically out of the bud up among the surrounding veg., and the hooks take hold. The stem often grows to immense lengths (500—600 ft.); the plants are troublesome in trop. forests because the hooks catch. The stripped stems (rattan canes *q.v.*), are largely used for making chair bottoms, baskets, cables, &c.
Calanda K. Schum. Rubiaceae (II. 1). 3 Afr., Austr.
Calandrinia H. B. et K. Portulacaceae. 80 sp. Vancouver to Chili, Austr. The fls. close very quickly in absence of sunlight.
Calandriniopsis Franz. (*Calandrinia* p.p.). Portul. 4 Chili.
Calanthe R. Br. Orchidaceae (II. 9). 120 warm. 8 pollinia, which, if re-introduced, strike the sides of rostellum and diverge into stigmas.
Calanthidium Pfitz. Orchidaceae (II. 9). 1 Burma. Long spur.
Calantica Jaub. ex Tul. Flac. (9) (Samyd. *BH.*) 5 Madag., E. Afr.
Calathea G. F. W. Mey. Marantaceae. 130 trop. Am., W.I. Std. β

(see fam.) present in most. The tubers of *C. Allouia* Lindl. (topee tampo) are eaten like potatoes in the W.I.
Calathodes Hook. f. et Thoms. (*Trollius* p.p. *EP.*). Ranunc. (2). 1 Himal.
Calathostelma Fourn. Asclepiadaceae (II. 1). 1 Brazil.
Calcaratus (Lat.), spurred.
Calceolaria L. Scrophulariaceae (II. 1). 225 S. Am., Mexico, N. Z. Many forms and hybrids cult. orn. fl.
Calceolate, slipper-shaped.
Calcicolous, living on chalk, **-philous**, chalk-loving.
Calcitrapa Hall. = Centaurea L. p.p. (Comp.).
Caldasia Lag. = Oreomyrrhis Endl. (Umbell.).
Caldcluvia D. Don. Cunoniaceae. 1 Chili.
Caldesia Parl. (*Alisma* L. *BH.*). Alismaceae. 3 palaeotrop.
Calea L. Compositae (5). 80 Am., esp. campos.
Caleana R. Br. Orchidaceae (II. 2). 4 temp. Austr.
Calectasia R. Br. Liliaceae (III). 1 S. and W. Austr.
Calendula L. Compositae (9). 15 Medit., *C. officinalis* L. (marigold) cult. A "hen-and-chickens" var. occurs, in which each principal head is surrounded by others, springing from the axils of the invol. br. Disc florets ♂, ray florets ♀. Three kinds of fr. occur.
Caleopsis Fedde (*Goldmania* Greenman). Compos. (5). 1 Mex.
Calepina Adans. Cruciferae (2). 1 Eur., Medit.
Calesiam Adans. (*Lannea* A. Rich.; *Odina BH.*). Anacard. (2). 15 trop. Afr. and As.
Caletia Baill. = Micrantheum Desf. (Euphorb.).
Calibanus Rose (*Dasylirion* p.p.). Liliaceae (VI). 1 Mex., a xero. with remarkable tuber and a few grass-like l.
Calibrachoa Cerv. Solanaceae (Inc. sed.). 1 Mex.
Calico bush (Am.), *Kalmia latifolia* L.
Calicorema Hook. f. (*Sericocoma* Fenzl.). Amarant. (2). 1 S. Afr.
California bluebell, *Nemophila*; **-hyacinth**, *Brodiaea*; **-lilac**, *Ceanothus*; **-nutmeg**, *Torreya*; **-poppy**, *Eschscholtzia*, *Platystemon*; **-redwood**, *Sequoia*.
Calimeris Nees = Aster Tourn. p.p. (Compos.).
Caliphruria Herb. Amaryllidaceae (I). 4 S. Am. Sta. with stipular appendages (see fam.). Cult. orn. fl.
Calisaya bark, *Cinchona Calisaya* Wedd.
Calla L. Araceae (III). 1 N. temp. and sub-arct., *C. palustris* L. Fls. ☿ with P, borne once in two years. Aquatic. *C. aethiopica* L. = Zantedeschia.
Callaeolepis Karst. (*Fimbristemma BH.*). Asclep. (II. 4). 1 C. Am.
Callaeum Small (*Jubelina* p.p.). Malpigh. (I). 1 Nicaragua
Calli- (Gr. pref.), beautiful.
Calliandra Benth. Leguminosae (I. 1). 100 warm Am., As. Cult. orn. flg. shrubs. (C).
Callianthemum C. A. Mey. Ranunculaceae (2). 5 Mts. of Eur. and Cent. As. See *Bot. Mag.* t. 7603, 1898.
Calliature wood, *Pterocarpus santalinus* L. f.
Callicarpa L. Verbenaceae (4). 40 trop. and subtrop.
Callichilia Stapf. (*Tabernaemontana* p.p.). Apocyn. (I. 3). 6 trop. Afr.

Callichlamys Miq. Bignoniaceae (1). 4 warm S. Am.
Callichroa Fisch. et Mey. = Layia Hook. et Arn. p.p. (Comp.).
Callicoma Andr. Cunoniaceae. 1 E. Austr. C o.
Calligonum L. Polygonaceae (II. 1). 20 N. Afr., W. As., S. Eur.
Callilepis DC. Compositae (4). 3 S. Afr.
Callionia Greene (*Potentilla* p.p.). Rosaceae (III. 2). 1 N. Am.
Calliopsis Reichb. = Coreopsis L. p.p. (Compos.).
Callipeltis Stev. Rubiaceae (II. 11). 3 Egypt to Persia.
Calliprora Lindl. = Brodiaea Sm. p.p. (Lili.).
Callipsyche Herb. (*Eucrosia* Ker-Gawl. *EP.*). Amaryllidaceae (1). 3 Ecuador, Peru. Cult. orn. fl.
Callirhoe Nutt. (*Malva* p.p. *EP.*). Malvaceae (II). 8 N. Am.
Callisia L. in Loefl. Commelinaceae. 4 trop. Am.
Callista D. Don = Erica Tourn. p.p. (Eric.).
Callistachys Vent. (*Oxylobium* Andr. *BH.*). Legum. (III. 2). 27 Austr.
Callistemma Boiss. (*Scabiosa* p.p. *BH.*). Dipsaceae. 1 E. Medit.
Callistemon R. Br. Myrtaceae (II. 1). 12 Austr., often cult. (bottle-brushes). The axis of the infl. grows on beyond the fl. and continues to produce l. (*cf.* Eucomis). Sta. conspicuous, as is often the case in the dry climate of Austr. (*cf.* Acacia). Cult. orn. flg. shrubs.
Callistephus Cass. Compositae (3). 1 Chi., Jap., *C. hortensis* Cass., cult. under the name China aster. *Bot. Mag.*, 1898, t. 7616.
Callisteris Greene (*Gilia*, *Cantua*, &c. p.p.) Polem. 10 N. Am.
Callisthene Mart. Vochysiaceae. 10 S. Am.
Callithamna Herb. = Stenomesson Herb. p.p. (Amaryll.).
Callitrichaceae (*EP.*; *Haloragidaceae* p.p. *BH.*). Dicots. (Archichl. Geraniales). Only genus Callitriche (*q.v.*). As usu. in water plants (*cf.* Ceratophyllaceae), the systematic position is doubtful. B.-H. unite C. with Haloragidaceae, but the differences are considerable. They have also been placed near Caryophyllaceae, Verbenaceae, Boraginaceae, &c., but seem on the whole nearest to Euphorbiaceae, where they are placed by Engler and by Warming (Tricoccae).
Callitriche L. Callitrichaceae. 25 (perhaps only vars. of 1 or 2), cosmop. (exc. S. Afr.). Several forms (water star-wort) in Brit. The submerged l. are longer and narrower than the floating, and the more so the deeper they are below the surface. Land forms also occur. Fl. unisex., naked, commonly with 2 horn-like bracteoles, protog.; ♂ of 1 sta.; ♀ of (2) cpls., transv. placed, 4-loc. by 'false' septum (*cf.* Labiatae), with 2 styles; 1 ov. in each loc., pend. anatr. with ventral raphe. Schizocarp. Fleshy endosp.
Callitris Vent. (excl. *Tetraclinis* Mast., *Widdringtonia* Endl.). Coniferae (Pinac.; see C. for gen. char.). 18 Austr. (cypress pine). L. and cone-scales in whorls. The cone ripens in 1 or 2 years. Wood valuable. Yield a sandarach resin.
Callixene Comm. ex Juss. = Luzuriaga Ruiz et Pav. (Lili.).
Callopsis Engl. Araceae (1). 1 E. Afr.
Callostylis Blume. Orchidaceae (II α, III). 1 Java.
Calluna Salisb. Ericaceae (IV. 1). 1, *C. vulgaris* Salisb. (heather or ling), Eur., Greenland, and from Newfoundland to Massachusetts (the only repres. of Ericoideae in Am.), covering large areas, together with sp. of Erica and Vaccinium. A low evergr. shrub, with linear

closely crowded wiry l. and racemes of fls. K coloured like the almost polypetalous C. The honey is more easily accessible than in Erica (fl. of class B) and there is a larger circle of visiting insects, including however many bees (heather honey is among the best). The stigma projects beyond the mouth of the fl.; insects touch it first and in probing for honey jostle the anthers. The fl. is also wind pollinated; the loose powdery pollen blows about easily and the stigma is not covered by the C.

Callus, new tissue covering a wound, usu. ± corky. *Cf.* Supplement.

Callyntranthele Ndz. Malpighiaceae (II). 1 Venezuela.

Calocephalus R. Br. Compositae (4). 12 temp. Austr.

Calochilus R. Br. Orchidaceae (II. 2). 7 E. Austr., New Caled., N.Z.

Calochortus Pursh. Liliaceae (V). 40 W. N.Am.

Calocrater K. Schum. Apocynaceae (II. 1). 1 Cameroons.

Calodendrum Thunb. Rutaceae (I). 2 S. and trop. Afr.

Calogyne R. Br. Goodeniaceae. 4 China, Austr.

Calolisianthus Gilg. Gentianaceae (I). 7 Brazil to W.I.

Caloncoba Gilg (*Oncoba* p.p.). Flacourt. (2). 14 trop. Afr.

Calonyction Choisy (*Ipomoea* L. p.p. *BH.*). Convolvulaceae (I). 5 trop. Am. Cult. orn. fl.

Calophaca Fisch. Leguminosae (III. 6). 10 S. Russia to Burma.

Calophanes Don (*Dyschoriste EP.*). Acanth. (IV. A). 40 trop.

Calophyllum L. Guttiferae (IV). 80 trop. chiefly Old World. *C. tacamahaca* Willd. and other sp. yield resins known as Tacamahac. (See Populus.) The young l. are usu. prettily coloured.

Calophysa DC. (*Maieta* Aubl. *EP.*). Melastom. (I). 10 trop. Am.

Calopogon R. Br. Orchidaceae (II. 7). 5 U.S.

Calopogonium Desv. Leguminosae (III. 10). 5 C. and S. Am., W.I.

Calopsis Beauv. ex Juss. (Leptocarpus R. Br.). Restion. 10 S. Afr.

Calopyxis Tul. (*Combretum* p.p. *BH.*). Combret. 10 Madag.

Calorchis Barb. Rodr. (*Ponthieva* R. Br.). Orch. (II. 2). 1 Brazil.

Calorhabdos Benth. Scrophulariaceae (III. 1). 4 E. As.

Calorophus Labill. (Hypolaena R. Br.). Restion. 3 Austr., Tasm., N.Z.

Calosacme Wall. = Chirita Buch.-Ham. = Didymocarpus Wall. p.p.

Calosanthes Blume = Oroxylum Vent. (Bignon.).

Caloscilla Jord. et Fourr. = Scilla L. p.p. (Lili.).

Calostemma R. Br. Amaryllidaceae (I). 3 sp. E. Austr. There is no embryo, but bulbils are said to be formed in the embryo sac.

Calostephane Benth. Compositae (4). 3 S. warm Afr.

Calostigma Decne. Asclepiadaceae (II. 1). 8 Brazil.

Calothamnus Labill. Myrtaceae (II. 1). 25 W. Austr. The axis goes on bearing l. beyond the fls. (*cf.* Callistemon). Sta. in bundles before the petals, the common axis of the bundle very large.

Calotheca Desv. = Briza L.; **do.** Spreng. = Aeluropus Trin.

Calotis R. Br. Compositae (3). 20 Austr.

Calotropis R. Br. Asclepiadaceae (II. 1). 3 trop. As., Afr. *C. gigantea* Ait. (madar, mudar, wara) yields a fibre from the bark, and a floss, used like kapok (Eriodendron), from the seeds.

Calpidia Thou. (*Pisonia* p.p. *EP.*). Nyctagin. 20 Malaya, New Cal.

Calpigyne Blume. Euphorb. (A. II. 2). 1 Celebes, Borneo. [Afr.
Calpocalyx Harms (*Erythrophloeum* p.p.). Legum. (I. 4). 4 W. trop.
Calpurnia E. Mey. Legum. (III. 1). 10 Afr. Pod narrowly winged.
Caltha (Rupp.) L. Ranunc. (2). 20 temp. *C. palustris* L. (marsh-marigold, king-cup) in Brit. K coloured. No honey-l.; honey by cpls.
Caltrops, *Tribulus*; **Calumba-root,** *Jateorhiza Columba* Miers (trop. Afr.); **false-** (Ceylon), *Coscinium fenestratum* Colebr.
Calvaria Comm. ex Gaertn. f. Sapot. (inc. sed.). 3 Madag.
Calvoa Hook. f. Melast. (1). 8 trop. Afr. Connective with scale.
Calyc- (Gr. pref.), cup; **-anthemy,** a monstrosity of the K imitating a C; **-iflorae** (*BH.*), the 3rd series of Polypetalae; **-ine,** belonging to K; **-oid,** like a K; **-ulus,** *Loranthaceae*, *Tofieldia*.
Calycacanthus K. Schum. Acanth. (IV. B). 1 New Guinea.
Calycadenia DC. = Hemizonia DC. p.p. (Comp.). 10 Calif.
Calycampe Berg. = Myrcia DC.
Calycanthus L. (incl. *Chimonanthus* Lindl. *q.v.*). The only genus of **Calycanthaceae** (*EP.*, *BH.*) (Dicots. Archichl. Ranales, pp. xix, l). 6 N. Am., Japan, Chi., N.E. Austr. Shrubs, usu. aromatic, with opp. simple l. and term. acyclic fls. on short shoots. P ∞, perig., spiral, with gradual transition from sepaloid to petaloid l.; A 5—30; G ∞, in hollowed axis, with 2 anatr. ov. in each. Achenes enclosed in axis; embryo large, with spirally wound cots. in slight endosp. *C. floridus* L. (Carolina allspice) cult. orn. shrub.
Calycera Cav. Calycer. 10 S. Am. Fr. all free, dimorphic.
Calyceraceae (*EP.*, *BH.*). Dicots. (Sympet. Campanulatae; Asterales *BH.*; pp. xlix, lii). 4/40 S. Am. Herbs with alt. exstip. l. Fls. in heads with invol. of br., ☿ or ♂ ♀, reg. or ·|·, epig., 4—6-merous. K leafy, C valv. or open, A in one whorl, filaments united, anthers free or slightly coherent at base, $\overline{G}$ 1-loc. with 1 pend. anatr. ov., and capitate stigma. Fr. achene-like, sometimes ± united, crowned by persistent K; embryo straight in slight endosp. Closely related to Comp. *Genera*: Boopis, Calycera, Acicarpha, Moschopsis.
Calyciflorae (*BH.*). The 3rd series of Polypetalae. *Cf.* p. li.
Calycinae (*BH.*). The 4th series of Monocots. *Cf.* p. liv.
Calycobolus Willd. = Breweria R. Br. (*BH.*) = Prevostia Choisy (Conv.).
Calycocarpum Nutt. ex Torr. et Gray. Menisperm. 1 Atl. N. Am. L. lobed. K 9, C 0, A 12.
Calycogonium DC. Melastom. (1). 25 W.I. G united to K. [in bud.
Calycolpus Berg. Myrt. (I. 1). 10 W.I., S. Am. K leafy, reflexed
Calycopeplus Planch. Euphorb. (A. II. 8). 3 Austr. [1 large sep.
Calycophyllum DC. Rubi. (I. 5). 3 W.I., S. Am. Wood useful.
Calycophysum Karst. et Triana. Cucurb. (3). 2 Colombia. [Climber.
Calycopteris Lam. Combret. 1 Indomal. Like Bucida, but l. opp.
Calycorectes Berg. Myrt. (I. 1). 12 S. Am. Like Eugenia, but (K).
Calycoseris A. Gray. Comp. (13). 2 Calif., Mex.
Calycosia A. Gray (*Psychotria* p.p. *EP.*). Rubi. (II. 5). 6 Polyn.
Calycothrix Meissn. (*Calythrix*). Myrt. (II. 2). 40 Austr. Cult. orn. shrubs. Embryo straight. A ∞. Seps. long and pointed.
Calycotome Link. Legum. (III. 3). 4 Medit. Stem branches thorny.
Calycotropis Turcz. Caryoph. (inc. sed.). 1 Mex.
Calyctenium Greene (*Rubus* p.p.). Ros. (III. 2). 1 Japan.

Calydermos Lag. = Calea L. p.p. (Compos.).
Calydorea Herb. Iridaceae (II). 10 Texas to S. Am.
Calymenia Pers. = Oxybaphus Vahl (*BH.*) = Mirabilis L. p.p.
Calymmanthera Schlechter. Orchidaceae (II. 20). 3 New Guinea.
Calypso Salisb. Orchidaceae (II. 4). 2 cold N. temp.
Calypso Thou. = Salacia L. (Hippocrat.).
Calypsogyne Neraud. Inc. sed. Nomen.
Calypteris Zipp. Inc. sed. 1, habitat?
Calyptocarpus Less. Compositae (5). 2 Texas, Mex.
Calyptranthes Sw. Myrtaceae (I). 80 trop. Am., W.I. Ed. fr.
Calyptrate, capped.
Calyptrella Naud. Melastomaceae (I). 5 trop. Am.
Calyptridium Nutt. Portulacaceae. 5 California.
Calyptrion Ging. (*Corynostylis* Mart.). Viol. 2 trop. S. Am.
Calyptrocalyx Blume. Palmae (IV. 1). 6 Austr., Moluccas.
Calyptrocarpus Less. Compositae (5). 2 Texas, Mex.
Calyptrocarya Nees. Cyperaceae (II). 5 Guiana, Brazil.
Calyptrochilum Krzl. Orchidaceae (II. 20). 1 Cameroons.
Calyptrogyne H. Wendl. Palmae (IV. 1). 3 Centr. Am.
Calyptronoma Griseb. (= last, *BH.*). Palmae (IV. 1). 4 trop. Am.
Calyptrostegia C. A. Mey = Pimelea Banks p.p. (Thymel.).
Calyptrotheca Gilg. Capparidaceae (II). 3 trop. Afr.
Calystegia R. Br. Convolvulaceae (I). 10 temp. and trop. 2 Brit., *C. Soldanella* R. Br. on the coasts, and *C. sepium* R. Br. in hedges. The fert. of this sp. depends largely on the visits of a hawk-moth (*Sphinx convolvuli*) and the distr. areas of the two correspond to some extent (*cf.* Aconitum). Often united to Convolvulus (*q.v.*).
Calythrix Labill. (*Calycothrix*). Myrt. (II. 2). 40 Austr. Cult. orn.
Calyx, the outer protective portion of the perianth, usu. of green l. (sepals). For descriptive terms, &c. see Perianth; **-tube**, the lower continuous portion of a gamosepalous calyx; **water-holding-**, *Parmentiera*, *Spathodea*.
Camarea St. Hil. Malpighiaceae (I). 10 E. S.Am.
Camaridium Lindl. Orchidaceae (II. 18). 15 trop. S. Am., W.I.
Camarotea Elliot. Acanthaceae (IV. A). 1 Madag.
Camarotis Lindl. (*Sarcochilus BH.*). Orchid. (II. 20). 2 E. Indies.
Camassia Lindl. Liliaceae (V). 4 N. Am. The bulbs (quamash) form a food for the Indians of N.Am.
Cambessedesia DC. Melastomaceae (I). 15 S. Brazil.
Cambium, the actually growing layer in a stem, &c.
Cambogia L. = Garcinia L. p.p. (Guttif.).
Camel-thorn, *Alhagi maurorum* Medic.
Camelina Crantz. Cruciferae (4). 8 Eur., Medit. *C. sativa* Cr. (gold of pleasure, Brit.) is used as a source of fibre in S. Eur.
Camelinus (Lat.), tawny.
Camellia L. (*Thea* L. p.p.). Theaceae. 8 Ind., China, Japan. *C. japonica* L. and others cult. orn. fls. *C. Thea* Link., *C. viridis* Link., and *C. Bohea* Lindl. = T. sinensis (again C. in recent papers).
Camelostalix Pfitzer (*Pholidota* p.p.). Orchid. (II. 3). 1 Java.
Cameraria (Plum.) L. Apocynaceae (I. 3). 2 W. Ind.

Camilleugenia Frappier (*Cynorchis* p.p.). Orchid. (II. 1). 1 Madag.
Camnium (Cl.), a succession due to cultivation.
Camoensia Welw. ex B. and H. Leguminosae (III. 1). 3 W. trop. Afr. *C. maxima* Welw. is a magnificent flowering creeper.
Camomile, *Anthemis*.
Campanales (*BH.*). The 3rd cohort of Gamopetalae.
Campanea Decne. Gesneriaceae (II). 10 C. and S. Am.
Campanocalyx Valeton. Rubiaceae (I. 7). 1 Borneo.
Campanolea Gilg et Schellenberg. Oleaceae. 1 Cameroons.
Campanula (Tourn.) L. Campanulaceae (I. 1). 300 N. temp. and trop. Mts., esp. Medit.; 8 Brit. incl. *C. rotundifolia* L. (harebell, blue-bell of Scotland). The pollen is shed in the bud, the sta. standing closely round the style and depositing their pollen upon the hairs. As the fl. opens the sta. wither, exc. the triangular bases that protect the honey, and the style presents the pollen to insects. After a time the stigmas separate and the fl. is ♀; finally the stigmas curl right back on themselves and effect self-pollin. (See fam. and *cf.* Phyteuma, Jasione.) Seeds light and contained in a caps., which if erect dehisces at the apex, if pend. at the base, so that the seeds (*cf.* Aconitum) can only escape when the plant is shaken, *e.g.* in strong winds. Several are cult. (Canterbury bells, &c.).
Campanulaceae (*EP.*, *BH.*). Dicots. (Symp. Campanulatae). 60 gen. 1000 sp., temp. and sub-trop., mostly perennial herbs (a few trees and shrubs), with alt., exstip. l., and usu. with latex. The infl. may term. the primary axis, or one of the second order. It is generally racemose, ending with a term. fl. in Campanuloideae. In some cases, instead of single fls. in the axils of the bracts of the raceme, small dich. occur (*cf.* Labiatae). Others have the whole infl. cymose (Canarina, Pentaphragma, &c.).

Fl. usu. ☿, reg. or ·|·, epig., generally 5-merous, the odd sepal post. in Campanuloideae, but anterior in the other groups. In these, however, a twisting of the axis through 180° takes place before the fl. opens (*cf.* Orchids), so that the odd sepal is finally post. K 5, open; C (5) valvate; A 5 epig.; anthers intr., sometimes united; $\overline{G}$ (5), (3) or (2), multi-loc. with axile plac. bearing ∞ anatr. ov. Style simple; stigmas as many as cpls. Caps. dehisc. in various ways in different gen., or berry. Fleshy endosp.

The nat. history of the fl. is of interest, both in itself and as exhibiting transitions to the Composite type. Honey is secreted by a disc at base of style and covered in most cases by the triangular bases of the sta., which fit closely together and only allow of the insertion of a proboscis between them. This, taken together with the size of the fls., their frequently blue colour and pendulous position, points to their being best adapted to the visit of bees, as is the case, but there are also many other visitors of various insect classes, so that this fam. cannot be placed in the fl. class H but must go into B. A few exceptions occur; the bulk of the fam. has large fls., conspicuous by themselves, but Phyteuma and Jasione have small fls. massed in heads, and come into class B′ along with the Compositae.

The general principle of the fl. mech. is the same throughout, and agrees with that of Compositae. The fl. is very protandr., and the style (with the stigmas closed up against one another) has the pollen shed upon it by the anthers, either in the bud or later. Usu. there is a bunch of hairs upon the style to hold the pollen. For some time the style acts as pollen-presenter to insects; after a time the stigmas separate and the ♀ stage sets in, and finally, in many cases, the stigmas curl back so far that they touch the pollen still clinging to their own style, and thus effect self-pollin. See genera, esp. Campanula, Phyteuma, Jasione, Lobelia, and *cf.* Compositae.

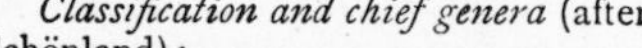

Floral diagram of Campanula; after Eichler.

Classification and chief genera (after Schönland):

I. *CAMPANULOIDEAE* (fl. actinomorphic, rarely slightly zygomorphic; anthers usu. free):

1. *Campanuleae* (cor. valvate; fl. symmetrical): Campanula, Phyteuma, Wahlenbergia, Platycodon, Jasione.
2. *Pentaphragmeae* (cor. valvate; fls. asymmetric, in cincinni): Pentaphragma (only genus).
3. *Sphenocleae* (cor. imbricate): Sphenoclea (only genus).

II. *CYPHIOIDEAE* (fl. zygomorphic; sta. sometimes united; anthers free): Cyphia, Nemacladus.

III. *LOBELIOIDEAE* (fl. zygomorphic, rarely almost actinomorphic; anthers united): Centropogon, Siphocampylus, Lobelia.

Campanulastrum Small (*Campanula* p.p.). Campan. (1). 1 N. Am.

Campanulatae. The 10th order of Dicotyledons (Sympet.).

Campanulate, bell-shaped.

Campanulopsis Zoll. et Morr. Campanul. (inc. sed.). 1 Malaya.

Campanulinae (Warming). The 9th cohort of Sympetalae.

Campanumoea Blume. Campanulaceae (I. 1). 5 Indomal.

Campbellia Wight = Christisonia Gardn. (Orobanch.).

Campderia Benth. (*Coccoloba* p.p. *EP.*). Polygon. (III. 1). 4 trop. Am.

Campe Dulac = Barbarea R. Br. (Crucif.).

Campeachy wood (W.I.), *Haematoxylon campechianum* L.

Campelia Rich. Commelinaceae. 1 trop. Am., W.I. Ed. fr.

Campereia Griff. Santalaceae. 2 Malaya. G.

Campestris (Lat.), growing in fields.

Camphor, an aromatic crystalline body, obtained by distillation from the wood or l. of *Cinnamomum Camphora* Nees et Eberm.; **ai-**, *Blumea balsamifera* DC.; **Barus** or **Borneo**, *Dryobalanops aromatica* Gaertn.; **ngai-**, = ai; Sumatra-, = Borneo.

Camphora (Bauh.) L. = Cinnamomum Tourn. (Laur.).

Camphorosma L. Chenopodiaceae (A). 8 E. Medit., Cent. As.

Campimia Ridl. Melastomaceae (I). 2 Malaya.

Campion, *Lychnis*, *Silene*; **bladder**, *S. inflata*; **moss**, *S. acaulis*.

Campnosperma Thw. Anacardiaceae (3). 10 trop.

Campomanesia Ruiz et Pav. Myrtaceae (I. 1). 80 S. Am. Ed. fr.

Campsiandra Benth. Leguminosae (II. 8). 3 trop. Am.

Campsidium Seem. (*Tecoma BH.*). Bignon. (2). 1 Chili.
Campsis Lour. (*Tecoma BH.*). Bignon. (2). 2 E. U.S., Japan.
Camptandra Ridl. (*Kaempfera* p.p.). Zingiber. (I). 7 trop. As., Chi.
Campteria Pr. = Pteris L. (Filic.).
Camptocarpus Decne. Asclepiadaceae (I). 5 Mauritius, Madag.
Camptolepis Radlk. Sapindaceae (I). 1 E. trop. Afr.
Camptoloma Benth. Scrophulariaceae (III. I). 2 trop. Afr.
Camptosema Hook. et Arn. Leguminosae (III. 10). 12 S. Am.
Camptosorus Link. Polypodiaceae. 2 N. Am., N. As. A xero. fern, whose prothalli can stand drought.
Camptostemon Mast. Bombacaceae. 2 N. Austr., Phil. Is. A (∞).
Camptostylus Gilg. Flacourtiaceae (I). 4 W. trop. Afr.
Camptotheca Decne. Nyssaceae. 1 China, Tibet.
Campuloclinium DC. = Eupatorium Tourn. p.p. (Compos.).
Campylandra Baker (*Tupistra* p.p. *BH.*). Lili. (VII). 3 E. As.
Campylanthus Roth. Scrophulariaceae (III. I). 5 Afr., Arabia, &c.
Campylia Lindl. ex Sweet = Pelargonium L'Hérit. p.p. (Geran.).
Campylobotrys Lem. = Hoffmannia Sw. (Rubiaceae).
Campylocentron Benth. Orchid. (II. 20). 25 trop. Am., W.I.
Campylochiton Welw. ex Hiern. (*Combretum* p.p. *EP.*). Comb. 1 trop. Afr.
Campylogyne Welw. ex Hemsl. (*Combretum* p.p. *EP.*). Comb. 1 trop. Afr.
Campyloneurum Presl. = Polypodium L. (Filic.).
Campylosiphon Benth. Burmann. 1 trop. S. Am. Saprophytic.
Campylospermum Van Tieghem = Ouratea Aubl. (Ochn.).
Campylostachys Kunth. Verbenaceae (2). 1 S. Afr.
Campylostemon Welw. Hippocrateaceae. 5 trop. W. Afr.
Campylotropous (ovule), curved into a U shape.
Campylus Lour. Inc. sed. 1 China.
Campynema Labill. Amaryllidaceae (IV). 1 Tasm. See fam.
Campynemanthe Baill. Amaryllidaceae (IV). 1 New Caled.
Camwood, *Baphia nitida* Afzel.
Canada balsam, *Abies balsamea* Mill.; **-pitch**, *Tsuga canadensis* Carr.; **-rice**, *Zizania aquatica* L.
Canaigre, *Rumex hymenosepalus* Torr.
Cananga Rumph. ex Hook. f. et Thoms. Anonaceae (I). 3 trop. E. As. to Austr. *C. odorata* Hook. f. is cult. for its fls., which yield the perfume known as ylang-ylang or Macassar oil.
Canariastrum Engl. Burseraceae. 1 trop. Afr. (? = *Uapaca*).
Canariellum Engl. Burseraceae. 1 New Caledonia.
Canarina L. Campanulaceae (I. I). 3 Canary Is., trop. Afr. Like Campanula, but usu. 6-merous, and with ed. berry fr.
Canarium (Rumph.) L. Burseraceae. 100 trop. As., Afr. *C. commune* L. (Java almond; ed. seed) furnishes the resin Manila Elemi (see Bursera). *C. strictum* Roxb. (Malabar) and other sp. furnish some of the black dammar of commerce (cf. Agathis).
Canary creeper, *Tropaeolum peregrinum* L. (*canariensis* Hort.); **-grass**, **-seed**, *Phalaris canariensis* L.; **-whitewood**, *Liriodendron tulipifera* L.
Canavalia DC. Leguminosae (III. 10). 12 trop. *C. ensiformis* DC.

(sword or sabre bean, overlook) cult. ed. pods. *C. obtusifolia* DC. is a common trop. shore plant.

Canbya Parry. Papaveraceae (II). 2 California, Mex.

Cancellate, latticed.

Cancrinia Kar. et Kir. Compositae (7). 1 Centr. As.

Candidus (Lat.), pure white.

Candle-nut, *Aleurites*; **-plant**, *Dictamnus*; **-tree**, *Parmentiera*; **-wood** (W. I.), *Sciadophyllum*, *Amyris*.

Candollea Labill. in Ann. Mus. Par. 1805 (*Stylidium* Sw., *q.v.*). Stylidiaceae. 85 Austr., N. Z., E. As.

Candollea Labill. 1806 = Hibbertia Andr. p.p. (Dillen.).

Candolleaceae = Stylidiaceae.

Candy-tuft, *Iberis amara* L.

Cane, a commercial term for stems of grasses (esp. bamboos), climbing palms, &c.; **bamboo-**, *cf.* bamboos; **-brake**, *Arundinaria*; **dumb-**, *Dieffenbachia*; **Malacca-**, *Calamus*; **rattan-**, *Calamus*, and *cf.* Rattan; **sugar-**, *Saccharum officinarum* L. **Tobago**, *Bactris minor* Jacq.; **Whangee-**, *Phyllostachys*.

Canella P. Br. (*Winterana* L.). 2 W. Ind., trop. Am. *C. alba* Murr. yields Canella bark, used as a tonic and stimulant.

Canella bark, see last.

Canellaceae = Winteranaceae.

Canephora Juss. Rubiaceae (I. 8). 3 Madagascar. Fls. in clusters at the top of a phyllodineous stalk with a 2-lobed calyculus.

Canescent, grey or hoary.

Canistrum Morren (*Aechmea* p.p. *BH.*). Bromel. (4). 4 Brazil.

Canker-berry (W. I.), *Solanum bahamense* L.

Canna L. Cannaceae. 60 trop. and subtrop. Am., *C. indica* L. cosmop. trop. Many sp., vars. and hybrids, cult. *C. indica* (Indian shot) is the basis of most of these. Habit like Zingiberaceae or Marantaceae, but C. can be distinguished even when not in fl. by possessing neither the ligule of the former nor the pulvinus of the latter. Infl. term. usu. composed of 2-fl. cincinni. The two fls. are homodromous, but the bracteole is to the right in one and to the left in the other (behind one or other of the two lat. sepals in the diagram). Fl. ☿, asymmetric, epig. K 3, C (3). The A is the most conspicuous part. There is a leafy sta. bearing half an anther on one edge, and a number of petaloid structures round it, usu. 3 but sometimes 1 or 4. One of these is the labellum (not = that of Zingiberaceae), and is rolled back on itself outwards. The other two are often termed the wings (α β in diagram). When a fourth std. (γ, *cf.* Marantaceae) is present it stands behind the fertile sta. Other sp. have only the labellum. $\overline{G}$ (3) with petaloid style, 3-loc.; ov. in 2 rows in each loc., anatr. Caps., usu. warty. Seed with perisperm and straight embryo.

Floral diagram of *Canna indica* (after Eichler). The bracteole is omitted. S = petaloid style; L = labellum; α β = staminodes.

As to the morphological explanation of the A, there are two views

Eichler (*Blütendiag.* I. p. 174) regards the labellum as a lat. sta. of the inner whorl, and the fertile sta. together with all the stds. as the post. sta. of the same whorl; the other sta. of the inner, and all the sta. of the outer, whorl are wanting. The older view looks upon β, γ, as the 2 post. sta. of the outer whorl, and the labellum, α, and the fertile sta. as the 3 sta. of the inner whorl. (*Cf.* this fl. with those of Musaceae, Zingiberaceae and Marantaceae.)

The pollen is shed upon the style in the bud; insects alight on the labellum, touch first the term. stigma and then the pollen. The rhiz. of *C. edulis* Ker-Gawl. is ed., containing much starch.

Cannabaceae, Cannabinaceae = § IV. of Moraceae (*q.v.*).

Cannabis (Tourn.) L. Moraceae (IV). 1 Cent. As., *C. sativa* L., the hemp. Infl. like Humulus ♂, dioec. Hemp is largely cult. both in temp. and trop. regions, in the former for the fibre, in the latter for the drug. A valuable fibre, used for ropes and other purposes, is obtained from the inner bark of the stem, much as flax is prepared from Linum, and for this purpose the plant is cult. in S. Eur., the eastern U.S., and other countries. In the trop., and esp. in India, the pl. is cult. for the sake of the narcotic resin which exudes from it, and which is used much like opium, both as a drug and as a stimulant. The drug occurs in three common forms, ganja, charas, and bhang. The first is the ♀ flg. tops with resin on them, packed together, the second, which comes from rather cooler climates, is the resin knocked off the twigs, bark, &c., and the third, which is largely obtained from the wild plants, is the mature l., with their resinous deposit, packed together. Asiatics are much addicted to the use of hemp as a narcotic. It is smoked, with or without tobacco, and an intoxicating liquor, hashish, is made from it. The resin has an intoxicating stimulating effect. In small quantities it produces pleasant excitement, passing into delirium and catalepsy if the quantity be increased. The names given to the plant among them indicate this use of it, *e.g.* leaf of delusion, increaser of pleasure, cementer of friendship. The sale of ganja and charas is kept in check in India by a stringent licensing system, but that of bhang, which is collected from wild plants, is hard to control. *Cf.* Literature (Watt).

Cannaceae (*EP.*; *Scitamineae* p.p. *BH.*). Monocotyledons (Scitamineae). Only genus Canna (*q.v.*).

Cannomois Beauv. Restiaceae. 8 S. Afr.

Cannon-ball tree, *Couroupita guianensis* Aubl.

Canotia Torr. 1 Calif., New Mexico, doubtfully placed in Rutaceae, but perhaps belonging to Celastraceae.

Canscora Lam. Gentianaceae (1). 18 palaeotrop.

Cansjera Juss. Opiliaceae. 4 trop. As., Austr.

Cantaloupe, melon, *Cucumis Melo* L.

Canterbury bell, *Campanula.*

Cantharospermum Wight et Arn. (*Atylosia BH.*). Leguminosae (III. 10). 20 Madag., trop. As. and Austr.

Canthium Lam. = Plectronia L. (Rubiaceae).

Canthopsis Miq. (*Randia* p.p. *EP.*). Rubiaceae (I. 8). 1 Timor.

Cantua Juss. Polemoniaceae. 8 Andes.

Cantuffa Gmel. (*Pterolobium* R. Br.). Legum. (II. 7). 5 palaeotrop.

Canus (Lat.), grey-white.
Caopia Adans. = Vismia Vand. (Guttif.).
Caoutchouc, see Rubber.
Capanemia Barb. Rodr. (*Quekettia EP.*). Orch. (II. 19). 2 Brazil.
Caparrosa, *Neea theifera* Oerst.
Cape aster, *Felicia*; **-chestnut**, *Calodendron*; **-cowslip**, *Lachenalia*; **-crocus**, *Gethyllis*; **-figwort**, *Phygelius*; **-forget-me-not**, *Anchusa*; **gooseberry**, *Physalis*; **-honeysuckle**, *Tecoma*; **-jasmine**, *Gardenia*; **-lily**, *Crinum*; **-pondweed**, *Aponogeton*; **-primrose**, *Streptocarpus*; **-tulip**, *Haemanthus*.
Caper, *Capparis spinosa*, L.
Caperonia St Hil. Euphorbiaceae (A. II. 2). 33 trop. Am., Afr.
Capet tree (W.I.), *Capparis verrucosa* Jacq.
Capillary, hair-like.
Capirona Spruce. Rubiaceae (I. 4). 1 S. Am. K like Mussaenda.
Capitania Schweinf. Labiatae (VII). 1 E. Afr.
Capitate, head-like.
Capitularia J. V. Suringar. Cyper. (III). 1 New Guinea.
Capitulum, a head of fl., *Compositae*, *Cornac.*, *Dipsac.*, &c.
Capnites Dum. = Corydalis Vent. (Papav.).
Capnoides Tourn. ex Adans. = Corydalis Vent. (Papav.).
Capnophyllum Gaertn. Umbelliferae (III. 6). 4 Medit., S. Afr.
Capnorea Rafin. (Hesperochiron S. Wats.). Hydrophyll. 18 Pac., N. Am.
Capparidaceae (*EP.*, *BH.*). Dicots. (Archichl. Rhoeadales; Parietales *BH.*). 40 gen., 450 sp., trop. and warm temp., many xero., with reduced, often inrolled, l. (*cf.* Empetrum). Herbs or shrubs, with alt. simple or palmate l., often with stips. (frequently repres. by thorns or glands). Fls. ☿, reg., usu. in racemes, bracteate but without bracteoles. The P resembles that of Cruciferae (K 2 + 2, C 4 diagonal), but great var. occurs in the A. In some sp. of Cleome there are 4 sta. in two whorls, but elsewhere there are more. Some sp. of Cleome, &c. show tetradynamous sta. In others, still further branching of the median sta. occurs and usu. the post. sta. is more branched than the ant. Staminody of some of the branches is frequent. Cpls. typically (2), transv. as in Cruciferae, with parietal plac. In many sp. of sub-order II the number rises to 10 or 12 by the addition of a second whorl of cpls. and by dédoublement. Ovules ∞, campylotropous.

A further complication is the presence of axial effigurations, &c. in the fls. A disc may occur between P and sta. (usually thicker at the post. side), or a gynophore between sta. and ov., or both. Or the disc may grow up in the centre to form an androphore on which the sta. are borne and above them there may be a gynophore also. From the disc there often grow out structures of various shapes and sizes; these may be scales quite free from one another, or, as in Cadaba, &c., may be united into a tube. Or the scales may, as in Steriphoma, &c., alt. with and be joined to the sepals.

Fr. a siliqua (with replum), nut, berry or drupe. Seed exalb. with embryo folded in various ways as in Cruciferae. Few are useful: see Capparis, &c.

Classification and chief genera (after Pax):

A. Mostly shrubs, with hairs or scales, rarely glandular. No replum.

I. *DIPTERYGIOIDEAE* (samara): Dipterygium.

II. *CAPPARIDOIDEAE* (berry): Capparis, Cadaba, Maerua, Koeberlinia.

III. *ROYDSIOIDEAE* (drupe): Roydsia.

IV. *EMBLINGIOIDEAE* (prostrate undershrubs; calyx-tube present; C (2); nut): Emblingia (only genus).

B. Glandular annuals; siliqua with replum.

V. *CLEOMOIDEAE*: Cleome, Polanisia.

Capparis (Tourn.) L. Capparid. (II). 200 warm. Many climb by recurved stip. thorns. Fertile sta. ∞. *C. spinosa* L. fl.-buds (Medit.) form capers (*cf.* cloves, Eugenia).

Capraea Opiz. = Salix L. (Salic.).

Capraria (Tourn.) L. Scroph. (III. 1). 4 warm Am., W.I. L. alt. C almost free.

Capreolatus (Lat.), tendrilled.

Caprificus Gasp. = Ficus Tourn. p.p. (Mor.); **caprification**, *cf.* Ficus.

Caprifoliaceae (*EP.*; *BH.* incl. *Adox.*). Dicots. (Sympet. Rubiales, p. xlix, lii). 18/275, temp. (chiefly N.), and trop. Mts. Usu. ♄ with decussate usu. exstip. simple l. (*cf.* Sambucus). Fls. ☿, reg. or ⫩, usu. in cymes and 5-merous with odd sep. post. K, C 5, A 5, epipet., $\overline{G}$ (2—5), usu. multi-loc. with 1—∞ pend. ov. in each on axile plac. Berry, drupe, or caps.; embryo small in fleshy endosp. Orn. shrubs. *Chief genera:* Sambucus, Viburnum, Symphoricarpus, Linnaea, Lonicera, Diervilla.

Caprifolium Tourn. ex L. = Lonicera L. p.p.

Capriola Adans. (*Cynodon* Rich.). Gramin. (11). 1 cosmop., 3 Austr.

Capsella Medic. Crucif. (4). 4 temp., sub-trop. *C. Bursa-pastoris* Medic. (shepherd's purse) in Brit.; a cosmop. weed, self-pollin. In early spring and late autumn sta. often ± aborted. L. variable in shape and degree of division in various situations. Solms (*Bot. Zeit.* 1900, p. 167) describes *C. Heegeri*, a new form with elongated fr., which has arisen from this, and is almost generically distinct.

Capsicum (Tourn.) L. Solan. (2). 30 C. and S. Am. (*cf.* Tubocapsicum). *C. annuum* L. cult. for fr. (chillies or red peppers); dried and ground they form Cayenne pepper. (Irish in *Rep. Miss. Bot. Gdn.*, 1898, for revision of cult. forms.)

Capsule, a dry dehiscent fr. (*q.v.*) of > 1 cpl.

Capura Blanco (*Otophora* Blume p.p. *EP.*). Sapind. (I). 3 Malaya.

Capura L. = Wikstroemia Endl. (Thymel.).

Caracalla Tod. = Phaseolus L. (Legum.).

Caracasia Szysz. (*Vargasia* Ernst.). Marcgrav. 2 Venez. Pets. free, A 3.

Caradesia Rafin. = Eupatorium L. (Comp.).

Caraea Hochst. = Euryops Cass. (Comp.).

Caragaea Tul. = Castelnavia Tul. et Wedd. (Podost.)

Caragana Lam. Legum. (III. 6). 40 C. As., Chi. Petiole persistent.

Caraguata (Plum.) Lindl. (*Guzmania* Ruiz. et Pav. p.p. *EP.*). Bromel. (1). 20 S. Am., W.I. Cult. orn. infl.

Caraguata fibre, *Bromelia*, *Eryngium*, *Furcraea*, &c.

Caraipa Aubl. Guttif. (I). (Ternstroem. *BH.*) 12 trop. S. Am. They yield useful hard timber (tamacoari) and medic. balsam. L. alt. Connective with term. gland. Seed 1 per loc.

Carallia Roxb. ex R. Br. Rhizophoraceae. 10 palaeotrop., exc. Afr. Disc. usu. double.
Caralluma R. Br. Asclepiadaceae (II. 3). 60 Medit. to E. Ind.
Caramba, Carambola, *Averrhoa Carambola* L.
Caranda Gaertn. Inc. sed. 1 Ceylon.
Carapa Aubl. Meliaceae (III). 10 trop. *C. procera* DC. and *C. guianensis* Aubl. seeds yield a good oil (carapa, touloucouna, andiroba, coondi). *C. moluccensis* Lam. among the mangroves (*q.v.*).
Carapichea Aubl. = Cephaelis Sw. (Rubiac.).
Carat, *Ceratonia Siliqua* L.
Caraway seed, *Carum Carvi* L.
Carbenia Adans. (*Cnicus* p.p. *EP.*). Compos. (11). 1 Medit.
Carbohydrates, bodies containing C, H, and O, in the proportions C_x, H_{2y}, O_y; cellulose, starch, sugar, &c.
Carcerulus, fruit of Labiatae.
Carda Nor. Inc. sed. Nomen.
Cardamine (Tourn.) L. (*BH.* incl. *Dentaria* L.). Cruciferae (2). 100 cosmop., chiefly temp. *C. pratensis* L. (cuckoo-flower) and others in Brit. *C. impatiens* L. has an explosive fruit like that of Eschscholtzia. *C. chenopodiifolia* Pers. (S. Am.) possesses two kinds of fr. Those formed on the upper part of the plant are normal siliquae; at the base, in the axils of the l. of the rosette cleist. fls. form which burrow into the soil and produce fr. there (cf. Arachis, Trifolium, &c.). In *C. pratensis* there is extensive veg. repr. by adv. buds on the radical l. and in *C.* (*D.*) *bulbifera* R. Br. by means of axillary bulbils. See Schulz, Monograph in *Engl. Jb.* 32, p. 280.
Cardaminopsis Hayek. Cruciferae (2). 4 *.
Cardamoms, *Elettaria Cardamomum* Maton, *Amomum*.
Cardamomum Noronha = Elettaria Maton (Zingib.).
Cardanthera Buch.-Ham. (*Synnema EP.*). Acanth. (IV. A). 10 palaeotrop.
Cardia Dulac = Veronica Tourn. (Scroph.).
Cardiaca (Tourn.) L. = Leonurus L. p.p. (Comp.).
Cardiacanthus Schau. (*Jacobinia* p.p. *BH.*). Acanth. (IV. B). 1 Mex.
Cardiandra Sieb. et Zucc. Saxifr. (III). 1 China, Japan. A ∞. G inf.
Cardinal flower, *Lobelia cardinalis* L.
Cardiobatus Greene (*Rubus* p.p.). Rosac. (III. 2). 1 N. Am.
Cardiocarpus Reinw. = Soulamia Lam. (Simarub.).
Cardiochlamys Oliv. Convolvulaceae (I). 1 Madag.
Cardiogyne Bur. (*Plecospermum BH.*). Morac. (I). 1 trop. Afr. The wood yields a dye.
Cardiopetalum Schlechtd. (*Stormia* Moore). Anon. (1). 1 Braz.
Cardiopteris Wall. Icacinaceae (Olacineae *BH.*). 3 Indomal. (C).
Cardiospermum L. Sapindaceae (1), 15 trop., esp. Am.
Cardoon, *Cynara Cardunculus* L.
Cardopatium Juss. (*Broteroa EP.*). Compositae (11). 2 Medit.
Carduncellus Adans. Compositae (11). 20 Medit.
Carduus (Tourn.) L. This gen., Cnicus and Cirsium are nearly allied, and scarcely any floras agree in the sp. assigned to them. See *Index Kewensis*.

Comp. (II). 35 Eur., Medit., As. (thistles). *C. nutans* L. &c. Brit.

Cardwellia F. Muell. Prot. (II). 1 Queensland.

Carelia Less. Comp. (2). 1 S. Braz. Hairy shrub with opp. l.

Carenophila Ridl. Zingib. (I). 1 Malay Penins.

Carex (Dill.) L. Cyper. (III). 900 cosmop., espec. temp., in marshes, &c. About 60 Brit. (sedges). Grass-like pl. with 1-fld. pseudo-spikelets in long spikes which are sometimes unisexual, sometimes with both ♂ and ♀ fls. The ♀ fl. has a second glume (*cf.* fam.). Fls. protog., wind-pollin. Much veg. repr. by offshoots. Many Brit. spp. are alpine; others, *e.g.* *C. arenaria* L. grow on sand-dunes, with the habit of Ammophila. *Cf.* monograph in *Pfl. R.*

Careya Roxb. Lecythid. (II). 5 Indomal. *C. arborea* Roxb. (patana oak) almost the only tree on the grassy expanses known as patanas in Ceylon. Seeds ∞; embryo like Barringtonia.

Cargillia R. Br. = Diospyros Lam. (Eben.).

Carica L. Caric. 30 warm Am. *C. Papaya* L. (papaw) universally cult. for ed. fr. in warm countries. C and K alt. The l. and the unripe fr. contain a milky juice in which is the proteid-ferment papaïn, collected in Ceylon, &c. for use in digestive salts. Meat wrapped in the l. and buried becomes tender through partial digestion of the fibres (Umney in *Kew Bull.* 1897). *C. candamarcensis* Hook. f. (mountain papaw) also cult. for ed. fr. in trop. Mts.

Caricaceae (*EP.*; *Passifl.* p.p. *BH.*). Dicots. (Archichl. Parietales, p. xxxv). 4/40 trop. Am., Afr. Small trees, branched or not, with a term. crown of palmate or digitate exstip. alt. l., and milky juice. Fls. reg., in loose axillary infls., unisexual, 5-merous; C twisted in bud. ♂ with long C-tube, and 2 whorls intr. epipet. sta.; ♀ with short C-tube, $\underline{G}$ (5), 1- or 5-loc. with short style and 5 stigmas; ov. ∞, anatr., usu. on parietal plac. Berry; endosp. oily. *Genera:* Carica, Jaracatia, Cylicomorpha, Vasconcellosia.

Caricature plant (Ceylon, &c.), *Graptophyllum hortense* Nees (Austr.).

Caries, decay; **Carina**, a keel, *Leguminosae.* [Timber valuable

Cariniana Casar. (*Couratari* p.p. *BH.*). Lecyth. (IV). 7 trop. Am.

Carinta W. F. Wight = Geophila D. Don (Rubi.).

Carionia Naud. Melastom. (I). 2 Phil. Is. Small trees. 6-merous.

Carissa L. (*Arduina* Mill.). Apocyn. (I. 1). 20 warm |✻. Shrubs with branch thorns. *C. Carandas* L. has ed. fr.

Carlemannia Benth. Rubi. (I. 2). 4 Himal. L. toothed. A 2.

Carlesia Dunn. Umbell. (III. 5). 1 China.

Carlina L. Comp. (II). 20 Eur., Medit., As. *C. vulgaris* L. (carline-thistle) Brit. *C. acaulis* L. is the weather thistle of the Alps, &c. The outer br. of invol. are prickly, the inner membranous and shining, spreading like a star in dry air, but closing in damp.

Carline thistle, *Carlina vulgaris* L.

Carlomohria Greene = Halesia Ellis (Styrac.).

Carlotea Arruda. Inc. sed. 2 Brazil. (? = Hippeastrum Herb.)

Carlowrightia A. Gray. Acanth. (IV. B). 10 S.W. U.S., Mex.

Carludovica Ruiz et Pav. Cyclanth. 40 trop. Am., W.I. Habit that of a small palm (a few climbers) with short stem and fan l. in whose axils arise the infls. Each is a cylindrical spadix, enclosed at first in a number of br. which fall off and leave it naked. Its surface is covered with fls. arranged as in the diagram (after Drude in *Nat. Pfl.*; F = ♀, m = ♂, fl.). The ♂ fl. has a rudimentary P, and ∞ sta., united below. The ♀ is sunk in and united with the tissue of the spadix. It has 4 very long stds. and 4 stigmas corresponding to the 4 plac. in the 1-loc. ov. When the spadix opens the ♀ fls. are ripe and the long stds. give a tangled appearance to the whole. After a few days the stigmas cease to be receptive and the anthers open. Afterwards the ♂ fls. drop and a multiple fr. is formed, composed of berries.

```
          m                   m
m     m       F       m       m
          m       m           m
          F    m     m        F
          m       m           m
m     m       F       m       m
          m                   m
```

The l. of *C. palmata* R. and P., gathered young, cut into thin strips and bleached, form the material of Panama hats.

Carmenocania Wernham. Rubiaceae (I. 7). 1 trop. Am.

Carmenta Nor. Inc. sed. Nomen.

Carmichaelia R. Br. Legum. (III. 6). 20 N.Z., Lord Howe's I. Xero. with flat green stems (phylloclades) and no green l. (*cf.* Bossiaea).

Carminatia Moç. Compositae (2). 1 Mex.

Carnarvonia F. Muell. Proteaceae (II). 1 Queensland.

Carnation, *Dianthus Caryophyllus* L.

Carna-uba, *Copernicia cerifera* Mart.

Carnegiea Britton et Rose (*Cereus* p.p.). Cactaceae (III. 1). 1 Texas (*Cereus giganteus, q.v.*).

Carnegiea Perkins. Monimiaceae. 1 New Caled.

Carneus (Lat.), flesh-coloured.

Carnivorous plants, see Insectivorous.

Carnosus (Lat.), fleshy.

Carob-tree, *Ceratonia Siliqua* L.

Carolina allspice, *Calycanthus*; **-jasmine,** *Gelsemium*.

Carolinea L. f. = Pachira Aubl. (*BH.*) = Bombax L. p.p.

Carolinella Hemsl. = Primula p.p. (Primul.). 4 China.

Carolofritschia Engl. Gesneriaceae (I). 1 trop. Afr.

Caropodium Stapf. et Wettst. Umbel. (III. 5). 1 Persia.

Caroxylon Thunb. = Salsola L. (Chenopod.).

Carp- (Gr. pref.), fruit; **-el,** the megasporophyll of the fl., bearing the ovules. In Gymnospermae the ovule is exposed, but in Angiospermae the cpl. is infolded, and the ovules borne on thickened placentae. Cpls. may be free (*apocarpous*) or united (*syncarpous*), in the latter case the ovary being uni- or multi-locular. The tip of the cpl. is the *style*, ending in the *stigma*; **-id,** diminutive of cpl.; **-ophore,** *Rosaceae, Umbelliferae*; **-ophyll,** carpel; **-ostrote** (Cl.), pl. migrating by means of fr.; **-otropic,** *cf.* Movements.

Carpacoce Sond. Rubiaceae (II. 7). 4 S. Afr.

Carpentaria Becc. (*Kentia* p.p. *EP.*). Palmae (IV. 1). 1 New Guin.

Carpenteria Torr. Saxifragaceae (III). 1 sp. Calif. Like Philadelphus, but ov. sup.; sta. ∞, cpls. 5—7.

Carpesium L. Compositae (4). 16 S. Eur., As. Pappus 0.

Carpet plant, *Ionopsidium acaule*; **-weed** (Am.), *Mollugo*.
Carpha Banks et Soland. Cyperaceae (I). 4 S. temp.
Carphalea Juss. Rubiaceae (I. 2). 1 Madag.
Carphephorus Cass. Compositae (2). 5 E. U.S.
Carphobolus Schott = Piptocarpha R. Br. (Comp.)
Carphochaete A. Gray. Compositae (2). 4 S.W. U. S., Mex.
Carpinus L. Betulaceae (I). 21 N. temp., chiefly E. As. *C. Betulus* L. Brit. (hornbeam). The young l. hang downwards as the shoot expands. The ♀ catkins are term. on long shoots, the ♂ are themselves short shoots. In the axil of each scale of the latter are 4—12 sta. each split almost to the base. No bracteoles are present, so that it is doubtful how many fls. of the possible 3 (see fam.) are repres. In the ♀ there are the 2 lat. fls. with all 6 bracteoles. On the top of the 2-loc. ovary is a small P. Fr. a 1-seeded nut with a 3-lobed leafy wing on one side, whose centre lobe corresponds to the bract α or β, the lat. lobes to the bracteoles α', β'; these unite and grow large after fert. The timber is little used.
Carpoceras Link. = Thlaspi Tourn. (Crucif.).
Carpodetus Forst. Saxifragaceae (V). 7 New Zealand, New Guin. G̅.
Carpodinus R. Br. ex Sabine. Apocyn. (I. 1). 50 trop. Afr. Rubber is obtained by grating and boiling from the rhiz. of *C. lanceolatus* K. Sch. &c. (*cf.* Clitandra; *Bot. Centr.* 72, p. 116).
Carpodiptera Griseb. Tiliaceae. 6 E. Afr., Cuba.
Carpolobia G. Don. Polygalaceae. 6 trop. W. Afr.
Carpolyza Salisb. (*Hessea* Berg.). Amaryllidaceae (I). 4 S. Afr.
Carponema Eckl. et Zeyh. Cruciferae (I). 4 S. Afr. Fr. indeh.
Carpopogon Roxb. = Mucuna Adans. (Legum.).
Carpotroche Endl. Flacourtiaceae (2). 6 trop. Am.
Carpoxylon H. Wendl. et Drude. Palmae (IV. 1). 1 New Hebrides.
Carrichtera Adans. Cruciferae (2). 1 Medit.
Carrierea Franch. Flacourtiaceae (4). 2 China.
Carrion-flower (Am.), *Smilax herbacea* L.; **-flowers**, fls. with a smell of carrion, visited esp. by carrion-loving flies, *Amorphophallus*, *Araceae*, *Stapelia*, &c.
Carronia F. Muell. Menispermaceae. 3 New S. Wales to New Guinea.
Carrot, *Daucus Carota* L.
Carruthersia Seem. Apocynaceae (II. 1). 4 Polynesia.
Carsonia Greene (*Cleome* p.p.). Capparid. (V). 1 N. Am.
Cartagena bark, *Cinchona cordifolia* Mutis.
Carteria Small. Orchidaceae (II. 2). 1 Florida, Bahamas.
Carthamus (Tourn.) L. Compositae (11). 25 Medit., Afr., As. *C. tinctorius* L. (safflower) cult. in Asia, &c.; its fls. are used in dyeing; powdered and mixed with talc they form rouge.
Cartiera Greene (*Streptanthus* p.p.). Crucif. (I). 6 N. Am.
Cartilaginous, firm and tough; endosp. of *Liliaceae*.
Cartonema R. Br. Commelinaceae. 6 trop. Austr.
Carum Rupp. ex L. (*BH.* incl. *Bunium* L., *Petroselinum* Hoffm.). Umbelliferae (III. 5). 20 sp. temp. and sub-trop. 3 Brit., of which *C. Carvi* L. is cult. for its fr. (caraway seeds).
Caruncle, a small hard aril, *Buxaceae*, *Euphorbiaceae*.
Carvalhoa K. Schum. Apocynaceae (II. 1). 2 E. trop. Afr.

Carya Nutt. Juglandaceae. 12 E. N. Am., the hickory trees, cultivated for their wood, which is very tough and elastic, and for the edible fruit (pecans, like walnuts).

Caryocar Linn. Caryocaraceae. 15 sp. trop. Am. The wood is very durable and is used in ship-building. The fruit is a large 4-stoned drupe; the seeds are the Souari- or Butter-nuts of commerce.

Caryocaraceae (*Rhizoboleae*) (*EP.*; *Ternstroemiaceae* p.p. *BH.*). Dicots. (Archichl. Parietales). 2 gen., 15 sp. trop. Am. Trees and shrubs with ternate opp. or alt. l. with deciduous stips. Fls. ☿ in racemes. K (5—6), C (5—6), A ∞, united into a ring or in 5 bundles. G̲ 4- or 8—20-loc. with as many styles. 1 pend. ov. per loc. Usu. drupe with oily mesocarp, and woody endocarp which splits into 4 mericarps; sometimes a leathery schizocarp. Little or no endosp. *Genera:* Anthodiscus, Caryocar.

Caryodendron Karst. Euphorbiaceae (A. II. 2). 2 trop. S. Am.

Caryophyllaceae (*EP.*; *BH.* excl. *Illecebraceae* or *Paronychiaceae*, and *Scleranthaceae*). Dicots. (Archichl. Centrospermae). 80 gen., 1300 sp. cosmop. (many Brit.), mostly herbs, a few undershrubs, with opp. simple usu. entire l., often stip.; the stem often swollen at the nodes, the branching dich. The infl. usu. term. the main axis and is typically a dich. cyme, but both in the veg. region and in the infl., of the two branches arising at any node, one (that in the axil of β) tends to outgrow the other and after two or three branchings the weaker one often does not develope at all, so that a cincinnus arises. The whole infl. is very char., and such an one is often called a caryophyllaceous infl.

Fls. ☿ and reg., but often not isomerous. As a type, the formula of Lychnis may serve: K (5), C 5, A 5+5, G̲ (5), with free central plac., uniloc. Ov. usu. ∞, in double rows corresponding to the

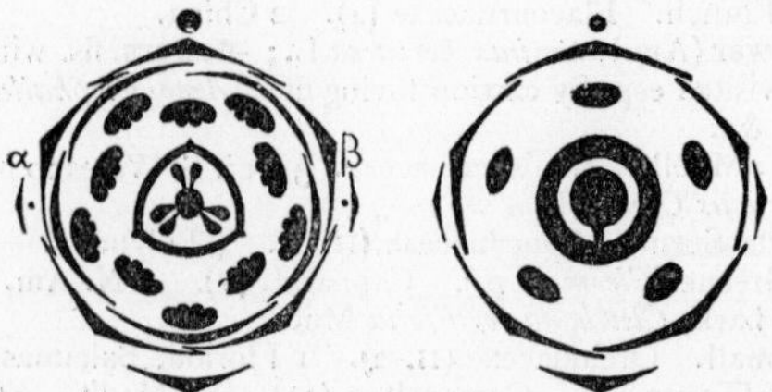

Floral diagrams of (1) *Silene inflata* and (2) *Paronychia sp.* (after Eichler), showing the ordinary type of fl. in Silenoideae and the most reduced type of Alsinoideae; α, β = bracteoles.

cpls., rarely few or 1 (Paronychieae), usu. campylotropous. In most cases the fl. is obdiplost. as may be recognised by the cpls. (when 5) being opp. the petals. Frequently, reduction of the number of parts occurs, *e.g.* G (3) or (2) or rarely (4); A 4+4, or 5, 3, 2, or 1, and in other cases the C may abort (Sagina sp., Herniaria, &c.). The ovary, sta., and corolla are sometimes borne on an androphore (*e.g.* Lychnis), an elongation of the axis between K and C. The petals sometimes have a ligule (*e.g.* Lychnis), and are often bifid. At the base of the ovary are often seen traces of the septa, which in the upper part do not develope; in some cases the plac. is basal.

Biologically, as well as morphologically, the fam. forms two distinct groups, a higher type, the *Silenoideae*, and a lower, the *Alsinoideae.* All secrete honey at the base of the sta., but while in the A. the fl. is wide open, so that short-tongued insects can reach the honey, in the S. a tube is formed by the gamosepalous K; in this stand the claws of the petals and the sta., partly filling it up, and rendering the honey inaccessible to any but long-tongued insects, esp. bees and Lepidoptera. The latter class, esp. in the Alps (see Müller's *Alpenblumen*), are the chief visitors, and many of the S. are adapted to them —by length of tube, red and white colours, night-flowering in many sp., or emission of scent only at night, &c. The fls. are commonly protandr. Many A. are gynodioec. (cf. Labiatae).

Fr. usu. a caps. containing several or ∞ seeds. It opens in nearly all cases by splitting from the apex into teeth which bend outwards, leaving an opening. The splitting may take place in as many, or in twice as many, lines as cpls. The seeds cannot escape from the capsule unless it be shaken, *e.g.* by wind or animals, and being small and light have a good chance of distr. Embryo usu. curved round the perisperm (in a few cases nearly straight).

Classification and chief genera (after Pax):

I. *ALSINOIDEAE* (flr. polysepalous; sta. often perig.).

a. Fruit a capsule opening by teeth.

1. *Alsineae* (styles free to base; l. exstip.): Stellaria, Cerastium, Sagina, Arenaria.
2. *Sperguleae* (do., but l. stip.): Spergula, Spergularia.
3. *Polycarpeae* (styles joined at base): Drymaria, Polycarpon.

b. Fruit an achene or nut.

4. *Paronychieae* (fls. all alike; stipules): Corrigiola, Paronychia, Illecebrum, Herniaria.
5. *Dysphanieae* (do., but l. exstip. alt.): Dysphania.
6. *Sclerantheae* (do., exstip. opp.): Scleranthus.
7. *Pterantheae* (fls. in 3's, the 2 lat. ± abortive): Pteranthus.

II. *SILENOIDEAE* (fl. gamosepalous, hypog.):

1. *Lychnideae* (calyx with commissural ribs): Silene, Lychnis.
2. *Diantheae* (no commissural ribs): Gypsophila, Dianthus.

BH. separate off groups 1, 4—7 as an independent fam. *Illecebraceae* (Monochlam. Curvembryae), retaining the rest (*Caryophylleae*) in Polypetalae Caryophyllinae. This is an unnatural separation of closely allied groups. See discussion of relationships of these fams. in *Nat. Pfl.* (Caryophyllaceae, p. 68).

Caryophyllata Tourn. = Geum Tourn. (Rosac.).

Caryophyllatus (Lat.), with long claw.

Caryophylleae (*BH.*). See above.

Caryophyllinae (*BH.*). The 4th cohort of Polypetalae.

Caryophyllus L. = Eugenia L. (*BH.*) = Jambosa DC. p.p. (Myrt.).

Caryopitys Small (*Pinus* p.p.). Pinaceae. 2 N. Am.

Caryopsis, achene with pericarp and testa united, *Gramineae*.
Caryopteris Bunge. Verbenaceae (5). 5 Himal. to Japan.
Caryospermum Blume (*Perrottetia* p.p. *EP.*). Celast. 3 Indomal.
Caryota L. Palmae (IV. 1). 10 Indomal. Stem columnar; l. bipinnate. Infl. of a number of equal branches hanging down like a brush. They appear in descending order, the oldest in the crown, the younger lower down in the axils of the old leaf-sheaths. Fls. in groups of 3, one ♀ between two ♂. Sta. 9—∞. Cpl. 1. Berry. *C. urens* L. (toddy palm) cult.; it yields palm sugar (see Arenga), sago (see Metroxylon), Kitul fibre, wood, &c.
Casasia A. Rich. Rubiaceae (I. 8). 5 W.I., Fla. G 1-loc.
Cascara sagrada, *Rhamnus Purshiana* DC.
Cascarilla Wedd. (*Ladenbergia* p.p. *EP.*). Rubiaceae (I. 4). 20 S. Am. The bark of some resembles that of Cinchona (see also Croton), but the amount of alkaloid is small.
Cascarilla bark, *Croton Cascarilla* Benn., *Cascarilla*.
Cascaronia Griseb. Leguminosae (III. 6). 1 Argentina.
Casearia Jacq. Flacourtiaceae (7) (Samydaceae *BH.*). 150 trop. *C. praecox* Griseb. (Cuba, trop. S. Am.), W.I. box (useful wood).
Caseola Nor. Inc. sed. Nomen.
Cashaw (W.I.), *Prosopis*.
Cashew nut, *Anacardium occidentale* L.
Casimirella Hassler. Icacinaceae. 1 Paraguay.
Casimiroa La Llave. Rutaceae (IV). 5 Cent. Am. Ed. fr. Exalb.
Casparya Klotzsch = Begonia L. p.p. (Begon.).
Cassandra D. Don (*Lyonia* p.p. *EP.*). Ericac. (II. 1). 1 N. temp.
Cassareep, *Manihot*.
Cassava, *Manihot*.
Cassebeera Kaulf. = Cheilanthes, Pellaea, &c. (Polypod.).
Cassebeeria Dennst. (*Sonerila* Roxb.). Melast. (I). 60 warm As.
Casselia Nees et Mart. Verbenaceae (I). 6 Brazil, Paraguay.
Cassia Tourn. ex L. Leguminosae (II. 5). 400 trop. and warm temp. (exc. Eur.). Trees, shrubs and herbs with paripinnate l. and stips. of various types. Fl. ·|·, but with petals almost equal in size. The sta. may be 10, but the 3 upper ones are usu. reduced to stds. or absent. The anthers usu. open by pores. The 5 upper sta. are generally short, the 2 lower are long and project outwards. In many two forms of fl. occur, one in which the lower sta. project to the left, the other in which they project to the right. It was once thought that this *enantiostyly* was a kind of heterostylism, but both types of fl. occur on one plant. It would appear to be simply a case of variation in symmetry (*cf.* Exacum, Saintpaulia). In many sp. a division of labour takes place among the sta. (*cf.* Heeria); the insect visitors eat the pollen of the short sta. and carry away on their bodies that of the long. There is no honey. Fr. often chambered up by 'false' septa running across it—outgrowths from the placenta.

Many cult. for the l., which when dried form the drug senna. Alexandrian senna from *C. acutifolia* Delile, Italian *C. obovata* Collad., Arabian *C. angustifolia* Vahl. *C. Fistula* L. (purging Cassia, pudding-pipe tree) has its seeds embedded in laxative pulp.
Cassia bark, *Cinnamomum Cassia* Blume; **-broom**, *Cassia*.

Cassida Tourn. ex Adans. = Scutellaria Riv. (Labiat.).
Cassidispermum Hemsl. Sapotaceae. 1 Solomon Is.
Cassie flowers, *Acacia Farnesiana* Willd.
Cassine L. Celastraceae. 40 S. Afr., Madag. *C. crocea* Presl yields saffron-wood. L. alt. or opp.
Cassinia R. Br. Compositae (4). 20 S. Afr., Austr., N.Z.
Cassinopsis Sond. Icacinaceae (Olacin. *BH.*). 4 S. Afr., Madag.
Cassiope D. Don. Eric. (II. 1). 7 boreal. L. much rolled back (see fam.; *cf.* Empetrum); in *C. Redowskii* G. Don it is hollow.
Cassipourea Aubl. Rhizophoraceae. 10 trop. Am.
Cassupa Humb. et Bonpl. Rubiaceae (I. 7). 2 N.W. S. Am.
Cassytha L. Lauraceae (II). 15 palaeotrop. Parasites with the habit of Cuscuta.
Castalia Salisb. = Nymphaea L. p.p. (*C. speciosa* Salisb. = N. alba).
Castanea Tourn. ex L. (incl. *Castanopsis* Spach). Fagaceae. 40 ✻ *C. vulgaris* Lam. (*sativa* Mill.) is the chestnut. The ♂ fls. are in dich. of 3—7, the ♀ in groups of 3, yielding 3 nuts, enclosed in the prickly cupule (*cf.* others of fam. and Aesculus). Fr. ed.; useful wood and bark (used in tanning). See fam. for fl. diagram.
Castanella Spruce (*Paullinia* p.p. *EP.*). Sapind. (I). 1 Brazil.
Castaneous, chestnut-coloured.
Castanopsis Spach (*Castanea* p.p. *EP.*). Fagaceae. 35 trop. As.
Castanospermum A. Cunn. Leguminosae (III. 1). 1 sub-trop. Austr., *C. australe* A. Cunn. (Australian chestnut), has ed. seeds.
Castanospora F. Muell. Sapindaceae (I). 1 warm E. Austr.
Castela Turp. Simarubaceae. 12 C. and S. Am., W.I.
Castelaria Small. Simarubaceae. 8 W.I. to California.
Castelnavia Tul. et Wedd. Podostemaceae. 7 Brazil.
Castilleja Mutis. Scrophulariaceae (III. 3). 90 N. Am., As., S. Am. (painted lady, paint-brush). The upper l., or sometimes only their outer ends, are brightly coloured, adding to the conspicuousness of the fls. (*cf.* Cornus, Poinsettia, &c.).
Castilloa Cervant. Moraceae (II). 10 trop. Am., Cuba. The latex of *C. elastica* Cerv. yields caoutchouc (C. American or Panama rubber, Caucho, Ulé; *cf.* Hevea, &c.).
Castor oil, *Ricinus communis* L.
Castratella Naud. Metastomaceae (I). 1 Colombia.
Casual, an occasional weed of cultivation, not naturalised.
Casuarina Linn. Casuarinaceae. 35 Austr., Polynes., &c. Trees, often of weeping habit, with long slender green branches, cylindrical and deeply grooved. At the nodes are borne whorls of scale l. like those of Equisetum. The stomata and green tissue are at the bases of the grooves, whilst the ridges are formed of sclerenchyma, so that the plant is markedly xero. Fls. unisex. The ♂ are borne in term. spikes on short lat. branches. The internodes are short and at every node is a cup (formed of the combined bracts) with several sta. hanging out over the edge. Each repres. a ♂ fl. and has a 2-leaved P and 2 bracteoles. The ♀ fls. are borne in dense spherical heads. Each is naked in the axil of a bract, has 2 bracteoles, and consists of 2 cpls., syncp., the post. loc. empty, the ant. containing 2 or more ov. The long styles hang out beyond the bracts and wind-fert.

occurs. Afterwards the whole head becomes woody (bracts as well) enclosing the ripening seeds. The seed is winged and is enclosed in the woody bracteoles. Exalb. Wood (beef-wood) valued for hardness; several sp. are used, known in Austr. as she-oak, forest-oak, &c. The green shoots are used as fodder for cattle.

Casuarinaceae (*EP.*, *BH.*). Dicots. (Archichl. Verticil.; Unisexuales *BH.*). Only genus Casuarina (*q.v.*). The place to be assigned to this fam. in the natural system has been much disputed. Its nearest allies seem to be Betulaceae. In 1891 Treub discovered the chalazogamic fert. (*cf. Chalazogamae*) and proposed to remove it from its place near the B. Later discoveries however show that these pl. too are chalazogamic, as also Juglans, and thus C. may still be kept beside them.

Casuarineae (*BH.*) = preceding.

Casuariniflorae (Warming). The 2nd cohort of Choripetalae.

Cat-brier (Am.), *Smilax*; **-claw** (W.I.), *Bignonia Unguis-cati* L.; **-mint, -nip**, *Nepeta Cataria* L.; **-'s ear**, *Hypochaeris*; **-'s foot**, *Antennaria*; **-'s tail**, *Typha*.

Catabrosa Beauv. Gramineae (10). 7 temp. (1 Brit.).

Catalpa Scop. Bignoniaceae (2). 10 Am., E. As. *C. bignonioides* Walt. (cult. orn. tree) yields a durable timber.

Catamixis Thoms. Compositae (12). 1 Himal.

Catananche L. Compositae (13). 5 Medit.

Catanthera F. Muell. Ericaceae (III. 1). 1 New Guinea.

Cataphyllary leaves, scales.

Catapodium Link. (*Festuca* p.p. *BH.*). Gramin. (10). 2 Medit.

Catappa Gaertn. = Terminalia L. p.p. (Combret.).

Catasetum Rich. Orchidaceae (II. 11). 40 trop. Am. Epiph. 3 widely different forms occur on different (or sometimes on the same) stocks. Long regarded as separate gen., it is now known that they are all forms of C. The old genus C. is the ♂ form, *Myanthus* Lindl. the ☿ and *Monachanthus* Lindl. the ♀. The labellum is uppermost in the fl. The pollinia are ejected with violence when one of the horns of the column is touched. (Darwin's *Orchids*, p. 178; Rolfe in *Linn. Soc. Journ.*, 27, 1890.)

Catch-fly, *Lychnis*, *Silene*.

Catechu, *Acacia Catechu* Willd.

Catesbaea L. Rubiaceae (I. 8). 10 W. Ind., Fla.

Catha Forsk. Celastraceae. 1 Arabia, Afr., *C. edulis* Forsk. The l. are used by Arabs like tea, under the name Khat or Cafta.

Catha G. Don = Celastrus L. (Celastr.).

Cathartolinum Reichb. (*Linum* p.p.). Linaceae. 50 N. Am.

Cathastrum Turcz. (*Pleurostylia EP.*). Celastr. 1 S. Afr.

Cathcartia Hook. f. Papaveraceae (II). 4 Himal., China.

Cathedra Miers. Olacaceae. 5 Brazil.

Cathestecum J. Presl. Gramineae (10). 2 Mex., Texas.

Catis O. F. Cook (*Euterpe* p.p. *EP.*). Palmae (IV. 1). 1 Brazil.

Catjang, dhal, *Cajanus indicus* Spreng.

Catkin, a pendulous spike, *Betulaceae*, *Fagaceae*, *Salicaceae*.

Catoblastus H. Wendl. Palmae (IV. 1). 3 trop. S. Am.

Catocoryne Hook. f. Melastomaceae (I). 1 Peru.

Catonia P. Br. Inc. sed. 1 Jamaica.
Catonia Raf. Inc. sed. 1 habitat?
Catonia Vell. Inc. sed. 1 Brazil.
Catopheria Benth. Labiatae (VIII). 3 trop. Am.
Catophractes D. Don. Bignoniaceae (2). 1 trop. Afr.
Catopsis Griseb. Bromeliaceae (1). 25 W.I., Mex., Andes.
Catosperma Benth. Goodeniaceae. 1 trop. Austr.
Catostemma Benth. Bombacaceae. 1 Guiana.
Cattleya Lindl. Orchidaceae (II. 6). 30 trop. Am., largely cult.; showy fls. The labellum encloses the column but is not united to it. From its base a nectary runs down into the ovary. The action of the parts of the fl. is like that of Epipactis (Darwin, *Orchids*, p. 143).
Cattleyopsis Lem. (*Laelia* p.p. *EP.*). Orchid. (II. 6). 2 W.I.
Catutsjeron Adans. (*Holigarna* Buch.-Ham.). Anacardiaceae (4). 5 Indomal.
Caucalis L. (incl. *Torilis* Adans.). Umbelliferae (III. 2). 25 N. temp., 5 Brit. (hedge-parsley, &c.).
Caucanthus Forsk. Malpighiaceae (1). 3 E. Afr., Arabia.
Cauda, a tail-like appendage; **-tus** (Lat.), tailed.
Caudex, a trunk or stock.
Caudicle, *cf. Orchidaceae.*
Caul- (Lat. pref.), stem; **-escens** (Lat.), with obvious stem; **-icle**, a diminutive stalk; **-iflory**, production of fl. from old stems, *Artocarpus*, *Averrhoa*, *Clavija*, *Crescentia*, *Cynometra*, *Ficus*, *Goethea*, *Kigelia*, *Theobroma*, *Theophrasta*; **-ine**, on the stem; **-caulis** (Lat. suff.), -stemmed; **-ocarpic**, fruiting repeatedly; **-ome**, organ of stem nature.
Caulanthus S. Wats. Cruciferae (1). 8 W. U.S. *C. procerus* Wats. (wild cabbage) ed.
Cauliflower, *Brassica oleracea* L. var.
Caulinia DC. = Posidonia Koen. p.p.; **do.** Willd. = Naias L. p.p.
Caulophyllum Michx. (*Leontice* p.p. *EP.*). Berb. 2 N.E. As., N. Am. (cohosh).
Caustis R. Br. Cyperaceae (II). 7 Austr.
Cautleya Royle (*Roscoea* p.p. *BH.*). Zingib. (1). 5 Himal.
Cavaleriea Leveillé. Hamamelidaceae. 1 China.
Cavanillesia Ruiz et Pav. Bombacaceae. 2 S. Am.
Cavendishia Lindl. Ericaceae (III. 2). 30 trop. Am.
Cayaponia Silva Manso. Cucurbitaceae (3). 70 warm Am., Afr.
Cayenne pepper, *Capsicum annuum* L.
Caylusea A. St Hil. Resedaceae. 2 E. Afr. to India.
Ceanothus L. Rhamn. 40 N. Am., often cult. orn. shrubs.
Ceara rubber, *Manihot Glaziovii* Muell.-Arg.
Cebu hemp, Manila hemp, *Musa textilis* Née.
Cecropia L. Moraceae (III). 45 trop. Am. Trees of rapid growth, with very light wood, used for floats, &c. Infl. a very complex cyme (see *Bot. Centr.* 57, p. 6). *C. peltata* L. is the trumpet tree, so called from the use made of its hollow stems by the Uaupès Indians (Wallace, *Amaz.* ch. XII). The hollows are often inhabited by fierce ants (*Azteca* sp.) which rush out if the tree be shaken, and attack the intruder. Schimper has made an investigation of this *symbiosis* (or

living together for mutual benefit) of plant and animal, showing that there is here a true case of myrmecophily as in *Acacia sphaerocephala* (*q.v.*). These ants protect the C. from the leaf-cutter ants. The internodes are hollow but do not communicate directly with the air. Near the top of each however is a thin place in the wall. A gravid ♀ ant burrows through this and brings up her brood inside the stem. The base of the leaf-stalk is swollen and bears food bodies (*cf.* Acacia) on the lower side, upon which the ants feed. New ones form as the old are eaten. Several other sp. show similar features. An interesting point, that goes to show the adaptive nature of these phenomena, is that in one sp. the stem is covered with wax which prevents the leaf-cutters from climbing up, and there are neither food-bodies nor the thin places in the internodes.

Cedar, *Cedrela, Cedrus, Toona,* &c.; **Atlantic,** *Cedrus atlantica* Manetti; **Australian red-,** *Toona*; **bastard-,** *Chickrassia* (W.I.), *Guazuma tomentosa* H. B. K.; **Bermuda-,** *Juniperus bermudiana* L.; **Japanese-,** *Cryptomeria*; **of Lebanon,** *Cedrus*; **Oregon-,** *Cupressus Lawsoniana* A. Murr.; **pencil-,** *Juniperus*; **red-,** *Juniperus*; **Siberian-,** *Pinus Cembra* L.; **W. Indian-,** *Cedrela*; **white-,** *Chamaecyparis, Chickrassia, Libocedrus*; **yellow-,** *Chamaecyparis*; **-wood,** *Toona.*

Cedrela P. Br. (*BH.* incl. *Toona, q.v.*). Meliaceae. 100 trop. Am. Many yield valuable timber, *e.g. C. odorata* L., the West Indian Cedar, used in cigar-boxes.

Cedrelopsis Baill. Meliaceae (I). 2 Madag.

Cedronella Riv. Labiatae (VI). 1 Canaries, Madeira. L. ternate.

Cedrus (Tourn.) Mill. Coniferae (Pinaceae; see C. for gen. char.). 3, *C. Libani* Barrel. (Cedar of Lebanon), *C. atlantica* Manetti (Atlantic Cedar; Algeria) and *C. Deodara* Loud. (Deodar; Himal., gregarious, and reaching to 40 ft. in girth); all probably vars. of one sp. Handsome evergreen trees (often planted for orn.) with needle l. and long and short shoots; the latter may grow for several years and even develope into long shoots. Fls. sol., in the position of short shoots. The cone ripens in 2—3 years. Wood durable and valued for building, &c.

Ceiba Gaertn. (*Bombax* L. p.p.; *Eriodendron* DC. *EP.*). Bombac. 10 trop. Am. *C. pentandra* Gaertn. is the silk-cotton (*cf.* Eriodendron).

Celandine, *Ranunculus Ficaria* L.; **greater-,** *Chelidonium majus* L.; **W. Indian,** *Bocconia.*

Celastraceae (*EP.*, *BH.*). Dicots. (Archichl. Sapindales; Celastrales *BH.*). 38 gen. with 480 sp., trop. and temp. Trees or shrubs with simple, often leathery, l. and cymose (rarely racemose) infl. Fl. small, reg., usu. ☿. K 4—5, free or united, C 4—5. There is usu. a well marked disc, on the upper side or edge of which are borne 4—5 sta. $\underline{G}$ (2—5), usu. with as many loculi, sometimes partly sunk in the disc. Ovules generally 2 in each loc., usu. erect, anatr. or apotr. Fr. a loculic. caps., samara, drupe, berry or indehi. caps. Seed usu. with brightly coloured aril. Endosp. usu. present. *Chief genera:* Euonymus, Celastrus, Cassine.

Celastrales (*BH.*). The 9th cohort of Polypetalae.

Celastrineae (*BH.*) = Celastraceae.

Celastrus L. Celastraceae. 50 trop. and subtrop. Climbing shrubs with fruit like Euonymus.
Celebnia Nor. Inc. sed. Nomen.
Celeriac, *Apium graveolens* L. var. *rapaceum*.
Celery, *Apium graveolens* L.; **-pine**, *Phyllocladus*.
Cellulose, the carbohydrate of which cell walls are composed.
Celmisia Cass. Compositae (3). 50 N.Z., Austr., &c.
Celome Greene (*Cleome* L. p.p.). Capparid. (V). 1 N. Am.
Celosia L. Amarantaceae (1). 35 trop. and temp., most interesting *C. cristata* L., the cock's-comb, a cult. (but now hereditary) monstrosity, in which fasciation of the fls. of the infl. occurs.
Celsa Vell. Zygophyllaceae. 1 Brazil.
Celsia L. Scrophulariaceae (I. 1). 40 Medit., Afr., As.
Celtidaceae = Ulmaceae p.p.
Celtis Tourn. Ulmaceae. 75 *, S. Afr. Like Ulmus, but intr. anthers, drupe, and curved embryo. Fr. of nettle-tree (*C. australis* L.) ed.; wood useful for turning; tree used as fodder in India.
Cenarrhenes Labill. Proteaceae (1). 1 Tasmania.
Cenchropsis Nash (*Cenchrus* p.p.). Gram. (5). 1 warm Am., W.I.
Cenchrus L. Gramineae (5). 25 trop. and warm temp. Spikelet surrounded by invol. of sterile spikelets, which in some sp. become hard and prickly, surrounding the fr. and acting as a means of distribution by animals (*cf.* Tribulus, &c.). *C. tribuloides* L. is a very troublesome pest in the wool-growing districts of N. Am.
Cenia Comm. ex Juss. (*Cotula* p.p. *EP.*). Compositae (7). 9 S. Afr.
Cenocentrum Gagnep. Malvaceae. 1 Indochina.
Cenolophium Koch (*Selinum* p.p. *BH.*). Umbel. (III. 5). 1 Eur., As.
Cenostigma Tul. Leguminosae (II. 8). 3 Brazil, Paraguay.
Censer-mechanism, *Aconitum*, and *cf.* Dispersal.
Centaurea L. Compositae (11). 600 cosmop., chiefly Medit.; several Brit. *e.g.* *C. nigra* L. (knapweed), *C. Scabiosa* L., *C. Cyanus* L. (blue-bottle or cornflower). In the last two the outer fls. are neuter with enlarged C (*cf.* Hydrangea). *C. Calcitrapa* L. (star-thistle) has long spiny invol. br. The fl. of C. shows the usual construction but the sta. are sensitive to contact and when touched (*e.g.* by insects probing) contract, thus forcing out the pollen at the top of tube. In *C. montana* L. and others there is a nectary on each br. of the invol. Numbers of ants are thus attracted.
Centaurium Gilib. (*Erythraea* Borkh.). Gent. (I). 30 N. Am.
Centaurodendron Johow. Compositae (11). 1 Juan Fernandez.
Centauropsis Boj. Compositae (1). 3 Madagascar.
Centaury, *Erythraea Centaurium* Pers.
Centella L. (*Hydrocotyle* p.p. *BH.*). Umbel. (I. 1). 20 S. Afr. to As.
Centema Hook. f. Amarantaceae (2). 5 trop. Afr.
Centemopsis Schinz. Amarantaceae (2). 3 S. and trop. Afr.
Centipeda Lour. Compositae (7). 5 Chili, Madag., trop. As., Austr.
Centotheca Desv. Gramineae (10). 3 trop. As., Afr.
Centradenia G. Don. Melastomaceae (I). 4 Mexico, Cent. Am. *C. rosea* Lindl. shows habitual anisophylly.
Centradeniastrum Cogn. Melastomaceae (I). 1 Peru.
Centranthera R. Br. Scrophular. (III. 2). 5 trop. As., China, Austr.

Centrantheropsis Bonati. Scrophular. (III. 2). 1 China.

Centranthus DC. Valerianaceae. 12 Medit., Eur. *C. ruber* DC. (red spur-valerian) cult. orn. C spurred at the base; at the end of the spur honey is secreted. The tube of the C has a partition dividing it into two, one containing the style, the other, lined with downward-pointing hairs, leading to the spur. Fl. protandr.; only long-tongued insects can obtain honey.

Centratherum Cass. Compositae (1). 15 trop.

Centric (l.), circular in section, with tissues distr. evenly all round, *Allium*, *Bobartia*, *Eleocharis*, *Juncus*, *Littorella*.

Centrifugal, away from centre; **-petal,** towards centre.

Centrilla Lindau. Acanthaceae (IV. B). 1 Cuba.

Centrocarpha D. Don = Rudbeckia L. p.p. (Compos.).

Centroglossa Barb. Rodr. (*Zygostates* Lindl. *EP.*). Orchidaceae (II. 19). 5 Brazil, Paraguay.

Centrolepidaceae (*EP.*, *BH.*). Monocotyledons (Farinosae; Glumaceae *BH.*). 6 gen., 32 sp. Austr., N.Z., S. Am., Polynes., S.E. As. Small grass-like herbs with spikes of small fls., ☿ or unisex., naked or with 1—3 hair-structures round them. A 1—2, $\underline{G}$ 1—∞, each with one pend. orthotr. ov. *Chief genus:* Centrolepis.

Centrolepis Labill. Centrolepidaceae. 20 Austr., E. As.

Centrolobium Mart. Leguminosae (III. 8). 3 trop. Am. Pod winged. *C. robustum* Mart. yields good timber (zebra wood).

Centromadia Greene (*Hemizonia* p.p.). Compos. (5). 5 Calif.

Centronia D. Don. Melastomaceae (1). 15 trop. Am.

Centropetalum Lindl. Orchidaceae (II. 20). 8 Andes.

Centroplacus Pierre. Euphorbiaceae (A. I. 1). 1 trop. Afr.

Centropogon Presl. Campanulaceae (III). 90 trop. Am., W.I.

Centrosema Benth. (*Bradburya EP.*). Legum. (III. 10). 30 Am.

Centrospermae. The 17th order of Dicots. (Archichl.). *Cf.* p. xiv.

Centrostegia A. Gray. Polygonaceae (I. 1). 2 California.

Centrostigma Schlechter. Orchid. (II. 1). 3 Nyassaland.

Centunculus Dill. ex L. Primul. 1 temp. and subtrop., incl. Brit.

Century, set of 100 dried plants.

Century plant, *Agave americana* L.

Cepa (Tourn.) L. = Allium Tourn. (Lili.).

Cephaelis Sw. (*Uragoga* L. *EP.*). Rubiaceae (II. 5). 130 trop., esp. Brazil. For ipecacuanha *cf.* Uragoga.

Cephal- (Gr. pref.), head.

Cephalacanthus Lindau. Acanthaceae (IV. B). 1 Peru.

Cephalandra Schrad. = Coccinia Wight et Arn. (Cucurb.).

Cephalanthera Rich. Orchidaceae (II. 2). 10 N. temp., 3 Brit. No rostellum; the pollen germinates *in situ*, fertilising its own stigma (Darwin, *Orchids*, p. 80). The lat. stds. (see fam.) are easily seen. Darwin regards C. as a degraded Epipactis (*cf.* Cephalopipactis).

Cephalanthus L. Rubiaceae (I. 6). 8 warm Am., As. Fl. in heads.

Cephalaralia Harms. Araliaceae (2). 1 Austr.

Cephalaria Schrad. Dipsacaceae. 35 Medit., Afr.

Cephalipterum A. Gray. Compositae (4). 1 S. and W. Austr.

Cephalobembix Rydberg. Compositae (6). 1 Mexico.

Cephalocarpus Nees. Cyper. (II). 1 Brazil. Habit of Dracaena.

Cephalocereus Pfeiff. (em. K. Schum.; *Cereus* Mill. p.p. *BH.*). Cactaceae (III. 1). 48 Brazil to Fla.
Cephalocroton Hochst. Euphorb. (A. II. 4). 6 trop. Afr.
Cephalocrotonopsis Pax (preceding, p.p.). Euph. (A. II. 4). 1 Socotra.
Cephalomappa Baill. Euphorbiaceae (A. II. 4). 1 Borneo.
Cephalomedinilla Merrill. Melastomaceae (I). 1 Phil. Is.
Cephalonema K. Schum. Tiliaceae. 1 trop. Afr.
Cephalopappus Nees et Mart. Compositae (12). 1 Bahia.
Cephalophilum Börner (*Polygonum* p.p.). Polyg. (II. 2). 1 N. Am., N. As.
Cephalophora Cav. (*Helenium* p.p. *EP.*). Compos. (6). 12 temp. S. Am.
Cephalopipactis × Aschers. et Graebn. Orchid. Hybrid between Cephalanthera and Epipactis.
Cephalosphaera Warb. (*Brochoneura* p.p.). Myristic. 1 trop. Afr.
Cephalostachyum Munro. Gramineae (13). 8 Indomal., Madag.
Cephalostemon R. Schomb. Rapateaceae. 5 Brazil, Guiana.
Cephalostigma A. DC. Campanulaceae (I). 7 trop.
Cephalotaceae (*EP.*; *Saxifragaceae* p.p. *BH.*). Dicots. (Archichl. Rosales). Only genus Cephalotus (*q.v.*).
Cephalotaxus Sieb. et Zucc. Conif. (Taxac. 7; see C. for gen. char.). 6 E. As. *C. Fortunei* Hook. cult. orn. shrub. All shoots of unlimited growth. Fls. dioec., the ♂ in heads in the axils of the l. of the preceding year, the ♀ stalked, of several pairs of l. each with a short axillary shoot bearing two ov. Seeds 1—2, with fleshy aril.
Cephalotomandra Karst. et Triana (*Pisonia* L. p.p. *EP.*). Nyctaginaceae. 1 Colombia.
Cephalotus Labill. Cephalot. 1 in marshes at King George's Sound, W. Austr. *C. follicularis* Labill. An interesting pl. with pitchers like Nepenthes or Sarracenia, though not nearly related to either. The lower l. of the rosette form pitchers, the upper are flat and green (*cf.* this division of labour with that in N. and S.), the rhiz. annually producing both. The pitcher has much the structure of N. and catches insects in the same way. Fl. ☿, apetalous, reg.; P 6, valvate; A 6+6; $\underline{G}$ 6, or ± united, each with 1 (rarely 2) basal erect anatr. ov. with dorsal raphe. Follicle with 1 seed; embryo small in fleshy endosp.
Ceramanthus Malme (*Sarcostemma* p.p.). Ascl. (II. 1). 2 S. Am.
Ceranthera Ellis. Labiatae (VI). 2 S.E. U.S.
Ceraria Pearson et E. L. Stephens. Portulac. 3 S. Afr.
Cerasee (W.I.), *Momordica*.
Cerasin, an insoluble constituent of gums, merely swelling in water; *Prunus*.
Cerasiocarpum Hook. f. Cucurbit. (2). 1 Malay Arch., Ceylon.
Cerastium (Dill.) L. (incl. *Moenchia* Ehrh.). Caryophyllaceae (I. 1). 100 N. temp., 5 or more Brit. (mouse-ear chickweed).
Cerasus (Tourn.) L. = Prunus L. *C. Avium* Moench., *Laurocerasus* Loisel., *lusitanicus* Loisel., *Padus* Delarb. = P. Avium, &c.; *C. vulgaris* Mill. = P. Cerasus.
Cerat- (Gr. pref.), horn.
Ceratandra Eckl. Orchidaceae (II. 1). 9 S. Afr.
Ceratandropsis Rolfe. Orchidaceae (II. 1). 2 S.W. Cape Col.

Ceratiola Michx. Empetraceae. 1 Atl. N. Am.
Ceratiosicyos Nees. Achariaceae. 1 S. Afr.
Ceratites Soland. ex Miers. Apocyn. (I. 3). 1 Rio de Janeiro.
Ceratocarpus Buxb. ex L. Chenopod. (A). 1 Persia, Afghan.
Ceratocaryum Nees (*Willdenowia EP.*). Restiaceae. 2 Cape Col.
Ceratocephalus Moench. = Ranunculus L. p.p. (Ranunc.).
Ceratochaete Lunell (*Zizania* p.p.). Gramin. (6). 2 N. Am.
Ceratochilus Blume. Orchidaceae (II. 20). 4 Indomal.
Ceratochloa Beauv. = Bromus Dill. p.p. (Gram.).
Ceratocnemum Coss. et Balansa (*Rapistrum* p.p. *EP.*). Cruciferae (2). 1 Morocco.
Ceratodiscus Batalin (*Corallodiscus* p.p. *EP.*). Gesn. (I). 1 Chi.
Ceratogyne Turcz. Compositae (7). 1 W. temp. Austr.
Ceratolacis Wedd. Podostemaceae. 1 Brazil.
Ceratolobus Blume. Palmae (III. 2). 2 Malay Arch.
Ceratominthe Briq. Labiatae (VI). 2 Andes.
Ceratonia L. Leguminosae (II. 5). 1 Medit., *C. Siliqua* L. (carob-tree). The pods (Algaroba, St John's bread) are full of juicy pulp containing sugar and gum, and are used for fodder. The seeds are said to have been the original of the carats of jewellers.
Ceratopetalum Smith. Cunon. 2 E. Austr. Light timber.
Ceratophyllaceae (*EP.*, *BH.*). Dicots. (Archichl. Ranales; Monochlam. *BH.*). Only genus Ceratophyllum (*q.v.*). As usu. with water-plants it is difficult to decide upon a position for the C. in the classification. The one free cpl. and several P leaves seem to place them in Ranales, and they are distinguished from Nymphaeaceae by the orthotr. ov., whorled l., &c. Eichler placed them in Urticinae.
Ceratophylleae (*BH.*) = preceding.
Ceratophyllum L. Ceratophyllaceae. 3 cosmop.; *C. demersum* L. and *C. submersum* L. Brit. (hornworts). Water-pl., rootless, with thin stems and whorls of much-divided submerged l. The pl. decays behind as it grows in front, so that veg. repr. occurs by the setting free of the branches. The old l. are translucent and horny, whence the name. Winter buds are not formed, the pl. merely sinking in autumn and rising in spring.

Fls. monoec., axillary, sessile, with sepaloid P. In the ♂, P about (12), hypog.; A 12—16 on convex recept., with oval non-cutinised pollen. In the ♀, P (9—10), hypog.; G 1, the midrib anterior; ovule 1, orthotr., pend. Achene crowned by the persistent style, which in *C. demersum* is hooked. Endosp. Fl. water-pollin.; the anthers break off and float up through the water (each has a sort of float at top of theca); the pollen is of the same specific gravity as water (*cf.* Zostera) and drifts about till it reaches a stigma.
Ceratopsis Lindl. = Epipogum S. G. Gmel. (*BH.*) = Galera Blume.
Ceratopteris Brongn. Parkeriaceae. 2 trop., subtrop. *C. thalictroides* Brongn. is aquatic. Its fronds are ed.
Ceratopyxis Hook. f. Rubiaceae (II. 3). 1 Cuba.
Ceratosanthes Burm. ex. Adans. Cucurb. (2). 10 Braz. to W.I.
Ceratosanthus Schur. = Delphinium Tourn. p.p. (Ranunc.).
Ceratosepalum Oliv. Tiliaceae. 1 E. trop. Afr.
Ceratostema Juss. (*Thibaudia* p.p. *EP.*). Eric. (III. 2). 25 S. Am.

Ceratostigma Bunge. Plumbaginaceae. 10 trop. Afr. to China. The total infl. is racemose, the partials dichasial.
Ceratostylis Blume. Orchidaceae (II. *a*. III). 50 Indomal., Polyn.
Ceratotheca Endl. Pedaliaceae. 5 trop. and S. Afr.
Ceratozamia Brongn. Cycadaceae. 6 Mexico.
Ceraunia Nor. Inc. sed. Nomen.
Cerbera L. (excl. *Tanghinia* Thou.). Apocyn. (I. 3). 6 Indomal., Madag. The floating fr. are familiar on the coast. L. alt.
Cerberiopsis Vieill. Apocyn. (inc. sed.). 1 New Caled.
Cercanthemum Van Tiegh. = Ouratea Aubl. (Ochnac.).
Cercestis Schott. Araceae (IV). 9 W. Afr.
Cercidiphyllaceae (*EP.*; *Magnoliaceae* p.p. *BH.*). See Supplement.
Cercidiphyllum Sieb. et Zucc. Cercidiph. 2 Japan. Useful wood.
Cercidium Tul. Leguminosae (II. 7). 8 warm Am.
Cercis L. Legum. (II. 4). 5 N. temp. *C. Siliquastrum* L. (Judas-tree; Judas is said to have hanged himself on one), cult. orn. tree in Brit. The fls. appear before the l., in bunches on the older twigs, and have a very papilionaceous look, the two lower pets. enclosing the essential organs. Serial buds in the axils. Good wood.
Cercocarpus H. B. et K. Rosaceae (III. 3). 10 Mex. to Oregon. C o.
Cercopetalum Gilg. Capparid. (II). 1 Cameroons.
Cercophora Miers. Lecythidaceae. 1 Amazon valley.
Cerdia Moç. et Sesse. Caryophyllaceae (I. 3). 2 Mex.
Cereals, the grasses (Gramineae) yielding food to man, wheat, rice, maize, oats, barley, rye, millet, &c.
Cereus Mill. (*BH.* incl. *Cephalocereus* Pfeiff., *Echinocereus* Engelm., *Echinopsis* Zucc., *Pilocereus* Lem.). Cactaceae (III. 1). 25 Am., W. Ind. Most are erect cylindrical forms, rarely branched, with ribs or less often mammillae (see fam.). *C. giganteus* Engelm. (Texas) is the largest of the cacti; it grows to 70 ft. high and 2 ft. thick with candelabra-like branching. *C. grandiflorus* Mill. is the night-flowering cactus, whose sweetly-scented fls. open in the evening and wither before morning. Others, *e.g.* *C. triangularis* Mill., behave in the same way. These sp. are mostly trailing forms with adv. r. upon the stems. A number of cases of close resemblance may be found between sp. of C. and sp. of Euphorbia. Fr. of most ed., often preserved. [*Cf.* Britton & Rose, *Cactaceae.*
Ceriferous, wax-producing.
Cerinthe (Tourn.) L. Boraginaceae (IV. 4). 7 Eur., Medit.
Ceriops Arn. Rhizophoraceae. 2 palaeotrop. coast.
Cerium Lour. Inc. sed. 1 China.
Cernuus (Lat.), nodding.
Cerolepis Pierre (*Camptostylus EP.*). Flac. (1). None described.
Ceropegia L. Asclepiadaceae (II. 3). 120 Afr., As., Austr. Erect or twining herbs or undershrubs, ± xero. Many have tuberous root-stocks, others are leafless and sometimes have fleshy Stapelia-like stems. The fls. form a trap like *Aristolochia Clematitis*. The C-tube widens at the base and at the top the teeth spread out, but in some they hold together at the tips, making a sort of umbrella. The tube is lined with downward pointing hairs, and small flies, attracted by the colour and smell, creep into the fl. and cannot escape till the hairs wither, when they emerge with pollinia on their proboscides

Ceropteris Link. Polypod. 8 trop. Am., Afr., Borneo. Silver fern.
Cerothamnus Tidestrom. Myric. 4 N. Am., W.I. Wax myrtle.
Ceroxylon Humb. et Bonpl. Palm. (IV. 1). 5 N. Andes. *C. andicolum* H. et B. and others secrete wax on the stems; it is used for gramophone discs, candles, &c.
Cerris Rafin. = Quercus L. (Fag.).
Ceruana Forsk. Comp. (3). 1 Egypt, trop. Afr.
Cervantesia Ruiz et Pav. Santal. 4 Andes.
Cervia Rodr. Convolv. (inc. sed.). 1 Spain.
Cervicina Delile = Wahlenbergia Schrad. p.p. (Campan.). [stds.
Cespedesia Goudot. Ochn. 5 trop. S. Am. Seps. all alike. A ∞, no
Cestichis Thou. (*Stichorchis EP., Liparis BH.*). Orchid. (II. 4). 40 Masc. to Japan and Polynes. 2 jointed l. on each tuber.
Cestrum L. (*Habrothamnus* Endl.). Solan. (4). 150 warm Am., W.I. ♄.
Ceterach Lam. et DC. Polypod. 5 | ✻. [Some cult. orn.
Cetra Nor. Inc. sed. Nomen. [long process. G 1 with one pend. ov.
Cevallia Lagasc. Loas. 1 Mex., New Mex., Texas. Connective with
Ceylon gooseberry (Am.) *Dovyalis*; **oak**, *Schleichera trijuga* Willd.
Chaboissaea Fourn. Gramin. (10). 1 Mex.
Chabraea DC. = Leuceria Lag. p.p. (Comp.).
Chadsia Boj. Legum. (III. 6). 12 Madag. Caulifloral. Fls. scarlet.
Chaenactis DC. Comp. (6). 25 W. U. S. L. opp.
Chaenanthe Lindl. (*Diadenium BH.*). Orchid. (II. 19). 1 Peru.
Chaenarrhinum Reichb. = Linaria Tourn. (Scroph.)
Chaenesthes Miers = Iochroma Benth. (Solan.).
Chaenocephalus Griseb. Comp. (5). 12 W.I., S. Am. L. alt.
Chaenolobus Small. = Pterocaulon Ell. (Comp.) [Japanese quince).
Chaenomeles Lindl. = Pyrus L. (Ros.). 3 Chi., Jap. (Chinese or
Chaenopleura Rich. ex DC. = Miconia Ruiz et Pav. p.p. (Melastom).
Chaenorrhinum Lange (*Linaria* p.p. *BH.*). Scroph. (II. 3). 20 Medit., W. As. Post. cpl. larger. [Stigma capitate.
Chaenostoma Benth. (incl. *Lyperia* Benth.). Scroph. (II. 5). 120 Afr.
Chaerefolium Haller (*Anthriscus* p.p.). Umbell. (III. 2). 3 Eur., N. As.
Chaerophyllopsis Boissieu. Umbell. (III. 2). 1 China.
Chaerophyllum L. Umbell. (III. 2). 40 N. temp. *C. temulum* L. (chervil) in Brit. *C. bulbosum* L. cult. ed. r.
Chaet- (Gr. pref.), hair.
Chaetacanthus Nees (*Calophanes BH.*). Acanth. (IV. A.) 4 Afr. E. and S.
Chaetachme Planch. Ulm. 2 warm Afr.
Chaetadelpha A. Gray. Comp. (13). 1 S.W. U.S. Zigzag twigs.
Chaetanthera Ruiz et Pav. Comp. (12). 30 Chile, Peru. Cushion pl.
Chaetanthus R. Br. Restion. 1 S.W. Austr.
Chaetaria Beauv. = Aristida L. p.p. (Gram.)
Chaetium Nees. Gramin. (5). 3 trop. Am., Cuba. Glume with callus.
Chaetobromus Nees = Danthonia DC. (Gramin.). 5 S. Africa.
Chaetocalyx DC. Legum. (III. 7). 12 warm Am., W.I. Twining herbs.
Chaetocarpus Thw. Euphorb. (A. II. 6). 7 trop. G 3-loc. Stigma
Chaetocephala Barb. Rodr. = Pleurothallis R. Br. 2 Braz. [multifid.
Chaetochlamys Lindau. Acanth. (IV. B). 4 trop. S. Am.
Chaetochloa Scribn. = Setaria Beauv. (Gramin.). 50 warm.
Chaetocyperus Nees = Eleocharis R. Br. p.p. (Cyper.).

Chaetogastra DC. = Tibouchina Aubl. (Melastom.).
Chaetolepis Miq. Melastom. (I). 12 trop. Am., W.I. No appendages to connective.
Chaetopappa DC. (*Distasis* DC). Comp. (3). 3 Mex., S.W. U. S.
Chaetosciadium Boiss. Umbell. (III. 2). 1 E. Medit. Fr. bristly.
Chaetospermum Swingle (*Limonia* p.p.). Rut. (V). 1 Phil. Is.
Chaetospora R. Br. = Schoenus L. (Cyper.).
Chaetostachys Valeton. Rubi. (II. 5). 1 New Guin.
Chaetostoma DC. Melastom. (I). 20 mid. and S. Braz. G 3-loc.
Chaetosus Benth. Apocyn. (I. 1). 1 New Guinea.
Chaetothylax Nees. Acanth. (IV. B). 7 S. and C. Am. Cult. orn. fl.
Chaetotropis Kunth. Gramin. (8). 1 Chile. Like Agrostis, but axis prolonged.
Chaeturus Link. Gramin. (8). 2 Spain, Portugal.
Chaff-weed, *Centunculus minimus* L. (N. temp. and subtrop.).
Chailletia DC. See Dichapetalum Thou. 120 trop.
Chailletiaceae. See Dichapetalaceae.
Chain-fern (Am.), *Woodwardia*.
Chalarothyrsus Lindau. Acanth. (IV. B). 1 Mex.
Chalaza, the base of the ovule; **-ogamic**, *cf.* Chalazogamae.
Chalazocarpus Hiern. Rubi. (I. 8). 1 Angola.
Chalazogamae, a division of Angiospermae, proposed by Treub as the outcome of his work upon Casuarina (*Ann. Buitenz.* X, 1891).

Both in the development of the macrospores (embryo-sacs), which elongated downwards into the chalaza, and in the process of fertilisation, which took place through the chalaza, the difference from other known Angiosperms was so great, that Treub proposed to rearrange them into Chalazogamae and Porogamae (fertilised in the ordinary way), but as the phenomenon has since been observed in many other genera, especially of the lower types, it cannot be regarded as of classificatory value (for literature see former editions).
Chalcanthus Boiss. (*Hesperis* L. *BH.*). Crucif. (4). 1 Persia.
Chalcas L. = Murraya Koen. (Rut.)
Chalcoelytrum Lunell (*Sorghastrum* p.p.). Gramin. (2). 1 S.E. U. S.
Chalepophyllum Hook. f. Rubi. (I. 3). 2 Guiana. 2 bracteoles. Seps. unequal.
Chalicium (Cl.), a gravel-slide formation.
Chalk-glands, *Plumbaginaceae*, *Saxifraga*; **-plant**, *Gypsophila*.
Chamabainia Wight. Urtic. (3). 2 Indomal.
Chamae- (Gr. pref.), ground-.
Chamaealoe Berger (*Aloe* p.p.). Lili. (III). 1 S. Afr.
Chamaeangis Schlechter (*Angraecum*, &c. p.p.). Orchid. (II. 20). 12 trop. Afr., Madag. Masc.
Chamaeanthus Schlechter. Orchid. (II. 20). 6 Java, Borneo, New Guin.
Chamaeanthus Ule. Commelin. 1 Amaz. valley.
Chamaebatia Benth. Ros. (III. 3). 2 Calif. Glandular, aromatic.
Chamaebatiaria Maxim. Ros. (I. 1). 1 N. Am.
Chamaebuxus (Tourn.) Spach. = Polygala L. p.p. (Polygal.).
Chamaecerasus (Tourn.) Medic. = Lonicera L. (Caprifol.).
Chamaecereus Britton et Rose. Cact. (II. 1). 1 Arg.
Chamaechaenactis Rydberg (*Chaenactis* p.p.). Comp. (6). 1 U.S.
Chamaecissos Lunell = Glechoma L. (Labiat.).
Chamaecistus S. F. Gray = Loiseleuria Desv. (Eric.).

Chamaecladon Miq., Schott (*Homalomena* p.p. *PR.*). Arac. (v). 40 Malaya, Cochinchina, New Guin., Phil. Is.
Chamaecrista Moench. = Cassia Tourn. p.p. (Legum.). 100 warm.
Chamaecyparis Spach (*Thuya*, *Cupressus* p.p.). Conif. (Pin.; see C. for gen. char.). 8 N. Am., Japan, Formosa, incl. *C.* (*Cupressus*) *Lawsoniana* Parl. (N.W. U.S.; Lawson's cypress), *C.* (*Cupr.*) *nutkaensis* Spach (Alaska to Oregon; Sitka or yellow cypress, yellow cedar); *C.* (*Cupr.*) *thyoides* Britton, Sterns, et Poggenb. (*C. spheroidea* Spach, *Thuya spheroidalis* Rich.; E.N. Am.; white cedar), *C.* (*Th.*) *obtusa* Sieb. et Zucc. (Japan, Formosa), *C.* (*Th.*) *pisifera* Sieb. et Zucc. (Japan; Sawara Cypress), &c. All yield good and useful timber.
Chamaedaphne Moench. (*Lyonia* p.p.; *Cassandra BH.*). Eric. (II. 1). 1 N. temp.
Chamaedorea Willd. Palm. (IV. 1). 60 warm Am. Small reedy palms, often forming suckers. Dioec. A 6 on fleshy disc.
Chamaedrys Moench, Schreb. = Teucrium Tourn. p.p. (Labi.).
Chamaegeron Schrenk (*Aster* p.p. *EP.*). Comp. (3). 1 C. As.
Chamaelaucium Desf. Myrt. (II. 2). 12 W. Austr. Heath-like. A 10, 10 stds.
Chamaele Miq. Umbell. (III. 5). 1 Japan.
Chamaelea (Tourn.) Adans., van Tiegh. (*Cneorum* p.p.). Cneor. 1 Canaries.
Chamaelirium Willd. Lili. (I). 1 Atl. N. Am. Dioec.
Chamaemeles Lindl. Ros. (II). 1 Madeira. G 1.
Chamaemelum Vis. = Matricaria Tourn. (Comp.).
Chamaenerion (Tourn.) Adans. (*Epilobium BH.*). Onagr. (2). 4 temp. and subtrop., exc. Austr. Young r. shoots used like asparagus.
Chamaeorchis Koch, L. C. Rich. (*Herminium BH.*). Orchid. (II. 1). 1 Mts. of Eur. *Cf.* Müller's *Alpenblumen*, p. 73.
Chamaepericlimenum Aschers. et Graebn. (*Cornus* p.p. *BH.*). Corn. 2 N. temp.
Chamaepeuce DC. = Cnicus Tourn. (*BH.*). = Cirsium Adans. p.p. (Comp.).
Chamaepitys Tourn. ex Rupp. = Ajuga Tourn. p.p. (Labi.).
Chamaeranthemum Nees. Acanth. (IV. B). 3 trop. Am.
Chamaeraphis R. Br. Gramin. (5). 4 trop. | ✻.
Chamaerhodos Bunge. Ros. (III. 2). 6 Siberia, N.W. Amer. A 5.
Chamaerops L. Palm. (I. 2). 2 W. Medit. *C. humilis* L. the only Eur. palm. Decorative. Dioec. Endosp. ruminate.
Chamaesaracha A. Gray. Solan. (2). 6 Am., Japan. Prostrate herbs.
Chamaesciadium C. A. Mey. Umbell. (III. 5). 2 E. Medit.
Chamaescilla F. Muell. Lili. (III). 2 Austr., Tasm. P twisted after flowering. Fl. blue.
Chamaesium H. Wolff. Umbell. (III. 5). 1 Tibet.
Chamaesphacos Schrenk. Labi. (VI. 4). 3 C. As.
Chamaesyce S. F. Gray = Euphorbia L. (Euph.).
Chamaexeros Benth. (*Acanthocarpus EP.*). Lili. (III). (Junc. *BH.*). 2 S.W. Austr.
Chamagrostis Borkh. = Mibora Adans. (Gramin.).
Chamarea Eckl. et Zeyh. Umbell. (III. 5). 1 S. Afr.
Chamartemisia Rydberg (*Tanacetum* p.p.). Comp. (7). 1 Nevada.
Chambeyronia Vieill. Palm. (inc. sed.). 3 New Caled.
Chamelum Phil. Irid. (II). 3 Chile, Arg. Caps. enclosed in spathe.
Chamira Thunb. Crucif. (I). 2 S. Afr. Lower l. opp.
Chamisal, *cf.* Chaparral.

Chamise, *Adenostoma fasciculatum* Hook. et Arn.
Chamisme Rafin. Rubiaceae (I. 2). 5 N. Am.
Chamissoa H. B. et K. Amarantaceae (2). 5 warm Am. Aril.
Chamissonia Endl. (*Oenothera* p.p. *BH.*). Onagr. (2). 15 warm Am.
Chamomile, *Anthemis*; **wild-**, *Matricaria*.
Champak, *Michelia Champaca* L.
Champereia Griff. Opiliac. (Santal. *BH.*). 4 Indomal.
Championia Gardn. Gesneriaceae (I). 1 Ceylon.
Chamula Nor. Inc. sed. Nomen.
Change of colour in flowers, *Arnebia*, *Brunfelsia*, *Cobaea*, *Diervilla*, *Fumaria*, *Lonicera*, *Ribes*.
Chaparral, the xero. scrub of the hills of Calif., incl. *Adenostoma*, *Arctostaphylos*, *Baccharis*, *Ceanothus*, *Eriodictyon*, *Garrya*, *Rhus*, dwarf oaks, currants, buckeye, roses, &c.
Chapeliera A. Rich. Rubiaceae (I. 8). 2 Madagascar.
Chapmannia Torr. et Gray. Leguminosae (III. 7). 1 Florida.
Chapmanolirion Dinter. Amaryllidaceae. 1 S.W. Afr.
Chaptalia Vent. Compositae (12). 35 warm Am., W.I.
Characheera Forsk. Acanthaceae (inc. sed.). 1 Arabia.
Charadrophila Marloth. Gesneriaceae (inc. sed.). 1 S. Afr.
Charas, *Cannabis*.
Charcoal, *Acer*, *Betula*, *Euonymus*, *Rhamnus*, &c.
Chardinia, Desf. Compositae (11). 1 W. As.
Chards, the late summer blanched l. of artichokes.
Charia C. DC. Meliaceae. 2 trop. Afr.
Charianthus D. Don. Melastomaceae (I). 8 W.I., Guiana.
Charidion Bong. Ochnaceae. 2 Brazil.
Charieis Cass. Compositae (3). 1 S. Afr.
Chariessa Miq. (*Villaresia BH.*). Icacinaceae. 4 E. Austr., Samoa.
Chariomma Miers (*Echites EP. BH.*). Apocyn. (II. 1). 7 trop. Am., W.I.
Charlock, *Brassica Sinapis* Vis.
Charpentiera Gaud. Amarantaceae (2). 2 Sandwich Is. Small trees.
Chartaceous, of papery texture.
Chartacalyx Maingay ex Mast. Tiliaceae. 1 Malaya.
Chartocalyx Regel (*Otostegia* Benth.). Labi. (VI). 1 W. As.
Chartolepis Cass. = Centaurea L. p.p. (Compos.).
Chartoloma Bunge (*Isatis* p.p. *BH.*). Crucif. (2). 1 Turkestan.
Chasalia Comm. ex DC. Rubiaceae (II. 5). 15 palaeotrop.
Chascotheca Urb. Euphorbiaceae (A. I. 1). 2 W.I.
Chasea Nieuwland (*Panicum* p.p.). Gramineae (5). 10 N. Am.
Chasmanthera Hochst. Menispermaceae. 2 trop. Afr.
Chasmogamic, open, not cleistogamic.
Chasmone E. Mey. = Argyrolobium Eckl. et Zeyh. (Legum.).
Chastenaea DC. = Axinaea Ruiz et Pav. (Melast.).
Chaubardia Reichb. f. (*Zygopetalum BH.*). Orch. (II. 14). 1 S. Am.
Chaulmoogra, *Gynocardia*, *Taraktogenos*.
Chaunochiton Benth. Olacaceae. 1 Brazil.
Chaunostoma J. D. Smith (*Satureia* p.p.). Lab. (VI). 1 C. Am.
Chavica Miq. (*Piper* L. p.p. *BH.*). Piperaceae. 5 Indomal.
Chawstick (W.I.), *Gouania*.

Chaydaia Pitard. Rhamnaceae. 2 Tonquin, Chi.
Chayote, *Sechium edule* Sw.
Chayotilla, *Hanburia.*
Chay-root, *Oldenlandia umbellata* L.
Cheatgrass (Am.), *Bromus.*
Checkerberry (Am.), *Gaultheria procumbens* L.
Cheilanthes Sw. Polypodiaceae. 120 trop. and temp. mostly xero.; pinnae often incurved and stomata protected by hairs (*cf.* Empetrum).
Cheilanthos St. Lag. Labiatae (inc. sed.). Nomen.
Cheiloclinium Miers (*Salacia* p.p. *EP.*). Hippocrat. 1 Brazil.
Cheilosa Blume. Euphorbiaceae (A. II. 6). 2 Java, Phil. Is. A 5—10.
Cheilotheca Hook. f. Pyrolaceae. 2 E. Indomal.
Cheiradenia Lindl. Orchidaceae (II. β. II). 1 Guiana.
Cheiranthera Brongn. Pittosporaceae. 4 Austr.
Cheiranthus L. Cruciferae (4). 20 Medit. and N. temp. *C. Cheiri* L. (wall-flower) Brit. Cult. orn. perf. fl.
Cheirodendron Nutt. (*Panax* L. *BH.*). Araliac. (1). 2 Hawaii.
Cheirolaena Benth. Sterculiaceae. 1 Mauritius.
Cheiropleuria Presl. Polypodiaceae. 1 E. As.
Cheiropterocephalus Barb. Rodr. (*Microstylis EP.*). Orchidaceae (II. 4). 1 Brazil.
Cheirostemon Humb. et Bonpl. (*Chiranthodendron* Cerv.). Sterculiaceae. 1 Mexico. Fls. large; petals 0; sta. 5, united below.
Cheirostylis Blume. Orchidaceae (II. 2). 12 trop. Afr. and As.
Chelidonium L. Papaveraceae (II). 5 Brit. to E. As., *C. majus* L., the greater celandine.
Chelidurus Willd. Inc. sed. 1, habitat?
Chelonanthus Gilg (*Lisianthus* L.). Gentian. (1). 10 trop. S. Am.
Chelone L. Scrophulariaceae (II. 4). 4 N. Am.
Chelonecarya Pierre = Raphiostyles Planch. (Icac.).
Chelonespermum Hemsl. Sapotaceae. 4 Solomon Is., Fiji.
Chelonistele Pfitzer (*Coelogyne*, &c. p.p.). Orchid. (II. 3). 5 Indomal.
Chelonopsis Miq. Labiatae (VI). 2 Japan, China.
Chemotropism, sensitiveness to chemical stimulus.
Chena, burning of forest for a couple of crops.
Chenolea Thunb. (*BH.* incl. *Bassia* All.). Chenopodiaceae (A). 3 Medit., S. Afr.
Chenopodiaceae (*EP.*; *BH.* incl. *Basellaceae*). Dicots. (Archichl. Centrospermae; Curvembryae *BH.*). 75 gen., 500 sp. with an interesting geographical distr., determined by the fact that they are nearly all halophytic. The 10 chief districts char. by their presence are (according to Bunge), (1) Austr., (2) the Pampas, (3) the Prairies, (4) and (5) the Medit. coasts, (6) the Karroo (S. Afr.), (7) the Red Sea shores, (8) the S.W. Caspian coast, (9) Centr. As. (Caspian to Himalayas—deserts), (10) the salt steppes of E. As. The presence of large quantities of salt in the soil necessitates the reduction of the transpiration, so that the pl. which grow in such situations exhibit xero. characters. They are mostly herbs (a few shrubs or small trees), with roots which penetrate deeply into the soil, and with l. of various types, usu. not large, often fleshy, and often covered with hairs, which frequently give a curious and very char. mealy feeling

to the pl. In some halophytes of this fam. the l. are altogether suppressed, and the pl. has curious jointed succulent stems like a miniature cactus (*e.g.* Salicornia). Each 'limb' embraces the next succeeding one by a sort of cup at its apex. Even more than in their external form, the C. show xero. structure in their internal anatomy.

Infl. often primarily racemose, but the partial infls. are always cymose, at first often dich., but with a tendency to the cincinnus form, by preference of the β-bracteole. The fls. are reg., small and inconspic., ☿ or unisex. P simple, rarely absent, persistent after flowering, 5, 3, 2 (rarely 1 or 4) ± united, imbr., sepaloid; A as many as or fewer than P segments, opp. to them, hypog. or on a disc; anthers bent inwards in bud; $\underline{G}$ (semi-inf. in Beta), 1-loc. with 2 (rarely more) stigmas; ov. 1, basal, campylotropous. Fr. usu. a small round nut or achene; embryo usu. surrounding the endosp., either simply bent or spirally twisted. Few are useful; see Beta, Spinacia, Chenopodium, &c.

Classification and chief genera (after Volkens).

A. *CYCLOLOBEAE.* Embryo ring-shaped, horseshoe-like, conduplicate or semicircular, wholly or partially enclosing endosp.; Polycnemum, Beta, Chenopodium, Spinacia, Atriplex, Camphorosma, Kochia, Corispermum, Salicornia.

B. *SPIROLOBEAE.* Embryo spirally twisted; endosp. wanting or divided into two masses by embryo; Sarcobatus, Suaeda, Salsola, Haloxylon, Halimocnemis.

Chenopodium (Tourn.) L. Chenopodiaceae (A). 90 temp., 9 Brit. (goosefoot, lamb's-quarters, Good King Henry, &c.). Fr. in many dimorphic; some have horiz. seeds, some vertical (esp. on the term. twigs of the cymes). *C. anthelminticum* (*ambrosioides*) L. (worm-seed or Mexican tea) essential oil is used as a vermifuge in the U.S. *C. Quinoa* Willd. is a food plant in S. Am.; its seeds are boiled like rice. It and other spp. are used as spinach.

Cherimolia, cherimoyer, *Anona Cherimolia* Mill.

Cherleria Hall. = Arenaria L. (*BH.*) = Alsine Scop. (Caryophyll.).

Cherry, *Prunus Cerasus* L.; **Barbados-**, *Malpighia*; **bastard-** (W.I.), *Ehretia*; **-bean**, *Vigna*; **broad-leaved-** (W.I.), *Cordia macrophylla* L.; **clammy-** (W.I.), *Cordia Collococca* L.; **Cornelian-**, *Cornus mas* L.; **Jamaica-** (W.I.), *Ficus pedunculata* Ait.; **-laurel**, *Prunus Laurocerasus* L.; **-pie**, *Heliotropium*; **W. Indian-**, *Malpighia*, *Bunchosia*; **winter-**, *Physalis Alkekengi* L.

Chersium (Cl.), a dry waste formation.

Chervil, *Anthriscus sylvestris* Hoffm., *Chaerophyllum temulum* L.

Chess (Am.), *Bromus*.

Chestnut, *Castanea vulgaris* Lam.; **Australian** or **Moreton Bay**, *Castanospermum australe* A. Cunn.; **horse-**, *Aesculus Hippocastanum* L.; **wild-**, *Brabejum*.

Chevalieria Gaudich. (*Aechmea* p.p. *BH.*). Bromel. (4). 5 S. Am.

Chevreulia Cass. Compositae (4). 8 S. Am.

Chewing gum, *Achras Sapota* L.

Chian turpentine, *Pistacia Terebinthus* L.

Chibaca Bertol. f. Lauraceae (inc. sed.). 1 S. Afr.

Chibou, *Bursera gummifera* L.
Chick-pea, *Cicer arietinum* L., *Cajanus indicus* Spr.
Chickrassia (*Chukrasia*) A. Juss. Meliaceae (II). 1 India, Ceylon, *C. tabularis* A. Juss. Timber valuable (Indian red wood, Chittagong wood, white cedar).
Chickweed, *Stellaria media* Cyrill.; (W.I.), *Drymaria cordata* Willd.; **African** (W.I.), *Mollugo*; **mouse-ear-**, *Cerastium*; **-wintergreen,** *Trientalis*.
Chicle gum, *Achras Sapota* L.
Chicory, *Cichorium Intybus* L.
Chileranthemum Oerst. Acanthaceae (IV. B). 1 Mexico.
Chilianthus Burchell. Loganiaceae. 3 S. Afr.
Chiliocephalum Benth. Compositae (4). 1 Abyssinia.
Chiliophyllum Phil. Compositae (3). 2 Chili, Andes.
Chiliotrichum Cass. Compositae (3). 5 temp. S. Am.
Chillies, *Capsicum annuum* L.
Chilocalyx Klotzsch (*Cleome* p.p. *BH.*). Capparid. (V). 2 E. Afr.
Chilocarpus Blume. Apocynaceae (I. 1). 10 Indomal.
Chilochloa Beauv. = Phleum L. p.p. (Gramin.).
Chiloglottis R. Br. Orchidaceae (II. 2). 6 Austr., N.Z.
Chilopogon Schlechter. Orchidaceae (II. *a*. III). 3 New Guinea.
Chilopsis D. Don. Bignoniaceae (2). 1 Mexico, S. U.S. L. alt.
Chiloschista Lindl. (*Sarcochilus* p.p. *BH.*). Orch. (II. 20). 2 Indomal.
Chimaphila Pursh. Pyrolaceae. 7 N. temp.
Chimarrhis Jacq. Rubiaceae (I. 1). 3 W.I., Andes.
Chimonanthus Lindl. (*Calycanthus* p.p. *EP.*). Calycanthaceae. 2 China, *C. fragrans* Lindl., cult. shrub with very fragrant fls. which come out early in the year before the l. and show marked protogyny with movement of sta., and *C. nitens* Oliv. (Hooker, *Ic. Pl.* t. 1600).
Chimonobambusa Makino (*Bambusa* p.p.). Gramin. (13). 2 Japan.
Chin, *cf.* Orchidaceae.
China aster, *Callistephus hortensis* Cass.; **-grass**, *Boehmeria nivea* Gaudich.; **-jute**, *Abutilon*; **-root** (W.I.), *Vitis sicyoides* Miq.; **-wythe** (W.I.), *Smilax Balbisiana* Kunth. And next.
Chinese date-plum, *Diospyros Kaki* L. f.; **-grass-cloth**, *Boehmeria nivea* Gaudich.; **-green indigo**, *Rhamnus chlorophora* Decne.; **-ivy**, **-jasmine**, *Trachelospermum*; **-sacred lily**, *Narcissus*.
Chinquapin (Am.), *Castanea pumila* Michx.
Chiococca P. Br. ex L. Rubi. (II. 3). 10 trop. Am., W.I. Fla. (A).
Chiogenes Salisb. Eric. (II. 2). 1 E. N. Am., 1 Japan (*cf.* Epigaea).
Chionachne R. Br. Gramineae (I). 5 Indomal., E. As., Austr. *C. cyathopoda* F. von Muell., valuable fodder-grass.
Chionanthula Börner (*Carex* p.p.). Cyper. (III). 2 N. palaeotemp.
Chionanthus Gaertn. = Linociera Sw. (*Mayepea* Aubl.) (Oleaceae).
Chionanthus Royen ex L. Oleaceae. 2 N. Am., China. *C. virginica* L. (snowdrop tree) cult. orn. flg. shrub.
Chione DC. Rubiaceae (II. 3). 5 W. Ind.
Chionium (Cl.), a snow formation.
Chionodoxa Boiss. Liliaceae (V). 4 Crete and As. Minor. *C. luciliae* Boiss. (glory of the snow) cult. orn. fl.

Chionographis Maxim. Liliaceae (I). 2 Japan. Fl. ·|·.
Chionolaena DC. Compositae (4). 8 Mexico, S. Am. Shrubs with the l. rolled back.
Chionopappus Benth. Compositae (12). 1 Peru.
Chionophila Benth. Scrophulariaceae (II. 4). 2 Rocky Mts.
Chionoptera DC. (*Pachylaena* Don). Comp. (12). 1 Andes.
Chionothrix Hook. f. Amarantaceae (2). 1 Somaliland.
Chiquito, *Combretum*.
Chiranthodendron Cerv. (*Cheirostemon*). Stercul. 1 Mexico.
Chiretta, *Swertia Chirata* Ham.
Chirimoya, *Anona Cherimolia* Mill.
Chirita Buch.-Ham. (*Didymocarpus* or *Roettlera* p.p.). Gesneraceae (I). 50 Indomal., some with epiphyllous infl. (*cf. B. Centr.* 74, p. 128).
Chironia L. Gentianaceae (I). 30 Afr., Madag.
Chiropetalum A. Juss. (*Argithamnia* Sw. *BH.*). Euphorbiaceae (A. II. 2). 20 S. Am. to Mexico.
Chisocheton Blume. Meliaceae (III). 50 Indomal.
Chitonanthera Schlechter. Orchidaceae (II. 15). 3 New Guinea.
Chitonia Moc. et Sesse. Zygophyllaceae. 1 Mexico.
Chitonochilus Schlechter. Orchid. (II. *a*. III). 1 New Guinea.
Chittagong wood, *Chickrassia tabularis* A. Juss.
Chive, *Allium Schoenoprasum* L.
Chlaenaceae (*EP.*, *BH.*). Dicots. (Archichl. Malvales; Guttiferales *BH.*). 7 gen., 25 sp. Madagascar. Trees with alt. entire stip. l.; fl. sol. or 2 in an invol., in racemose infl., ☿, reg. K 3—5, C 5—6, A 10—∞, $\underline{G}$ (3), 3-loc., each with 2 ov. Caps. 3 or 1-loc. Endosp. *Chief genus:* Leptochlaena.
Chlaenandra Miq. Menispermaceae. 1 New Guinea.
Chlainanthus Briq. Labiatae (VI). 1 Asia.
Chlamydacanthus Lindau. Acanthaceae (IV. B). 1 Madag.
Chlamydeous, with perianth.
Chlamydites J. K. Drumm. Compositae (8). 1 Tibet.
Chlamydoboea Stapf. Gesneraceae (I). 1 China, Burma.
Chlamydocardia Lindau. Acanthaceae (IV. B). 3 W. Afr.
Chlamydocarya Baill. Icacinaceae. 8 trop. W. Afr.
Chlamydojatropha Pax et K. Hoffm. Euphorb. (A. II. 2). 1 Cameroons.
Chlamydostylus Baker = Nemastylis Nutt. p.p. (Irid.).
Chlamyphorus Klatt (*Gomphrena* p.p.). Amarant. (3). 1 Brazil.
Chledium (Cl.), a ruderal formation.
Chlidanthus Herb. Amaryllidaceae (I). 4 S. Am. Sta. with lat. appendages (see fam.).
Chloanthes R. Br. Verbenaceae (3). 10 Austr.
Chlora Ren. ex Adans. (*Blackstonia* Huds.). Gentianaceae (I). 3 Eur., Medit. *C. perfoliata* L. (yellow-wort) on chalk in Brit.
Chloradenia Baill. (*Adenogynum EP.*). Euph. (A. II. 2). 1 Malaya.
Chloraea Lindl. Orchidaceae (II. 2). 100 S. Am., W.I.
Chloranthaceae. Dicots. (Archichl. Piperales; Micrembryae *BH.*). 3 gen., 35 sp., trop. and subtrop. Herbs, shrubs, or trees, with opp. stip. l. Fls. small, in spikes or cymes, ☿ or unisex., sometimes with sepaloid P; A 1—3, united to one another and to ovary;

G 1; ov. few, pend., orthotr. Endosp. oily; perisperm embryo minute. *Chief genera:* Chloranthus, Hedyosmum.

Chloranthus Sw. Chloranth. 10 E. As., E. Ind. P 1, anterior; the centre sta. has a complete anther, the lat. each half (*cf.* Fumaria).

Chloridion Stapf. Gramineae (5). 1 trop. Afr.

Chloris Sw. Gramineae (11). 60 trop. and warm temp. Several are useful pasture-grasses in Austr., &c.

Chloro- (Gr. pref.), green, yellow; **-phyll**, the green colouring matter of l.; **-in the fl.** Deherainia; **-plastids**, carriers of.

Chlorocodon Hook. f. Asclepiadaceae (I). 2 E. and S.E. Afr.

Chlorocrambe Rydberg (*Caulanthus* p.p.). Cruc. (1). 1 N. Am.

Chlorocyathus Oliv. Asclepiadaceae (I). 1 Delagoa Bay.

Chlorocyperus Rikli = Cyperus L. (Cyperac.).

Chlorogalum Kunth. Liliaceae (III). 6 Calif. *C. pomeridianum* Kunth has a large bulb whose inner parts are used as a substitute for soap (*cf.* Saponaria). The outer layers yield a quantity of fibre.

Chloromyrtus Pierre (*Eugenia* p.p. *EP.*). Myrt. (I). 1 trop. Afr.

Chloropatane Engl. Monimiaceae. 2 trop. Afr.

Chlorophora Gaudich. Moraceae (I). 3 W. Afr., trop. Am. The wood of the latter (*C. tinctoria* Gaudich.) forms the yellow dye fustic.

Chlorophytum Ker-Gawl. Liliaceae (III). 110 warm. In *C. comosum* Baker infl. often replaced by veg. repr.; long shoots develope in the axils of the br., weigh the stem down to the soil and take root. Cult. orn.

Chloropyron Behr. = Cordylanthus Nutt. (Scroph.).

Chlorosa Blume. Orchidaceae (II. 2). 1 Java. C 1; scape scaly.

Chlorospatha Engl. Araceae (VI). 1 Colombia. ♀ fls. in whorls.

Chloroxylon Rumph. Rutaceae (II) (Meliaceae, *BH.*). 1 E. Ind., *C. Swietenia* DC. (satinwood). Timber very lasting, largely used in veneering. The tree also yields a gum.

Chloroxylum P. Br. Inc. sed. Quid?

Chloryllis E. Mey. (*Dolichos* p.p. *BH.*). Legum. (III. 10). 1 S. Afr.

Choananthus Rendle. Amaryllidaceae (I). 2 Ruwenzori.

Chocho, *Sechium edule* Sw.

Chocolate, *Theobroma*.

Chodanthus Hassler (*Adenocalymma* p.p.). Bign. (1). 1 Braz.

Choisya H. B. et K. Rutaceae (I). 1 Mexico. Cult. orn. shrub.

Choke-berry (Am.), *Pyrus arbutifolia* L.

Chomelia Jacq., non L. (*Anisomeris* Presl *EP.*). Rubiaceae (II. 2). 30 trop. S. Am., Afr.

Chomelia L., non Jacq. (*Tarenna* Gaertn. *BH.*). Rubi. (I. 8). 30 trop. As., Afr.

Chondilophyllum Panch. ex Guillaumin (*Meryta* Forst. p.p.). Araliaceae. 1 New Caledonia.

Chondodendron Ruiz et Pav. Menispermaceae. 6 Brazil, Peru. A 6 or (3). G 6. The root of some spp. furnishes Radix Pareirae bravae.

Chondrilla (Tourn.) L. Compositae (13). 20 N. temp.

Chondrobollea × Hort. Orchidaceae. Hybrid of Chondrorhyncha and Bollea. Also **Chondropetalum** × Hort. Hybrid with Zygopetalum.

Chondrophylla A. Nelson (*Gentiana* p.p.). Gentian. (I). 2 N. Am.

Chondrorrhyncha Lindl. Orchid. (II. β. II). 2 Colombia. Cult.
Chondrosea Haw. = Saxifraga Tourn. p.p. (Saxifr.).
Chondrostylis Boerlage. Euphorb. (A. II. 2). 1 Malaya.
Chondrosum Desv. = Bouteloua Lag. p.p. (Gramin.).
Chonemorpha G. Don. Apocynaceae (II. 1). 2 Indomal.
Chordospartium Cheesem. Leguminosae (III. 6). 1 N.Z.
Choretrum R. Br. Santalaceae. 5 Austr.
Chorilaena Endl. Rutaceae (I). 3 W. Austr.
Chorilepis Van Tiegh. (*Loranthus* p.p.). Loranth. (I). 3 Malaya, Phil. Is.
Chorioluma Baill. (*Sideroxylon* p.p. *EP.*). Sapot. (I). 1 New Caled.
Choriophyllum Benth. Euphorb. (A. I. 1). 2 Malay Arch.
Choripetalae (Warming) = Archichlamydeae.
Choripetalous, polypetalous.
Chorisia H. B. et K. Bombacaceae. 5 S. Am. *C. speciosa* St Hil. (paina de seda) gives a useful silky cotton from the pods.
Chorisis, branching in floral organs.
Chorispora R. Br. Cruciferae (4). 12 E. Medit., Centr. As.
Choristega Van Tiegh. (*Loranthus* p.p.). Loranth. (I). 2 Celebes.
Choristegeres Van Tiegh. (ditto). Loranth. (I). 1 Borneo.
Choristigma F. Kurtz. Asclepiadaceae (II. 1). 1 Argentina.
Choristylis Harv. Saxifrag. (V). 2 S. Afr. Fl. ♂♀ perig. G 2-loc.
Choritaenia Benth. (*Pappea* Sond. et Harv. *EP.*). Umbelliferae (III. 6). 1 S. Afr.
Chorizandra R. Br. Cyperaceae (II). 4 Austr.
Chorizanthe R. Br. Polygon. (I. 1). 35 Am. Some have an ochrea, usu. absent in this group. Fls. usu. single inside the invol. (*cf.* Eriogonum).
Chorizema Labill. Leguminosae (III. 2). 15 Austr.
Chortolirion Berger (*Haworthia* p.p.). Lili. (III). 4 Afr.
Chowlee (India), *Vigna Catjang* Walp.
Christ's thorn, *Paliurus aculeatus* Lam.
Christensenia Maxon. Marattiaceae. 1 Phil. Is.
Christiana DC. Tiliaceae. 1 Madag. to Guiana.
Christisonia Gardn. Orobanchaceae. 10 trop. As. Roots parasitic on those of bamboos or Acanthaceae, united to a dense meshwork. The flg. shoots spring up, die, and decay, in a fortnight.
Christmannia Dennst. Inc. sed. 1 E. Indies.
Christmas gambol (W.I.), *Ipomoea sidifolia* Choisy; **-pride** (W.I.), *Ruellia paniculata* L.; **-rose**, *Helleborus niger* L.
Christolea Cambess. Cruciferae (4). 2 W. and C. As.
Christophine (W.I.), *Sechium edule* Sw.
Christopteris Copeland. Polypodiaceae. 2 S.E. As.
Chroilema Bernh. Compositae (3). 1 Chili.
Chromanthus Phil. Portulacaceae. 1 Chili.
Chromolepis Benth. Compositae (5). 1 Mexico.
Chromoplastids, carriers of colouring matters.
Chronopappus DC. Compositae (1). 1 Minas Geraes.
Chrozophora Neck. Euphorbiaceae (A. II. 2). 10 Medit., India, W. Afr. *C. tinctoria* A. Juss. and *C. verbascifolia* Juss. are characteristic plants of the Medit. region. The former, once medicinal, is

still sometimes used as the source of the dye turn-sole, tournesol, or bezetta rubra.

Chrysactinia A. Gray. Compositae (6). 3 Mex., S.W. U.S.

Chrysalidocarpus H. Wendl. (*Hyophorbe* p.p. *EP*.). Palmae (IV. 1). 1 Madag., *C. lutescens* H. Wendl. a favourite orn. palm, branching at the r. and forming tufts of stems.

Chrysanthellum L. C. Rich. Compositae (5). 4 trop.

Chrysanthemum (Tourn.) L. (incl. *Pyrethrum* Hall.). Compositae (7). 180 Eur., As., Afr., Am. *C. segetum* L. (corn-marigold) and *C. Leucanthemum* L. (ox-eye or dog daisy) Brit. The autumn-flowering C. are cult. forms of *C. indicum* L. and *C. sinense* Sabine (China, Japan). As in Dahlia, all florets have become ligulate (Hemsley in *Gard. Chron.* 1889, p. 521, &c.; Henry in *Gard. Chron.*, 1902, p. 301, and discussion by Hooker in Curtis, *Bot. Mag.* t. 7874). *C. Parthenium* Bernh. (feverfew, Eur.), a popular remedy against fevers; *C. cinerariaefolium* Vis. yields Dalmatian, and *C. roseum* Adam. Persian, insect powder (the dried and powdered fls.), *Kew Bull.* 1898, p. 297.

Chryseus (Lat.), **chryso-** (Gr. pref.), golden yellow.

Chrysithrix L. Cyperaceae (II). 2 S. Afr., 1 W. Austr.

Chrysobalanaceae (Warming) = Rosaceae (§ VI).

Chrysobalanus L. Rosaceae (VI). 4 Afr., Am. Style basal, so that the flr. is slightly ·|·. *C. Icaco* L. (coco plum), W. Ind., fr. ed.

Chrysocephalum Walp. = Helichrysum Vaill. p.p. (Comp.).

Chrysochamela Boiss. (*Cochlearia* p.p. *BH.*). Cruc. (4). 3 E. Medit.

Chrysochlamys Poepp. et Endl. Guttiferae (V). 10 trop. Am.

Chrysocoma L. Compositae (3). 10 S. and trop. Afr. *C. Linosyris* L. see Aster.

Chrysocoptis Nutt. (*Coptis* p.p.). Ranunc. (2). 1 N.W. Am.

Chrysocychnis Lindau et Reichb. f. Orch. (II. 13). 2 Colombia.

Chrysoglossum Blume. Orchid. (II. *a*. II). 10 Indomal., Polynes.

Chrysogonum L. (excl. *Moonia* Arn.). Compositae (5). 1 E. U.S.

Chrysoliga Willd. = Nesaea Comm. (Lythrac.).

Chrysoma Nutt. = Solidago Vaill. (Compos.).

Chrysophthalmum Schulz-Bip. Compositae (4). 2 W. As.

Chrysophyllum L. Sapotaceae (I). 100 trop., esp. Am. Serial buds form in each leaf-axil in some sp. and the undeveloped ones subsequently give rise to fls. borne on the old wood (cauliflory, *q.v.*). *C. Cainito* L. (star-apple, W. Ind.), cult. ed. fr.

Chrysopogon Trin. (*Andropogon* L. p.p. *EP*.). Gram. (2). 12 trop., subtrop.

Chrysopsis Ell. Compositae (3). 30 N. Am.

Chrysosplenium Tourn. ex L. Saxifragaceae (I). 60 N. temp., temp. S. Am., 2 Brit. (golden saxifrage). Rhiz. bears both veg. and fl. shoots. Infl. cymose. The small greenish fls. are perig. and apet., homogamous. *Cf.* Adoxa.

Chrysothamnus Nutt. (*Bigelovia* p.p.). Compos. (3). 50 Am.

Chthamalia Decne. (*Gonolobus BH.*). Asclep. (II. 4). 6 trop. Am.

Chthonocephalus Steetz. Compositae (4). 3 temp. Austr.

Chukrasia (*Chickrassia*, *q.v.*) A. Juss. Meli. (II). 1 Indomal.

Chuncoa Pav. = Terminalia L. p.p. (Combret.).

Chuquiraga Juss. Compos. (12). 50 S. Am. In each axil are thorns, probably repres. l. of an undeveloped branch; above is a normal branch.

Churrus, charas, *Cannabis*.

Chusquea Kunth. Gramineae (13). 70 Am. Like Bambusa (*q.v.*). Char. of high plateau in S. Am.

Chydenanthus Miers (*Barringtonia* p.p. *BH.*). Lecyth. 1 Java.

Chylismia Nutt. (*Oenothera* p.p.). Onagr. (2). 10 W. U.S.

Chylocauly, stem succulence; **-phylly**, leaf succulence.

Chymococca Meissn. Thymelaeaceae. 1 S. Afr.

Chymsydia Alboff (*Agasyllis EP.*). Umbell. (III. 6). 1 Caucasus.

Chysis Lindl. Orchidaceae (II. 9). 6 trop. Am. Cult.

Chytranthus Hook. f. Sapindaceae (I). 10 trop. W. Afr.

Chytroglossa Reichb. f. Orchidaceae (II. 19). 2 Brazil.

Cibotium Kaulf. Cyatheaceae. 10 trop. Am., Polynesia, As. The famous Tartarian lamb of early travellers was the rhiz. of *C. barometz* Link.

Cicatrix, a scar.

Cicca L. = Phyllanthus L. p.p. (Euph.). 1 S. As.

Cicely, *Myrrhis odorata* Scop.

Cicendia Adans. Gentianaceae (I). 1, *C. pusilla* Griseb., S.W. Eur. and Channel Is. (For *C. filiformis* Delarb. see Microcala.)

Cicer (Tourn.) L. Legum. (III. 9). 15 W. As. Accessory buds in axils in some. *C. arietinum* L. (chick-pea, gram), cult. food S. Eur., Ind.

Cichorium (Tourn.) L. Compos. (13). 8 Medit., Eur., N. As. *C. Intybus* L. (chicory), Brit. The r., roasted and ground, are mixed with coffee. *C. Endivia* L. (endive), a pot-herb; its l. being blanched.

Ciconium Sweet = Pelargonium L'Hérit. p.p. (Geran.).

Cicuta (Tourn.) L. Umbelliferae (III. 5). 20 N. temp. *C. virosa* L. (cow-bane or water-hemlock) Brit. Highly poisonous.

Cienfuegosia Cav. (*Fugosia* Juss.). Malv. (4). 30 Am., Afr., Austr.

Cienkowskia Regel et Rach. Boragin. (?). 1, habitat?

Cilia, hair-like bodies; **-te**, with fine projecting hairs.

Cimicifuga L. (*Actaea* L. p.p. *EP.*). Ranunc. (2). 12 N. temp. *C. foetida* L. (bugbane, Eur.), used as preventive against vermin. R. of *C. racemosa* Nutt. (black snake-root, N. Am.) emetic.

Cinchona L. Rubiaceae (I. 5). 40 Andes. Trees. Fl. heterostyled in some. The source of Peruvian or Jesuit's bark, from which are extracted the valuable drugs (alkaloids) quinine, cinchonidine, &c. The tree used to be cut down to obtain the bark and there was danger of extinction until cult. was started on a large scale. An expedition to the Andes in 1859 brought it to the east, where Ceylon took up its cult., and upon so large a scale as to reduce the price of quinine from 12*s.* to 1*s.* an ounce. Decrease in price, the lack of any improvement in the barks, and attacks of disease, made the cult. die out in Ceylon, and Java, where improvement was taken in hand, now almost monopolises it. India grows a good deal for supply to natives through the post offices. Several sp. are used, *e.g.* *C. Calisaya* Wedd. (yellow, and some crown, bark), *C. Ledgeriana* Moens (yellow bark, the richest in alkaloid), *C. cordifolia* Mutis (Cartagena bark), *C. officinalis* L. (*condaminea* H. & B.) (Loxa, crown or brown bark), *C. succirubra*

Pav. (red bark). (Markham, *Travels in Peru and India*; Reimers, *Les quinquinas de culture*, 1900.)

Cinchonidin, *Cinchona*.

Cincinnobotrys Gilg. Melastomaceae (1). 2 trop. Afr.

Cincinnus, a monoch. cyme in which the successive lat. branches fall alt. on either side of the relatively main axis; *Bignoniaceae*, *Boraginaceae*, *Canna*, *Caryophyllaceae*, *Chenopodiaceae*, *Commelinaceae*, *Crassulaceae*, *Geranium*, *Helianthemum*, *Heliconia*, *Hydrophyllaceae*, *Hyoscyamus*, *Linaceae*, *Solanaceae*, *Strelitzia*, *Tradescantia*, *Urtica*, *Verbenaceae*.

Cineraria L. p.p. Compositae (8). 35 Afr., Madag. Many sp. of Senecio are often included in this genus. Cult. orn. fl.

Cinereus (Lat.), ash grey.

Cinga Nor. Inc. sed. Nomen.

Cinna L. Gramineae (8). 2 N. temp. A 1.

Cinnagrostis Griseb. Gramineae (8). 1 Argentina.

Cinnamodendron Endl. Winteranaceae. 3 Brazil, W. Ind.

Cinnamomeous, light yellowish brown.

Cinnamomum (Tourn.) L. Laur. (1). 80 Indomal., E. As. Young leaves often red. *C. zeylanicum* Nees (Ceylon) is the cinnamon. The pl. is coppiced in cult., and the bark of the twigs peeled off and rolled up is the spice. *C. Cassia* Blume (China, Japan) yields Cassia bark, often used to adulterate cinnamon. Its fl. buds are used as a spice (*cf.* Eugenia). *C. Camphora* T. Nees & Eberm. (China, Japan, Formosa) is the camphor. The old trees are felled, and the wood cut into chips and distilled with steam, but in cult. the camphor is distilled from young shoots.

Cinnamon, *Cinnamomum zeylanicum* Nees, (Am.) *Canella*; **wild-** (Ceylon), *Litsea zeylanica* Nees, (W.I.) *Canella alba* Murr., *Pimenta acris* Kostel.

Cinnamosma Baill. Winteranaceae. 2 Madag. K 3, C (4—6).

Cinquefoil, *Potentilla reptans* L.

Cionosicyos Griseb. Cucurbit. (3). 1 Jamaica.

Cipadessa Blume. Meliaceae (III). 4 Indomal., Madag.

Cipre (W.I.), *Cordia Gerascanthus* L.

Cipura Aubl. Iridaceae (II). 1 trop. Am.

Cipuropsis Ule. Bromeliaceae (1). 1 Peru.

Circaea Tourn. ex L. Onagraceae (2). 9 N. temp. and arctic; 2 Brit. (enchanter's nightshade). Fl. dimerous with one whorl sta. Fr. hooked.

Circaeaster Maxim. Chloranthaceae. 1 Himal., China. K 2—3, C 0, A 1—2, G 1—4; fr. hooked. (Hooker, *Icones Pl.*, t. 2366.)

Circinate (aestivation), l. rolled up like watch-springs, *Filicineae Leptospor.*, *Marsileaceae*, petals of *Hamamelidaceae*.

Circinus Med. (*Hymenocarpus* Savi). Legum. (III. 5). 1 Medit.

Circumscissile, opening by splitting off a lid, *Anagallis*.

Cirrhaea Lindl. Orchidaceae (II. 13). 5 Brazil.

Cirrhiferous, tendril-bearing: **cirrhose**, tendrilled.

Cirrhopetalum Lindl. Orchidaceae (II. 16). 70 Indomal., Masc.

Cirsium (Tourn.) Adans. (*Cnicus* L. p.p. *EP.*). Compositae (11). 200 N. temp.

Cissampelos L. Menispermaceae. 25 trop. and subtrop. ♂ infl.

cymose. In ♂, K 4, C (2—4), rarely free, (A) in column; in ♀, K 1, C 1, rarely 2—3, G 1. *C. Pareira* L. (trop.), false Pareira root.

Cissus L. (*Vitis* p.p. *BH.*). Vit. 325 warm. Fl. ☿. C 4. Gilg in *Engl. Jb.* 46.

Cistaceae (*EP.*, *Cistineae BH.*). Dicots. (Archichl. Parietales, pp. xxxiii, l). 7/200 in dry sunny places, espec. on chalk or sand, a few S. Am., the rest N. temp. (espec. Medit.). Shrubs and herbs with opp. rarely alt. l., often inrolled (*cf.* Ericaceae), stip. or not. Ethereal oil and glandular hairs usu. present. Fl. sol. or in cymes, ☿, reg. K 5, the two outer usu. smaller than the inner (sometimes regarded as bracteoles, but these are found lower down); C 5, 3, or 0 (in cleistog. fls.), conv. to right or left according as 3 inner seps. overlap to left or right; A usu. ∞ on a subovarial disc, developed in descending order; G̲ (5—10 or 3) 1-loc. with parietal often projecting plac. each bearing ∞ or 2 ascending orthotr. or anatr. ov.; styles free or not. Caps. usu. loculic.; endosp. and curved embryo. *Genera:* Cistus (C 5, ov. ∞, caps. 10—5-valved), Helianthemum (do. but 3-valved), Halimium, Tuberaria, Fumana, Hudsonia, Lechea. [Monographed in *Pfl. R.*, 1903.]

Cistanche Hoffmgg. et Link. Orobanch. 12 Medit., Afr., As.

Cistanthera K. Schum. Tili. 4 C. and W. trop. Afr.

Cistiflorae (Warming). The 10th order of Choripetalae.

Cistineae (*BH.*) = Cistaceae. **Cistula** Nor. Inc. sed. Nomen.

Cistus (Tourn.) L. Cist. 20 Medit. *C. villosus* L. var. *creticus*, and *C. ladaniferus* L. yield the resin ladanum (not laudanum), formerly offic. Many cult. orn. shrubs (cool-house). *Cf.* fam.

Citharella Nor. Inc. sed. Nomen.

Cithareloma Bunge. Crucif. (4). 2 Turkestan.

Citharexylum Mill. Verben. (1). 25 warm Am. Fr. often tightly enclosed in K. Drupe with 2 stones. Timber (fiddlewood, from bois fidèle).

Citriobatus A. Cunn. Pittospor. (2). 2 S.W. Austr.

Citriosma Tul. (*Citrosma* Ruiz et Pav.) = Siparuna Aubl. (Monim.).

Citron, *Citrus medica* L.

Citronella oil, *Cymbopogon Nardus* Rendle, *C. Winterianus* Jowitt.

Citrophorum Neck = Citrus L. p.p. (Rut.).

Citropsis Swingle et Kellermann (*Limonia* p.p.). Rut. (v). 5 trop. Afr.

Citrullus Forsk. Cucurb. (3). 4 Afr., Medit., trop. As. *C. vulgaris* Schrad. the watermelon, *C. Colocynthis* Schrad. (colocynth) fr. a drug.

Citrus L. Rut. (v). 10 palaeotrop. and subtrop. ♄ with usu. simple l., which show a joint at meeting of blade and stalk, indicating their derivation from cpd. l. like those of most of the fam. (*cf.* Berberis). Axillary thorns in some = met. l. of branch shoot. Fls. ☿ in corymbs. K, C 4—8; A ∞ in irreg. bundles, corresponding to an outer whorl only; G̲ (∞) (6 or more). A second whorl sometimes appears. Berry with leathery epicarp, the flesh made up of large cells which grow out from inner layer of pericarp.

Many cult. in warm countries, espec. California, the W. Indies, Brazil, the Medit. region, &c., for their fr. *C. Medica* L., the citron, is the parent sp. of several varieties, *e.g.* var. *Limonum* the lemon, var. *acida* the lime, var. *Limetta* the sweet lime. *C. aurantium* L. is the orange, with its vars. *Bergamia*, the Bergamot orange (from which the perfume is obtained), *Bigaradia* or *amara* the Seville or bitter orange, used in marmalade, *C. decumana* the shaddock, or pomelo, with its var. the grape-fruit, *C. sinensis*, the Malta or Portugal orange, *C. suntara* Engl., the suntara or kumquat, and others. *C. nobilis* Lour. is the true mandarin orange. *Cf.* De Candolle, *Orig. of Cult. Plts.* p. 176; Engler in *Nat. Pfl.*; Bonavia, *Oranges...of India and Ceylon.*

Cladanthus Cass. Compositae (7). 2 S. Spain, Morocco.

Claderia Hook. f. Orchidaceae (II. 5). 1 Perak.

Cladium P. Br. Cyperaceae (II). 30 trop. and temp., esp. Austr. *C. Mariscus* R. Br. (*germanicum* Schrad.), Brit.

Cladode, phylloclade of one internode.

Cladogynos Zipp. ex Span. Euphorb. (A. II. 2). 1 Malay Is., S.E. As.

Cladopus Möller. Podostem. 2 Java, Japan.

Cladostemon A. Br. et Vatke. Capparid. (II). 1 Zanzibar.

Cladostigma Radlk. Convolv. (I). 1 Abyssinia. Ed. fr. Unisexual.

Cladothamnus Brongn. Ericaceae (I. 1). 1 N.W. N. Am. Tall shrub.

Cladothrix Nutt. Amarantaceae (3). 3 W. N. Am.

Cladrastis Rafin. Leguminosae (III. 1). 1 E. As., 1 E. N. Am. (*cf.* Epigaea) (*C. tinctoria* Rafin., yellow-wood); its wood yields a yellow dye.

Clambus Miers = Phyllanthus L. p.p. (Euph.).

Claoxylon A. Juss. Euphorbiaceae (A. II. 2). 60 palaeotrop. A 10—200.

Clappia A. Gray. Compositae (6). 2 Texas, Mexico.

Clarionea Lag. = Perezia Lag. p.p. (Compos.).

Clarisia Ruiz et Pav. Moraceae (II). 4 Peru, Brazil.

Clarkeifedia Kuntze (*Patrinia* p.p.). Valer. 1 Himalaya.

Clarkella Hook. f. Rubiaceae (I. 2). 1 Himalaya.

Clarkia Pursh. Onagraceae (2). 8 W. N. Am. Cult. orn. fl. Mech. of fl. as in Epilobium.

Clary, *Salvia pratensis* L.; **wild-** (W.I.), *Heliotropium*.

Clastopus Bunge ex Boiss. (*Vesicaria BH.*). Cruc. (4). 3 Persia.

Clathrate, latticed.

Clathrospermum Planch. (*Popowia EP.*). Anon. (1). 12 trop. Afr.

Clathrotropis Harms (*Diplotropis* p.p.). Legum. (III. 1). 2 Braz.

Clausena Burm. f. Rutaceae (V). 20 palaeotrop. Some ed. fr.

Clausia Trotzky (*Hesperis BH.*). Crucif. (4). 5 C. and N. As.

Clavapetalum Pulle (*Platea* p.p.). Icacinaceae. 1 Surinam.

Clavate, club-shaped.

Clavija Ruiz et Pav. Theophrastaceae. 40 trop. Am. Trees of palm-like habit, often with fls. on the old wood (cauliflory).

Clavipodium Desv. ex Grüning. Euphorb. (B. II). 1 Austr.

Clavistylus J. J. Smith. Euphorb. (A. II. 2). 1 Java.

Claw, a narrowed base of a petal, *Cheiranthus*, *Caryophyllac.*

Claytonia Gronov. ex L. Portulacaceae. 24 N. temp. and arctic; 2 nat. in Brit. No stips. Fls. in sympodial cymes. Before pollin. the fl.-stalk is erect; fl. protandr., with outward movement of the sta. after dehisc. Honey, at base of each petal, accessible to short-tongued insects. After pollin., the stalk bends down through 180°, to return once more to the erect position when fr. ripe. The caps. contains 3 seeds and splits into 3 valves, the seeds lying across the lines of splitting. The inner surfaces of the valves contract as they dry and shoot out the seeds (*cf.* Buxus, Viola).

Cleanthe Salisb. Iridaceae (II). 1 Cape Colony.
Cleanthes D. Don (*Trixis BH.*). Compos. (12). 3 S. Braz., Arg.
Clearing-nut, *Strychnos potatorum* L. f.
Clearweed (Am.), *Pilea*.
Cleavers, *Galium Aparine* L.
Cleft, cut halfway down.
Cleghornia Wight (*Baissea BH.*). Apocyn. (II. 1). 4 Indomal.
Cleidion Blume. Euphorbiaceae (A. II. 2). 18 trop.
Cleisocratera Korth. (*Psychotria* p.p. *EP.*). Rubi. (II. 5). 1 Borneo.
Cleisostoma Blume. Orchidaceae (II. 20). 20 Indomal.
Cleistachne Benth. Gramineae (2). 2 trop. As., Afr.
Cleistanthus Hook. f. ex Planch. Euphorb. (A. I. 2). 110 palaeotrop.
Cleistes L. C. Rich. (*Pogonia BH.*). Orchid. (II. 2). 12 S. Am.
Cleistochlamys Oliv. Anonaceae (1). 1 Mozambique.
Cleistogamy, the production of closed self-pollinating fl., *Amphicarpaea*, *Cardamine*, *Commelina*, *Halenia*, *Lamium*, *Leersia*, *Lespedeza*, *Malpighia*, *Montia*, *Ononis*, *Oxalis*, *Parochetus*, *Viola*, esp. the last.
Cleistoloranthus Merrill. Loranth. (1). 1 Phil. Is.
Cleistopholis Pierre. Anonaceae (1). 5 trop. Afr.
Clematicissus Planch. (*Vitis* p.p.). Vitaceae. 1 W. Austr.
Clematis Dill. ex L. (incl. *Atragene* L.). Ranunculaceae (3). 220 cosmop. *C. vitalba* L. (traveller's joy) Brit. Mostly climbing shrubs with opp., usu. cpd., l. Lower sides of petioles sensitive to contact. The petiole bends once round the support, thickens and lignifies. Fls. in cymes; K coloured; no pets. or honey secretion. The style often remains persistent upon the fr. and becomes hairy, thus forming a mech. for wind-distr.
Clematoclethra Maxim. Dillen. (Ternstr. *BH.*). 10 China.
Clemensia Merrill. Meliaceae (II). 1 Phil. Is.
Clementsia Rose (*Sedum* p.p.). Crassulaceae. 1 Rocky Mts.
Cleobula Vell. Inc. sed. 1 Brazil.
Cleobulia Mart. Leguminosae (III. 10). 3 Brazil.
Cleome L. Capparidaceae (V). 70 trop., subtrop. Disc usu. more developed on post. side; may bear scales. Gynophore varies in length.
Cleomella DC. Capparidaceae (V). 10 N. Am.
Cleomodendron Pax. Capparidaceae (inc. sed.). 1 Somaliland.
Cleonia L. Labiatae (VI). 1 W. Medit.
Clermontia Gaudich. Campanulaceae (III). 12 Sandwich Is. The latex is used as bird lime. Some have ed. fr.
Clerodendron L. Verbenaceae (4). 150 trop., subtrop. *C. Thompsonae* Balf., often cult. orn. fl., has red C and white K. The sta. project so as to form the landing place for insects, and when they are ripe the style is bent down. Afterwards the sta. roll up and the style takes their place. *C. fistulosum* Becc. has hollow internodes inhabited by ants (myrmecophily, *q.v.*).
Clethra Gronov. Clethraceae. 30 trop., subtrop. Shrubs and trees with alt. l.; fls. in racemes or panicles, without bracteoles, ☿, reg. K 5, C 5, polypet.; A 5 + 5, hypog.; no disc; anthers bent outwards in bud; pollen in single grains; ov. 3-loc.; style with 3 stigmas. Caps. loculic.; endosp.

Clethraceae (*EP.*; *Ericaceae* p.p. *BH.*). Dicots. (Sympet. Ericales). Only genus Clethra, *q.v.*

Clevelandia Greene ex Brandegee. Scroph. (III. 3). 1 Calif.

Cleyera DC. (*Eurya* Thunb. p.p. *EP.*). Theac. 9 warm Am., As.

Clianthus Banks et Soland. (*Donia* G. Don). Leguminosae (III. 6). 2 Austr., N.Z. Cult. orn. fl.

Clibadium L. Compositae (5). 15 trop. Am., W.I.

Clidemia D. Don (incl. *Sagraea EP.*). Melastom. (I). 100 trop. Am. Ed. fr.

Cliff-brake (Am.), *Pellaea*.

Cliffortia L. Rosaceae (III. 5). 50 S. Afr. Axis hollow in ♀ only.

Cliftonia Banks et Gaertn. f. Cyrillaceae. 1 S.E. U.S.

Climacorachis Hemsl. et Rose. Leguminosae (III. 7). 2 Mex.

Climbing fern (Am.), *Lygodium*; **-plants** abound in trop. forests, where they usu. grow large and woody (*lianes*), and are rarer elsewhere. Four chief groups: (1) **twiners**, whose tips nutate in search of support, Apios, Apocynaceae, Araliaceae, Aristolochiaceae, Basella, Bauhinia, Bignoniaceae, Bowiea, Calystegia, Camoensia, Ceropegia, Cassytha, Combretaceae, Connaraceae, Convolvulaceae, Cuscuta (sensitive stems, like tendrils), Cynanchum, Dipladenia, Freycinetia, Gnetum, Hoya, Ipomoea, Jasminum, Lardizabalaceae, Loasaceae, Lonicera, Lygodium, Malpighiaceae, Menispermaceae, Phaseolus, Phytocrene, Plumbago, Polygonum, Rhodochiton, Ruscus, Schizandra, Solanum, Tamus, Thunbergia, Wistaria; (2) **climbers with sensitive organs**, usu. *tendrils*, which may be modified *stems*, Antigonon, Landolphia, Passiflora, Vitis, *leaves*, Bignoniaceae, Cucurbitaceae, Cobaea, Corydalis, Leguminosae (Lathyrus, Vicia, &c.), Mutisia, *sensitive hooks* which clasp and become woody, Ancistrocladus, Artabotrys, Bauhinia, Gouania, Hugonia, Landolphia, Paullinia, Strychnos, Uncaria, Unona, Uvaria; *sensitive l.* occur in Gloriosa, Littonia, &c., *petioles* in Clematis, Dalbergia, Fumaria, Hablitzia, Maurandia, Rhodochiton, Tropaeolum, *midrib* in Nepenthes, *lat. branches* in Hippocratea, Macherium, Salacia, Securidaca, Uvaria; (3) **hook climbers**, sprawling, and catching by hooks (*cf.* above), Caesalpinia, Calamus, Capparis, Combretaceae, Desmoncus, Dipladenia, Galium, Hugonia, Lycium, Pereskia, Plectocomia, Smilax, Ventilago; (4) **root climbers** with special negatively heliotropic adv. r. that adhere to the support, Araceae, Araliaceae, Begonia, Bignoniaceae, Clusia, Ficus, Hedera, Hoya, Kendrickia, Norantea, Piper, Rhus, Salacia, Sapindaceae, Tecoma.

Climbers are often of anatomical interest, presenting many abnormal features, esp. the trop. lianes. For details, see Darwin, *Climbing Plants*; Schenk, *Biologie und Anatomie der Lianen*.

Clinacanthus Nees. Acanthaceae (IV. B). 1 Malaya.

Clinandrium (orchids), anther-bed.

Clinogyne Salisb. Marantaceae. 20 trop. Afr.

Clinopodium L. = Calamintha Tourn. (*BH.*) = Satureia L. p.p.

Clinostigma Wendl. Palmaceae (IV. 1). 5 Samoa, New Hebrides, &c.

Clintonia Dougl. = Downingia Torr. (Campanul.).

Clintonia Rafin. Liliaceae (VII). 6 E. As., N. Am.

Clistax Mart. Acanthaceae (IV. B). 2 Brazil.

Clistoyucca Trel. (*Yucca* p.p.). Liliaceae (VI). 1 N. Am.
Clitandra Benth. Apocynaceae (I. 1). 20 W. and C. trop. Afr. Rubber is obtained from the r. of *C. Henriqueziana* K. Sch.
Clitoria L. Leguminosae (III. 10). 35 trop. and subtrop. Fls. inverted and the essential organs therefore touch an insect's back.
Clivia Lindl. Amaryllidaceae (I). 3 S. Afr. Cult. orn. fl.
Cloezia Brongn. et Gris. Myrtaceae (II. 1). 6 New Caled.
Cloiselia Sp. Moore. Compositae (12). 1 Madag. Tree.
Clomenŏlepis Cass. Compositae (inc. sed.). Nomen.
Clonodia Griseb. Malpighiaceae (II). 3 N. Brazil, Bolivia.
Closia Remy. Compositae (6). 5 Chili.
Closing of fl. in shade or cold, *Anagallis*, *Bellis*, *Calandrinia*, *Eschscholtzia*, *Paeonia*, *Tragopogon*.
Clotbur (Am.), *Xanthium*.
Cloudberry, *Rubus Chamaemorus* L.
Clove gilliflower, **-pink**, *Dianthus Caryophyllus* L., var.
Clovenberry bush (W.I.), *Samyda serrulata* L.
Clover, *Trifolium*; **bush** or **Japanese-**, *Lespedeza*.
Cloves, *Eugenia caryophyllata* Thunb., (W.I.) *Pimenta acris* Kostel.; **Madagascar-**, *Ravensara aromatica* Sonn.
Clozelia A. Chevalier (*Antrocaryon* Pierre). Anacardiaceae (2). 1 Ivory Coast.
Clubmoss, *Lycopodium*; **-rush**, *Scirpus*.
Clusia L. Guttiferae (V). 200 warm Am., mostly climbing epiph., clasping the host by anastomosing aerial r., and frequently strangling it (*cf.* Ficus). Fr. fleshy probably carried by birds.
Clusiaceae (Warming) = Guttiferae.
Clusianthemum Vieill. (*Garcinia* p.p. *BH.*). Guttif. (V). 2 New Caled.
Clusiella Planch. et Triana. Guttiferae (V). 1 Colombia.
Cluster bean, *Cyamopsis*; **-pine**, *Pinus Pinaster* Ait.
Cluytia Boerh. ex L. Euphorbiaceae (A. II. 5). 50 Afr., Arabia.
Cluytiandra Muell.-Arg. Euphorbiaceae (A. I. 1). 5 trop. Afr.
Clybatis Phil. (*Leuceria* p.p. *EP.*). Compos. (12). 1 Chili.
Clypea Blume = Stephania Lour. (Menisp.).
Clypeate, shield-shaped.
Clypeola L. Cruciferae (4). 12 Medit.
Clytostoma Miers (*Pithecoctenium* Mart. *BH.*). Bignoniaceae (1). 2 temp. S. Am. Cult. orn. fl., often under name Bignonia.
Cnemidiscus Pierre. Sapindaceae (1). 1 Cochinchina.
Cnemidophacos Rydb. (*Astragalus* p.p.). Legum. (III. 6). 4 N. Am.
Cnemidostachys Mart. = Sebastiana Spreng. p.p. (Euph.).
Cneoraceae (*EP.*; *Simarubaceae* p.p. *BH.*). Dicots. (Archichl. Geraniales). Only genus Cneorum, *q.v.* Near to Zygophyllaceae, but separated because only one whorl of sta. with no ligules, and no stipules, but oil-glands in the l.
Cneoridium Hook. f. Rutaceae (I). 1 S. Calif.
Cneorum L. Cneoraceae. 12 Medit., Canaries. Shrubs with alt. leathery exstip. l. with oil-glands; fl. sol. or in racemes, 3—4-merous, ☿, reg. with column or bolster-like disc. A 3—4, $\underline{G}$ (3—4), lobed, with 2 ov. in each; style 1. Schizocarp.

Cnesmone Blume. Euphorb. (A. II. 2). 1 Indomal. Climbing shrub.
Cnestidium Planch. Connar. 1 Panama.
Cnestis Juss. Connar. 25 warm Afr., As. K. valv. Caps. hairy within.
Cnicothamnus Griseb. Comp. (12). 1 Argentina.
Cnicus L. p.p. [*BH.* and others incl. *Cirsium*, making 120 *]. Comp. (11). 1 Medit. (*C. Benedictus* L., offic.). The genus is much confused with Carduus and Cirsium.
Cnidium Cusson (*Selinum BH.*). Umbellif. (III. 5). 20 N. palaeotemp., S. Afr.
Cnidoscolus Pohl. = Jatropha L. p.p (Euphorb.). 54 trop.
Coach whip, *Fouquieria splendens* Engelm.
Coadunate, adnate, connate.
Coarctate, crowded together.
Coaxana Coulter et Rose. Umbellif. (III. 5). 1 Mexico.
Cobaea Cav. Polemoniaceae. 15 trop. Am. *C. scandens* Cav. cult. orn. climber of very rapid growth. It climbs by aid of tendrils (leaf-structures) which are much branched, the branches ending in sharp hooks. The tendril nutates with great rapidity and is highly sensitive to contact (as may be seen by rubbing one side and watching it for 5 min.); the hooks prevent the nutation from dragging away a branch before it has had time to clasp its support (Darwin, *Climbers*, p. 106). The closed bud stands erect on an erect stalk, but when going to open, the tip of the stalk bends over. Fl. very protandr. with movement of sta. and styles. At first greenish with unpleasant smell (fly-fl.), it becomes purple with pleasant honey-like smell (bee-fl.). Afterwards the stalk goes through several contortions (*cf.* Linaria).
Cobnut, *Corylus*, (W.I.) *Omphalea triandra* L.
Cobresia Pers. (*Kobresia* Willd.). Cyper. (III). 30 N. temp.
Coburgia Sweet = Stenomesson Herb. p.p. (Amaryll.).
Coca, *Erythroxylum Coca* Lam.; **cocaine**, ditto.
Coccineus (Lat.), scarlet.
Coccinia Wight et Arn. Cucurbitaceae (4). 20 warm As., Afr. The fr. of *C. indica* W. and A. is eaten as a veg. in India.
Coccoceras Miq. Euphorbiaceae (A. II. 2). 3 Indomal.
Coccocypselum P. Br. Rubiac. (I. 7). 10 trop. Am. Heterostyled.
Coccoderma Miers. Menispermaceae. Nomen.
Coccoglochidion K. Schum. Euphorb. (A. I. 1). 1 New Guinea.
Coccoloba L. (*Coccolobis* P. Br.). Polygonaceae (III. 1). 150 trop. and subtrop. Am. *C. uvifera* L., and others, ed. fr. (seaside grape).
Cocconerion Baill. Euphorb. (inc. sed.). 2 New Caled.
Coccothrinax Sargent. Palmaceae (I. 2). 10 warm Am., W.I.
Coccule, portion of a divided coccus.
Cocculus DC. Menispermaceae. 15 trop. and subtrop.
Cocculus indicus, *Anamirta Cocculus* Wight et Arn.
Coccus, a mericarp.
Cochineal, *Nopalea*, *Opuntia*.
Cochlanthera Choisy (*Clusia BH.*). Guttif. (V). 1 Venezuela.
Cochlanthus Balf. f. Asclepiadaceae (I). 1 Socotra.
Cochlea, a closely coiled legume.
Cochlear, spoon-shaped.

Cochlearia Tourn. ex L. Cruciferae (2). 20 Eur., As. Minor. *C. officinalis* L. (scurvy-grass) in Brit. with ± fleshy l., chiefly at the seaside and on mts. (*cf.* Armeria). The thick root of *C. Armoracia* L. (horse-radish) is a condiment.
Cochleate, coiled shell-shaped.
Cochlianthus Benth. Leguminosae (III. 10). 1 Nepal.
Cochlioda Lindl. Orchid. (II. 19). 5 trop. S. Am. Cult.
Cochliostema Lem. Commelinaceae. 1 Ecuador, *C. odoratissima* Lem., cult. orn. perf. fl. The filaments of the fertile sta. develope both lat. and beyond the anthers into large wings. Anther-loculi spiral.
Cochlospermaceae (*EP.*; *Bixineae* p.p. *BH.*). Dicots. (Archichl. Parietales). 3 gen., 18 sp. trop. Trees and shrubs usu. with lobed l. and racemose infl. of large ☿, reg. or slightly ·|· fl. K 4—5, C 4—5, A ∞, $\underline{G}$ (3—5) with ∞ ov. in each on axile or parietal plac. Caps. Oily endosp.
Cochlospermum Kunth. Cochlospermaceae. 12 trop., mostly xero.; some have stout tuberous underground stems; many drop their l. and flower in the dry season. Some cult. orn.
Cochranea Miers. Boraginaceae (III). 10 Chili.
Cockburnia Balf. f. Globulariaceae. 1 Socotra.
Cockle (Am.), *Lychnis*; **-bur** (Am.), *Xanthium*.
Cock's comb, *Celosia cristata* L.; **-head** (W.I.), *Desmodium tortuosum* DC.; **-foot grass**, *Dactylis glomerata* L.; **-spur** (W.I.), *Pisonia aculeata* L.; **-spur thorn** (Ceylon), *Acacia eburnea* Willd.
Coco, *Colocasia antiquorum* Schott; **-de-mer**, *Lodoicea Seychellarum* Labill.; **-nut**, *Cocos nucifera* L., *Lodoicea*; **-plum**, *Chrysobalanus Icaco* L.; **water nut**, *Nipa fruticans* Thunb.; **-wood** (W.I.), *Inga vera* Willd.
Cocoa, *Theobroma Cacao* L., and other spp.
Cocops O. F. Cook. Palmaceae (IV. 2). 1 W. Indies.
Cocos L. Palmae (IV. 2). 60 trop., esp. *C. nucifera* L. (coconut), cult. throughout trop. It grows esp. well near to the sea, and its fibrous and woody fr. is capable of floating long distances uninjured, hence it forms a char. feature of marine island veg., and indeed probably became widely distr. in early times. It is a tall palm with large pinnate l. and a dense monoec. infl. The stem rarely stands vertically, but makes a gradual curve; this would appear to be due to heliotropism. Fr. large, one-seeded. The outer layer of the pericarp is fibrous, the inner very hard (the shell of the coconuts sold in shops). At the base are 3 marks, corresponding to the 3 loc. of the ovary, two of which have become obliterated. Under one of these is the embryo. The thin testa is lined with white endosp., enclosing a large cavity, partly filled with a milky fluid. This palm furnishes many of the necessaries of life to the inhabitants of the tropics, and its products are largely exported from Ceylon, the Philippines, &c. The large l. are woven into cadjans for thatching, mats, baskets, &c.; their stalks and midribs make fences, brooms, yokes, and many other articles of furniture. The bud or "cabbage" at the apex of the stem makes an excellent vegetable and is made into pickles and preserves. When flowering the infl.-axis is tapped for toddy, a drink like the Mexican pulque (*cf.* Agave), containing sugar. Evap. of toddy

furnishes a sugar known as jaggery; its fermentation gives an alcoholic drink, from which distillation produces the strong spirit known as arrack, while further fermentation gives vinegar. The fr. while young contain a pint or more of a sweetish watery fluid, a refreshing drink; it decreases as the nut ripens. The kernels are eaten raw, or in curries, milk is expressed from them for flavouring, and oil is extracted by boiling or by pressure, in the latter case the kernels being first dried into what is known as copra. The refuse cake or poonac, left after the expression of the oil, is a valuable fattening food for cattle. The great use of the oil is for soap-making and margarine. In recent years a large industry has sprung up in desiccated coconut, largely used in confectionery, the kernel being sliced and dried in special desiccators. The outer wood of the stem (porcupine wood) is used for rafters, orn. articles, &c. The thick outer husk, rarely seen in Europe upon the nut, contains a large number of long stout fibres running lengthwise. The nut is placed in water till the soft tissues between these fibres decay, and the fibre (coir) is then beaten out; or sometimes the fibre is obtained by special machinery. [E. B. Copeland, *The Coconut*; Hunger, *Cocos nucifera*,

Cocos or **cocus wood**, *Brya Ebenus* DC. [*Nature*, 124, 1929, p. 133.]

Codia Forst. Cunoniaceae. 9 New Caledonia.

Codiaeum Rumph. ex A. Juss. Euphorb. (A. II. 5). 6 Indomal., Polynes., Austr. *C. variegatum* Blume cult., esp. in trop., for its coloured l.; usu. known as Crotons, and also used as hedges. Some have curious l., often twisted, or with two blades separated by a length of petiole.

Codlins and cream, *Epilobium hirsutum* L.

Codon L. Hydrophyllaceae. 2 S. Afr. 10—12-merous.

Codonacanthus Nees. Acanthaceae (IV. B). 2 Khasias, China.

Codonanthe Hanst. Gesneriaceae (I). 10 trop. Am.

Codonocarpus A. Cunn. ex Hook. (*Gyrostemon* Desf. *EP.*). Phytolaccaceae. 3 Austr.

Codonocephalum Fenzl. Compositae (4). 2 W. As.

Codonopsis Wall. Campanulaceae (I). 25 As. Cult. orn. fl.

Codonorchis Lindl. (*Pogonia BH.*). Orchid. (II. 2). 2 temp. Am.

Codonosiphon Schlechter. Orchid. (II. 16). 3 New Guinea.

Codonostigma Klotzsch (*Scyphogyne BH.*). Eric. (IV. 2). 1 S. Afr.

Codonura K. Schum. Apocynaceae (II. 1). 1 Cameroons.

Coelachne R. Br. Gramineae (9). 5 Indomal., China, Austr., Madag.

Coelachyrum Nees (*Eragrostis* p.p. *BH.*). Gram. (11). 2 S.W. As.

Coelanthum E. Mey. Aizoaceae (I). 2 S. Afr.

Coelarthron Hook. f. (*Andropogon* p.p. *EP.*). Gramin. (2). 1 Indomal.

Coelebogyne J. Sm. = Alchornea Sw. p.p. (Euphorb.).

Coelia Lindl. Orchidaceae (II. 6). 5 trop. Am., W.I.

Coelidium Vog. Leguminosae (III. 3). 8 S. Afr.

Coelina Nor. Inc. sed. Nomen.

Coeliopsis Reichb. f. Orchid. (II. 13). 1 Panama.

Coelocarpum Balf. f. Verbenaceae (I). 2 Socotra, Madag.

Coelocaryon Warb. Myristicaceae. 5 trop. Afr.

Coelococcus H. Wendl. (*Metroxylon* p.p.). Palm. (III). 2 Polynes.

Coelodepas Hassk. Euphorbiaceae (A. II. 2). 6 Indomal.

Coelodiscus Baill. Euphorbiaceae (A. II. 2). 5 Indomal. A ∞.
Coeloglossum Hartm. (*Habenaria* p.p. *BH.*). Orch. (II. 1). 2 N. temp.
Coelogyne Lindl. (*BH.* incl. *Pleione* D. Don). Orchidaceae (II. 3). 120 Indomal.
Coelonema Maxim. Cruciferae (4). 1 China.
Coeloneurum Radlk. Solanaceae (4). 2 San Domingo.
Coelopleurum Ledeb. (*Archangelica BH.*). Umbel. (III. 5). 6 N. Am., E. As.
Coelopyrum Jack. Inc. sed. 1 Malaya.
Coelorachis Brongn. (*Rottboellia* L.). Gram. (2). 12 trop.
Coelospermous, with boat-shaped seeds.
Coelospermum Blume. Rubiac. (II. 9). 12 Malaya, Austr., Polyn.
Coelostegia Benth. Bombacaceae. 3 Malaya.
Coelostelma Fourn. Asclepiadaceae (II. 4). 1 Brazil.
Coemansia March (*Pentapanax* p.p.). Araliac. (2). 1 Brazil.
Coffea L. Rubiaceae (II. 4). 45 palaeotrop., esp. Afr. *C. arabica* L. (Arabian coffee) largely cult. in S. Brazil, Java, Jamaica, and elsewhere, often under the shade of large trees. *C. liberica* Hiern (Liberian coffee) cult. usu. at lower elevations; its produce is not so good. Other sp. are also used. The fr. is a 2-seeded drupe, resembling a cherry. The pulp and the endocarp (which covers the two seeds like a layer of parchment) are mechanically removed. The seed, or coffee-bean, has a deep groove on the ventral side; by soaking it in water the endosperm is softened and the embryo may be dissected out. The stimulating property depends on the presence of the alkaloid caffeine. Coffee cultivation was from 1850 to 1880 the mainstay of Ceylon agriculture, but was killed out largely by the attacks of a fungus (*Hemileia vastatrix*) and the green bug. By far the largest cult. is that of Brazil, which in 1912 exported £45 million worth of coffee. (Raoul, *Culture du Caféier*, Paris.)
Coffee, *Coffea arabica* L., &c.; **Kentucky-**, *Gymnocladus*.
Coffin nail, *Anacardium occidentale* L.
Cogniauxia Baill. Cucurbitaceae (3). 4 trop. Afr.
Cogswellia Spreng. (*Peucedanum* p.p.). Umbelliferae (III. 6). 70 N. Am.
Cogwood, *Zizyphus chloroxylon* Oliv.; (W.I.), *Ceanothus*.
Cohesion, union of members of same whorl, *e.g.* petals.
Cohnia Kunth (*Cordyline* p.p. *BH.*). Lili. (VI). 3 Masc., New Caled.
do. Reichb. f. = Cohniella Pfitz.
Cohniella Pfitz. (*Cohnia* Reichb. f.). Orchid. (II. 19). 1 C. Am.
Cohort, a group of allied fams., now termed an order.
Cohosh (Am.), *Cimicifuga*; **blue-**, *Caulophyllum*.
Cohune nut, *Attalea cohune* Mart.
Coilochilus Schlecht. Orchid. (II. 2). 1 New Caled.
Coincya Rouy (*Raphanus* p.p. *BH.*). Crucif. (2). 1 Spain.
Coinochlamys T. Anders. Loganiaceae. 5 W. Afr.
Coir, *Cocos nucifera* L.
Coix L. Gramineae (I). 6 India, China, esp. *C. Lachryma* L. (Job's tears) with inverted pear-shaped body at base of infl., the sheath of the br. of the infl., hollowed out and containing the 1-fld. ♀ spikelet;

the ♂ project beyond the mouth; cult. for food in Khasia Hills and Burma; used in medicine in China.

Cola Schott et Endl. Sterculiaceae. 50 Afr. *C. vera* K. Schumann and *C. acuminata* Schott et Endl. (possibly identical) are the source of the kola nuts which form a principal article of trade in W. Africa. The nuts contain much caffein, and when chewed confer considerable power of sustaining fatigue; they are consequently a staple in the diet of the negroes (*cf.* Erythroxylon). The tree is as yet rarely cult., but is very common in W. Afr. The nuts are skinned after keeping for a few days, and packed between l. to keep them damp. Exalb.

Colax Lindl. (*Lycaste* Lindl. *BH.*). Orchidaceae (II. 14). 3 Brazil. Cult.

Colchicaceae (Warming) = Liliaceae (suborder 1).

Colchicum L. Liliaceae (1). 45 Eur., W. As., N. Afr. *C. autumnale* L. (autumn crocus or meadow saffron), Brit. Below the soil is a large corm (fig. and description of corm &c. below). In autumn the fl. projects out of the soil. The P-tube is long, and the ovary remains below ground, protected from cold, &c. The protog. fl. is visited by

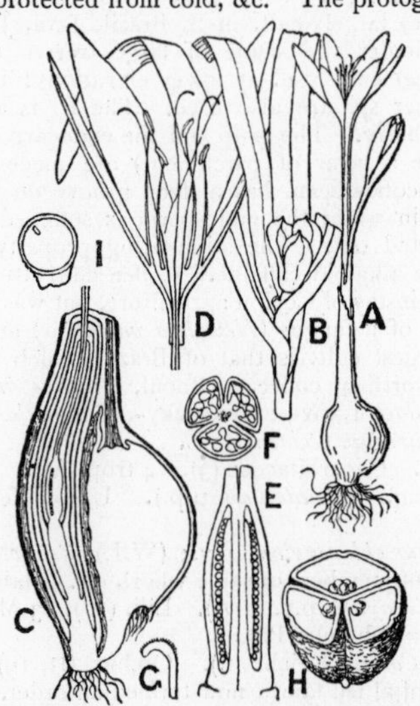

A, pl. in fl. in autumn, ×⅛. B, l. and opening fr. in following summer, ×⅛. C, underground portion of flg. pl. cut lengthwise; the thick outer line repres. the brown membrane enveloping the whole; to the right is the corm formed from the base of last year's shoot, a withered portion remaining at the apex; to the left is the flg. axis, a lat. shoot from the base of the corm; from the base of the axis spring r. and above are the l., sheathing and foliage; the fl. arises in the axil of one of the uppermost foliage l., which will appear above ground with the fr. next spring, when the lower portion of the axis will swell to form a new corm. Reduced. D, section of upper part of fl. ×½. E, ovary cut lengthwise. F, cross-section ovary. G, a single stigma. H, cross-section fr. I, ditto seed. BEGHI after Berg and Schmidt. E to G, and I enlarged, H×½.

bees. In spring the l. appear and the capsule is brought above ground by the lengthening of its stalk. The seeds and corms are used in medicine, in gout.

Coldenia L. Boraginaceae (II). 15 trop., subtrop.

Colea Boj. Bignoniaceae (4). 18 Madag., Masc.

Coleanthera Stschegl. Epacridaceae (3). 3 W. Austr.

Coleanthus Seidl. Gramineae (8). 1 N. temp. |※.

Colebrookea Sm. Labiatae (VI). 1 India.

Coleocoma F. Muell. Compositae (4). 1 trop. Austr.

Coleogyne Torr. Rosaceae (III. 3). 1 W.U.S., C o.

Coleonema Bartl. et Wendl. Rutaceae (I). 5 S. Afr.

Coleosanthus Cass. = Brickellia Ell. (Compos.).

Coleospadix Becc. (*Ptychosperma EP.*). Palm. (IV. 1). 2 New Guin.

Coleostachys A. Juss. Malpighiaceae (II). 1 N. S. Am.

Coleotrype C. B. Clarke. Commelin. 3 S.E. Afr., Madag.

Coleus Lour. Labiatae (VII). 150 palaeotrop. Many forms and hybrids with varieg. and coloured leaves, cult. *C. elongatus* Trimen is a peculiar sp. found only on the top of one mountain in Ceylon, and must have arisen by mutation (*Ann. Perad.* IV. 1).

Colic-root (Am.), *Aletris.*

Colignonia Endl. Nyctaginaceae. 7 Andes.

Collabium Blume. Orchidaceae (II. a. II). 3 Malaya.

Colladonia DC. = Prangos Lindl. p.p. (Umbellif.).

Collaea DC. = Galactia P. Br. p.p. (Legum.).

Collar, junction of root and shoot.

Collards (Am.), a form of cabbage.

Collateral branches, buds, cf. Buds.

Collecting (notes for field botanists, travellers and collectors).

OUTFIT. Any or all of the following may be needed, according to the places to be visited, and the kind of work to be done. All that is needed should be taken from the start, as it is usually difficult to get suitable things quickly elsewhere; extra supplies of paper, &c. may be sent to the "Poste restante" at places to be visited en route.

Portfolios for pressing plants as collected, lightly made of two strong cloth-covered pasteboards (17 in. × 11 in.) with encircling straps and handle, and to contain 30—50 sheets of paper. Specimens as collected are put at once into these, and time is thus saved in making large collections, *e.g.* on a journey in new country.

Collecting tins or vasculums of various sizes for bringing plants home for further study. When slung on the back, the hinges should be on the lower side of the lid, and the bolt should slide downwards to fasten, otherwise it is liable to work loose. Small specimens are best carried in *small round-cornered tobacco or tooth-powder tins*, not among large ones in a general vasculum.

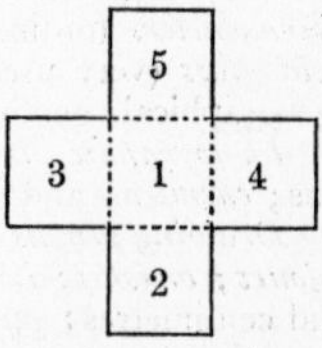

5

3 1 4

2

Presses for drying pl.; each of two outer frames of ¼ inch iron rod 17½ × 11½ inches, filled in with stout wire netting soldered to the iron. The papers lie between these frames and the whole is strapped with two stout straps to obtain the pressure.

Lattices, 17 × 11 inches, for admitting air between the masses of plants in the press, made of two sets of parallel thin laths fastened together.

Drying paper in sheets 17 × 11 inches in ample quantity; stout Manila is best, blotting paper is too fragile. *Mounting paper* in sheets 16½ × 10½ inches (standard size of Kew herbarium) or sheets of newspaper or other common paper for preservation of dry specimens removed from the press. Unfolded *envelopes* of thin paper cut into the shape shown, for seeds, flowers, &c.; place the specimen on 1 and fold over the wings 2, 3, 4, 5 in order. 2 must be the same size as 1.

Waxcloth for tying up bundles of dried and mounted specimens; *waterproof canvas* for covers for presses, &c. in case of rain.

Corrosive sublimate (mercuric chloride) and *alcohol* for poisoning specimens; made up as required in the proportion of 1 part to 50. Large *dish* for poisoning. *Naphthalin* for keeping away insects.

Kerosine tins or other square tins with large lids for preserving specimens in alcohol (lids that push in airtight, as in many tobacco tins, are the best); *soldering apparatus* for fastening up when full.

Bottles with stoppers for preserving delicate specimens; neckless *glass tubes*, with corks, of various sizes. Bottles are easily packed in joints of bamboo, tubes in small tins.

Muslin for wrapping alcohol specimens. Each should be wrapped with its label (in Indian ink, or better on metal) in a piece of muslin and packed in the tin; specimens cannot then become mixed together, and can be closely packed.

Alcohol for preserving; ordinary methylated spirit is best for most things, but some require 70 % alcohol, and some absolute alcohol.

Formalin, *picric acid*, *chromic acid*, *glycerin*, or other preservatives.

Butterfly-net, *killing-bottle*, *insect boxes*, *entomological pins*, if ecological work is to be done.

Hunting-knife, cutlass, or kukri for lopping creepers, &c.; *pruning shears* for cutting branches; strong *pocket knives;* strong narrow-bladed *trowels; geological hammer;* strong *rope* for climbing, &c.

Travelling microscope and *lenses; dissecting microscope; pocket lenses;* microscope *slides; cover-slips* in alcohol or oil; *scalpels;* dissecting *needles; scissors* large and small and with fine points; *razors* for section-cutting; *forceps; dishes; watch-glasses; camel-hair brushes.*

Reagents and *mountants* for simple microscopic work, *e.g.* iodine, glycerine, haematoxylin, gold-size, canada balsam in xylol, alcohol, oil of cloves.

Compass (prismatic by preference); *spirit-level; aneroid barometer; thermometers* (ordinary, maximum and minimum, wet and dry bulb); *field glass* (very useful for studying cliffs, ravines, trees, &c.); *maps* (geographical, geological, outlines for marking distribution, &c.).

Photographic camera and *lenses; tripod; films* or *plates* in soldered tins; *chemicals* and *dishes* for developing, fixing, &c.

Drawing pencils (hard, medium, soft); drawing *cards; sketch-block; colours; brushes; india-rubber; ink; compasses; ruler; scales* in inches and centimetres; *gum* and *brush; pins; pens; pencils; stylograph.*

Spirit-lamp; tape-measure; string, twine and *thread; thin wire;* sheet-*lead* or *zinc* for labels (if latter, also solution of platinic chloride for writing on it); *glue-pot* and *glue* for mounting.

Note-books with numbered detachable pages, so that the descr. of each specimen can be separated; consecutively numbered and perforated *labels* for specimens, the numbers to correspond to those in note-book. The labels may be joined to the pages or in sheets like postage stamps. More than one of each number will usu. be needed.

Collecting and Preserving. The following hints will be found useful.

Decide the general object of the work in advance, and collect principally for the furtherance of that object.

In collecting for subsequent distr., collect enough specimens to go round, but do not seriously diminish a plant in its native locality.

Do not collect immediately on arrival; first become familiar with the plants and their local features and distribution. Better results are obtained by choosing certain localities as headquarters and working these thoroughly, than by rushing through a large district.

Do not collect herbarium material in wet weather.

Collect specimens which are as typical as possible, but also take some illustrating the range of variation, the difference of habit and size on different soils or situations, &c.

Collect entire pl. if possible, incl. r. In shrubs or trees, twigs with l. in all stages, portions of stem-bark and anything else necessary for a complete descr. Do not forget rad. l., buds, fl., ripe and unripe fr., seeds.

If a large collection is being made, it is quicker to use the portfolio than the vasculum, and to press each specimen as soon as obtained.

Large flowers or heads (*e.g.* thistles), fruits, roots, tubers, &c. may be sliced in half before pressing, or the surface only sliced off. Notes and sketches should be made of the original appearance.

L. of Conifers, Heaths, Succulents, &c. fall when dried, unless previously immersed a few seconds in boiling water. Do not immerse fl.

Thorny and prickly plants should first be placed between boards and pressed down with the feet; the prickles would otherwise tear the papers.

Delicate water plants should be arranged upon sheets of white paper under water, and always remain on these sheets while drying.

It saves time in drying delicate specimens to keep each always in a folded sheet of very thin paper.

Place extra fl., small fragments, seeds, &c., in small envelopes, numbered to correspond with the specimens; do not have any small parts loose, or confusion may result.

Place all specimens in the press the day they are collected. Withered plants may be soaked in water; if the stem be cut 2—3 in. above the former cut and *under* water it will often revive quickly.

Label every specimen with its consecutive number in such a way that the number cannot be lost. Punched labels are best, tied on with thread. See that all envelopes, &c. have the same number.

Spread out the specimens naturally. If many l. &c. overlap, place bits of drying paper between. If stems have to be cut, mark the corresponding ends by stars on the paper. Spread out some fl., leave others unspread, and divide some in the antero-post. plane. Divide some fr. lengthwise and crosswise.

Arrange the specimens on the sheets so that they form a steady pile without lumps in the middle. Place a lattice upon every five inches of specimens. When all are ready place in the press and draw the straps as tight as possible, or better, place about 10 lbs. weight upon it. Tighten the straps as the plants shrink.

Change drying papers at least once daily: dry used paper in the sun or by the fire; use warm driers where possible. See that petals, &c. do not stick to the paper: if necessary put slips of tissue paper under.

In changing the papers, put the outer specimens inside, so that all shall dry evenly. Drying should be as rapid as possible to prevent loss of colour, blackening, &c.

Fully dried plants no longer feel cold on the cheek, and are stiff and brittle.

Dried specimens should be poisoned by a brief immersion in 2 % solution of mercuric chloride in alcohol. They should then be dried in the air, mounted (with glue) or laid between sheets of paper, and tied up in wax-cloth with a little naphthalin to keep out insects.

Material for subsequent microscopic examination or for museums must usu. be preserved in alcohol. Cut into small portions, attach label (best of zinc written on with solution of platinic chloride, but paper and pencil or Indian ink will do temporarily); place in methylated spirit for a few days, wrapped in muslin, and finally preserve in large tin. A few inches of spirit at the bottom, enough to keep all specimens moist when the tin is soldered, will suffice for most material. Specimens for embryological, delicate histological, cytological, and other investigations, and delicate plants or organs, must be separately preserved from the first in absolute alcohol in bottles or tubes. Labels should be put inside these. Contents of bottles may be written on the ground surface of the stoppers, so as to be legible through the neck.

Museum material may also be preserved in formalin (1 part of ordinary solution to 10 or more of water). Some special preservatives, *e.g.* picric and chromic acids, are used in special cases.

Specimens illustrative of economic uses of plants and their products should be collected in less known districts, *e.g.* samples of gums, resins, caoutchoucs, oils, fibres, timbers (portions of trunks, or slabs 8 × 4 × 4 inches), food-products, drugs, dyes, tans, &c. In all cases the exact origin should be verified, and herbarium specimens taken, bearing numbers to correspond with those placed on the products.

From less known countries, endeavour to bring back living seeds (ripe, well dried, dry in canvas bags, or packed in charcoal in tins if to be long kept), bulbs and tubers (gathered when dry and with withered leaves), succulent plants (gathered dry and loosely packed), living plants (planted in earth in Wardian cases or sometimes in bamboo pots, if possible some weeks before moving). Cuttings may sometimes be brought in oiled silk wrappers; pseudobulbs in boxes with air-holes; tree ferns with the fronds removed, and a ball of earth round the root.

RECORDING. The following hints are worth noting.

Make all notes immediately upon observation of the facts; never trust to memory, nor delay recording.

Make all notes about individual specimens upon detachable sheets, numbered to correspond with the specimens; never describe two or more on the same sheet; never use the same number twice.

Make no record till satisfied of its truth and accuracy.

Accompany all notes with maps, drawings, sketches, or photographs as far as possible.

Sketch and photograph all peculiarities of habit, characteristic forms of vegetation, and other features of interest. Mark all plants in such pictures with numbers corresponding to their numbers in your collection, and write a full description of each picture before leaving the spot. If a photograph is taken, make a rough sketch (from the picture on the focussing screen or finder) of the scene and put numbers to the plants.

Label all specimens as collected with consecutive numbers, and subsequently with permanent labels (about 3 × 2 inches) giving name of herbarium, collection, tour or district in which they were collected, date, locality, and collector, as well as the number.

As each specimen is gathered, record date, exact locality, elevation above sea, habit, colour of fl. and fr., scent, presence or absence of honey, floral mechanism, insect visits, and any other features and facts that cannot be ascertained from the specimens preserved.

Note the comparative frequency of each species, the kind of situation and soil it affects, and the species with which it is found in association.

Endeavour to note the chief general forms of vegetation and the local grouping of pl. in districts studied. Pay special attention to ecological and geographical questions.

Record native names (question several different persons before deciding), economic uses, and points of general or ethnological interest.

Further details of the subjects treated in this section may be found in *Hints for Collectors* (Kew Bulletin, 1914, p. 97), the *Admiralty Manual of Scientific Enquiry*, Dammer's *Handbuch für Pflanzensammler*, Stuttgart, 1891, Asa Gray's *Structural Botany*, &c.

Collective (fr.), resulting from several fl., *Ficus*, *Morus*, *Platanus*.

Collet, collar.

Colleters, glandular hairs.

Colletia Comm. ex Juss. Rhamnaceae. 15 S. Am. Habit peculiar; in each axil are 2 serial buds; the upper gives a triangular thorn, the lower fls. or a branch of unlimited growth.

Colliguaja Molina. Euphorbiaceae (A. II. 7). 6 temp. S. Am.

Collinsia Nutt. Scrophul. (II. 4). 25 N. Am., often cult. orn. fl. The fl. resembles, in shape and mech., that of Leguminosae.

Collinsonia L. Labiatae (VI). 2 Atl. N. Am.

Collinus (Lat.), on low hills.

Collococcus P. Br. Inc. sed. Nomen.

Collomia Nutt. Polemoniaceae. 10 W. Am. The seed coat has a covering of cells with mucilaginous walls which swell when wetted (*cf.* Brassica, Linum, &c.). Cult. orn. fl.

Collyris Vahl = Dischidia R. Br. (Asclep.).

Colmeiroa F. Muell. Saxifragaceae (V). 1 Lord Howe I.

Colobanthus Bartl. Caryophyllaceae (I. 1). 15 S. Am., Austr., N.Z. Petals 0. Sta. in one whorl.

Colocasia Schott. Araceae (VI). 8 Indomal. Tuberous herbs or small shrubs. Monoec. Sta. in synandria. *C. antiquorum* Schott (taro, coco, or scratch-coco), cult. in trop. for its rhiz., which when boiled loses its poisonous nature and forms valuable food.

Colocynth, *Citrullus Colocynthis* Schrad.

Colocynthis (Tourn.) L. = Citrullus Neck. (Cucurb.).

Cologania Kunth (*Amphicarpaea EP.*). Legum. (III. 10). 30 Am., As.

Colonist, weed of cult. land, rare elsewhere.

Colophony, a form of resin.

Coloptera Coulter et Rose. Umbell. (III. 6). 3 N.W. U.S.

Colosanthera Pohl. Inc. sed. Nomen.

Colour, change in fl., *cf.* Change; **of young l.**, *Amherstia*, *Brownea*, *Cinnamomum*, *Dryobalanops*, *Haematoxylon*.

Colpias E. Mey. Scrophulariaceae (II. 3). 1 S. Afr.

Colpodium Trin. Gramineae (10). 12 N. temp.

Colpoon Berg. Santalaceae. 3 S. Afr.

Colpothrinax Griseb. et H. Wendl. Palm. (I. 2). 1 Cuba.

Colquhounia Wall. Labiatae (VI). 5 Indomal.

Colt's foot, *Tussilago Farfara* L.; (W.I.) *Piper umbellatum* L.

Colubrina Rich. ex Brongn. Rhamnaceae. 20 trop., subtrop.

Columbaria J. et C. Presl = Scabiosa Tourn. (Dipsac.).

Columbia Pers. Tiliaceae. 15 trop. As.

Columbine, *Aquilegia vulgaris* L.

Columella, central axis of fr., *Geranium*, *Thuja*.

Columellia Ruiz et Pav. Columell. 3 N. Andes. Shrubs with evergr. opp. exstip. l. Fls. in cymes, ☿, nearly reg. K 5, C (5), A 2, short and thick with irreg. broad connective and 1 twisted pollen sac. No disc. G̲ (2), imperfectly 2-loc.; ov. ∞, anatr.; style short and thick with broad 2—4-lobed stigma. Caps., enclosed in K. Endosp.

Columelliaceae. Dicots. (Sympet. Tubiflorae; Personales *BH.*). Only genus Columellia (*q.v.*). [Van Tieghem, *Ann. Sc. Nat.* 8. xviii. 155.]

Column, *cf.* Orchidaceae.

Columnea Plum. ex L. Gesneraceae (I). 75 trop. Am., several climbers and epiphytes. Anisophylly is frequent.

Columniferae (Warming). The 12th cohort of Choripetalae.

Coluria R. Br. Rosaceae (III. 2). 4 Siberia, China.

Colutea (Tourn.) L. Leguminosae (III. 6). 12 S. Eur. to Himal. *C. arborescens* L. (bladder-senna) cult. Its l. have similar properties to senna (Cassia) and are used to adulterate the latter. The pods are inflated and burst on being squeezed.

Coluteocarpus Boiss. Cruciferae (2). 1 W. As. Mts.

Colvillea Boj. ex Hook. Leguminosae (II. 7). 1 Madag.

Colza, *Brassica Napus* L.

Coma, a tuft of hairs.

Comandra Nutt. Santalaceae. 4 Eur., N. Am.

Comanthosphace Sp. Moore. Labiatae (VI). 4 Japan.

Comarella Rydberg (*Potentilla* p.p.). Rosac. (III. 2). 2 N. Am.

Comarobatia Greene (*Rubus* p.p.). Rosac. (III. 2). 1 N.W. Am.

Comarostaphylis Zucc. = Arctostaphylos Adans. p.p. (Eric.).

Comarum L. = Potentilla L. (Rosac.).

Combretaceae (*EP.*, *BH.*). Dicots. (Archichl. Myrtiflorae; Myrtales *BH.*). 16 gen., 480 sp. trop. and subtrop. Trees and shrubs with alt. or opp. simple stalked entire exstip. l.; many climbers, some twining, some with hooks (persistent bases of petioles); usu. rich in tannin. Fls. usu. sessile in racemose infls., usu. ☿ and reg., 3—8-merous. Typically K 5, usu. valv., C 5 or 0, A 5+5, rarely ∞, $\overline{G}$ 1-loc. with 2—5 anatr. pend. ov. and simple style. Disc on summit of ovary, sometimes with outgrowths. Dry 1-seeded fr., often winged at angles. No endosp.; cots. usu. spirally twisted. *Chief genera:* Terminalia, Combretum, Quisqualis.

Combretocarpus Hook. f. Rhizophor. 1 Borneo. Like Anisophyllea.

Combretodendron A. Chevalier. Combret. 1 trop. Afr.

Combretopsis K. Schum. (*Lophopyxis* Hk. f.). Icacin. 1 New Guin.

Combretum L. Combret. 350 warm, exc. Austr. K deciduous, C present, A usu. 8—10. Climbers or erect; l. alt. or opp. Chiquito, a butter-like body, from fr. of *C. butyrosum* Tal. (trop. Afr.).

Comesperma Labill. (*Bredemeyera* p.p. *EP.*). Polygal. 25 Austr.

Cometes L. Caryoph. (I. 7). 2 W. As., Abyss.

Cometia Thou. Euphorb. (A. I. 1). 2 Madag. G 1-loc; 1 style.

Comfrey, *Symphytum officinale* L.

Cominia P. Br. = Allophylus L. (Sapind.).

Cominsia Hemsl. Marant. 1 Moluccas, New Guinea, Solomons.

Commelina L. Commelin. 115 trop. and subtrop. Infl. with sheathing bracts; fl. horiz., sta. and style projecting. In many the upper 3 sta. sterile with cross-like anthers, but lobes juicy, bees piercing them for honey. *C. benghalensis* L. has subterranean cleist. fls. Some have ed. rhiz.; many cult. orn. fl.

Commelinaceae (*EP.*, *BH.*). Monocots. (Farinosae; Coronarieae *BH.*, pp. vii, liv). 30/400 mostly trop. and subtrop. herbs with jointed stems and alt. sheathing l. Infl. usu. a cincinnus like Borag. Fl. ☿, usu. reg., commonly blue; usu. formula K 3, C 3, rarely (3), differing in colour and texture from K, A 3+3, often hairy, but some often absent or stds., $\underline{G}$ (3), 3-loc. with a few orthotr. ov. in each. Caps. loculic. or indeh. Endosp. copious, seed often with aril. *Chief genera:* Commelina, Aneilema, Tradescantia, Cyanotis, Dichorisandra.

Commensalism, living together for mutual benefit.

Commersonia Forst. Stercul. 10 trop. As., Austr. Pets. cap-like, stds. 3-partite.

Commersorchis Thou. Orchid. (inc. sed.). 1 Mascarenes.

Commianthus Benth. = Retiniphyllum Humb. et Bonpl. pp. (Rubi.).

Commicarpus Standley (*Boerhaavia* p.p.). Nyctag. 5 warm Am., W.I.

Commidendron Burch. Comp. (3). 5 St. Helena. Trees; l. crowded at ends of twigs. *C. gummiferum* DC. yields a gum.

Commilobium Benth. = Pterodon Vog. (Legum.).

Commiphora Jacq. (*Balsamodendron* Kunth). Burser. 90 warm As., Afr. Axis cup-like. Resin exudes and collects in lumps. Several yield myrrh, used in medicine, incense, &c. *C. opobalsamum* Engl. is said to yield balm of Gilead; others yield bdellium and other resins.

Commissure (Umbellif.), face by which the cpls. cohere.

Common receptacle, the receptacle of all fl. on a head.

Communis (Lat.), social, general.

Community (Cl.), a mixture of individuals of 2 or more spp.

Comocladia P. Br., L. Anacard. (3). 15 W.I., C. Am. 3—4-merous.

Comolia DC. Melastomaceae (I). 20 S. Am.
Comomyrsine Hook. f. (*Weigeltia* p.p. *EP.*). Myrsin. (II). 4 S. Am.
Comopycna O. Ktze. = Pycnocoma Benth. (Euphorb.).
Comoroa Oliv. (*Teclea* p.p. *EP.*). Rutaceae (IV). 1 Comoro Is.
Comose, hairy in tufts.
Comostemum Nees = Androtrichum Brongn. (Cyper.).
Comparettia Poepp. et Endl. Orchidaceae (II. 19). 5 trop. Am. Cult.
Compass-plants, *Silphium laciniatum* L., *Lactuca Scariola* L.
Comperia C. Koch (*Orchis BH.*). Orchid. (II. 1). 1 S.E. Eur.
Compital, where veins intersect at an angle.
Complanate, flattened.
Complete (fl.), with two whorls of perianth.
Complicate, folded on itself.
Compositae (*EP.*, *BH.*). Dicots. (Sympet. Campanulatae; Asterales *BH.*). The largest fam. of flg. pl., comprising about 900 genera, with over 13,000 sp.—more than 10 °/₀ of the total. They are distr. over the greater part of the earth. Although so large a fam. they are well marked in their characters and cannot be confounded with any other, though they have a superficial likeness to Dipsaceae and Calyceraceae.

Living in almost every conceivable situation, they present great variety in veg. habit, often within a single genus, *e.g.* Senecio (*q.v.*). Water and marsh plants and climbers are rare, and so also are epiphytes. This latter is interesting, for the distr. mech. of these pl. is admirably suited to an epiph. existence, and xero. is not uncommon. The enormous majority are herbaceous pl.; trees and shrubs are comparatively rare (about 1½ °/₀). It is worthy of note that the latter often form an important feature in the Composite flora of oceanic islands (see Wallace's *Island Life*).

L. usu. alt., frequently rad., opp. in Heliantheae, whorled in a few cases, *e.g.* *Zinnia verticillata*; stips. rarely present. R. usu. a tap-root, sometimes tuberous as in Dahlia, &c., often thickened like that of a carrot, *e.g.* Taraxacum, Cichorium, &c. For details of veg. organs refer to individual gen.; *e.g.* Aster, Barnadesia, Bellis, Bidens, Cichorium, Dahlia, Espeletia, Gnaphalium, Helianthus, Helichrysum, Lactuca, Mutisia, Petasites, Senecio, Silphium, Taraxacum, &c. All tribes exc. 12 and 13 contain oil-passages in the root, stem, &c. In 13 (Cichorieae), laticiferous vessels are present, commonly containing a milky white latex (*e.g.* lettuce, dandelion).

Infl. of racemose type, the fls. arranged in heads (*capitula*), or rarely in spikes. These heads are again arranged in many cases into larger infls.—racemes, corymbs, &c., or even into cpd. heads (Echinops, &c.). In this last case, however, the smaller heads contain only one fl. each. Head surrounded by an invol. of bracts, usu. green, which performs for all the fls. of the head the functions that in most plants are performed by the calices of the individual fls., viz. protection of the bud and of the young fr. Fls. arranged upon a common receptacle—the enlarged end of the axis—of various shapes, most frequently flat, slightly convex or even spindle-shaped. The shape and surface-condition of the receptacle are chars. of importance in classification of the fam. It may be smooth or hairy, &c.; there may (Helianthus, &c.) or may not (Calendula, &c.) be, upon it, scaly br. belonging to the individual flrs. In Cynareae these br. are divided so as to form numerous bristles.

In the simplest case the fls. of a single head are all alike and ☿, but there are many deviations from this type. The fls. may be all actinomorphic (*tubular*) or all ·|· (*ligulate*); see below. Very commonly however, as in daisy or sunflower, there is a distinction into a *disc* of actinomorphic fls., and a marginal *ray* of ·|· fls. Or, as in Centaurea sp., the outer florets may be actinomorphic but different in size from the central. The number of ray-florets varies in different sp., but according to definite rules.

The *distribution of sexes* among the fls. of a head varies much. The most common case is gynomonoecism, the ray-florets ♀, the disc ☿. The very large ray-florets of Centaurea sp. and others are completely sterile (*cf.* Hydrangea, Viburnum, &c.). Cf. also Tussilago, Petasites, &c.

The *flower* is fully epig., usu. 5-merous. K absent in Ambrosia and its allies, Siegesbeckia, &c.; in some cases it appears only as a slightly 5-lobed rim upon the top of the inf. ovary (*cf.* Rubiaceae and Umbelliferae); usu. it takes the form of hairs or bristles—the *pappus*—and enlarges after fert. into a parachute (Dandelion) or into hooked bristles (Bidens) to aid in distr. (see below). C (5), valvate in bud; actinom. (tubular) or ·|·. Of the latter form there are two varieties, labiate (lipped) and ligulate (strap-shaped). The latter term, strictly speaking, should be applied to those corollas which are strap-shaped in form with 5 teeth at the end repres. the petals, but is usu. also given to those lipped forms where the lower lip is strap-shaped and ends in 3 teeth. Sta. 5, epipet. with short filaments, alt. with the petals. Anthers intr., cohering by their edges (*syngenesious*), forming a tube around the style (*cf.* Lobelia). $\overline{G}$ (2), with a simple style that forks at the end into two stigmas, an ant. and a post. (see diagram). The construction of the style and stigma is of importance in the classification. There is often a brush of hairs on the style below the stigmas. Only the inner (upper) surfaces of the stigmas are as a rule receptive to pollen. Ovary 1-loc. with 1 erect, basal, anatr. ov., which gives an exalb. seed with straight embryo, enclosed in the dry indeh. pericarp. This fr. is usu. termed an achene, but of course is, if one adhere strictly to definitions, a pseudo-nut, as its pericarp is partly axial, and there is > one cpl. It is often crowned with a pappus (see below).

Floral Diagram of Composite fl. with pappus (after Eichler). The small outer lines represent the pappus-bristles.

Natural History of the Flower. Being massed together in heads, the individual fls. may be, and usu. are, comparatively very small, and the advantage is gained that a single insect visitor may fert. many fls. in a short time without having to fly from one to the other, while there is no loss of conspicuousness, and a considerable saving of corolla-material, &c. Throughout the fam., the same type of mech. of the individual fl. is found, the differences being slight and unimportant. It is simple, but effective. Honey is secreted by a ring-shaped nectary round the base of the style, and protected from rain and from short-lipped insects by the tube of the C. The depth of the tube varies within fairly wide limits, but is never so small as to permit the shortest-lipped insects to obtain the honey. As a fam., the C. all belong to Müller's fl. class B′, but there is considerable variety in the depth of tube, &c., and therefore also in the composition of the group of visiting insects to each. Thus the long-tubed purple-flowered Centaureas, &c. are mainly visited by bees and Lepidoptera, while the short-tubed yellow Leontodons or white Achilleas are visited mainly by flies.

At the time when the fl. opens, the style, with its stigmas tightly closed against one another, is comparatively short, reaching up to, or projecting a small distance into, the anther tube. The pollen is shed into this, and as the style grows it presses the pollen little by little out at the upper end of the tube where it will come into contact with visiting insects. At last the style itself emerges and the stigmas separate. The fl. is now ♀. Finally, in a great many cases, the stigmas curl so far back that they touch the pollen upon their own style, so that every fl. is certain to set seed, even though it be by self-fert. In a few cases, *e.g. Senecio vulgaris*, insect visitors are very rare, and the fl. depends entirely on self-fert. The mech. is about the simplest and most perfect that exists for attaining the desired ends. A striking contrast is seen in the orchids; they have bizarre fls. with most elaborate mechs., and an enormous number of seeds in every caps. An interesting modification of the mech. is found in *Cynareae* (see Centaurea) where the sta. are irritable. See also Artemisia (wind-fert.).

The invol. bracts, or ray-florets, or both, often close up over the central fls. in cold or wet weather, thus protecting the fls.

Natural History of the Fruit. The ripening fr.-head is generally protected from injury by the invol. bracts, which bend inwards over it, performing the function of a K. The calices of the individual fls. are thus rendered useless in this respect and are, in most C., used for purposes of distr. of the fr. In most cases, the K, after the fert. of the fl., grows into the familiar pappus, as seen in dandelions or thistles, usu. composed of fine hairs, often branched, but in some cases, *e.g.* Achyrachaena, leafy and membranous. The hairs are hygroscopic and spread out in dry air; this often helps to lever the fr. off the receptacle. In Adenostemma the pappus is sticky. In Bidens and others the pappus is formed of stout barbed bristles; the fr. adheres to animals. In Arctium the invol. br. become hooked at the tips and cling to animals. In Xanthium the recept. is provided with hooks. In Siegesbeckia the bracts are sticky. A few genera, *e.g.* Helianthus, Bellis, &c., have no special arrangements at all, and the frs. remain upon the common receptacle till jerked off by wind or otherwise.

General Considerations. The C. are generally regarded as occupying the highest position in the Veg. Kingdom. Their success may be put down perhaps to the concurrence of several useful peculiarities, viz.

(1) the massing of the fls. in heads, surrounded by invol. bracts: from this there results

(*a*) greater conspicuousness, especially when ray-florets are developed; (*b*) a saving of material in the corollas, &c.; (*c*) the fact that one insect visitor may fertilise many fls. in a short time without having to fly from one to another;

(2) the very simple and effective floral mechanism, which ensures

(*d*) protection of honey and pollen; (*e*) exclusion of the very short-lipped (allotropous) insects, but not too great specialisation for a very narrow circle of visitors; (*f*) prevention of self- and chance of cross-fertilisation till the last possible moment; (*g*) certainty of self-fertilisation if the cross fails;

(3) the use of the calices of individual fls. for purposes of seed-distribution, and the very perfect character of the mechanism.

These considerations should be compared with the features of rival fams., *e.g.* Cruciferae, Gramineae, Rubiaceae, Leguminosae.

Economic uses. The C. furnish but few useful plants (other than border or greenhouse pl.). See Lactuca, Cichorium, Cynara, Helianthus, Carthamus, Chrysanthemum, Tanacetum, &c.

Classification and chief genera (after Hoffmann). The classification of the C. and the determination of their genera is a matter of no small difficulty; we shall give only the primary groupings and their chief genera. [There are several exceptions to the characters given below.]

[*Abbreviations:* cap. = capitulum; tub. = tubular; lig. = ligulate; homog. = fls. in head all similar as to sex; heterog. = fls. of different sex in one head, *e.g.* ray ♀ and disc ☿.]

A. *TUBULIFLORAE*. Fls. of disc not ligulate. No latex.

1. *Vernonieae* (cap. homog.; fls. tub., never yellow; anthers arrow-shaped at base, pointed or rarely tailed, with filaments inserted high above the base; stigmas semi-cylindrical, long, pointed, hairy outside); stigmatic papillae all over inner surface: Vernonia, Elephantopus.
2. *Eupatorieae* (cap. homog.; fls. tub., never pure yellow; anthers blunt at base, with filaments inserted at base; stigmas long, but blunt or flattened at tip, with very short hairs; stigmatic papillae in marginal rows): Ageratum, Eupatorium, Mikania, Adenostemma.
3. *Astereae* (cap. heterog. or homog.; all or only central fls. tub.; anthers as in 2; stigmas flattened with marginal rows of papillae, and terminal hairy unreceptive portions): Solidago, Bellis, Aster, Erigeron, Baccharis, Callistephus, Olearia.
4. *Inuleae* (as 3; corolla in tub. fls. with 4—5-toothed limb; anthers tailed at base; styles various): Blumea, Filago, Antennaria, Gnaphalium, Helichrysum, Inula.

5. *Heliantheae* (style with crown of long hairs above the division; anthers usu. rounded at base with basally inserted filaments; corolla of disc fls. actinom.; pappus not hairy; invol. bracts not membranous at margins; recept. with scaly br.): Espeletia, Silphium, Xanthium, Zinnia, Siegesbeckia, Helianthus, Dahlia, Bidens, Cosmos, Tithonia.
6. *Helenieae* (as 5, but recept. without scaly br.): Helenium, Tagetes.
7. *Anthemideae* (as 6, but invol. br. with membranous tip and edges; pappus 0 or abortive): Achillea, Anthemis, Chrysanthemum, Matricaria, Tanacetum, Artemisia.
8. *Senecioneae* (as 5 and 6, but pappus hairy): Tussilago, Petasites, Senecio, Doronicum.
9. *Calenduleae* (cap. with ♀ ray fls., and usu. ♂ disc fls., with undivided style; anthers pointed at base; recept. not scaly; no pappus): Calendula.
10. *Arctotideae* (style, below or at point of division, thickened or with circle of hairs; cap. with lig. ray fls.; anthers acute at base or with longer or shorter point and with filaments inserted above the base): Arctotis.
11. *Cynareae* (style as in 10; cap. homog. or with neuter, rarely ♀, not ligulate, ray fls.; anthers usu. tailed; recept. usu. bristly; Echinops, Carlina, Arctium, Carduus, Cnicus, Cynara, Centaurea, Carthamus, Saussurea.
12. *Mutisieae* (cap. homog. or heterog.; ray fls. when present usu. 2-lipped; disc fls. actinom. with deeply-divided limb, or 2-lipped): Barnadesia, Mutisia, Stifftia, Gerbera.

B. *LIGULIFLORAE.* All fls. ligulate. Latex.

13. *Cichorieae*: Cichorium, Rhagadiolus, Picris, Crepis, Hieracium, Leontodon, Taraxacum, Lactuca, Tragopogon, Scorzonera, Sonchus.

Compound (l.), where the stalk bears several leaflets; (head), *Angianthus*, *Echinops*; (fr.), aggregate, *Anona*, *Ranunculus*, *Rubus*.

Compressed, flattened.

Compsoneura Warb. (*Myristica* p.p.). Myrist. 6 trop. Am.

Conamomum Ridl. Zingiberaceae (I). 2 Malay Penins.

Conandrium Mez. Myrsinaceae (II). 3 Malaya.

Conandron Sieb. et Zucc. Gesneraceae (I). 1 Japan.

Conanthera Ruiz et Pav. Amaryllidaceae (III). 5 Chili.

Conanthus S. Wats. = Nama L. p.p. (Hydrophyll.). 7 N. Am.

Conceptacle, reproductive cavity.

Conceveiba Aubl. Euphorbiaceae (A. II. 2). 6 trop. S. Am.

Conchium Sm. = Hakea Schrad. (Proteac.).

Conchopetalum Radlk. Sapindaceae (II). 1 Madagascar.

Conchophyllum Bl. (*Dischidia BH.*). Asclep. (II. 3). 5 Malaya.

Concinnus (Lat.), neat.

Concolor (Lat.), of uniform colour.

Concrescence, union of originally distinct organs by growth of the tissue beneath them. Organs in the earliest stages of development are usu.

separate, and most often remain so, but frequently there is a subsequent growth of tissue under them, carrying them out upon a basal portion which most often (*e.g.* in sympet. fls.) has a similar structure to the organs themselves, so that they look as if joined together by their bases. The diagram shows this process on the right, but not on the left. It is common in fls., less so in other organs. It is not necessary for the concrescent organs to be similar; *e.g.* sta. are often united to pets., l. to stems (*cf.* Solanaceae, &c.). The phenomenon goes under many names—adnation, connation, adhesion, cohesion, &c. *Cf.* figures of *Zostera*, *Solanaceae*, &c.

leaf | leaf | stem | common tissue | leaf | leaf

Concrete, growing together.

Condalia Cav. Rhamnaceae. 12 warm Am.

Condaminea DC. Rubiaceae (I. 1). 3 Andes.

Condiments, or spices, veg. products used rather for the flavour than the food value, *e.g.* alexanders, almond, allspice, angelica, anise, asafoetida, balm, basil, camphor, caper, caraway, cardamoms, cassia, cayenne, celery, chillies, cicely, cinnamon, chives, cloves, coriander, cress, cucumber, cummin, curry-leaf, dill, fennel, fenugreek, garlic, ginger, horse-radish, Indian cress, Japan pepper, leek, lemon, lettuce, mace, marjoram, mint, mustard, myrrh, nutmeg, onion, parsley, pennyroyal, pepper, peppermint, pimento, rhubarb, rosemary, sage, samphire, savory, shallot, star-anise, tansy, thyme, turmeric, vanilla, watercress, &c.

Conduplicate (l.), folded lengthwise; (embryo), *Cruciferae*.

Condylocarpus Desf. Apocynaceae (I. 3). 10 trop. S. Am.

Cone, infl. of *Coniferae*, *Cycadaceae*, *Lycopodium*, &c.; **-fl.** (Am.), *Rudbeckia*.

Confertus (Lat.), crowded.

Confluent, blending.

Congdonia Muell.-Arg. Rubiaceae (II. 5). 1 Rio de Janeiro.

Congea Roxb. Verbenaceae (6). 5 Burma, Malaya. Cult. orn.

Congenital, grown to.

Congo pea, *Cajanus indicus* Spreng.

Congou, *Thea*.

Coniferae. The most important class of Gymnosperms, and like the others better represented in former ages than now. They form 2 fams. with 41 gen. and 380 sp. Like their past history, their present geographical distr. is of interest. Most are erect evergr. trees, and grow in dense forests, forming char. features of the veg. in many regions (esp. temp. and subtrop. and mountains). Beginning in the north we find *Juniperus nana* beyond the limit of trees. This limit is largely marked by the C. and the birch. Within it, in the N. temp. zone, are broad areas covered with C. (Larix, Abies, Pinus, &c.). Going S., their importance decreases, and at about 40° N. they become practically confined to the mountains. Here we find in Japan and China a region of development char. by Cephalotaxus, Pseudolarix, Cryptomeria, Cunninghamia, Sciadopitys, Chamaecyparis, Keteleeria, Glyptostrobus, Taiwania, &c.,

mostly endemic gen. In Pacific N. Am. is another region, with *Pseudotsuga Douglasii*, Sequoia, Taxodium, *Chamaecyparis*, *Lawsoniana*, *Thuja gigantea*, and *Libocedrus decurrens*, together with endemic Abies, Tsuga, Pinus, &c. The Himal. forms another great centre, with many peculiar sp., *e.g. Cedrus Deodara*, *Pinus excelsa*, and others, Picea sp., Tsuga sp., &c. The C. of the ✳ are separated from those of the ✳ by a broad band of trop. forests, &c., partially broken by groups of C. on the Mts. of the Indomal. region and Am. In Austr. we find Araucaria, Agathis, Podocarpus, Callitris, Microcachrys, Athrotaxis, Actinostrobus, &c. In Tasm., N.Z. and Chili appear Phyllocladus, Fitzroya, &c. S. Am. has Araucaria sp., Podocarpus sp., and others. Few gen. and sp. of C. appear in both N. and S. hemispheres; each sp. is limited to a well-defined area.

Trees or shrubs, usu. monopodial, often of considerable or even (Sequoia) gigantic size. Typically, as may be seen in a fir or larch plantation, a certain amount of growth is made each year and a number of branches are also formed much at the same level, so that in trees of moderate size the number of 'whorls' of branches is an index of the age. Later on the lower branches usu. die off and the branching near the apex becomes less reg. The main stem is radially symmetrical, but the branches, which often grow almost horiz., have a tendency to dorsiventrality, expressed in a two-ranked arrangement of the l., twisting of the l. on their stalks, and so on. Many C. show a difference in their shoots; some (*long shoots*, or *shoots of unlimited growth*) grow continuously onwards, except for the interruption in winter; others (*short shoots*, *shoots of limited growth*, or *spurs*) grow only to a definite size, usu. very small, and bear a few l. Intermediate conditions occur in Larix, Cedrus, Taxodium, &c. When both kinds occur the foliage l. are often borne on the short shoots only (see Pinus &c. for details). The green l. are usu. entire and are either needle-like, flat and linear, or closely appressed scales (Cupressus, &c.). Mention may be made of the curious 'double-needles' of Sciadopitys and the flat green short shoots of Phyllocladus (*q.v.*).

Anatomically, the C. resemble Dicots. in all important points. A very general feature (exc. Taxus) is the presence of resin passages in all parts of the pl. The l. exhibit a somewhat peculiar internal structure, suited to xero. pl., under which class most C. come, living in cold soil, as most do, and often with evergr. l.

In the fl. we are met with great difficulties. There are two theories about its morphology, those of Eichler (*Blüthendiag.* or *Nat. Pfl.*) and of Celakovsky (see Warming's *System. Bot.* or *Bot. Jahresb.* 1890, p. 324, also Noll in *Bot. Centr.* 60, p. 131). We cannot discuss these (see Worsdell, in *Ann. of Bot.* 14, 1900, p. 39), but shall merely state both. As the order is usu. classified according to the Eichlerian view, we have adopted this in the classification and the details of the gen.

The fls. of C. appear as a rule in the form of *cones*, and are always unisex., mon- or dioecious. They are never term. on the main stem as in Cycads, but are usu. borne lat. near to its apex. Sometimes (as in Pinus ♂) the cones are massed together in spikes or heads.

Both theories agree about the ♂ fl., which is usu. a cone or catkin of sta. on a central axis. The sta. may be flat, but is commonly ± peltate, and bears a number of pollen-sacs (not > 9 as a rule) on its lower surface (see Pinus, Taxus, &c.). In the ♀, the cone (to avoid for the present the word flower) consists typically of an axis bearing leaf-like organs. The most familiar case is Pinus (*q.v.*), where each l. borne on the axis is a small scale, bearing on its upper surface a very large scale (these latter show on the outside of the cone) on the upper side of which, again, are the two ovules. We may diagrammatically represent it thus, using 'cover-scale' to express the lower, 'ovuliferous scale' (*epimatium*) the upper, of the two scales. In Cryptomeria, &c. we find a large scale borne directly on the axis, with a little flap on its upper side near the outer end, and the ovules at the base. The flap is, by both theorists, supposed to represent the ovuliferous scale, and so we have what is illustrated by the second diagram. Then in *Cupresseae*, &c. we find only one scale, and here the two theorists differ. In the other fam., *Taxaceae*, still further difficulties meet us. In Microcachrys the ovule is borne upon a l. of the cone, but in Phyllocladus it is axillary and in Taxus term. (see these gen.). In most C. there is only one integument, but in *Taxaceae* a second commonly appears, forming an aril, ± fleshy, round the seed as it ripens.

cover-scale
——
ovules
ovulif. scale
cover-scale
——
ovules

ovulif. sc.}
cover-scale}
——
ovules
ovulif. sc.}
cover-scale}
——
ovules

Now as to the explanation of the facts. Eichler regards the whole cone as one ♀ fl. with a number of cpls. (the 'cover-scales'). The cpl. may bear the ovule directly, as in the latter cases above mentioned, or may develope upon its upper surface a placenta (ovulif. scale) which bears the ovules. Cryptomeria thus represents a stage in this evolution, and the whole may be compared with the division of a l. into a sterile and fertile part, as in Ophioglossum. The rival theory of Celakovsky regards each ovule or pair of ovules with its appurtenances as a ♀ fl. (one cpl. to each ovule or pair) so that the cone is a spike of fls. A series may be thus drawn: Podocarpus (one cpl., one ovule with two integuments, the whole in the axil of a cover-scale, which is therefore to be regarded as a *bract*), Taxus (fl. reduced to ovule, aril = outer integument); then in the *Pinaceae* we have spikes of fls. (cones), the cover-scale being the bract, the ovuliferous scale the combined outer integuments of the ovules of two cpls. (or three, the keel on the middle of the scale in Pinus, &c. repres. the third): a fusion of the bract with the fl. in its axil is supposed to have gone on, and we get next the Cryptomeria type, and finally that of *Cupresseae*.

Ovules orthotr., exc. Podocarpus. For development of the ovule, fert., &c., see text-books. The cone often becomes hard and woody as the seeds ripen; in other cases it becomes fleshy. The seeds contain an embryo with 2—15 cotyledons, and rich endosp.

Natural History. The C. are entirely wind-fert.; the pollen is light and powdery, sometimes provided with air-bladders (*e.g.* Pinus), and is produced in enormous quantities. About the time it is shed the scales of the ♀ cones open to receive it and the grains adhere to the sticky fluid at the apex of the ovule. Fert. often does not take place for a long time afterwards (see Pinus).

The seeds in many genera with woody cones (*e.g.* Pinus) are winged for wind-carriage; in other genera they are animal-distributed, *e.g.* Juniperus (cone fleshy), Taxus (fleshy aril), &c.

Further details of morphology, life history, &c. under *Gymnospermae*, *Pinus* and other gen. See also *Retinospora* for the peculiar case of pl. retaining the 'seedling' form throughout life.

Economically the C. are most important, furnishing the greater proportion of our timber, as well as resins, tars, turpentines, &c. See gen., esp. Abies, Pinus, Larix, Tsuga, Libocedrus, Juniperus, Taxus, &c.

Classification and Key to Genera (after Eichler and Engler):

Fam. 1. TAXACEAE. Mostly dioecious; cone-formation imperfect; cpls. usu. few or even 1 terminal, with 1—2 ov. each; seeds projecting beyond cpls., or even naked, with fleshy aril or drupaceous testa; chiefly ⁂.

A. Anther with 2 pollen-sacs; cpls. 1—∞, with 1 ov., often very small; ovuliferous scale in all but Pherosphaera, often united to integument. I. **PODOCARPOIDEAE.**

a. Ovuliferous scale 0; ov. at base of cpl., erect; l. scaly. 1. *Pherosphaereae.*
1. Pherosphaera.

b. Ovuliferous scale present; l. usu. linear. 2. *Podocarpeae.*

α. Ov. scale and integument separate.

I. Cpls. many; ov. scale membranous, little enlarged.

1. Cpls. whorled, thick, obtuse; seeds free; l. scaly. 2. Microcachrys.

2. Cpls. spiral, imbr.; seeds in groove at base, small; fr. cpls. united; l. linear. 3. Saxegothaea.

II. Cpls. 1—few; ov. scale developed; young ov. ± pend., ultimately mostly upright, rarely stationary, enclosed in ov. scale. 4. Dacrydium.

β. Ov. scale completely curved into itself, united with integument of pend. ov., falling with seed; cpls. usu. small, much shorter than ov. 5. Podocarpus.

B. Anther with 2 loc.; cpls. with 1 ov.; seeds surrounded by cupule; twigs phylloclades with tooth-like l.-rudiments. II. **PHYLLOCLADOIDEAE.**

Only genus 6. Phyllocladus.

C. Anther with 3—8 loc.; cpls. with 2 ov., or fl. reduced to 1 ov. term. on axis covered with scale l.; ov. scale 0; seeds with cupule, exc. in 7. III. **TAXOIDEAE.**

a. ♀ fl. of several decussate cpls.; cpl. with 2 ov. 1. *Cephalotaxeae.*
7. Cephalotaxus.

b. ♀ fl. reduced to 1 ov. term. on axis covered with scale l.
2. *Taxeae.*

α. ♀ fl. in pairs in axil of l., each with 4 decussate scales; anther 4-loc. 8. Torreya.

β. ♀ fl. usu. single, only one of pair developed, the common axis with scale l.; anther 6—8-loc.
9. Taxus.

Younger ♀ fl. unknown; position doubtful, ? Podocarpoideae; sta. 2-loc.; ♀ fl. term. or 2—3 at tip of twig; cpls. 1—2.
10. Acmopyle.

Fam. 2. PINACEAE. Mostly monoecious; cones perfect; seeds concealed between scales; testa woody or leathery; no aril.

A. L. spirally arranged; sta. with several long pollen-sacs; cpls. simple, with 1 reversed ov. in centre.
I. *Araucarieae.*

Seeds free from cpl. 11. Agathis.
,, united to cpl. 12. Araucaria.

B. L. spirally arranged; cover and ov. scales, the latter usu. large, with 2 ov. II. *Abieteae.*

a. Long shoots only present.

α. Needles 4-angled; cone pend.; scales persistent.
13. Picea.

β. Needles flat.

I. L. with 1 central resin canal; cone pend.; scales persistent. 14. Tsuga.

II. L. with 2 lat. resin canals; cone pend. or erect; sta. fl. sol. or umbellate.
15. Pseudotsuga.

III. Cone upright with persistent scales.
16. Keteleeria.

IV. Cone upright with deciduous scales.
17. Abies.

b. Long and short shoots both present.

α. Long shoots with scale l. only; the green (needle) l. on the short shoots. 18. Pinus.

β. Needle l. on both shoots.

I. Needles evergr.; fr. 2—3 yrs. in ripening.
19. Cedrus.

II. Deciduous; fr. 1 yr. in ripening.
Cone scales persistent. 20. Larix.
Cone scales deciduous. 21. Pseudolarix.

C. L. spirally arranged; scales rudimentary or weakly developed into cover and ov. scales; ovules 2—8, axillary and erect, or reversed on edges of cpls. III. *Taxodieae.*

a. Long shoots with scale l.; short shoots = double needles.
22. Sciadopitys.

b. Long shoots only.

α. Seed reversed.

I. Cpl. minute. China, Cochinchina.
Ovules 3. 23. Cunninghamia.
Ovules 2. 24. Taiwania.

II. Cpl. with ridge-like inner scale. Tasmania, Austr. 25. Athrotaxis.
III. Cpl. shield-shaped, no distinct ov. scale. N. Am. 26. Sequoia.

β. Seed erect.
I. Cpl. with toothed scale. 27. Cryptomeria.
II. Cpl. shield-shaped, no distinct scale.
Cone scales persistent. N. Am. 28. Taxodium.
Cone scales deciduous. China. 29. Glyptostrobus.

D. L. opp. or whorled, rarely alt., often heterophyllous; ovule erect. IV. *Cupresseae*.

a. Cone woody when ripe; cpls. valvate. 1. Actinostrobinae.
α. Branchlets compressed; cones sol., axis not produced beyond scales; scales 4; N. Afr. 30. Tetraclinis.
β. Branchlets angular; cones paniculate, axis produced beyond scales.
Scales 6 unequal; Austr. 31. Callitris.
,, 8 equal; Austr. 32. Actinostrobus.
,, 4 equal; trop. and S. Afr. 33. Widdringtonia.
γ. Branchlets flattened or angular; dioecious; ♂ cones sol. term.; axis produced; sharp point on back of each scale near top; Chili, Tasm. 34. Fitzroya.

b. Cone woody when ripe, cpls. imbr.; whorls of all fl. 2-merous. 2. Thujopsidinae.
α. Cpl. with 4—5 seeds. 35. Thujopsis.
β. Cpl. with 2 (1—3) seeds.
Cpls. 4, upper pair fertile. 36. Libocedrus.
Cpls. 6—8, both upper pairs fertile. 37. Thuja.
Cpls. 6—8 pair. 38. Fokienia.

c. Cone woody when ripe; cpl. peltate; whorls of all fls. 2-merous. 3. Cupressinae.
α. Cpls. strongly woody when ripe. 39. Cupressus.
β. Cpls. slightly woody when ripe; twig system flat in one plane. 40. Chamaecyparis.

d. Cone, berry or drupe-like when ripe. 4. Juniperinae.
Only genus. 41. Juniperus.

Conimitella Rydberg (*Heuchera* p.p.). Saxifr. (I). 1 W. U.S.

Coniogeton Blume = Buchanania Roxb. (Anacard.).

Coniogramme Fée. Polypodiaceae. 3 warm |✻.

Conioselinum Fisch. (*Ligusticum* L. p.p. *BH.*). Umbelliferae (III. 6). 7 N. palaeotemp.

Conium L. Umbell. (III. 4). 2 N. temp. |✻, S. Afr. *C. maculatum* L. (hemlock, very poisonous) Brit. Biennial. Stem dotted red.

Conjugate, coupled.

Connaraceae (*EP.*, *BH.*). Dicots. (Archich. Rosales, *EP.*, *BH.*). 16 gen., 160 sp., trop.; closely allied to Leguminosae, chiefly distinguished by the absence of stips. and the (usual) presence of > 2 free cpls. Mostly twining shrubs with alt. exstip. l. and panicles of reg. fls. K 5 or (5), imbr. or valvate; C 5; A 10 or 5 sometimes joined below; G 5 or 1 or 4, each with 2 erect orthotr. ov. Fr. usu. one follicle with one seed, album. or not, arillate. *Chief genera:* Connarus, Rourea, Cnestis.

Connaropsis Planch. Oxalidaceae. 5 Malay Arch.

Connarus L. Connaraceae. 70 trop. Am., Afr., As.

Connate (l.), concrescent, *Lonicera*.

Connective, the prolongation of the filament into the anther; elongated in *Begonia*.

Connellia N.E. Br. Bromeliaceae (2). 2 Guiana.

Connivent, converging.

Conobea Aubl. Scrophulariaceae (II. 6). 7 Am., W.I.

Conocarpus L. Combretaceae. 2 trop. Am., Afr., W.I., Fla.

Conocephalus Blume. Moraceae (III). 15 Indomal. The l. of *C. suaveolens* Blume possess water-secreting glands.

Conoclinium DC. = Eupatorium Tourn. p.p. (Compos.).

Conomitra Fenzl (*Glossonema BH.*). Asclep. (II. 1). 1 Kordofan.

Conomorpha A. DC. Myrsinaceae (II). 40 trop. S. Am., W.I.

Conophallus Schott = Amorphophallus Blume p.p. (Arac.).

Conopharyngia G. Don (*Tabernaemontana* L. p.p.; *Plumeria* Tourn. p.p. *BH.*). Apocynaceae (I. 3). 25 trop. and S.E. Afr.

Conopholis Wallr. Orobanchaceae. 1 Carolina to Mex.

Conophora DC. Nieuwland (*Cacalia* p.p.). Comp. (8). 8 N. Am.

Conopodium Koch. Umbelliferae (III. 5). 20 Eur., As., N. Afr. *C. denudatum* Koch (*Bunium flexuosum* With.) in Brit. (earth nut). The tuberous roots are ed. when roasted.

Conospermum Sm. Proteaceae (1). 35 Austr.

Conostegia D. Don. Melastomaceae (1). 15 trop. Am.

Conostephium Benth. Epacridaceae (3). 5 W. Austr.

Conostylis R. Br. Amaryllid. (III). (Haemodor., *BH.*) 35 W. Austr.

Conothamnus Lindl. Myrtaceae (II. 1). 3 W. Austr.

Conradia Mart. = Pentarhaphia Lindl. (*BH.*) = Gesneria L. p.p.

Conradina A. Gray. Labiatae (VI). 1 Florida.

Conringia Heist. ex L. Cruciferae (4). 6 Medit., Centr. Eur.

Constantia Rodrig. (*Sophronitis* p.p.). Orchid. (II. 6). 1 Braz.

Consuegria Mutis. Inc. sed. Nomen.

Contabescent (anther), shrivelling.

Contarinia Vand. Verbenaceae (?). 1 Brazil.

Contortae (Engler), the 5th order of Sympetalae. *Cf.* p. xlii.

Contorted (aestivation), *cf.* Aestivation.

Contortoduplicate, twisted and folded.

Contrayerva (W.I.), *Aristolochia*.

Conuleum A. Rich. = Siparuna Aubl. (Monim.). 1 Fr. Guiana.

Convallaria L. Liliaceae (VII). 1 N. temp. (incl. Brit.), *C. majalis* L., lily of the valley, in woods. The stock developes a few scales and

2 green l. annually. Fls. homogamous, self-fert. Cult. orn. fl.
Convallariaceae (Warming) = Liliaceae (§§ VI—XI).
Convolute (aestivation), *cf.* Aestivation.
Convolvulaceae (*EP.*; *BH.* incl. *Nolan.*). Dicots. (Sympet. Tubiflorae; Polemoniales *BH.*; pp. xlv, liii). 50/1000, trop. and temp., herbs, shrubs or rarely trees, many climbing, some thorny xero., Cuscuta a climbing parasite. Some with tuberous roots or stems, others with rhiz.; latex often present. L. alt., usu. stalked, rarely stip., often with accessory axillary buds. Infl. dich. with tendency to cincinnus or bostryx; br. and bracteoles present, sometimes close to K.

Fl. ☿, reg. hypog. usu. 5-merous. K, rarely (K), imbr., odd sep. post., seps. sometimes unequal; (C) of various shapes, usu. induplicate-valv., sometimes conv.; A 5, alt. with C, epipet., on base of C, anthers usu. intr.; $\underline{G}$ on honey-secreting disc (2), rarely (3—5) or only joined by style, 2-loc. with axile plac.; ov. 2, rarely 1 or 4, per loc., erect, anatr. or ½-anatr., micropyle facing outwards and downwards; ov. with one integument. Berry, nut, caps.; endosp. Fl. usu. large and showy. Many have extrafloral nectaries on petiole. Few of economic value except for handsome fls. (*cf.* Ipomoea).

Classification and chief genera: closely related to Solan., Borag., and other Tubiflorae. *Cf. Nat. Pfl.*

I. *CONVOLVULOIDEAE* (independent green pl.).
1. *Dichondreae* (G usu. divided, forming 2 or 4 1-seeded mericarps): Dichondra (2 meri.), Falkia (4), only gen.
2. *Dicranostyleae* (G simple; style long ± bifid, or 2), 5-merous, stigma capitate or slightly lobed): Breweria, Dicranostyles, Evolvulus.
3. *Hildebrandtieae* (do. stigma irreg. lobed): Hildebrandtia (only gen.).
4. *Convolvuleae* (style united to stigma): Argyreia, Porana, Aniseia, Mina, Quamoclit, Exogonium, Ipomoea, Pharbitis, Jacquemontia, Convolvulus, Calystegia.
5. *Erycibeae* (style extremely short): Erycibe (only gen.).

II. *CUSCUTOIDEAE* (leafless parasites; no cots.): Cuscuta (only gen.). Dichondraceae and Cuscutaceae are sometimes made separate fams.

Convolvulus (Tourn.) L. Convolv. (I. 4). 180 temp., a few trop. *C. arvensis* L. (Brit.; bindweed) has sweetly scented fls., more visited by insects than the large but scentless fls. of *Calystegia sepium*. Smaller fls. with short sta. appear on some stocks; these appear to be due to the action of a fungus (*cf.* Lychnis). Veg. repr. by adv. stem buds produced on the root. From incisions in the rhiz. of *C. scammonia* L. flows a resinous purgative juice (scammony). Some yield rosewood oil. Cult. orn. fl.
Convolvulus, *Calystegia*, *Convolvulus.*
Conyza L. Comp. (3). 60 temp. and subtrop. Head androgynous.
Conyzella Rupr. = Erigeron L. (Comp.). 2 N. Am.
Conyzoides DC. = Carpesium L. (Comp.).
Conzattia Rose. Legum. (II. 7). 1 Mex.
Cooba (Austr.), *Acacia salicina* Lindl.; **Coondi**, *Carapa*.
Cookia Sonner. = Clausena Burm. f. (Rut.).
Cooperia Herb. Amaryllid. (I. 1). 2 Mex., Tex. (evening star).
Copaiba Adans., **Copaifera** L. Legum. (II. 2). 30 trop. Am., Afr. Some

S. Am. sp. yield the resin Balsam of Copaiba, and resins (copals) are also obtained from the Afr. sp. Timber good (purpleheart).

Copaiva tree (W.I.), *Copaifera*.

Copal, a hard resin, *Agathis, Copaifera, Hymenaea, Trachylobium*; **Manila**, **Kauri-**, *Agathis*.

Copernicia Mart. Palmae (I. 2). 10 trop. Am., W.I. *C. cerifera* Mart. (wax- or Carna-uba-palm, Brazil) has its l. coated with wax, removed by shaking; it is used in making gramophone records, candles, &c. The wood, l., &c., are also useful.

Copianthus Hill. Amarantaceae?. 1 Indomal.

Copisma E. Mey. = Rhynchosia Lour. p.p. (Legum.).

Copper-beech, *Fagus sylvatica* L. var.

Copra, dried endosp. of *Cocos nucifera* L.

Coprosma Forst. Rubiaceae (II. 7). 45 N.Z., Austr., Malaya, Chili. The stipules of some are glandular, and some have peculiar openings (? domatia) on the backs of the l.

Copse, coppice wood with occasional standard trees.

Coptis Salisb. Ranunculaceae (2). 10 N. temp. and arctic.

Coptocheile Hoffmgg. Gesneriaceae (inc. sed.). 1 Brazil?

Coptophyllum Korth. Rubiaceae (I. 7). 1 Sumatra.

Coptosapelta Korth. Rubiaceae (I. 5). 4 Malaya.

Coptosperma Hook. f. (*Tarenna* p.p.). Rubiac. (I. 8). 1 trop. Afr.

Coquilla, coquilho nut, *Attalea funifera* Mart.

Coquito palm, *Jubaea spectabilis* H. B. et K.

Coral-berry (Am.), *Symphoricarpus*; **-creeper**, *Kennedya*; **-root**, *Corallorhiza*; **-tree**, *Erythrina*.

Coralliokyphos Fleischm. et Rech. Orchid. (II. 2). 1 Samoa.

Corallobotrys Hook. f. Ericaceae (III. 1). 1 Khasias.

Corallocarpus Welw. ex Benth. et Hook. f. Cucurb. (2). 35 warm.

Corallodiscus Batalin. Gesneriaceae (1). 1 N. China.

Corallonema Schlechter. Asclepiad. (II. 1). 1 Bolivia.

Corallorhiza Hall. Orchidaceae (II. 4). 15 N. temp. *C. innata* R. Br. (coral-root) Brit. Saprophytes with much branched fleshy rhiz., no r., and scaly l. [*Cf.* Epipogum.]

Corallospartium Armstrong. Leguminosae (III. 6). 1 N.Z.

Corbularia Salisb. = Narcissus Tourn. p.p. (Amaryll.).

Corchoropsis Sieb. et Zucc. Tiliaceae. 2 Japan, China.

Corchorus (Tourn.) L. Tiliaceae. 40 warm. *C. capsularis* L. and *C. olitorius* L. (India, &c.) furnish the chief supply of the fibre jute or gunny; annuals about 10 feet high, little branched. The stems are cut and retted in water, and the fibre beaten out (*cf.* Linum).

Cord-grass, *Spartina*.

Cordate, heart-shaped.

Cordeauxia Hemsl. Leguminosae (II. 3). 1 trop. Afr.

Cordia L. Boragin. (1). 280 warm. Trees or shrubs; fr. ed.; that of *C. Myxa* L. (sebestens; Egypt to Austr.) formerly medic. Some have good timber, *e.g. C. Gerascanthus* L. (trop. Am., W.I., prince-wood), and *C. sebestana* L. (trop. Am., W.I., aloewood). [Mez in *Engl. Jahrb.* XII.]

Cordiaceae (Warming) = Boraginaceae (§ 1).

Cordifolius (Lat.), cordate-leaved.

Cordobia Niedenzu. Malpighiaceae. 2 S. Am.
Cordyla Lour. Leguminosae (II. 9). 1 trop. Afr. Pods ed. Apet.
Cordylanthus Nutt. (*Adenostegia* Benth.). Scroph. (III. 3). 12 N. Am.
Cordyline Royen ex Adans. Liliaceae (VI). 15 trop., warm temp. Decorative; habit of Dracaena. The l. of some sp. yield fibre.
Cordylocarpus Desf. (*Rapistrum* p.p. *BH.*). Crucif. (2). 1 N. Afr.
Cordylogyne E. Mey. Asclepiadaceae (II. 1). 1 S. Afr.
Corema D. Don. Empetraceae. 2 W. Eur., Atl. N. Am.
Coreocarpus Benth. (*Coreopsis* p.p. *EP.*). Comp. (5). 2 California.
Coreopsis L. Compositae (5). 80 Am., trop. Afr., Sandw. Is. Many cult. orn. fl.
Corethrodendron Fisch. et Basiner. Legum. (III. 7). 1 Soongaria.
Corethrogyne DC. Compositae (3). 4 Calif.
Coriaceous, leathery.
Coriander, *Coriandrum sativum* L.
Coriandrum (Tourn.) L. Umbelliferae (III. 3). 3 Medit. The fr. (coriander-seeds) of *C. sativum* L. are used in flavouring.
Coriaria Niss. ex L. The only genus of Coriariaceae. 10 Medit. to Japan, N.Z., Chili to Mexico, mostly shrubs with opp. or whorled l., sometimes becoming alt. at the ends of the shoots. The inconspic. protog. fls. are in racemose infls. K 5, C 5, A 5+5, $\underline{G}$ 5. The petals are keeled on the inner side, and after fert. grow fleshy and enclose the cpls. forming a pseudo-drupe. Ov. 1 in each loc., pend., anatr.; raphe dorsal. Endosp. thin. *C. myrtifolia* L. (W. Medit.) yields tan, others a black dye.
Coriareae (*BH.*) = Coriariaceae.
Coriariaceae (*EP.*, *BH.*). Dicots. (Archichl. Sapindales). Only genus Coriaria (*q.v.*). The only nearly related order is Empetraceae. Placed as anomalous order at end of Disciflorae *BH.*
Coridothymus Reichb. f. (*Thymus* p.p. *BH.*). Labi. (VI). 1 Medit.
Corion Mitch. = Spergularia J. et C. Presl (Caryoph.).
Coriophyllus Rydberg (*Cymopterus* p.p.). Umbel. (III. 6). 4 N. Am.
Coris Tourn. Primulaceae. 2 Medit. Fl. ·|·.
Corispermum B. Juss. ex L. Chenopodiaceae (A). 16 N. temp. P ·|·.
Cork, the substance of which the water-tight bark is composed; **-oak**, *Quercus suber* L.; **-tree, Indian**, *Millingtonia hortensis* L. f.; **-wood**, *Ochroma*, (Am.) *Leitneria*, (W.I.) *Anona palustris*.
Corm, the base of a stem swollen into a bulbous shape with reserves; *Colchicum* (and fig.), *Amorphophallus*, *Arisaema*, *Bowiea*, *Crocus*, *Cyclamen*, *Eranthis*, *Hablitzia*, *Testudinaria*.
Cormonema Reissek. Rhamnaceae. 4 trop. Am.
Cormophyte, a flowering plant or fern.
Corn, in Engl. wheat, in Am. maize; **broom-**, *Sorghum vulgare* Pers.; **Chinese-** (W.I.), *Setaria italica* Beauv.; **-cockle**, *Lychnis Githago* Scop.; **-flower**, *Centaurea Cyanus* L.; **Guinea-**, *Sorghum vulgare* Pers.; **Indian-**, *Zea Mays* L.; **Kaffir-**, *Sorghum vulgare* Pers.; **-marigold**, *Chrysanthemum segetum* L.; **-salad**, *Valerianella*.
Corna Nor. Inc. sed. Nomen.
Cornaceae (*EP.*, *BH.* incl. *Alang.*, *Garry.*, *Nyss.*). Dicots. (Archichl.

Umbelliflorae, Umbellales *BH.* pp. xxxix, lii). 15/100 N. and S. temp., and trop. Mts. ♄, rarely herbs, with opp. or alt. simple l., usu. petiolate entire, exstip. Infl. dich. or pleioch., usu. condensed to corymbs or umbels, or even (Cornus) heads with invol. Fls. ☿ or ♂ ♀, reg., 4—5-merous. K 4—5, small, or 0, C 4—5—0, usu. valv., A 4—5, $\overline{G}$ (4—1, usu. 2); disc epig., style simple with lobed stigma; loc. 1—4, each with 1 pend. anatr. ov., raphe usu. dorsal. Drupe or berry, with 1—4-loc. stone or 2 separate stones. Endosp. Cornus and others are very near to Caprifol. *Chief genera:* Cornus, Aucuba, Griselinia. [*Cf. Pfl. R.*, 1910.]

Cornel, *Cornus sanguinea* L.; **cornelian cherry**, *Cornus mas* L.

Cornella Rydberg (*Cornus* p.p.). Corn. 3 N. temp. and arct.

Cornicina DC.=Anthyllis L. p.p. (Legum.).

Cornidia Ruiz et Pav.=Hydrangea L. p.p. (Saxifr.).

Corniola Adans.=Genista L. (Legum.).

Cornish moneywort, *Sibthorpea europaea* L.

Corniveum Nieuwland (*Dicentra* p.p.). Papaver. (III). 1 N.W. Am.

Cornucopiae L. Gramin. (8). 1 E. Medit. Fl. in small heads; when fr. ripe these bend over and break off with a sharp point; they adhere to animals, and are said to burrow like Stipa.

Cornuella Pierre. Sapot. (inc. sed.). 1 Venezuela.

Cornulaca Del. Chenopod. (B). 4 Egypt to Afghanistan. P ·|·.

Cornus (Tourn.) L. Corn. 60 N. temp., and trop. Mts. 2 Brit., *C. sanguinea* L. (cornel, dogwood) and *C. suecica* L. a dwarf herb of the Highlands, giving off annual stems from the creeping stems, with fls. in umbels, invol. by 4 large white br. L. usu. opp. Fl. usu. ☿, C 4, valv., G usu. 2-loc. *C. florida* L. (N. Am.) and others yield useful wood. Preserve from fr. of *C. mas* L. (Cornelian cherry, Eur., As. Min.), whose fl. appear in spring before l.

Cornutia Plum. ex L. Verben. (4). 6 trop. Am., W.I. A 2; stds. filiform.

Cornutioides L.=Premna L. (Verben.).

Corokia A. Cunn. Corn. 3 N.Z. Fls. ☿. G 2—3-loc. L. alt.

Corolla (adj. **corolline**), the inner, usu. coloured, envelope of the fl.

Corollonema Schlechter. Asclep. (II. 1). 1 Bolivia.

Coromandel wood, *Diospyros quaesita* Thw., &c.

Corona, *Amaryllid.*, *Asclepiad.*, *Napoleona*, *Nectouxia*, *Passiflor.*

Coronanthera Vieill. ex C. B. Clarke in DC. Gesner. (I). 10 New Caled. Shrubs or small trees.

Coronaria L.=Lychnis L. p.p. (Caryoph.).

Coronarieae (*BH.*). The 3rd series of Monocots. *Cf.* p. liv.

Coronilla Tourn. ex L. Legum. (III. 7). 20 Eur., Medit. Fl. like Lotus, but honey usu. secreted by outer surface of K, insects poking between claws of pets. Buds and ripening fr. bend down, open fls. and ripe fr. upwards. Cult. orn. fl. shrubs.

Coronocarpus Schum. et Thonn.=Aspilia Thou. (Comp.).

Coronopus Rupp. ex L. (*Senebiera* DC.). Crucif. (2). 20 subtrop., Eur.

Coronopus Miller=Plantago L. (Plantag.).

Coroya Pierre. Legum. (III. 8). 1 Cochinchina.

Corpse-plant (Am.), *Monotropa*.

Corpusculum, *Asclepiadaceae*.

Correa Andr. Rut. (I. 3). 6 temp. Austr. Cult. orn. shrubs (Austr. fuchsia). (C.) 4-merous.

Corrigiola L. Caryophyllaceae (I. 4). 12 Medit., Andes, S. Afr., Eur. 1 Brit.

Corsia Becc. Burmanniaceae. 1 New Guinea.

Corsiaceae (Beccari), Burmanniaceae p.p.

Corsican pine, *Pinus Laricio* Poir.

Cortaderia Stapf. Gramineae (10). 10 S. Am. Pampas grass.

Cortesia Cav. Boraginaceae (II). 2 temp. S. Am.

Cortex, tissue between vascular bundles and epidermis.

Cortia DC. Umbelliferae (III. 5). 2 Himalaya.

Cortusa L. Primulaceae. 2 Mts. of Eur. and As. Cult. orn. fl.

Corunastylis Fitzgerald. Orchidaceae (II. 2). 1 Austr.

Coryanthes Hook. Orchidaceae (II. 13). 6 trop. S. Am., epiphytic. Fl. pend.; seps. bent back and fairly large, pets. small. Labellum complex, forming a bucket-like organ with dome above; the mouth faces upwards, and the edges are incurved; there is also an overflow pipe projecting towards the seps. and closely covered in by the bent end of the column, with the stigma and anther. From the base of the column project two horns which secrete a thin watery fluid that drips into the bucket, keeping it full to the level of the overflow pipe. The dome (above) is composed of succulent tissue attractive to bees; these fight for places on it to drill the tissue; every now and then one gets pushed off and falls into the bucket. It can neither fly nor climb out, and has to squeeze through the overflow pipe. In so doing it first passes the stigma, fertilising it if it bears any pollen, and then, passing the anther, is loaded with new pollinia. [Darwin's *Orchids*, p. 173, and *cf.* Stanhopea.]

Corybas Salisb. = Corysanthes R. Br. (Orchid.).

Corycium Swartz. Orchidaceae (II. 1). 10 S. Afr.

Corydalis Vent. Papaveraceae (III). 140 Medit., Eur., As. *C. claviculata* DC. Brit., a (leaf) tendril-climbing annual. Most are perennial herbs with underground tubers. In *C. cava* Schweigg. et Kort., and others, the main axis forms a tuber, which dies away below, each annual shoot arising from the axil of a scale-l. of older date. In *C. solida* Sw., and others, the tuber is a swollen root-structure belonging to the current annual shoot. Fls. transv. ·|· (see fam. for diagram); twisting through 90° brings it vertical; only one petal is spurred and contains the honey secreted by a staminal outgrowth. Its mech. resembles that of Leguminosae. The inner pets., united at the tip, enclose stigma and anthers; the upper pet. covers the fl. Bees alighting push down the inner pet. and cause the essential organs to emerge. In some, *e.g. C. ochroleuca* Koch and *C. lutea* DC., the emergence is explosive (*cf.* Genista). The fls. of *C. cava* are self-sterile.

Corylopsis Sieb. et Zucc. Hamamelidaceae. 25 China, Japan. Fls. ☿, in spikes with coloured bracts at base.

Corylus (Tourn.) L. Betulaceae (I). 8 N. temp. *C. avellana* L., hazel-nut (Brit.). Shrubby (largely owing to extensive formation of suckers), with monoecious catkinate fls. (the ♀ catkin sessile and elliptical in outline, rather resembling a bud). Both are laid down in autumn; the ♂ catkins are visible all winter, but the ♀ are not obvious until the red stigmas come out early in the year. Anemoph.;

the fact of flg. before the appearance of the l. renders their chance of fert. greater. On the inner side of the br. in the ♂ catkin are found 2 scales and, adnate to these, 4—8 sta., each branched nearly to the base. Here only the central fl. of the possible 3 (*cf.* diagram of fam.) is present, with its bracteoles *α*, *β*. In the ♀ catkin, on the other hand, we have the two lat. and not the central fl. as shown in the second diagram (* = missing fl.). At the time of fert. the ovary is minute, but the long red stigmas are easily identified. After fert. the ovary (2-loc. at first) gives a one-seeded nut, enclosed in a cup of green leafy nature, really the combined bract and bracteoles *α*, *α′*, *β′*, very much developed.

	stem	
*	♂ fl.	*
α		*β*
	bract	

	stem	
α′		*α′*
α ♀ fl.	*	♀ fl. *β*
β′		*β′*
	bract	

The fl. is chalazogamic (*cf. Chalazogamae*). The nuts of this and other sp. are valuable as dessert fr., &c. (hazel-nut, cob-nut, filbert), and have been cultivated from very early times (*cf.* Goeschke, *Die Haselnuss*, Berlin, 1887). Wood elastic, but cannot be obtained in large boards. Oil from the seeds.

Corymb, a raceme in which the stalks of the lat. fl. elongate to bring all to one level, *Cruciferae*, *Iberis*.

Corymbis Thou. Orchidaceae (II. 2). 12 trop.

Corymbium L. Compositae (I). 7 S. Afr. L. narrow, ||-veined.

Corymborchis Thou. (*Corymbis BH.*). Orchid. (II. 4). 16 trop.

Corymbostachys Lindau. Acanthaceae (IV. B). 1 Madag.

Corynaea Hook. f. Balanophoraceae. 4 Andes.

Corynanthe Welw. Rubiaceae (I. 5). 5 trop. Afr.

Corynella DC. Leguminosae (III. 6). 3 W.I.

Corynephorus Beauv. (*Weingaertneria* Bernh.). Gramineae (9). 3 Eur. *C.* (*W.* or *Aira*) *canescens* Beauv., Brit.

Corynephyllum Rose. Crassulaceae. 1 Mexico.

Corynitis Spreng. Leguminosae (III. 6). 2 Cuba.

Corynocarpaceae (*EP.*, *Anacardiaceae* p.p. *BH.*). Dicots. (Archichl. Sapindales). Only genus Corynocarpus, *q.v.*

Corynocarpus Forst. Corynocarpaceae. 3 New Hebrides, New Caled., N. Zealand. Trees or shrubs with alt. leathery l. and panicles of ☿ fl. A in two whorls, inner sta. stds.; G (2), one fertile, with one pend. ov. Compressed drupe. No endosp.

Corynostylis Mart. (*Calyptrion EP.*). Violaceae. 2 trop. S. Am.

Corynotheca F. Muell. Liliaceae (III). 3 trop. and W. Austr.

Corynula Hook. f. Rubiaceae (II. 7). 1 Colombia.

Corypha L. Palmae (I. 2). 6 Ceylon, Indomal. The gigantic infl. terminates the life of the tree. *C. umbraculifera* L. (talipot palm, Ceylon, S. Ind.) grows to a great size, up to 80 feet. The l. are used as umbrellas, and for thatching, also as writing material (a metal stylus being used).

Coryphantha Lem. = Mamillaria Haw. p.p. (Cact.).

Coryphium (Cl.), an alpine meadow formation.

Corysanthes R. Br. Orchidaceae (II. 2). 50 N.Z. to Malaya.

Corythea S. Wats. Euphorbiaceae (A. II. 7). 1 Mexico.

Corytholoma Decne. (*Gesneria* p.p.). Gesn. (II). 60 trop. Am.

Coscinium Colebr. Menispermaceae. 6 Indomal.
Cosmanthus Nolte = Phacelia Juss. p.p. (Hydrophyll.).
Cosmea Willd. = Cosmos Cav. (Compos.).
Cosmelia R. Br. Epacridaceae (2). 1 S.W. Austr.
Cosmibuena Ruiz et Pav. (1802). Rubiaceae (I. 5). 6 trop. Am. Good bud-protection by the stips. of the last-opened l.
Cosmibuena Ruiz et Pav. (1794) = Hirtella L. (Rosaceae).
Cosmos Cav. (*Cosmea* Willd.). Compos. (5). 20 Am., W.I. Orn. fl.
Cosmostigma Wight. Asclepiadaceae (II. 3). 1 Indomal.
Cossinia (*Cossignia*) Comm. ex Lam. Sapind. (II). 3 Masc., New Cal.
Cossonia Durieu (*Raffenaldia BH.*). Cruciferae (2). 3 N. Afr.
Costaea A. Rich. (*Purdiea BH.*). Cyrillaceae. 3 Cuba, Colombia.
Costate (diminutive **costulate**), ribbed.
Costera J. J. Smith. Ericaceae (III. 1). 1 Borneo.
Costularia C. B. Clarke. Cyperaceae (II). 9 Masc., S. Afr.
Costus L. Zingiberaceae (II). 140 trop. Labellum very large, lat. stds. wanting, sepals and petals comparatively small. Projecting in the centre is the fertile petaloid sta. with anther on its ant. face; the style reaches just above this. The fl. mech. thus resembles Iris. Cult. orn. pl.
Cota J. Gay = Anthemis Mich. p.p. (Compos.).
Cotinus (Tourn.) L. (*Rhus* L. p.p. *BH.*). Anacard. (3). 2 N. temp.
Cotoneaster Rupp. Rosaceae (II). 50 N. temp. *C. vulgaris* Lindl. Brit. In the Alps visited solely by a wasp (*Polistes gallica*) whose nests are often attached to the rocks where the pl. grows. Fl. protog. with self-fert. in default of insects. Several cult. orn. shrubs.
Cottea Kunth. Gramineae (10). 1 trop. Am. to New Mexico.
Cottendorffia Schult. f. Bromeliaceae (2). 1 Bahia.
Cotton, the fibre of *Gossypium*, and loosely, of other *Malvaceae* and *Bombacaceae*. The fibre most used, and extensively cult. in the U.S., India, Brazil, trop. Afr., Japan, W.I., &c. It is the fine silky fibre enveloping the seed, and in *G. barbadense* and others comes clean away, but in *G. herbaceum* and most spp. leaves a 'fuzz' adhering to the seed. There are many grades upon the market: the longest and finest 'staple' is that of Sea Island, *G. barbadense* L., and the next best Egyptian and some Brazilian and American. The bulk of the supply is American 'Upland,' and the poorest qualities come from India. For details see Watt, *Wild and Cult. Cotton Plants of the World*; Willis, *Agriculture in the Tropics*. **-grass**, *Eriophorum*; **-rose** (Am.), *Filago*; **-sedge**, *Eriophorum*; **silk-**, *Eriodendron*, *Chorisia*; **-thistle**, *Onopordon*; **-tree**, *Bombax*; **-weed**, *Diotis*; **-wood tree**, *Populus*.
Cottonia Wight. Orchidaceae (II. 20). 2 Ceylon to China.
Cottony, with soft long hairs.
Cotula (Tourn.) L. (incl. *Cenia* Juss. *EP.*). Compositae (7). 50 cosmop., esp. ⁕. Cult. orn. fl.
Cotylanthera Blume. Gentianaceae (I). 3 E. Indomal., Mariannes.
Cotyledon Tourn. ex L. (incl. *Echeveria* DC.). Crassulaceae. 100 Afr., Eur., As., Mexico, S. Am. *C. Umbilicus* Linn. (penny-wort) Brit. Pets. united into a tube. L. succulent. Cult. orn. fl.
Cotyledon, a seed l.

Cotylelobiopsis Heim. Dipterocarpaceae. 1 Borneo.
Cotylelobium Pierre. Dipterocarpaceae. 5 Indomal.
Cotyliform, dish- or wheel-shaped.
Cotylodiscus Radlk. Sapindaceae (1). 1 Madagascar.
Cotylonychia Stapf. Sterculiaceae. 1 trop. Afr.
Coublandia Aubl. (*Muellera* L. f.). Legum. (III. 8). 3 trop. Am.
Couch grass, *Agropyron repens* Beauv.
Coudenbergia March (*Pentapanax EP.*). Araliac. (2). 1 Brazil.
Couepia Aubl. Rosaceae (VI). 45 S. Am.
Coula Baill. Olacaceae. 2 trop. Afr.
Coulterella Vaizey et Rose. Compositae (5). 1 Lower Calif.
Coulterophytum Robinson. Umbelliferae (III. 6). 5 Mex.
Couma Aubl. Apocynaceae (I. 1). 5 Brazil, Guiana.
Coumarin, *Anthoxanthum*.
Coumarouna Aubl. (*Dipteryx*, *q.v.*). Legum. (III. 8). 8 trop. Am.
Country almond (Ceylon), *Terminalia Catappa* L.; **-walnut**, *Aleurites triloba* Forst.
Coupoui Aubl. Rubiaceae (inc. sed.) (Apocyn. *BH.*). 1 Guiana.
Couralia Splitg. Bignoniaceae (2). 4 trop. S. Am.
Courantia Lemaire (*Cotyledon* Tourn.). Crassul. 1 Mexico.
Couratari Aubl. Lecythidaceae. 8 S. Am. The bark yields a soft fibre used for making clothing.
Courbonia Brongn. Capparidaceae (II). 12 trop. Afr. C o.
Courimari Aubl. Inc. sed. 1 Guiana.
Couroupita Aubl. Lecythid. 9 trop. S. Am., W.I. The fls. of *C. guianensis* Aubl. are borne on the old stems and followed by large spherical woody caps. (whence the name cannon-ball tree). Good timber.
Coursetia DC. Leguminosae (III. 6). 15 Brazil to Calif.
Courtoisia Nees. Cyperaceae (1). 2 trop. As., Afr.
Cousinia Cass. Compositae (11). 240 E. Medit., W. As.
Coussapoa Aubl. Moraceae (III). 18 trop. S. Am.
Coussarea Aubl. Rubiaceae (II. 8). 45 Brazil, Venezuela.
Coutarea Aubl. Rubiaceae (I. 5). 6 trop. Am., W.I.
Couthovia A. Gray. Loganiaceae. 5 Polynesia, Malay Arch.
Coutoubea Aubl. Gentianaceae (1). 4 trop. S. Am., W.I.
Covellia Gasp. = Ficus Tourn. p.p. (Morac.).
Cover-scale, *Coniferae*.
Covilhamia Kunth. Sterculiaceae. 1 Borneo.
Covillea Vail. = Larrea Cav. (Zygophyll.).
Cow-bane, *Cicuta virosa* L.; **-berry**, *Vaccinium Vitis-Idaea* L.; **-itch**, *Mucuna pruriens* DC.; **-parsnip**, *Heracleum Sphondylium* L.; **-pea**, *Vigna sinensis* Endl.; **-tree**, *Brosimum*; **-wheat**, *Melampyrum*.
Cowage, *Mucuna pruriens* DC.
Cowania D. Don. Rosaceae (III. 2). 3 Mexico, S.W. U.S.
Cowiea Wernham. Rubiaceae (I. 8). 1 Borneo.
Cowrie pine, *Agathis australis* Steud.
Cowslip, *Primula veris* Lehm.
Coxella Cheesem. et Hemsl. Umbellif. (III. 5). 1 Chatham Is.
Crab grass (Am.), *Panicum*, *Eleusine*; **-'s eyes**, *Abrus precatorius* L.; **-wood** (W.I.), *Carapa guianensis* Aubl.

Crabbea Harv. Acanthaceae (IV. A). 12 trop. and S. Afr.

Cracca Benth. ex Oerst. Leguminosae (III. 6). 6 trop. Am.; **do.** L. = Tephrosia Pers.; **do.** (Riv.) Medic. = Vicia Tourn. p.p.

Craibia Harms et Dunn. Leguminosae (III. 6). 15 trop. Afr.

Craibiodendron W. W. Smith. Ericaceae (II. 1). 5 Burma, China.

Crambe Tourn. ex L. Cruciferae (2). 20 Eur., Medit., As., Afr. Is. Patagonia. *C. maritima* L. (sea-kale) on coast of Brit. has l. fleshy and waxy. The young l. blanched form a veg.

Cranberry, *Vaccinium Oxycoccus* L.

Crane's bill, *Geranium pratense* L., &c.

Cranichis Sw. Orchidaceae (II. 2). 25 trop. Am., W.I.

Craniolaria L. Martyniaceae. 3 S. Am.

Craniospermum Lehm. Boraginaceae (IV. 2). 3 temp. As.

Craniotome Reichb. Labiatae (VI). 1 Himalaya.

Cranocarpus Benth. Leguminosae (III. 7). 2 Brazil.

Crantzia Scop. (*Alloplectus* Mart. *EP.*). Gesneriaceae (I). 35 trop. Am.; **do.** Nutt. Umbelliferae (III. 5). 1 Am., Austr., N.Z.; **do.** Pohl. Inc. sed. Nomen.

Craspedia Forst. f. Compositae (4). 4 temp. Aust., N.Z.

Craspedodictyum Copeland (*Gymnogramme* p.p.). Polypodiaceae. 2 Malay Arch., Polynesia.

Craspedorachis Benth. Gramineae (11). 2 trop. Afr.

Craspidospermum Boj. ex DC. Apocynaceae (I. 1). 1 Madag.

Crassocephalum Moench. (*Gynura EP.*). Comp. (8). 30 warm Afr., As.

Crassula Dill. ex L. (incl. *Dinacria* Harv., and *Tillaea* Michx. *EP.*). Crassul. 300 cosmop. (*cf. Trans. R. S., S. Afr.* xvii, 151), usu. succulent-l. xero. In *C. lycopodioides* Lam. the l. are narrow and closely packed, giving to the pl. the habit of a Lycopodium. In *C.* (*Rochea*) *falcata* Wendl. the connate decussate l. stand almost edgewise, and are very fleshy; some of the epidermal cells are swollen above the rest into large bladders which meet one another over the whole surface. At first living, when the l. is mature they are dead and full of air, their walls infiltrated with quantities of silica. A protection against evap. is thus afforded. In *C. nemorosa* Endl. there is veg. repr. by the formation of young plants in the infl. in place of fls.

Crassulaceae (*EP.*, *BH.*). Dicotyledons (Archichl. Rosales *EP.*, *BH.*). 25 gen., 1450 sp. cosmop., chiefly S. Afr., a very natural group. Most are perenn. living in dry (esp. rocky) places and exhibit xero. chars., fleshy l. and stem, often tufted growth, close packing of l., waxy surface, sunk stomata, &c. Veg. repr. frequent; usu. by rhiz. or offsets; some form bulbils, &c. (*e.g.* Crassula), others form adv. buds upon the l. (*e.g* Bryophyllum). Fls. usu. in cymes (cincinni), ☿ or rarely unisex., actinom. with very reg. construction. Formula K *n*, C *n*, A *n*+*n*, $\underline{G}$ *n*, where *n* represents any number from 3 to 30. K persistent; C sometimes (*e.g.* Cotyledon) gamopet.; A frequently obdipl. Insertion of parts usu. perig., but recept. not deeply hollowed. Cpls. frequently slightly united at the base; at the base of each commonly a honey-secreting scale; ov. usu. ∞. Fr. usu. a group of follicles with very small seeds. Endosp. none or very little. Fls. mostly protandr. and chiefly visited by flies, &c., their honey being easily obtainable. *Chief genera:* Sedum, Sempervivum, Cotyledon Bryophyllum, Crassula.

Crassus (Lat.), thick.

Crataegus Tourn. ex L. (*Mespilus EP.* The boundaries of these two genera and of *Pyrus* are ill-defined.) Rosaceae (II). 100 N. temp. Some hundreds of spp. have in recent years been described from the U.S., but there is some possibility that they may arise through hybridisation (*cf. Journ. of Hered.*, June 1916). *C. Oxyacantha* L. (hawthorn or may) in Brit. The thorns are modified branches. Collateral buds appear in the axils. Fls. of class AB. The wood is a substitute for that of box in engraving, &c.

Crataemespilus × G. Camus. Hybrid, Crataegus—Mespilus. 2 Eur.

Crataeva L. Capparidaceae (II). 10 trop.

Crateranthus E. G. Baker. Lecythidaceae. 1 Nigeria.

Crateriform, cup-shaped.

Crateriphytum Scheff. ex Koord. Loganiaceae. 1 Moluccas.

Craterispermum Benth. Rubiaceae (II. 1). 10 trop. Afr., Seychelles.

Craterosiphon Engl. et Gilg. Thymelaeaceae. 2 Cameroons.

Craterostemma K. Schum. Asclepiadaceae (II. 3). 1 S.E. Afr.

Craterostigma Hochst. Scrophulariaceae (II. 6). 5 trop. and S. Afr.

Cratoxylon Blume. Guttiferae (II). 12 Indomal.

Cratylia Mart. Leguminosae (III. 10). 6 S. Am.

Cratystylis Sp. Moore (*Olearia* p.p. in part.). Comp. (3). 3 Austr.

Crawfurdia Wall. Gentianaceae (I). 10 warm As.

Creaghia Scortech. (*Mussaendopsis EP.*). Rubiac. (I. 5). 1 Malaya.

Creaghiella Stapf. Melastomaceae (I). 1 Borneo.

Creeper, Canary, *Tropaeolum peregrinum* L.; **trumpet-**, *Tecoma radicans* Juss.; **Virginian-**, *Parthenocissus*.

Creeping plant, one with stolons or runners, rooting at the nodes, *Agropyron*, *Agrostis*, *Ajuga*, *Fragaria*, *Ranunculus*, &c.

Cremanium D. Don = Miconia Ruiz et Pav. p.p. (Melast.).

Cremanthodium Benth. Compositae (8). 50 Himal., China.

Cremaspora Benth. Rubiaceae (II. 1). 6 trop. Afr., Madag.

Cremastra Lindl. Orchidaceae (II. 10). 2 Nepal, Japan.

Cremastus Miers (*Bignonia BH.*). Bignon. (I). 3 Brazil.

Cremnium (Cl.), a cliff formation.

Cremnophila Rose (*Sedum* p.p.). Crassulaceae. 1 Mex.

Cremocarp, a mericarp.

Cremocarpus Boiv. ex Baill. Rubiaceae (II. 7). 1 Comoros.

Cremolobus DC. Cruciferae (I). 10 Andes.

Crenamon Raf. Inc. sed. 1 N. Am.

Crenate (l.), teeth pointing forward, rounded; notches sharp.

Crenea Aubl. Lythraceae. 2 trop. S. Am., Trinidad.

Crenium (Cl.), a spring formation.

Creochiton Blume. Melastomaceae (I). 3 Java, Phil. Is.

Creosote plant, *Larrea mexicana* Moric.

Crepe-flower, *Lagerstroemia*.

Crepidopsis Arv. Touv. Compositae (13). 1 Mex.

Crepidospermum Hook. f. Burseraceae. 2 Northern S. Am.

Crepinella Marshal. Araliaceae (I). 1 Brit. Guiana.

Crepis (Vaill.) L. (incl. *Barkhausia* Moench.). Compositae (13).

240 N. Hemisph., S. Afr., S. Am.; 6 in Brit. (hawk's beard). Like Hieracium.

Crescentia L. Bignon. (4). 5 warm Am. Fls. on old stems, succeeded by gourd-like berries; the epicarp is woody, and after removal of the pulp forms a calabash (*C. Cujete* L., calabash tree, most used).

Cress, *Lepidium sativum* L.; **American-**, *Barbarea praecox* R. Br.; **bitter-**, *Cardamine*; **Indian-**, *Tropaeolum*; **penny-**, *Thlaspi*; **rock-**, *Arabis*; **water-**, *Nasturtium officinale* R. Br.; **winter-**, *Barbarea*; **yellow-**, *Barbarea*, *Nasturtium*.

Cressa L. Convolvulaceae (I). 5 trop. and subtrop.

Crest, a ridge or outgrowth.

Cretaceous, chalky.

Cribriform, sieve-like.

Crinitus (Lat.), with soft hairs.

Crinodendron Molina (*Tricuspidaria* R. et P.). Elaeocarp. 2 Chili.

Crinum L. Amaryllidaceae (I). 130 trop. and subtrop., esp. on sea-coasts. Large bulbous pl. with showy fls. The seed of *C. asiaticum* L. (Goebel, *Pflanzenbiol. Schild.* I. p. 128) has a very thin corky covering and is suited to distr. by water and early germination. The ovule has no integuments, and the testa is replaced by a formation of cork at the outside of the endosp. Cult. orn. fl.

Crioceras Pierre (*Tabernaemontana* p.p.). Apocyn. (I. 3). 2 trop. Afr.

Crisp, crispate, crisped, curled.

Cristaria (Heist.) Cav. Malvaceae (2). 30 Chili, Peru.

Cristatella Nutt. Capparidaceae (V). 2 S.W. U.S.

Cristatus (Lat.), crested.

Crithmum L. Umbelliferae (III. 5). 1 *C. maritimum* L., the samphire, on rocky coasts, Medit., Eur. (incl. Brit.). It has much divided and very fleshy l. Used for making pickles.

Crocidium Hook. Compositae (8). 1 W. N. Am.

Crocion Nieuwland (*Viola* p.p.). Violaceae. 4 N. Am.

Crockeria Greene ex A. Gray. Compositae (6). 1 Calif.

Crocodiloides Adans. = Berkheya Ehrh. (Compos.).

Crocopsis Pax. Amaryllidaceae (I). 1 Peru.

Crocosmia Planch. (*Tritonia* p.p. *EP.*). Iridaceae (III). 1, *C. aurea* Planch., trop. and S. Afr. Cult. orn. fl.

Crocus (Tourn.) L. Iridaceae (I). 60 Medit., Eur., 2 nat. in Brit. Below ground is a corm (*cf.* Colchicum), covered with a few scaly l., in whose axils may arise one or more buds, giving rise to new corms on the top of the old. The l. are dorsiv., and curiously grooved on the back. The fl. is often single and term.; in some sp. there is a small cyme. The fl. closes at night and in dull weather. The tube of the P is so long that the ovary remains below the soil and is protected from the weather (*cf.* Colchicum). The fl. is protandr. and visited by bees and Lepidoptera. Honey is secreted by the ovary, and the anthers face outwards so as to touch any insect alighting on the petals and seeking honey. The stigmas are branched. Birds often bite off the fls. in gardens (? for honey); they seem to prefer the yellow fls., leaving the blue and white alone.

The dried stigmas of *C. sativus* L. form saffron, once largely used as an orange yellow dye, but now chiefly employed in flavouring and colouring dishes, liqueurs, &c. [See Kronfeld's *Geschichte des Safrans*, &c., Wien 1892. Cult. orn. fl. (Maw, *The genus C.*).]

Crocus, autumn, *Colchicum autumnale* L.

Crocyllis E. Mey. Rubiaceae (II. 7). 1 S. Afr.

Croftia King et Prain. Zingiberaceae (I). 1 India.

Croftia Small (*Schaueria* p.p.). Acanth. (IV. B). 1 N. Am.

Croixia Pierre. Sapotaceae (II). 1 Malaya.

Crookea Small (*Ascyrum* p.p.). Guttif. (II). 1 N. Am.

Croomia Torr. ex Torr. et A. Gray. Stemonaceae. 3 E. U.S., Japan.

Crosnes, *Stachys Sieboldi* Miq.

Crossandra Salisb. Acanthaceae (IV. B). 25 trop. As., Afr., Madag. The seeds of many sp. are covered with scales which spread out and become sticky when wetted (*cf.* Linum). Cult. orn. fl.

Cross-fertilisation or **-pollination,** pollination from a distinct plant; *cf.* Floral mechanisms, Flower classes, &c.

Cross-wort, *Galium.*

Crossandrella C. B. Clarke. Acanthaceae (IV. B). 1 Uganda.

Crossonephelis Baill. Sapindaceae (I). 1 Nossi Bé.

Crossopetalum P. Br. = Myginda L. (Celastr.).

Crossopteryx Fenzl. Rubiaceae (I. 5). 2 trop. Afr.

Crossosoma Nutt. The only genus of Crossosomataceae. 3 S.W. U.S., Mex. Shrubs with small stiff l. and sol. fl. Like Rosaceae Spiraeoideae, but seeds kidney-shaped, with rich endosp. Aril. (Engler.)

Crossosomataceae (*EP.*; *Dilleniaceae* p.p. *BH.*). Dicots. (Archichl., Rosales). Only genus (*q.v.*) Crossosoma.

Crossostemma Planch. ex Benth. in Hook. Passifl. 1 W. trop. Afr.

Crossostephium Less. Compositae (7). 1 China, Phil. Is.

Crossostylis Forst. Rhizophoraceae. 6 Polynesia.

Crossotropis Stapf. Gramineae (11). 3 warm Afr., Arabia.

Crotalaria Dill. ex L. Leguminosae (III. 3). 350 trop. and subtrop. *C. juncea* L. (India, Austr.), an annual about 8 ft. high, is largely cult. for the fibre obtained from its stems by maceration in water (*cf.* Linum), known as Sunn-hemp, Bombay or Madras hemp, &c. *C. retusa* L. (trop.) is also employed.

Croton L. Euphorbiaceae (A. II. 1). 600 trop. and subtrop. Fls. mon- or dioecious, little reduced from the type of the fam. *C. Tiglium* L. (trop. As.) is the source of croton oil (a powerful purgative drug, expressed from the seeds). *C. Cascarilla* Benn. and *C. Eluteria* Benn. (Bahamas) yield Cascarilla bark, used as a tonic (*cf.* Cascarilla). *C. lacciferus* L. (India, Ceylon) yields a lac, used in varnish-making, and several Brazilian spp. a dragon's blood resin.

Croton (of trop. gardens), *Codiaeum variegatum* Bl.

Croton-oil, *Croton Tiglium* L.

Crotonogyne Muell.-Arg. Euphorbiaceae (A. II. 2). 10 trop. Afr.

Crotonogynopsis Pax. Euphorbiaceae (A. II. 2). 1 trop. Afr.

Crotonopsis Michx. Euphorbiaceae (A. II. 1). 2 N. Am.

Crow-berry, *Empetrum nigrum* L.; **-foot,** *Ranunculus*; **-foot-grass,** *Dactyloctenium.*

Crowea Smith. Rutaceae (I). 4 Austr.

Crown-bark, *Cinchona*; **-beard** (Am.), *Verbesina*; **-Imperial,** *Fritillaria imperialis* L.; **-palm** (W.I.), *Maximiliana.*

Crucianella L. Rubiaceae (II. 11). 4 Eur., Medit. Cult. orn. fl.

Cruciate, cross-shaped.

Cruciferae (*EP.*, *BH.*). Dicots. (Archichl. Rhoeadales; Parietales *BH.*). 220 gen., 1900 sp., cosmop., but chiefly N. temp. and esp. Medit.; a very natural fam., well marked off from others, though approaching Papaveraceae and Capparidaceae. Herbs, a few undershrubs; some ann., many perenn., forming each year a new shoot term. in the infl. L. usu. alt., exstip., with unicellular simple or branched hairs. For other peculiarities of veg. organs see gen., *e.g.* Brassica, Anastatica, Subularia, Vella, &c. Infl. usu. a raceme or corymb, and nearly always without bracts or bracteoles.

Fl. usu. ☿, reg., hypog., with typical formula K 2 + 2, C 4, A 6, $\underline{G}$ (2). The K has two whorls, the C only one, alt. with the K as a whole. The petals usu. spread out in the form of a cross and are often clawed; the sta. in two whorls, an outer of 2 short, an inner of 4 long, sta. (tetradynamous); anthers intr. The two cpls. are placed transv., and have parietal plac., but the ov. is 2-loc. on account of the presence of an antero-post. partition, the *replum* or so-called spurious septum, an outgrowth of the placentae. Stigmas 2, on short style, above the placentae (*cf.* Papaveraceae). Ovules anatr. or campylotr.

Floral Diagram (after Eichler).

The explanation of the morphology of this fl. has given rise to much dispute. It is usu. regarded as a typically 2-merous fl. (*cf.* Papaveraceae), and the 4 petals and 4 inner sta. are supposed to be due to branching. Others regard it as 4-merous (*e.g.* Klein in *Bot. Centr.* 58, p. 197). Full discussion in Eichler's *Blüthendiagr.* or in Asa Gray's *Struct. Bot.* p. 206.

On the bases of the sta. are the nectaries, the honey being secreted into the often gibbous bases of the inner sepals. The sepals often stand almost straight up, and the petals are then provided with claws and spread out horiz. beyond the sepals. The honey is thus concealed to some extent and protected from rain. The majority of the order exhibit this construction more or less, thus coming into the biological fl.-class AB. In many gen. the fls. are arranged in corymbs, thus getting the advantage of many fls. massed together on one level (*cf.* Umbelliferae and Compositae). Insects visiting the fls. touch the anthers with one side of their bodies and the stigma with the other, and may in this way effect cross-fert., as they go sometimes to one, sometimes to the other, side of the fl. Dichogamy is frequent, but not well marked, and in almost all self-fert. ultimately occurs. [Müller, *Fert. of Fls.*]

Fr. a caps. of pod-like form; if at least three times as long as broad it is called a *siliqua*, if shorter a *silicula*. It is divided into two by the replum and is usu. thin and membranous. The valves break away from below upwards, leaving the replum with the seeds pressed against it and adhering. The fr. may be flattened in two ways, either ∥ or ⊥ the replum; this char. is of systematic importance. It may also be jointed between the seeds as in a lomentum (Leguminosae). Achene-like one-seeded fr. occur in a few gen. Others have subterranean fr. (Cardamine sp., &c.).

The chars. of the seed are also of great importance in classification. The seed is exalb.: the testa is often mucilaginous, swelling up when wetted (*e.g.* the familiar case of mustard seed). The ovules being campylotr., the embryo sacs, and embryos, are curved, usu. with the radicle in one half of the seed, the cots. in the other. The shape of the embryo and the position of the radicle with regard to the cots. are important. The chief cases are: (1) radicle *incumbent* (or embryo *notorhizal*), *i.e.* lying on the back of one cot., the cots. not being folded on themselves; this may be shown thus o∥, the o repres. the radicle; (2) *accumbent* (or embryo *pleurorhizal*), o=, the radicle against the edges of the cots.; (3) *orthoplocous* (cots. *conduplicate*), o>>; (4) *spirolobous*, as in (1) but cots. once folded, o∥∥; (5) *diplecolobous*, ditto twice or more folded, o∥∥∥∥.

For plants of economic value see esp. Brassica (which gives a number of valuable vegetables), Sinapis, Nasturtium, Lepidium, &c. All C. are harmless, and most are rich in sulphur compounds (to which the smell of boiling cabbages is due), and are thus useful in scurvy, &c.

Classification and chief genera (after Prantl):

The grouping of the smaller divisions of the fam. and the defining of the genera is a most difficult task. Many classifications have been devised. Prantl (in *Nat. Pfl.*) bases his largely upon the hairs borne on the leaves. Others rely on characters of fruit and embryo, &c. In any case the identification of a cruciferous genus is a difficult matter.

A. Hairs simple or none: no glandular hairs.

1. *Thelypodieae* (stigma equally developed all round; style undivided or prolonged above middle of cpls., or turned back): Pringlea, Thelypodium, Heliophila.
2. *Sinapeae* (stigma better developed over placentae): Subularia, Lepidium, Iberis, Cochlearia, Alliaria, Sisymbrium, Cakile, Isatis, Vella, Sinapis, Brassica, Raphanus, Crambe, Nasturtium, Cardamine, Lunaria.

B. Hairs branched (a few exceptions): sometimes also glandular hairs.

3. *Schizopetaleae* (stigma equal all round): Schizopetalum, Physaria.
4. *Hesperideae* (stigma better developed over placentae): Capsella, Draba, Arabis, Erysimum, Cheiranthus, Alyssum, Anastatica, Malcomia, Hesperis, Matthiola, Conringia.

Cruckshankia Hook. et Arn. Rubiaceae (I. 2). 5 Chili.

Cruddasia Prain. Leguminosae (III. 10). 1 N. India.

Crudia Schreb. (*Apalatoa* Aubl.). Legumin. (II. 3). 20 trop.

Cruentus (Lat.), blood coloured.

Crula Nieuwland (*Acer* p.p.). Aceraceae. 7 E. As.

Crumenaria Mart. Rhamnaceae. 5 trop. Brazil.

Crunocallis Rydberg (*Claytonia* p.p.). Portul. 1 Arct. As. Am.

Crupina Dill. ex L., Cass. Compositae (11). 2 S. Eur. to Persia.

Crusea Cham. et Schlechtd. Rubiaceae (II. 10). 10 Mex., C. Am.
Crustaceous, hard and brittle.
Cruzia Phil. Labiatae (VI). 1 Patagonia.
Crymium (Cl.), a polar barren formation.
Cryosophila Blume (*Copernicia BH.*). Palmae (I. 2). 1 Mex.
Cryphiacanthus Nees (*Ruellia* p.p.). Acanth. (IV. A). 10 S. Am.
Crypsis Ait. Gramineae (8). 1 Medit. Seed ejected from fr.
Cryptadenia Meissn. Thymelaeaceae. 5 Cape Col. Cult. orn.
Cryptandra Sm. Rhamnaceae. 30 temp. Austr.
Cryptangium Schrad. Cyperaceae (II). 20 trop. Am.
Cryptantha Lehm. (*Eritrichium BH.*). Borag. (IV. 2). 80 Pacif. Am.
Cryptanthe Benth. et Hook. f. = preceding.
Cryptanthopsis Ule. Bromeliaceae (4). 2 Brazil (Bahia).
Cryptanthus Otto et Dietr. Bromeliaceae (4). 10 Brazil. Cult. orn. fol.
Cryptarrhena R. Br. Orchidaceae (II. 19). 3 W.I., Guiana, Mex.
Crypteronia Blume. Sonneratiaceae (Lythr. *BH.*). 4 Malaya.
Cryptocarpus H. B. et K. Nyctaginaceae. 2 W. coast Am.
Cryptocarya R. Br. Lauraceae (II). 70 trop. and subtrop. The fr. of *C. moschata* Nees et Mart. (Brazilian nutmegs) used as spice.
Cryptocentrum Benth. (*Mystacidium EP.*). Orchid. (II. 20). 4 Ecuador.
Cryptochilus Wall. Orchidaceae (II. 5). 2 Himalaya.
Cryptochloris Benth. (*Tetrapogon EP.*). Gramin. (11). 1 Patagonia.
Cryptocoryne Fisch. Araceae (VII). 40 Indomal. Marsh plants. Some sp. are apparently 'viviparous' in their germination, like mangroves (see Goebel's *Pflanzenbiol. Schild.* I. p. 132).
Cryptodiscus Schrenk. Umbelliferae (III. 4). 4 W. As.
Cryptogamae. A term used to distinguish those pl. which do not produce seeds. All the higher C. exhibit alternation of generations (see *Pteridophyta*), and the distinction between them and Phanerogams depends on the fact that in C. the *macrospore or spore falls out of its sporangium*, germinates upon the ground or in water and gives rise to an *independent* ♀ (or ☿) prothallus; in the P. on the other hand, it does not do so.

The C. form 3 great groups, Thallophyta, Bryophyta, and Pteridophyta, each usu. regarded as equivalent to Spermaphyta.

Cryptogamae Vasculares = Pteridophyta.
Cryptogramma R. Br. (*Allosorus* Bernh.). Polypodiaceae. 5 Eur., As., Am. *C. crispa* R. Br. (parsley-fern, curled rockbrake) Brit.
Cryptogyne Hook. f. Sapotaceae (I). 1 Madag.
Cryptolepis R. Br. Asclepiadaceae (I). 20 palaeotrop.
Cryptomeria D. Don. Coniferae (Pinaceae; see C. for gen. char.). 1 Japan, *C. Japonica* D. Don. (Japanese cedar), often cult. Timber good.
Cryptophaseolus O. Ktze. (*Canavalia* p.p. *EP.*). Legum. (III. 10). 1 Annam.
Cryptophoranthus Barb. Rodr. (*Pleurothallis BH.*). Orchid. (II. 8). 10 trop. Am., W.I.
Cryptophragmium Nees (*Gymnostachyum BH.*). Acanth. (IV. B). 15 trop. As.
Cryptopus Lindl. Orchidaceae (II. 20). 1 Madag.

Cryptosepalum Benth. Legum. (II. 3). 10 trop. Afr. One large petal only. A 3.
Cryptospora Kar. et Kir. Cruciferae (4). 1 W. As.
Cryptostegia R. Br. Asclepiadaceae (1). 2 trop. Afr., Madag. Cult. orn. fl.
Cryptostemma R. Br. (*Arctotis* p.p. *EP.*). Comp. (10). 4 S. Afr.
Cryptostephanus Welw. Amaryllidaceae (1). 2 trop. W. Afr. Berry.
Cryptostylis R. Br. Orchidaceae (II. 2). 12 Indomal.
Cryptotaenia DC. Umbelliferae (III. 5). 5 Medit. to N. Am.
Cryptotaeniopsis Dunn (*Carum* p.p. in part). Umb. (III. 5). 18 E. As.
Ctenanthe Eichl. Marantaceae. 12 trop. Am.
Ctenium Panz. Gramineae (11). 7 Am., Afr., Masc.
Ctenodon Baill. (*Aeschynomene* p.p. *EP.*). Legum. (III. 7). 1 Brazil.
Ctenolophon Oliv. Linaceae (formerly Olac.). 2 Malaya.
Ctenophrynium K. Schum. Marantaceae. 1 Madag.
Ctenophyllum Rydb. (*Phaca* p.p.). Leguminosae (III. 6). 1 N. Am.
Ctenopsis De Notar. (*Festuca* p.p. *EP.*). Gramin. (10). 1 trop. Afr.
Cuba bark (W.I.), **bast,** *Hibiscus elatus* Sw.; **-hemp** (Aust.), *Furcrea.*
Cubanthus Millspaugh (*Pedilanthus* p.p.). Euphorb. (A. II. 8). 2 Cuba.
Cubeba Raf. = Piper L. (Piper.).
Cubebs, *Piper Cubeba* L.
Cubilia Blume. Sapindaceae (inc. sed.). 2 Phil. Is., Celebes.
Cuckoo flower, *Cardamine,* &c.; **-pint,** *Arum maculatum* L.
Cucubalus (Tourn.) L. Caryophyllaceae (II. 1). 1, *C. baccifer* L., N. temp. (introd. in Brit.). Fr. a berry.
Cucullaria Schreb. = Vochysia Juss. (Vochys.).
Cucullate, hooded, cowled.
Cucullus, *Asclepiadaceae.*
Cucumber, *Cucumis sativus* L.; **calabash-,** *Lagenaria*; **squirting-,** *Ecballium*; **-tree** (Am.), *Magnolia.*
Cucumeropsis Naud. Cucurbitaceae (2). 2 trop. W. Afr.
Cucumis (Tourn.) L. Cucurb. (3). 40 trop., subtrop. *C. Melo* L. (melon), *C. sativus* L. (cucumber) cult. from early times. Tendrils simple, regarded as of l. nature (see fam.), the stem portion suppressed.
Cucurbita (Tourn.) L. Cucurbitaceae (3). 10 Am., but many so long cult. that their origin is doubtful. For tendrils see fam. Fls. monoecious. Germination interesting. On the lower side of the hypocotyl a peg is formed which holds one side of the testa firmly while the expansion of the plumule splits off the other side. The position of the peg is determined by gravity.

C. Pepo L. is the pumpkin, with its vars. the vegetable marrow and squash; *C. maxima* Duchesne the giant pumpkin, cult. in N. Am.
Cucurbitaceae (*EP.*, *BH.*). Dicots. (Sympet. Cucurbitales; Polypet. Passiflorales *BH.*). 90 gen., 750 sp., wanting in the colder regions, most abundant in the trop., chiefly climbing ann. herbs with very rapid growth and abundance of sap in their stems and other tissues. L. alt. roundish, entire or lobed. They climb by tendrils, about whose morphological nature there has been much discussion; they have been considered by various authors as "roots, stems, leaves,

stipules, shoots, flower-stalks or organs sui generis." According to Müller (*Nat. Pfl.*) the tendrils of *Cucurbita Pepo*, with their frequent abnormalities, give a proof of their true nature. Every variety is found, from simple threads to long leafy tendrils, in which the l. show all transitions to tendrils. Müller, therefore, considers the twining portion of the tendril to be a met. l., the lower stiff portion a stem. The tendrils of C. are very sensitive and show very well all the phenomena of tendril-climbing.

Fls. diclinous, rarely ☿, in infls. of various types (see *Nat. Pfl.*, or Eichler, *Blüthendiagr.*). K and C typically (5) each, reg.; A typically 5, but great var. is introduced by cohesions, &c.; it is almost always ·|·. In Fevillea we find 5 sta. with biloc. anthers, the simplest type; it is noteworthy that the usual 4-loc. anther never occurs in C., and no trace of the missing loc. is to be found in either lobe of the anther of Fevillea. In the rest of the fam. the A is more complex. In Thladiantha two pairs of sta. stand apart from the fifth sta. In Sicydium these pairs show union of their members at the base, and in others the union is more complete, until, as in Bryonia, &c., the A apparently has only 3 sta., of which 2 have 4-loc. anthers due to unions. The more the sta. depart from the simple type the more curved do the loculi of the anthers become, till in Cucurbita, &c. the pollen-sacs are twisted in a most extraordinary manner (*cf.* Columellia). In Cyclanthera the sta. are all united into a column with two ring-shaped pollen chambers running round the top (*cf.* the *flowers* of Cyclanthus). $\bar{G}$ 1—10-loc., with 1—∞ anatr. ov. in each loc.; the most common type is, however, a 3-loc. ovary with axile plac. projecting deep into the cavity. Stigmas as many as cpls., usually forked. Fr. usu. fleshy, of the type of the melon or cucumber—berry-like, sometimes called a pepo. Seeds exalb. In Zanonia, Ecballium, Cyclanthera, &c. (*q.v.*), the mode of seed-dispersal is interesting. Several have ed. fr., *e.g.* Cucurbita, Cucumis, Sechium, Lagenaria, &c.

The relationships of this fam. have been much disputed. It has been placed near Passifloraceae, Loasaceae and Begoniaceae, but most probably it comes near to the Campanulaceae.

Classification and chief genera (after Pax):

A. Pollen-sacs not fused into a ring.
  a. Sta. free or only united at base.
    1. *Fevilleeae* (sta. 5, rarely 4): Fevillea, Zanonia, Thladiantha.
    2. *Melothrieae* (sta. 3, rarely 2 or 4; pollen-sacs straight or slightly curved): Melothria, Telfairia.
    3. *Cucurbiteae* (do., but pollen-sacs S or U shaped): Acanthosicyos, Momordica, Luffa, Bryonia, Ecballium, Cucumis, Lagenaria, Trichosanthes, Cucurbita.
  b. Sta. united into a column.
    4. *Sicyoideae:* Echinocystis, Sechium, Sicyos.

B. Pollen-sacs fused into a ring.
    5. *Cyclanthereae:* Cyclanthera (only genus).

Cucurbitaceous, gourd-like.

Cucurbitales (*EP.*). The 9th order of Dicots. Sympetalae. P. xlviii.

Cucurbitella Walp. Cucurbitaceae (2). 4 temp. S. Am.

Cudrania Tréc. Moraceae (II). 4 Japan to Austr., New Cal.
Cudweed, *Gnaphalium.*
Culcasia P. Beauv. Araceae (I). 15 trop. Afr.
Culcitium Humb. et Bonpl. Compos. (8). 20 Andes. Like Espeletia.
Cullenia Wight. Bombacaceae. 1 India, Ceylon. C o.
Cullumia R. Br. Compositae (10). 15 S. Afr.
Cullumiopsis Drake del Castillo. Compositae (4). 1 Madag.
Culm, the stem of a grass.
Cultivation, see Economic and ornamental plants.
Culver's physic, -root, *Veronica virginica* L.
Cumbu, *Pennisetum typhoideum* Rich.
Cumin seed, *Cuminum Cyminum* L.
Cumingia Vidal. Bombacaceae. 1 Phil. Is.
Cuminia Colla. Labiatae (VI). 3 Juan Fernandez.
Cuminum (Tourn.) L. Umbelliferae (7). 1 *C. Cyminum* L., Medit. The fr. (cumin seeds) are sometimes used like caraway seeds.
Cumminsia King ex Prain = Cathcartia Hk. f. (Papav.).
Cuneal, cuneate, cuneiform, wedge-shaped.
Cunila L. Labiatae (VI). 15 Am.
Cunninghamia R. Br. Coniferae (Pinaceae; see C. for genus characters). *C. sinensis* R. Br., the only sp., in S. China and Cochin-China.
Cunonia L. Cunoniaceae. 1, *C. capensis* L., S. Afr., 11 New Caled. Bud-protection by stipules.
Cunoniaceae (*EP.*; *Saxifragaceae* p.p. *BH.*). Dicot. (Archichl. Rosales). 26 gen., 250 sp., chiefly between 13° and 35° S. Shrubs and trees with opp. or whorled leathery l., stip. (the stip. often united in pairs as in Rubiaceae). Fl. small, usu. ☿. Receptacle usu. flat. K 4—5; C 4—5, usu. smaller than calyx, often absent; A 8—10 or ∞ or 4—5; $\underline{G}$ usu. (2), rarely 2; ovary usu. 2-loc., generally with ∞—2 ovules in 2 rows in each loc. Fruit usu. a capsule, rarely drupe or nut. Endosperm. *Chief genera:* Cunonia, Weinmannia.
Cunuria Baill. Euphorbiaceae (A. II. 3). 2 N. Brazil.
Cup, a hollow floral receptacle, *Myrtaceae, Rosaceae,* &c.; **-flower,** *Nierembergia*; **-plant** (Am.), *Silphium perfoliatum* L.
Cupania L. Sapindaceae (I). 32 warm Am. Wood of some is useful. *C. sapida* Voigt (*C. edulis* Schum. et Thonn.) = Blighia.
Cupaniopsis Radlk. Sapindaceae (I). 28 Austr., Polynesia.
Cuphea P. Br. Lythraceae. 200 Am. L. decussate; usu. there is one fl. at each node, standing *between* the two l.; this is really the axillary fl. of the l. below, and its peduncle is 'adnate' to the main stem. Many covered with sticky glandular hairs. Cult. orn. fl.
Cupheanthus Seem. (*Jambosa, Syzygium* p.p. ? *EP.*). Myrtaceae (I). 1 New Caled.
Cuphocarpus Decne. et Planch. Araliaceae (I). 1 Madag.
Cupia DC. = Randia L. (Rubiac.).
Cupirana Miers (*Coupoui BH.*). Apocynaceae (I. I). 2 Guiana.
Cuprea bark, *Remijia.*
Cupreous, copper-coloured.
Cupressaceae (Warming) = Pinaceae § Cupresseae.
Cupressus Tourn. ex L. [Synonymy: *C. fastigiata* DC. = *C. semper-*

virens L.; *C. pendula* Staunt. = *C. funebris* Endl.; *C. nootkatensis* Lamb. = *Chamaecyparis nutkatensis* Spach.; *C. thujoides* L. = *Ch. sphaeroidea* Spach.; *C. juniperoides* L. = *Callitris arborea* Schrad.; *C. japonica* L. = *Cryptomeria jap.* Don.

Coniferae (Pinaceae; see C. for gen. char.). 12 Medit., As., N.Am. The gen. habit is xero., the l. being much reduced and closely appressed to the stems. *C. sempervirens* L. is the cypress of the Medit. region; *C. funebris* Endl. the funereal cypress of China and Thibet, with 'weeping' branches; *C. macrocarpa* Hartn. (Monterey cypress, Calif.) is largely planted for timber and shade in warm countries. Several yield useful timber, *e.g. C. Lawsoniana* Murr. (Calif., Oregon), *C. Lindleyi* Klotzsch (Mexico), *C. torulosa* Don (W. Himal.), *C. sempervirens*, &c. (see Camus, *Les Cyprès*, Paris, 1914).

Cupule, *Fagaceae, Betulaceae.*

Cupuliferae (*BH.*) = Betulaceae + Fagaceae; (Warming) = Fagaceae.

Curanga Juss. Scrophulariaceae (II. 6). 1 Indomal.

Curare, *Strychnos toxifera* Schomb.

Curatella L. Dilleniaceae. 5 trop. Am., W. I.

Curculigo Gaertn. Amaryllid. (III). 3 trop. Ovary loculi imperfect.

Curcuma L. Zingiber. (I). 55 Indomal., Chi. *C. angustifolia* Roxb. tubers furnish east indian arrowroot. *C. longa* L. yields the yellow dye turmeric (dried and ground rhiz.). The tubers of *C. Zedoaria* Rosc. yield zedoary, used in the East as a tonic and perfume.

Curima O. F. Cook (*Bactris EP.*). Palmae (IV. 2). 2 W. Indies.

Curinila Roem. et Schult. Asclepiadaceae (inc. sed.). 1 Malaya.

Curled rockbrake, *Cryptogramma crispa* R. Br.

Curly greens, *Brassica oleracea* L. var.

Curmeria Linden et André = Homalomena Schott p.p. (Arac.).

Curraniodendron Merrill. Saxifragaceae (V). 1 Phil. Is.

Currant, *Ribes, Vitis*; **Australian-,** *Leucopogon*; **black-,** *Ribes nigrum* L.; **-bush** (W.I.), *Clidemia, Miconia*, &c.; **flowering-,** *Ribes sanguineum* Pursh; **-tree** (W.I.), *Beureria, Jacquinia.*

Curroria Planch. Asclepiadaceae (I). 1 S. Afr.

Curry-leaf (Ceyl., India), *Murraya Koenigii* Spreng.

Curtia Cham. et Schlechtd. Gentian. (I). 10 Guiana to Uruguay.

Curtisia Ait. Cornaceae. 1 S. Afr., *C. faginea* Ait., yielding a hard and useful timber (assegai-wood).

Curvembryae. The 1st series (*BH.*) of Monochlamydeae. The 7th cohort (Warming) of Choripetalae.

Cuscuaria Schott (*Scindapsus* p.p. *EP.*). Araceae (II). 1 Malay Archipelago.

Cuscus (khas-khas), *Vetiveria zizanioides* Stapf.

Cuscuta (Tourn.) L. Convolvulaceae (II). 100 trop. and temp.; 3 Brit. (dodder, scald, &c.). Many have extended their boundaries through being carried about with their host plants. Leafless and rootless total parasites. The stem twines and is sensitive to contact like a tendril so that it clasps the support tightly; it rarely makes more than three turns about the same branch of the host. At the points in close contact suckers are developed which penetrate the tissues of the host, growing into organic union with them and drawing off all the food materials required by the parasite, which has no green tissue of its own. The seeds of C. germinate later than those of the host plant; a very short anchorage root is formed and the stem nutates in search of a host; as soon as it has clasped one the root dies away. Much damage is often done by these plants: most of the Brit. sp. confine themselves to particular host pl., but others attack a variety of pl. For details see Kerner's *Nat. Hist. of Plants*, vol. I., and papers by Peirce in *Ann. of Bot.* 1893—4.

Cushion plants, with cushion-like growth reducing evap.

Cusickia M. E. Jones. Umbelliferae (III. 6). 1 N. Am.

Cusparia Humb. Rutaceae (I). 22 S. Am. *C. febrifuga* Humb. (*C. trifoliata* Eng.) yields Angostura or Cusparia bark, sometimes used in place of cinchona bark. (C) ⫩.

Cuspidaria DC. Bignoniaceae (I). 5 Brazil, Bolivia.

Cuspidate, with rigid point.

Cussonia Thunb. Araliaceae (I). 25 S. and trop. Afr., Madag.

Custard-apple, *Anona squamosa* L., *reticulata* L.

Cutandia Wilk. Gramineae (10). 6 Medit.

Cutch, *Acacia Catechu* Willd., *Rhizophora*.

Cuthbertia Small (*Tradescantia* p.p.). Commelin. 2 N. Am.

Cuticle, the thin detachable skin of a plant.

Cutting grass (W.I.), *Scleria flagellum-nigrorum* Berg.

Cuttsia F. Muell. Saxifragaceae (V). 1 E. Austr.

Cuviera DC. Rubiaceae (II. 1). 10 trop. Afr. Several are ant-inhabited with hollow swellings of the stem above the nodes.

Cyamopsis DC. Leguminosae (III. 6). 3 trop. Afr., As. *C. psoraloides* DC. is largely cultivated in India as fodder (guar).

Cyanaeorchis Barb. Rodr. Orchidaceae (II. 7). 1 Brazil.

Cyanandrium Stapf. Melastomaceae (I). 2 Borneo.

Cyananthus Wall. Campanul. (I). 10 Mts. mid. and E. As. Ov. sup.

Cyanastraceae (*EP.*, *Pontederiaceae* p.p. *BH.*). Monocots. (Farinosae). Only genus Cyanastrum, *q.v.*

Cyanastrum Oliv. Cyanastraceae. 5 trop. Afr. Herbs with tuber or tuberous rhiz., and racemes or panicles of ☿ reg. fls. P (3 + 3), A (6), $\bar{G}$ (3), 3-loc. with 2 ov. in each. Fr. 1-seeded. Perisperm.

Cyanea Gaudich. Campanulaceae (III). 28 Sandw. Is.

Cyanella L. Amaryllidaceae (III.). (Haemodor. *BH.*) 7 S. Afr.

Cyaneus (Lat.), full blue.

Cyanocarpus Bailey. Proteaceae (II). 2 Queensland.

Cyanodaphne Blume. Lauraceae (II). 2 Malay Archipelago.

Cyanostegia Turcz. Verbenaceae (3). 4 W. Austr.

Cyanothyrsus Harms. (*Daniella* p.p.), Legumin. (II. 3). 3 trop. Afr.

Cyanotis D. Don. Commelinaceae. 50 palaeotrop.

Cyanus (Tourn.) L. = Centaurea L. (Comp.).

Cyathanthus Engl. Moraceae (I). 1 Cameroons.

Cyathea Sm. Cyatheaceae. 240 trop. and subtrop. Tree ferns, forming a char. feature in the scenery of various regions. *C. medullaris* Sw. (N.Z.) and *C. dealbata* Sw. are well known. Their pulpy pith is eaten by the natives.

Cyatheaceae. Filicineae Leptosporangiatae (Homosporous). 9 gen. with 360 sp. chiefly trop. and subtrop., mostly tree ferns with stout erect stems, covered with adv. roots and a palm-like crown of l. at the top. These show circinate vernation, &c., very well. The sori are marginal or on the under side of the l., naked or with a cup-shaped indusium; the sporangia are shortly stalked and have a complete excentric annulus. *Chief genera:* Cyathea, Alsophila, Dicksonia, Hemitelia.

Cyathium, an infl. reduced to look like a single fl., *Euphorbia*, *Anthostema*.

Cyathocalyx Champ. ex Hook. f. et Thoms. Anon. (4). 9 Indomal.

Cyathocephalum Nakai. Compositae (8). 2 Japan, Manchuria.

Cyathochaeta Nees. Cyperaceae (11). 4 Austr.

Cyathocline Cass. Compositae (3). 2 India.

Cyathodes Labill. (*Styphelia* p.p. *EP.*), Epacrid. 15 Austr. Polynes.

Cyathogyne Muell.-Arg. Euphorbiaceae (A. I. 1). 5 trop. Afr.

Cyathopsis Brongn. et Gris. (*Styphelia* p.p. *EP.*). Epacridaceae (3). 2 Indomal.

Cyathopus Stapf. Gramineae (8). 1 Indomal.

Cyathoselinum Benth. (*Seseli* p.p. *EP.*). Umbellif. (III. 5). 1 Dalmatia.

Cyathostelma Fourn. Asclepiadaceae (II. 1). 2 Brazil.

Cyathostemma Griff. Anonaceae (1). 7 Malaya.

Cyathula Lour. Amarantaceae (2). 10 Afr., As., S. Am.

Cybele, a flora.

Cybianthus Mart. Myrsinaceae (11). 35 trop. S. Am., W.I.

Cybistax Mart. Bignoniaceae (2). 3 S. Am. The l. of *C. Sprucei* K. Sch. are used as a blue dye, by boiling them with the cloth.

Cycadaceae (chiefly after Eichler). Gymnospermae. 9 genera with about 75 sp., the survivors of a group of plants which in past ages figured more largely in the flora of the earth, reaching their maximum about the end of the Triassic and beginning of the Jurassic period. They represent the lowest type of living seed-plants and in appearance and habit are like tree-ferns. The stem is usu. short and stout, only growing to any noteworthy height in Cycas itself, and is often tuberously swollen; it shows a secondary growth in thickness. It has a long primary tap root. In some sp. a sort of felt-work of roots is formed at the base of the stem, and a number of short lat. branches of these stand erect and may emerge from the soil (see *Nat. Pfl.*). The stem has usu. a crown of leaves, and its lower portion is covered with scales. There are, in all except a few sp. of Macrozamia, two sorts of l., foliage- and scale-l., borne spirally upon the stem, and alt. with one another, as a rule several circles of scales before each circle of foliage l., which they protect in the bud. The scales are really l. bases whose blades abort. The foliage l. are very char. They possess usu. a thickened, woody, ± sheathing base, which often persists after the fall of the rest of the l. There is a stout rachis or petiole, frequently thorny at the base, the thorns being 'metamorphosed' leaflets. Upon its upper side are two grooves, from which spring the leaflets, which may or may not be opp. to one another; there is usu. no term. leaflet. The leaflets may be entire or toothed and are usu. very rigid and leathery. Three types of nervature occur:

(1) midrib, no lateral nerves: Cycas.
(2) midrib and lateral nerves: Stangeria.
(3) numerous parallel or wavy, simple or forked nerves running longitudinally: the other genera.

The fls. are dioec. and usu. take the form of *cones*; these are term., and so the stem becomes a sympodium, except in Cycas and some spp. of Encephalartos, &c., where the stem 'grows through' the fl. or fls. The size of the cones varies considerably. Each consists essentially of a central axis bearing a number of fertile l. or sporophylls; occasionally the lowest l. are sterile as in Coniferae. In the ♂ cone, the l. (scales) are generally of a sort of nail shape (*cf.* Equisetum), and bear *sori* upon the lower side, each of 2—6 sporangia (pollen-sacs), arranged with the lines of dehiscence radiating from the common centre. In the ♀ cone the scale (cpl.) is of somewhat similar shape but bears as a rule only two sporangia (ovules), whose apices are directed towards the axis of the cone. Cycas (*q.v.*) has no proper cone, but the stem bears a whorl of cpls. in place of ordinary l. The ovule is large, orthotr. with one integument. The pollen is carried by the wind to the micropyle, where it germinates.

The ov. grows into a large seed; testa two-layered, the inner woody, the outer fleshy. Endopleura on the seed. Nucellus reduced to a thin cap on the top of the seed, the bulk of which is endosp., with straight embryo in centre. 2 cots., usu. united at the tips.

The C. are exclusively trop. and subtrop. Of the genera, 4, 7, 8, 9 are from Am., 3 and 6 Austr., 2 and 5 Afr., whilst Cycas is found in E. Ind., Austr., and the islands of Ind. and Pacif. Oceans.

Classification and Genera (after Eichler):

I. *Cycadeae* (cpls. with 8—4, rarely 2 ovules; stem growing through the ♀ fl.; leaflet with midrib only): 1. Cycas.

II. *Zamieae* (ovules 2; stem not growing through):

Pinna pinnately nerved	2. Stangeria.
,, longitudinally nerved	
Leaf bipinnate	3. Bowenia.
,, once pinnate	
Ov. on swelling of cpl.	4. Dioon.
,, sessile	
Scales peltate. Afr.	5. Encephalartos.
,, pointed. Austr.	6. Macrozamia.
,, peltate. Am.	7. Zamia.
,, two-horned	8. Ceratozamia.
,, in ♂ flat, in ♀ peltate.	9. Microcycas.

Cycas L. Cycadaceae. 16 trop. E. Ind., Austr., Polynes. For gen. char., &c., see fam. The ♀ pl. does not bear a cone, but a whorl of cpls. of a woolly brown appearance; in notches upon the margins of these are the naked ovules, usu. 4—8 in number. Stems reaching 50 ft. in some sp., usu. unbranched. The pith of *C. circinalis* L. (trop. As., sometimes called sago-palm) and *C. revoluta* Thunb. (Japan) yields a sago. Literature in Coulter and Chamberlain, *Morphology of Gymnosperms* (*q.v.*).

Cyclachaena Fresen. (*Iva EP.*). Compositae (5). 2 N. Am.

Cycladenia Benth. Apocynaceae (II. 1). 2 California.

Cyclamen (Tourn.) L. Primulaceae (2). 18 Eur. (mostly alpine), Medit. *C. europaeum* L. Brit. (sow-bread). There is a stout corm (*cf.* Colchicum) due to thickening of the hypocotyl. The P-lobes are bent back and the fl. is pend., with loose-pollen mechanism (*cf.* Acanthus, Erica). After fert. the stalk usu. coils up spirally, drawing the ripening fr. down to the soil (*cf.* Vallisneria); in *C. persicum* Sibth. et Sm. it bends over and forces the fr. into the ground (*cf.* Arachis). Cult. orn. fl.

Cyclanthaceae (*EP.*, *BH.*). Monocots. (Synanthae; Nudiflorae *BH.*). 6 gen., 45 sp. trop. Am.; they help to char. the flora of this region. Climbers, epiph., rhiz.-herbs, or small shrubs, of palm-like habit, with curious spadix infls. on which the ♂ and ♀ fls. alt. in various ways (see Carludovica and Cyclanthus). Fr. multiple, fleshy. Endosp. The fam. is nearly related to Palmae, Pandanaceae and Araceae. *Chief genera:* Carludovica, Cyclanthus.

Cyclanthera Schrad. Cucurbitaceae (5). 30 trop. Am. Sta. combined into a column as in section 4, but here the anther-loculi fused into 2 ring-shaped loculi running completely round the top of the column. *C. explodens* Naud. has explosive fr. (*cf.* Ecballium); the pericarp is extremely turgid on its inner surface, and the fr. dehisces into valves, each of which rolls back on itself with a jerk.

Cyclantheropsis Harms. (*Gerrardanthus* p.p.). Cucurb. (4). 1 trop. Afr.

Cyclanthus Poit. Cyclanthaceae. 4 trop. Am., W.I. The rhiz. bears large l., forked into two at the top. Infl. term. on a long stalk, as a large cylindrical spadix with big bracts at base, resembling a number of discs piled upon one another, with their edges sharpened to a thin rim. In some two ‖ spirals compose the spadix, each with a sharpened edge. In the former case every other disc bears ♂ fls., in the latter one of the spirals, the other being ♀. The ♂ fls. occupy a groove at the edge of the rim; each has 6 sta. and no P. The ♀ fls. are embedded in the disc; ovaries united into a long continuous chamber running all round the disc and containing numerous placentae. Ps united all round the disc; on their inner sides they bear stds. Fr. multiple, consisting of a number of seeds embedded in a general fleshy mass formed of ovaries and spadix. *Cf.* Carludovica.

Cyclea Arn. Menispermaceae. 20 trop. As.

Cyclic (fl.), with all members in whorls.

Cyclo- (Gr. pref.), circle; **-spermous**, with embryo coiled round endosp.

Cyclobothra D. Don in Sweet = Calochortus Pursh (Lili.).

Cyclocampe Steud. Cyperaceae (11). 3 Mauritius, New Cal. (?).

Cyclocarpa Afzel., emend. Urban. Leguminosae (III. 7). 1 W. Afr.

Cyclocheilon Oliv. (*Holmskioldia* Retz.). Verben. (4). 2 trop. Afr.

Cyclocotyla Stapf. Apocynaceae (I. 1). 1 Congo.

Cyclodium Presl. Polypodiaceae. 2 W. I., trop. S. Am.

Cyclolepis Gill. Compos. (12). 1 temp. S. Am. Char. in N. Patag.

Cyclolobium Benth. Leguminosae (III. 8). 4 Brazil, Guiana.

Cycloloma Moq. Chenopodiaceae (A). 1 Central N. Am.

Cyclonema Hochst. = Clerodendron L. p.p. (Verb.).

Cyclopeltis J. Sm. Polypodiaceae. 4 trop. E. As. and Am.

Cyclophorus Desv. (*Niphobolus* Kaulf.). Polypod. 90 trop. and subtrop.

Cyclophyllum Hook. f. Rubiaceae (II. 1). 1 New Caled.
Cyclopia Vent. Leguminosae (III. 2). 10 S. Afr. Exstip.
Cycloptychis E. Mey in Drège. Cruciferae (1). 2 S. Afr.
Cyclospathe O. F. Cook. Palmaceae (IV. 1). 1 Bahamas.
Cyclostemon Blume. Euphorbiaceae (A. I. 1). 50 trop. Afr., As.
Cycnia Griff. Rosaceae (inc. sed.). 1 Burma.
Cycniopsis Engl. (*Browallia* p.p.). Scrophular. (III. 2). 3 trop. Afr.
Cycnium E. Mey. Scrophulariaceae (III. 2). 15 trop. and S. Afr.
Cycnoches Lindl. Orchidaceae (II. 11). 8 trop. Am. Fl. like that of Catasetum in mechanism and polymorphism.
Cydista Miers (*Bignonia BH.*). Bignon. (1). 2 trop. Am.
Cydonia Tourn. ex Mill. (*Pyrus* Tourn. *BH.*). Rosaceae (II). 5 Eur., N. As. *C. vulgaris* Pers. (*P. Cydonia* L.) is the quince (ed. fr.); *C. japonica* Pers. (*P. japonica* Thunb.) cult. orn. wall shrub.
Cylicodaphne Nees = Litsea Lam. p.p. (Laur.).
Cylicodiscus Harms. (*Erythrophloeum* p.p.). Legum. (I. 5). 1 Gaboon.
Cylicomorpha Urb. (*Jacaratia* p.p.). Caricaceae. 2 trop. Afr.
Cylindria Lour. Inc. sed. 1 China.
Cylindrocarpa Regel. (*Phyteuma* p.p. *EP.*). Campan. (I. 1). 1 W. As.
Cylindrocline Cass. Compositae (4). 1 Mauritius.
Cylindrolepis Boeck. Cyperaceae (1). 1 S. Afr.
Cylindropsis Pierre (*Carpodinus* p.p.). Apocyn. (I. 1). 3 trop. Afr.
Cylindrosolen O. Ktze. = next.
Cylindrosolenium Lindau. Acanthaceae (IV. B). 1 Peru.
Cylista Ait. Leguminosae (III. 10). 4 palaeotrop.
Cymaria Benth. Labiatae (1). 3 Malaya, Burma.
Cymbalaria Medic. (*Linaria BH.*). Scroph. (II. 3). 9 Medit. W. Eur.
Cymbalariella Nappi (*Saxifraga* p.p.). Saxifr. (1). 12 N. temp. |*.
Cymbaria L. Scrophulariaceae (III. 3). 3 Russia, temp. As.
Cymbia Standley (*Krigia* p.p.). Compositae (13). 1 S.W. U.S.
Cymbidium Sw. Orchidaceae (II. 17). 40 Afr. to Austr. and Japan. Cult. orn. fl.
Cymbiform, boat-shaped.
Cymbocarpa Miers (*Gymnosiphon BH.*). Burmanniaceae. 1 trop. S. Am.
Cymbocarpum DC. Umbelliferae (III. 6). 4 W. As.
Cymbonotus Cass. (*Arctotis* p.p. *EP.*). Compositae (10). 1 temp. Austr.
Cymbopetalum Benth. Anonaceae (2). 5 Mexico, trop. Am.
Cymbopogon Spreng. (*Andropogon* p.p.). Gramineae (2). 60 trop. Char. of savannas of trop. Afr. Several yield essential aromatic oils, *e.g.* *C. Nardus* Rendle and others (Ceylon; citronella), *citratus* Stapf (Ceylon, S. India; lemon-grass), *C. Martini* Stapf (India; palma rosa or geranium oil), used in soaps, perfumery, &c. *Cf.* Stapf, under Andropogon.
Cymbosema Benth. Leguminosae (III. 10). 1 Brazil.
Cymbosepalum Baker. Leguminosae (II. 2). 1 Madag.
Cyme, an infl. in which each successive branch ends in a fl. after bearing one or more bracteoles, from whose axils the branching is continued. According to the number of branches borne on each

successive branch, the cyme is termed *mono-*, *di-* or *pleio-chasial*. Dich. cymes occur in Caryophyllaceae, Gentianaceae, &c., and very commonly tend to become monochasial in the later branchings. Monochasia are of four types; if each successive branch is upon the same side of the relatively main axis, and in the same plane, it is a *drepanium*, Juncaceae, &c.; if on the same side but at right angles, a *bostryx* or screw, Hemerocallis, Hypericum, &c.; if it fall alt. on one side and the other in the same plane, a *rhipidium*, Iris, &c.; if at right angles, a *cincinnus*, Boraginaceae, Helianthemum, Hydrophyllaceae, Pentaphragma, Tradescantia, &c.; **cymose**, of cyme nature, *Hydrangea*.

Cymelonema Presl (*Urophyllum* p.p. *EP.*). Rubi. (I. 7). 1 Phil. Is.

Cyminosma Gaertn. = Acronychia Forst. (Rut.).

Cymodocea Kon. Potamogetonaceae. 7 trop. and subtrop.

Cymophora Robinson. Compositae (5). 1 Mexico.

Cymophyllus Mackenzie (*Carex* p.p.). Cyperaceae (III). 1 S.E. U.S.

Cymopterus Rafin. Umbelliferae (III. 5). 25 W. N. Am.

Cynanchum L. (incl. *Vincetoxicum* Rupp.). Asclepiadaceae (II. 1). 120 trop. and temp., many twiners, and xero. with fleshy stems and reduced l.; fls. fert. by carrion-flies which get the pollinia attached to their proboscides.

Cynapium Nutt. = Ligusticum L. (Umbell.).

Cynara Vaill. ex L. Compositae (11). 11 Medit. *C. Scolymus* L. is the true artichoke (*cf.* Helianthus); young fl.-heads enclosed in the invol. bracts, a valuable pot-herb. The blanched summer growth (chards) is also ed. *C. Cardunculus* L. is the cardoon, whose l. are blanched and eaten like celery; it has spread over great areas on the Pampas, where it was introduced.

Cynaropsis O. Ktze. (*Cynara* p.p.). Compositae (inc. sed.). 1 Canaries.

Cyno- (Gr. pref.), dog-.

Cynocrambaceae (*Thelygonaceae*) (*EP. Urticaceae* p.p. *BH.*). Dicots. (Archichl. Centrospermae). One genus, Cynocrambe (*q.v.*), which is so anomalous that it has been placed near to Urticaceae (united *BH.*), Phytolaccaceae (united by Warming), Chenopodiaceae, Begoniaceae, Santalaceae, Monimiaceae, &c. (see *Nat. Pfl.*).

Cynocrambe Tourn. ex Adans. (*Thelygonum* L.). Cynocrambaceae (only gen.). 2 Canaries, Medit., C. As. Herbs with fleshy stip. l., the basal opp. Fls. unisex., the ♂ opp. the l., with P 2—5, A 10—30; ♀ in 3-fld. axillary cymes, with P 3—4; $\underline{G}$ 1, style basal, ov. 1. Drupe. Endosp.

Cynoctonum E. Mey. = Vincetoxicum Moench. (*BH.*) = Cynanchum L.

Cynodon Rich. Gramineae (11). 3 Austr., 1 *C. Dactylon* Pers. (dog's-tooth or Bermuda grass), cosmop. (incl. Brit.). It grows with creeping stems on sandy soil and is used for binding dunes; useful pasture. Spikes digitate, spikelets 1-fld.

Cynoglossum (Tourn.) L. Boraginaceae (IV. 1). 60 temp. and subtrop. 2 Brit., incl. *C. officinale* (hound's tongue). Formerly offic. Fr. hooked.

Cynomarathrum Nutt. (*Peucedanum* p.p.). Umbell. (III. 6). 5 N. Am.

Cynometra L. Leguminosae (II. 2). 40 trop. *C. cauliflora* L. is a good example of stem-fruiting or cauliflory.

Cynomoriaceae (*EP.*; *Balanophoraceae* p.p. *BH*). Dicots. (Archichl. Myrtiflorae). Only genus Cynomorium, *q.v.*

Cynomorium Mich. ex. L. Cynomoriaceae. 1 Medit., *C. coccineum* L. Rhiz. brownish, total parasitic herbs with polygamous fls. ☿ fl. with epig. sta. Ovule 1, pend.

Cynorchis Thou. (*Cynosorchis*). Orchid. (II. 1). 15 trop. Afr., Madag.

Cynosciadium DC. Umbelliferae (III. 5). 3 N. Am.

Cynosurus L. Gramineae (10). 5 Old World temp., 2 Brit. (dog's-tail grass), one, *C. cristatus* L., a valuable pasture and fodder.

Cypella Herb. Iridaceae (II. 1). 5 temp. S. Am. One sp. unfolds its fls. in great numbers at definite times.

Cypellium Desv. Inc. sed. 1 Guiana.

Cyperaceae (*EP.*, *BH.*). Monocots. (Glumiflorae; Glumaceae *BH.*). 85 gen., 2600 sp., cosmop., chiefly marsh-pl. Grass-like pl. (sedges), mostly perenn. with creeping sympodial rhiz. The new shoot of each year is adnate, for an internode or more, to the parent shoot, so that the branching seems at first sight extra-axillary. The aerial shoot is usu. grass-like, but the stem solid and angular with 3 ranks of l. The l. is sheathing at the base, but the sheath is entire, not split as in a grass. The unit of infl. is again a spikelet; the total infl. may be a spike or panicle as in grasses. In many sedges the spikelet is cymose—a sympodium—and should perhaps be termed a pseudo-spikelet. The fl. is borne in the axil of a glume and may be ☿ or unisexual; it is usu. naked but may have a P of 6 (or ∞) small scales or hairs; A 3, G̲ (3) or (2), 1-loc., with long feathery (anemoph.) stigmas; ovule 1, basal, anatr. In Carex, &c., the ♀ fl. is borne in the axil of a second glume (the *utricle*) which closely enwraps it (in the figure it is shown diagrammatically). The fls. are wind-pollinated. Fr. an achene, the testa not adhering to the pericarp. The sedges are of little economic value; see Cyperus.

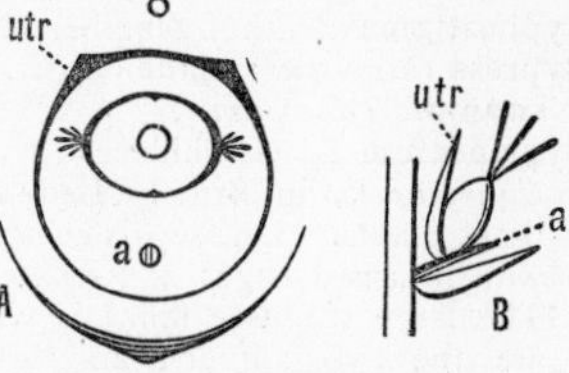

Diagrams of Carex (after Eichler). A, diagram of a 2-carpelled ♀ flr.; B, side view of ♀ flr. a. = axis of spikelet; utr. = utricle.

Classification and chief genera (after Engler):

I. *SCIRPOIDEAE* (fls. ☿ in many-fld. spikelets, or single ♂ ♀ with or without trichomes): Cyperus, Eriophorum, Scirpus, Eleocharis, Fimbristylis.

II. *RHYNCHOSPOROIDEAE* (fls. ☿ or ♂ ♀ with or without trichomes in few-fld. spike-like cymes aggregated into spikes or heads): Schoenus, Cladium, Rhynchospora, Mapania, Scleria.

III. *CARICOIDEAE* (fls. ♂ ♀, naked, usu. in many-fld. spikes; ♀ enclosed by utricle): Carex, Uncinia.

Cyperorchis Blume. Orchidaceae (II. 17). 3 Himal. Cult. orn. fls.

Cyperus L. (incl. *Mariscus* Gaertn.). Cyperaceae (I). 400 trop. and warm temp. (2 Brit.). Herbs with sympodial rhiz. and leafless or leafy shoots above ground. Infl. umbel- or head-like. *C. Papyrus* L. (paper-reed) is a river-side plant with shoots 3—12 feet high. From the stems was made the ancient writing paper, papyrus. The stem was split into thin strips, which were pressed together while still wet. The rhiz. is ed., and also the root-tubers of several sp.; the stems (whole or split) of many are used for basket making, &c.

Cyphel, *Arenaria Cherleria* Hook.

Cyphia Berg. Campanulaceae (II). 25 Afr. [Cyphiaceae, Warming.]

Cyphocarpa Lopriore. Amarantaceae (2). 10 trop. and S. Afr.

Cyphocarpus Miers. Campanulaceae (II). 1 Chili.

Cyphochilus Schlechter. Orchidaceae (II. *a*. III.). 6 New Guinea.

Cyphochlaena Hackel. Gramineae (4). 1 Madag.

Cyphokentia Brongn. Palmae (IV. 1). 10 New Caled.

Cypholepis Chiov. (*Eragrostis* p.p.). Gramin. (10). 1 Arabia.

Cypholophus Wedd. Urticaceae (3). 10 Malaya, Polynesia.

Cyphomandra Mart. ex Sendtn. Solanaceae (2). 30 S. Am. *C. betacea* Sendt. (tree tomato) cult. ed. fr.

Cyphomeris Standley (*Lindenia* p.p.). Nyctagin. 2 Mexico.

Cyphophoenix H. Wendl. ex Benth. et Hook. f. Palmae (IV. 1). 2 New Cal.

Cyphosperma H. Wendl. (*Cyphokentia*). Palmaceae (IV. 1). 2 New Cal.

Cyphostigma Benth. Zingiberaceae (I). 15 Ceylon, Malaya.

Cypress *Cupressus*; **-pine** (Austr.), *Callitris*; **Sitka-**, *Chamaecyparis*; **swamp-**, *Taxodium*.

Cypripedium L. Orchidaceae (I. 2). 30 N. temp. and subtrop. (*C. Calceolus* L. in Brit.). Lady's-slipper orchids. Terrestrial acranthous plants. Lat. sepals completely united. Labellum slipper-like with inturned edge; at its base is the column, partly enclosed in it. The large std. (see fam.) is visible outside the labellum; under it are the two anthers, and lower down the flat stigma. Pollen glutinous not united into pollinia. Insects (mostly bees) visiting the fl. get inside the labellum and cannot get out by the way they entered, so have to pass out by the openings at the base, in doing which they brush against the stigma and then the anthers.

Cypselea Turp. Aizoaceae (II). 1 W. Indies.

Cypselocarpus F. Muell. Chenopodiaceae (inc. sed.). 1 W. Austr.

Cypselodontia DC. Compositae (4). 1 S. Afr.

Cyrilla Garden. Cyrillaceae. 3 warm Am., marsh plants with evergr. l., and fls. in racemes below them.

Cyrillaceae (*EP.*, *BH.*). Dicots. (Archichl. Sapindales; Olacales *BH.*). 3 gen., 6 sp. Am. Evergr. shrubs with alt., exstip. l. and racemes of ☿, reg. flrs. K 5, imbr., persistent; C 5 or (5), imbr.; A 5 + 5 or 5, with intr. anthers; $\underline{G}$ (5—2) multi-loc. with 1 (rarely 2—4) pend. anatr. ov. in each loc.; raphe dorsal, micropyle facing upwards and inwards. Embryo straight, in endosp. *Genera:* Cliftonia, Costaea, Cyrilla.

Cyrtandra Forst. Gesneriaceae (1). 250 Malaya, China, Polynesia.

Cyrtandraceae = Gesneriaceae.

Cyrtandromoea Zoll. Gesneriaceae (I). 10 Malay Archipelago.
Cyrtandropsis Lauterb. Gesneriaceae (I). 1 New Guinea.
Cyrtanthera Nees = Jacobinia Moric. (Acanth.).
Cyrtanthus Ait. Amaryllid. (I). 16 S. and trop. Afr. Cult. orn. fl.
Cyrtocarpa H.B. et K. Anacardiaceae (2). 1 Mexico.
Cyrtoceras Benn. = Hoya R. Br. p.p. (Asclep.).
Cyrtochilum H.B. et K. (Oncidium Sw. p.p.). Orchid. (II. 19). 115 [Andes.
Cyrtodeira Hanst. = Episcia Mart. p.p. (Gesner.).
Cyrtogonone Prain. Euphorbiaceae (A. II. 2). 1 trop. Afr.
Cyrtomium Presl (*Polystichum* p.p.). Polypodiaceae. 4 E. As.
Cyrtonora Zipp. Inc. sed. 1 New Guinea.
Cyrtopera Lindl. = Eulophia R. Br. (Orchid.).
Cyrtopodium R. Br. Orchidaceae (II. 10). 5 trop. Am. Cult. orn. fl.
Cyrtorchis Schlechter. Orchidaceae (II. 20). 15 trop. Afr.
Cyrtosia Blume (*Galeola BH.*). Orchidaceae (II. 2). 4 S.E. As.
Cyrtosperma Griff. Araceae (IV). 11 trop. The rhiz. of *C. edule* Schott is ed. when cooked (cult. in Polynes.).
Cyrtostachys Blume. Palmaceae (IV. 1). 5 Malaya. Ornamental.
Cyrtostylis R. Br. Orchidaceae (II. 2). 3 Austr., N. Z.
Cyrtoxiphus Harms (*Cylicodiscus*). Legum. (I. 5). 1 trop. Afr.
Cystacanthus T. Anders. Acanthaceae (IV. B). 4 Further India.
Cystochilum Barb. Rodr. (*Cranichis EP.*). Orchid. (II. 3). 1 Brazil.
Cystolith, a concretion in cells of Urticaceae, &c., showing as a lighter coloured dot when held up to the light.
Cystopteris Bernh. Polypodiaceae. 15 temp. and subtrop. 2 Brit., incl. *C. fragilis* Bernh. (bladder-fern). In *C. bulbifera* Bernh. adv. buds on petioles give veg. repr.
Cystopus Blume = Odontochilus Blume (Orchid.).
Cystorchis Blume. Orchidaceae (II. 2). 8 Malay Archipelago.
Cystostemma Fourn. Asclepiadaceae (II. 1). 1 S. Brazil.
Cystostemon Balf. f. Boraginaceae (IV. 4). 1 Socotra.
Cytherea Salisb. = Calypso Salisb. (Orchid.).
Cytinaceae (*BH.*) = Rafflesiaceae + Hydnoraceae. Multiovulatae Terrestres.
Cytinus L. Rafflesiaceae. 4 Afr., Medit.
Cytisopsis Jaub. et Spach. Leguminosae (III. 5). 1. W. As.
Cytisus L. (incl. *Sarothamnus* Wimm., excl. *Laburnum* L.). Leguminosae (III. 3). 40 Eur., Medit. *C.* (*S.*) *scoparius* Link, the broom, Brit. The l. in this sp. are reduced to scales and assim. is chiefly performed by the stems. The fl. has an explosive mech., in general like Genista (*q.v.*), but different in detail. The style is very long and there are two lengths of sta., so that pollen is shed near the tip of the keel (where also is the stigma) and also about half way along its upper side. When an insect alights on the fl. (there is no honey), the keel begins to split from the base towards the tip, and presently the pollen of the short sta. is shot out upon the lower surface of the visitor; immediately afterwards, the split having reached the tip, the other pollen and the style spring violently out and strike the insect on the back. As the stigma touches first there is thus a chance of a cross, if the insect bear any pollen. Afterwards the style bends right round and the stigma occupies a position just above the short sta.,

so that another chance of cross-fert. is afforded if other insects visit the fl. (in most exploding fls. there is only the one chance). Other sp. have simple mechanisms like Trifolium. The fr. explodes by a twisting of the valves.

C. Adami Poit is a curious graft-hybrid between *C. purpureus* Scop. and *Laburnum vulgare*. The latter was used as the stock; the shoots above the graft exhibit hybrid characters (see Darwin, *Variation under Domest.* ch. XI). Recently this matter of *chimeras* (half-and-half shoots, &c.) and graft-hybrids has been much investigated. See review in *Bot. Gazette*, 51, 1911, p. 147.

Daboecia D. Don (*Dabeocia*). Ericaceae (I. 3). 1 Atl. Eur. (incl. Ireland), *D. polifolia* D. Don (St. Dabeoc's heath). Cult. orn. fl.

Dacrydium Soland. Coniferae (Taxac. 4; see C. for gen. char.). 16 Malaya, N.Z., Tasm., S. Am. Most are dioecious. Fruit scales 1 or 2 or more. Seed arillate. *D. Franklinii* Hook. f. (Huon pine; Tasm.) and *D. cupressinum* Soland. (red pine; N.Z.) good timber.

Dacryodes Vahl. Burseraceae. 1 W. Indies.

Dactylaena Schrad. Capparidaceae (V). 3 Brazil.

Dactylanthera Welw. nomen. Guttiferae.

Dactylanthus Hook. f. Balanophoraceae. 1 New Zealand.

Dactyliandra Hook. f. Cucurbitaceae (2). 1 trop. W. Afr.

Dactylis L. Gramineae (10). 1 Eur. (incl. Brit.), Medit., As., *D. glomerata* L., cock's-foot, a valuable pasture grass.

Dactylocladus Oliv. Melastomaceae (III). 1 Borneo.

Dactyloctenium Willd. (*Eleusine* p.p. *BH.*). Gram. (11). 5 warm.

Dactyloid, finger-like.

Dactyloides Nieuwland (*Saxifraga* p.p.). Saxifr. (I). 2 N. Am.

Dactylopetalum Benth. Rhizophoraceae. 8 trop. Afr., Madag.

Dactylophyllum Spach = Gilia Ruiz et Pav. p.p. (Polemon.).

Dactylorhynchus Schlechter. Orchidaceae (II. 16). 1 New Guinea.

Dactylostalix Reichb. f. (*Cremastra BH.*). Orchid. (II. 10). 1 Japan.

Dactylostelma Schlechter. Asclepiadaceae (II. 1). 1 Bolivia.

Dactylostemon Klotzsch = Actinostemon Klotzsch p.p. (Euph.).

Dadap, *Erythrina*.

Dadia Vell. Compositae (inc. sed.). 1 Brazil.

Daedalacanthus T. Anders. (*Eranthemum* p.p.). Acanth. (IV. A). 14 Indomal.

Daemia R. Br. Asclepiadaceae (II. 1). 4 palaetrop.

Daemonorops Blume ex Schult. f. (*Calamus* p.p. *EP.*). Palmaceae (III. 2). 75 Indomal.

Daffodil, *Narcissus Pseudo-narcissus* L.

Dagger-plant (W. I.), *Yucca*.

Dahlia Cav. Compositae (5). 10 Mexico. Perenn. herbs with tuberous roots. Many vars. of *D. variabilis* Desf. and other sp. are cult. orn. fl.; the double forms have the disc florets ligulate as well as the ray (*cf.* Chrysanthemum). (Hemsley in *Gard. Chron.* 1879.)

Dahlstedtia Malme (*Camptosema* p.p.). Legum. (III. 10). 1 Brazil.

Daikon, see Radish.

Dais Royen ex L. Thymelaeaceae. 2 Natal, Madag. Cult. orn.

Daisy, *Bellis perennis* L.; **Australian-**, *Vittadinia*; **bush-**, *Olearia*,

Haastia; **dog-**, *Chrysanthemum Leucanthemum* L.; **globe-**, *Globularia*; **Michaelmas-**, *Aster*; **ox-eye-**=dog; **-tree**, *Montanoa*.

Dal, pigeon-pea, *Cajanus indicus* Spreng.

Dalbergia L. f. Legum. (III. 8). 120 warm. Many lianas. *D. variabilis* Vog., a shrub with pend. twigs in the open, becomes a liana in forest, with short lat. shoots sensitive to contact. Fr. winged, indeh. Many yield valuable wood, *e.g. D. nigra* Allem. (rosewood, Brz.) and other Am. spp.; *D. melanoxylon* Guill. et Perr. (Afr. blackwood, W. trop. Afr.); *D. latifolia* Roxb. (blackwood or E. Indian rosewood, India), and *D. Sissoo* Roxb. (shisham, sissoo, India).

Dalea L. Legum. (III. 6). 150 Am. Ov. collat. Claws of 4 lower pets. united to A.

Dalechampia Plum. ex L. Euphorb. (A. II. 2). 60 warm. *D. Roezliana* Müll.-Arg. (cult. orn. infl.) has a complex infl. (*cf.* diagram), enclosed in 2 large pink or white outer br. (the big brackets). Above these on axis is a smaller br. (small bracket), with 3-fld. cyme of ♀ fls. (F) in axil. Above is ♂ part of infl., starting with 4 br. (asterisks); above these, ant., are 9—14 ♂ fls., and post. a yellow cushion of rudimentary ♂ fls., secreting resin in some sp.

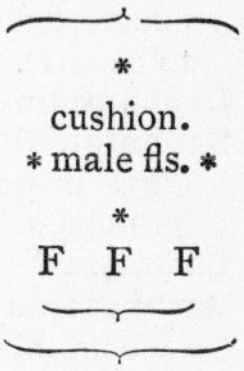

*
cushion.
* male fls. *
*
F F F

Dalembertia Baill. Euphorb. (A. II. 7). 4 Mex. A 1 enclosed in K 1.

Dalenia Korth. Melastom. (I). 1 Borneo. K-tube with deciduous cap.

Dalhousiea R. Grah. Legum. (III. 1). 2 palaeotrop.

Dalibarda L.=Rubus Tourn. p.p. (Ros.).

Dallachya F. Muell. Rhamn. 1 E. Austr., Polyn. No endosp.

Dalmatian insect powder, *Chrysanthemum cinerariaefolium* Vis.

Dalucum Adans. (*Melica* p.p.). Gramin. (10). 6 N. temp.

Dalzellia Wight=Terniola Tul. (*BH.*)=Lawia Tul. (Trist.).

Damapana Adans.=Smithia Ait. (Legum.).

Damask rose, *Rosa damascena* Mill.

Damasonium Mill. Alism. 4 Eur., Medit., Calif., Austr.

Damasonium Schreb.=Ottelia Pers. (Hydrochar.).

Dame's violet, rocket, *Hesperis matronalis* L.

Dammar, a hard resin, *Agathis*, *Dipterocarpaceae*, *Shorea*; **black-**, *Canarium*; **white-**, *Vateria*.

Dammara Gaertn.=Protium Burm. f. (Burser.).

Dammara (Rumph.) Lam.=Agathis Salisb. (Conif.).

Dammaropsis Warb. Mor. (II). 1 New Guinea.

Dammera K. Schum. et Lauterb. Palm. (I. 2). 2 New Guinea.

Damnacanthus Gaertn. f. Rubi. (II. 9). 4 E. As. Thorny shrubs.

Dampiera R. Br. Gooden. 60 Austr. K small or 0. Syngenesious.

Damrongia Kerr ex Craib. Gesner. (I). 1 Siam.

Damson, *Prunus insititia* L., var.; **bitter-** (W.I.), *Simaruba amara* Aubl.; **-plum** (W.I.), *Chrysophyllum*.

Danaa All.=Physospermum Cusson. (Umbell.).

Danae Medic. Lili. (VII). 1 W. As. Erect shrub; phylloclades. (P).

Danaea Sm. Maratt. (III). 30 Am. Stem branched (rare in M.). Synangia very long, sometimes from midrib to margin of l., opening by term. pore.

Danais Comm. ex Vent. Rubi. (I. 5). 20 Madag., Masc.

Dancing girls, *Mantisia saltatoria* Sims.
Dandelion, *Taraxacum officinale* Weber.
Dangleberry (Am.), *Gaylussacia*.
Danielia Mello. Bignoniaceae (I). 1 Brazil.
Daniella J. J. Benn. Leguminosae (II. 3). 8 trop. W. Afr.
Danthonia DC. Gramineae (9). 150 trop. and temp., esp. S. Afr.
Dapania Korth. Oxalidaceae. 2 Malaya.
Daphnales (*BH.*). The 5th series of Monochlamydeae.
Daphnandra Benth. Monimiaceae. 4 Austr.
Daphne Tourn. ex L. Thymelaeaceae. 40 Eur., temp. and subtrop. As.; *D. Mezereum* L. (mezereon) and *D. Laureola* L. (spurge-laurel) Brit. Honey is secreted by the base of the ovary, and the depth of the tube preserves it for long-tongued insects; the fl. belongs to class F. Several cult. orn. fl. Bark used for paper in India.
Daphnidium Nees = Lindera Thunb. p.p. (Laur.).
Daphniphyllum Blume. Euphorbiaceae (A. I. 3). 25 Indomal., E. As. Often made into a separate family.
Daphnopsis Mart. et Zucc. Thymelaeaceae. 25 S. Am., Mex., W. I.
Darlingia F. Muell. Proteaceae (II). 1 Queensland.
Darlingtonia Torr. Sarraceniaceae. 1 Calif., a pitcher pl. like Sarracenia, but top of tube bent over and a fish-tail-shaped flap in front.
Darnel grass, *Lolium temulentum* L.
Dartus Lour. Solanaceae (inc. sed.). 1 E. As.
Darwinia Rudge. Myrtaceae (II. 2). 25 Austr. Heath-like shrubs.
Dasheen, tuberous-rooted taro, *Colocasia antiquorum* Schott.
Dasiogyna Rafin. Inc. sed. 1 N. Am.
Dasistoma Rafin. = Gerardia L. (Scroph.).
Dasus Lour. Inc. sed. 1 Cochin-china.
Dasycephala Benth. et Hook. f. (*Diodia* L. *EP.*). Rubiaceae (II. 10). 5 trop. Am.
Dasycoleum Turcz. (*Chisocheton EP.*). Meliac. (III). 4 Mal. Arch.
Dasylepis Oliv. Flacourtiaceae (I). 2 W. Afr.
Dasylirion Zucc. Liliaceae (VI). 10 Texas, Mex. Aloe-like, xero.; stems woody, often tuberous; hard l. Fls. dioec., in gigantic infl. Cf. *Cordyline*.
Dasyloma DC. = Oenanthe Tourn. p.p. (Umbell.)
Dasymaschalon Hook. f. et Thoms. Anon. (4). 8 trop. As.
Dasynema Schott = Sloanea L. (Elaeocarp.).
Dasypoa Pilger (*Poa* p.p. *EP.*). Gramineae (10). 1 Peru.
Dasypogon R. Br. Liliaceae (III.) (Junc. *BH.*). 2 S.W. Austr.
Dasyspermum Neck. Inc. sed. Farrago Umbelliferarum.
Dasysphaera Volkens. Amarantaceae (2). 2 E. Afr.
Dasystachys Baker (*Chlorophytum* p.p. *EP.*). Lili. (III). 15 trop. Afr.
Dasystephana Adans. = Gentiana Tourn. p.p. (Gent.).
Date, *Phoenix dactylifera* L.; **-plum**, *Diospyros Lotus* L., &c.
Datisca L. Datiscaceae. 2 N. Am., W. As.
Datiscaceae (*EP.*, *BH.*). Dicots. (Archichl. Parietales; Passiflorales *BH.*). 3 gen. 5 sp., trop. and temp. Trees or herbs with exstip. l. and racemes or spikes of reg., usu. dioec., sometimes apet. fls. ♂ fl.: K 3—9, free or united; C 4—9 or 0; A 4—9 or ∞; ♀: K 3—8,

united to one another and to the ovary; C o; $\overline{G}$ (3—8), with free styles; 1-loc. with parietal plac. and ∞ anatr. ov. Caps. Little endosp. *Genera:* Datisca, Tetrameles, Octomeles. Affinities doubtful (see *Nat. Pfl.*); probably allied to Begoniaceae.

Datura L. Solanaceae (3). 15 trop. and warm temp. *D. Stramonium* L. (thorn-apple; escape in Brit.) has a 4-loc. ov. (see fam.) giving a 4-valved caps. covered with spines. The l. and seeds are medic. Some cult. orn. fl.

Daubenya Lindl. Liliaceae (v). 3 S. Afr.

Daucophyllum Rydberg. Umbelliferae (III. 5). 2 Rockies.

Daucus (Tourn.) L. Umbelliferae (III. 8). 60 Eur., As., Afr., Am. *D. Carota* L. (carrot) Brit., biennial with thickened root. The cult. form has much more fleshy roots than the wild. In the centre of the umbel is usu. a red term. fl. After fert. the peduncles all bend inwards until the frs. are ripe and then spread out again allowing the burred mericarps to adhere to animals.

Davallia Sm. Polypodiaceae. 80 mostly trop. Sori marginal.

Daveaua Willk. Compositae (7). 1 Portugal.

Davidia Baill. Nyssaceae. 1 Tibet, China.

Davidsonia F. Muell. Cunoniaceae. 1 N.E. Austr. L. alt.

David's root (W. I.), *Chiococca.*

Daviesia Sm. Leguminosae (III. 2). 55 Austr.

Davilla Vand. Dillen. 35 trop. Am., W.I. The two inner sepals are larger; after fert. they grow woody or leathery and enclose the fr.

Davya DC. = Meriania Sw. p.p. (Melast.).

Day-flower (Am.), *Commelina*; **-lily** (Am.), *Hemerocallis.*

Deadly dwale (W. I.), *Acnistus*; **-nightshade,** *Atropa Belladonna* L.

Dead-finish (Austr.), *Acacia tetragonophylla* F. Muell.; **-nettle,** *Lamium.*

Deal, *Pinus sylvestris* L., &c.

Dealbate, whitened.

Deanea Coulter et Rose. Umbelliferae (III. 6). 8 Mexico.

Debesia O. Ktze. (*Acrospira*). Liliaceae (III). 1 trop. Afr.

Debregeasia Gaud. Urticaceae (3). 5 Abyss., S. and E. As. *D. edulis* Wedd. (janatsi; Japan) ed. fr., useful fibre (*cf.* Boehmeria).

Deca- (Gr. pref.), **decem** (Lat.), ten; **-androus,** with 10 sta.

Decabelone Decne. Asclepiadaceae (II. 3). 3 S. Afr.

Decaceras Haw. (*Anisotoma BH.*). Asclepiadaceae (II. 3). 2 S. Afr.

Decachaeta DC. Compositae (2). 1 Mexico.

Decadia Lour. Inc. sed. 1 Cochin-China.

Decagonocarpus Engl. Rutaceae (1). 1 Amazon valley.

Decaisnea Hook. f. et Thoms. Lardizabalaceae. 1 Himal., China, *D. insignis* H. f. et T., with ed. fr. (Hooker's *Himal. Journ.*, XXV.).

Decalepis Boeck. (*Boeckeleria* Durand). Cyper. (II). 1 S. Afr.

Decalepis Wight et Arn. Asclepiadaceae (1). 1 Dekkan.

Decaloba M. Roem. = Passiflora L. p.p. (Passifl.).

Decanema Decne. Asclepiadaceae (II. 1). 2 Madagascar.

Decanemopsis Costantin et Galland. Asclep. (II. 1). 1 Madag.

Decaneurum DC. = Centratherum Cass. (Compos.).

Decaptera Turcz. Cruciferae (1). 1 Chili.

Decaschistia Wight et Arn. Malvaceae (4). 8 trop. As.

Decaspermum Forst. Myrtaceae (1). 12 Indomal.

Decaspora R. Br. = Trochocarpa R. Br. (Epacrid.).
Decastelma Schlechter. Asclepiadaceae (II. 1). 1 W. Indies.
Decatoca F. Muell. Epacridaceae (3). 1 New Guinea.
Decatropis Hook. f. Rutaceae (I). 1 S. Mexico.
Decazesia F. Muell. Compositae (4). 1 W. Austr.
Deciduous (l.), falling in autumn, or at the beginning of the dry season; (perianth), falling after fertilisation.
Decipiens (Lat.), deceiving.
Deckenia H. Wendl. (*Acanthophoenix BH.*). Palmae (IV. 1). 1 Seychelles.
Deckera Sch.-Bip. = Picris L. p.p. (Comp.).
Declieuxia H. B. et K. Rubiaceae (II. 5). 33 trop. S. Am., W. I.
Declinate, bent downwards or forwards.
Decodon J. F. Gmel. (*Nesaea BH.*). Lythraceae. 1 N. Am.
Decompound, several times divided.
Decumaria L. Saxifragaceae (III). 2 China, S.E. U.S.
Decumbent (stem), bending upwards from prostrate base.
Decurrent (l.), continued by wing on stem, as in thistles.
Decussate (l.), each pair of opp. l. ⊥ to the next pair.
Dedea Baill. Saxifragaceae (V). 2 New Caledonia.
Dedoublement, branching, *Polygonaceae*.
Deer-berry (Am.), *Vaccinium stamineum* L.; **-grass** (Am.), *Rhexia*.
Deeringia R. Br. Amarantaceae (I). 6 Indomal., Madag.
Definite growth (stem), when the buds grow rapidly to their full elongation, and stop, *Aesculus*, *Pinus*, &c.; (infl.), when the branches each in turn term. in a fl. (cymes, *q.v.*).
Deflersia Schweinf. ex Penzig. Euphorb. (inc. sed.). 1 Erythrea.
Deflexed, bent sharply outwards.
Defoliation, leaf-casting.
Degenerate fl., one which has gone back to an earlier type.
Degenia Hayek. (*Lesquerella* p.p.). Crucif. (4). 1 Croatia.
Deguelia Aubl. (*Derris* Lour. *BH.*). Legum. (III. 8). 40 trop.
Dehaasia Blume. Lauraceae (II). 10 Malay Archipelago.
Deherainia Decne. Theophrastaceae. 2 Mex., W. I., incl. *D. smaragdina* Decne. with large green fls. (coloured by chlorophyll).
Dehiscence, mode of opening; *cf.* Fruit, Stamen.
Deianira Cham. et Schlecht. Gentianaceae (I). 5 Brazil.
Deidamia Nor. ex Thou. Passifloraceae. 6 Madagascar.
Deinacanthon Mez (*Rhodostachys* Phil.). Bromel. (4). 1 Argentina.
Deinandra Greene = Hemizonia DC. (Comp.).
Deinanthe Maxim. Saxifragaceae (III). 1 Japan.
Deinbollia Schum. et Thonn. Sapindaceae (I). 15 warm Afr., Madag.
Dekindtia Gilg. Oleaceae. 1 trop. Afr.
Dekinia Mart. et Gal. (*Lepechinia* p.p. *E.P.*). Labiat. (VI). 1 Mex.
Delamerea Sp. Moore. Compositae (4). 1 Brit. E. Afr.
Delaportea Thorel et Gagnep. Leguminosae (I. 1). 1 Laos.
Delarbrea Vieill. Araliaceae (2). 3 New Caled., New Guinea.
Delavaya Franch. Sapindaceae (II). 1 Yunnan.
Delima L. = Tetracera L. p.p. (Dillen.).
Deliquescent (stem), breaking up into branches.

Delissea Gaudich. Campanulaceae (III). 7 Sandwich Islands.
Delognaea Cogn. Cucurbitaceae (3). 1 Madagascar.
Delopyrum Small (*Polygonella* p.p.). Polygon. (II. 2). 2 U. S.
Delostoma D. Don. Bignoniaceae (2). 5 trop. Andes.
Delpechia Montr. Inc. sed. 2 New Caled.
Delphinium Tourn. ex L. Ranunculaceae (2). 175 N. temp. *D. Ajacis* L. (larkspur) Brit. Several cult. orn. fl. Fls. ·|· in racemes; the post. sepal is drawn out into a spur containing the spurs of the two post. petals, in which the honey is secreted. (*Cf.* with Aconitum, which is far more frequently robbed by humble-bees.) The fl. is protandr. with movement of sta., fert. by humble-bees. The open fl. projects horiz., but subsequently the stalk bends up and the follicles stand erect so that the seeds can only escape if shaken, *e.g.* by strong wind (censer-mechanism).
Delphyodon K. Schum. Apocynaceae (II. 1). 1 New Guinea.
Delpinoa H. Ross (*Agave* p.p. *EP.*). Amaryll. (II). 1 N. Am.
Delpinoella Spegazz. Cruciferae (inc. sed.). 1 Patagonia.
Delpinophytum Spegazz. Cruciferae (2). 1 Patagonia.
Delpya Pierre ex Bonati (*Vandellia* p.p.). Scrophulariaceae (II. 6). 1 Cochin-China.
Delpydora Pierre. Sapotaceae (1). 1 trop. Afr.
Deltoid, the shape of an equilateral triangle.
Dematophyllum Griseb. Zygophyllaceae (?). 1 Argentina.
Demazeria Dum. Gramineae (10). 4 Medit., S. Afr. *D.* (*Brizopyrum*) *sicula* Dum. is a cult. ornam. grass.
Demersus (Lat.), sub-aqueous.
Demeusia De Wild. et Durand. Amaryllidaceae (1). 1 Congo.
Demidium DC. (*Amphidoxa EP.*). Compositae (4). 1 Madagascar.
Democrita Vell. Inc. sed. 1 Brazil.
Dendrobangia Rusby. Icacinaceae. 1 Bolivia.
Dendrobium Sw. Orchidaceae (II. 15). 750 trop. As., Japan, Austr., Polynes. Epiphytes; cult. orn. fl. For floral mechanism see Darwin's *Orchids*, p. 138.
Dendrocalamus Nees. Gramineae (13). 12 Indomal., China. *D. giganteus* Munro (the giant bamboo), the largest known bamboo (*cf.* bamboos), grows with great rapidity (see Lock in *Ann. Perad.*, II. 1904, p. 211), even as much as 46 cm. a day. *D. strictus* Nees (male bamboo) has solid stems, used for lances, &c. Nut fr.
Dendrochilum Blume. Orchidaceae (II. 16). 75 Indomal.
Dendrocolla Blume = Sarcochilus R. Br. p.p. (Orchid.).
Dendroconche Copeland (*Polypodium* p.p.). Polypod. 1 Phil. Is.
Dendrocousinia Millspaugh. Euphorbiaceae (A. II. 7). 2 N. Am.
Dendroid, tree-like.
Dendromecon Benth. Papaveraceae (II). 20 California.
Dendron (Gr.), a tree.
Dendropanax Decne. et Planch. (*Gilibertia* Ruiz et Pav. *EP.*). Araliaceae (1). 25 trop. and subtrop.
Dendrophthoe Mart. = Loranthus L. p.p. (Loranth.).
Dendrophthora Eichl. Loranthaceae (II). 30 W.I., trop. Am.
Dendrophylax Reichb. f. Orchidaceae (II. 20). 3 W. Indies.
Dendropogon Rafin. = Tillandsia L. (Bromel.).

Dendroseris D. Don. Compositae (13). 7 Juan Fernandez.
Dendrosicyos Balf. f. Cucurbitaceae (2). 1 Socotra.
Dendrosma Panch. et Sebert. Rutaceae (inc. sed.). 1 New Caled.
Dendrostylis Karst. et Triana (*Mayna EP.*). Flac. (2). 8 S. Am.
Denekia Thunb. Compositae (4). 2 trop. Afr.
Denhamia Meissn. Celastraceae. 4 trop. Austr.
Denisia Post et O. Ktze. (*Phryma* p.p.). Phrymaceae. 1 S. Afr.
Denisonia F. Muell. Verbenaceae (3). 1 Australia.
Denizen, a pl. probably foreign, but maintaining its place.
Dennettia E. G. Baker. Anonaceae (I). 1 S. Nigeria.
Dennstaedtia Bernh. Polypodiaceae. 60 trop., S. Am., Austr.
Dens (Lat.), a tooth.
Dentaria (Tourn.) L. (*Cardamine* p.p. *BH.*). Crucif. (2). 20 N. temp.
Dentate (dim. **denticulate**), with small teeth pointing outwards.
Dentella Forst. Rubiaceae (I. 2). 1 Indomal.
Deodar, *Cedrus Deodara* Loud.
Deonia Pierre ex Pax. (*Blachia EP.*). Euphorb. (A. II. 5). 1 Cochin-China.
Depauperate, diminutive.
Dependent, hanging down.
Deplanchea Vieill. (*Diplanthera BH.*). Bignon. (2). 6 Malaya, Austr.
Deppea Cham. et Schlechtd. Rubiaceae (I. 3). 9 C. Am., Mex.
Depresmenilia F. Muell. (*Pityrodia* p.p. *EP.*). Verben. (3). 1 Austr.
Dermatobotrys Bolus. Scrophul. (inc. sed.). 1 Zululand.
Dermatocalyx Oerst. Scrophulariaceae (II. 4). 1 Costa Rica.
Deroemeria Reichb. f. (*Habenaria* p.p. *BH.*). Orchidaceae (II. 1). 4 trop. Afr., Abyssinia.
Derris Lour. (*Deguelia* Aubl.). Leguminosae (III. 8). 50 trop.
Desbordesia Pierre ex Van Tiegh. (*Irvingia* p.p.). Simarubaceae. 5 trop. Afr.
Descending (aestivation), see Aestivation.
Deschampsia Beauv. Gramineae (9). 20 temp. and frigid. *D. caespitosa* Beauv. (*Aira*) and *D. flexuosa* Trin. in Brit. (hair grass); of tufted growth; rough fodder grasses.
Description of plants. Root, stem, leaf, flower, and fruit, &c. are described for floras, &c. in concise technical terms (original descriptions of new species must be in Latin), which are mostly given here under fl., l., &c. The descriptions of families in this book may serve as examples for large groups, and as examples of a species described in full detail we may refer to any numbers of the *Journ. Linn. Soc.* or to Lindley's *Descriptive Botany*, from which we quote as instances:

lilac (l.): l. opp., exstip., roundish-cordate, very acute, thin, smooth, rather longer than the linear channelled petiole.

buttercup (fl.): fl. term., sol., on long angular and furrowed peduncles, reg., ☿, hypog. Sepals 5, polysep., oval, coloured at edge, reflexed, with shaggy hairs. Petals 5, polypet., roundish, concave, with wedge-shaped basal nectaries, bright yellow. Stamens ∞, polyandrous, spiral; filament yellow, slender; anther linear, adnate, extrorse. Carpels ∞, apocarpous, superior, collected into a nearly spherical head, greenish; stigmas sessile, recurved; ovules solitary, ascending, anatropous.

But if all the species in a genus are known, it is obvious that for purposes of description to enable identification, such a description is much too long, and the skill of the describer will be shown in describing those characters only in full (or as fully as necessary) which are essential to the discrimination of the species among its congeners.

Descurainia Webb et Berth. (*Sisymbrium* p.p. *BH.*) Cruciferae (4). 45 N. temp., S. Am.

Desdemona Sp. Moore. Scrophulariaceae (inc. sed.). 1 Brazil.

Desfontainia Ruiz et Pav. Loganiaceae. 3 Andes. Ovary 5-loc.

Desmanthodium Benth. Compositae (5). 4 Mexico, C. Am.

Desmanthus Willd. Leguminosae (I. 3). 15 Am., Madagascar.

Desmiograstis Börner. Cyperaceae (III). 1 N. temp.

Desmochaeta DC. = Pupalia Juss. (Amarant.).

Desmodium Desv. Leguminosae (III. 7). 170 trop. and subtrop. In *D. gyrans* DC. (telegraph plant), during the day, if the temperature be not below 72° F. the two small lat. leaflets of each l. move steadily round in elliptical orbits. See Darwin's *Movements of Plants.* At night the leaves sleep, drooping downwards. Several are useful as fodder, and are cult.

Desmogyne King et Prain. Ericaceae (III. 1). 1 India.

Desmoncus Mart. Palmae (IV. 2). 25 trop. Am., climbing palms with reedy stems, and hooks like Calamus.

Desmonema Miers. Menispermaceae. 7 warm Afr., Madag. A (6—3), [G 3.

Desmoscelis Naud. Melastomaceae (1). 2 trop. S. Am.

Desmostachya Stapf. Gramineae (10). 1 trop. As. and Afr.

Desmostachys Planch. Icacinaceae. 3 Madagascar, trop. Afr.

Desmothamnus Small (*Andromeda* p.p.). Eric. (II. 1). 2 Florida.

Desmotrichum Blume (*Dendrobium* p.p.). Orch. (II. 15). 27 Malaya.

Despeleza Nieuwland (*Lespedeza* p.p.). Legum. (III. 7). 4 U.S.

Desplatzia Bocq. Tiliaceae. 2 W. trop. Afr.

Desvauxia R. Br. = Centrolepis Labill. (Centrolep.).

Detandra Miers (*Sychnosepalum* Eichl.). Menisp. 4 trop. S. Am.

Detarium Juss. Legumin. (II. 2). 4 trop. Afr. Pith of pod ed.

Determinate, definite, ending with a bud.

Dethawia Endl. (*Seseli* p.p. *BH.*). Umbellif. (III. 5). 1 Pyrenees.

Detris Adans. = Felicia Cass. (Comp.).

Deuterocohnia Mez. (*Dyckia*). Bromeliaceae (2). 3 S. Am.

Deutzia Thunb. Saxifragaceae (III). 40 N. temp. and trop. Ovary inf. 3—4-loc. The fruit splits septicidally into its cpls. which open each at its apex. The seed is provided with a winged testa, very light.

Deverra DC. = Pituranthos Viv. (Umbell.).

Devil-in-a-bush, *Nigella*; **-'s bean** (W.I.), *Capparis jamaicensis* Jacq.; **-'s bit scabious,** *Scabiosa Succisa* L.; **-'s cotton,** *Abroma augusta* L. f.

Devillea Tul. et Wedd. Podostemaceae. 1 Brazil.

Dewberry, *Rubus caesius* L.

Dewevrea M. Micheli. Leguminosae (III. 6). 1 trop. Afr.

Dewevrella De Wild. Apocynaceae (II. 1). 1 trop. Afr.

Deweya Torr. et A. Gray (*Arracacia BH.*). Umbell. (III. 4). 4 W. N. Am.

Dewildemania O. Hoffm. Compositae (I). 1 Congo.
Dewindtia De Wild. Leguminosae (II. 3). 1 trop. Afr.
Dextrorse, to the right.
Deyeuxia Clar. (*Calamagrostis* p.p. *EP.*). Gramineae (8). 120 temp.
Dhak tree, *Butea frondosa* Roxb.
Dhal, pigeon pea, *Cajanus indicus* Spreng.
Di- (Gr. pref.), two; **-adelphous,** in two groups; **-androus,** with two sta.; **-carpellary,** with two cpls.; **-chlamydeous,** with distinct K and C; **-chogamy,** see article below; **-chotomy,** actual forking of growing apex; **-clinism** (**-clinous**), with separate ♂ and ♀ fl.; **-cotyledons,** one of the great divisions of angiosperms; **-cyclic,** in two whorls; **-dymous,** twinned; **-dynamous,** with two sta. longer than rest, *Labiatae*; **-merous,** with two members in each whorl; **-midiate,** halved; **-morphism,** see article below; **-oecism,** see article below; **-photic,** with two surfaces unequally lighted; **-plecolobous,** *Cruciferae*; **-plochlamydeous,** see dichlamydeous; **-plostemonous,** sta. in two whorls, outer alt. with C; **-ptera,** flies, &c.; **-stichous,** in two ranks; **-thecous,** with two thecae; **-varicate,** very divergent; **-vergens** (Lat.), separating.
Dia- (Gr. pref.), transverse; **-heliotropism,** transv. h., *e.g.* in runners, &c.; **-phragm,** a dividing membrane; **-tropism,** a placing of organs transv. to a stimulus.
Diacalpe Blume. Polypodiaceae. 1 trop. As.
Diacarpa Sim. Sapindaceae. 1 E. Afr.
Diacattleya ×, **Dialaelia** × Hort. Orchidaceae. Hybrids of Diacrium with Cattleya and Laelia.
Diacidia Griseb. Malpighiaceae (II). 1 trop. S. Am.
Diacrium Benth. Orchidaceae (II. 6). 4 Mexico to Guiana.
Diadenium Poepp. et Endl. Orchidaceae (II. 19). 1 Peru.
Diagram, floral, see Floral Diagram.
Dialiopsis Radlk. Sapindaceae (II). 1 trop. Afr.
Dialium L. Leguminosae (II. 5). 20 trop. Petals 2, 1, or 0; sta. 2, or rarely 3. *D. guineense* Willd. (trop. Afr.; velvet tamarind) pod contains an ed. pulp; wood useful, resists salt water. *D. indum* L. (Java; tamarind plum) and others have also ed. fr.
Dialyanthera Warb. Myristicaceae. 2 Peru, Colombia.
Dialycarpa Mast. Bombacaceae. 1 Borneo.
Dialyopsis Radlk. Sapindaceae (II). 1 trop. Afr.
Dialypetalae, Polypetalae.
Dialypetalum Benth. Campanulaceae (III). 2 Madagascar.
Diamorpha Nutt. Crassulaceae. 2 E. U.S.
Diandriella Engl. Araceae (V). 1 New Guinea.
Diandrolyra Stapf. Gramineae (5). 1, habitat unknown.
Dianella Lam. Liliaceae (III). 15 trop. As., Austr., Polynes., N.Z. Berry.
Dianthera Gronov. (*Justicia* p.p. *EP.*). Acanthaceae (IV. B). 80 trop.
Dianthoseris Sch. Bip. Compositae (13). 2 Abyssinia.
Dianthus L. Caryophyllaceae (II. 2). 250 Eur., As., Afr., esp. Medit., mostly in dry sunny situations (4 in Brit.; pinks). Genus readily known by the bracts under the K. Fls. very protandrous (class F), largely visited by butterflies. Many cult. orn. fl., *e.g. D. barbatus* L.

(Sweet William), *D. Caryophyllus* L. (carnation, picotee, clove-pink), *D. chinensis* (China or Indian pink), &c.

Diapedium Koen. = Dicliptera Juss. (Acanth.).

Diapensia L. Diapensiaceae. 4, one Himal., *D. lapponica* L. circum-polar boreal. Tufted, like ∞ alpine and arctic pl.; fl. protog.

Diapensiaceae (*EP.*, *BH.*). Dicots. (Sympet. Ericales *EP.*, *BH.*). 6 gen., 9 sp., ⁑, chiefly alpine and arctic evergr. under-shrubs, with rosettes of l.; fls. sol. or in racemes, with two bracteoles, ☿, actinom., without a disc. K (5) or 5, C (5) nearly polypet., A 5, epipet., opp. sepals, with frequently 5 stds. opp. petals; anthers transv., each lobe opening by longitudinal slit; pollen simple; $\underline{G}$ (3) with axile plac. bearing ∞ anatr. or amphitr. ov.; style simple with 3-lobed capitate stigma. Fruit a loculic. caps. Embryo cylindrical, endosp. fleshy. *Chief genera:* Diapensia, Shortia, Galax.

Diaperia Nutt. (*Evax* p.p.). Compositae (4). 4 N. Am.

Diaphananthe Schlechter. Orchid. (II. 20). 20 trop. Afr.

Diaphycarpus Calest. (*Carum* p.p.). Umbell. (III. 5). 1 Medit.

Diarrhena Beauv. Gramineae (10). 3 N. Am., E. As.

Diarthron Turcz. Thymelaeaceae. 2 C. As.

Diascia Link et Otto. Scrophulariaceae (II. 2). 30 S. Afr.

Diaspasis R. Br. Goodeniaceae. 1 S.W. Austr.

Diasperus L. = Phyllanthus L. (Euph.).

Diaspis Niedenzu. Malpighiaceae (I). 1 Brit. E. Afr.

Diastatea Scheidw. Campanulaceae (inc. sed.). 1 Mexico.

Diastema Benth. Gesneriaceae (II). 18 trop. Am. Cult. orn. fl.

Diateinacanthus Lindau. Acanthaceae (IV. B). 1 Centr. Am.

Diatenopteryx Radlk. Sapindaceae (I). 1 S. Am.

Diberara Baill. (*Nebelia BH.*). Bruniaceae. 5 S. Afr.

Dicaelospermum C. B. Clarke. Cucurbitaceae (2). 1 S. India.

Dicarpidium F. Muell. Bombacaceae. 1 Austr.

Dicaryum Willd. (*Geissanthus EP.*). Myrsinaceae (II). 2 S. Am.

Dicella Griseb. Malpighiaceae (II). 3 Brazil, Paraguay.

Dicellandra Hook. f. Melastomaceae (I). 3 trop. W. Afr.

Dicellostyles Benth. Malvaceae (4). 2 Ceylon, Sikkim.

Dicentra Bernh. Papaveraceae (III). 15 As., N. Am. *D. Cucullaria* Bernh. (Dutchman's breeches) and others cult. orn. fl. The rhiz. of many sp. (§ *Cucullaria*) resembles a succession of bulbs, on account of the fleshiness of the scale l. and of the sheathing bases of the fol. l. The materials formed in the l. during the growing season are stored up in the fleshy base, which survives the winter, while the rest of the l. dies. Fls. in racemes, pend. Each outer petal has a large pouch at its base. The inner petals are spoon-shaped and cohere at the tip, forming a hood which covers the anthers and stigma. The pend. position and complex structure of the fl. render it suited to bees, which hang on to it and probe for honey first one side, then the other, in the pouches of the petals. In so doing they push aside the hood and touch the stigma, on which there is usu. pollen from its own sta.

Dicerandra Benth. = Ceranthera Ell. (Labiatae).

Diceratella Boiss. Cruciferae (4). 3 W. As., trop. Afr.

Dicerostylis Blume (*Hylophila EP.*). Orchidaceae (II. 2). 1 Malaya.

Dichaea Lindl. Orchidaceae (II. 20). 60 trop. Am., W. I. Monopodial creeping epiphytes with sheathing l. Cult. orn. fl.
Dichaelia Harv. (*Brachystelma BH.*). Asclep. (II. 3). 10 S. Afr.
Dichaeopsis Pfitz. (*Dichaea* Lindl. p.p.). Orchidaceae (II. 20). 5 trop. Am.
Dichaetanthera Endl. Melastomaceae (I). 16 Madagascar, Masc.
Dichaetaria Nees (*Gymnopogon* Beauv.). Gramin. (11). 1 Indomal.
Dichaetophora A. Gray (*Boltonia* p.p. *BH.*). Comp. (3). 1 Texas.
Dichapetalaceae (*EP.*; *Chailletiaceae BH.*). Dicots. (Archichl. Geraniales *EP.*, *BH.*). 3 gen., 125 sp. trop. Woody pl. with entire stip. l. Fls. in cymose umbels, &c., sometimes epiphyllous, usu. reg., ☿ or unisex., typically 5-merous. K and C free or united, the petals often bifid; axis continued into a cup-like disc or scales; A 5, sometimes epipet.; $\underline{G}$ (2—3), each with 2 ov. Drupe with 1- or 2-loc. stone; no endosp.; sometimes a caruncle. *Chief genus* Dichapetalum.
Dichapetalum Thou. (*Chailletia* DC.). Dichapet. 120 trop. Several have epiphyllous infl. (*cf.* Erythrochiton), probably arising by a development like infl. of Solanaceae, or thorns of Cactaceae.
Dichasial cyme, one in which each successive branch bears two branches upon itself, *Acanthaceae*, *Asclepiadaceae*, *Begonia*, *Bignoniaceae*, *Caryophyllaceae*, *Castanea*, *Convolvulaceae*, *Cornaceae*, *Labiatae*, *Linaceae*, *Sanicula*, *Saxifragaceae*, *Ulmus*, *Urtica*, *Verbenaceae*.
Dichazothece Lindau. Acanthaceae (IV. B). 1 Rio de Janeiro.
Dichelachne Endl. Gramineae (8). 3 Austr., N. Zealand.
Dichelostemma Kunth. (*Brodiea* Sm.). Lili. (IV). 8 N. Am.
Dicheranthus Webb. Caryophyllaceae (I. 7). 1 Canaries.
Dichilanthe Thw. Rubiaceae (II. 2). 2 trop. As.
Dichiloboea Stapf. Gesneriaceae (I). 2 E. trop. As.
Dichilus DC. Leguminosae (III. 3). 4 S. Afr.
Dichoespermum Wight = Aneilema R. Br. p.p. (Commelin.).
Dichogamy, ripening of sexes at different times; sta. ripe before stigma, *protandry*, Aeschynanthus, Aconitum, Aquilegia, Bignonia, Borago, Campanula, Campanulaceae, Caryophyllaceae, Clerodendron, Compositae, Crassulaceae, Crocus, Delphinium, Dipsacaceae, Echium, Empetrum, Epilobium, Geraniaceae, Gesneriaceae, Gladiolus, Labiatae, Malva, Monarda, Oxalis, Phacelia, Phyteuma, Rosaceae, Saxifraga, Scabiosa, Stellaria, Teucrium, Thymus, Umbelliferae, Valeriana; stigma ripe before sta., *protogyny*, Alopecurus, Amorpha, Anthurium, Aesculus, Araceae, Callitriche, Carex, Chimonanthus, Colchicum, Coriaria, Epimedium, Euphrasia, Ficus, Fragaria, Helleborus, Humulus, Juncus, Magnolia, Mirabilis, Parietaria, Paris, Plantago, Potamogeton, Pyrus, Scrophularia, Thalictrum.
Dichoglottis Fisch. et Mey. = Gypsophila L. p.p. (Caryophyll.).
Dichondra Forst. Convolvulaceae (I). 6 trop., some amphicarpic.
Dichondropsis T. S. Brandegee. Convolvulaceae (I). 1 Mexico.
Dichopogon Kunth. Liliaceae (III). 2 Austr. Cult. orn.
Dichopsis Thw. (*Palaquium* Blanco *q.v.*). Sapotaceae (I). 50 Indomal.
Dichorisandra Mikan. Commelinaceae. 30 trop. Am. Infl. racemose (*cf.* fam.); its branches often pierce the leaf-sheath.
Dichosciadium Domin. (*Azorella* p.p.). Umbell. (I. 2). 1 Austr.

Dichostemma Pierre. Euphorb. (A. II. 8). 3 trop. Afr.
Dichostylis Beauv. = Scirpus L. (Cyper.)
Dichotomanthes S. Kurz. Ros. (V). 1 Yunnan.
Dichroa Lour. Saxifrag. (III). 10 China, E. Indomal. G isomerous.
Dichroanthus Webb et Berth. = Cheiranthus L. p.p. (Crucif.).
Dichrocephala L'Hérit. ex DC. Comp. (3). 6 warm Afr., As. Pappus 0.
Dichrolepis Welw. (*Eriocaulon* p.p. *EP.*). Eriocaulon. 1 trop. Afr.
Dichromena Michx. Cyper. (I). 12 Am., W.I. P 0. Stigmas 2.
Dichrostachys Wight et Arn. Legum. (I. 4). 10 warm |✻. Stips often thorny. Spike of two colours, upper fls. ☿, lower neuter.
Dichrotrichum Reinw. Gesner. (I). 10 Malay Arch., Phil. Like Tri-
Dickinsia Franch. Umbell. (I. 2). 1 Chi. [chosporum; hair of 2 colours.
Dicksonia L'Hérit. (excl. *Cibotium*, *q.v.* for Tartarian lamb). Cyath. 25 warm and ✻, usu. tree ferns, *e.g.* *D. antarctica* Labill. (Austr., N.Z.). Sori marginal.
Dicladanthera F. Muell. Acanth. (IV. B). 1 W. Austr.
Diclidanthera Mart. Styrac. 2 Brazil.
Diclidium Schrad. ex Nees = Mariscus Gaertn. (*BH.*) = Cyperus L. p.p.
Diclidocarpus A. Gray (*Trichospermum BH.*). Tili. 2 Java, Fiji.
Dicliptera Juss. Acanth. (IV. B). 100 trop and subtrop. Fls. in cymes.
Diclis Benth. Scroph. (II. 3). 6 Afr., Madag. Creeping herbs.
Diclytra Borckh. = Dicentra Bernh. (Papav.) [side of midrib.
Dicoelia Benth. Euphorb (A. I. 1). 1 Borneo. Pets. concave either
Dicoma Cass. Comp. (12). 30 Afr., Madag., trop. As. [with pappus.
Dicoria Torr. et A. Gray. Comp. (5). 5 W. U.S., Mex. Fr. winged,
Dicorynia Benth. Legum. (II. 5). 4 Guiana, N. Braz. A 2.
Dicoryphe Thou. Hamamelid. 15 Madag., Comoros.
Dicotyledons, one of the two chief divisions of Angiosperms; p. x.
Dicraea (Thou.) Tul. Podostem. 12 Madag., trop. Afr., Ceylon, India. Thallus (root) drifting from attached base, exogenously branched, with marginal secondary shoots. Fr. isolobous.
Dicraeanthus Engl. Podostem. 1 trop. Afr.
Dicraeopetalum Harms. Legum. (III. 1). 1 Somaliland. [pappus.
Dicranocarpus A. Gray. Comp. (5). 1 Tex., Mex. Some fr. with no
Dicranolepis Planch. Thymel. 25 trop. Afr. Fls. 1—2 in axils.
Dicranopteris Bernh. = Gleichenia Sm. (Polypod.). [3 Himal., Chi.
Dicranostigma Hook. f. et Thoms. (*Chelidonium* p.p.). Papav. (II).
Dicranostyles Benth. Convolv. (I. 2). 2 trop. S. Am.
Dicranotaenia Finet. Orchid. (II. 20). 1 Dahomey.
Dicrastylis Drumm. Verben. (3). 12 N. and W. Austr. A 5. Style
Dicraurus Hook. f. Amarant. (3). 1 Tex., Mex. [5-fid.
Dicrypta Lindl. = Maxillaria Ruiz et Pav. (Orchid.).
Dictamnus L. Rut. (I. 2). 1 Eur., As., *D. albus* L. (*D. Fraxinella* Pers.), (dittany, candle-plant). Volatile and inflammable ethereal oil is secreted, so that on hot calm days the air round the pl. may sometimes be ignited. Fl. ·|·; unripe sta. bent down. Fr. elastic-dehisc.
Dictyandra Welw. ex Benth. et Hook. f. Rubi. (I. 8). 2 W. trop. Afr. K large, conv. Anther loc. chambered.
Dictyanthus Decne. in DC. Asclep. (II. 4). 4 Mex. Fls. large. [S. Am.
Dictyocaryum H. Wendl. (*Iriartea* p.p. *EP.*). Palm. (IV. 1). 2 trop.
Dictyochloa Camus (*Ammochloa* p.p.). Gramin. (10). 1 N. W. Afr.

Dictyoloma A. Juss. Rutaceae (I. 6). 2 Brazil, Peru.
Dictyoneura Blume (*Cupania* p.p. *BH.*). Sapind. (I). 3 Malay Arch.
Dictyophleba Pierre (*Landolphia* p.p.). Apocyn. (I. 1). 1 trop. Afr.
Dictyosperma Regel (*Pirea EP.*). Cruciferae (2). 1 Turkestan.
Dictyosperma Wendl. et Drude. Palmae (IV. 1). 3 Mascarenes.
Dictyostega Miers. Burmanniaceae. 5 trop. Am. and Afr.
Dictyoxiphium Hook. Polypodiaceae. 1 Cent. Am.
Dicyclophora Boiss. (*Pycnocycla BH.*). Umbell. (III. 1). 1 Persia.
Dicymbe Spruce ex Benth. et Hook. f. Leguminosae (II. 8). 1 Braz.
Dicypellium Nees. Lauraceae (I). 1 Brazil, *D. caryophyllatum* (Mart.) Nees. Wood valuable; bark (Cassia caryophyllata) smells like cloves.
Dicyrta Regel (*Achimenes* p.p. *EP.*). Gesner. (II). 2 Guatemala.
Didactyle Lindl. = Bulbophyllum Thou. (Orchid.).
Didelotia Baill. Leguminosae (II. 3). 4 trop. Afr.
Didelta L'Hérit. Compositae (10). 3 S.W. Afr.
Didesmandra Stapf. Dilleniaceae. 1 Borneo.
Didesmus Desv. = Rapistrum Tourn. p.p. (Crucif.).
Didiciea King et Pantl. Orchidaceae (II. 6). 1 Sikkim.
Didieraceae, a fam. sometimes created for Didierea.
Didierea Baill. Sapindaceae (?). 4 Madag. Anomalous plants with the habit of cactus-like Euphorbias, and of doubtful affinity. See *Nat. Pfl.* III. 5, p. 461, *Kew Bull.* 1898, p. 97.
Didiplis Rafin. (*Peplis* p.p. *EP.*). Lythraceae. 1 N. Am.
Didiscus DC. (*Trachymene BH.*). Umbell. (I. 1). 20 Malaya, Austr.
Didissandra C. B. Clarke. Gesneriaceae (I). 30 India, China.
Didymaea Hook. f. Rubiaceae (II. 11). 1 Mexico.
Didymanthus Endl. Chenopodiaceae (A). 1 W. Aust.
Didymeles Thou. Inc. sed. 1 Madagascar.
Didymia Phil. (*Mariscus* p.p. *BH.*). Cyperaceae (II). 1 Chili.
Didymocarpaceae = Gesneriaceae.
Didymocarpus Wall. (*Rottlera* Vahl). Gesneriaceae (I). 120 Indomal., China, Madag., Austr., trop. Afr.
Didymochlaena Desv. Polypodiaceae. 1 trop.
Didymochlamys Hook. f. Rubiaceae (I. 7). 1 Colombia. Epiphytic.
Didymopanax Decne. et Planch. Araliaceae (I). 24 trop. Am.
Didymopelta Regel et Schmalh. (*Astragalus* p.p. *BH.*). Leguminosae (III. 6). 1 Turkestan.
Didymophysa Boiss. Cruciferae (2). 1 Persia.
Didymoplexis Griff. (*Leucorchis* p.p. *EP.*). Orch. (II. 2). 10 Indomal.
Didymosperma H. Wendl. et Drude. Palmae (IV. 1). 8 Indomal.
Didymotheca Hook. f. Phytolaccaceae. 5 Austr., Tasmania.
Dieffenbachia Schott. Arac. (V). 30 trop. Am., W.I. Fls. ♂♀, naked, the ♂ is a synandrium of 4 or 5 sta. *D. Sequine* Scott is the 'dumb cane' of the W. Ind., formerly used in torturing slaves; it renders speechless a person who chews a piece of the stem.
Diellia Brackenridge. Polypodiaceae. 8 Hawaiian Is.
Dielsia Gilg. Restionaceae. 1 Austr.
Dielsina O. Ktze. (*Polyceratocarpus* Engl. et Diels). Anonaceae (4). 1 trop. Afr.
Dielytra Cham. et Schlecht. = Dicentra Bernh. (Papav.).

Dienia Lindl. = Microstylis Nutt. (Orchid.).
Dierama C. Koch. Irid. (III). 2 S. and trop. Afr. Sta. short.
Diervilla (Tourn. ex L.) Adans. (*Weigelia* Thunb.). Caprifol. 10 E. As., N. Am. *D. florida* Sieb. et Zucc., &c. cult. orn. shrubs. G (2). Fl. suited to bees; changes colour after fert. (*cf.* Ribes, Fumaria, &c.).
Dietes Salisb. = Moraea L. p.p. (Irid.).
Dieudonnaea Cogn. Cucurb. (3). 1 Peru.
Diffuse, loosely spreading.
Digera Forsk. Amarant. (2). 1 palaeotrop.
Digitalin, *Digitalis*. A poisonous alkaloid, offic.
Digitalis (Tourn.) L. Scroph. (III. 1). 25 Eur., W. As., Canary Is. *D. purpurea* L. (foxglove) Brit. Racemes one-sided by twisting of peduncles. Fert. by bees. A calcifuge sp. L. offic. for digitalin.
Digitaria Heist. ex Adans. (*Panicum* p.p.). Gramin. (5). 50 warm.
Digitate (l.), palmate with 5 or 7 leaflets.
Diglyphosa Blume (*Chrysoglossum* p.p. *BH.*). Orchid. (II. *a*. II.). 1 Java, Celebes.
Dignathe Lindl. Orchid. (II. 19). 1 Mex.
Dignathia Stapf. Gramin. (3). 2 E. trop. Afr.
Digomphia Benth. Bignon. (2). 2 Guiana, Braz. Std. very long.
Digraphis Trin. = Phalaris L. p.p. (Gramin.).
Digyroloma Turcz. Acanth. (inc. sed.) 1 Madras.
Diholcos Rydberg (*Astragalus* p.p.). Legum. (III. 6). 5 N. Am.
Dilatris Berg. Haemodor. 2 S. Afr. $\overline{G}$. Ov. 1 per loc.
Dildo (W. I.), *Cereus Swartzii* Griseb., *Cephalocereus*.
Dilkea Mast. Passiflor. 6 N. Braz. A 6, united at base.
Dill, *Peucedanum graveolens* Benth. et Hook. f.
Dillenia L. (excl. *Wormia* Rottb.). Dillen. 20 Indomal. Fr. often enclosed in fleshy K.
Dilleniaceae (*EP.*; *BH.* incl. *Crossosom.*). Dicots. (Archichl. Parietales, Ranales *BH.*; pp. xxxi, l). 16/400, trop. and subtrop, well repres. in the Austr. scrub. Usu. ♄ (many lianas), with alt. usu. leathery l., stip. or not, veins of 2nd. and later orders ‖; sometimes phylloclades. Infl. cymose, often raceme-like by reduction, or fls. sol. Fl. usu. reg. ☿. K 5, 3, 4, or ∞, spiral, imbr., persistent; C usu. 5, imbr.; A ∞, rarely 10 or less, hypog., free or united at base, anthers usu. adnate, versatile in Actinidia and Saurauia; $\underline{G}$ ∞—1, free or slightly united, styles usu. free, ov. ∞—1, ascending, anatr., with ventral raphe, plac. unthickened. Fr. dehisc. or not; funicular aril, united to testa. Endosp. copious; embryo small, straight. Some give useful timber; tannin. *Chief gen.*: Dillenia, Hibbertia, Wormia, Tetracera, Saurauia.
Dillwynia Sm. in Kon. et Sims. Legum (III. 2). 10 Austr. Exstip.
Dilobeia Thou. Prot. (I). 1 Madag.
Dilodendron Radlk. Sapind. (I). 1 S. Braz. Oil from seed.
Dilophia T. Thoms. Crucif. (2). 3 C. As.
Dimacria Lindl. in Sweet = Pelargonium L'Hérit. (Geran.).
Dimeresia A. Gray. Comp. (4). 1 Oregon. Head 2-fld., each in br.
Dimeria R. Br. Gramin. (2). 15 Indomal., S. Chi. Spikelet 1-fld.
Dimerocostus O. Ktze. Zingiber. (II). 4 W. S. Am.
Dimerostemma Cass. Comp. (5). 1 Braz. Glandular herb; l. alt.
Dimetopia DC. = Trachymene Rudge (*BH.*) = Didiscus DC. (Umbell.).
Dimorphandra Schott. Legum. (II. 1). 12 trop. Am. Episepalous sta. reduced to stds. *D. Mora* Benth. et. Hook. f. gives good timber.

Dimorphanthera F. Muell. (*Agapetes* p.p.). Eric. (III. 2). 10 Malaya, Australia.

Dimorphanthes Cass. = Conyza L. (Comp.).

Dimorphanthus Miq. = Aralia Tourn.

Dimorphism, appearing in two forms, *e.g. flower*, Asperula, Cassia, Exacum, Saintpaulia, and *cf.* Dioecism, Heterostylism; *fruit*, Cardamine, Chenopodium, Dimorphotheca; *inflorescence*, Trifolium; *leaf*, Anisophyllea, Bidens, Dischidia, Ficus, Hedera, Heteranthera, Platycerium, Polygonum, Polypodium, Ranunculus, Sagittaria, Salvinia, Trapa, and *cf.* Water-plants; *plant*, Littorella; *pollen*, Faramea; *root*, Araceae, Ficus, Jussieua, Orchidaceae; *shoot*, Marcgravia, Salacia; *stamens*, Heeria, Monochaetum.

Dimorphocalyx Thw. Euphorbiaceae (A. II. 5). 6 Indomal.

Dimorphochlamys Hook. f. Cucurbitaceae (3). 3 trop. W. Afr.

Dimorphocoma F. Muell. et Tate. Compositae (7). 1 C. Austr.

Dimorphotheca Vaill. ex L. Compositae (10). 20 S. and trop. Afr. There are two kinds of fr. on the head (*cf.* Calendula).

Dinacria Haw. (*Crassula* p.p. *EP.*). Crassulaceae. 2 S. Afr.

Dinebra Jacq. Gramineae (11). 1 trop. Afr., As.

Dinemagonum A. Juss. Malpighiaceae (1). 3 Chili.

Dinemandra A. Juss. ex Endl. Malpighiaceae (1). 6 Peru, Chili.

Dinklagea Gilg. Connaraceae. 1 Liberia.

Dinochloa Buese. Gramineae (13). 6 Malay Archip.

Dinophora Benth. Melastomaceae (1). 2 trop. W. Afr.

Dinoseris Griseb. Compositae (12). 1 Argentina.

Dintera Stapf. Scrophulariaceae (II. 6). 1 trop. Afr.

Dinteracanthus C. B. Clarke ex Schinz. Acanth. (IV. A). 3 S. Afr.

Dioclea H.B. et K. Leguminosae (III. 10). 20 trop.

Diodia Gronov. Rubiaceae (II. 10). 35 trop. and subtrop. *D. maritima* Schum. et Thonn. is common to Afr. and Am.

Dioecism (-ious), ♂ fl. on one pl., ♀ on another; *Antennaria*, *Arisaema*, *Aucuba*, *Cannabis*, *Mercurialis*, *Myrica*, *Rhamnus*, *Rhus*, *Salix*, *Taxus*.

Diolena Naud. Melastomaceae (1). 6 trop. S. Am.

Diomedia Cass. = Borrichia Adans. (Comp.).

Dionaea Ellis. Droseraceae. 1 Carolina, *D. muscipula* Ellis (Venus' fly-trap), in damp mossy places on the 'pine-barrens.' Short rhiz. bearing a rosette of l., which lie close to the soil. Each has a lower and an upper blade; the former may be regarded as a winged petiole, the latter has a quadrangular shape and the margins project as long teeth close together. The two halves of this part of the l. are bent upwards so as to present a flat V-form in section. The edge of each half is green, the inner part of the surface is covered with reddish dots, which under the microscope are seen to be digestive glands; unless stimulated, no secretion is carried on. On each half of the l. are three long hairs—the trigger-hairs—jointed at the base so that they fold downwards when the l. closes. The slightest touch to one of these, or a more vigorous stimulus to the surface of the l., causes an immediate closing. The teeth cross one another, and if an insect cause the movement, it is thus captured. The closing of the l. still continues till the two halves are tightly squeezed together. Then the digestive glands commence to secrete a ferment which acts upon the proteids of the prey and renders them soluble, when they are absorbed by the l. (*cf.* Drosera). When the process is complete the l. opens again. [Macfarlane in *Contrib. from Bot. Lab. Pennsylv. Univ.* I. 1892.]

Dioncophyllum Baill. Flacourtiaceae (5). 1 Congo.

Dionychia Naud. Melastomaceae (1). 2 Madagascar.

Dionysia Fenzl. Primulaceae (1). 20 alpine Persia, Afghanistan.

Dioon Lindl. Cycadaceae. 3 Mexico. The seeds are ground into meal, which contains much starch.

Dioscorea Plum. ex L. Dioscoreaceae. 600 trop. and subtrop. *D. pyrenaica* Bub. et Bordère (Pyrenees) is the only Eur. sp. They have twining annual stems arising from tubers which in different sp. are of different morphological nature. In *D. Batatas* Dcne., &c. the tuber arises by a lateral hypertrophy of the hypocotyl, and is variously regarded as a rhiz. or a root; in *D. sinuata* Vel., &c. it arises by lateral hypertrophy of the internodes above the cotyledon; in *D. pentaphylla* L., &c. it arises from the internode just above the cotyledon together with the hypocotyl, whilst in *D. villosa*, L., *D. quinqueloba* Thunb., &c., there is a fleshy rhiz. The tubers are known as yams; they contain much starch and are largely cult. for food in trop., esp. Am. The best are perhaps *D. alata* L. (white yam), *D. cayennensis* Link (negro yam), *D. trifida* L. f. (cush-cush; yampi). They are propagated by 'eyes' like potatoes. Small axillary tubers often form on the main stem and may also be used.

Dioscoreaceae (*EP.*, *BH.*). Monocots. (Liliiflorae; Epigynae *BH.*). 9 gen., 220 sp., trop. and warm temp., climbing herbs or shrubs with tubers or rhizomes at the base (morphology varied; see gen.). L. alt., net-veined, often arrow-shaped; infl. racemose; fls. reg., usu. dioec., inconspic. P (6), tubular at base; A 6, or 3 and 3 stds.; $\overline{G}$ (3) usu. 3-loc. with axile, rarely 1-loc. with parietal, plac.; ov. usu. 2 in each loc., anatr. one above the other. Capsule or berry; embryo in horny endosp. The tubers of Dioscorea are valuable as food stuffs; those of Testudinaria are also used. *Chief genera:* Dioscorea, Testudinaria, Tamus.

Dioscoreophyllum Engl. Menispermaceae. 5 trop. Afr.

Dioscoreopsis O. Ktze. = Dioscoreophyllum Engl. (Menisp.).

Diosma L. Rutaceae (1). 11 S. Afr. Heath-like xerophytes.

Diosphaera Buser. Campanulaceae (I. 1). 3 E. Medit.

Diospyrinae (Warming). The 2nd cohort of Sympetalae.

Diospyros L. Ebenaceae. 240 warm. Many sp. yield the valuable wood ebony (*q.v.*). The sapwood is white and soft, the heart-wood hard and black. *D. reticulata* Willd. (Mauritius) and *D. Ebenum* Koen. (Ceylon) yield the finest ebony. *D. quaesita* Thw. (Ceylon) yields calamander wood. *D. Embryopteris* Pers. (gaub; India) fr. contains a sticky pulp, used for caulking. *D. Kaki* L. f. (Chinese date plum, persimmon) fr. is used as a sweetmeat when dried, *D. Lotus* L. (date-plum, temp. As.). *D. virginiana* L. (N. Am. ebony or persimmon, U.S.) cult. for both wood and fr. (*cf. Kew Bull.* 1911, p. 234).

Diotacanthus Benth. Acanthaceae (IV. B). 2 Indomal.

Diothonea Lindl. Orchidaceae (II. 6). 5 W. trop. S. Am.
Diotis Desf. Compositae (7). 1 coasts of Brit., W. Eur., Medit. *D. candidissima* Desf. (*D. maritima* Sm.), cotton-weed.
Dipanax Seem. (*Pterotropia* Hillebr.). Aral. (1). 1 Hawaii.
Dipcadi Medic. Liliaceae (V). 40 Afr., Medit., trop. As. Cult. orn. fl.
Dipelta Maxim. Caprifoliaceae. 4 China.
Dipentaplandra O. Ktze. = Pentadiplandra Baill. (Tili.).
Dipentodon Dunn. Celastraceae. 1 China (*Kew Bull.* 1911, 310).
Diphaca Lour. (*Ormocarpum* Beav.). Legum. (III. 7). 9 |* warm.
Diphalangium Schau. Liliaceae (IV). 1 Mexico.
Diphasia Pierre. Rutaceae (IV). 1 trop. Afr.
Dipholis A. DC. Sapotaceae (I). 8 W.I., Fla. C-lobes 3-fid.
Diphylax Hook. f. (*Habenaria* p.p.). Orchid. (II. 1). 1 Sikkim.
Diphyllarium Gagnep. Leguminosae (III. 10). 1 Cochin-China.
Diphylleia Michx. Berberidaceae. 2 Atl. N. Am., Japan (umbrella-leaf).
Diphysa Jacq. Leguminosae (III. 6). 12 Mexico, Cent. Am.
Dipidax Laws. ex Salisb. Liliaceae (I). 2 S. Afr.
Diplachne Beauv. Gramineae (10). 30 trop. and subtrop.
Diplacrum R. Br. (*Scleria BH.*). Cyperaceae (II). 3 trop.
Diplacus Nutt. = Mimulus L. p.p. (Scroph.).
Dipladenia A. DC. Apocynaceae (II. 1). 25 S. Am. Most are lianes climbing by hooks. Cult. orn. perf. fl.
Diplandra Hook. et Arn. Onagraceae (2). 1 Mexico.
Diplanthemum K. Schum. Tiliaceae. 1 trop. Afr.
Diplanthera Banks et Soland. ex R. Br. Bignon. (2). 4 Austr., Malaya.
Diplanthera Thou. (*Halodule* Endl.; *Cymodocea BH.*). Potamogetonaceae. 2 trop.
Diplarche Hook. f. et Thoms. Ericaceae (I. 3). 2 Sikkim.
Diplarpea Triana. Melastomaceae (I). 1 Colombia.
Diplarrhena Labill. Iridaceae (II). 2 S. Austr., Tasm.
Diplasia Rich. Cyperaceae (II). 2 trop. S. Am., W. Ind.
Diplaspis Hook. f. (*Huanaca* Cav.). Umbell. (I. 2). 2 Austr., Tasm.
Diplaziopsis C. Chr. Polypodiaceae. 1 E. As., Polynesia.
Diplazium Sw. Polypodiaceae. 280 trop., Chi., Jap.
Diplectria Rchb., O. Ktze. Melast. (I). 17 Malaya. Cult. orn. fl.
Diplocalymma Spreng. Inc. sed. 1, habitat?
Diplocaulobium Kränzlin (*Dendrobium* p.p. *EP.*). Orchidaceae (II. 15). 30 Malaya to Fiji.
Diplocentrum Lindl. Orchidaceae (II. 20). 3 Indomal.
Diplochita DC. = Miconia Ruiz et Pav. (Melast.).
Diploclinium Lindl. = Begonia L. p.p. (Begon.).
Diploclisia Miers (*Cocculus* p.p. *BH.*). Menisp. 4 E. As.
Diplocrater Hook. f. (*Tricalysia* p.p. *EP.*). Rubiac. (I. 8). 2 trop. Afr.
Diplocyatha N.E. Br. Asclepiadaceae (II. 3). 1 S. Afr.
Diplocyathium H. Schmidt (*Euphorbia* p.p.). Euph. (A. II. 8). 1 Eur.
Diplodiscus Turcz. Tiliaceae. 1 Phil. Is.
Diploglottis Hook. f. Sapindaceae (I). 2 Austr.
Diplokeleba N.E. Br. Sapindaceae (I). 1 Argentina.
Diploknema Pierre. Sapotaceae (I). 1 Borneo.

Diplolaena R. Br. Rutaceae (I). 4 W. Austr.
Diplolegnon Rusby. Gesneriaceae (I). 1 S. Am.
Diplolepis R. Br. Asclepiadaceae (II. 1). 2 S. Am.
Diplolophium Turcz. Umbelliferae (III. 5). 2 trop. Afr.
Diplomeris D. Don. Orchidaceae (II. 1). 4 Himal., China.
Diplopappus Cass. = Aster Tourn. p.p. (Comp.).
Diplopeltis Endl. Sapindaceae (II). 3 Austr., Madag.
Diplophractum Desf. Tiliaceae. 1 Java.
Diplopogon R. Br. Gramineae (8). 1 W. Austr.
Diploprora Hook. f. Orchidaceae (II. 20). 3 trop. As.
Diplopterys A. Juss. Malpighiaceae (I). 7 warm S. Amer., W.I.
Diplopyramis Welw. (*Oxygonum* p.p. *EP.*). Polygon. (II. 2). 1 trop. Afr.
Diplora Baker. Polypodiaceae. 2 S.E. As.
Diplorrhynchus Welw. Apocynaceae (I. 3). 5 trop. Afr.
Diplospora DC. (*Tricalysia* p.p. *EP.*). Rubi. (I. 8). 15 trop. As., China.
Diplosporopsis Wernham. Rubiaceae (I. 8). 2 S. Nigeria.
Diplostephium H. B. et K. Compositae (3). 20 trop. Andes.
Diplostigma K. Schum. Asclepiadaceae (II. 1). 1 E. Afr. steppes.
Diplotaenia Boiss. (*Peucedanum* p.p. *BH.*). Umbell. (III. 6). 1 Persia.
Diplotaxis DC. Cruciferae (2). 20 Eur., Medit. (2 Brit.).
Diplothemium Mart. Palmaceae (IV. 2). 4 S. Am.
Diplotropis Benth. Leguminosae (III. 1). 7 trop. Am.
Diplusodon Pohl. Lythraceae. 50 Brazil.
Diplycosia Blume. Ericaceae (II. 2). 20 Indomal.
Dipodium R. Br. Orchidaceae (II. 17). 5 Austr., Malaya.
Dipoma Franch. Cruciferae (2). 1 Yunnan.
Diporidium Wendl. f. ex Bartl. et Wendl. f. = Ochna L. (Ochn.).
Diposis DC. Umbelliferae (I. 2). 2 temp. S. Am.
Dipsacaceae (*EP.*, *BH.*). Dicots. (Sympet. Aggregatae; Asterales *BH.*). 10 gen., 150 sp., chiefly N. temp., |✱, and trop. and S. Afr. Most are herbs with opp. exstip. l. (connate in Dipsacus), and cymes (Triplostegia, Morina) or heads of fls. That the heads are also cymose is indicated by the fact that the fls. do not open in strictly centripetal order. The outer fls. have the corolla more or less drawn out on one side (*cf.* Compositae, Cruciferae, &c.); bracteoles of the ordinary kind are rare (Triplostegia). Most have an epicalyx, a cup-shaped organ springing from the base of the ovary, and usu. regarded as composed of the two united bracteoles. K and C $\underline{5}$-merous or 4-merous by union of two members; A 4, epipetalous; $\overline{G}$ (2), 1-loc. with one pend. anatr. ov. Fls. usu. protandr. of the flower class B′. Fr. an achene (*cf.* Compositae) usu. enclosed in the epicalyx; endosperm. Several are cult. orn. fl.; Dipsacus yields teasels. *Chief genera:* Knautia, Dipsacus, Scabiosa.
Dipsacales (Warming). The 7th cohort of Sympetalae.
Dipsacus L. Dipsaceae. 12 Medit., Eur., Afr. *D. sylvestris* Mill. (teasel), Brit. The connate leaves form troughs round the stem in which rain-water collects. The protandr. fls. are chiefly visited by bees. *D. fullonum* L. (fuller's teasel) has hooked bracts; the fr.-heads are used for raising the nap upon cloth (*Kew Bull.* 1912, p. 345).

Dipteracanthus Nees = Ruellia L. p.p. (Acanth.).
Dipteranthemum F. Muell. Amarant. (2). 1 Austr. [3 Brazil.
Dipteranthus Barb. Rodr. (*Zygostates* p.p. *EP.*). Orchid. (II. 19).
Dipteris Reinw. Polypod. 5 As., Polynes.
Dipterocarpaceae (*EP.*; *BH.* incl. *Ancistroclad.*). Dicots. (Archichl. Parietales; Guttiferales *BH.*; pp. xxxiii, l). 25/350 palaeotrop., chiefly Ind. Usu. tall, little branched trees with entire, leathery, evergreen, usu. alt. stip. l., and resin passages. Sometimes gregarious in growth. Infl. racemose, of ☿, reg., 5-merous fls. Twigs, infl., K, C, G usu. hairy. K 5; C 5, conv., often connate at base; A 5—10—15 or more, connective usu. with term. process; G (3), 3-loc. with 2-∞ ov. in each, style frequently on a stylopodium. Fr. usu. a 1-seeded nut enclosed in K, some seps. enlarged into wings. No endosp. Valuable timber, and resins. *Chief gen.:* Dipterocarpus, Dryobalanops, Shorea, Vatica, Vateria. (*BH.* chars. incl. Ancistr.)
Dipterocarpus Gaertn. f. Dipterocp. 70 Indomal. Large amplexicaul stips. protect the young bud (*cf.* Magnolia, &c.). Stylopodium. Several yield wood-oil or Gurjun balsam, a resin obtained by tapping, and used as a varnish. Many yield useful timber.
Dipterocome Fisch. et Mey. Comp. (9). 1 W. As. Fr. 2-winged.
Dipterodendron (incl. *Dilodendron*) Radlk. Sapind. (1). 2 trop. Am.
Dipteronia Oliv. Acer. 2 Cent. Chi. Mericarp winged all round.
Dipteropeltis Hallier f. Convolv. (1). 1 Cameroons.
Dipterosiphon Huber. Burmann. 1 Para.
Dipterostemon Rydberg (*Brodiaea* pp.). Lili. (IV). 4 W. N. Am.
Dipterygium Decne. (*Pteroloma* Hochst.). Capparid. (I). (Crucif. *BH.*) 3 Panjab to Nubia. Fr. a samara (*cf.* fam.).
Dipteryx Schreb. (*Coumarouna* Aubl.). Legum. (III. 8). 10 trop. Am. L. opp. Fr. 1-seeded indeh. 3 lower seps. mere teeth, 2 upper wing-like. *D. odorata* Willd. (Tonquin or Tonka bean) used in perfumery, snuff, &c. Some yield valuable timber.
Diptychandra Tul. Legum. (II. 8). 3 Brazil, Bolivia.
Diptychocarpus Trautv. Crucif. (4). 1 C. As.
Dipyrena Hook. Verben. (1). 1 temp. S. Am. L. alt. Stones 2, 2-loc.
Dirachma Schweinf. ex. Balf. f. Geran. 1 Socotra. L. alt. 8-merous.
Dirca L. Thymel. 2 N. Am. K almost 0, C 0, A 8, G 1-loc.
Dircaea Decne. = Gesnera Mart. (*BH.*) = Corytholoma Decne. p.p.
Dirichletia Klotzsch. Rubi. (I. 2). 15 trop. Afr., Madag. [orn. fl.
Disa Berg. Orchid. (II. 1). 110 S. and trop. Afr., Madag., Masc. Cult.
Disaccanthus Greene (*Streptanthus* p.p.). Crucif. (1). 5 W. N. Am.
Disachoena Zoll. et Mor. Umbell. Nomen.
Disakisperma Steud. Gramin. (inc. sed.). 1 Mex.
Disandra L. = Sibthorpia L. (Scroph.).
Disanthus Maxim. Hamamel. 1 Japan.
Disarticulate, to separate at a joint.
Disc, a flattening of the receptacle above the K, *Anacardiaceae*, *Celastraceae*, *Rutaceae*; epigynous in *Umbelliferae*, &c.; **-flower**, *Compositae*; **-oid**, like a disc.
Discaria Hook. Rhamn. 15 S. Andes, Brazil, N.Z., Austr. Cult. orn.
Dischidia R. Br. (incl. *Conchophyllum* Blume). Asclep. (II. 3). 70 Indomal., Polynes., Austr. Epiphytic, climbing by advent. roots, and

with fleshy l. covered by wax. The curious pitcher-plant, *D. Rafflesiana* Wall., besides the ordinary l., has pitcher-l. Each is a pitcher with incurved margin, about 10 cm. deep. Into it grows an adv. r. developed from the stem or petiole just beside it. The pitcher may hang with its mouth upwards or may stand horizontally or upside down. It usu. contains a lot of *débris*, largely carried into it by nesting ants. Most contain ± rain water, so that perhaps they act as humus collectors and water reservoirs. The inner surface is waxy, so that the water cannot be absorbed by the pitcher itself, but must be taken up by the roots.

Developmental study shows the pitcher to be a l. with its lower side invaginated. The existing sp. illustrate all stages. Many, *e.g. D. bengalensis* Colebr., have bi-convex l.; others have the under surface concave, *e.g. D.* (*C.*) *Collyris* Wall., and the roots are developed under and sheltered by the concave l. A further invagination would lead to *D. Rafflesiana.* (Treub in *Ann. Buitenz.* III. 1883, Haberlandt's *Tropenreise*, p. 168, and two papers in *Ann. of Bot.* 1893.)

Dischidiopsis Schlechter (*Dischidia* p.p.). Asclep. (II. 3). 2 N. G., Phils.

Dischisma Choisy. Scrophulariaceae (II. 7). 10 S. Afr.

Dischistocalyx (*Distichocalyx*) Lindau. Acanth. (IV. A). 7 trop. Afr.

Disciflorae (*BH.*). The 2nd series of Polypetalae.

Disciphania Eichl. Menispermaceae. 8 trop. S. Am.

Discocactus Pfeiff. (*Echinocactus* p.p. *E.P.*). Cact. (III. 1). 3 trop. Am., W.I.

Discocalyx Mez. Myrsinaceae (II). 8 Phil. Is., Polynesia.

Discocarpus Klotzsch. Euphorbiaceae (A. I. 1). 3 Brazil, Guiana.

Discoglypremna Prain. Euphorbiaceae (A. II. 2). 1 trop. Afr.

Discogyne Schlechter. Saxifrag. (V). 1 New Guinea. *Cf. Engl. Jb.* 82,

Discolobium Benth. Leguminosae (III. 7). 6 Brazil, Paraguay. [123.

Discoluma Baill. (*Chrysophyllum* p.p.). Sapot. (I). 1 Brazil.

Discontinuous distribution, *cf.* Geographical Distribution.

Discophora Miers (*Kummeria* Mart.). Icacin. 2 trop. S. Am.

Discopleura DC. Umbelliferae (III. 5). 2 N. Am.

Discopodium Hochst. Solanaceae (2). 1 trop. Afr.

Discostigma Hassk. = Garcinia L. p.p. (Guttif.).

Discrete, separate.

Disella Greene (*Sida* p.p.). Malvaceae (2). 4 N. Am.

Diselma Hook. f. (*Fitzroya* p.p.). Coniferae. 1 Tasmania.

Disemma Labill. = Passiflora L. p.p. (Passifl.).

Disepalum Hook. f. Anonaceae (1). 4 Malaya. 2-merous.

Disparago Gaertn. Compositae (4). 5 S. Afr.

Disperis Sw. Orchidaceae (II. 1). 40 trop. and S. Afr., Madag., As.

Disperma C. B. Clarke. Acanthaceae (IV. A). 7 trop. Afr.

Dispersal of seeds may be *occasional*, as by floating trees, ice, &c., tornados, mud on birds' feet, the voiding of the crops of carnivorous birds, &c. (see *Origin of Species*, chap. XII), or *regular*, by ways which may be classed in four heads. By **wind** are carried *directly* the spores of ferns, &c., seeds of Pyrola, Orchidaceae, some Caryophyllaceae, &c., by *censer-mechanisms* (see Aconitum), Campanula,

Caryophyllaceae, Delphinium, Iridaceae, Liliaceae, Papaver; *winged seeds* in Bignoniaceae, Bromeliaceae, Casuarina, Millingtonia, Pinus, Zanonia; *winged fruits* in Abronia, Aceraceae, Bignoniaceae, Carpinus, Dipterocarpaceae, Fraxinus, Liriodendron, Malpighiaceae, Ptelea, Pterocarpus, Rumex, Serjania, Terminalia, Tripteris, Ulmus, Ventilago; *hairs*, forming a *parachute mechanism*, in seeds of Apocynaceae, Asclepiadaceae, Epilobium, Gossypium, Salix, &c., in fruits of Anemone, Clematis, Compositae, Eriophorum, Typha, Valerianaceae, &c.

By **animals** are carried, as *inside* passengers, the seeds in edible fruits (*q.v.*), and as *outside* passengers the *hooked fr.* of Asperula, Bidens, Blumenbachia, Cenchrus, Circaea, Daucus, Galium, Geum, Harpagophytum, Martynia, Medicago, Tragoceros, Triumfetta, Xanthium, &c., the *glandular fr.* or seed of Allionia, Boerhaavia, Pisonia, Plumbago, Siegesbeckia, &c. By **water** Cerbera, Cocos, Crinum, Nuphar, Nymphaea, Potamogeton, &c. By **explosive mechanisms** are scattered the seeds of Alstroemeria, Balsaminaceae, Biophytum, Buxus, Cardamine, Cyclanthera, Dorstenia, Ecballium, Elaterium, Eschscholtzia, Geranium, Hura, Impatiens, Ricinus, Ulex, Viola, &c. As a general rule, the dispersal of seed by any of these mechanisms is only to a very small distance, but they may at any time be of great importance by enabling transport over long distances.

Disporopsis Hance. Liliaceae (VII). 4 S.E. China.

Disporum Salisb. Liliaceae (VII). 15 N. temp. As. and Am.

Dissanthelium Trin. Gramineae (10). 4 California to Mexico.

Dissected, deeply divided.

Dissepiment, septum.

Dissiliaria F. Muell. Euphorbiaceae (A. I. 1). 3 warm Austr.

Dissochaeta Blume. Melastomaceae (I). 25 Indomal.

Dissochondrus O. Ktze. (*Setaria BH.*). Gramineae (5). 1 Hawaii.

Dissomeria Hook. f. Flacourtiaceae (9) (Samyd. *BH.*). 1 W. Afr.

Dissothrix A. Gray. Compositae (2). 1 N.E. Brazil.

Dissotis Benth. Melastomaceae (I). 50 Afr.

Distal, furthest from axis.

Distasis DC. (*Chaetopappa* DC.). Compositae (3). 2 Texas, Mexico.

Disteganthus Lem. Bromeliaceae (4). 2 Guiana.

Distegia Klatt (*Didelta EP.*). Compositae (10). 1 Austr.

Distegocarpus Sieb. et Zucc. = Carpinus L. (Betulac.).

Distemma Lem. = Passiflora (L.) (Passifl.).

Distemon Wedd. Urticaceae (3). 1 Indomal.

Distemonanthus Benth. Leguminosae (II. 5). 1 Guinea.

Disterigma Niedenzu ex Drude (*Vaccinium* p.p.). Ericaceae (III. 1). 3 trop. Andes.

Distiacanthus Linden (*Bromelia* p.p.). Bromeliaceae (4). 2 S. Am.

Distichella Van Tiegh. (*Dendrophthora* p.p.). Loranth. 3 W.I.

Distichia Nees et Meyen. Juncaceae. 3 Andes.

Distichlis Rafin. Gramineae (10). 4 Am. *D. maritima* Rafin. also Austr., used for binding sandy soil (*cf.* Ammophila, Carex).

Distichocalyx (*Dischistocalyx*) T. Anders. Acanth. (IV. A). 7 trop. Afr.

Distichostemon F. Muell. Sapindaceae (II). 1 N. Austr. Apet.
Distictella O. Ktze. = Distictis Bur., non DC. (Bignon.).
Distictis Bur., Mart. Bignoniaceae (I). 5 Brazil, Guiana.
Distoecha Phil. Compositae (13). 1 Chili.
Distomanthera Turcz. Saxifragaceae (inc. sed.). 1 S. Am.
Distomocarpus O. E. Schulz. Crucif. (2). 1 Morocco.
Distribution of seeds, see Dispersal; **of sexes**, see Dioecism, Monoecism, Andro- and Gyno-mon- and di-oecism, Polygamy, Sex-distr.
Distylium Sieb. et Zucc. Hamamelidaceae. 8 E. As., Indomal.
Dita bark, *Alstonia scholaris* R. Br.
Ditassa R. Br. Asclepiadaceae (II. 1). 75 S. Am.
Ditaxis Vahl ex A. Juss. (*Argithamnia BH.*). Euph. (A. II. 2). 50 Am., W.I.
Ditch-grass (Am.), *Ruppia maritima* L.
Dithyrea Harv. (*Biscutella* p.p. *BH.*). Cruc. (3). 2 S.W. U.S.
Dithyrocarpus Kunth. = Floscopa Lour. (Commel.).
Ditta Griseb. Euphorbiaceae (A. II. 7). 1 Cuba.
Dittander, *Lepidium latifolium* L.
Dittoceras Hook. f. Asclepiadaceae (II. 3). 1 Sikkim.
Dittostigma Phil. Solanaceae (4). 1 Chili.
Diuranthera Hemsl. (*Paradisea* p.p.). Lili. (III). 2 China.
Diuris Sm. Orchidaceae (II. 2). 20 Austr.
Divi-divi, *Caesalpinia Coriaria* Willd.
Division of labour (sta.), *Cassia*, *Commelina*, *Heeria*.
Dizygostemon Radlk. (*Beyrichia* p.p. *BH.*). Scroph. (II. 6). 1 Brazil.
Dizygotheca N.E. Br. Araliaceae (I). 5 New Caledonia.
Dobera Juss. Salvadoraceae. 3 trop. Afr., As.
Dobinea Buch.-Ham. Anacardiaceae (5) (Sapindaceae *BH.*). 1 Himalaya. ♀ fl. naked.
Dobrowskya Presl = Lobelia L. (*BH.*) = Monopsis Salisb. p.p.
Dock, *Rumex*.
Docynia Decne. Rosaceae (II). 3 Himal., Burma.
Dodartia (Tourn.) L. Scrophulariaceae (II. 6). 1 S. Russia, W. As.
Dodder, *Cuscuta*.
Dodecadenia Nees. Lauraceae (I). 3 Himal.
Dodecadia Lour. Flacourtiaceae (inc. sed.). 1 China.
Dodecaspermum Forst. Inc. sed. Nomen.
Dodecatheon L. Primulaceae (I). 30 N. Am., N.E. As. Like Cyclamen. Cult. orn. fl. (American cowslip).
Dodonaea L. Sapindaceae (II). 50 trop., esp. Austr.
Doellingeria Nees (*Aster* L. p.p.). Compositae (3). 6 N. Am.
Dog-bane (Am.), *Apocynum*; **-daisy**, *Chrysanthemum Leucanthemum* L.; **-rose**, *Rosa canina* L.; **-'s tail grass**, *Cynosurus*; **-'s tooth grass**, *Cynodon Dactylon* Pers.; **-violet**, *Erythronium*; **-wood**, *Cornus sanguinea* L., (W.I.) *Piscidia*.
Dolia Lindl. Nolanaceae. 18 W. S.Am.
Dolianthus C. H. Wright. Loganiaceae. 1 New Guinea.
Dolichandra Cham. (*Macfadyena BH.*). Bignon. (2). 1 S. Brazil.
Dolichandrone Fenzl. Bignoniaceae (2). 10 Madag. to Malaya.
Dolichanthera Schlechter et Krause. Rubi. (I. 7). 1 New Caled.
Dolichodelphys K. Schum. et Krause. Rubiaceae (I. 8). 1 Peru.

Dolichogyne DC. = Nardophyllum Hook. et Arn. (Comp.).
Dolicholobium A. Gray. Rubiaceae (I. 5). 5 Fiji to New Guinea.
Dolicholus Medic. = Rhynchosia Lour. (Legum.).
Dolichometra K. Schum. Rubiaceae (I. 2). 1 E. trop. Afr.
Dolichopsis Hassler. Leguminosae (III. 10). 1 Paraguay.
Dolichos L. Leguminosae (III. 10). 60 warm. *D. Lablab* L. largely cult. in the trop. for its ed. pods. *D. biflorus* L. (horse-gram) cult. in India, &c. for feeding horses and cattle.
Dolichosiphon Phil. Solanaceae (inc. sed.). 1 Chili.
Dolichostylis Turcz. (*Stenonema EP.*). Crucif. (inc. sed.). 1 Colombia.
Doliocarpus Roland. Dilleniaceae. 25 trop. S. Am. W. I.
Dollee-wood (W.I.), *Myristica surinamensis* Roland.
Dolophragma Fenzl (*Arenaria* p.p. *BH.*). Caryoph. (I. 1). 2 Nepal.
Dolosanthus Klatt (*Vernonia* p.p.). Compositae (1). 1 trop. Afr.
Domatia, *cf.* Acarodomatia.
Dombeya Cav. Sterculiaceae. 80 Afr., Madag.
Domeykoa Phil. Umbelliferae (I. 2). 1 Chili.
Dominant, very abundant and widespread.
Domingoa Schlechter (*Epidendrum* p.p.). Orch. (II. 6). 2 W. Ind.
Donacodes Blume = Amomum L. p.p. (Zingib.).
Donaldsonia Baker f. Passifloraceae. 1 trop. Afr.
Donatia Forst. Stylidiaceae, formerly Saxifragaceae (I). 2 Chili, New Zealand.
Donax Lour. (*Clinogyne BH.*). Marantaceae. 2 Indomal.
Dondia Adans. (*Suaeda* Forsk.). Chenopodiaceae (B). 15 N. Am.
Dondia Spreng. = Hacquetia Neck.
Donella Pierre (*Chrysophyllum* p.p.). Sapot. (1). 3 trop. Afr.
Donia G. Don (*Clianthus* p.p.). Leguminosae (III. 6). 2 Austr., N. Zealand. Cult. orn. fl. under the name *C. Dampieri* Cunn.
Doniophyton Wedd. Compositae (12). 3 Chili, Argentina.
Donnellia C. B. Clarke (*Callisia* p.p.). Commelin. 1 C. Am.
Donnellsmithia Coulter et Rose. Umbell. (III. 4). 1 Guatemala.
Dontostemon Andrz. Cruciferae (4). 8 Centr. As.
Donzellia Tenore. Euphorbiaceae (inc. sed.). 1 Brazil.
Doob grass, *Cynodon Dactylon* Pers.
Doodia R. Br. Polypodiaceae. 5 Ceylon to Austr. and N.Z.
Doon (Ceylon), *Doona.*
Doona Thw. Dipterocarpaceae. 11 Ceylon. Timber, resin.
Doorweed (Am.), *Polygonum aviculare* L.
Dopatrium Buch.-Ham. ex Benth. Scrophul. (II. 6). 10 palaeotrop.
Doratoxylon Thou. Sapindaceae (II). 1 Mascarenes.
Dorema D. Don. Umbelliferae (III. 6). 4 W. Centr. As. *D. ammoniacum* D. Don is the source of the gum-resin gum-ammoniacum (medic.), obtained by puncturing the stem.
Doria Thunb. = Othonna L. (*BH.*) = Senecio Tourn. (Comp.).
Doritis Lindl. Orchidaceae (II. 20). 5 Indomal.
Dormant buds, buds which do not develop with the rest.
Doronicum Tourn. ex L. Compositae (8). 25 N. temp. |✱
Dorothea Wernham. Rubiaceae (I. 8). 1 S. Nigeria.
Dorsal (surface), lower, away from axis, but not very consistently used **dorsi-fixed** (anther), jointed to filament by its whole length; **-ventral**

with upper and lower sides differing in structure, leaves, creeping shoot, many fl., *e.g. Aconitum*, *Delphinium*, *Labiatae*, *Leguminosae*, *Orchidaceae*. *Cf.* esp. *Podostemaceae*, and see *Boraginaceae*.

Dorstenia Plum. ex L. Moraceae (I). 120 trop. Herbs or shrubs with peculiar cymose infl. The common recept. of the fls. is a flat or hollowed fleshy structure, often > an inch wide. Fls. unisexual, sometimes all of one sex on one receptacle, sometimes intermingled with several ♂ round one ♀, sunk in the receptacle round whose edge project a number of bracts. P-segments completely united. Sta. in the ♂ usu. 2. The fr. when ripe is shot out of the receptacle; the latter becomes very turgid and presses on the fr. and at length ejects it as one might fillip away a bit of soap between finger and thumb.

Dortmanna L.=Lobelia L. (Campan.).

Doryalis (*Dovyalis*) E. Mey. Flacourtiaceae (4). 25 Afr., Ceylon. Some (*cf.* Aberia) have ed. fr.

Doryanthes Correa. Amaryllidaceae (II). 3 Austr.

Dorycnium L. Leguminosae (III. 5). 10 Medit.

Doryopteris J. Sm. Polypodiaceae. 45 trop. and subtrop.

Doryphora Endl. Monimiaceae. 1 New S. Wales.

Dorystephania Warb. Asclepiadaceae (II. 3). 1 Phil. Is.

Dorystoechas Boiss. et Heldr. Labiatae (VI). 1 W. As.

Dossinia C. Morr. Orchidaceae (II. 2). 1 Borneo, cult. orn. l. under the name *Anoectochilus Lowii* Hort.

Dossinimaria × Rolfe. Orchidaceae. Hybrid of last and Haemaria.

Douarrea Montr. Inc. sed. 2 New Caled.

Double coconut, *Lodoicea Sechellarum* Labil.; **-flower,** fl. with sta. changed to petals (in Compositae, with disc fl. changed to ray fl.); **-needles,** *cf.* Coniferae.

Douglas fir, *Pseudotsuga Douglasii* Carr.

Douglasia Lindl. Primul. (I). 6 arct. N. Am.

Doum palm, *Hyphaene*.

Dove-orchid, *Peristeria elata* Hook.; **-wood** (W.I.), *Alchornea*.

Dovea Kunth. Restionaceae. 10 S. Afr. Used for thatch.

Dovyalis (*Doryalis*) E. Mey. Flacourtiaceae (4). 25 Afr., Madag., Ceylon. *Cf.* Aberia.

Downingia Torr. (incl. *Clintonia* Dougl.). Campanul. (III). 3 Pac. Am. *D. pulchella* Torr. has no twisting of the floral axis, or not > 90°.

Down tree (W.I.), *Ochroma Lagopus* Sw.

Downy, covered with fine soft hairs.

Doxantha Miers (*Bignonia* p.p. *BH.*). Bignon. (I). 1 U.S.

Doyerea Grosourdy ex Bello (*Corallocarpus* p.p. *EP.*). Cucurbitaceae (2) (Myrtaceae *BH.*). 2 W.I., Venezuela.

Draba Dill. ex L. Cruciferae (4). 150 N. temp. and arctic, and south-west. N. Am.; 5 in Brit. (whitlow-grass), incl. *D. verna* L. which occurs in Eur. in a vast number of vars. which breed true, and were distinguished as sp. by Jordan (*cf.* works on Mendelism). Most are tufted, ± xero. with hairy or fleshy l.

Dracaena Vand. Liliaceae (VI). 40 Old World warm. Mostly trees, whose stems branch and grow in thickness (extra-fascicular combium). The famous dragon-tree of Teneriffe (*D. Draco* L.), blown down in

1868, was 70 ft. high and 45 ft. in girth and was supposed to be 6000 years old. A resin exudes from the trunk of this sp. (dragon's blood); the original dragon's blood appears to be that of *D. Cinnabari* Balf. f. (Socotra). [*Cf.* Pleomele, and see N. E. Brown in *Kew Bull.* 1914, p. 273.]

Dracamine Nieuwland (*Cardamine* p.p.). Crucifer. (2). 4 Atl. U.S.

Dracocephalum L. Labiatae (IV). 50 N. temp.

Dracontioides Engl. Araceae (IV). 1 S. Brazil.

Dracontium L. Araceae (IV). 10 trop. Am. The sympodial rhiz. gives rise yearly to one enormous l. and an infl. The l. has 3 chief divisions, and the lat. ones develope dichot. at first. Fl. ☿ with P.

Dracontomelum Blume. Anacardiaceae (2). 6 Malaya to Fiji.

Dracophyllum Labill. (excl. *Sphenotoma* R. Br.). Epacridaceae (2). 25 N.Z., Austr., New Caled. The sheathing l. leave ring-scars when they fall.

Dracunculus (Tourn.) Adans. Araceae (VII). 2 Medit. Fert. like Arum.

Dragon-root (Am.), *Arisaema*; **-'s blood**, **-tree**, *Dracaena.*

Drakaea Lindl. Orchidaceae (II. 2). 4 Austr.

Drake-Brockmania Stapf. Gramineae (10). 1 Brit. Somaliland.

Draperia Torr. Hydrophyllaceae. 1 California.

Drapetes Banks. Thymelaeaceae. 6 S. Am., N.Z. to New Guinea.

Drebbelia Zoll. Olacaceae. 1 Bali.

Dregea E. Mey. Asclepiadaceae (II. 3). 5 S. Afr. to China.

Drejera Nees (*Jacobinia BH.*). Acanthaceae (IV. B). 3 trop. Am.

Drejerella Lindau. Acanthaceae (IV. B). 3 W. Indies.

Drepananthus Maingay ex Hook. f. Anonaceae (4). 3 Malay Penin., Sumatra.

Drepanium, a monoch. cyme with each successive branch on same side of relatively main axis, and in same plane, *Juncus*, *Marantaceae.*

Drepanocarpus G. F. W. Mey. Leguminosae (III. 8). 8 trop. Am., Afr.

Drepanolobus Nutt. ex Torr. et Gray = Hosackia Dougl. p.p.

Drepanostemma Jumelle et Perrier. Asclep. (II. 1). 1 Madag.

Driessenia Korth. Melastomaceae (I). 5 Malaya.

Drimia Jacq. Liliaceae (V). 25 Afr.

Drimiopsis L. et Paxt. Liliaceae (V). 10 S. and trop. Afr. Cult. orn. fl.

Drimycarpus Hook. f. Anacardiaceae (4). 1 E. Himal.

Drimys Forst. Magnoliaceae. 20 S. Am., and N.Z. to Borneo. There is a distinction between calyx and corolla (*cf.* Illicium). The bark of *D. Winteri* Forst. (Winter's bark) is medicinal.

Drimyspermum Reinw. = Phaleria Jack (Thymel.).

Drinks, *cf.* Alcohol; infusion drinks from seeds of *Coffee*, *Thea*, *Theobroma*, *Cola*, *Paullinia*, l. of *Thea*, *Ilex*, *Catha*, *Priva*, *Stachytarpheta*, and root of *Cichorium.*

Driodium (Cl.), a dry thicket formation.

Drip-tip, *cf.* *Acer*, and *Artocarpus*, *Begonia*, *Boehmeria*, *Ficus.*

Droguetia Gaudich. Urticaceae (5). 4 trop. As., Afr., Madag.

Droogmansia De Wild. (*Desmodium* p.p.). Legu. (III. 7). 4 trop. Afr.

Drooping of young l., *Aesculus*, *Bauhinia*, *Cinnamomum*, *Dryobalanops*; **of young shoot**, *Amherstia*, *Brownea*, *Saraca*.

Dropper, young immature bulb.

Dropseed grass (Am.), *Sporobolus*, *Muhlenbergia*.

Dropwort, *Filipendula vulgaris* Moench.; **water-**, *Oenanthe*.

Drosera L. Droseraceae. 90 trop. and temp. 3 in Brit. (sundew). *D. rotundifolia* L. abundant in bogs. Herbs usu. with creeping rhiz. and rosettes of l., insectivorous. The blade of the l. is circular in some sp., elongated in others, and is set with curious tentacles; these are emergences containing vascular bundles and ending in swollen reddish heads which secrete a sticky glistening fluid. Flies and other insects mistaking it for honey are held by it. The tentacles are exceedingly sensitive to continued pressure even by the lightest bodies; the result is to cause an inward and downward movement of the head of the tentacle, finally placing the fly upon the blade of the l. At the same time the stimulus passes to the surrounding tentacles causing them also to bend downwards to the same point. The victim is thus smothered and now the glandular heads of the tentacles secrete a ferment which acts upon the proteids and brings them into solution, when they are taken up by the l. Afterwards the tentacles expand once more and recommence the secretion of the sticky fluid. The food thus obtained is of benefit to the pl., though it can live without it. D. is able to live in very poor soil. The extra materials obtained are devoted chiefly to seed-production. If the stimulus produced by the capture of an insect be very powerful, the l. itself may bend into a cup form, and this feature is very marked in some sp., the l. bending almost double over the prey.

The fls. of the Brit. sp. rarely open, but self-pollinate in bud.

Droseraceae (*EP.*, *BH.*). Dicots. (Archichl. Sarraceniales; Rosales *BH.*). 5 gen., 100 sp., Drosera cosmopolitan, the rest more local. Herbs, usu. with perenn. rhiz. and rosettes of l.; Aldrovanda a water-plant. All are insectivorous; Dionaea and Aldrovanda have sensitive l. which shut up when touched, the others catch their prey by sticky tentacles upon the l. (see genera). Fls. usu. in cincinni, rarely in racemes or sol., ☿, reg., 5—4-merous, usu. hypog. K (5); C 5, imbr.; no disc; A usu. 5, pollen in tetrads (*cf.* Ericaceae); $\underline{G}$ (2, 3, or 5); plac. usu. parietal, rarely axile or free-central; style long; stigmas simple or branched; ov. 3—∞, anatr. Loculic. caps.; seed with endosp. and small basal embryo. *Genera:* Dionaea, Aldrovanda, Drosophyllum, Drosera, Roridula.

Drosophyllum Link. Droseraceae. *D. lusitanicum* Link, Morocco, Portugal, S. Spain. The l. have glands of two kinds—stalked, secreting a sticky fluid (*cf.* Drosera), and sessile, which only secrete when stimulated by nitrogenous matter, and then secrete a digestive ferment. Insects alight on the glands and are entangled; they struggle for a while and finally sink down and die, and are digested by the ferment. The taller glands have no power of movement, but are able to secrete a ferment as well as the sessile ones.

Drudea Griseb. Caryophyllaceae (I. 3). 1 Peru.

Drudeophytum Coulter et Rose (*Arracacia* p.p.). Umb. (III. 4). 5 N. Am.

Drugs are obtained from ∞ pl.: *cf. e.g. Abrus*, *Aconitum*, *Aegle*, *Aloe*, *Alpinia*, *Alstonia*, *Anchusa*, *Aralia* (ginseng), *Atropa* (belladonna), *Bamboos*, *Brayera*, *Brucea*, *Canella*, *Cannabis* (hemp), *Capsicum*, *Carica*, *Carum* (caraway), *Cascarilla*, *Cassia* (senna), *Cinchona* (quinine, &c.), *Cinnamomum* (camphor), *Cistus*, *Citrullus* (colocynth), *Citrus*, *Coix*, *Cola*, *Colchicum*, *Colutea*, *Commiphora*, *Convolvulus* (scammony), *Croton*, *Curcuma*, *Datura*, *Digitalis* (digitalin), *Dorema* (gum-ammoniacum), *Dracaena*, *Drimys*, *Elettaria* (cardamom), *Erythroxylon* (cocaine), *Eucalyptus*, *Eugenia*, *Ferula* (asafoetida), *Gentiana*, *Glycyrrhiza* (liquorice), *Guaiacum*, *Ipomoea* (jalap), *Lewisia*, *Lindera*, *Mentha*, *Menyanthes*, *Myroxylon*, *Papaver* (opium), *Peucedanum* (dill), *Picraena*, *Pilocarpus*, *Piper*, *Podophyllum*, *Polygala*, *Pringlea*, *Rhamnus* (cascara), *Rheum* (rhubarb), *Ricinus* (castor-oil), *Ruta* (rue), *Santalina*, *Sassafras*, *Schoenocaulon*, *Smilax* (sarsaparilla), *Strophanthus*, *Strychnos* (strychnine), *Styrax*, *Tamarindus*, *Toluifera*, *Trigonella* (fenugreek), *Uragoga* (ipecacuanha), *Urginea* (squill), *Veratrum*, *Verbascum*, *Zingiber* (ginger), &c. See Dragendorff, *Die Heilpflanzen*, Stuttgart, 1898.

Drummondita Harv. (*Philotheca EP.*). Rutaceae (I). 1 Austr.

Drupaceae (Warming) = Rosaceae (sub-order V).

Drupaceous, drupe-like; **drupe**, a fleshy fr. with hard endocarp, within which is the seed, *Cornaceae*, *Juglans*, *Prunus*.

Drupatris Lour. Inc. sed. 1 Cochin-China.

Drusa DC. (*Bowlesia BH.*). Umbelliferae (I. 2). 3 Am., Canaries.

Dry fr., esp. achenes and nuts (indehiscent), follicles, legumes and capsules (dehiscent); and schizocarps; **-ing pl.**, *cf.* Collecting.

Dryadaea L. = Dryas L. (Ros.).

Dryadorchis Schlechter. Orchidaceae (II. 20). 2 New Guinea.

Dryandra R. Br. Proteaceae (II). 50 Austr. Like Banksia.

Dryas L. Rosaceae (III. 2). 2 arctic. *D. octopetala* L. (alpine in Brit.) is androdioec. in the Alps. Style feathery after fert. (*cf.* Clematis, Geum).

Drymaria Willd. Caryophyllaceae (I. 3). 40 trop. and S. temp.

Drymocallis Fourr. (*Potentilla* p.p.). Rosac. (III. 2). 20 N. Am.

Drymoda Lindl. Orchidaceae (II. 16). 1 Burma.

Drymoglossum Presl. Polypodiaceae. 10 palaeotrop., Jap., Chi. *D. carnosum* (Wall.) J. Sm. has succulent leaves.

Drymonia Mart. Gesneriaceae (I). 15 trop. Am., W. Ind.

Drymophila R. Br. Liliaceae (VII). 2 E. Austr., Tasm.

Drymophloeus Zipp. Palmaceae (IV. 1). 15 Malaya, N. Austr.

Drymotaenium Makino. Polypodiaceae. 2 Japan, Formosa.

Drynaria (Bory) J. Sm. Polypodiaceae. 20 palaeotrop. *D. quercifolia* (L.) J. Sm. has dimorphic l., some projecting, assimilating and spore-bearing, the others small, close to rhiz., collecting humus.

Dryobalanops Gaertn. f. Dipterocarpaceae. 7 Borneo, Malaya. *D. aromatica* Gaertn. &c. yield Borneo or Sumatra camphor, used chiefly in China. The young l. are red, and hang down. A ∞.

Dryopetalon A. Gray. Cruciferae (2). 1 Mexico. Pets. 5—7-lobed.

Dryopteris Adans. (incl. *Cyclosorus*, *Lastrea*, *Leptogramma*, *Meniscium*, *Nephrodium*, *Phegopteris*). 1000 cosmop. *D. Filix-mas* (L.) Schott (shield-fern) and others Brit. This sp. has a stout nearly erect rhiz. with large pinnate l. The var. *cristatum* Moore shows apospory.

Dryostachyum J. Sm. Polypodiaceae. 5 Malay Archipelago.

Drypetes Vahl. Euphorbiaceae (A. I. 1). 150 trop.

Drypis L. Caryophyllaceae (II. 1). 1 S.E. Eur.

Duabanga Buch.-Ham. Sonneratiaceae. 2 Indomal.

Dubautia Gaudich. Compositae (5). 6 Hawaiian Is. L. ||-veined.

Duboisia R. Br. Solanaceae (5). 2 Austr., New Caled.

Duboscia Bocq. Tiliaceae. 1 trop. W. Afr.

Dubouzetia Panch. Elaeocarpaceae. 6 New Caled.

Dubrueilia Gaudich. = Pilea Lindl. p.p. (Urtic.).

Duchesnea Smith (*Fragaria* p.p. *BH.*). Rosac. (III. 2). 2 S. As.

Duck's meat, duckweed, *Lemna*.

Ducosia Vieill. ex Guillaumin (*Dubouzetia* p.p.). Elaeo. 1 N. Cal.

Ducrosia Boiss. Umbelliferae (III. 6). 3 W. As.

Dudleya Britton et Rose (*Cotyledon* p.p. *EP.*). Crassul. 60 Calif.

Duffin bean, *Phaseolus lunatus* L.

Dugesia A. Gray. Compositae (5). 1 Mexico.

Dugezia Montr. = Lysimachia L. p.p. (Primul.).

Duguetia A. St. Hil. (*Aberemoa* Aubl.). Anonaceae (1). 30 trop. S. Am., W.I. *D. quitarensis* Benth. &c. furnish Jamaica and Cuba lancewood. Fr. formed of the individual berries or achenes united to the fleshy recept.

Dulacia Vell. (*Liriosma BH.*). Olacaceae. 15 trop. S. Am.

Dulcis (Lat.), sweet.

Dulichium Pers. (*Websteria* Wright). Cyper. (1). 1 N. Am.

Dumasia DC. Leguminosae (III. 10). 3 trop. As., Afr., Madag.

Dumb-cane, *Dieffenbachia Seguine* Schott.

Dumerilia Lag. ex DC. = Jungia L. (Comp.).

Dumoria A. Chevalier. Sapotaceae (1). 1 trop. Afr. Good wood.

Dumose, shrubby.

Dunalia H. B. et K. Solanaceae (2). 15 W. S.Am. to Mexico.

Dunbaria Wight et Arn. Leguminosae (III. 10). 15 trop. As., Austr.

Dune-plants, *cf. Ammophila*, *Carex*, *Elymus*, *Hippophaë*, &c.

Dunnia Tutcher. Rubiaceae (I. 4). 1 China.

Duparquetia Baill. (*Oligostemon BH.*). Legumin. (II. 5). 1 W. Afr.

Dupontia R. Br. (*Graphephorum BH.*). Gramin. (10). 2 Arctic.

Duramen, the heart-wood.

Durandea Planch. (*Hugonia EP.*). Linaceae. 5 New Guinea, Polynes.

Durandia Boeck. Cyperaceae (II). 1 Costa Rica.

Duranta L. Verbenaceae (1). 10 trop. Am., W.I. Cult. orn. shrubs.

Duravia Greene (*Polygonum* p.p.). Polygon. (II. 2). 4 Calif.

Durian, *Durio zibethinus* Murr.

Durieua Boiss. et Reut. = Daucus Tourn. p.p. (Umbell.).

Durio Adans. Bombacaceae. 12 Indomal. *D. zibethinus* Murr. produces the durian fr., with delicate flavour and disagreeable smell. Seed with fleshy aril.

Duroia L. f. Rubiaceae (I. 8). 10 S. Am. Myrmecophilous (*cf.* Acacia). *D. petiolaris* Hk. f. and *D. hirsuta* K. Sch. have stems swollen just below the infl. The swollen part is hollow and entrance is obtained by two longitudinal slits; it is inhabited by ants, which bite through the thin tissue of the slits. *D. saccifera* Benth. et Hk. f. has 'ant-houses' on the l. At the base, on the under side, are two pear-shaped organs formed by outgrowth of the l. The entrance is upon the upper side, protected from rain by a little flap.

Dusenia O. Hoffm. (*Duseniella EP.*). Compos. (12). 1 Patagonia.

Duseniella K. Schum. Compositae (12). 1 Patagonia.

Dussia Krug. et Urb. Leguminosae (III. 1). 1 Martinique.

Dutaillyea Baill. Rutaceae (I). 1 New Caled.

Dutch clover, *Trifolium repens* L.; **-grass** (W.I.), *Panicum molle* Sw.; **rushes**, *Equisetum*.

Dutchman's breeches, *Dicentra*; **-pipe**, *Aristolochia*.

Duthiea Hackel. Gramineae (10). 2 Kashmir, Afghanistan.

Duvalia Haw. Asclepiadaceae (II. 3). 15 S. Afr.

Duvaliella Baill. Dipterocarpaceae. 1 Penang.

Duvaljouvea Palla. (*Cyperus* p.p.). Cyperaceae (I). 2 As., Eur.

Duvaua Kunth = Schinus L. p.p. (Anacard.).

Duvaucellia Bowditch. Oleaceae. 1 trop. Afr.

Duvernoya E. Mey (*Adhatoda* p.p. *BH.*). Acanthaceae (IV. B). 25 Afr.

Dwale, *Atropa Belladonna* L.

Dyckia Schult. f. Bromeliaceae (2). 70 warm S. Am.

Dyera Hook. f. Apocynaceae (I. 3). 3 Malaya.

Dyerophyton O. Ktze. (*Vogelia* Lam.). Plumbaginaceae. 3 palaeotrop.

Dyer's greenweed, *Genista tinctoria* L.; **-weld**, *Reseda lutea*, L.

Dyes (vegetable), *cf.* esp. *Alkanna*, *Baphia* (cam wood), *Bixa* (annatto), *Caesalpinia* (sappan), *Carthamus* (rouge), *Chlorophora* (fustic), *Cladrastis*, *Crocus* (saffron), *Crozophora*, *Curcuma* (turmeric), *Garcinia*, *Haematoxylon* (logwood), *Indigofera* (indigo), *Isatis* (woad), *Lawsonia*, *Maclura* (fustic), *Morinda*, *Nopalea*, *Peganum* (turkey red), *Pterocarpus*, *Reseda*, *Rhamnus*, *Rhus*, *Rubia* (madder).

Dypsidium Baill. (*Dypsis* p.p.). Palmae (IV. 1). 3 Madagascar.

Dypsis Noronha ex Thou. Palmae (IV 1). 10 Madag.

Dyschoriste Nees (*Calophanes BH.*). Acanthaceae (IV. A). 50 trop.

Dysodia Cav. Compositae (6). 35 Am.

Dysodiopsis Rydberg (*Dysodia* p.p.). Compositae (6). 1. S.W. U.S.

Dysolobium Prain. Leguminosae (III. 10). 4 Indomal.

Dysophylla Blume. Labiatae (VI). 20 E. As., Austr.

Dysopsis Baill. Euphorb. (A. II. 2). 1 Andes, Juan Fernandez.

Dysoxylum Blume. Meliaceae (III). 140 Indomal. *D. Fraseranum* Benth. (E. Austr.; Austr. mahogany) and others, good timber.

Dysphania R. Br. Caryophyllaceae (I. 5). 3 Austr. L. alt.

Dyssochroma Miers. Solanaceae (3). 4 trop. Am.

E- (Lat. pref.), without; **-bracteate**, **-calcarate**, **-costate**, **-dentate**, **-glandulose**, **-marginate** (notched), **-rostrate**, **-strophiolate**, **-valvate**, &c. And *cf.* Ex.

Eagle-wood, *Aquilaria*, *Agallocha* Roxb. (Burma).

Earina Lindl. Orchidaceae (II *a.* III). 6 N.Z., Polynesia.

Earth-nut, *Arachis hypogaea* L., *Conopodium denudatum* Koch.

East Indian arrowroot, *Curcuma*, *Tacca*; **-hemp**, *Crotalaria juncea* L.; **-rosewood**, *Dalbergia latifolia* Roxb.; **walnut**, *Albizzia Lebbek* Benth.

Eastwoodia Brandegee. Compositae (3). 1 Lower California.

Eatonella A. Gray. Compositae (6). 2 Nevada, California.
Eatonia Rafin. Gramineae (10). 5. N. Am.
Eau de Créole, *Mammea*.
Ebenaceae (*EP.*, *BH.*). Dicots. (Sympet. Ebenales *EP.*, *BH.*). 7 gen., 320 trop. (esp. Indomal.), trees and shrubs with alt., opp. or whorled, simple, leathery, usu. entire l. Fls. axillary, sol. or in small cymes, reg., usu. dioec., bracteolate, 3—7-merous. (K) persistent; (C) convolute; A epipet. at base of tube, usu. in 2 whorls but frequently ∞ by branching; stds. usu. present in ♀ fls., (G) 2—16-loc., with 1—2 anatr. ov. pend. in each loc.; styles 2—8, free or united below. Fr. usu. a berry with fewer seeds than there were ovules, sometimes dehiscent. Embryo straight or slightly curved, in abundant cartilaginous endosp. Many yield valuable wood, *e.g.* Diospyros. *Genera:* Royena, Euclea, Maba, Diospyros, Tetraclis.
Ebenales. The 4th order of Sympetalae (*EP.*), the 6th (*BH.*).
Ebeneous, black as ebony.
Ebenus L. Leguminosae (III. 7). 14 Medit. to Beluchistan.
Ebermaiera Nees (*Staurogyne EP.*). Acanthaceae (1). 40 trop. exc. Afr.
Ebony, wood of many Ebenaceae, esp. *Diospyros*, blackened by a deposition of a gum-resin in the heartwood; Gürke gives a list of forms, *Nat. Pfl.* IV. 1, p. 164; Ceylon and S. Indian ebony, the most important, is from *D. Ebenum* Koen.; **American-, green-, Jamaica-, W. Indian-**, *Brya Ebenus* DC.
Eburopetalum Becc. Anonaceae (4). 1 Borneo.
Eburophyton A. A. Heller (*Chloraea* p.p.). Orch. (II. 2). 1 Calif.
Ecad (Cl.), a habitat form due to origin by adaptation.
Ecastaphyllum P. Br. (*Dalbergia* p.p. *EP.*). Legum. (III. 8). 6 trop. Am., W.I.
Ecballium A. Rich. Cucurbitaceae (3). 1 Medit., *E. Elaterium* A. Rich. (squirting cucumber). The ripe fr. is highly turgid; as it drops from the stalk, a hole is made in its lower end, and through this the contraction of the pericarp squirts the seeds, mixed with a watery fluid. A purgative (elaterium) is prepared from the fr.
Ecbolium Kurz. Acanthaceae (IV. B). 8 trop. Afr.
Ecbolium Riv. ex L. = Justicia L. (Acanth.).
Ecclinusa Mart. Sapotaceae (1). 6 N. Brazil.
Eccremocarpus Ruiz et Pav. Bignoniaceae (3). 3 Peru. See fam. The valves of the fr. hang together at the top.
Ecdeiocolea F. Muell. Restionaceae. 1 S.W. Austr.
Ecdysanthera Hook. et Arn. Apocynaceae (II. 1). 10 Indomal., China.
Echeandia Ortega. Liliaceae (III). 10 Mexico to Guiana.
Echenais Cass. = Cnicus Tourn. p.p. (*BH.*) = Cirsium Adans. p.p.
Echetrosis Phil. Compositae (7). 1 temp. S. Am.
Echeveria DC. (*Cotyledon* p.p.). Crassulaceae. 150 Am.
Echidiocarya A. Gray (*Plagiobotrys* p.p. *EP.*). Borag. (IV. 2). 1. Arizona.
Echidnium Schott. Araceae (IV). 2 trop. S. Am.
Echidnopsis Hook. f. Asclepiadaceae (II. 3). 4 E. Afr. Xerophytes with succulent stems.

Echin- (Gr. pref.), spiny.
Echinacanthus Nees. Acanthaceae (IV. A). 8 Himal., Java.
Echinacea Moench. (*Rudbeckia* p.p.). Compositae (5). 2 N. Am.
Echinanthus Cerv. (*Tragus EP.*). Gramineae (3). None described.
Echinaria Desf. Gramineae (10). 1 Medit.
Echinocactus Link et Otto. Cactaceae (III. 1). 250 Texas to Chili. Ribbed cacti (see fam.).
Echinocarpus Blume (*Sloanea* p.p. *EP.*). Tiliaceae. 6 E. As., Austr.
Echinocephalum Gardn. (*Melanthera* p.p.). Comp. (5). 3 Brazil.
Echinocereus Engelm. (*Cereus* Haw. *BH.*). Cactaceae (III. 1). 20 Am.
Echinochlaenia Börner. (*Carex* p.p.) Cyper. (III). 3 Tasm., N.Z.
Echinochloa Beauv. (Panicum L. p.p.). Gramin. (5). 20 warm.
Echinocystis Torr. et Gray. Cucurbit. (4). 25 Am., W.I. Tuberous climbing herbs. *E. lobata* Torr. et Gray often cult. Its tendrils are very sensitive and nutate rapidly; they become straight and erect as they come round towards the main axis, thus avoiding contact.
Echinodorus Rich. Alismaceae. 20 Am., Afr.
Echinolaena Desv. (*Panicum* p.p. *EP.*). Gramineae (5). 2 S. Am., Madag.
Echinopanax Decne. et Planch. (*Fatsia BH.*). Araliaceae (1). 1 N. Am., Japan, *E. horridus* D. et P., an obstacle to travellers.
Echinopepon Naud. (*Echinocystis* Torr. et Gray). Cucurb. (4). 15 N. Am.
Echinophora Tourn. ex L. Umbelliferae (III. 1). 8 Medit. One cpl. is aborted. The umbel has one ☿ fl. in the centre, surrounded by ♂ fls. The spiny stalks of the latter enclose the fr.
Echinopogon Beauv. Gramineae (8). 1 Austr., N.Z.
Echinops L. Compositae (11). 75 E. Eur., Afr., As. The spherical head is really cpd., formed of ∞ small 1-fld. heads, each with its own invol. The fls. are largely visited by bees.
Echinopsilon Moq. = Chenolea Thunb. (*BH.*). = Bassia All. p.p.
Echinopsis Zucc. (*Cereus* p.p.). Cactaceae (III. 1). 25 S. Am.
Echinopterys A. Juss. Malpighiaceae (1, but forming a link between 1 and 2, as it has a flat torus). 1 Mexico. Mericarp spiny.
Echinospermum Sw. (Lappula p.p. *EP.*). Boraginaceae (IV. 2). 50 temp. *E. Lappula* Lehm. cult. The fls. change from white to red and blue (see fam.). Fr. hooked.
Echinostachys Brongn. (*Aechmea* p.p.). Bromel. (4). 6 S. Am. Cult. orn. infl.
Echinothamnus Engl. Passifloraceae. 1 S.W. Afr.
Echiochilon Desf. Boraginaceae (IV. 5). 2 N. Afr., Aden.
Echioglossum Blume (*Cleisostoma BH.*). Orch. (II. 20). 3 Indomal.
Echioides (Tourn.). Desf. = Nonnea Medic. (Borag.).
Echirospermum Saldanha da Gama. Leguminosae. Nomen.
Echites P. Br. Apocynaceae (II. 1). 40 Am., W.I.
Echium Tourn. ex L. Boraginaceae (IV. 5). 30 Eur., Medit. *E. vulgare* L. (viper's bugloss) Brit. (offic.). Fl. ·|·, protandr., gynodioec., bee-visited.
Echyrospermum Schott. Leguminosae (inc. sed.). Nomen.
Ecklonea Steud. (*Trianoptiles EP.*). Cyperaceae (II). 2 Austr., S. Afr.

Eclipta L. Compositae (5). 4 Austr., S. Am. Pappus 0.
Eclopes Gaertn. = Relhania L'Hérit. p.p. (Comp.).
Ecology, relations of plants to their environment.
Economic Botany, the study of pl. from the point of view of their uses to man; **-products**, of value in the arts as food, &c., may be divided into groups: (1) gums, resins, rubbers or caoutchoucs, gutta-perchas, &c., (2) oils, (3) dyes and tanning stuffs, (4) fibres, (5) drugs, (6) edible products, (7) timbers, and (8) miscellaneous, such as cork, vegetable ivory, weights, beads, &c. For more detail see under each of these heads, and consult Wiesner, *Die Rohstoffe des Pflanzenreichs*, Vienna, 1903; Watt, *The Commercial Products of India*; De Candolle, *Origin oj Cultivated Plants*; *Kew Bulletin* and other technical journals.
Ecphymacalyx Pohl. Inc. sed. Nomen.
Ecpoma K. Schum. Rubiaceae (I. 7). 1 trop. Afr.
Ecpomanthera Pohl. Inc. sed. Nomen.
Ectadiopsis Benth. Asclepiadaceae (1). 6 trop. and S. Afr.
Ectadium E. Mey. Asclepiadaceae (1). 2 S. Afr.
Ectasis D. Don = Erica L. p.p. (Eric.).
Ectinocladus Benth. Apocynaceae (II. 1). 1 W. Afr.
Ectotropic, hyphae running between epidermal cells.
Ectrosia R. Br. Gramineae (10). 4 Austr.
Edaphic, of the soil.
Eddoes (W.I.), *Colocasia antiquorum* Schott.
Edelweiss, *Leontopodium alpinum* Cass.
Edgaria C. B. Clarke. Cucurbitaceae (2). 1 Sikkim.
Edgeworthia Meissn. Thymelaeaceae. 2 Himalaya, China.
Edible products, or foodstuffs in a wide sense, are obtained esp. from stores of reserves in pl., *e.g.* the seeds of *cereals*, Avena (oat), Coix, Eleusine, Euchlaena, Hordeum (barley), Oryza (rice), Panicum (millet), Paspalum, Pennisetum (bulrush millet), Secale (rye), Setaria, Sorghum (Guinea corn), Triticum (wheat), Zea (maize), Zizania, &c.; the seeds of many *Leguminosae*, *e.g.* Arachis (peanut), Cajanus (cowpea), Cicer (chickpea), Dolichos, Glycine (soy), Lathyrus, Lens (lentil), Phaseolus (beans, &c.), Pisum (pea), Psophocarpus, Vicia (bean), Voandzeia, &c.; the seeds of Araucaria, Bertholletia (brazil-nut), Brosimum, Carya, Caryocar, Castanea (chestnut), Castanospermum, Cocos (coconut), Corylus (hazelnut, filbert), Dioon, Fagopyrum (buckwheat), Juglans (walnut), Lecythis, Nelumbium, Pistacia (pistachio), Telfairia, Trapa, &c.; the *underground reserves* of Allium (onion, &c.), Alocasia, Araceae, Arracacia, Arum, Beta (beetroot), Brassica (turnip, &c.), Canna, Colocasia (taro), Commelina, Daucus (carrot), Dioscorea (yam), Helianthus (Jerusalem artichoke), Ipomoea (sweet potato), Manihot (cassava, tapioca), Maranta (arrowroot), Ophiopogon, Oxalis, Pachyrhizus, Peucedanum (parsnip), Plectranthus, Priva, Raphanus, Scilla, Scorzonera, Selinum, Stachys, Solanum (potato), Tragopogon, Tropaeolum, Ullucus, Xanthosoma, &c.; from *reserves in the stems* of many trees, esp. palms; Acer (sugar), Alsophila, Arenga (sugar), Borassus (sugar, sago), Caryota (sugar, sago), Cycas, Cocos (sugar), Encephalartos, Metroxylon (sago), Oreodoxa, Saccharum (sugar), &c.; from *reserves in l. and infl.* in

Brassica, Cynara, many palms, &c. Other l. are also eaten, *e.g.* Apium (celery), Ceratopteris, Chenopodium, Crambe (sea-kale), Eremurus, Foeniculum (fennel), Lactuca (lettuce), Lepidium (cress), Myrrhis, Rheum (rhubarb), Scorzonera, Spinacia (spinach), Tetragonia, &c.; similarly the young shoots of Asparagus, Bambusa, &c. This leads on to *condiments* or *spices* (see Condiments).

Many *fleshy fr.* are also eaten; the greatest food value attaches to Artocarpus (bread-fr., jak), Musa (banana, plantain), and Phoenix (date), but others are Aberia, Achras, Anacardium (cashew), Ananas (pine-apple), Anona (custard-apple, &c.), Artabotrys, Averrhoa, Bactris, Benincasa, Blighia, Borassus (palmyra-palm), Byrsonima, Carica (papaw), Celtis, Cereus, Chrysobalanus, Chrysophyllum, Citrullus, Citrus (orange, lemon, &c.), Coccinia, Coccoloba, Cucumis (melon, cucumber), Cucurbita (pumpkin, marrow), Debregeasia, Decaisnea, Dialium, Diospyros (kaki), Durio (durian), Eriobotrya (loquat), Eugenia (rose-apple, &c.), Feronia, Ficus (fig), Fragaria (strawberry), Garcinia (mangosteen), Gaylussacia (huckleberry), Glycosmis, Hymenaea, Juniperus, Lantana, Lapageria, Litchi (litchi), Macadamia, Maclura, Mammea, Mangifera (mango), Mimusops, Monstera, Morus (mulberry), Myrtus, Nephelium (rambutan), Opuntia (prickly pear), Osmanthus, Pappea, Passiflora (granadilla, &c.), Pereskia, Persea (avocado), Peumus, Prunus (plum, cherry, apricot, peach, &c.), Psidium (guava), Punica (pomegranate), Pyrus (pear, apple, &c.), Ribes (gooseberry, currant), Rubus (raspberry, &c.), Sechium, Spondias, Tamarindus (tamarind), Vaccinium (cranberry, bilberry, &c.), Vitellaria, Vitis (grape), Zanthoxylum, Zizyphus, &c.

Drinks (*q.v.*, and Alcohol), narcotics (*q.v.*), &c may also be mentioned here. For food for animals *cf.* Fodder, and Bee-flowers.

Edithcolea N. E. Br. Asclepiadaceae (II. 3). 2 E. Afr., Socotra.

Edmondia Cogn. Cucurbitaceae (3). 1 Venezuela.

Edraianthus A. DC. = Wahlenbergia Schrad. (*BH.*) = Hedraianthus A. DC.

Edulis (Lat.), edible.

Edwardsia Salisb. = Sophora Linn. p.p. (Legum.).

Edwinia A. A. Heller (*Jamesia* p.p.). Saxifragaceae (III). 2 N. Am.

Eel-grass, *Zostera*; **-trap pl.**, *Biovularia*, *Genlisea*, *Polypompholyx*, *Utricularia*.

Eenia Hiern et Sp. Moore. Compositae (4). 1 Damaraland.

Effete, functionless from age.

Effigurations, outgrowths of receptacle, *Capparidaceae*, *Orchidaceae*, *Passifloraceae*.

Effuse, expanded.

Efulensia C. H. Wright (*Deidamia EP.*). Passifloraceae. 1 trop. Afr.

Eganthus Van Tiegh. Olacaceae. 1 Brazil.

Egassea Pierre ex Wildem. Scytopetalaceae. 3 trop. Afr.

Egeria Neraud. Rubiaceae. Nomen.

Egg-apparatus, the ovum and synergidae; **-fruit**, **-pl.**, *Solanum Melongena* L.

Eggersia Hook. f. (*Neea* p.p. *EP.*). Nyctaginaceae. 1 W. Indies.

Eglantine, *Rosa Eglanteria* L.

Egletes Cass. Compositae (3). 6 trop. Am., Mexico.

Egyptian bean, lotus, *Nelubium*, *Nymphaea*; **-lily,** *Richardia*.
Ehretia L. Boraginaceae (II). 50 warm, chiefly |✻. Timber.
Ehrharta Thunb. Gramineae (7). 25 S. Afr., Masc., N.Z. Useful pasture grasses for sandy soil.
Eichhornia Kunth. Pontederiaceae. 5 S. Am., W.I. The sympodium is very complex. Each shoot in turn is pushed to one side by the axillary shoot of its last l. but one; with this shoot it is combined, however, up to the last l. of the axillary shoot. After leaving the axillary shoot, each shoot bears another l., and then ends in the infl., which is enclosed in a spathe, and at first glance appears to spring from the stalk of the last l. In *E. azurea* Kunth. the fls. are dimorphic, in *E. crassipes* Solms trimorphic heterostyled. This last sp. has, when floating freely, large bladder-like swollen petioles, but in soil these are not nearly so large. They cause the plant to float high and it is easily blown about by wind, and has become a very troublesome weed (water hyacinth) in Florida, Java, Australia, &c.
Eichleria Progel. Oxalidaceae. 2 E. Brazil.
Eichlerodendron Briquet (*Xylosma* p.p.). Flacourt. (4). 1 Brazil.
Eicosia Blume. Orchidaceae. Nomen.
Ekebergia Sparrm. Meliaceae (III). 12 S. and trop. Afr., Madag.
Elachanthera F. Muell. Liliaceae (X). 1 Austr.
Elachanthus F. Muell. Compositae (7). 2 temp. Austr.
Elacholoma F. Muell. et Tate. Pedaliaceae. 1 Austr.
Elaeagia Wed. Rubiaceae (I. 3). 2 N. Andes.
Elaeagnaceae (*EP.*, *BH.*). Dicots. (Archichl. Myrtiflorae; Daphnales *BH.*). 3 gen., 25 sp., chiefly on steppes and coasts, $\underline{✻}$; much branched shrubs, often with leathery l., entire, opp. or alt., and covered, as are all parts, with scaly hairs. There are frequently thorns on the surface (reduced shoots). Infl. racemose; fls. ☿ or unisexual, 2- or 4-merous. In the ♂ the recept. is often flat, but in the ☿ or ♀ fl. it is tubular as in Thymelaeaceae, and may be fused with the ovary. No petals. Sta. as many, or twice as many, as sepals. $\underline{G}$ 1 with one erect anatr. ov. Pseudo-drupe. Seed with little or no endosp. *Chief genera:* Hippophaë, Elaeagnus.
Elaeagnus (Tourn.) L. Elaeagnaceae. 30 As., Eur., N. Am. (oleaster). The fr. of some is ed. Cult. orn. shrubs.
Elaeis Jacq. Palmae (IV. 2). 2, one trop. Am., the other, *E. guineensis* Jacq. trop. Afr. (oil-palm) from whose fr. the palm-oil, used for railway axles &c., is obtained by boiling.
Elaeocarpaceae (*EP.*; *Tiliaceae* p.p. *BH.*). Dicots. (Archichl. Malvales). 7 gen., 120 sp. trop. and subtrop., trees and shrubs with alt. or opp., stip. l., and racemes, panicles or dichasia of fls. Disc usu. present. K 4 or 5, free or united, valvate; C 4 or 5, rarely united, often 0, the petals often much divided at the ends, valvate or imbr. but never conv.; A ∞, free, on the disc, which is sometimes developed to an androphore; anthers 2-loc. usu. opening by two pores (sometimes confluent) at the apex; $\underline{G}$ sessile, with 2—∞ (rarely 1) loc.; ovules in each loc. ∞ or 2, anatr., pend. with ventral raphe; style simple, sometimes lobed at apex. Capsule or drupe; embryo straight, in abundant endosp. *Chief genera:* Elaeocarpus,

Sloanea, Aristotelia. The grounds upon which they are separated from Tiliaceae are chiefly anatomical.

Elaeocarpus Burm. ex L. Elaeocarpaceae. 90 trop.

Elaeodendron Jacq. f. (*Cassine* p.p. *EP.*). Celastraceae. 30 trop. and subtrop. *E. croceum* DC. (saffranhout, S. Afr.) good timber.

Elaeogene Miq. Euphorbiaceae (inc. sed.). 1 Sumatra.

Elaeoluma Baill. (*Myrsine* p.p. *BH.*, *Chrysophyllum* p.p. *EP.*). Sapotaceae (I). 1 Brazil.

Elaeophorbia Stapf. (*Euphorbia* p.p.). Euphorb. (A. II. 8). 1 trop. Afr.

Elaeoselinum Koch ex DC. Umbelliferae (III. 7). 8 W. Medit.

Elaphoglossum Schott. Polypodiaceae. 330 trop. and subtrop.

Elaphrium Jacq. = Bursera Jacq. (Burs.). 80 warm Am.

Elater, *Equisetum*.

Elaterioides O. Ktze. (*Elateriospermum* Bl.). Euph. (A. II. 3). 2 Malaya.

Elateriopsis Ernst (*Cyclanthera BH.*). Cucurb. (4). 6 S. Am.

Elaterium Jacq. Cucurbitaceae (4). 12 trop. Am. The fr. is explosive like that of Ecballium.

Elaterium, Ecballium.

Elatinaceae (*EP.*, *BH.*). Dicots. (Archichl. Parietales; Guttiferales *BH.*). 2 gen., 30 sp., trop. and temp. Undershrubs, herbs, or annual water-pl.; the latter are able to live on land, altering their structure to suit the changed conditions (*cf.* Littorella). L. opp. or whorled, simple with interpet. stip. Fls. ☿, reg., solitary or in dichasia, 2—6-merous. K hypog., free or united; C imbr.; A in 2 whorls, or inner aborted; $\underline{G}$ syncarpous, multiloc., with free styles; plac. axile; ov. ∞, anatr. Capsule septifragal; seed straight or curved; endosp. thin or none. *Genera:* Bergia, Elatine.

Elatine Linn. Elatinaceae. 15 trop. and temp. *E. hexandra* DC. and *E. Hydropiper* L. (water pepper or pipe-wort) in Brit.

Elatineae (*BH.*) = Elatinaceae.

Elatinoides Wettst. (*Linaria* p.p.). Scroph. (II. 3). 24 Eur., As., Afr.

Elatostema Forst. Urticaceae (2). 120 trop. |✻. *E. acuminatum* Brongn. is apogamous. Some show water secretion from the l.

Elatostematoides C. B. Robinson. Urticaceae (2). 10 Phil. Is.

Elattostachys Radlk. Sapindaceae (I). 10 Indomal., Polynesia.

Elatus (Lat.), tall.

Elcismia Robinson (*Celmisia* p.p.). Compositae (4). 45 S. temp.

Elcomarhiza Barb. Rodr. Asclepiadaceae (inc. sed.). 1 Brazil.

Elder, *Sambucus nigra* L.; **American witch-**, *Fothergilla*; **dwarf-** (W.I.), *Pilea grandis* Wedd.

Elecampane, *Inula Helenium* L.

Elegia L. Restionaceae. 20 S. Afr.

Eleiotis DC. Leguminosae (III. 7). 1 India, Ceylon.

Elemi, balsams, *Burseraceae*, *Commiphora*, *Copaifera*, *Dipterocarpus*, *Liquidambar*, *Pistacia*, *Styrax*, *Toluifera*, etc.

Eleocharis R. Br. Cyperaceae (I). 90 cosmop. *E. palustris* R. Br. (spike-rush) on turfy moors in Brit. The green tissue is centric. The tubers of *E. tuberosus* Schult. (E. As.) are used as food.

Eleogiton Link = Scirpus L. p.p. (Cyper.).

Elephant-apple, *Feronia Elephantum* Correa; **-'s ear,** *Begonia*; **-'s foot** (Am.), *Elephantopus*.
Elephantella Rydberg (*Pedicularis* p.p.). Scrophul. (III. 3). 2 N. Am.
Elephantopus L. Compositae (I). 20 trop. *E. scaber* L. is an abundant and troublesome weed.
Elephantorrhiza Benth. Leguminosae (I. 5). 2 trop. and S. Afr.
Elettaria Maton. Zingiberaceae (I). 1 Indomal., *E. Cardamomum* Maton. Fls. on leafless shoots from the rhiz. Cult. in the mountains of Ceylon and S. India (cardamoms). The ripe fr. are picked and dried; the seeds form a strongly flavoured spice, mainly used in India.
Elettariopsis Baker. Zingiberaceae (2). 20 Indomal.
Eleusine Gaertn. Gramineae (11). 10 trop. and subtrop. *E. coracana* Gaertn. (ragi, kurakkan) is cult. as a cereal in Ceylon, India, Africa, &c., and others are useful fodders.
Eleutheranthera Poit. ex Bosc. Compositae (5). 1 trop. Am.
Eleutheranthus (*Eleuthranthes*) F. Muell. Rubi. (II. 7). 1 W. Austr.
Eleutherine Herb. Iridaceae (II). 1 trop. S. Am., W.I. Bulb.
Eleutherococcus Maxim. (*Acanthopanax* p.p. *EP.*). Aral. (I). 2 China.
Eleutheropetalous, polypetalous.
Eleutherospermum C. Koch (*Pleurospermum* p.p. *EP.*). Umbel. (III. 4). 2 W. As.
Eleutherostemon Herzog. Ericaceae (III. 2). 1 Bolivia.
Eliaea Cambess. Guttiferae (II). 1 Madagascar.
Elichrysum, *cf.* Helichrysum.
Elionurus Humb. et Bonpl. ex Willd. Gramineae (2). 20 trop. and subtrop.
Elisena Herb. Amaryllidaceae (I). 3 Peru.
Elisma Buchen. Alismaceae. 1 Eur. (incl. Brit.), *E. natans* Buchen.
Elissarrhena Miers (*Anomospermum EP.*). Menisperm. 1 Brazil.
Elizabetha Schomb. Leguminosae (II. 3). 2 Brit. Guiana.
Elk-horn fern, *Platycerium*.
Elleanthus Presl. Orchidaceae (II. 7). 50 trop. Am., W. Ind.
Ellertonia Wight. Apocynaceae (I. 3). 4 trop. As., Madagascar.
Elliottia Muehlb. ex Nutt. Ericaceae (I. 1). 1 S. Atl. U.S.
Ellipanthus Hook. f. Connaraceae. 8 Indomal.
Ellipeia Hook. f. et Thoms. Anonaceae (1). 10 Malaya.
Elliptical, narrowish, tapering equally to both ends.
Ellisia L. Hydrophyllaceae. 4 N. Am.
Ellisiophyllum Maxim. Hydrophyllaceae. 1 Japan.
Elm, *Ulmus campestris* L. &c.; **Spanish-** (W.I.), *Cordia*, *Hamelia*.
Elmera Rydberg (*Heuchera* p.p.). Saxifragaceae (I). 1 N. Am.
Elmeria Ridl. (*Hornstedtia* Retz.). Zingiberaceae (I). 2 Phil. Is.
Elodea Michx. Hydrocharitaceae. 6 Am.; *E. canadensis* Michx (American water-weed) arrived in Brit. about 1842 and rapidly spread over the inland waters of Eur. Only the ♀ plant is known in Eur., and the spreading is therefore due to veg. repr. chiefly by the breaking off of twigs. Submerged pl., slightly rooted, with whorls of l., in whose axils are the usual squamulae. ♂ fl. P 6, A 9; it breaks off as a bud and comes to the surface (*cf.* Vallisneria), where it opens. The ovary of the ♀ fl. grows to such a length as to bring the fl. to the surface, where it is pollinated. P 6, stds. 3, $\overline{G}$ (3); enclosed below in

a 2-leaved spathe. The pl. does not form a true winter bud; the l. are merely a little more closely grouped together.

Elongate, drawn out.

Elsholtzia Willd. Labiatae (VI). 30 As., Eur., Abyss.

Elutheria M. Roem. Meliaceae (II). 2 Peru to Venezuela.

Elvasia DC. Ochnaceae. 5 N. Brazil, Guiana.

Elvira Cass. Compositae (5). 3 trop. Am.

Elymus L. Gramineae (12). 50 N. temp., S. Am. *E. arenarius* L. (lyme grass) on dunes in Brit. (*cf.* Ammophila); its l. are coated with wax.

Elyna Schrad. (*Kobresia* Willd. p.p.). Cyper. (III). 5 N. palaeotemp.

Elynanthus Beauv. Cyperaceae (II). 30 *.

Elynanthus Nees = Tetraria P. Beauv. (Cyper.).

Elytranthe Blume (*Loranthus* p.p. *BH.*). Loranth. (I). 50 Indomal.

Elytraria Michx. (*Tubiflora* Gmel.). Acanth. (I). 5 trop., subtrop.

Elytropappus Cass. Compositae (4). 6 S. Afr. *E. Rhinocerotis* L. is a char. pl. of the karroo.

Elytrophorus Beauv. Gramineae (10). 2 palaeotrop.

Elytropus Muell.-Arg. Apocynaceae (II. 1). 1 Chili. Many bracts.

Emarginate, notched.

Embelia Burm. f. Myrsinaceae (II). 120 trop. and subtrop., exc. Am.

Emblic myrobalan, *Phyllanthus Emblica* L.

Emblingia F. Muell. Capparidaceae (IV). 1 W. Austr.

Embolanthera Merrill. Hamamelidaceae. 1 Phil. Is.

Embothrium Forst. Proteaceae (II). 5 Andes, Chili, E. Austr.

Embryo, the young pl. contained in the seed; **adventitious-**, *Alchornea*, *Funkia*, *Nothoscordum*.

Embryopteris Gaertn. = Diospyros L. (Eben.).

Emeorhiza Pohl. Rubiaceae (II. 10). 2 S. Am.

Emergences, surface outgrowths arising from other tissues as well as epidermis, *Cactaceae*, *Drosera*, *Rosa*, *Ribes*.

Emerus Tourn. ex Mill. = Coronilla L. (Legum.).

Emex Neck. Polygonaceae (I. 2). 1 Medit., S. Afr., Austr. The fr. is surrounded by the P, 3 of whose l. are spiny.

Emicocarpus K. Schum. et Schlechter. Asclep. (II. 1). 1 S.E. Afr.

Emilia Cass. (*Senecio* Tourn. p.p. *EP.*). Compositae (8). 5 palaeotrop.

Emiliomarcelia Th. et H. Durand (*Trichoscypha* p.p.). Anacardiaceae (3). 4 Congo.

Eminia Taub. (*Rhynchosia* p.p. *BH.*). Leguminosae (III. 10). 2 E. trop. Afr.

Eminium Schott. Araceae (VII). 4 W. and C. As., Egypt.

Emmenanthe Benth. Hydrophyllaceae. 1 W. N. Am.

Emmenopteryx Oliv. Rubiaceae (I. 5). 1 China.

Emmenosperma F. Muell. Rhamnaceae. 2 Austr.

Emmeorrhiza Pohl. Rubiaceae (II. 10). 2 trop. S. Am.

Emmer, *Triticum dicoccum* Schrank.

Emmotum Desv. Icacinaceae. 5 Brazil.

Emorya Torr. Loganiaceae. 1 Texas.

Empedoclea A. St. Hil. (*Tetracera* p.p. *EP.*). Dilleniaceae. 1 Brazil.

Empetraceae (*EP.*, *BH.*). Dicots. (Archichl. Sapindales; anomalous

Monochlamydeae *BH.*). 3 gen., 4 sp., * and Andes, occupying similar positions to Ericaceae; heath-like habit. The l. are incurved backwards, forming a cavity on the under side partly filled up by hairs into which the stomata open. Infl. racemose, usu. dioec. In all but Corema the fls. are on 'short shoots' which arise lat. from the main axis and bear only scales below the infl. K 3, C 3, A 3, G (2—9). Loculi=cpls.; ovules 1 in each, anatr. or nearly campylotr., erect on axile plac., with ventral raphe. Drupe with 2—9 stones; seed albuminous with no caruncle. *Genera:* Corema, Empetrum, Ceratiola.

Empetrum (Tourn.) L. Empetr. 2, incl. *E. nigrum* L. (crow-berry), on moors, N. temp. (incl. Brit.), S. Andes, Falkl., Tristan. For habit, fl., &c. see fam. Flr. dioec. and anemoph., but sometimes ☿ and protandr. (*Cf.* Good in *Linn. Soc. Journ.* 47, p. 489.)

Emplectanthus N.E. Br. Asclepiadaceae (II. 3). 2 S. Afr.

Emplectocladus Torr. (*Prunus* p.p. *EP.*). Rosaceae (V). 1 N.W. Am.

Empleuridium Sond. et Harv. Rutaceae (I). 1 S. Afr.

Empleurum Ait. Rutaceae (I). 1 S. Afr. L. officinal (buchu).

Empogona Hook. f. Rubiaceae (I. 8). 2 E. trop. and S. Afr.

Enallagma Baill. Bignoniaceae (4). 4 C. Am., W.I. L. alt. Berry.

Enalus L. C. Rich. Hydrochar. 1 Indian and Pac. Oceans. See Enhalus.

Enantia Oliv. Anonaceae (4). 3 W. Afr.

Enantioblastae (Warming). The 4th cohort of Monocotyledons.

Enantiophylla Coulter et Rose. Umbelliferae (III. 6). 1 Guatemala.

Enantiostyly, *Cassia* (q.v.), *Klugia*, *Leguminosae*, *Marantaceae*, *Saintpaulia*.

Enargea Banks (*Luzuriaga* Ruiz et Pav.). Lili. (X). 3 S. Am., N.Z.

Enarthrocarpus Labill. Cruciferae (2). 7 E. Medit., N. Afr.

Encelia Adans. Compositae (5). 40 W. U.S. to Chili. Pappus usu. 0.

Enceliopsis A. Nelson (*Encelia* p.p.). Compositae (5). 5 N. Am.

Encephalartos Lehm. Cycadaceae. 10 Afr. The Kaffirs prepare a meal from the pith (*cf.* Cycas).

Encephalosphaera Lindau. Acanthaceae (IV. B). 1 Colombia.

Enchanter's Nightshade, *Circaea.*

Encholirium Mart. (*Dyckia BH.*). Bromeliaceae (2). 6 Brazil.

Enchosanthera King et Stapf (*Anplectrum* p.p.). Melastomaceae (I). 1 Indo-China.

Enchylaena R. Br. Chenopodiaceae (A). 1 Austr.

Enchysia Presl=Laurentia Neck. (Campan.).

Enckea Kunth=Piper L. p.p. (Piper.).

Encopa Griseb. Scrophulariaceae (II. 6). 1 Cuba.

Encyclia Hook.=Epidendrum L. (Orchid.).

Endacanthus Baill. Icacinaceae. 1 Madagascar.

Endemic, confined to a small section of country, island, &c.

Endiandra R. Br. Lauraceae (II). 20 Indomal., Austr., Polynesia.

Endive, *Cichorium Endivia* L.

Endlicheria Nees (*Ayendron BH. Aniba EP.*). Laur. (II). 3 trop. Am.

Endo- (Gr. pref.), within; **-carp**, the innermost layer of fr. in a drupe, &c.; **-chylous**, with internal water-storing tissue; **-gamy**, fusion of ♀ gametes; **-genous**, arising from internal tissues; **-gens**, Monocotyledons; **-parasite**, pl. living within the tissues of the host;

-phytic, living within another; **-pleura**, inner seed coat, *Cycadaceae*; **-rhizal**, monocotyledonous; **-sperm**, the nutrient tissue outside embryo in seed, fleshy in *Berberis*, &c., bony in *Phoenix*, *Phytelephas*, horny in *Coffea*, &c., mealy in *Frankeniaceae*, ruminate in *Anonaceae*, and *cf.* *Gymnospermae*; **-tropic**, with hyphae entering the cells.

Endocellion Turcz. ex Herd. Compositae (inc. sed.). 1 Russia.

Endodesmia Benth. Guttiferae (III). 1 W. trop. Afr.

Endolithodes Bartl. = Synisoon Baill. (Rubiaceae).

Endomallus Gagnep. Leguminosae (III. 10). 2 Cochin-China.

Endonema A. Juss. Penaeaceae. 2 S. Afr.

Endopogon Nees = Strobilanthes Blume p.p. (Acanth.).

Endopogon Rafin. Rubiaceae (inc. sed.). 1 N. Am.

Endorima Rafin. (*Balduina* Nutt.). Compositae (5). 3 N. Am.

Endosiphon T. Anders. ex Benth. et Hook. f. Acanth. (IV A). 1 trop. Afr.

Endospermum Benth. Euphorbiaceae (A. II. 6). 12 Malaya, China.

Endosteira Turcz. Tiliaceae. 1 St Vincent.

Endostemon N.E. Br. (*Ocimum* p.p.). Labiatae (VII). 1 S. and trop. Afr.

Endressia J. Gay (*Ligusticum* p.p. *BH.*). Umbellif. (III. 5). 1 Pyrenees.

Endusa Miers. Olacaceae. 2 Peru.

Enetophyton Nieuwland (*Utricularia* p.p.). Lentibular. 1 U.S.

Engelhardtia Leschen. Juglandaceae. 10 Indomal., China.

Engelmannia Torr. et Gray. Compositae (5). 1 S.W. U.S., Mex.

Englerastrum Briquet. Labiatae (VII). 2 trop. Afr. (A).

Englerella Pierre. Sapotaceae (inc. sed.). 1 French Guiana.

Engleria O. Hoffm. Compositae (3). 2 S. trop. Afr.

Englerocharis Muschler. Cruciferae (4). 2 Peru.

Englerodaphne Gilg. Thymelaeaceae. 1 E. Afr.

Englerodendron Harms. Leguminosae (II. 3). 1 E. trop. Afr.

Englerodoxa Hörold. Ericaceae (III. 2). 1 Ecuador.

Englerophytum Krause. Sapotaceae (I). 1 Cameroons.

Englypha Chod. et Hassler. Aristolochiaceae. 1 Paraguay.

Engram, record produced on the organism. *New Phyt.* V. 200.

Enhalus Rich. Hydrocharitaceae. 1 Indomal., in salt water. The ♀ fls. float horiz. at low water, and catch the ♂ fls. which (*cf.* Vallisneria) break off and float. As the tide rises, the ♀ fls. stand vertically, and the pollen, heavier than water, sinks down upon the stigmas. The testa bursts when the seed is ripe, and the embryo is freed.

Enhydra (*Enydra*) Lour. Compositae (5). 9 trop. and subtrop.

Enhydrias Ridl. Hydrocharitaceae. 1 Malaya.

Enicosanthum Becc. Anonaceae (1). 1 Borneo.

Enicostema Blume. Gentianaceae (1). 1 trop. Xero. and coast.

Enkianthus (*Enkyanthus*) Lour. Ericaceae (II. 1). 10 Himal. to Japan.

Enkleia Griff. (*Linostoma* Wall.). Thymel. 1 Further India.

Ennealophus N.E. Br. Iridaceae (II). 1 Amazon valley.

Enneapogon Desv. ex Beauv. (Pappophorum p.p.). Gram. 8 warm.

Enomegra Aven Nelson (*Argemone* p.p.). Papav. (II). 2 Rockies.

Ensate, ensiform, sword-shaped.

Enslenia Nutt. Asclepiadaceae (II. 1). 3 N. U.S. to Colombia.

Entada Adans. (*Pusaetha* L.). Legum. (I. 5). 20 warm. Seeds of *E. scandens* Benth. (nicker bean), a trop. climber with pods 1 m. long, are carried to Eur. by the Gulf Stream drift.
Entandrophragma C. DC. Meli. (II). 10 trop. Afr. [very light.
Entelea R. Br. Tili. 1 N.Z. K. G 4—6-loc. Caps. spiny. Wood
Enterolobium Mart. Legum. (I. 1). 8 trop. Am., W.I. Pod spiral.
Enteropogon Nees. Gramin. (11). 4 palaeotrop. Spikelet awned.
Enterosora Baker. Polypod. 1 C. Am., Jamaica.
Enterospermum Hiern. Rubi. (I. 8). 1 E. Afr. coast.
Enthomanthus Moç. et Sesse ex Ramirez. Caprifol. 2 Mex.
Entire, without marginal notches.
Entolasia Stapf. Gramin. (5). 2 trop. Afr. [by specialisation for it.
Entomophily (fl.), insect-pollination; fls. divided into 8 fl.-classes (*q.v.*)
Entoplocamia Stapf. Gramin. (11). 2 S. and trop. Afr.
Entrecasteauxia Montr. Inc. sed. 1 New Caled.
Enydra (*Enhydra*) Lour. Comp. (5). 10 warm. Marsh pl.
Enzyme, an unorganised or soluble ferment.
Eomecon Hance. Papaver. (II). 1 E. China. (K).
Epacridaceae (*EP.*; *Epacrideae BH.*). Dicots. (Sympet. Ericales, pp. xli, lii). 30/400, chiefly Austr. Tasm., where they repres. the Eric. of other continents, but also Ind., Sandw. Is., N.Z., S. Am. Like Eric. (§ IV) in habit and look; shrubs or trees, usu. small, stems ± oblique, sparingly branched, with narrow, entire, rigid l., usu. close together and alt., rarely opp. or whorled. L. sometimes sheathing, leaving no scar when they fall, or leaving one, in which case the impression is of Monocot. habit. Fls. in term. racemes or spikes, or sol., usu. white or red, ☿, ⊕. K 5, C (5), A 5 (exc. Oligarrhena), epipet, or hypog. at edge of disc, anthers opening by one central longitudinal slit and without horns or other appendages, pollen simple or in tetrads. G (5), cpls. opp. pets., usu. 5-loc. with axile plac. and simple style, sometimes in depression at top of ov. with capitate stigma; ov. in each loc. 1—∞, anatr., usu. pend. Loculic. caps. (from ∞-ov. loc.) or drupe (from 1-ov.). Embryo straight, in copious endosp. A few yield ed. fr., or are cult. orn. fl.

Classification and chief genera (after Drude):

Each loc. with many ov. Caps. loculic.

1. *Prionoteae* (A hypog. free, anther-loc. divided): Prionotes (loc. ∞-seeded), Lebetanthus (few-seeded); only gen.
2. *Epacrideae* (A usu. epipet.; anther-loc. without separation after dehiscence): Sprengelia (l. sheathing, A free, C deeply divided), Richea, Dracophyllum, Sphenotoma, Epacris (l. base stalk-like, leaving scar, C imbr., placenta at centre).

Each loc. with 1 ov. Fr. indeh. Usu. 5-merous.

3. *Styphelieae*: Styphelia (C valv.; anthers free, moveable on fil. C smooth or bearded in tube, G 5-loc.), Acrotriche, Pentachondra, Oligarrhena (A 2).

Epacris Forst. Epacrid. (2). 40 S. E. Austr., Tasm., New Caled., N.Z. Cult. orn. fl.
Epactium Willd. Inc. sed. 1 Peru.
Epallage DC. Comp. (5). 5 Madag. L. alt.
Epaltes Cass. Comp. (4). 12 trop. L. usu. decurrent. Pappus 0.
Epatitis Rafin. Comp. (inc. sed.). 1 Oregon.

Eperua Aubl. Leguminosae (II. 3). 6 N. Braz., Guiana. *E. purpurea* Benth., a showy tree of the caatingas. *E. falcata* Aubl. (wallaba, Br. Guiana) yields a good timber.

Ephebepogon Nees et Meyen (*Pollinia* p.p. *EP.*). Gram. (2). 1 China.

Ephedra Tourn. ex L. Gnetaceae. 35 warm temp. Shrubs, much branched, with opp. connate l. reduced to scales, so that the stem performs the work of assim. Fls. diclinous, with no trace of cpls. in ♂, or of sta. in ♀; ♂ in spikes, ♀ in pairs or solitary, usu. bracteate. The ♂ has a P of 2 antero-post. united l., beyond which the axis is prolonged and bears 2—8 sessile 2-loc. anthers. The ♀ has a tubular P and one erect orthotr. ovule with a long micropyle projecting at the top of the fl.; the fl. or fls. are enclosed by bracts which become red and fleshy after fert. and enclose the fr. The seed is enclosed in the P, which becomes woody, and the fleshy bracts cover this again. There are two cots. in the embryo; seed album.

Ephedranthus Sp. Moore (*Guatteria EP.*). Anonaceae (1). 1 Brazil.

Ephemeral, lasting a day; fruiting two or three times a season.

Ephippiandra Decne. Monimiaceae. 1 Madagascar.

Ephippianthus Rchb. f. (*Liparis* p.p. *BH.*). Orchid. (II. 4). 1 Saghalien.

Epi- (Gr. pref.), upon; **-basal**, in front of basal wall; **-calyx**, an extra calyx of apparent stip. nature, *Bombacaceae*, *Dipsacaceae*, *Fragaria*, *Lythraceae*, *Malvaceae*, *Potentilla*, *Rhodotypos*, *Rosaceae*; **-carp**, the outer layer of a fleshy fr.; **-chil**, end of labellum of orchid, when distinct from base; **-cotyl**, stem of seedling above cotyledons; **-dermis**, outer skin of plant; **-geal** (germination), with cotyledons above ground; **-gyny (-gynous)**, fl. when ovary is immersed in hollow receptacle, and other organs are epigynous, *Begoniaceae*, *Compositae*, *Iridaceae*, *Rubiaceae*, *Umbelliferae*, &c.; **-petalous** (sta.), inserted upon petal, *Labiatae*, &c.; **-phyllous** (infl.), *Chailletia*, *Chirita*, *Erythrochiton*; (sta.), inserted upon perianth, *Proteaceae*, &c.; **-physis**, a protuberance round the hilum of a seed; **-phytes**, see separate article below; **-sepalous**, inserted upon a sepal; **-sperm**, outer coat of seed; **-spore**, *Marsiliaceae*, *Salviniaceae*; **-tropous** (ovule), with raphe towards axis.

Epiblastus Schlechter (*Dendrobium* p.p.). Orchid. (II. 15). 8 Austr., N.G.

Epiblema R. Br. Orchidaceae (II. 2). 1 S.W. Austr. Column winged.

Epicampes J. et C. Presl. Gramineae (8). 15 Calif. to Argentina.

Epicattleya × Rolfe. Orchid. Hybrid Epidendrum—Cattleya.

Epicharis Blume (*Dysoxylum* p.p. *EP.*). Meliaceae (III). 4 E. As.

Epicladium Small (*Epidendrum* p.p.). Orchid. (II. 6). 1 Florida.

Epiclastopelma Lindau. Acanthaceae (IV. A). 1 E. Afr.

Epicranthes Blume (*Bulbophylium* p.p. *BH.*). Orchid. (II. 16). 2 Malaya.

Epidendrum L. Orchidaceae (II. 6). 400 trop. Am. Labellum often ± united to column; a canal runs from the junction down into the ovary. Cult. orn. fl.

Epidiacrum × Rolfe. Orchid. Hybrid of last with Diacrium.

Epifagus Nutt. (*Epiphegus EP.*). Orobanchaceae. 1 N. Am.

Epigaea L. Ericaceae (II). 2 sp., *E. asiatica* Maxim. Japan, *E.*

repens L., the (trailing arbutus, mayflower) Atl. U.S. Fls. tetramorphic (Darwin, *Forms of Flrs.* p. 297).

Epigynae (*BH.*). The 2nd series of Monocotyledons.

Epigynium Klotzsch = Vaccinium L. p.p. (Eric.).

Epigynum Wight. Apocynaceae (II. 1). 8 Indomal.

Epilaelia × Rolfe. Orchid. Hybrid Epidendrum—Laelia.

Epilasia Benth. et Hook. f. (*Scorzonera* p.p. *BH.*). Compositae (13). 5 Centr. and W. As.

Epilobiaceae, Onagraceae.

Epilobium Dill. ex L. Onagraceae (2). 160 temp. and arctic; 9 in Brit. (willow-herbs). Fl. reg., but in some slightly ·|· by the bending of sta. and style, which project and make a landing-place for insects. Of Brit. sp. several may be noticed, as the fls. form a series in regard to cross-pollination, &c. In *E. angustifolium* L. the fls. are large and autogamy almost impossible. Honey is secreted by the upper surface of the ovary. The sta. are ripe when the fl. opens, and project horiz., while the style, with its stigmas closed, is bent downwards. Afterwards the sta. bend down and the style up, and the stigmas open. This is the plant in which C. K. Sprengel (1793, see biography in *Nat. Science*, 1893) made the first discovery of dichogamy. In *E. hirsutum* L. sta. and stigma are ripe together, but the stigma projects beyond the sta.; if not pollinated it bends back and touches the anthers. *E. parviflorum* Schreb. is a small-flowered homogamous sp. rarely visited by insects; 4 sta. are shorter, 4 longer, than the style; the former are useful for cross-pollination, the latter for self. The seed has a tuft of hairs aiding wind-carriage.

Epiluma Baill. (*Chrysophyllum* p.p.). Sapotaceae (1). 1 New Caled.

Epimatium, ovuliferous scale (Coniferae).

Epimedium (Tourn.) L. (incl. *Vancouveria* C. Morr. et Dcne.). Berberidaceae. 10 N. temp. *E. alpinum* L. nat. in Brit. It has, like most E., a 2-merous fl., which is pend., with glandular hairs on the stalk. It is protog., and after a time the valves of the anthers bend upwards and roof over the stigma and the ♂ stage begins. Finally self-pollination occurs by the elongation of the style carrying the stigma among the valves. The nectaries are of a curious shoe-like pattern. The seeds have a membranous aril.

Epinetrum Hiern. Menispermaceae. 2 trop. Afr. (A).

Epipactis Adans. Orchidaceae (II. 2). 10 N. temp.; 2 Brit., *E. latifolia* All., and *E. palustris* Crantz (helleborine). There are two stds. at the sides of the column; the anther is acrotonic. The labellum has a hinged term. portion, which by its rebound causes the insect to fly somewhat upwards in leaving the flr. In so doing it rubs the rostellum, which instantly becomes very viscid and cements the pollinia (which have no true caudicles) to the insect. The chief visitors are wasps. See Darwin's *Orchids*, p. 93.

Epipetrum Phil. (*Dioscorea* p.p. *BH.*). Dioscoreaceae. 3 Chili.

Epiphegus Spreng. Orobanchaceae. 1 N. Am.

Epiphora Lindl. (*Polystachya BH.*). Orchidaceae (II. 5). 1 S. Afr.

Epiphronitis × Veitch. Orchid. Hybrid, Epidendrum—Sophronitis.

Epiphyllanthus Berger (*Cereus* p.p.). Cact. (III. 1). 1 Brazil.

Epiphyllum Haw. Cactaceae (III. 1). 5 Brazil, often cult.

Epiphyte, a plant which clings to another for support, but is not parasitic, and is not usu. attached to the soil. Abundant in the wetter trop., esp. S. Am. The group is made up of pl. which possess in common 3 general adaptations: (1) a good seed-dispersal mechanism for wind or birds, (2) a capacity to attach themselves at once to the support on germination, usu. by clasping roots, and (3) fairly well-marked xero. chars. to enable them to stand the droughts to which their situation renders them esp. liable; *Aeschynanthus*, *Araceae*, *Bromeliaceae*, *Bulbophyllum*, *Clusia*, *Columnea*, *Dischidia*, *Filices*, *e.g. Asplenium*, *Platycerium*, *Polypodium*, &c., *Ficus*, *Hydnophytum*, *Marcgravia*, *Myrmecodia*, *Oncidium*, *Orchidaceae*, *Phalaenopsis*, *Phyllocactus*, *Piper*, *Rhipsalis*, *Rhododendron*, *Scuticaria*, *Tillandsia*, *Vanilla*, &c. See Schimper, *Die epiph. Vegetation Amerikas*, Jena, 1888, and *Plant Geography*; Goebel, *Pflanzenbiol. Schilderungen*.

Epipogum S. G. Gmel. Orchidaceae (II. 2). 1 Eur. (incl. Brit.), As., *E. aphyllum* Sw. a leafless saprophyte with branched rhiz. and no r.; endotropic mycorhiza. Fl. as in Epipactis, but without twisting of the recept.

Epipremnopsis Engl. Araceae (I). 1 Indomal.

Epipremnum Schott. Araceae (II). 15 Indomal.

Epiprinus Griff. Euphorbiaceae (A. II. 2). 1 Further India.

Epirrhizanthes Blume = Salomonia Lour. p.p. (Polygal.).

Episcia Mart. Gesneriaceae (I). 30 trop. Am., W.I.

Epistephium Kunth. Orchidaceae (II. 2). 7 trop. S. Am.

Epistylium Sw. = Phyllanthus L. p.p. (Euph.).

Epitaberna K. Schum. Rubiaceae (I. 8). 2 Cameroons.

Epithema Blume. Gesneriaceae (I). 10 Indomal., trop. Afr.

Epithymum Lunell (*Cuscuta* p.p.). Convolv. (II). 5 W. U.S.

Epitrachys C. Koch = Cnicus L. (*BH.*) = Cirsium Tourn. (Comp.).

Equisetaceae. Pteridophyta (Equisetineae). An order with one surviving genus (Equisetum *q.v.*), formerly well repres. Many large fossils.

Equisetales (*Equisetineae*). A main division of Pteridophyta (*q.v.*), containing the single living fam. Equisetaceae.

Equisetum L. Equisetaceae (only genus). 25 cosmop.; 9 in Brit. (horsetails), chiefly in swampy places. Perenn. herbs with sympodial rhiz. which send up aerial shoots each year, of one or two kinds; in some sp. the ordinary green shoot bears the repr. spike at the end, while in the others there is a special repr. shoot, usu. appearing early in the year, and often without chlorophyll, the ordinary shoots performing assim. work only. The stem is very distinctly jointed, and at the nodes are borne whorls of united l. closely pressed against the stem, and of little or no use in assim. The branches emerge through the leaf-sheath and thus appear at first sight endogenous; in reality they are exogenous, but formed so much later than the l. that their points of origin are already covered by the leaf-sheath, and so they are compelled to burrow through it. Stages in this process may easily be observed. The surface of the stem is grooved; the ridges are occupied by mechanical tissue, whilst the green tissue and stomata are at the base of the furrows. This is a marked xero. structure and is repeated very closely in Casuarina. In several sp. the internodes of the rhiz. are swollen into tubers, which serve for hibernation and veg. repr.

The spike is very like the ♂ fl. of a Conifer, and has as much right to the title of flower. It is an axis with short internodes, bearing a dense mass of sporophylls. Each is shield-shaped and bears a number of sporangia upon the under side of the head (*i.e.* towards the stem), arranged like the horses of a 'merry-go-round.' The spores are of one kind only; each has, running round it, two spiral cuticularised bands of membrane, formed from the outer wall and termed *elaters*. These are hygroscopic, unfolding in damp air. In the rolling up again on drying, the elaters of one spore become entangled with those of others and cause them to adhere together, so that several prothalli may be formed near to one another when they germinate. This is advantageous, for the prothalli are dioec., though so far as we can tell the spores are all alike. The prothallus is fairly large, the ♂ being smaller than the ♀.

The stems of *E. hyemale* L. (Dutch rushes) are used for polishing, the mechanical tissues contain much silica, as do those of most.

Equitant (vernation), *cf.* Vernation.

Eragrostis Host. Gramineae (10). 250 cosmop., mostly subtrop.

Eranthemum L. (excl. *Pseuderanthemum* Radlkf.). Acanthaceae (IV. A). 25 trop. As.

Eranthis Salisb. Ranunculaceae (2). 7 N. palaeotemp. *E. hyemalis* Salisb. (winter aconite, nat. in Brit.) has a thick rhizome or row of tubers, one formed each year. The sol. term. fls. appear in February, before the l.; each has an invol. of three green l., a 'calyx' of 6 segments, and several honey-l. or petals.

Erasma R. Bruniaceae. Nomen.

Ercilla A. Juss. Phytolaccaceae. 2 Chili, Peru. *E. volubilis* A. Juss., climbs by adhesive discs, endogenous just above the axils.

Erechtites Rafin. Compositae (8). 15 Am., Austr., N.Z.

Erect (ovule), erect with stalk at base (fl. held erect).

Eremaea Lindl. Myrtaceae (II. 1). 6 W. Austr.

Eremaeopsis O. Ktze. = Eremaea Lindl. (Myrt.).

Eremalche Greene (*Malvastrum* p.p.). Malvaceae (2). 3 W. U.S.

Eremanthus Less. Compositae (1). 20 Brazil.

Eremia D. Don. Ericaceae (IV. 2). 30 S. Afr.

Eremiastrum A. Gray. Compositae (3). 2 Calif., Arizona.

Eremiopsis N.E. Br. Ericaceae (IV. 2). 1 S. Afr.

Eremium (Cl.), a desert formation.

Eremobium Boiss. (*Malcolmia BH.*). Cruciferae (4). 3 N. Afr.

Eremocarpus Benth. Euphorbiaceae (A. II. 1). 2 Pac. N. Am.

Eremocarya Greene. Boraginaceae (IV. 2). 3 Pac. N. Am.

Eremochlaena Baill. Chlaenaceae. 1 S. Madagascar.

Eremochloa Buese. Gramineae (2). 6 SE. As.

Eremochloe S. Wats. Gramineae (10). 2 W. N.Am.

Eremocitrus Swingle (*Triphasia* p.p.). Rutaceae (V). 1 N. Austr.

Eremocrinum M. S. Jones. Liliaceae (III). 1 California, Utah.

Eremogone Fenzl. = Arenaria L. p.p. (Caryophyll.).

Eremolaena Baill., *cf.* Eremochlaena.

Eremolepis Griseb. Loranthaceae (II). 5 trop. Am., W.I.

Eremolithia Jepson. Caryophyllaceae (I. 6). 1 California.
Eremoluma Baill. (*Lucuma* p.p. *EP.*). Sapotaceae (I. 6). 1 Guiana.
Eremomastax Lindau (*Paulowilhelmia BH.*). Acanth. (IV. A). 1 W. Afr.
Eremopanax Baill. Araliaceae (1). 3 New Caledonia.
Eremophila R. Br. (*Pholidia EP.*). Myoporaceae. 30 Austr.
Eremophyton Beguinot. Cruciferae (2). 1 N. Afr.
Eremosis Gleason (*Vernonia* p.p.). Compositae (1). 15 Mex., C. Am.
Eremosparton Fisch. et Mey. Leguminosae (III. 6). 1 W. and C. As.
Eremospatha G. Mann et H. Wendl. Palmaceae (III. 2). 5 trop. Afr.
Eremostachys Bunge. Labiatae (VI). 40 mid. and W. As.
Eremosyne Endl. Saxifragaceae (I). 1 S.W. Austr.
Eremothamnus O. Hoffm. Compositae (8). 1 S. Afr.
Eremurus Bieb. Liliaceae (III). 20 alpine W. and Cent. As. Fl. protog.; the petals crumple up before the essential organs are ripe. The l. of *E. aurantiacus* Baker are eaten in Afghanistan.
Eria Lindl. Orchidaceae (II. 15). 325 trop. As. Epiphytes; cult.
Eriachaenium Sch.-Bip. Compositae (9). 1 Tierra del Fuego.
Eriachne R. Br. Gramineae (9). 25 trop. As., Austr.
Eriadenia Miers. Apocynaceae (II. 1). 1 trop. S. Am.
Eriander H. Winkler. Rutaceae (IV). 1 trop. Afr.
Eriandrostachys Baill. Sapindaceae (I). 1 Madagascar.
Erianthus Michx. Gramineae (2). 25 trop. *E. Ravennae* Beauv. orn.
Eriastrum Wooton et Standley (*Gilia* p.p.). Polemon. 2 New Mexico.
Eriaxis Rchb. f. (*Galeola BH.*). Orchidaceae (II. 2). 1 New Caledonia.
Eribroma Pierre (*Sterculia* p.p. *EP.*). Sterculiaceae. 1 trop. Afr.
Erica (Tourn.) L. Ericaceae (IV). 500 Eur. (esp. Medit.) and S. Afr. (see fam.). 5 in Brit.; the two common heaths, *E. cinerea* L. and *E. Tetralix* L., cover great areas of moor. In habit like Calluna. Fl. bell-shaped and pendulous, visited and fert. mainly by bees. Honey is secreted by the disc, and insects hanging on to the fl. and probing for it must shake the sta. and receive a shower of the loose powdery pollen from the pores in the tips of the anthers. In the wider mouthed sp. the anthers have horn-like projections at the back, which ensure contact with the insect's proboscis. The stigma projects beyond the sta. so as to be touched first.

Many S. Afr. sp. cult. *E. scoparia* L. is the heath of S. France, &c. (*bruyère*), several feet high; its rootstocks furnish 'briar' wood pipes. The roots of heaths possess endotropic mycorhiza.

Ericaceae (*EP.*, *BH.* excl. *Vacciniaceae*, incl. *Pyrolaceae* p.p., *Clethraceae*. Dicots. (Sympet. Ericales *EP.*, *BH.*). 50 gen., 1350 sp. Owing to their numbers and their social habit they form very char. parts of the veg. in many portions of the globe. Cosmop. except in deserts and in hot damp trop. regions. The *Ericoideae* are confined to Africa, Medit. and Europe, the two great masses of them being however separated by the Sahara, though sp. of Erica, &c. occur in each (see Drude in *Nat. Pfl.* or *Pflanzengeog.* for full discussion of the

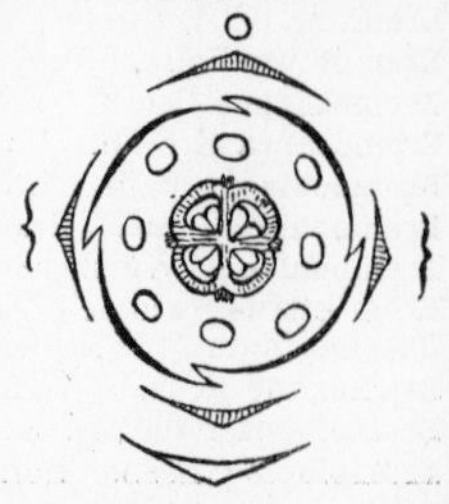

distr.; also gen., espec. Rhododendron, Vaccinium, Calluna, Erica.)

The distr. in moors and swamps, and in peaty soil, is correlated with possession of xero. chars. They are woody, from small under-shrubs to large shrubs and even trees, of two types of habit. Ericoideae are evergreen with no true winter-buds or scale-l.; the whorled l. are needle-like, often rolled back on themselves to form a groove or chamber on under side (*cf.* Empetrum). The other tribes usu. form true winter-buds, though the l. may last over winter; the bud is covered with scale-l., which drop as it elongates, leaving a gap on the stem, while the foliage-l. tend to form term. rosettes. L. usu. elliptical, opp., alt., or whorled, exstip., entire or nearly so, leathery, often hairy, with strongly cuticularised upper epidermis, and often water-storing tissue under it. Many are epiphytic.

Infl. usu. term. on strongly growing shoot; a sympodium tends to be formed. Fls. sol., or oftener racemosely grouped, each with br. and 2 bracteoles, ☿, ⊕ or slightly ·|·. K 4—5, persistent, sometimes accrescent; C (4—5) or 4—5 (*Ledeae*), usu. bell-shaped; A 8—10, obdipl., hypog. or rarely slightly epipet. or 4—5, anthers intr., often with projecting appendages, the thecae often spreading at top, and opening by apical pores, pollen in tetrads. Below the G is a fleshy disc secreting honey; G (4—5), opp. pets., sup. or inf., 4—5-loc. (2—3 in Sympieza, Tripetaleia, 7 in Befaria), with axile plac. and ∞—1 anatr. ov. in each; style simple stigma capitate. Caps., drupe, or berry, usu. ∞ small seeds; embryo cylindrical in copious endosp.

The fls. of the Brit. sp. are mostly suited to bees by size and hanging position, and have 'loose-pollen' mech. The stigma projects so far as to be first touched, and in probing for the honey at the base of the fl. the bee touches the sta. or their horns, and by shaking them causes the fall of pollen from anther-tips. Calluna is partly anemoph. *Cf.* C., Kalmia (explosive), Erica, &c.

[**BH. chars.** Shrubs and trees, l. alt., opp., or whorled, exstip.; usu. persistent. Infl. various. Fls. reg. ☿. K (4—5) or 4—5; C usu. (4—5), A usu. 8—10, sometimes adnate to base of C, usu. dehisc. by pores; disc various or 0; $\underline{G}$ (2—12), multiloc. with style and peltate, capitate or lobed stigma; ov. usu. ∞ in each loc., anatr. on axile plac. Caps., rarely drupe or berry, with small seeds. Endosp.]

Classification and chief genera (after Drude):

I. *RHODODENDROIDEAE* (septic. caps.; seed with ribbed loose coat, often winged; C falling after flg.; sta. with upright or long adnate anthers, with no appendages):

1. *Ledeae* (polypet.): Tripetaleia (C 3), Befaria (C 7), Ledum (C 5). [Menziesia (included).
2. *Rhododendreae* (·|·): Rhododendron (sta. exserted),
3. *Phyllodoceae* (⊕): Leiophyllum (C free, racemes), Loiseleuria (A 5, caps. 2—3-valved), Kalmia (anthers held in hollows of C), Phyllodoce (A 10 free, C bell-shaped), Bryanthus (A 8, C deeply divided), Daboecia (do. toothed).

II. *ARBUTOIDEAE* (berry or loculic. caps.; seed triangular or ovate, not winged; C falling; anthers much folded, with peg-like appendages, or prolonged into tubes, shedding the pollen upwards; G sup.):

1. *Andromedeae* (dry caps. with small K at base): Cassiope (l. closely overlapping), Leucothoë (plac. apical, C spherical in bud), Andromeda (do., C cup-shaped), Lyonia (caps. valve with swollen edge), Epigaea (C salver-shaped, anthers with longitudinal slits).
2. *Gaultherieae* (caps. or berry; K fleshy round caps., or leafy; anthers blunt at tip or with two short processes): Gaultheria (K fleshy round caps., anther-loc. 2-pointed), Pernettya (K dry, berry), Chiogenes (berry nearly inf.).
3. *Arbuteae* (K as small disc at base of berry or drupe; anthers with two long processes): Arbutus (berry loc. many-seeded), Arctostaphylos (1-seeded), Arctous (l. annual).

III. *VACCINIOIDEAE* (as II, but G inf.):
1. *Vaccinieae* (ovary sharply defined from peduncle): Gaylussacia (G 10-loc., anthers not spurred), Vaccinium (5-loc., sta. straight, spurred), Disterigma.
2. *Thibaudieae* (K decurrent on ov., and going over into peduncle): Agapetes, Macleania, Thibaudia (A (10), horned).

IV. *ERICOIDEAE* (fr. usu. loculic. caps. or nut; seeds round, not winged; C persistent after flg.; anther with short connective, thecae spreading above, often appendaged):
1. *Ericeae* (> 1 seed per loc.): Calluna (caps. septicid.), Erica (loculic.; large disc, sepals equal), Macnabia, Philippia.
2. *Salaxideae* (1 per loc.); Eremia, Simocheilus, Salaxis.

Ericaceous, heath-like.
Ericala Renealm. ex S. F. Gray = Gentiana Tourn (Gentian.).
Ericales, the 1st order of Sympet., p. xl; (*BH.*), the 4th of Gamopet.
Ericameria Nutt. (*Aplopappus BH.*). Comp. (3). 12 W. U.S. L. ericoid, often glandular and scented.
Ericetal, growing on moors.
Erichsenia Hemsl. Legum. (III. 2). 1 Austr.
Ericinella Klotzsch. Eric. (IV. 1). 8 S. and W. Afr., Madag. K ·|·.
Ericoid (l.), narrow, needle-like, rolled back.
Erigenia Nutt. Umbell. (III. 4). 1 E. U.S. Tuberous herb.
Erigeron L. Comp. (3). 180 cosmop., esp. N. Am.; 2 Brit. (flea-bane).
Erinacea (Tourn.) Adans. Legum. (III. 3). 1 S.W. Eur. Branch thorns.
Erinna Phil. Lili. (IV). 1 Chile. A 3 with 3 stds.
Erinocarpus Nimmo ex J. Grah. Tili. 1 S. Ind. Androphore. Fr. spiny.
Erinus L. Scroph. (III. 1) 1 Pyrenees, Alps.
Erinosma Herb. = Leucojum L. p.p. (Amaryll.).
Erio- (Gr. pref.), woolly; **-phorous**, very cottony or woolly.
Eriobotrya Lindl. Ros. (II). 12 warm As. *E. japonica* Lindl. has ed. fr. (loquat), largely cult. in As., Medit., N. Am., &c.
Eriocarpum Nutt. = Aplopappus Cass. p.p. (Comp.).
Eriocaucanthus Chiov. Malpigh. (I). 3 trop. and S. Afr.
Eriocaulaceae (*EP.*, *Eriocauleae BH.*). Monocots. (Farinosae; Glumaceae *BH.*; pp. vii, liv). 9/600, mostly trop. and subtrop., esp. S. Am. Perenn. herbs with often grass-like l. Fls. in invol. heads, inconspic., unisexual, 2—3-merous, reg. or ·|·. P usu. 2 whorls, differing in texture. ♂ with usu. (C), A 4—6 or 3—2 with 2- or 1-thecous anthers; ♀ with $\underline{G}$ (2—3)-loc. with 1 orthotr. pend. ov. in each. Caps. loculic. Endosp. floury. *Chief genera:* Eriocaulon, Paepalanthus. [*Pfl. R.*]

Eriocaulon L. Eriocaulaceae. 250 trop. and subtrop. *E. septangulare* With. in the eastern U.S. and also in the Scottish Hebrides and the west coast of Ireland (the only repres. of the fam. in Eur.).
Eriocephalus L. Compositae (7). 20 S.W. Afr. (capok-bosch).
Eriocereus Riccob. (*Cereus* p.p.). Cactaceae (III. 1). 9 warm Am.
Eriochilus R. Br. Orchidaceae (II. 2). 6 Austr.
Eriochlamys Sond. et F. Muell. Compositae (4). 2 S. Austr.
Eriochloa H. B. et K. Gramin. (5). 25 trop., subtrop. Fodders.
Eriochrysis Beauv. = Saccharum L. p.p. (Gramin.). 5 trop. Afr., Am.
Eriocnema Naud. Melastomaceae (1). 2 Minas Geraës.
Eriocoelum Hook. f. Sapindaceae (1). 3 Guinea.
Eriocoma H. B. et K. (*Montanoa* Ll. et Lex.). Compos. (5). 20 trop. Am.
Eriodendron DC. (*Ceiba* Medic.). Bombacaceae. 9 trop., chiefly Am. *E. anfractuosum* DC. (silk-cotton, kapok) has its seeds enveloped in silky hairs, which are used for stuffing cushions, &c. [See Kingsley's *Westward Ho*, c. XXI.]
Eriodes Rolfe. Orchidaceae (II. 9). 1 Khasias.
Eriodictyon Benth. Hydrophyllaceae. 4 W. N.Am.
Erioglossum Blume. Sapindaceae (1). 2 S.E. As.
Eriogonum Michx. Polygonaceae (I. 1). 170 N. Am., esp. W. U.S. Differs from most of the fam., having no ocreae, and cymose umbels or heads of fls. The partial infls. (of a few or many fls. with special invol. of united br.) are combined into heads, &c.
Eriogynia Hook. (*Spiraea* p.p.). Rosaceae (I. 1). 1 N.W. Am.
Eriolaena DC. Sterculiaceae. 8 Indomal.
Eriolithis Gaertn. Rosaceae (inc. sed.). 1 Peru.
Erioneuron Nash (*Triodia EP.*). Gramineae (10). 1 N. Am.
Erionia Nor. Inc. sed. Nomen.
Eriope Humb. et Bonpl. Labiatae (VII). 20 trop. and subtrop. S. Am.
Eriopetalum Wight (*Brachystelma BH.*). Asclepiad. (II. 3). 4 Indomal.
Eriophorum L. Cyperaceae (1). 15 N. temp. chiefly on wet moors. 4 in Brit. (cotton-grass, cotton-sedge). The ♀ fls. are massed together; each has a P of bristles which after fert. grow out into long hairs acting as a means of distr. for the fr. The hairs are sometimes used in stuffing pillows, &c.
Eriophyllum Lag. Compositae (6). 25 N.W. Am.
Eriophyton Benth. Labiatae (VI). 1 Himalaya.
Eriopsis Lindl. Orchidaceae (II. 14). 4 trop. S. Am. Cult. orn. fl
Eriosema DC. Leguminosae (III. 10). 90 trop. and subtrop.
Eriosolena Blume = Daphne L. p.p. (Thymel.).
Eriospermum Jacq. Liliaceae (III). 50 Afr. Cult. orn. fl.
Eriosphaera Less. Compositae (4). 1 S. Afr.
Eriospora Hochst. Cyperaceae (II). 5 trop. Afr.
Eriostemon Sm. Rutaceae (1). 16 Austr., New Caled.
Eriosyce Phil. (*Echinocactus* p.p. *EP.*). Cactaceae (III. 1). 1 Chili.
Eriothrix Cass. Compositae (8). 1 Bourbon.
Erioxylum Rose et Standley. Malvaceae (4). 2 W. Mexico.
Erisma Rudge. Vochysiaceae. 7 N. Brazil, Guiana.
Erismadelphus Mildbraed. Vochysiaceae. 1 Cameroons.
Erismanthus Wall. Euphorbiaceae (A. II. 5). 2 Penang, Sumatra.

Erithalis P. Br. Rubiaceae (II. 3). 6 Florida, W. Indies.
Eritrichium Schrad. (*BH.* incl. *Cryptantha* Lehm.). Boraginaceae (IV. 2). 50 temp.
Erlangea Sch.-Bip. Compositae (I). 20 trop. Afr.
Ernestia DC. Melastomaceae (I). 3 trop. S. Am.
Ernestimeyera O. Ktze. = Alberta E. Mey (Rubiac.).
Ernodea Sw. Rubiaceae (II. 10). 6 W.I., S.E. U.S.
Erocallis Rydberg (*Claytonia* p.p.). Portulacaceae. 1 Rockies.
Eroded, erose, slightly, irreg. toothed, as though gnawed.
Erodendrum Salisb. = Protea L. (Proteac.).
Erodiophyllum F. Muell. Compositae (3). 2 Austr.
Erodium L'Hérit. Geraniaceae. 65 temp. (2 Brit.—Stork's-bill). Like Geranium. The awn twists into a corkscrew with free end and is very hygroscopic (used for weather indicators, &c.). The mericarp has a sharp point with backward-pointing hairs. When it falls, the free end of the awn often catches against surrounding objects. If dampness supervene, the awn untwists and lengthens, and the fr. is driven into the soil. When dry the awn curls up, and the process may be repeated (*cf.* Stipa).
Erophila DC. (*Draba* p.p. *EP.*). Cruciferae (4). 4 Eur., Medit., 1 Brit.
Erosion Lunell (*Eragrostis* p.p.). Gramineae (10). 2 W. N. Am.
Erpetion DC. = Viola Tourn. (Viol.).
Erubescens (Lat.), blush-red.
Eruca Tourn. ex Adans. Cruciferae (2). 10 Medit. Oil is obtained from the seed of *E. sativa* Mill.
Erucago Tourn. ex Adans. = Bunias L. p.p. (Crucif.).
Erucaria Cerv. (*Bouteloua EP.*). Gramineae (11). 7 Mexico.
Erucaria Gaertn. Cruciferae (2). 6 Medit.
Erucastrum Presl (*Brassica* p.p. *BH.*). Crucif. (2). 15 Medit., Eur.
Erucastrum Schimp. et Spann. Cruciferae (2). 15 Medit., Mid-Eur.
Ervatamia Stapf. (*Tabernaemontana* p.p.). Apocyn. (I. 3). 40 palaeotrop.
Ervilia Link = Vicia Tourn. p.p. (Legum.).
Ervum Tourn. ex L. = Vicia Tourn. p.p. For *E. Lens* L. see Lens.
Erycibe Roxb. Convolvulaceae (I). 18 Indomal.
Erycina Lindl. Orchidaceae (II. 19). 1 Mexico.
Eryngiophyllum Greenman. Compositae (5). 1 Mexico.
Eryngium (Tourn.) L. Umbelliferae (II. 1). 220 trop. and temp. (exc. S. Afr.). 2 Brit. (eryngo or sea-holly) on coast, prickly herbs with thick r. and fleshy l. coated with wax. Fls. in cymose heads, blue, visited by bees. Fibre (Caraguata fibre) is obtained from the l. of *E. pandanifolium* Cham. et Schlecht.
Eryngo, *Eryngium.*
Erysimum (Tourn.) L. Cruciferae. 80 Medit., Eur., As. (*E. cheiranthoides* L., treacle mustard, in Brit.)
Erythaea S. Wats. Palmaceae (I. 2). 2 S. California.
Erythraea Renealm ex Borck. Gentianaceae (I. 2). 30 temp. *E. Centaurium* Pers. (centaury), Brit.
Erythrina L. Leguminosae (III. 10). 35 trop. and subtrop. *E. crista-galli* L. cult. Its bright red fls. are inverted; the wings are nearly aborted; the keel forms at its base a honey sac. *E. indica* Lam.

largely planted as shade, and as support. *E. caffra* Thunb. (S. Afr.,

Erythro- (Gr. pref.), red. [Kaffir-boom) very light timber.

Erythrocephalum Benth. Comp. (12). 12 trop. Afr. Pappus scaly.

Erythrochiton Nees et Mart. Rut. (I. 5). 5 trop. Am. The infl. is borne on surface of l. by adnation. K coloured. (C).

Erythrochlamys Guerke. Labiat. (VII). 1 trop. Afr.

Erythrococca Benth. (incl. *Caloxylon* p.p.). Euphorb. (A. II. 2). 30 trop. and S. Afr. *Cf.* Prain in *Ann. of Bot.* 1911.

Erythrocoma Greene. Ros. (III. 2). 5 W. N. Am. [Malaya.

Erythrodes Blume (*Physurus* Rich. p.p.). Orchid. (II. 2). 12 Polynes.,

Erythronium L. Lili. (V). 7 N. temp. P leaves reflexed.

Erythropalum Blume. Olac. 3 Himal. to Malaya. Climbers.

Erythrophloeum Afzel. ex R. Br. Legum. (II. 1). 8 Afr., China, N. Austr. 10 fertile sta. *E. guineense* G. Don (Sierra Leone, red-water tree) has poisonous bark, used as ordeal by native tribes.

Erythrophysa E. Mey. Sapind. (II). 2 S. Afr., Madag. Petiole winged.

Erythropsis Endl. (*Sterculia* p.p.). Sterc. 2 Indomal.

Erythropyxis Pierre. Scytopet. 1 Gaboon.

Erythroselinum Chiov. (*Pastinaca* p.p.). Umbell. (III. 6). 1 Ethiopia.

Erythrospermum Lam. Flacourt. (I). 8 Madag. to Malay Penins.

Erythrotis Hook f. = Cyanotis D. Don p.p. (Commelin.).

Erythroxylaceae (*EP.*, *Linaceae* p.p. *BH.*). Dicots. (Archichl. Geraniales, pp. xxv, li). 2/200 trop. ♄ with usu. alt., entire stip. l. Fl. ☿, reg., usu. heterost.; K or (K) 5, persistent, quincuncial or valvate, C 5, conv or imbr., often with appendages on upper side, A 5 + 5, united at base, G̲ (3—4), usu. 1 only fertile, ov. 1—2 pend. Drupe; endosp. or not. *Gen.*: Erythroxylum, Aneulophus. (*Pfl. R.* 1907.)

Erythroxylum P. Br. Erythroxyl. 200 warm, chiefly Amer. Branches often covered with distichous scales (rudimentary l.). *E. Coca* Lam. (Peru, coca), l. chewed or infused, enable the user to undergo much fatigue; cocaine is made from them (Mortimer, *History of C.*, 1901).

Escallonia Mutis ex L. f. Saxifrag. (V). 60 S. Am., esp. Andes. Ḡ, 2—3-loc., with 4—6 plac. pend. into loc., and ∞ ovules.

Escalloniaceae (Warming), Saxifragaceae, § V.

Escape, a pl. escaped from cultivation, and maintaining itself.

-escens (Lat. suffix), -ish, becoming.

Eschatogramme Trevisano. Polypod. 1 trop. Am.

Eschenbachia Moench. (*Erigeron* p.p.). Comp. (3). 50 warm.

Eschscholtzia Cham. Papaver. (II). 150 Pac. N. Am., cult. orn. fl. Fl. perig. with concave recept. (K) falling as a cap. In dull weather each pet. rolls up on itself, enclosing some sta. Valves of ripe fr. tend to curl spirally, and fr. explodes.

Eschweilera Mart. (*Lecythis* p.p. *BH.*). Lecythid. (IV). 80 trop. Am. Seed sessile. A like Lecythis. [10 Malay Arch.

Eschweileria Zipp. (*Schefflera*, *Boerlagiodendron*, p.p. *EP.*). Aral. (1).

Escobedia Ruiz et Pav. Scroph. (III. 2). 2 trop. Am. Root used for

Escontria Rose (*Cereus* p.p.). Cact. (III. 1). 1 Mex. [dyeing.

Esculentus (Lat.), edible.

Esenbeckia H. B. et K. Rut. (I. 5). 18 trop. Am., W.I. Bark of some Braz. spp. (angostura brasiliensis, quina) used like angostura.

Esmeralda Rchb. f. (*Arachnanthe BH.*). Orchid. (II. 20). 1 Sikkim.

Esmeraldia Fourn. Asclepiadaceae (II. 1). 1 Venezuela. Corona 0.
Espadaea A. Rich. Solanaceae (4). (Verben. *BH.*) 1 Cuba.
Esparto, *Stipa tenacissima* L., *Ampelodesma*, *Lygeum*.
Espeletia Mutis. Compositae (5). 11 Andes. Char. pl. of the alpine region (Paramo). Aloe-like xero. with dense hairs.
Espinal (formation), spiny woodland (S. Am.).
Esquirolia Léveillé. Oleaceae (?). 1 China.
Essence of violets, *Iris florentina* L.
Essential oils, cf. oils; **-organs of fl.**, sta. and cpls.
Esterhazya Mikan. Scrophulariaceae (III. 2). 3 Brazil.
Estival, pertaining to summer.
Esula Rupp. = Euphorbia L. p.p. (Euph.).
Etaballia Benth. (*Inocarpus BH.*). Leguminosae (III. 8). 1 Guiana.
Etaerio, aggregate (of fruit).
Eteriscius Desv. Rubiaceae (inc. sed.). 1 Guiana.
Ethulia L. Compositae (1). 3 palaeotrop.
Etiolation, yellowing and attenuation for want of light.
Etiology, the study of causes.
Ettow (W.I.), *Cordia Sebestana* L.
Eu- (Gr. pref.), true, typical; **-cyclic**, whorled with same number of organs in every whorl; **-geogenous**, weathering readily; **-tropous** (insects), long-tongued bees and hawk-moths.
Euadenia Oliv. Capparidaceae (II). 2 trop. Afr.
Eubrachion Hook. f. Loranthaceae (II). 2 S. Am.
Eucalyptus L'Hérit. Myrtaceae. 230 Austr., 2 or 3 Indomal. (blue-gum, iron-bark, stringy-bark, blood-wood, mallee, &c.). One of the most characteristic genera of the Austr. flora, easily known by the operculum of the fl. bud. Trees and shrubby trees. Some sp. reach an enormous size; *E. regnans* F. Muell. is officially recorded as reaching 326 ft. in height and 25 ft. 7 in. in girth at 6 ft., on Mt. Baw Baw near Melbourne (*cf.* Sequoia). The l. at first formed are often opp. and dorsiv., the later ones alt. and isobil., more suited to the climate. The barks vary much, but being easily recognized, are a valuable aid in the classification. The most common is smooth bark (gum trees) which exfoliates in patches; other kinds are bark scaly all over the trunk (blood-woods, &c.); bark thick and fibrous, the fibres set longitudinally (stringy-barks), or felted; bark hard and furrowed, often black with age (iron-barks). Infl. usu. an umbel which by lengthening of the axis passes to a panicle or corymb. The floral recept. is hollow and becomes woody in the fr. The K is thrown off as a lid when the fl. opens.

On account of their rapid growth and economic value, these trees are now largely cult. in warm climates. Many yield valuable timber, *e.g.* *E. rostrata* Schlecht., *E. marginata* Sm. (jarrah), *E. diversifolia* F. Muell. (karri), &c.; *E. Globulus* Labill. (blue-gum) and others yield oil of eucalyptus; others yield oils, kino, &c.
Eucephalus Nutt. (*Aster* p.p.). Compositae (3). 10 N. Am.
Euceraea Mart. Flacourtiaceae (7). 1 Amazon valley.
Euchaetis Bartl. et Wendl. Rutaceae (1). 5 S. Afr.
Eucharidium Fisch. et Mey. Onagraceae (2). 3 California.
Eucharis Planch. et Linden. Amaryllidaceae (1). 6 trop. S. Am.

Sta. from margin of corona. Cult. orn. fl. (Eucharis lily).
Euchilopsis F. Muell. Legum. (III. 2). 1 W. Austr.
Euchilus R. Br. = Pultenaea Sm. p.p. (Legum.).
Euchlaena Schrad. Gramin. (I). 1 Mex., *E. mexicana* Schrad. (teosinte), used as cereal and fodder. Like Zea in habit and infl., but ♀ spikelets free from one another, not forming 'cob.'
Euchlora Eckl. et Zeyh. Legum. (III. 3). 1 S. Afr. L. simple, exstip.
Euchresta Bennett. Legum. (III. 8). 3 Himal. to Japan.
Euchroma Nutt. = Castilleja L. p.p. (Scroph.).
Euclasta Franch. (*Andropogon* p.p.). Gramin. (2). 1 trop. Afr., Am.
Euclea Murr. Eben. 30 Afr., Arabia. L. alt., opp., or whorled. Fr. ed. *E. Pseudebenus* E. Mey (Orange R. ebony), &c., good wood.
Euclidium R. Br. Crucif. (4). 1 E. Medit.
Euclisia Greene (*Streptanthus* p.p.). Crucif. (1). 15 Calif.
Eucnide Zucc. (*Mentzelia* p.p. *BH.*). Loas. 10 Mex., S.W. U.S. G (5).
Eucomis L'Hérit. Lili. (V). 10 S. and trop. Afr. Spike crowned by tuft of br. Sta. broadened at base. Cult. orn. fl.
Eucommia Oliv. The only gen. of **Eucommiaceae** (*EP.*; *Magnol.* p.p. *BH.*). (Dicots. Archichl. Rosales, pp. xxiii, l). 1 China, *E. ulmoides* Oliv. Tree with alt. exstip. l. and latex. Fls. naked, unisexual, reg. A 6—10. G (2), one abortive, with anatr. pend. ov. Samara. Endosp. Yields medicinal bark and rubber. Hook., *Kew Bull.* 1921, 177; [*Ic. Pl.* tt. 1950, 2361.
Eucorymbia Stapf. Apocyn. (I. 3). 1 Borneo.
Eucosia Blume. Orchid. (II. 2). 2 Java, New Guinea.
Eucrinum Nutt. = Fritillaria Tourn. (Lili.)
Eucrosia Ker-Gawl (incl. *Callipsyche*). Amaryllid. (I. 2). 4 Peru, Ecu-[ador. L. stalked.
Eucryphia Cav. Eucryph. 4 Chile, Austr., Tasm.
Eucryphiaceae (*EP.*; *Rosaceae* p.p., near *Quillaja*, *BH.*). Dicots. (Archichl. Parietales; pp. xxxiii, li). 2/5, Chile, Austr., Tasm., New Caled. ♄ with evergr. opp. stip. l., and sol. reg. ☿ hemicyclic fl. K 4, decid. as hood, C 4, conv., asymm.; A ∞, G (5—18), each with ∞ pend. ov. Styles and ripe cpls. free, but joined by threads to axis. Endosp.; seeds winged. *Gen.*: Eucryphia, Paracryphia.
Eucrypta Nutt. (*Ellisia* p.p.). Hydrophyll. 3 N. Am.
Eudema Humb. et Bonpl. (*Braya* p.p. *BH.*). Crucif. (4). 10 Andes.
Eudesmia R. Br. = Eucalyptus L'Hérit. (Myrt.).
Eufragia Griseb. = Bartsia L. (*BH.*) = Parentucellia Viv. (Scroph.).
Eugeissona Griff. Palm. (III. 2). 3 Malay Pen. to New Guinea. Dioec.
Eugenia Mich. ex L. (*BH.* incl. *Jambosa*, *Myrciaria*, *Syzygium*, &c.). Myrt. (I). 750 warm. K. Ov. 4—∞ per loc. Berry. Cots. fleshy, plumule small. Many have ed. fr., *e.g. E. Michelii* Lam. (trop. Am., Brazil cherry), &c. The dried fl. buds of *E. caryophyllata* Thunb. form the spice cloves.
Eugeniopsis Berg. = Marlieria Cambess. p.p. (Myrt.).
Euglypha Chod. et Hassler. Aristoloch. 1 Paraguay.
Euklisia Rydberg (*Streptanthus* p.p.). Crucif. (1). 4 U.S. (*Cf.* Euclisia.)
Eulalia Kunth. = Pollinia Trin. p.p. (Gramin.).
Eulenburgia Pax. Cucurb. (3). 1 trop. Afr.
Eulobus Nutt. ex Torr. et Gray. Onagr. (2). 1 Calif. Ripe caps. bent [downwards.
Eulophia R. Br. (excl. *Acrolophia*). Orchid. (II. 10). 200 warm |✻.
Eulophidium Pfitz. Orchid. (II. 18). 4 Braz., trop. Afr., Mauritius.

Eulophiella Rolfe. Orchidaceae (II. 10). 1 Madagascar. Cult. orn. fl.

Eulophiopsis Pfitz. Orchidaceae (II. 17). 2 S. Afr., Madag., E. Ind.

Eulophus Nutt. Umbelliferae (III. 5). 5 N. Am.

Eulychnia Phil. (*Cereus* p.p. *EP.*). Cactaceae. 4 Chili.

Eumorphia DC. Compositae (7). 4 S. Afr.

Eunanus Benth. = Mimulus L. p.p. (Scroph.).

Eunomia DC. (*Aethionema* p.p. *BH.*). Cruciferae (2). 10 Mts. of E. Medit.

Euonymus L. Celastraceae. 100 N. temp., and S.E. As. *E. europaeus* L., the spindle-tree, in Brit. Several sp. have curious outgrowths of cork upon their stems. The fls. are polygamous and protandrous. On the ripe seed is a bright red fleshy aril, serving in bird-dispersal. The development of the aril may easily be studied by examining seeds of various ages. The wood is used for spindles, pegs, &c., and furnishes good charcoal.

Euosmia Humb. et Bonpl. Rubiaceae (I. 7). 1 Venezuela.

Eupatoriastrum Greenman. Compositae (2). 1 Mexico.

Eupatoriopsis Hieron. Compositae (2). 1 Brazil.

Eupatorium (Tourn.) L. (incl. *Conoclinium* DC.). Compositae (2). 450 mostly Am., a few in Eur., As., trop. Afr. *E. cannabinum* L., hemp-agrimony, in Brit. Its fls. are largely visited by butterflies.

Euphorbia L. Euphorbiaceae (A. II. 8). 750 chiefly subtrop. and warm temp. (12 in Brit.). They differ very much in vegetative habit. The British sp. of spurge are herbs and so are many others, but shrubs are also frequent. The chief interest centres in those sp. that inhabit very dry places and have consequently a xerophytic habit. Most of these forms closely resemble Cactaceae (*q.v.*), and sometimes when not in flr. it is very difficult to decide from the outside appearance whether one has to do with a Euphorbia or a Cactus. The presence of latex of course distinguishes the former. It is very interesting to see how similar conditions of life have called forth, in three different fams. not nearly allied to one another, such a similarity of habit as is seen in Euphorbia, the Cactaceae, and Stapelia (Asclepiadaceae). As in the cacti, we get almost spherical forms, ridged forms, cylindrical forms, &c. Many are armed with thorns. In all cases it is the stem which is fleshy. The outer tissue is green and does the assimilating work of the plant; the inner portion of the stem consists mainly of parenchymatous storage tissue.

For morphology *cf.* Goebel (*Pflanzenbiol. Schild.* p. 56). He divides the pl. into the following groups:

I. L. normal, well developed, serving a long time as assim. organs. (1) Shoot not water-storing: *e.g.* the British sp. (2) Storage in tubers below ground: *E. tuberosa* L. (3) Stem as reserve for water, &c., but not green: *E. bupleurifolia* Jacq. (cylindrical stem covered with corky scales = l. bases; l. borne in wet season, drop in dry). (4) Stem fleshy, green, leafy in wet season only: *E. neriifolia* L., &c.

II. L. abortive, dropping off early. Assim. and storage carried on in stem. Various types occur here (*cf.* Cactaceae) approaching ± nearly to perfectly spherical form. Somc common ones are (1) *E. Tirucalli* L. (Zanzibar), with thin cylindrical shoots. *E. pendula*

Link is very similar and resembles Rhipsalis in Cactaceae. (2) *E. xylophylloides* Brongn. has flattened shoots (*cf.* Phyllanthus § *Xylophylla*, and Epiphyllum in Cactaceae). (3) *E. Caput-Medusae* L. has a stout stock giving off a number of thinner branches at the top. These are covered with little cushion-like papillae, closely crowded, which are really l. bases; the l. proper is undeveloped. Many sp. show this structure. (4) *E. mamillaris* L. has a thorn in the axil of each cushion (=a metamorphosed infl.-axis). If the cushions, as in the cacti, become 'fused,' we get a ridged stem, as is seen in (5) *E. polygona* Haw. (cf. *Echinopsis cereiformis* in Cactaceae), *E. grandicornis* and many others. Most of these sp. exhibit pairs of stout thorns which are the stips. of the abortive l. By the two horizontal thorns one can tell one of these pl. from a cactus, which has a group of thorns. (6) *E. meloformis* Ait. is nearly spherical but ribbed, whilst in (7) *E. globosa* Sims (*cf.* Echinocactus) we have an almost perfect sphere. [*Cf.* Cactaceae, and Stapelia, and compare all these succulent forms with one another. See also Goebel, *loc. cit.*]

Besides the above, note *E. splendens* Boj. and *E. Bojeri* Hook., pl. with thick stems and green l., the latter dropped in the dry season.

The other chief point of interest in E. is the *cyathium*, or infl. condensed to simulate a single fl. The resemblance is almost perfect. The general branching of the plant is cymose (dichasial). The partial infl. forms a cyathium by the non-development of its internodes, the absence of the P of the individual fls. and the reduction of each ♂ fl. to one sta. There is a perianth-like organ of 5 l., really bracts, and between these are 4 curious horn-like bodies (U-shaped in fig.), which are the combined stips. of the bracts. Then follow a number of sta. arranged with the oldest nearest to the centre and each with a peculiar joint half-way up the stalk. In the middle of the cyathium is a 3-carpelled ovary on a long stalk, usu. ripe for pollination before any sta. ripen.

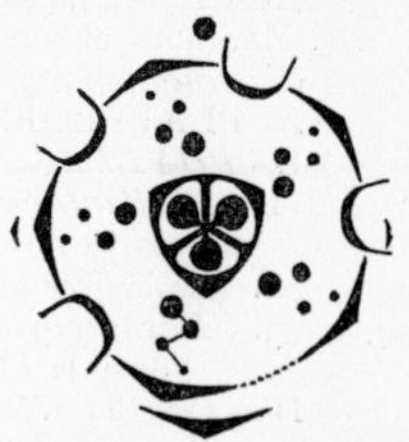

Diagram of central cyathium of infl. of *Euphorbia Peplus* L. (after Eichler, modified).

That this cyathium is an infl. and not a fl., consisting of a lot of ♂ fls., each of 1 sta., round a single ♀, is shown by the centrifugal (cymose) order of ripening of organs, and the joint on the sta.; at this point in the allied gen. Anthostema, there is a P, which shows that the sta. is really a reduced ♂ fl.

In *E.* § *Poinsettia* the infl. is rendered conspicuous by the bright red colour of the larger upper bracts. These sp. often cult. orn. infl.

The fruit explodes when ripe; the carpels split off from the central axis and open at the same moment.

Euphorbiaceae (*EP.*, *BH.* incl. *Buxaceae*). Dicots. (Archichl. Geraniales; Unisexuales *BH.*). 220 gen., 4000 sp., cosmop., except arctic. Few sp. have a very wide range; the most widely-ranging genus is Euphorbia. Closely related to Geraniales by the structure of the gynoeceum, &c., although separated a good deal from the other fams. of the order by the amount of reduction in most of its fls.

Most are shrubs or trees, a few herbaceous (*e.g.* the Brit. sp.). Many are xero.; a number of Australian sp. are of ericoid habit; several, esp. S. Afr., Euphorbias are cactus-like; others resemble Lauraceae, or possess phylloclades (*e.g.* Phyllanthus sp.). A few are lianes. L. usu. alt.; some have opp. l., some opp. l. above and alt. below. Stips. usu. present, but may be repres. by branched hair-like bodies (Jatropha), glands, or thorns. Nearly all contain latex in special laticiferous cells.

Infl. usu. complex; almost every type occurs. Often the first branching is racemose and all subsequent ones cymose. In some cases, *e.g.* Dalechampia and Euphorbia (*q.v.*), the partial infls. are so condensed as to give the appearance of single fls. The fls. are always unisexual, monoec. or dioec., reg., hypog. The P may be present as two whorls usu. 5-merous; more often there is only one (calyx) and frequently the fl. is naked. Sta. 1—∞, free or united in various ways. Ricinus has branched sta. *Phyllanthus cyclanthera* has the sta. united, with a ring-like common anther. $\underline{G}$ usu. (3), with axile placentae, and 3 loc. Styles usu. 2-lobed. The ovules are constant throughout the family and form its best distinctive feature; they are 1 or 2 in each loc., collateral, pendulous, anatropous, with ventral raphe. The micropyle is usu. covered by a caruncle, which is also found on the seed. The fruit is almost invariably a 'schizocarp-capsule.' It splits into cpls. often elastically, and at the same time each cpl. opens ventrally, letting the seed escape. See albuminous. [**BH. chars.** incl. those of Buxaceae, esp. dorsal raphe, and loculic. caps. or drupe.]

Most E. are poisonous. Several are important economic plants, *e.g.* Manihot (rubber, cassava), Hevea (rubber), Croton, Ricinus, &c.

Classification and chief genera (after Pax):

A. PLATYLOBEAE (cotyledons much broader than radicle):

I. *PHYLLANTHOIDEAE* (ovules 2 per loc.; no latex):

1. *Phyllantheae* (embryo large, little shorter than endosp.; ♂ calyx imbricate): Phyllanthus.
2. *Bridelieae* (do., but ♂ calyx valvate): Bridelia.
3. *Daphniphylleae* (embryo short, 4—6 times shorter than endosp.): Daphniphyllum.

II. *CROTONOIDEAE* (ovules 1 per loc.; latex usu. present):

1. *Crotoneae* (sta. bent inwards in bud): Croton.
2. *Acalypheae* (sta. erect in bud; fl. usu. apetalous; ♂ calyx valvate; infl. a raceme, spike, or panicle, axillary or term.): Mercurialis, Acalypha, Ricinus, Dalechampia, Tragia.
3. *Jatropheae* (do.; infl. a dichasial panicle): Hevea, Jatropha.
4. *Adrianeae* (do.; infl. a simple term. spike or raceme): Manihot.
5. *Cluytieae* (♂ calyx imbr.; ♂ fls. with petals, in groups or cymes, these partial infls. axillary or in complex infls.): Codiaeum, Cluytia.
6. *Gelonieae* (do. but apetalous): Gelonium.
7. *Hippomaneae* (do.; apetalous; infl. axillary or term., spike-like, the partial infl. cymes): Stillingia, Hura, Hippomane.

8. *Euphorbieae* (cyathium): Anthostema, Euphorbia.

B. STENOLOBEAE (cotyledons as wide as radicle):

I. *PORANTHEROIDEAE* (ovules 2 per loc.): Poranthera.

II. *RICINOCARPOIDEAE* (ovules 1 per loc.): Ricinocarpus.

Euphorbiodendron Millspaugh (*Euphorbia* p.p.). Euph. (A. II. 8). 12 trop. Am., W.I.

Euphorbiopsis Léveillé (*Euphorbia* p.p.). Euph. (A. II. 8). 1 S.E. As.

Euphoria Comm. ex Juss. Sapindaceae (I). 6 trop. and subtrop. As.

Euphorianthus Radlk. Sapindaceae (I). 1 Malay Archipelago.

Euphoriopsis Radlk. Sapindaceae (I). 1 Indomal.

Euphrasia L. Scrophulariaceae (III. 3). 100 sp. extra-trop. *E. officinalis* L. (eyebright) in Brit. Semi-parasites with loose-pollen fls. (see fam.). The 4 anthers lie close under the upper lip of the fl.; the two upper cohere and also the upper to the lower on each side; the lower lobe of each has a projecting spine. Insects probing for honey shake the spines and receive a shower of pollen from among the anthers. The stigma protrudes beyond the sta. in most fls. so as to be touched first, but every stage can be found from highly protog. fls. with very protruding stigmas to almost homog. fls. whose stigma does not protrude and with self-fert.

Euphrona Vell. Inc. sed. 1 Brazil.

Euphronia Mart. Rosaceae (I. 2). 1 Brazil.

Euphrosine Allem. Inc. sed. Nomen.

Euphrosyne DC. Compositae (5). 1 Mexico.

Euplassa Salisb. Proteaceae (II). 8 trop. Am.

Eupomatia R. Br. Eupomatiaceae. 2 N.E. Austr., New Guinea. Fl. deeply perig., naked; A ∞, G ∞. Oil cells.

Eupomatiaceae (*EP. Anonaceae* p.p. *BH.*). Dicots. (Archichl. Ranales). Only genus Eupomatia, *q.v.*

Euptelea Sieb. et Zucc. Trochodendraceae. 3 Japan to Bengal.

Eureiandra Hook. f. Cucurbitaceae (3). 6 trop. Afr.

Euroschinus Hook. f. Anacardiaceae (3). 5 New Caled., E. Austr.

Eurotia Adans. Chenopodiaceae (A). 2 Medit., W. As., N. Am.

Eurya Thunb. Theaceae. 80 Mexico, S. Am., W. and E. Ind.

Euryale Salisb. Nymphaeaceae (III). 1 S.E. As. Fl. epigynous. The seeds and roots are eaten in China.

Eurybia Cass. = Olearia Moench. (Comp.).

Eurybropsis DC. = Vittadinia A. Rich. (Comp.).

Eurycentrum Schlechter (*Cystorchis* p.p.). Orch. (II. 2). 2 N. G., Solomons.

Eurycles Salisb. Amaryllidaceae (I). 2 N. Austr., Malaya.

Eurycoma Jack. Simarubaceae. 3 Malaya. Sta. 5, stds. 5.

Eurygania Klotzsch (*Thibaudia* p.p. *EP.*). Eric. (III. 2). 8 Andes.

Eurylepis D. Don = Erica Tourn. p.p. (Eric.).

Eurylobium Hochst. Verbenaceae (2). 1 S. Afr.

Euryloma D. Don = Erica Tourn. p.p. (Eric.).

Euryops Cass. Compositae (8). 35 S. Afr. to Socotra, Arabia.

Eurypetalum Harms. Leguminosae (II. 2). 1 Guinea.

Euryptera Nutt. (*Peucedanum* p.p.). Umbellif. (III. 6). 6 N. Am.

Eurysolen Prain. Labiatae (III). 1 Indomal.

Euryspermum Salisb. = Leucadendron R. Br. (Prot.).

Eurystegia D. Don = Erica Tourn. p.p. (Eric.).
Eurystyles Wawra (? = *Stenoptera EP.*). Zingib. or Orchid. 1 Brazil.
Eurytaenia Torr. et Gray. Umbelliferae (III. 5). 1 Texas.
Euscaphis Sieb. et Zucc. Staphyleaceae. 1 Japan. Aril.
Eusideroxylon Teijsm. et Binn. Lauraceae (I). 1 Borneo.
Eusporangiatae. See Filicales.
Eustegia Rafin. Melastomaceae (inc. sed.). 3, habitat?
Eustegia R. Br. Asclepiadaceae (II. 1). 5 S. Afr.
Eustephia Cav. Amaryllidaceae (I). 2 Peru, Argentina.
Eustephiopsis R. Fries. Amaryllidaceae (I). 2 Argentina.
Eustigma Gardn. et Champ. Hamamelidaceae. 2 Hongkong, Tonquin.
Eustoma Salisb. Gentianaceae (I. 1). 5 warm Am., W.I.
Eustrephus R. Br. Liliaceae (X). 1 E. Austr.
Eutacta Link = Araucaria Juss. p.p. (Conif.).
Eutaxia R. Br. Leguminosae (III. 2). 8 Austr. L. opp.
Euterpe Gaertn. Palmae (IV. 1). 10 trop. Am. *E. edulis* Mart. (Assai palm) ed. fr.; a beverage is prepared by soaking it in water.
Eutetras A. Gray. Compositae (6). 1 Mexico.
Euthamia Ell. (*Solidago* p.p.). Compositae (3). 10 N. Am.
Euthemis Jack. Ochnaceae. 6 Indomal.
Euthystachys A. DC. Verbenaceae (2). 1 S. Afr.
Eutoca R. Br. = Phacelia Juss. p.p. (Hydrophyll.).
Eutrema R. Br. Cruciferae (2). 12 C. and E. As., Arctic.
Eutriana Trin. = Bouteloua Lag. (Gramin.).
Euxena Calest. (*Arabis* p.p.). Cruciferae (4). 1 France.
Euxolus Rafin. = Amarantus L. (Amarant).
Euxylophora Huber. Rutaceae (I). 1 Amazon valley. Good wood.
Euzomodendron Coss. Cruciferae (4). 1 S. Spain.
Evacidium Pomel (*Filago* p.p. *EP.*). Compositae (4). 1 N.W. Afr.
Evandra R. Br. Cyperaceae (II). 2 S.W. Austr.
Evansia Salisb. = Iris Tourn. (Irid.).
Evax Gaertn. Compositae (4). 15 Medit., N. Am.
Evelyna Poepp. et Endl. = Elleanthus Presl (Orchid.).
Evening primrose, *Oenothera*.
Everardia Ridl. Cyperaceae (II). 1 Roraima (Brit. Guiana).
Everettia Merrill. Melastomaceae (II). 1 Phil. Is.
Everettiodendron Merrill. Euphorbiaceae (A. I. 1). 1 Phil. Is.
Evergreen, bearing green l. throughout the year.
Everlasting, *Achyrachaena*, *Ammobium*, *Antennaria*, *Gnaphalium*, *Helichrysum*, *Helipterum*; **-grass** (Am.), *Eriochloa*; **mountain-**, *Antennaria*; **-pea** (Am.), *Lathyrus*.
Eversmannia Bunge. Leguminosae (III. 7). 1 Persia.
Evodia Forst. Rutaceae (I). 45 trop., exc. Am.
Evodianthus Oerst. (*Carludovica* p.p. *BH.*). Cyclanthaceae. 2 Costa Rica, W.I.
Evolution, the development of new forms from old.
Evolvulus L. Convolvulaceae (I). 90 trop. and subtrop.
Evonymus (*Euonymus q.v.*) L. Celastraceae. 80 N. temp. and S.E. As.
Evota Rolfe. Orchidaceae (II. 1). 3 S.W. Cape Colony.
Ewartia Beauverd. Compositae (4). 3 S.E. Austr., Tasmania.

Ex- (Lat. pref.), not, without, outside, *e.g.* **-albuminous**, without albumen; **-centric**; **-cluded**, exserted; **-current**, with single straight main stem, *Pinus*; **-ogamy**, tendency of allied gametes to avoid pairing; **-ogenous**, arising from the external layers; **-ogens**, Coniferae and Dicotyledons; **-otropism**, tendency of lat. r. to grow away from main r.; **-serted**, protruding; **-stipulate**, &c.

Exacum L. Gentianaceae (I). 30 sp. palaeotrop. The style is bent to one side or other of the fl.; both occur on the same plant (enantiostyly, *q.v.*).

Exarrhena R. Br. = Myosotis L. p.p. (Borag.).

Excelsus (Lat.), lofty.

Excoecaria L. Euphorbiaceae (A. II. 7). 30 sp. trop., exc. Am. For *E. sebifera* Muell.-Arg. see Sapium.

Excoecariopsis Pax. Euphorbiaceae (A. II. 7). 1 S.W. Afr.

Excremis Willd. Liliaceae (III). 1 Andes.

Exechostilus K. Schum. Rubiaceae (II. 1). 1 trop. Afr.

Exfoliate, to peel off.

Exoacantha Labill. Umbelliferae (III. 8). 1 Syria.

Exocarpus Labill. Santalaceae. 15 Austr., Malaya, Madag. Timber.

Exocarya Benth. Cyperaceae (II). 1 S.E. Austr.

Exochaenium Griseb. in DC. (*Belmontia* E. Mey.). Gent. (I). 20 warm Afr., Madag.

Exochogyne C. B. Clarke. Cyperaceae (II). 1 Amazon valley.

Exochorda Lindl. Ros. (I. 2). 3 Centr. As. Caps. Cult. orn. shrubs.

Exogonium Choisy (*Ipomoea* p.p. *BH.*). Convolvulaceae (I). 18 trop. Am. *E. Purga* Benth. (jalap) cult. for medic. resin.

Exolobus Fourn. Asclep. (II. 4). 4 Brazil. Corona double.

Exomicrum Van Tiegh. = Ouratea Aubl. (Ochn.).

Exomis Fenzl. Chenopod. (A). 1 S. Afr., St Helena.

Exorrhiza Becc. (*Kentia* p.p. *EP.*). Palm. (IV. 1). 1 Fiji.

Exostemma Rich. Rubiaceae (I. 5). 30 W.I., warm Am. Febrifugal alkaloids are contained in the bark.

Exostyles Schott. Leguminosae (II. 9). 2 Brazil.

Exotanthera Turcz. (*Rinorea EP.*). Violaceae. 1 Madagascar.

Exothea Macfadyen. Sapindaceae (II). 2 W.I., C. Am., Fla.

Exploding anthers, *Broussonetia*, *Pilea*, *Urtica*; **-pollen**, &c., *Caladenia*, *Compositae* (*Cynareae*), *Corydalis*, *Cytisus*, *Genista*, *Kalmia*, *Medicago*, *Posoqueria*, *Pterostylis*, *Ulex*, &c.; **-fruit**, *cf.* Dispersal.

Extra- (Lat. pref.), beyond; **-axillary**, outside the axil; **-tropical**, outside the tropics; **-floral nectaries**, *cf.* Nectaries.

Extrorse, opening away from centre of fl.

Eye, a bud, *Helianthus*, *Solanum*; **-bright**, *Euphrasia officinalis* L.

Eylesia Sp. Moore. Scrophulariaceae (III. 2). 1 trop. Afr.

Eyrythalia Renealm. = Gentiana Tourn. (Gent.).

Eysenhardtia H. B. et K. Leguminosae (III. 6). 4 Texas to Guatemala.

Eystathes Lour. Inc. sed. 1 Cochin-China.

F (fl.-class), fls. suited to Lepidoptera, *Angraecum*, *Cuphea*, *Dianthus*, *Labiatae*, *Lonicera*, *Lychnis*, *Oenothera*, *Primula*, and *cf.* Butterfly and Moth fls.

Faba (Tourn.) L. = Vicia L. (Legum.).

Faberia Hemsl. Compositae (13). 1 China.
Fabiana Ruiz et Pav. Solanaceae (4). 15 S. S.Am. Cult. orn. shrubs.
Fabricia Gaertn. = Leptospermum Forst. (Myrt.).
Fabricia Scop. (*Alysicarpus EP.*). Leguminosae (III. 7). 16 palaeotrop.
Facelis Cass. Compositae (4). 3 temp. S. Am.
Facies, external appearance.
Facultative, incidental.
Fadogia Schweinf. Rubiaceae (II. 1). 30 Afr.
Fadyenia Hook. Polypodiaceae. 1, *F. prolifera* Hook., W. Ind. The sterile l. produce buds at the tips.
Fagaceae (*EP.*; *Cupuliferae* p.p. *BH.*). Dicots. (Archichl. Fagales). 5 gen., 350 sp.; three chief centres of distr.—Fagus, Castanea § *Eucastanea* and Quercus N. extra-trop., Pasania and Castanopsis in trop. As. and Calif., Fagus § *Nothofagus* in S. Am., N.Z., and

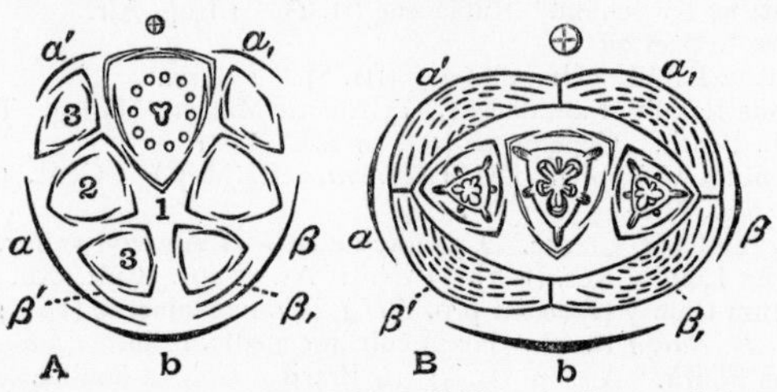

Floral diagrams of *Castanea vulgaris*, after Eichler. A, diagram of ♂ cyme in axil of catkin-leaf, the sta. and rudimentary gynoeceum only shown in the first fl. The sequence of the fls. is indicated by the figures 1, 2, 3. B, diagram of ♀ partial infl. *b* = bract, *α β* = bracteoles, *α′ β′ α, β,* = bracteoles of second order.

S. Austr. Most are trees with simple l. and scaly stipules that drop off as the l. expand. The fls. come out in the axils of the l. of the current year and are diclinous and anemoph., arranged in catkins or small spikes (exc. Fagus ♂). In general there is a close resemblance to Betulaceae, and, as in that fam., the fls. are usu. in dich. cymes in the axils of the catkin-l.; there are often, however, > three fls.

P bract-like, (4—7). ♂ fl. with as many to twice as many or ∞ sta. undivided, with or without rudimentary style. ♀ fls. usu. in dich. of 3 in Castanea, 2 in Fagus, 1 in Quercus, &c. $\bar{G}$ usu. (3) with 3 styles (exc. sp. of Castanea); loculi 3, usu. visible before fert. Plac. axile, each bearing 2 pend. anatr. ov. with 2 integuments. Fr. a 1-seeded nut. Seeds without endosp.

The group of nuts is surrounded by a cup-like organ termed a *cupule*; in the oak there is one nut in each cupule, in the beech two, in the chestnut three. About the morphology of this organ there has been much discussion. Eichler (see diagram above, fig. B, and *Blüthendiagr.*) regards it as the combined bracteoles *α′ β′ α, β,*, Prantl (Engler's *Bot. Jahrb.* VIII. 1887) as an axial outgrowth. See also Celakovsky in *Pringsheim's Jahrb.* XXI. 1890, and *cf.* Betulaceae. The cupule only becomes clearly visible after fert.

Some of the F. show signs of peculiar development of the embryo-sac, and other interesting features (see Chalazogamae).

The order includes several important economic plants, chiefly valuable for their timber, *e.g.* oak (Quercus), beech (Fagus), chestnut (Castanea), &c.

Classification and genera (after Prantl):

1. *Fageae* (fls. in dich., rarely sol. in axils of foliage-l.; lat. and single fr. 3-angled): Fagus (♂ fl. sol. or in dich. of 3; ♀ in 3 or sol.): Nothofagus (♂ in dich. of many; ♀ in 2s).
2. *Castaneae* (♀ fls. in dich. or single in the axils of catkin-l.; fr. rounded at sides):

Style cylindrical, with pointed stigma, ♂ catkins erect.
Cupule with spines or hard papillae. Castanea.
Cupule with scales. Pasania.
Style various, crowned by stigma, ♂ catkins pend. Quercus.

Fagales (*EP.*), the 11th order of Dicots. Archichlamydeae. *Cf.* p. xii.

Fagara L. (*Zanthoxylum BH.*). Rutaceae (I). 140 trop.

Fagelia Neck. Leguminosae (III. 10). 1 S. Afr.

Fagelia Schwencke=Calceolaria L. (Scroph.).

Fagonia Tourn. ex L. Zygophyllaceae. 20 Medit., S. Afr., Calif., Chili.

Fagopyrum Tourn. ex Hall. Polygonaceae (II. 2). 4 As. Fls. like Polygonum, but heterosyled, with long and short-styled forms. *F. esculentum* Moench. (buck-wheat) largely cult., esp. in N. Am., for its fr. (seed), in which there is a floury endosp. Also used as green fodder, and a good honey-plant.

Fagraea Thunb. Loganiaceae. 20 E. Ind. to Austr., often epiphytic. Some sp. have nectaries at the outside of the base of the fl.

Faguetia L. Marchand. Anacardiaceae (3). 1 Madag.

Fagus (Tourn.) L. (*BH.* incl. *Nothofagus* Blume). Fagaceae (I). 4 N. temp. *F. sylvatica* L. (beech, Brit. and large parts of Eur.) often forms homogeneous forests, and is accompanied by a peculiar undergrowth, *e.g. Asperula odorata, Lathrea squamaria*, &c. ♂ fls. in pendulous cymose heads, ♀ in pairs; each cupule encloses two nuts. The wood is hard, and much used in the arts; an oil is expressed from the nuts. Beech hedges in many districts; when growing low it does not drop its l., as it does when it takes the tree form, and thus affords good shelter in winter. A variety with red sap in the cells of the epidermis (copper-beech) is often cult. The beech only flowers every few years, and saves up material in the interval (*cf.* Agave).

Falcaria Riv. ex Rupp. Umbelliferae (III. 5). 4 Medit., W. As.

Falcate, sickle-shaped.

Falconeria Hook. f. Scrophulariaceae (III. 1). 1 W. Himalaya.

Falkia L. f. Convolvulaceae (I). 6 Afr.

Fallugia Endl. Rosaceae (III. 2). 1 N. Am.

False acacia, *Robinia*; **-asphodel** (Am.), *Tofieldia*; **-bromegrass**, *Brachypodium*; **-fruit**, the product of ovary with any other organ that developes, *e.g.* axis; **-hellebore** (Am.), *Veratrum*; **-hemp**, *Datisca*; **-indigo** (Am.), *Amorpha*, *Baptisia*; **-jalap**, *Mirabilis*; **-lettuce** (Am.), *Mulgedium*; **-mallow** (Am.), *Malvastrum*; **-nettle** (Am.), *Boehmeria*; **-oat-grass**, *Arrhenatherum*; **-septa**, partitions chamber-

ing ovary into abnormal or unusual loculi, *Boraginaceae*, *Cruciferae*, *Gaylussacia*, *Linaceae*; **-whorl**, *Labiatae*.
Family, a group of allied genera, *e.g. Compositae*, *Cruciferae*.
Fan-palm, *Chamaerops*, *Sabal*, *Thrinax*, &c.
Fanninia Harv. Asclepiadaceae (II. 1). 1 Cape Colony.
Fans, *cf. Andropogon*, *Bamboos*, *Borassus*, &c.
Faradaya F. Muell. Verbenaceae (4). 6 Austr., Polynes.
Faramea Aubl. Rubiaceae (II. 8). 100 trop. S. Am., W. Ind. See Müller's *Fert. of Fls.*, p. 304 (dimorphic pollen).
Farfugium Lindl. = Senecio Tourn. (*BH.*) = Ligularia Cass. (Comp.).
Fargesia Franch. (*Phyllostachys* p.p. *EP.*). Gramineae (13). 1 China.
Farinaceous (endosp.), of starchy consistence.
Farinosae (Engler). The 8th order of Monocotyledons. *Cf.* p. iv.
Farinosus (Lat.), covered with mealy powder.
Farkleberry (Am.), *Vaccinium arboreum* Marshall.
Farmeria Willis. Podostemaceae. 2 Ceylon, S. India.
Faroa Welw. Gentianaceae (I). 12 Afr.
Farquharia Stapf. Apocynaceae (II. 1). 1 S. Nigeria.
Farsetia Turra p.p. Cruciferae (4). 10 E. Medit.
Fasciation, lateral union of stems, branches, &c., *Celosia*.
Fascicle, a tuft of branches (adj. *fasciculate*).
Fascicularia Mez. Bromeliaceae (4). 4 Chili.
Fastigiate, many branches ‖ to stem, *Populus* (Lombardy poplar).
Fatoua Gaudich. Moraceae (I). 1 Austr. to Japan, Polynesia.
Fats, *cf.* oils.
Fatsia Decne. et Planch. (excl. *Echinopanax* Decne. et Planch., and *Tetrapanax* C. Koch). Araliaceae. 1 Japan, cult. orn. fol. For *F. papyrifera* Benth. et Hook. f. see Tetrapanax.
Faujasia Cass. Compositae (8). 3 Madagascar, Mascarenes.
Faurea Harv. Proteaceae (I). 10 S. and trop. Afr., Madag.
Fauria Franch. Saxifragaceae (I). 1 N. Japan.
Fawcettia F. Muell. Menispermaceae. 1 E. Austr. K 9, CA 6, G 3.
Faxonanthus Greenman. Scrophulariaceae (I. 1). 1 Mexico.
Faxonia T. S. Brandegee. Compositae (5). 1 Lower California.
Faya Neck. = Crenea Aubl. (Lythrac.).
Feather-foil (Am.), *Hottonia*; **-grass**, *Stipa*, (Am.) *Leptochloa*.
Fedia Gaertn. p.p. Valerianaceae. 1 Medit. Other sp. *cf.* Valerianella.
Fedtschenkoa Regel. Cruciferae (4). 1 Turkestan.
Feeria Buser (*Trachelium* p.p.). Campanulaceae (I). 1 Morocco.
Fegimanra Pierre. Anacardiaceae (I). 2 trop. Afr.
Feijoa Berg (*Orthostemon EP.*). Myrtaceae (I). 2 Brazil.
Felicia Cass. Compositae (3). 60 S. Afr. to Abyssinia.
Female fl., *Aucuba*, *Begonia*, *Bryonia*, *Rhamnus*, *Sagittaria*.
Fendlera Engelm. et Gray. Saxifragaceae (III). 3 S.W. U.S., Mex.
Fendlerella A. A. Heller (*Fendlera EP.*). Saxifrag. (III). 1 N. Am.
Fennel, *Foeniculum*; **-flower**, *Nigella sativa* L.; **giant-**, *Ferula*.
Fenugreek, *Trigonella Foenum-graecum* L.
Fenzlia Benth. = Gilia Ruiz et Pav. p.p. (Polemon.).
Fenzlia Endl. Myrtaceae (I). 2 Austr.
-fer (Lat. suffix), bearing.
Feral, wild.

Ferdinanda Lag. (*Zaluzania* Pers. p.p.). Compositae (5). 1 C. Am.
Ferdinandusa Pohl. Rubiaceae (I. 5). 10 W.I., trop. S. Am.
Feretia Delile. Rubiaceae (I. 8). 2 Upper Nile, trop. Afr.
Fergusonia Hook. f. Rubiaceae (II. 5). 1 Ceylon, S. India.
Ferment, *cf. Carica*, *Droseraceae*.
Fern, *Filicineae*; **beech-**, *Dryopteris*; **bird's nest-**, *Asplenium*; **bladder-**, *Cystopteris*; **bristle-**, *Trichomanes*: **elkhorn-**, *Platycerium*; **filmy**, *Hymenophyllum* (and fam.); **hard-**, *Lomaria*, *Blechnum*; **hart's tongue**, *Phyllitis*; **holly-**, *Polystichum*; **lady-**, *Athyrium*; **maiden-hair-**, *Adiantum*; **northern-**, *Blechnum*; **oak-**, *Dryopteris*; **parsley-**, *Cryptogramma*; **prickly shield-**, *Polystichum*; **royal-**, *Osmunda*; **shield-**, *Dryopteris*; **staghorn-**, *Platycerium*; **tree-**, *Cyathea*, &c.; **walking-**, *Asplenium*.
Fernandezia Lindl. = Lockhartia Hook. (Orchid.).
Fernandia Baill. Bignoniaceae (2). 1 Angola.
Fernelia Comm. ex Lam. Rubiaceae (I. 8). 4 Mascarenes.
Fernseea Baker. Bromeliaceae (4). 1 Itatiaia Mt (near Rio).
Feronia Correa. Rutaceae (V). 1 India to Java, *F. elephantum* Correa (elephant-apple or wood-apple; wood useful, and yields a gum; fr. ed.).
Feroniella Swingle. Rutaceae (V). 2 Indo-China.
Ferraria L. Iridaceae (II). 10 Afr. Cult. orn. fl.
Ferreirea Allem. Leguminosae (III. 1). 1 Rio de Janeiro.
Ferrugineus (Lat.), rust-coloured.
Fertile, capable of giving fruit.
Fertilisation, the union of ♂ and ♀ elements; **cross-**, between two fls. on different pl.; **self-**, within the same fl.
Ferula Tourn. ex L. Umbelliferae (III. 6). 60 Medit., Cent. As. *F. communis* L. cult. (giant-fennel). It only flowers after storing up materials for some years (*cf.* Fagus, Agave). *F. Narthex* Boiss. and *F. Assa-foetida* L. are the sources of the drug asafoetida, obtained by notching the roots; used as a condiment in Persia, &c. under the name 'food of the gods,' and as a stimulant in medicine. *F. galbaniflua* Boiss. et Buhse and *F. rubricaulis* Boiss. are the sources of the medic. gum galbanum.
Ferulago Koch. Umbelliferae (III. 6). 40 Medit., S. Eur.
Fescue-grass, *Festuca*.
Festuca (Tourn.) L. Gramineae (10). 100 cosmop.; 5 in Brit. (fescue-grass). The l. roll inwards in dry air (*cf.* Stipa). Many good pasture-grasses. When growing on mountains often viviparous (see fam.).
Fever-bush (Am.), *Lindera*; **-few**, *Chrysanthemum*, *Matricaria*; **-wort** (Am.), *Triosteum*.
Feuillea Gled. = Fevillea L.
Fevillea L. Cucurbitaceae (I). 6 trop. Am. 5 sta. all alike.
Fibigia Medic. (*Farsetia* p.p. *BH.*). Cruciferae (4). 12 E. Medit.
Fibraurea Lour. Menispermaceae. 4 trop. and subtrop. As.
Fibres, the strengthening tissues of plants, largely used in the arts for spinning, brush-making, plaiting, paper, rough weaving, tying, &c.; those of the bast are most generally useful. The chief *stem* or *leaf fibres* are perhaps Abroma, Abutilon, Agave (sisal, &c.), Ampelodesma, Arenga, Attalea (piassaba), Boehmeria (rhea, ramie), Borassus

(palmyra), Broussonetia, Camelina, Cannabis (hemp), Carludovica, Caryota (kitul), Chlorogalum, Cocos (coconut, coir), Copernicia, Corchorus (jute), Cordyline, Couratari, Crotalaria (Sunn-hemp), Cyperus, Debregeasia, Eryngium (caraguata), Furcraea (Mauritius hemp), Hibiscus, Jubaea, Laportea, Lardizabala, Leopoldinia (piassaba), Linum (flax), Lygeum, Maoutia, Marsdenia, Mauritia, Musa (Manila hemp), Pandanus, Phormium (New Zealand flax), Raphia (raffia), Sabal, Sansevieria (bowstring hemp), Spartium, Stipa (esparto), Tillandsia, Villebrunea, Yucca, &c. The chief *surface fibres* (on seeds, &c.) are Bombax, Calotropis, Chorisia, Cochlospermum, Eriodendron (kapok), Gossypium (cotton). Special or peculiar cases are Antiaris, Broussonetia, Lagetta, Luffa, &c. See Dodge, *Useful Fiber Plants*, Washington, 1897.

Fibrillose, with fibres.

Fibrocentrum Pierre. Sapotaceae (inc. sed.). 1 Brazil.

Fibrous root, one in tufts of uniform length, as in grasses.

Ficalhoa Hiern. Ericaceae (II). 1 trop. Afr.

Ficaria (Dill.) Hall = Ranunculus L. p.p. (Ranunc.).

Ficinia Schrad. Cyperaceae (I). 50 S. and trop. Afr.

Ficoidales (*BH.*). The 14th cohort of Polypetalae.

Ficoideae (*BH.*) = Aizoaceae.

Ficus Tourn. ex L. Moraceae (II). 800 warm, chiefly E. Ind. and Polynes., &c. Trees and shrubs of the most various habit. In general alt. entire l. with stips. which envelope the bud (acting as a protection to it against heat, &c.) and soon after their unfolding drop off. Adv. roots are very common.

F. elastica Roxb. (indiarubber tree) grows as a stout independent tree, usu. commencing epiphytically, and often reaching a great size. At its base are developed buttress-roots, radiating out in all directions; their depth is often several feet, while their thickness is only a few inches. From the branches are given off adv. roots which grow downwards and enter the soil. These grow in thickness and form great pillars supporting the branches. The l. are entire, and leathery, with a glossy surface. The stips. protect the bud. Rubber is obtained by tapping (*cf.* Hevea).

F. indica L. and *F. benghalensis* L. (banyan) show similar habit. The aerial roots form supporting pillars, and by their means the tree may reach immense size. (The banyan is sacred in India; the young roots are provided with tubes of bamboo to protect them, and the ground is prepared for them.) See plate in *Nat. Pfl.* of the famous tree at Calcutta.

F. religiosa L. (Peepul or Bo-tree) is similar, but its l. have a long acuminate apex, combined with an easily wetted surface. From the apex (*drip-tip*) the rain drips off rapidly after a shower and the l. is soon dry. In very wet trop. forests this property is of some importance.

F. Sycomorus L. (sycomore or mulberry fig) N. Afr. and *F. Carica* L. (fig) Eur., Medit., are also erect trees.

F. repens Rottl. is a small climbing sp. which takes hold of its support by aerial roots (as in ivy); these secrete a gummy substance containing caoutchouc, and then absorb the fluid constituents, leaving the caoutchouc as a cement, fastening the roots to their support

(Darwin, *Climbing Plants*, p. 185). *F. Thwaitesii* Miq. and other climbing sp. are heterophyllous, the l. on the climbing shoots small and different in shape.

F. Benjamina L. and other sp. climb up other trees giving off aerial clasping (negatively heliotropic) roots which surround the trunk. These roots thicken and unite into a network and finally often strangle the 'host' altogether. These sp. often become epiph. by the dying away of their lower portions, but like the Aroids they maintain communication with the ground by long aerial roots. Sometimes they commence as epiphytes and send down aerial roots to the soil.

The infl. is hollowed out, and consists of a number of fls. inside a pear-shaped common recept., which opens by a narrow mouth at the top. Within the mouth, in most, are the ♂ fls., while the rest of the cavity is filled with ♀ fls. (Sachs, *Physiol.* p. 434). The ♂ has a P and 1 or 2 sta., the ♀ a smaller P. Infl. as a whole protog.; mode of pollination extraordinary (*cf.* Yucca), there being a special insect (Blastophaga, a small wasp) adapted to Ficus fls. The gravid ♀ enters a fig infl. and lays eggs in the ovary; the ♂ wasps thus formed fertilise the ♀s and these as they emerge are pollinated by the ♂ fls. and carry the pollen to new figs. For further details and an account of the peculiar process of 'caprification,' see Müller's *Fert. of Fls.* p. 521, *Nat. Pfl.*, Cunningham on *F. Roxburghii* (rev. in *Bot. Centr.* 45, p. 344), and papers in *Bot. Jahrb.* II. 1890, p. 245.

Many sp. bear the fls. on old parts of the stem (cauliflory). Fr. multiple, composed of a lot of drupes inside the common fleshy recept.; that of *F. Carica* L. is the common fig.

Lac (shellac, &c.) is produced on several by the punctures of a small hemipterous insect (*cf.* Butea). Several, esp. *F. elastica* Roxb., yield caoutchouc. The buttress-roots are used as planks.

-fid, fidus (Lat.), cleft.

Fiddle-wood, *Citharexylum.*

Fiebrigia K. Fritsch. Gesneriaceae (II). 1 Bolivia.

Fiebrigiella Harms. Leguminosae (III. 7). 1 Bolivia.

Field botanists, notes for, see Collecting; **-madder,** *Sherardia.*

Fieldia A. Cunn. Gesneriaceae (I). 1 Australia.

Fig, *Ficus Carica* L.; **Hottentot-,** *Mesembryanthemum*; **Indian-,** *Opuntia*; **mulberry-,** *Ficus Sycomorus* L.; **-wort,** *Scrophularia.*

Figuierea Montr. Rubiaceae (inc. sed.). 1 New Caled.

Filago L. Compositae (4). 12 Eur., As., Am., N. Afr.; 3 Brit.

Filament, the stalk of a stamen.

Filbert, *Corylus.*

Filetia Miq. Acanthaceae (IV. B). 5 Sumatra, Malay Pen.

Filicales. One of the main divisions of Pteridophyta, char. by well-developed l. with vigorous growth, often large and much-branched; stem usu. short in proportion to the l. area, and not much branched. Sporangia borne on the l., usu. very numerous.

Classification (after Engler):

I. FILICALES LEPTOSPORANGIATAE. Sporangia from single superficial cells; prothallus above ground, usu. flattish (see below).

1. Eufilicineae. 2. Hydropterideae.

2. MARATTIALES. Sporangia from cell complex; prothallus flattish, antheridia on both sides, archegonia below.

3. OPHIOGLOSSALES. Sporangia from cell complex; prothallus wholly or partially subterranean, tuberous or cylindrical with sunken antheridia and archegonia; embryo often long subterranean. Fertile l. with branches bearing the sporangia.

For further details see next art., Pteridophyta, and the families. *Cf.* also *Nat. Pfl.*; Hooker and Baker, *Synopsis Filicum*; Christensen, *Index Filicum* (for nomenclature); Christ, *Die Farnkräuter der Erde*, 1897; Bower, papers on morphology and phylogeny in *Phil. Trans.* and *Ann. Bot.* of the last 25 years, and *Ferns*, Cambridge, *Origin of a Land Flora*, &c.; Seward, *Fossil Botany*, &c., &c.

Filicales Leptosporangiatae. The first order of Filicales, grouped as follows:

Sub-order 1. *EUFILICINEAE*. Sporangium wall usu. with a special ring or annulus of thickwalled cells, by whose means it opens; homosporous, with mono- or di-clinous prothalli.

1. *Hymenophyllaceae:* herbs with mesophyll usu. one cell thick, and marginal sori term. on naked veins.
2. *Cyatheaceae:* usu. tree or large ferns, with complete and oblique annulus.
3. *Polypodiaceae:* usu. herbaceous, with imperfect, vertically placed annulus, not closed at base, rarely absent.
4. *Parkeriaceae:* water ferns, sporangia sol. on anastomosing veins, almost spherical, with ± perfect, sometimes wanting, vertical annulus, and no true indusium, but inrolled l. margin.
5. *Matoniaceae:* herbs with dichotomous l., sporangia with complete oblique annulus, grouped at base of umbrella-like indusium.
6. *Gleicheniaceae:* herbs with l. repeatedly dichotomous, and sporangia with equatorial annulus; sori on the veins below.
7. *Schizaeaceae:* mostly small herbs with sessile sporangia, with complete annulus at apex, sol. on l. margin or in axils of bract-like segments.
8. *Osmundaceae:* short-stemmed ferns with sterile and fertile l. and naked sori, sporangia with annulus at one side of apex.

Sub-order 2. *HYDROPTERIDINEAE*. Sporangia usu. many in sori, enclosed in metam. l. segments or indusium-like covers; spores of two kinds; macrosporangia with one macrospore, microsporangia with many.

1. *Marsiliaceae:* sporocarps pluriloc.; sori 2—∞ in l. apex, ♂ and ♀ mixed; ♀ prothallus with one archegonium, ♂ of one veg. cell and 2 antheridia.
2. *Salviniaceae:* sporocarps uniloc.; sori unisexual, on special water l. (Salvinia) or submerged lobes of water l. (Azolla); ♀ prothallus with a few archegonia, ♂ as in Marsiliaceae.

1. *Eufilicineae.* These plants with the Marattiaceae are generally known as Ferns. An outline of the general life history will be found under Pteridophyta.

The fertilised ovum on the prothallus developes directly and without any resting period into a fern-plant. There is no intermediate period of rest as there is in flowering-plants when the seed is ripe. The prothallus continues to assimilate food and supply the young fern until the latter is able to do so for itself. The primary root remains small or withers away, and new ones are adv. formed from the stem or from the l. bases, as the pl. grows. The mature pl. may be of almost any size from the tiny filmy ferns (Hymenophyllum) to the large tree ferns (*e.g.* Cyathea, Alsophila). The stem grows by an apical cell, 2- or 3-sided, cutting off segments alt. on each face. From these by further divisions arise the tissues and members. The l. form a little way behind the growing apex as in fl. pl. One segment (but not every one) gives one l.; the l. grows by an apical cell also. The stem may be erect, or may climb (as in many epiph.), or creep on the surface, or below it as a rhiz. Its growth is slow and branching infrequent. The l. are borne upon it, the internodes being as a rule short in erect, long in creeping stems. The phyllotaxy is not so definite as in fl. pl., but the l. are very commonly in ranks or straight lines dependent on the position of the segments cut off from the apical cell of the stem. The lat. buds arise either on the l. (as in Dryopteris, § Nephrodium) or on the stem; in the latter case they are rarely axillary; but usu. beside the l. The growing tips of stem and l. are often protected by brown scales, which are mere trichomes or superficial outgrowths.

The l. is usu. large with apical growth and circinate (coiled) vernation. The growth often lasts for a long time, or even permanently (Lygodium). The l. blade is usu. branched pinnately.

The repr. organs are borne upon the l. The unit is the sporangium or spore capsule, a small rounded body, stalked in fams. 2, 3 and 8 but sessile in the others. The caps. has a wall one cell thick, and in this is a group of cells with peculiarly thickened cell-walls, termed the *annulus*, by whose agency (its cells being hygroscopic) the opening of the sporangium is effected. Sometimes, as in many Polypodiaceae, the opening is explosive. The mech. is in principle similar to that by which anthers dehisce. The annulus may have various forms (see fams.), but the commonest is that of a row of cells running round the sporangium for about $\frac{3}{4}$ of its circumference.

The sporangia are usu. collected into groups (*sori*). The sorus may be naked, but is more usu. covered by an *indusium*, sometimes merely a fold of the l. itself, but more commonly a special outgrowth from the l., either epidermal or derived from the more deeply placed layers of tissue as well. The sori are usu. found on the veins of a l., often in the angle where a vein forks. They do not as a rule occur on all the l. Very often certain l. are fertile, the others not. In this case the fertile l. have usu. no green tissue at all, their pinnae being entirely covered with sori, *e.g.* Osmunda sp. In other cases, *e.g.* Aneimia sp., one part of a l. is sterile, the other fertile. Or again the sori, and this is most common, may be borne simply on the ordinary l. They are almost always on the lower surface only; they may entirely cover it, but more often are localised.

The spores are all of one kind and if sown under suitable conditions give rise to *prothalli*, flat green expansions living for a short or long period independently upon the soil (numbers may be seen where ferns are growing). On the under surface are borne the repr. organs *antheridia* (♂) and *archegonia* (♀). The spermatozoids swim to the ova in the water which collects under the prothalli. The fert. ovum developes directly into a new fern-pl.

Two interesting modifications of the life cycle as above described are known. In *Pteris cretica*, *Dryopteris Filix-mas*, *Aspidium falcatum* and *Todea africana*, there occurs *apogamy* or the omission of the sexual process from the life-history (see diagram in Pteridophyta). The new fern-plant is produced from the prothallus by a process of budding; a growing point developes from the cells of the prothallus. The cycle thus runs:

Fern-plant → sporophylls → sporangia
↑ ↓
← . . . . . . ← prothallus

The other case, *apospory*, is found in *Athyrium Filix-foemina* var. *clarissima*, and in *Polystichum angulare* var. *pulcherrimum*, &c. Here spore-formation is replaced by a process of budding which gives rise to prothalli on the backs of the l., so that the life-cycle runs

Fern plant → . . . . →
↑ ↓
fertilised ovum ← {spermatozoid ← antheridium / ovum ← archegonium} ← prothallus

The latter must not be confused with the 'vivipary' of *Asplenium bulbiferum*, &c., where the leaf-tissue buds directly into new pl., which for a time remain attached, but ultimately grow independently (*cf.* Bryophyllum, &c.).

A very large number of ferns are shade- and moisture-loving plants. Many however are xero. and alpine forms with reduced transpiration, exhibiting the familiar char. of such plants—reduced surface, thick cuticle, hairiness, incurving of leaves (*cf.* Ericaceae), and even, though rarely, succulence (*Polypodium adnascens*, *Drymoglossum carnosum*, &c.). The tree ferns and many others have water storage tissue in the stem. Many are epiphytic, esp. in the trop., though they may be found growing in this way even in Britain. *Cf.* Platycerium, Polypodium, &c. The spores, consisting only of one cell, are much lighter than is possible for a seed, and may be carried by wind to enormous distances.

2. *Hydropteridineae* or *Rhizocarpae*. The two fams. of this group, though they have much in common, are probably derived from different stocks. For details *cf.* fams.

As in the homosporous forms, so here the embryo gives rise directly to a new leafy pl., usu. aquatic, and exhibiting a creeping stem with a dorsiv. arrangement of the l. Roots may or may not be formed. The stem grows by an apical cell. The sporangia are enclosed in capsular structures termed *sporocarps*. In the Salv. this body contains one sorus only, in the Mars. more than one. The sorus in the former has one kind of sporangium only, in the latter usu. both. The spores germinate in water; the megaspore gives rise to a small green ♀ prothallus which remains enclosed in the burst spore. Its free surface bears a few archegonia. The microspore gives rise (sometimes without escaping from the sporangium) to a rudimentary ♂ prothallus and antheridia. From the latter the spermatozoids escape and swim to the ♀ organ.

Filices, ferns proper, homosporous leptosporangiate Filicales.

Filicineae = Filicales.

Filicinean, relating to ferns.

Filicium Thw. Sapindaceae (II). 3 trop. As. and Afr.

Filiform, thread-like.

Filipendula Tourn. ex L. (*Spiraea* p.p. *BH.*; *Ulmaria* p.p., *q.v.*). Rosaceae (III. 4). 10 N. temp.

Fillaeopsis Harms. Leguminosae (I. 5). 1 trop. Afr.

Filmy ferns, *Hymenophyllaceae*.

Fimbriate, fringed.

Fimbristemma Turcz. Asclepiadaceae (II. 4). 1 trop. S. Am.

Fimbristylis Vahl. Cyperaceae (I). 225 chiefly trop.

Findlaya Bowdich. Inc. sed. 1 Madeira.

Findlaya Hook. f. Ericaceae (III. 2). 1 Trinidad.

Finger-grass (Am.), *Panicum*.

Fingerhuthia Nees ex Lehm. Gramineae (10). 1 S. Afr., Afghanistan.

Fingrigo (W.I.), *Pisonia aculeata* L.

Finlaysonia Wall. Asclepiadaceae (I). 1 Further India.

Finschia Warb. Proteaceae (II). 1 New Guinea.

Fintelmannia Kunth. Cyperaceae (II). 4 Brazil, Madagascar.

Fiorin-grass, *Agrostis alba* L.

Fir, *Abies*; **Douglas-**, *Pseudotsuga Douglasii* Carr.; **Scotch-**, *Pinus sylvestris* L.; **silver-**, *Picea alba* Link; **spruce-**, *Picea excelsa* Link; **umbrella-**, *Sciadopitys verticillata* Sieb. et Zucc.

Fire-bush, *Crataegus pyracantha* Medic.; **-pink** (Am.), *Silene*.

Firmiana Marsigli (*Sterculia* p.p. *BH.*). Sterculiaceae. 10 As.

Fischera Spreng. = Platysace Bunge (*BH.*) = Trachymene Rudge.

Fischeria DC. Asclepiadaceae (II. 1). 12 trop. Am., W.I.

Fissicalyx Benth. Leguminosae (III. 8). 1 Venezuela.

Fissiparous, splitting.

Fissipes Small (*Cypripedium* p.p.). Orchidaceae (I. 2). 1 N. Am.

Fistular, herbaceous and hollow, *Umbelliferae*.

Fistularia L. (*Rhinanthus* p.p.). Scroph. (III. 3). 9 N. temp.

Fitchia Hook. f. Compositae (13). 2 Polynesia.

Fittonia E. Coen. Acanthaceae (IV. B). 2 Peru, cult. orn. fol.

Fitzgeraldia F. Muell. (*Cananga* p.p.). Anonaceae (1). 1 Austr.

Fitzroya Hook. f. Coniferae (Pinaceae; see C. for gen. char.). 2 Chili, Tasm.

Five-finger (Am.), *Potentilla*; (W.I.) *Syngonium*.

Fixed light position, that taken up by l. with regard to light.

Fixed oils, *cf.* Oils.

Flabellaria Cav. Malpighiaceae (I). 1 W. Afr.

Flabellate, **flabelliform**, fan-shaped.

Flacourtia (Comm.) L'Hérit. Flacourtiaceae. 15 trop. As., Afr. *F. Ramontchi* L'Hérit. (Madagascar plum), &c. have ed. drupes.

Flacourtiaceae (*EP.*; *Bixinieae* p.p., *Samydaceae BH.*). Dicots. (Archichl. Parietales). 70 gen., 500 sp. trop. and subtrop. trees and shrubs, mostly with alt. stip. leathery l., often ± two-ranked. Fls.

sol., axill., or in cymose or racemose mixed infls., often ∞, reg., 4—more-merous, sometimes partly spiral. Peduncle often jointed near base. Axis convex; disc, or glands, scales, &c., between C and A. K 2—15 or (2—15), imbr. or valv., C 15—0, A usu. ∞, sometimes united in antipet. groups, anthers usu. opening by lat. slits; G̲ (2—10) or ½-inf. (inf. in Bembicia), 1- (rarely multi-) loc. with parietal plac. which often project into ov., and sometimes unite; ov. ∞, anatr.; styles = plac., or united. Usu. berry or caps.; seeds 1 or many, often with aril; embryo straight in endosp. Some have ed. fr.; a few supply timber, or oil.

Classification and chief genera (after Engler):

1. *Erythrospermae* (fl. ☿; P usu. ∞, spiral, A 5—8 with lineal anthers; caps.); Erythrospermum, Berberidopsis.
2. *Oncobeae* (fl. ☿; K 3—5, C 4—12 imbr., A ∞ with lineal anthers, G (3—10) each with ∞ ov.; fr. not, or late, dehisc.); Oncoba, Mayna, Carpotroche.
3. *Pangieae* (dioec.; K 2—5, C 5—8 with scales at base, A ∞—5, G (2—6) each with ∞—1 ov.; berry or berry-like caps.); Pangium, Hydnocarpus, Gynocardia.
4. *Flacourtieae* (K 4—6 imbr., C usu. 0, A ∞ with short anthers, G as last; berry or caps.); Flacourtia, Xylosma, Azara.
5. *Scolopieae* (fl. ☿; K 4—6 almost valv., C small or 0, A ∞ perig. with short anthers, G (3—6), each with ∞—1 ov., 1- or multi-loc.); Scolopia, Prockia, Banara.
6. *Paropsieae* (*Passiflor.* p.p. *BH.*) (K 5, axis slightly tubular, with disc or gynophore, C 5, often corona, A ∞—20 or 9—5, perig. or at base of gynophore, sometimes united, G (3—5), usu. with ∞ ov.; palaeotrop.); Barteria, Paropsia.
7. *Casearieae* (*Samydaceae* p.p. *BH.*) (K 4—5 imbr., C 0, A ∞ or few, sometimes stds., perig., G (2—6), usu. (3), each with ∞—2 ov.); Casearia, Samyda.
8. *Abatieae* (*Samydac.* p.p. *BH.*) (fl. ☿; K 4, valv., C 0, A ∞—8, perig., no stds., G (2—4) with ∞ ov.; l. opp.); Abatia.
9. *Homalieae* (do. *BH.*) (K, C 4—15, A 4—15 or ∞ in bundles, ante-pet., perig. or epig.; l. spiral, rarely paired); Homalium.
10. *Phyllobotryeae* (fl. ☿ or polyg., K, C 3—5, A 5—∞, hypog., G (2—4), 1-loc. with ∞ ov.; l. alt. with epiphyllous infl.); Phyllobotryum.

Flag, sweet, *Acorus Calamus* L.; **-yellow,** *Iris Pseudacorus* L.

Flagellaria L. Flagell. 4 warm |✻. Climbers. P. petaloid.

Flagellariaceae (*EP.*, *BH.*). Monocots. (Farinosae; Calycinae *BH.*, pp. v, liv). 3/10 warm |✻. Stout stems, sometimes climbing, with long, many-nerved, usu. sheathing l. and panicles; fls., reg., ☿ or ♂ ♀. P homoclam., 3 + 3, A 3 + 3, G̲ (3), 3-loc. each with 1 axile anatr. ov. Fr. 3-loc. or with 3—1 stones. Endosp. *Chief genus* Flagellaria.

Flagenium Baill. Rubi. (I. 8). 3 Madag.

Flamboyante, *Poinciana, Colvillea*; **flame-tree** (Austr.), *Nuytsia, Sterculia.*

Flamingo-plant, *Anthurium;* **flannel-flower,** *Actinotus.*

Flanagania Schlecter. Asclep. (II. 1). 1 S. Afr.

Flaveria Juss. Comp. (6). 20 Am., W.I. L. opp. No pappus.

Flavescent, becoming yellow, yellowish; **flavus** (Lat.), yellow.

Flax, *Linum usitatissimum* L.; **New Zealand-**, *Phormium tenax* Forst.; **purging-**, *Linum*; **spurge-**, *Daphne Gnidium* L.
Flea-bane, *Erigeron*, *Pulicaria*; (W.I.), *Vernonia arborescens* Sw.
Fleischmannia Sch.-Bip. Compositae (2). 4 Centr. Am.
Flemingia Roxb. ex Ait. (*Moghania EP.*). Legum. (III. 10). 20 palaeotrop.
Fleshy fr., see Dispersal of seeds, Edible products; **leaves**, *Agave*, *Aizoaceae*, *Aloe*, *Anacampseros*, *Bromeliaceae*, *Chenopodiaceae*, *Crassulaceae*, *Dischidia*, *Gesneriaceae*, *Glaux*, *Mesembryanthemum*, *Orchidaceae*, *Saxifragaceae*, *Suaeda*, *Yucca*; **stem**, *Cactaceae*, *Ceropegia*, *Euphorbia*, *Stapelia*, &c.
Fleur-de-lis, *Iris*.
Fleurya Gaudich. Urticaceae (1). 8 trop.
Flexularia Rafin. Gramineae (inc. sed.). 1 N. Am.
Flexuose (stem), zigzag.
Flindersia R. Br. Rutac. (II) (Meliac. *BH.*). 15 E. Austr., Malaya.
Flixweed, *Sisymbrium Sophia* L.
Floating heart (Am.), *Limnanthemum*.
Floerkea Willd. Limnanthaceae. 1 N. Am.
Flomosia Rafin. = Verbascum Tourn. (Scroph.).
Flora, a catalogue of the pl. growing in a country.
Floral (*cf.* also under Flower) **diagram** (*cf.* those given here under many fams.), an imaginary section through the bud, showing the arrangement of parts, aestivation, &c.; it may also be used (*cf.* Polygonaceae) to express theoretical views as to multiplication or suppression of organs. At the top is the original stem upon which the fl. is a branch, and at bottom the bract; lat. are the bracteoles; then follow K, C, A, and G, showing their relative positions to one another and to the br. When free they are shown separate; when concrescent, they are joined by lines; the anthers show the mode of opening, the ovary the placentation, stigmas, &c.; **-envelope**, the perianth; **-formula**, a convenient way of showing many features of a fl., largely used here. K 3, C 3, A 3, $\underline{G}$ 3, means calyx of 3 free sepals, corolla of 3 free petals, &c.; ovary superior. K (3), C (3), A 3 + 3, $\overline{G}$ (3), means calyx (corolla) of 3 concrescent sepals (petals), stamens in two whorls of 3 each, free, ovary of 3 concrescent carpels, inferior, and so on; **-kingdoms**, see Floral Regions; **-leaves**, the parts of the fl., esp. K and C; **-mechanisms**, mechanisms to contrive as far as possible cross-fertilisation for a fl., and to ensure that the visiting insect shall receive pollen or touch the stigma, or to ensure self-fertilisation. They may be classed as follows (see individual headings for examples): *Anemophily*, see Pollination by Wind; *Cleistogamy* (production of self-fertilising fl.); *Dichogamy* (ripening of ♂ and ♀ at different times, with or without movements of sta. and style); *Dioecism* and other sex-distributions (*q.v.*); *Explosive mechanisms*; *Heterostylism*; *Loose-pollen mechanisms*; *Piston-mechanisms*; *Pollen-prepotency*; *Pollination by Animals*; *Pollination by Water*; *Pollination by Wind*; *Self-sterility*; *Sensitive stamens*; *Sensitive stigmas*; *Special mechanisms*, such as Asclepiadaceae, Ficus, Orchidaceae, Salvia, Yucca, &c.; *Style-projection*; *Trap Flowers*, &c. See Knuth, *Handbook of Floral Pollination*; Oxford; **-regions**,

regions char. by the possession of a considerable number of local (endemic) forms; the greater their number, and the higher their systematic rank, the more natural is the region. Engler divides the world as follows: **I.** Northern Extra-tropical Floral Kingdom, with 9 regions, (1) *Arctic*, (2) *Sub-Arctic* or Conifer, (3) *Mid-European*, (4) *Macronesian* (Azores, Madeira, Canaries, Cape Verdes), (5) *Mediterranean*, including land all round that sea, (6) *Central Asiatic*, (7) *Temp. E. Asiatic*, (8) *Pacific N. Am.*, (9) *Atlantic N. Am.*: **II.** Palaeotropic Floral Kingdom, with 9 regions, (1) *N. Afr.—Indian desert*, (2) *Afr. forest and steppe*, (3) *S.W. S. Afr.*, (4) *S. Atl. islands*, (5) *Madagascar and islands*, (6) *Nearer India*, (7) *Monsoonia* (warmer Himal., Malaya, N. Austr., Polynesia) (this and 6 are usu. united in this book as Indomalaya, and sometimes called E. or W.), (8) *E. China and S. Jap.*, (9) *Hawaiian*: **III.** Centr. and S. American Floral Kingdom, with 5 regions, (1) *Mid-American Xero.* (S.W. U.S., Mex.), (2) *Trop. Am.*, (3) *Andine*, (4) *Galapagos*, (5) *Juan Fernandez*: **IV.** Austral Floral Kingdom, with 6 regions, (1) *Antarctic S. Am.*, (2) *Antarctic Continental*, (3) *Kerguelen*, (4) *New Zealand*, (5) *Australia*, (6) *Tristan da Cunha*, *St Paul*, *Amsterdam*: **V.** Oceanic Floral Kingdom, with 3 regions, *Boreal*, *Tropical*, and *Austral*; **-symmetry** shows two chief cases, if radial the fl. is *regular* or *actinomorphic* (even if the cpls. be fewer in number), *Ranunculaceae*, *Rosaceae*, &c., if not, some members being omitted in the outer whorls, or all members of a whorl not alike, it is *irregular* and may be *zygomorphic* (divisible into two halves, each the reflection of the other), *Labiatae*, *Scrophulariaceae*, &c., or *asymmetrical* (not so divisible), *Valerianaceae*. Cf. Floral Diagram, &c.

Flores verbasci, *Verbascum*.

Florestina Cass. Compositae (6). 3 Mexico.

Floret, small fl. of a cluster.

Floribundus (Lat.), producing many fls.

Florida Velvet Bean, *Mucuna*.

Floridus (Lat.), showy.

-florus (Lat. suffix), -flowered.

Flos (Lat.), a flower.

Floscopa Lour. Commelinaceae. 15 trop. and subtrop.

Flotovia Spreng. = Chuquiraga Juss. (Compos.).

Flourensia DC. Compositae (5). 10 Arizona to Argentina.

Flower, a repr. short shoot, consisting of an axis (*receptacle*, *q.v.*, *thalamus*, *torus*), bearing essential organs or *sporophylls*, the *androeceum* or *stamens* (*q.v.*), and *gynoeceum* or *carpels* (*q.v.*), or only one of them in diclinous fl.; also usu. some accessory organs or *perianth* (*q.v.*), most often divided into an outer green whorl or *calyx*, and inner coloured one or *corolla*; **and insects**, the relations between fls. and the insects which pollinate them, *cf.* Flower-classes, Floral Mechanisms, &c.; **-axis**, the receptacle; **-bud**, the young fl., in which the l. are packed in a definite way (aestivation, *q.v.*); **-classes**, the classes into which fls. may be divided according to their relations so insects, &c.; **W** (wind-pollinated), **Po.** (offering pollen only), **A** (with freely exposed honey), **AB** (partly concealed honey), **B** (fully concealed honey), **B′** (do. in aggregated infls.), **F** (Lepidoptera fls. with long tubes), **H** (bee fls. with long tubes, zygomorphism, &c.); see individual classes for examples; **colours of -** (usu. in corolla) are due to *chloroplastids* or bodies carrying chlorophyll (rare), *Deherainea*, *chromoplastids* or bodies carrying colours, or to coloured cell-sap; all colours change readily to white, and there are several cases of change (*q.v.*) of one colour to another; bees are inclined to prefer blue, butterflies red and white; **-cup**, a hollow receptacle; **-de-luce**, Iris; **-description**, *cf.* Description; **-, doubling of**, change of sta. to petals, or in Compositae of tubular to ligulate fl.; **-fence** (Barbados), *Caesalpinia pulcherrima* Sw.; **-mechanisms**, see Floral; **-movements**, protecting against cold and wet, *e.g.* a bending downwards, *Anemone*, *Bellis*, *Daucus*, *Fragaria*, *Linum*, *Papaver*, or a closing of the petals, *Anagallis*, *Bellis*, *Calandrinia*, *Eschscholtzia*, *Tragopogon*; **-pride** (W.I.), *Caesalpinia pulcherrima* Sw.; **-tube**, the concrescent portion.

Flowering ash, *Fraxinus*; **-currant**, *Ribes sanguineum* Pursh; **-fern**, *Osmunda*; **-rush**, *Butomus umbellatus* L.

Fluckigeria Rusby (*Kohlerianthus* Fritsch, *EP.*). Gesneriaceae (1). 1 Bolivia.

Flueckigeria O. Ktze. (*Ledenbergia* Klotzsch). Phytolaccaceae. 1 trop. S. Am., W.I.

Flueggea Rich. = Ophiopogon Ker-Gawl. (Lili.).

Flueggea Willd. Euphorbiaceae (A. I. 1). 6 palaeotrop.

Flueggeopsis K. Schum. (*Phyllanthus* p.p. *EP.*). Euphorb. (A. I. 1). 3 Malaya.

Fluitans (Lat.), floating.

Fluviales = Helobiae.

Fluviatilis (Lat.), growing in streams.

Fly-flowers, *Amorphophallus*, *Araceae*, *Arum*, *Asarum*, *Cobaea*, *Compositae*, *Crassulaceae*, *Cynanchum*, *Hedera*, *Helicodiceros*, *Paris*, *Stapelia*, *Umbelliferae*, *Veronica*; **-orchis**, *Ophrys muscifera* Huds.; **-trap, American**, *Apocynum*; **- -, Venus'**, *Dionaea muscipula* Ellis.

Fockea Endl. Asclepiadaceae (II. 3). 6 Afr.

Fodder. The food of grazing animals, &c. The grasses (fresh or dry) and Leguminosae (esp. the pods) are most generally useful. Innumerable pl. are used in different countries; among the most important are *Acacia*, *Agrostis*, *Alopecurus* (fox-tail grass), *Andropogon*, *Anthoxanthum*, *Anthyllis*, *Arachis*, *Aristida*, *Astragalus*, *Atriplex*, *Avena* (oat), *Bouteloua* (mesquit grass), *Brassica*, *Briza*, *Bromus*, *Buchloe* (buffalo grass), *Celtis*, *Cenchrus*, *Ceratonia* (algaroba), *Chionachne*, *Chloris*, *Chrysopogon*, *Cicer* (chick-pea), *Cyamopsis*, *Cynodon* (Bermuda grass), *Cynosurus* (dog's tail grass), *Dactylis* (cock's foot grass), *Daucus*, *Deschampsia*, *Desmodium*, *Dolichos* (horse-gram), *Ehrharta*, *Eleusine* (ragi), *Eragrostis*, *Eriochloa*, *Eruca*, *Ervum*, *Fagopyrum* (buckwheat), *Festuca* (fescue), *Galega*, *Glyceria*, *Gossypium* (cotton-seed), *Heteropogon*, *Hippocrepis*, *Holcus*, *Hordeum* (barley), *Imperata*, *Ischaemum*, *Lathyrus*, *Leersia*, *Lespedeza*, *Lolium* (rye grass), *Lotus*, *Lupinus* (lupin), *Medicago* (lucerne, &c.), *Melica*, *Melilotus*, *Milium*, *Mucuna* (Florida velvet bean), *Muehlenbergia*, *Musa*, *Onobrychis* (sainfoin), *Ornithopus*, *Oryza* (rice), *Panicum* (millet, Guinea grass, &c.), *Paspalum*, *Pennisetum* (bajri), *Phaseolus* (gram, beans), *Phleum* (timothy), *Pisum* (pea), *Poa* (meadow grass), *Secale* (rye), *Sesamum* (gingelly), *Setaria* (Italian millet), *Sorghum* (Guinea corn), *Spergula*, *Symphytum*, *Trifolium* (clover, &c.), *Tripsacum*, *Triticum* (wheat), *Vicia* (vetch), *Zea* (maize), *Zizyphus*.

Foeniculum Tourn. ex L. Umbelliferae (III. 5). 4 Medit., Eur., 1 Brit. (fennel). The young l. of *F. officinale* All. are a good veg. when blanched like celery, and the fr. is a condiment.

Foetid horehound, *Ballota nigra* L.

Foetidia Comm. ex Lam. Lecythidaceae. 3 Madag., Masc.

Fokienia A. Henry et H. H. Thomas. Coniferae (Pinaceae, see C. for gen. char.). 1 E. China.

Folia Jaborandi, *Pilocarpus*.

Foliaceous, leaf-like, leaf-bearing.

Foliage plants, cult. for orn. foliage, *e.g. Begonia*, *Caladium*, *Codiaeum*, *Coleus*, many *Coniferae*, *Cordyline*, *Cortaderia*, *Dracaena*, *Eryngium*, many *Ferns*, *Fittonia*, *Gunnera*, *Gesneria*, many *Palmae*, *Panax*, *Pelargonium*, *Phormium*, *Rheum*, *Rhus*, *Selaginella*, *Smilax*, *Sonerila*, many trees.

Folium (Lat.), a leaf; **-folius** (Lat. suffix), leaved.

Follicle, a dry dehisc. fr. of one cpl., dehisc. on ventral side only; *Aconitum*, *Apocynaceae*, *Asclepiadaceae*, *Banksia*, *Crassulaceae*.

Folotsia Costantin et Bois. Asclepiadaceae (II. 1). 1 Madag.

Fonna Lunell (*Phlox* p.p.). Polemoniaceae. 2 W. U.S.

Fontainea Heckel. Euphorbiaceae (A. II. 5). 1 New Caled., E. Austr.

Fontanesia Labill. Oleaceae. 1 Sicily, W. As. Chi. Hedge plant.

Fontanus (Lat.), growing in or near a spring.

Food, see Edible Products, Fodder; **-bodies**, *Acacia*, *Cecropia*; **- of the gods**, *Ferula*.

Fool's parsley, *Aethusa Cynapium* L.

Foot, organ attaching fern plant to prothallus.

Foramen, an aperture.

Forbesia Eckl. (*Curculigo* p.p. *BH.*). Amaryllid. (III). 12 Afr.

Forbidden fruit (W.I.). *Citrus aurantium* L. var. *paradisi*.

Forchhammeria Liebm. Capparidaceae (III). 3 Mex., W.I.

Forcipella Baill. Acanthaceae (IV. B). 1 Madag.

Forcipella Small (*Siphonychia EP.*). Caryophyll. (I. 4). 1 N. Am.

Fordia Hemsl. Leguminosae (III. 6). 3 S. China.

Fordiophyton Stapf. Melastomaceae (I). 2 S. China.

Forest, a close assemblage of trees, allowing no break in the overhead canopy; homogeneous (of one sp.), or diversified; **-oak**, *Casuarina*.

Forestiera Poir. Oleaceae. 15 Am., W.I.

Forficaria Lindl. Orchidaceae (II. 1). 1 S. Afr.

Forgesia Comm. ex Juss. Saxifragaceae (V). 1 Bourbon.

Forget-me-not, *Myosotis*.

Fork-veined, veins forking into two, as in ferns.

Forms of vegetation, groups of pl., of various fams., presenting a general resemblance in external habit, often correlated with resemblance in conditions of life, *e.g.* trees, epiphytes, &c.

Formula, floral, see Floral formula.

Forrestia A. Rich. Commelinaceae. 20 palaeotrop.

Forsellesia Greene (*Glossopetalon* A. Gray). Celastr. 4 N. Am.

Forskohlea L. Urticaceae (5). 5 Medit. to India.

Forstera L. f. (*Phyllachne* p.p. *EP.*). Stylidiaceae. 4 Tasm., N.Z.
Forsteronia G. F. W. Mey. Apocynaceae (II. 2). 30 trop. Am., W.I.
Forsythia Vahl. Oleaceae. 2 China. Cult. orn. fl. shrubs.
Forsythiopsis Baker. Acanthaceae (IV. A). 2 Madag.
Fortunearia Rehder et Wilson. Hamamelidaceae. 1 China.
Fortunella Swingle (*Citrus* p.p.). Rutaceae (V). 4 E. As. (cumquats).
Fortuynia Shuttl. ex Boiss. Cruciferae (2). 3 Persia, Afghanistan.
Fothergilla Murr. Hamamelidaceae. 2 Atl. N. Am. (Am. witch elder), Cashmir. Fl. apet., A ∞.
Fouquieria H. B. et K. Fouquieriaceae. 5 warm N. Am., incl. *F. splendens* Engelm. (ocotilla, coach-whip), used for hedges. Shrubs with deciduous l., the midribs persistent and thorny, and showy fl. in racemes, &c., ☿, reg., 5-merous. C (5), A 10—15, G̲ (3) with 4—6 ov. on plac. in middle of ventral side. Fr. spherical, 3-loc.; seeds with long hairs or wings. Endosp. oily. Wax obtained from bark.
Fouquieriaceae (*EP.*; *Tamaricaceae* p.p. *BH.*). Dicots. (Archichl. Parietales). Only gen. Fouquieria (*q.v.*) *Bull. Torr. Bot. Club*, 31, p. 45
Fourcroya Spreng. = Furcraea Vent. (Amaryllid.).
Four-o'clock, *Mirabilis Jalapa* L.
Fourniera Scribner. Gramineae (3). 1 Mexico.
Fournieria Van Tiegh. (*Cespedesia EP.*). Ochnaceae. 1 C. Am.
Foveolaria Ruiz et Pav. Styraceae. 6 Peru.
Fowl-meadow grass (Am.), *Poa*, *Glyceria*.
Fox-glove, *Digitalis purpurea* L.; **-grape**, *Vitis Labrusca* L.; **-tail grass**, *Alopecurus pratensis* L., (Am.) *Spartina patens* Muhl.
Fragaria (Tourn.) L. Rosaceae (III. 2). 10 ✳̲, Chili. *F. vesca* L. (wild strawberry), Brit. Veg. repr. by runners is well shown. Fl. protog. (class AB), with epicalyx. Fr. of a number of achenes (the so-called seeds) upon a fleshy recept. The fl. bends down after fert., while the fr. ripens. In Am. the cult. forms tend to become dioec. or polyg. Several sp. cult. for the ed. fr.
Franchetia Baill. = Cephalanthus L. (Rubi.).
Franciscea Pohl = Brunfelsia L. p.p. (Solan.).
Francoa Cav. Saxifragaceae (II). 2 Chili. Cult. orn. fl. (wedding flower).
Frangipani, *Plumeria*.
Frangula Tourn. ex Hall. = Rhamnus L. p.p. (Rhamn.).
Frangulinae (Warming), the 16th order of Choripetalae.
Frankenia L. Frankeniaceae. 45 sea-coasts, temp. and subtrop. *F. laevis* L., sea-heath, in Brit. Halophytes with inrolled hairy l. (*cf.* Empetrum).
Frankeniaceae (*EP.*, *BH.*). Dicots. (Archichl. Parietales; Caryophyllinae *BH.*). 4 gen., 60 sp. of salt-loving plants, trop. and temp. herbs with jointed stems; l. opp., inrolled, stip. (?). Fls. in dichasia, ☿, reg. K (4—7), C 4—7, A usu. 6 in two whorls, sta. slightly united at base; G̲ usu. (3), 1-loc. with parietal plac., only the lower parts of which bear ovules; ov. ∞, anatr., ascending; style forked. Caps. loculic. Mealy endosp.; embryo straight. *Chief genera:* Frankenia, Niederleinia. Closely related to Tamaricaceae and Guttiferae; the agreement with Caryophyllaceae, near to which it is sometimes placed, *e.g.* by *BH.*, is more in habit than in structure.

Frankincense, *Boswellia-Carteri* Birdw.; **-pine**, *Pinus Taeda* L.
Franklandia R. Br. Proteaceae (I). 2 W. Austr.
Franseria Cav. Compositae (5). 16 Am.
Frantzia Pittier. Cucurbitaceae (4). 2 C. Am.
Frasera Walt. (*Swertia EP.*). Gentianaceae (I. 3). 8 N. Am.
Fraunhofera Mart. Celastraceae. 1 Brazil.
Fraxinus Tourn. ex L. Oleaceae. 60 ⚹ esp. N. Am., E. As., and Medit. *F. excelsior* L., ash, in Brit. Serial accessory buds in axils. Has large pinnate l. with grooved petioles. Water is said to enter this groove and be absorbed by the l.; the hollow is usu. inhabited by acarids, forming a *domatium*. The fls. appear before the l. in densely crowded short racemes. Each ☿ consists merely of 2 sta. ⊥ 2 cpls., and is anemoph.; but polygamy is the rule in this sp. and every possible combination of the three types of fl. (☿, ♂, ♀) occurs in various places, sometimes all on one tree, or two on one and one on another, and so on. Fr. a samara or one-seeded nut with terminal wing aiding in wind distr. *F. Ornus* L., the 'flowering ash' of S. Eur., has K and C. The firm elastic wood of the ash is valuable.

The weeping ash is a variety propagated veg. from a single tree which appeared as a sport at Wimpole in Cambridgeshire.
Free, not ad- nor con-nate.
Free-central placenta, one running up through centre of a 1-loc. ovary, which looks like a multi-loc. ov. that has lost its septa. Cf. *Primulaceae* (diagram), *Caryophyllaceae*.
Freerea Merrill. Icacinaceae. 1 Phil. Is.
Freesia Klatt. Iridaceae (III). 3 Cape Col. Cult. orn. perf. fl.
Fregea Reichb. f. Orchidaceae (II. 7). 1 C. Am.
Fremontia Torrey. Sterculiaceae. 1 California.
French bean, *Phaseolus vulgaris* L.; **-honeysuckle**, *Hedysarum*; **-jujubes**, *Zizyphus*; **-marigold**, *Tagetes*; **-rye-grass**, *Arrhenatherum avenaceum* Beauv.; **-weed**, (W.I.), *Commelina*.
Frenela Mirb. = Callitris Vent. p.p. (Conif.).
Frerea Dalz. Asclepiadaceae (II. 3). 1 S. India.
Fresenia DC. Compositae (3). 3 S. Afr.
Freycinetia Gaudich. Pandanaceae. 70 Ceylon to N.Z. and Polynes., usu. climbing shrubs with infl. and fl. like Pandanus. The bracts are fleshy and usu. brightly coloured. In Java, Burck observed pollination effected by a bat (*Pteropus edulis*) which devoured the coloured bracts; in so doing it received pollen upon its head and carried it to the ♀ fl. Fr. a berry, not, as in Pandanus, a drupe.
Freyera Reichb. (*Biasolettia EP.*, *Chaerophyllum* p.p. *B.H.*). Umbelliferae (III. 2). 6 Medit.
Freylinia Colla. Scrophulariaceae (II. 4). 2 S. Afr.
Freziera Sw. ex Willd. (*Eurya* p.p. *EP.*). Theaceae. 10 trop. Am.
Fridericia Mart. Bignoniaceae (1). 1 S. Brazil.
Friedlandia Cham. et Schlechtd. = Diplusodon Pohl (Lythr.).
Frijole, *Phaseolus vulgaris* L.
Frijolite, *Sophora*.
Fringe-tree (Am.), *Chionanthus*.
Fritillaria (Tourn.). Liliaceae (V). 50 N. temp. *F. Meleagris* L.

(snake's head) Brit. Large nectaries at base of P. The bud stands erect and so does the caps., but the open fl. is pend. *F. Imperialis* L. (Crown Imperial) and others cult. orn. fl.

Fritillary, Fritillaria.

Fritzschia Cham. Melastomaceae (1). 3 Brazil.

Froelichia Moench. Amarantaceae (3). 10 warm Am. Fr. enclosed in the P, which forms two wings

Frog-bit, *Hydrocharis*; **-orchis**, *Habenaria* (*Coeloglossum*) *viridis* R. Br.

Frommia H. Wolff. Umbelliferae (III. 5). 1 Nyassaland.

Frondous, frondose, leafy.

Propiera Bouton ex Hook. f. (*Psiloxylon* p.p. *EP.*). Flacourtiaceae (inc. sed.) (Myrtaceae *BH.*). 1 Mauritius.

Froriepia C. Koch (*Carum* p.p. *BH.*). Umbelliferae (III. 5). 1 W. As.

Frost-weed (Am.), *Helianthemum.*

Fruit, the product of that process of growth initiated by the act of fert.; *true* fr. is the product of ovary only, *false* fr. or *pseudocarp* of ovary with any other organ that developes. *Simple* fr. where the fl. gives one indivisible fr.; *aggregate* where several similar fr. come from one fl., as in raspberry, buttercup, Ochna, Rubus, &c.; *multiple* or *collective*, where several fl. combine to give one fr., as in fig, mulberry, plane. They may be *dry* or *fleshy*, may open (*dehiscent*), or not (*indehiscent*): some, called *schizocarps*, break up into one-seeded portions (*mericarps*).

Dry indeh. fr. are divided into *achenes* and *nuts*, the former defined as the product of one, the latter of > one cpl.; but in practice the large are nuts, the small achenes. True achenes in Ranunculus, Potentilla, &c., but the name is also given to the fr. of Compositae, Gramineae (this variety, with pericarp and testa united, is sometimes called a *caryopsis*), Labiatae, &c. True nuts, from sup. ov., in Betulaceae, but the term is applied to the large one-carpelled fruit of Anacardium, &c. A var. of achene or nut is the winged one-seeded indeh. *samara* of ash, elm, Banisteria, Liriodendron, Ptelea, Seguieria, Ventilago, &c.

Schizocarps various, *e.g.* the *lomentum* of many Leguminosae (a pod constricted between seeds, breaking into one-seeded portions), the schizocarps of Euphorbiaceae, Geraniaceae, Malpighiaceae, many Malvaceae, Sapindaceae, Umbelliferae.

Dry dehisc. fr. of several kinds, esp. the *follicle*, *legume*, and *capsule*. Follicle of one cpl., dehisc. along ventral side only, Aconitum, Asclepiadaceae, Apocynaceae, Crassulaceae. Legume similar but dehisc. along both sides, as in most Leguminosae. Dry fr. of > 1 cpl. are capsules, but special forms have special names, *e.g.* the pod-like *siliqua* of Cruciferae, the *pyxis* of Anagallis, &c. (capsule opening by a lid split off by *circumscissile* dehiscence), and others. The way in which it dehisces is of systematic importance. It usu. splits from apex down. If the splits, as in Epilobium, Iris, &c., run down the midrib of each cpl., the dehisc. is *loculicidal*: if, as in Hypericum, the fr. breaks into its component cpls., leaving the placental axis standing, it is *septicidal*; if the outer wall of the fr. breaks away, leaving the septa standing, it is *septifragal.* The portions into which the fr. splits are termed *valves.* In some Campanulas,

Papaver, &c., the dehiscence is *porous*, little openings forming in the pericarp.

The commonest fleshy fr. are the *berry* and *drupe*. The former contains no hard part but the seeds; these are surrounded by fleshy tissue and there is a firmer skin (*epicarp*) on the outside. Berries may be derived from sup. ovaries, as in Berberis, Solanum, Vitis, &c. or inf., as in Ribes, Vaccinium, &c. In rare cases the berry dehisces, Akebia, Myristica, or is constricted between the seeds, Maerua, Unona. The drupe (*e.g.* cherry) has a skin (*epicarp*) on the surface, then a fleshy mass of tissue (*mesocarp*) and a hard shell or stone (*endocarp*), all forming part of the pericarp; within the stone is the seed or kernel, usu. without a hard coat. Drupes from sup. ovaries occur in Prunus, &c., from inf. in Cornaceae, Juglans, &c. There may be one stone or *pyrene* (Prunus) or several (Cornus).

Other fleshy fr. are the *pome* of Pyrus, &c. in which the fleshy receptacle encloses, and is united to, the core or product of the G proper; the *pepo* or gourd of Cucurbitaceae, *e.g.* cucumber (a variety of the berry with hard epicarp), the peculiar pseudo-berry of Juniperus (*q.v.*) &c., the fr. of strawberry (fleshy recept. bearing achenes), rose (fleshy recept. enclosing achenes), Anacardium (fleshy recept. bearing nut), Gaultheria (caps. enclosed in fleshy calyx), Urera, &c. (achene in fleshy perianth), and so on. Aggregate fleshy fr. in Anonaceae (berries), Rubus (drupes), &c. Multiple fleshy fr. frequent in Moraceae (*e.g.* mulberry, fig, bread-fruit), Ananas, Anona, Carludovica, &c.

The style and stigma often fall away as the fr. ripens, but frequently remain in a ± shrivelled or in an enlarged condition. Sometimes the style forms a hook, as in Geum, a plume, as in Clematis, or an *awn*, as in Geraniaceae (this name is applied to any long thread-like organ on a fruit; *cf.* Gramineae).

Other interesting morphological features in fruits: *cf.* Heterocarpy, Aesculus, Bertholletia, Chenopodium, Leontodon, Nymphaeaceae, Nyctaginaceae, Palmae (*e.g.* Phytelephas, Lodoicea, &c.), Pandanaceae, &c.

Frutex, a shrub; **frutescent, fruticose**, shrubby.

Fuchsia (Plum.) L. Onagraceae (2). 65 C. and S. Am., N.Z. Many cult. orn. fl. Many show two buds in each axil, one above the other. Fl. suited to bees, humming-birds, &c. Berry ed.

Fuernrohria C. Koch. Umbelliferae (III. 3). 1 Armenia.

Fuertesia Urb. Loasaceae. 1 San Domingo.

Fuertesiella Schlechter. Orchidaceae (II. 2). 1 San Domingo.

Fugacious, falling early.

Fugosia Juss. (*Cienfuegosia EP.*). Malvaceae (4). 30 Am., Afr., Austr.

Fuirena Rottb. Cyperaceae (1). 25 trop. and subtrop.

Fuliginous, sooty.

Fuller's teasel, *Dipsacus fullonum* L.

Fulvous, tawny.

Fumana Spach (*Helianthemum* p.p.). Cistaceae. 8 Medit., Eur., W. As.

Fumaria Tourn. ex L. Papaveraceae (III). 40 Eur., As., Afr., chiefly

Medit., 2 in Brit. (fumitory). Many climb by sensitive petioles (*cf.* Clematis). Fl. like Corydalis. *F. capreolata* L. var. *pallidiflora* Jord. (Brit.) shows colour-change in its fl.; before pollination white, it gradually turns pink or carmine (*cf.* Ribes, Diervilla). [*Jl.* 44, 47.

Fumariaceae (Warming) = § III of Papaver. *Kew Bull.* 1921, p. 97; *Linn.*

Fumariola Korshinsky. Papaveraceae (III). 1 Turkestan.

Fumitory, *Fumaria.*

Funastrum Fourn. Asclepiadaceae (II. 1). 2 trop. S. Am.

Funereal cypress, *Cupressus funebris* Endl.

Funicle, the stalk of the ovule; **funiculate** (ovule), stalked.

Funifera, Leandr. ex C. A. Mey. Thymelaeaceae. 2 Brazil.

Funkia Spreng. (*Hosta* Tratt.). Liliaceae (III). 5 Japan, China. Embryos are formed in the seeds by outgrowth of the nucellus-tissue round the embryo-sac (*cf.* Alchornea). Seeds winged. Cult. orn. fl.

Funtumia Stapf (*Kickxia* Blume p.p.). Apocynaceae (II. 1). 3 trop. Afr. *F. elastica* Stapf is the chief source of Lagos or Iré rubber.

Furcate, forked.

Furcraea Vent. Amaryllidaceae (II). 20 trop. Am. Like Agave; infl. even larger. *F. gigantea* Vent. yields fibre (Mauritius hemp).

Furcroya Rafin. = Furcraea Vent. (Amaryll.).

Furfuraceous, with soft scales.

Furze, *Ulex europaeus* L., &c.

Fusaea W. E. Safford. Anonaceae (I). 1 Guiana, Venezuela.

Fusanus R. Br. Santalaceae. 5 Austr., N.Z.

Fuscous, dusky.

Fusiform, spindle-shaped.

Fustic, *Chlorophora*, *Maclura*, *Zanthoxylum*; **young-**, *Rhus.*

Gabila Baill. (*Pycnarrhena EP.*). Menispermaceae. 1 Timor.

Gabunia K. Schum. (*Tabernaemontana* p.p.). Apocynaceae (I. 3). 7 W. Afr.

Gad-bush (W.I.), *Arceuthobium gracile* Engelm.

Gaertnera Lam. Rubiaceae (II. 5). 30 trop. Afr. and As. G.

Gagea Salisb. Liliaceae (IV). 30 N. temp. Old World. *G. lutea* Ker-Gawl. in Brit. Fl. protog. In the l.-axils of some are buds which, if fert. does not occur, develope into bulbils and drop off.

Gagernia Klotzsch. Ochnaceae. 1 Guiana.

Gagnebina Neck. Leguminosae (I. 4). 1 Mauritius, Madag.

Gagnepainia K. Schum. (*Hemiorchis* p.p.). Zingiber. (I). 3 S.E. As.

Gahnia Forst. Cyperaceae (II). 35 ✳, esp. Austr.

Gaiadendron G. Don (*Loranthus* p.p. *BH.*). Loranth. (I). 4 Andes, Austr.

Gaillardia Fouger. Compositae (6). 15 Am. Cult. orn. fl.

Gaillonia A. Rich. Rubiaceae (II. 10). 12 Nubia to India.

Gaimardia Gaudich. in Freyc. Centrolepid. 3 temp. S. Am., N.Z., Austr.

Galactia P. Br. Leguminosae (III. 10). 70 trop. and subtrop. Latex, which is rare in the fam., is found in this plant.

Galactites Moench. (*Lupsia EP.*). Comp. (11). 3 Medit., Canaries.

Galactodendron Rchb. (**-um** Kunth) = Brosimum Sw. (Morac.).

Galactoxylon Pierre (*Bassia* p.p.). Sapotaceae (I). 1 Malay Arch.

Galagania Lipsky. Umbelliferae (III. 5). 1 C. As.

Galanthus L. Amaryllidaceae (I). 10 Eur., Medit. *G. nivalis* L. (snowdrop) in Brit. Bulb with 1-fl. scape. P in two whorls. On the inner surface of the inner P-l. are green grooves secreting honey. The bud is erect, but the open fl. pendulous, visited by bees. The sta. dehisce by apical slits and lie close against the style. Each has a process outwards from the anther. The stigma projects and is first touched by an insect; in probing for honey it shakes the sta. and receives a shower of pollen (*cf.* Erica). Autogamy may occur in old fls. The fl. remains open a long time. Cult. orn. fl.

Galapee tree (W.I.). *Sciadophyllum.*

Galarhoeus Haw. = Euphorbia L. p.p. (Euph.).

Galatea, Galatella Cass. = Aster Tourn. p.p. (Comp.).

Galax L. Diapensiaceae. 1 Virginia, Georgia.

Galaxia Thunb. Iridaceae (I). 4 S. Afr.

Galba (W.I.), *Calophyllum Calaba* Jacq.

Galbanum, gum, *Ferula.*

Galbulimima F. M. Bailey. Magnoliaceae. 1 Austr.

Gale, sweet, *Myrica Gale* L.

Galeana La Llave. Compositae (6). 1 Mexico.

Galeandra Lindl. Orchidaceae (II. 5). 7 trop. Am. Epiphytes.

Galearia Zoll. et Morr. Euphorbiaceae (A. II. 5). 16 Malaya. A 10.

Galeata Wendl. Inc. sed. 1 Indomal.

Galeate, helmet-shaped.

Galedupa Lam. (*Pongamia* Vent.). Legum. (III. 8). 1 trop. As., Austr.

Galega Tourn. ex L. Leguminosae (III. 6). 3 S. Eur., W. As. *G. officinalis* L. sometimes cult. as a fodder-plant (goat's rue).

Galenia L. Aizoaceae (II). 18 S. Afr.

Galeobdolon Adans. = Lamium Tourn. p.p. (Labi.).

Galeola Lour. Orchidaceae (II. 2). 10 Malay Archipelago.

Galeopsis L. Labiatae (VI). 7 N. temp. |*. 3 in Brit., incl. *G. Tetrahit* L. (hemp-nettle) with swollen upper ends to internodes, acting as pulvini.

Galeorchis Rydberg (*Orchis* p.p.). Orchidaceae (II. 1). 1 N. Am.

Galeottia A. Rich. (*Zygopetalum BH.*). Orchidaceae (II. 14). 2 Colombia.

Galera Blume (*Epipogum BH.*). Orchidaceae (II. 2). 3 As.

Galingale (Am.), *Cyperus.*

Galiniera Delile. Rubiaceae (I. 8). 1 Abyssinia.

Galinsoga Ruiz et Pav. Compositae (5). 5 Mexico to Argentina. *G. parviflora* Cav. now a common weed in Eur. and near Kew.

Galipea Aubl. Rutaceae (I). 6 S. Am.

Galium L. Rubiaceae (II. 11). 250 cosmop.; 10 in Brit. (bed-straw, &c.). Herbs with whorls of l. and stips. (see fam.); fls. in dichasial panicles, small with honey freely exposed (class A) on the epig. disc, usu. protandrous with ultimate self-pollination. *G. Aparine* L. (goose-grass or cleavers; Brit.) is a feeble hook-climber with small reflexed hooks on the stem. The schizocarp is also provided with hooks.

Gallesia Casar. Phytolaccaceae. 1 Peru, Brazil.

Gallitrichum Fourn. = Salvia Tourn. (Labiatae).

Gallnuts, *cf.* Myrobalans.

Galopina Thunb. Rubiaceae (II. 7). 2 S. Afr.
Galphimia Cav. Malpighiaceae (II). 12 warm Am. Cult. orn. shrubs.
Galpinia N.E. Br. Lythraceae. 1 Transvaal.
Galpinsia Britton (*Oenothera BH.*). Onagraceae. 6 N. Am.
Galtonia Decne. Liliaceae (V). 2 S. Afr. Cult. orn. fl. (spire lily).
Galvesia Domb. ex Juss. Scrophulariaceae (II. 3). 3 Peru to Calif.
Galypola Nieuwland (*Polygala* p.p.). Polygalaceae. 1 U.S.
Gama grass (Am.), *Tripsacum.*
Gambeya Pierre (*Chrysophyllum* p.p. *EP.*). Sapot. (I). 5 trop. Afr., Am.
Gambir, *Uncaria Gambier* Roxb.
Gamblea C. B. Clarke. Araliaceae (I). 1 Sikkim.
Gamboge, *Garcinia Morella* Desr., &c.
Gamete, a sexual reproductive cell.
Gametophyte, the sexual generation.
Gamo- (Gr. prefix), united; **-petalae** (*BH.*), Sympetalae; **-petalous, -phyllous, -sepalous,** with concrescent C, P, K; **-tropic** (movement), before fert.
Gamocarpha DC. = Boopis Juss. (Calycer.).
Gamogyne N.E. Br. Araceae (V). 2 Malaya.
Gamolepis Less. Compositae (8). 12 S. Afr.
Gamopoda Baker. Menispermaceae. 1 Madag.
Gamosepalum Hausskn. Cruciferae (4). 2 W. As. Gamosepalous.
Ganja, *Cannabis sativa* L.
Ganophyllum Blume. Sapindaceae (II) (Burser. *BH.*). 1 Phils. to Austr.
Ganua Pierre ex Dubard (*Illipe* p.p.). Sapot. (I). 6 Malaya.
Ganymedes Salisb. = Narcissus Tourn. p.p. (Amaryll.).
Garapatica Karst. (*Alibertia BH.*). Rubiaceae (I. 8). 1 Colombia. Fr. ed.
Garberia A. Gray. Compositae (2). 1 Florida.
Garcia Rohr. Euphorbiaceae (A. II. 3). 1 trop. Am., W.I.
Garcilassa Poepp. et Endl. Compositae (5). 1 Peru.
Garcinia L. Guttiferae (V). 200 palaeotrop. trees or shrubs with leathery l. Sta. free or united into bundles or into a common mass. Berry; seed arillate. The resin of *G. Morella* Desr. and other sp., obtained by cutting notches in the stem, forms gamboge. The fr. of many is ed., esp. that of *G. Mangostana* L. (mangosteen), the aril of the seed of which is a delicacy. Some yield useful timber.
Gardenia Ellis. Rubiaceae (I. 8). 80 palaeotrop., largely cult. orn. perf. fl. Some sp. have apparently whorls of leaves, 3 in each, really a case of condensation of two whorls of 2 into one with extreme anisophylly of one whorl; the fourth l. is reduced to a minute scale. The stipules of many secrete a resinous fluid.
Gardeniopsis Miq. Rubiaceae (II. 4). 1 Sumatra, Borneo.
Gardneria Wall. ex Roxb. Loganiaceae. 3 India to Japan.
Gardoquia Ruiz et Pav. (*Satureia* p.p. *EP.*). Labiatae (VI). 30 W. Am.
Garget (Am.), *Phytolacca.*
Garhadiolus Jaub. et Spach (*Rhagadiolus BH.*). Comp. (13). 4 W. As.
Garidella Tourn. ex L. = Nigella L. (Ranunc.).
Garjan oil, *Dipterocarpus.*

Garlic, *Allium sativum* L. (S. Eur.), *ursinum* L. (Brit.); **-pear tree** (W.I), *Crataeva gynandra* L.; **-shrub** (W.I.), *Bignonia alliacea* Lam.
Garnieria Brongn. et Gris. Prot. (1). 1 New Caled.
Garnotia Brongn. in Duperr. Gramin. (8). 12 Indomal., China, Jap.
Garnotiella Stapf. Gramin. (8). 1 Phil. Is. *Kew Bull.* 1910, 302.
Garretia Welw. (*Khaya EP.*). Meli. (11). 1 trop. Afr.
Garrya Dougl. ex Lindl. The only gen. of **Garryaceae** (*EP.*; *Corn.* p.p. *BH.*). (Dicots. Archichl., Garryales; pp. xi, lii). 18 W.U.S., Mex., W.I. Shrubs with 4-angled twigs and opp. evergr. l., petioles united at base. Fl. in catkin-like panicles (♂ long-stalked), 1—3 in axil of each br., unisexual. ♂ P usu. 4, A 4; ♀ naked, G (2—3), uniloc. with 2 pend. anatr. ov. with dorsal raphe, on parietal plac. Fr. berry-like, with thin pericarp and 1—2 seeds. Endosp. Cult. orn. shrubs.
Garryales. The 4th order of Dicots. Archichl.; p. x. [(*Pfl. R.*, 1910.)
Garuga Roxb. Burser. 7 E. Indomal. L. imparipinnate. Disc cup-like.
Garugandra Griseb. (*Gleditschia* p.p. *EP.*). Legum. (II. 7) (Anacard.
Garuleum Cass. Comp. (9). 5 S. Afr. No pappus. [*BH.*). 1 Arg.
Gaslondia Vieill. (*Syzygium* p.p. *EP.*). Myrt. (1). 1 New Caled.
Gasparillo (W.I.), *Esenbeckia*.
Gasteria Duval. Lili. (11). 50 S. Afr. Xero. with succulent l. closely packed, but often growing in shade of grass. Cult. orn. pl.
Gastonia Comm. ex. Lam. Aral. (1). 5 Madag., Masc. 10—15-merous.
Gastranthus Moritz ex Benth. et Hook. f. Acanth. (IV B). 1 Venezuela.
Gastridium Beauv. Gramin. (8) 2 Medit. Glumes persistent on axis.
Gastridium Blume = Dendrobium Sw. (Orchid.).
Gastrochilus D. Don = Saccolabium Blume (Orchid.).
Gastrochilus Wall. Zingiber. (1). 30 Sikkim to Java. Labellum hollow.
Gastrocotyle Bunge. Borag. (IV. 2). 1 Egypt to Panjab.
Gastrodia R. Br. Orchid. (II. 2). 12 Indomal. to N.Z. Leafless.
Gastroglottis Blume = Liparis Rich. p.p. (Orchid.).
Gastrolepis Van Tiegh. Icacin. 1 New Caled.
Gastrolobium R. Br. Legum. (III. 2). 35 W. Austr. L. usu. opp. or
Gastronema Herb. = Cyrtanthus Ait. p.p. (Amaryllid.). [whorled.
Gatesia A. Gray. Acanth. (IV. B). 1 S.U.S.
Gaub tree, *Diospyros Embryopteris* Pers. (Indomal.).
Gaudichaudia H. B. et K. Malpigh. (1). 15 Mex. to Venezuela. Mericarp elevated on carpophore formed from wing of cpl.
Gaudinia Beauv. Gramin. (9). 3 Medit., Azores. Spikelet many-fld.
Gaultheria Kalm. ex. L. Eric. (II. 2). 120 Am., W.I., Indomal., Jap. to Tasm. Shrubby. Fl. 5-merous. Fr. berry-like, but really a caps. enclosed in fleshy K (not adherent). Many have ed. fr., e.g. *G. procumbens* L. (U.S., winter-green, checker-berry, partridge-berry), *G. Shallon* Pursh. (N.W. Am., sallal, shallon). Wintergreen oil distilled from some.
Gaura L. Onagr. (2). 25 N. Am. Sta. with scale at base; anther chambered by horiz. septa in each loc. (*cf.* Circaea). Nut. Cult. orn. fl.
Gaurella Small (*Oenothera* p.p.). Onagr. (2). 3 N. Am.
Gauropsis Presl (*Clarkia* p.p. *EP.*). Onagr. (2) 1 Mex.
Gaussia H. Wendl. Palm. (IV. 1). 1 Cuba. Stem swollen below.
Gauze tree (W.I.), *Lagetta*. [G 2-loc.
Gavarretia Baill. (*Conceveiba* p.p.). Euphorb. (A. II. 2). 1 Amazonas.
Gaya H. B. et K. Malv. (2). 15 trop. Am. Like Sida. No epicalyx.

Gaylussacia H. B. et K. Ericaceae (III. 1). 40 Am. (huckleberry). The 5 loc. of the ovary are made into 10 by partitions growing out from the midribs of the cpls., as in Linum.
Gayoides Small (*Abutilon* p.p. *EP.*, *Sida* p.p. *BH.*). Malv. (2). 2 N. Am.
Gayophytum A. Juss. Onagraceae (2). 6 Chili to Calif.
Gazania Gaertn. Compositae (10). 24 Cape Colony. Cult. orn. fl.
Gean, *Prunus Avium* L.
Geanthemum R. E. Fries. Anonaceae (1). 2 Brazil. *Cf.* Anona.
Geanthus Phil. Liliaceae (IV). 2 Chili.
Gearum N.E. Br. Araceae (VII). 1 Goyaz.
Geaya Costantin et Poisson. Ericaceae (IV. 1). 1 Madag.
Geigeria Griesselich. Compositae (4). 30 S. and trop. Afr.
Geijera Schott. Rutaceae (1). 5 E. Austr., New Caled., Loyalty Is.
Geissanthera Schlechter. Orchidaceae (II. 20). 2 New Guinea.
Geissanthus Hook. f. Myrsinaceae (II). 25 equatorial S. Am.
Geissaspis Wight et Arn. Leguminosae (III. 7). 8 trop. Afr., As.
Geissois Labill. Cunoniaceae. 6 Austr. to Fiji.
Geissolepis Robinson. Compositae (5). 1 Mexico.
Geissoloma Lindl. ex Kunth. Geissolomataceae. *G. marginatum* Kunth, Cape Col., a small xero. shrub, the only sp. L. opp. evergr., with sol. axillary fls., ☿. K 4, C 0, A 4+4, G (4) each with 2 pend. ov. Caps. 4-loc. Endosp.
Geissolomataceae (*EP.*; *Penaeaceae* p.p. *BH.*). Dicots. (Archichl. Myrtiflorae). Only genus, Geissoloma, *q.v.*
Geissomeria Lindl. Acanthaceae (IV. B). 10 trop. Am.
Geissopappus Benth. Compositae (6). 3 trop. S. Am.
Geissorhiza Ker. Iridaceae (III). 40 S. Afr., Madag. Cult. orn. fl.
Geissospermum Allem. Apocynaceae (I. 3). 2 trop. Brazil. *G. laeve* Baill. has offic. bark, cortex Pereirae.
Geissostegia Benth. = Erica Tourn. (Eric.).
Geitonogamy, pollination from another fl. on same pl.
Geitonoplesium A Cunn. Liliaceae (X). 2 E. Austr.
Gelasine Herb. Iridaceae (II). 2 temp. S. Am.
Geleznowia Turcz. Rutaceae (1). 3 W. Austr.
Gelonium Roxb. Euphorbiaceae (A. II. 6). 25 warm As., Afr., Madag.
Gelsemium Juss. Loganiaceae. 2 N. Am., As. *G. sempervirens* Ait. (Carolina jasmine) cult. The peduncle bears numerous bracteoles.
Geminate, in pairs.
Gemmae, buds, *Hymenophyllaceae*.
Gendarussa Nees = Justicia L. p.p. (Acanth.).
General, used in sense opposed to partial.
Generations, alternation of, *Pteridophyta*.
Generic name, see Nomenclature.
Genetyllis DC. = Darwinia p.p. (Myrt.).
Genianthus Hook. f. (*Secamone* p.p. *EP.*). Asclepiad. (II. 2). 4 Indomal.
Geniculate, bent sharply.
Geniosporum Wall. ex Benth. Labiatae (VII). 15 Afr., Madag., Indomal.

Geniostemon Engelm. et Gray. Gentianaceae (I). 2 Mexico.

Geniostoma Forst. Loganiaceae. 40 Madag. to N.Z.

Genip tree (W.I.), *Melicocca*, &c.

Genipa (Tourn.) L. Rubiaceae (I. 8). 6 warm Am., W.I.

Genista L. Leguminosae (III. 3). 90 Eur., N. Afr., W. As.; 3 in Brit. *G. anglica* L. (needle-gorse or petty whin) has large thorns (branches). The fl. has an explosive mechanism, typical of many of the fam. (*q.v.*). In *G. tinctoria* L., the dyer's greenweed (Müller's *Fert. of Fls.* p. 189), there is no honey; the style and tube of sta. are enclosed in the keel, which is united along the top seam as well as the bottom. The sta. shed their pollen almost in the apex of the keel, but not so near it as to pollinate the stigma. When the fl. opens there is a tension of the sta.-tube on the lower side tending to bend it upwards; this is resisted by an opposite one in the keel and wings, but if an insect alight on the wings and press them down, the upper seam of the keel gives way and an explosion follows. In it the style flies out, striking the under side of the insect, thus probably becoming cross-pollinated, and is followed by a shower of pollen which gives the insect a fresh coating to take to another fl.

A yellow dye is obtained from the fls. of this sp., which when mixed with woad gives a fine green (Kendal green).

Genlisea A. St Hil. Lentibulariaceae. 12 trop. Am. and Afr.

Gentian, Gentiana.

Gentiana Tourn. ex L. Gentianaceae (I). 400 cosmop. exc. Afr., chiefly alpine; 5 (gentian) in Brit. Most are alpine pl. of tufted growth. Fls. of interest (see *Nat. Pfl.*, Müller's *Fert. of Fls.*, *Alpenblumen*, &c.). The genus shows an ascending series of fls., adapted to higher and higher types of insects. *G. lutea* L. is a primitive type, with freely exposed honey, yellow homogamous fl. and short-tongued visitors. *G. purpurea* L., *G. Pneumonanthe* L. (Brit.), &c. are blue long-tubed humble-bee fls. *G. verna* L. (Brit.), *G. Amarella* L. (Brit.) and *G. campestris* L. (Brit.) are long-tubed butterfly fls., sometimes protandr.

The gentians form one of the most striking features of the flora of the Alps, occurring in large masses and with very conspicuous fls.; *G. acaulis* L. is the most beautiful. In the Brit. Mts. they are rare. The root of *G. lutea* furnishes a tonic.

Gentianaceae (*EP.*, *BH.*). Dicotyledons (Sympet. Contortae; Gentianales *BH.*). 80 gen., 800 sp. in every part of the globe and in great variety of situations—arctic and alpine pl., halophytes, saprophytes (Voyria, &c.), marsh pl. (Menyanthes, &c.), water pl. (Limnanthemum), &c. They are mostly herbaceous (often perennial); a few shrubs. The perennial herbs have usu. a rhizome. L. opp., exstip., usu. entire. The infl. is usu. a dichasial cyme like Caryophyllaceae; as in that fam., the lat. branches often become monochasial. Other cymose infls. also occur. Bracts and bracteoles present or not. Fls. reg., ☿, 4—5-merous (rarely more). K usu. (5), imbr.; C (5), bell- or funnel-shaped, or sometimes salver-shaped, conv. (exc. Bartonia, Obolaria, &c., and § II); A as many as petals, alt. with them, epipet.; anthers various, usu. introrse; $\underline{G}$ with a glandular disc at base, (2), placed in the antero-posterior plane.

Placentae usu. parietal, but they commonly project far into the cavity and spread out at their ends; occasionally the ovary is 2-loc. with axile plac.; ovules usu. ∞, anatr.; style simple; stigma simple or 2-lobed. Fr. usu. a septicidal caps. with ∞ seeds rarely a berry (Chironia, &c.); seeds small; embryo small, in abundant endosp.

The flowers of G. are insect-fertilised. The genus Gentiana has been very fully studied; see also Menyanthes (dimorphic).

Classification and chief genera (after Engler):

I. *GENTIANOIDEAE* (l. opp.: C conv. or imbr.): Exacum, Erythraea, Chlora, Gentiana, Swertia.

II. *MENYANTHOIDEAE* (l. alt.; C induplicate-valvate): Menyanthes, Limnanthemum.

Gentianales (*BH.*) The 7th cohort of Gamopetalae.

Gentianella Moench. = Gentiana Tourn. p.p. (Gent.).

Gentilia A. Chevalier et Beille. Euphorbiaceae (A. I. 2). 2 trop. Afr.

Genus, see Nomenclature.

Genyorchis Schlechter. Orchidaceae (II. 16). 3 trop. Afr.

Geo- (Gr. prefix), earth-; **-carpic**, producing subterranean fr., *Amphicarpaea*, *Arachis*, *Cardamine*, *Trigonella*, *Voandzeia*; **-graphical distribution**, *cf.* textbooks; **-philous**, geocarpic; **-tropism**, irritability to gravity.

Geobalanus Small. Rosaceae (VI). 2 Florida.

Geocardia Standley = Geophila D. Don (Rubiac.).

Geocarpon Mackenzie. Aizoaceae (II). 1 Missouri.

Geocharis Ridl. Zingiberaceae (I). 2 Malaya.

Geochorda Cham. et Schlecht. Scrophulariaceae (II. 6). 1 warm S. Am.

Geococcus J. Drumm. ex Harv. Cruciferae (4). 1 N.W. Austr.

Geodorum Jacks. Orchidaceae (II. 10). 10 Indomal.

Geoffraea L. Leguminosae (III. 8). 4 trop. Am.

Geoffraya Bonati. Scrophulariaceae (II. 6). 1 Cambogia.

Geomitra Becc. (*Bagnisia* p.p. *EP.*). Burmanniaceae. 2 Borneo.

Geonoma Wild. Palmae (IV. 1). 85 trop. Am., W.I. Style lateral.

Geopanax Hemsl. Araliaceae (I). 1 Seychelles.

Geophila D. Don. Rubiaceae (II. 5). 15 trop.

Geoprumnon Rydberg (*Astragalus* p.p. *EP.*). Leguminosae (III. 6). 6 N. Am.

Georchis Lindl. = Goodyera R. Br. (Orchid.).

Georgina Willd. = Dahlia Cav. (Comp.).

Geosiris Baill. Burmanniaceae. 1 Madag.

Geostachys Ridl. Zingiberaceae (I). 10 S.E. As.

Geracium Reichb. = Crepis Vaill. p.p. (Comp.).

Geraniaceae (*EP.*; *BH.* incl. *Oxalid.*, *Limnanth.*, *Tropaeol. Balsamin.*). Dicots. (Archichl. Geraniales *EP.*, *BH.*). 11/750, cosmop., mostly herbs, often hairy; Sarcocaulon fleshy. L. opp. or alt., often stip. Fl. usu. reg., ☿, 5-merous. K 5, or (5) imbr. with valvate tips, persistent; C 5, imbr. or conv.; A as many or 2 or 3 times as many as petals, united at base, obdipl. when > 1 whorl, anther usu. versatile; $\underline{G}$ (5) or (2—3) or (3—5), with 1—2 or 2—∞ ovules in each on axile plac.; ovules usu. pend. with ventral raphe and micropyle facing upwards; style long with 5 stigmas. Fls. usu. protandr. Fr. usu. a schizocarp, the cpls. splitting off from a central beak (the persistent style); each takes with it a strip of the tissue of the style, forming an *awn*, which is usu. hygroscopic (*cf.* Geranium, Erodium). Embryo straight or folded, in endosp. *Chief genera:* Geranium, Erodium, Pelargonium, Sarcocaulon. [**BH. chars.** Herbs with alt. or opp. l. Fl. ☿, reg. or ·|·. Recept. hardly disc-like, often with 5 glands alt. to C. K 5 or less, C 5 or less, or 0, imbr., rarely conv.; A twice as many as K, often ± connate, G̲ (3—5, rarely 2), multiloc.; ovules 1—2 per loc., pend. or not, raphe various. Caps., schizocarp, or rarely berry. Endosp. little or 0.]

Geraniales. The 23rd order (Engler) of Dicots. (Archichl.). The 7th cohort (*BH.*) of Polypetalae. *Cf.* pp. xxii, li.

Geranium (Tourn.) L. Geraniaceae. 300 cosmop., esp. temp. (12 in Brit., incl. *G. pratense* L., meadow cranesbill, and *G. Robertianum* L., herb Robert). Infl. cymose, either dich. with cincinnus-tendency (by preference of the β-bracteole), or a cincinnus alone, which is straightened out into a sympodium. The nectaries are at the base of the sta. These stand at first round the undeveloped style; after dehiscence they move away, and finally the stigmas open. The fr. explodes, the awn twisting up so that the cpls. are carried up and outwards. In many sp. they open at the same time and the seeds are shot out. The G. of greenhouses is really a Pelargonium.

Geranium (of greenhouses), *Pelargonium*; **-grass, -oil,** Cymbopogon.

Gerardia L. Scrophulariaceae (III. 2). 40 Am. W.I.

Gerardiina Engl. Scrophulariaceae (III. 2). 1 trop. Afr.

Gerardiopsis Engl. (*Anticharis* Endl.). Scrophular. (I. 2). 1 trop. Afr.

Gerascanthus P. Br. = Cordia L. p.p. (Borag.).

Gerbera Gronov. Compositae (12). 35 Afr., As. Cult. orn. fl.

Germainia Bal. et Poitr. (*Anthistiria* p.p. *BH.*). Gram. (2). 2 S.E. As.

German pellitory, *Anacyclus.*

Germander, *Teucrium.*

Germen, the ovary.

Germination, *cf. Acacia, Cucurbita, Streptocarpus, Ulex, Vivipary.*

Gerontogaeous, Old World.

Geropogon L. = Tragopogon Tourn. (Comp.).

Gerrardanthus Harv. ex Benth. et Hook. f. Cucurbitaceae (1). 4 trop. Afr.

Gerrardiana Oliver. Flacourtiaceae (9) (Samydaceae, *BH.*). 1 S. Afr.

Gertrudia K. Schum. Flacourtiaceae (3). 1 New Guinea.

Geruma Forsk. Inc. sed. 1 Arabia.

Gesneria L. Gesneriaceae (II). 50 trop. Am., W.I.

Gesneriaceae (*EP.*, *BH.*). Dicots. (Sympet. Tubiflorae; Personales *BH.*). 85 gen., 1100 sp. trop. and subtrop., mostly herbaceous or slightly woody; shrubs and trees are rare. L. usu. opp., rarely whorled or alt., entire or toothed, never divided, exstip. Some are root-climbers, and amongst these are a few epiphytes, *e.g.* Aeschynanthus, usu. with fleshy water-storing l. Many are tuberous, *e.g.* the Sinningia (Gloxinia) of greenhouses. A number repr. veg. by means of curious runners or suckers, covered with scale-leaves, usu.

formed below ground, *e.g.* Naegelia, Isoloma, &c. A peculiar morphology and life-history is found in Streptocarpus (*q.v.*).

Fls. sol. or in cymose infls. of various types, ☿, usu. markedly ·|·. K (5), usu. with very stout teeth, generally valvate; C (5), often 2-lipped, imbr. (in Ramondia, &c. it is nearly rotate and reg.); A usu. 4, didynamous, or 2, or 5 (Ramondia, &c.), alt. with corolla lobes; stds. often found. At the base of the flower-tube is a disc, whose various shapes form important marks in distinguishing gen.; it may be ring-shaped (thin or thick), 5-angled, 5-lobed, or reduced to 5 or fewer glands. G sup., or ± inf. (see below); always (2), 1-loc. with parietal plac. which sometimes project inwards so far that it becomes imperfectly 2-loc.; ovules ∞, anatr.; style simple; stigma often bilobed. Fr. usu. a caps., splitting loculic. into 2 valves, each of which may again split into 2; sometimes (Ramondia) the caps. is septicidal, or opens only at the tip, or the fr. may be ± fleshy or berry-like. Seeds small and numerous, with endosperm (§ II) or without (most of § I). Embryo straight.

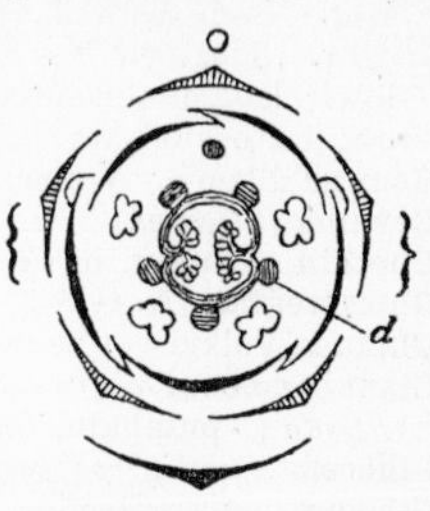

Floral diagram of Gesneria, after Eichler; *d*=disc-gland.

Fls. mostly protandrous; their large size and bright colours suit them to insects. Saintpaulia (*q.v.*), Klugia, and others exhibit two types of symmetry on the same plant, the fls. (and usu. the l.) on the left side of the infl. being like the reflections of those on the right (*enantiostyly*).

Germin. interesting, esp. in Streptocarpus (*q.v.*). The cots. are epigeal, and usu. thin, one larger than the other and often growing subsequently to some size: buds are often found in their axils. Anisophylly is very common, and usu. alt. on one side and the other.

None of the G. are economic plants; many are hothouse favourites.

Classification and chief genera (after Fritsch):

"The relationships to allied orders, especially Scrophulariaceae, Orobanchaceae and Bignoniaceae, are so close that it is almost impossible to draw the dividing lines. The B. are most sharply marked off by the structure and formation of their fruit and seed, and often by their divided leaves. The O. might very well be placed in G. as a parasitic sub-order. The placentation and structure of the ovary is the chief mark of distinction between the G., O., and S."

I. *CYRTANDROIDEAE* (ovary free, sup.): Ramondia, Saintpaulia, Didymocarpus, Streptocarpus, Aeschynanthus, Besleria, Cyrtandra, Columnea.

II. *GESNERIOIDEAE* (ovary more or less inf.): Achimenes, Isoloma, Gesneria.

Gesnouinia Gaudich. Urticaceae (4). 1 Canaries.

Gestroa Becc. Violaceae. 1 Malaya.

Getah (Malay) = gutta.

Gethyllis Plum. ex L. Amaryllidaceae (1). 10 Cape Col. Some ed. fr.

Gethyum Phil. Liliaceae (IV). 1 Chili.

Geum L. Rosaceae (III. 2). 40 N. and S. temp., arctic. *G. rivale* L. (water avens) with a thick rhizome and large protog. fls., and *G. urbanum* L. (wood avens) with smaller nearly homogamous fls., in Brit. Both, with many others, have a hook on each achene aiding distr. The style in a newly opened fl. has a Z-like kink in it. The lower half of this after fert. gets larger and more woody, while the upper drops off.

Geunsia Blume. Verbenaceae (4). 5 Malay Archipelago.

Gevuina (*Guevina*) Molina. Proteaceae (II). 1 Chili. Ed. nut.

Gherkin, young fr. of *Cucumis sativus* L.

Ghiesbreghtia A. Gray. Scrophulariaceae (I. 1). 1 Mexico.

Ghikaea Volkens et Schweinf. Scrophulariaceae (III. 2). 1 trop. Afr.

Giant bamboo, *Dendrocalamus*, *Gigantochloa*; **-cactus**, *Cereus*; **-fennel**, *Ferula*; **-pumpkin**, *Cucurbita*; **-sugar pine**, *Pinus*.

Gibbesia Small (*Siphonychia EP.*). Caryophyllaceae (I. 4). 1 N. Am.

Gibbous, with projecting broad pouch.

Gidgee (Austr.), *Acacia homalophylla* A. Cunn.

Giesekia (*Gisekia*) L. Phytolaccaceae. 5 Afr., India.

Gifdoorn (S. Afr.), *Sarcocaulon*.

Gifola Cass. = Filago L. (Comp.).

Giganthemum Welw. (*Camoensia EP.*). Leguminosae (III. 1). 1 trop. Afr.

Gigantochloa Kurz. Gramineae (13). 10 Indomal. Giant bamboos (*q.v.*), used in Java, &c. for building.

Gigasiphon Drake del Castillo (*Bauhinia* p.p.). Leguminosae (II. 4). 1 Madag.

Gigliolia Becc. Palmaceae (IV. 1). 2 Borneo.

Gigliolia Barb. Rodr. (*Octomeria EP.*). Orchidaceae (II. 6). 2 Brazil.

Gilgia Pax. Euphorbiaceae (A. II. 2). 1 Somaliland.

Gilgiochloa Pilger. Gramineae (9). 1 E. Afr.

Gilia Ruiz et Pav. Polemoniaceae. 120 temp. and subtrop. Am.

Gilibertia Ruiz et Pav. Araliaceae (1). 20 trop. Am., As., Japan, Chi.

Gill (Am.), *Nepeta Glechoma* Benth.

Gillbeea F. Muell. Cunoniaceae. 1 N.E. Austr.

Gillenia Moench. Rosaceae (I. 1). 2 N. Am. Cult. orn. fl.

Gilletiella De Wild. et Durand. Acanthaceae (II). 1 Congo.

Gillettia Rendle (*Anthericopsis* Engl.). Commelinaceae. 1 E. Afr.

Gilliesia Lindl. Liliaceae (IV). 3 Chili. Cult. orn. fl.

Gilliflower, clove, *Dianthus Caryophyllus* L.; **wall-**, wallflower.

Gilruthia Ewart. Compositae (4). 1 W. Austr.

Gin, *Juniperus*.

Ginalloa Korth. Loranthaceae (II). 4 Indomal.

Gingelly, gingili, *Sesamum indicum* L.

Ginger, *Zingiber officinale* Rosc.

Gingidium F. Muell. = Aciphylla Forst. (Umbellif.).

Ginginsia DC. = Pharnaceum L. (Aizo.).

Ginkgo L. Ginkgoaceae. 1, *G. biloba* L. (*Salisburia adiantifolia* Sm.), the maidenhair tree, perhaps found wild in W. China, but carefully preserved as sacred in temple gardens. It grows in the open in Eur., reaching 100 feet; l. deciduous in autumn, resembling those of maidenhair fern, and very often with a deep median division, *forked* in venation (*cf.* ferns and cycads), scattered on long shoots, or crowded at the apex of short shoots, which sometimes elongate into long. Below the l. on the short shoot are a few scale l. Fls. dioecious, in the axils of the uppermost scales or lowest green l. on a short shoot (position different from that usual in Coniferae with long and short shoots). ♂ a stalked central axis, bearing scattered rather loosely disposed sta., each of which is a slender filament ending in an apical scale and two or more pollen-sacs with longitudinal opening. The pollen grain forms a rudimentary prothallus of a few cells, and the generative nuclei produce two large spirally coiled spermatozoids (*cf.* cycads). The ♀ has the form of a long stalk with two term. elliptical ovules enclosed at the base by a collar-like envelope repres. a reduced carpellary l. Each ov. consists of a nucellus surrounded by one integument, which in the ripe seed forms a thick fleshy aril-like covering round a hard woody shell. In the mature ov. the greater part of the nucellus tissue is reduced to a thin papery layer enclosing a large embryo-sac with usually 2 archegonia. Fert. occurs before or *after* the ovule has fallen from the tree. The embryo has 2 cots.

The seed is edible, and yields an oil, and the timber is useful.

Ginkgo thus represents a very old type, with relationships to the Cycadales and the Filicales. Fossil species are found in the Carboniferous, Permian, Triassic, and Jurassic, and in the Tertiary of England.

For details see Coulter and Chamberlain, *Morphology of Gymnosperms*; Fujii on floral morphology in *Bot. Mag.*, Tokio, 1895; Seward and Gowan in *Ann. Bot.* 1900, p. 108; Ikeno on fertilisation in *Ann. Sci. Nat. Bot.* XIII. 1901, p. 303; Lyon on embryology in *Minn. Bot. Stud.* III. p. 275.

Ginkgoaceae. The only fam. of Ginkgoales, with one gen. Ginkgo (*q.v.*), formerly placed in Coniferae.

Ginkgoales. The 2nd class of Gymnosperms.

Ginora L. (*Ginoria* Jacq.). Lythraceae. 7 Mex., W.I.

Ginseng, *Panax Ginseng* C. A. Mey.

Giorgiella De Wild. Passifloraceae. 1 Congo.

Gipsywort, *Lycopus europaeus* L.

Giraldia Baroni (*Atractylis* p.p. *EP.*). Compositae (11). 1 China.

Giraldiella Damm. Liliaceae (V). 1 China.

Girardinia Gaudich. Urticaceae (1). 6 trop. As., Afr. Stinging hairs.

Gireoudia Klotzsch = Begonia L. p.p. (Begon.).

Girgensohnia Bunge. Chenopodiaceae (B). 4 W. and C. As.

Gironniera Gaudich. Ulmaceae. 8 Indomal., Polynesia.

Gisekia (*Giesekia*) L. Phytolaccaceae (Aizoaceae *BH.*). 5 trop. Afr. and As.

Githago Adans. = Lychnis L. (*BH.*) = Agrostemma L. (Caryoph.).

Githopsis Nutt. Campanulaceae (I). 1 California.

Giulianettia Rolfe. Orchidaceae (II *a*. III). 1 New Guinea.

Givotia Griff. Euphorbiaceae (A. II. 5). 2 S. India, Ceylon, Madag.

Gjellerupia Lauterbach. Opiliaceae. 1 New Guinea.

Glaber (Lat.), **glabrous**, hairless.
Glabraria L. = Litsea Lam. (Laur.).
Glacial zone, see Zones of Vegetation.
Gladdon, *Iris foetidissima* L.
Gladiate, sword-shaped.
Gladiolus (Tourn.) L. Iridaceae (III). 250 Afr., Eur., As. Fls. often protandrous. L. isobil. Cult. orn. fl.
Gland, an organ secreting fluid, *e.g.* nectary, oil-gland, water-pore; *cf.* Insectivorous Pl., Plumbaginaceae, Saxifragaceae; **-ular hair**, a sticky secreting hair, *Cuphea*, &c.
Glandonia Griseb. Malpighiaceae (II). 1 Amazon valley.
Glans (Lat.), a nut.
Glareal, growing on dry exposed ground.
Glass-wort, *Salsola*; (Am., W.I.) *Salicornia*.
Glastonbury thorn, a var. of hawthorn.
Glaucescent, becoming sea-green, or ± sea-green.
Glaucidium Sieb. et Zucc. Ranunculaceae (I). 2 Japan, China.
Glaucium Tourn. ex Hall. Papaveraceae (II). 25 Eur., As. *G. flavum* Crantz, yellow horned-poppy, on sea-shores in Brit.
Glaucothea O. F. Cook. Palmaceae (I. 2). 1 California.
Glaucous, sea-green, covered with a bloom like a plum.
Glaux (Tourn.) L. Primulaceae. *G. maritima* L., sea milkwort, the only sp., N. temp. coasts (incl. Brit.), a halophyte with fleshy l. The seedling dies after producing in the axil of one cot. a hibernating shoot, with a root of its own. From this fresh plants arise veg., the process being repeated for several years before flowering. Runners with scale l. in whose axils renewal-shoots form appear before the flowering period. The fl. has no C, but a coloured K.
Glaziocharis Taub. ex Warm. Burmanniaceae. 1 Rio de Janeiro.
Glaziophyton Franch. (*Arundinaria* p.p. *EP.*). Gramin. (13). 1 Brazil.
Glaziostelma Fourn. Asclepiadaceae (II. 1). 1 Brazil.
Glaziova Bur. Bignoniaceae (I). 1 Brazil. Tendrils with discs at tip (*cf.* Parthenocissus).
Gleadovia Gamble et Prain. Orobanchaceae. 1 Indomal.
Glechoma L. (*Nepeta* L. *BH.*). Labiatae (VI). 6 | ✻.
Glechon Spreng. Labiatae (VI). 12 Brazil, Paraguay.
Gleditschia Clayton. Leguminosae (II. 7). 11 subtrop. and trop. Stems usu. with stout branched thorns (stem structures, arising in l. axils). The thorn comes from the uppermost of a series of sub petiolar buds one above the other in the axil. No winter buds form, and the young apex of each twig dies off in winter, the next year's growth starting lat. Some used for hedges; some useful timber.
Glehnia F. Schmidt. Umbelliferae (III. 6). 1 E. As., W. N. Am.
Gleichenia Sm. Gleicheniaceae. 100 trop., ✻̅. Creeping rhiz.; l. repeatedly branched in an apparently dichot. way.
Gleicheniaceae. Filicales Leptosporangiatae. 2 gen., 100 sp., trop., subtrop. and S. temp., small ferns with creeping rhiz. and dichot. branched l. Sorus of 2—8 sessile sporangia, without indusium, with complete transverse annulus, dehiscing longitudinally. *Chief genus*. Gleichenia.
Gleniea Hook. f. Sapindaceae (I). 1 Ceylon.

Glinus L. (*Mollugo* L. p.p. *BH.*). Aizoaceae (I). 6 trop. and subtrop.
Gliricidia H. B. et K. Leguminosae (III. 6). 5 trop. Am., W.I.
Glischrocolla A. DC. (*Endonema BH.*). Penaeaceae. 1 S. Afr.
Glischrothamnus Pilger. Aizoaceae (I). 1 Brazil.
Globba L. Zingiberaceae (I). 80 Indomal. There is a short K; above this is the C tube, from the end of which spring 3 petals, a large labellum and 2 stds., also the slightly petaloid fertile sta., projecting beyond which is the style. The ovary is 1-loc. with parietal plac. The lower cymes are usu. replaced by bulbils; the mass of one of these consists of a root, springing lat. from the axis.
Globe daisy, *Globularia*; **-flower**, *Trollius*; **-thistle**, *Echinops*.
Globose, almost spherical.
Globularia Tourn. ex L. Globulariaceae. 18 Medit., Eur.
Globulariaceae (*EP.*; *Selagineae* p.p. *BH.*). Dicots. (Sympet. Tubiflorae). 3 gen., 20 sp., Eur., Medit., Afr. Herbs or shrubs with alt., exstip., simple l. and heads or spikes of fls. with or without invol. of bracts. Fl. ☿. K (5), persistent; C (5), median-zygomorphic; the upper lip of 2 petals is shorter than the 3-petalled lower lip; A 4, didynamous, epipetalous; $\underline{G}$ 1-loc., with 1 pend. anatr. ov. Fr. a one-seeded nut, free in base of calyx; embryo straight, in endosp. *Chief genus:* Globularia.
Globulea Haw. = Crassula Dill. p.p. (Crassul.).
Globulostylis Wernham. Rubiaceae (II. 1). 2 Nigeria.
Glochidia, *Azolla*.
Glochidion Forst. Euphorbiaceae (A. I. 1). 160 trop. As., Polynes.
Glochidopleurum Koso-Poljansky. Umbelliferae (III. 5). 1 Cyprus.
Glockeria Nees. Acanthaceae (IV. B). 5 Mexico, C. Am.
Gloeocarpus Radlk. Sapindaceae (I). 1 Phil. Is.
Gloeospermum Triana et Planch. Violaceae. 5 trop. Am. Exalb.
Glomera Blume. Orchidaceae (II. *a*. III). 12 Malay Archip., Polynesia.
Glomerate, collected into heads.
Glomeropitcairnia Mez. Bromeliaceae (3). 2 Venezuela, W.I.
Glomerule, a cluster of short-stalked fls.
Gloriosa L. Liliaceae (I). 5 trop. As., Afr. They climb by aid of the l., whose tips twine like tendrils. Fl. pendulous, with sta. and style projecting horiz. Cult. orn. fl.
Glory of the snow, *Chionodoxa*.
Glosocomia D. Don, **Glossocomia** Reichb. = Codonopsis Wall. (Campan.).
Glossocalyx Benth. Monimiaceae. 3 trop. W. Afr.
Glossocardia Cass. Compositae (5). 1 Indomal.
Glossocarya Wall. Verbenaceae (5). 3 Indomal.
Glossochilus Nees. Acanthaceae (IV. A). 2 S. Afr.
Glossodia R. Br. Orchidaceae (II. 2). 5 Austr.
Glossogyne Cass. Compositae (5). 5 Indomal., China.
Glossolepis Gilg. Sapindaceae (I). 1 Cameroons.
Glossonema Decne. Asclepiadaceae (II. 1). 6 trop. Afr. and As.
Glossopetalon A. Gray. Celastraceae. 3 S.W. U.S.
Glossopholis Pierre. Menispermaceae. 4 trop. Afr.
Glossorhyncha Ridl. Orchidaceae (II. 5). 3 Malay Archipelago.

Glossostelma Schlechter. Asclepiadaceae (II. 1). 1 Angola.
Glossostemon Desf. Sterculiaceae. 1 Persia.
Glossostephanus E. Mey. Asclepiadaceae (II. 1). 1 S. Afr.
Glossostigma Wight et Arn. Scrophulariaceae (II. 6). 3 warm |✻.
Glossostylis Cham. et Schlecht. = Alectra Thunb. (*BH.*) = Melasma Berg. p.p. (Scrophular.).
Glossula Lindl. (*Habenaria* p.p. *EP.*). Orchidaceae (II. 1). 1 China.
Gloxinia L'Hérit. Gesneriaceae (II). 6 trop. Am. *G. speciosa* Lodd., &c., often cult. orn. fl., *cf.* Sinningia.
Glucose, grape sugar.
Glumaceae (*BH.*). The 7th series of Monocotyledons.
Glumaceous, glume-like.
Glumicalyx Hiern. Scrophulariaceae (III. 1). 1 S. Afr.
Glumiflorae. The 4th order (Engler) or 2nd (Warming) of Monocotyledons.
Gluta L. Anacardiaceae (1). 6 trop. As., Madag. The sap of *G. Renghas* L. yields a good varnish.
Glyceria R. Br. Gramineae (10). 40 cosmop., esp. N. Am. 2 in Brit. Pasture grasses in wet meadows.
Glycine L. (incl. *Soja* Moench.). Leguminosae (III. 10). 16 palaeotrop. *G. Soja* Sieb. et Zucc. and *G. hispida* Maxim. yield Soja beans, eaten in Japan, &c., and used as green fodder. An oil is obtained from the seeds.
Glycosmis Correa. Rutaceae (V). 6 Indomal. Fr. ed.
Glycyderas Cass. Compositae (3). 1 Madag.
Glycyrrhiza Tourn. ex L. Leguminosae (III. 6). 12 temp. and subtrop. An extract of the rhiz. of *G. glabra* L. is Spanish liquorice.
Glyphaea Hook. f. Tiliaceae. 2 trop. Afr.
Glyphosperma S. Wats. Liliaceae (III). 1 North Mexico.
Glyptopetalum Thw. Celastraceae. 7 Indomal.
Glyptopleura Eaton. Compositae (13). 2 Utah to California.
Glyptostrobus Endl. (*Taxodium* p.p. *BH.*). Coniferae (Pinaceae; see C. for gen. char.). 2 China, *G. pendulus* Endl. and *G. heterophyllus* Endl.
Gmelina L. Verbenaceae (4). 8 Indomal.
Gnaphalium L. Compositae (4). 135 cosmop., 4 in Brit. (cudweed). *G. supinum* L., alpine in Scotland, is a tufted hairy xero. [*G. dioicum* L. = Antennaria, *G. Leontopodium* L. = Leontopodium.]
Gnaphalodes A. Gray. Compositae (4). 3 temp. Austr.
Gnephosis Cass. Compositae (4). 15 temp. Austr.
Gnetaceae. The only fam. of Gnetales, comprising 3 very distinct gen. with about 45 sp. trop. and subtrop. They are distinguished from the Coniferae by the absence of resin, by the presence of vessels in the secondary wood, and of a P. [*Cf.* Pearson, *Gnetales.*]

Classification and genera (after Engler):

I. *EPHEDROIDEAE* (♂ P 2, A 2—8 of sessile 2-loc. anthers; ♀ P pipe-like, ov. with simple integument. P hard when ripe, br. fleshy): Ephedra.

II. *TUMBOOIDEAE* (♂ P 4, A 6 with 3-loc. anthers; ♀ P pipe-like, ov. with 1 integument. Stem tuberous with 2 permanent l.): Tumboa (Welwitschia).

III. *GNETOIDEAE* (♂ P tubular, A 2 sessile on thread-like elongated axis; ♀ P pipe-like, ov. with 2 integuments. Usu. climbing; fls. in spikes, P becoming fleshy): Gnetum.

Gnetales, a class of Gymnospermae; only fam. Gnetaceae.

Gnetum L. Gnetaceae. 35 trop. Most are climbing shrubs, a few erect shrubs or small trees. L. decussate, exstip., simple, evergr., leathery. Fls. dioec., in spikes which are frequently grouped into more complex infls. The spike bears decussate bracts, in whose axils are condensed partial infls. of a large number of flrs. (*cf.* Labiatae), about 3—8 in the ♀, but more (up to 40) in the ♂. These fls. form whorls round the stem, and are intermingled with numerous hair-structures. At the top of each nodal group of the ♂ infl. in most is a single ring of ♀ fls., usu. with only 1 integument and infertile, sometimes with 2 or even 3 integuments and fertile. The ♂ has a tubular (2-leafed) P, from the top of which the axis projects; at the tip of the axis, right and left, are two sessile 1-loc. anthers. The ♀ has a tubular P like that of Ephedra, surrounding a single orthotr. erect ovule with two integuments; the inner of these projects at the apex of the fl. But there is much difference of opinion as to the morphology of these three envelopes. After fert. the P becomes fleshy, the outer integument woody, forming a drupe-like fr. *G. Gnemon* L. (Malaya) and other sp. are cult. for the ed. fr. [See Gymnospermae, and Karsten in Cohn's *Beiträge* VI., *Bot. Zeit.* 1892, *Ann. Buitenz.* XI. &c.]

Gnidia L. Thymelaeaceae. 125 Afr., Madag., Indomal.

Gnomonia Lunell (*Festuca* p.p.). Gramineae (10). 6 W. U.S.

Goa bean, *Psophocarpus tetragonolobus* DC.

Goat's beard, *Tragopogon pratensis* L., (Am.) *Spiraea Aruncus* L.; **-rue**, *Galega*, (W.I.) *Tephrosia cinerea* Pers.

Goatweed, *Aegopodium Podagraria* L., (Ceylon, &c.) *Ageratum conyzoides* L., (W.I.) *Capraria*, *Stemodia*.

Gobbo, *Hibiscus esculentus* L.

Gochnatia H. B. et K. Compositae (12). 12 Mexico to S. Am.

Godetia Spach (*Oenothera* p.p. *BH.*). Onagr. (2). 25 W. Am. Cult. orn. fl.

Godmania Hemsl. Bignoniaceae (2). 1 Panama, Venezuela.

Godoya Ruiz et Pav. Ochnaceae. 4 Peru, Colombia, Brazil.

Goebelia Bunge = Sophora L. p.p. (Legum.).

Goeldinia Huber. Lecythidaceae. 2 Brazil.

Goeppertia Griseb. (*Bisgoeppertia* O. Ktze.). Gentian. (1). 2 Cuba.

Goeppertia Nees = Aydendron Nees.

Goethalsia Pittier. Tiliaceae. 1 Panama.

Goethartia Herzog. Urticaceae (3). 1 Bolivia.

Goethea Nees. Malvaceae (3). 2 Brazil. Several buds in each axil, some of which give rise years later to fls., borne on the old wood. Epicalyx brightly coloured. The C does not spread out, but the styles first emerge and afterwards the sta. (reverse of usual behaviour in Malvaceae). Honey is secreted at the base of the K. The styles are twice as numerous as the cpls. (*cf.* Pavonia).

Goetzea Wydler. Solanaceae (4). 1 Porto Rico.

Gold-of-pleasure, *Camelina sativa* Cr.

Goldbachia DC. Cruciferae (2). 2 N. temp. |✻ and Yunnan.

Golden club (Am.), *Orontium*; **-drop**, *Onosma*; **-feather**, *Chrysanthemum Parthenium* Bernh., var. *aureum*; **-fern**, *Gymnogramma argentea* Mett., var. *aurea*; **-lily**, *Lycoris*; **-pine**, *Pseudolarix*; **-rod**, *Solidago*; **-saxifrage**, *Chrysosplenium*; **-seal**, *Hydrastis*; **-thistle**, *Scolymus hispanicus* L.; **-thread** (Am.), *Coptis trifolia* Salisb.; **-top** (Am.), *Lamarckia aurea* Moench.; **-tuft** (W.I.), *Pterocaulon*; **-wattle**, *Acacia*.

Goldfussia Nees = Strobilanthes Blume (Acanth.).

Goldmanella Greenman (*Goldmania* p.p.). Compositae (5). 1 Mexico.

Goldmania Greenman. Compositae (5). 1 Mexico.

Goldmania Rose. Leguminosae (I. 5). 2 Mexico.

Gold-mohur tree, *Poinciana regia* Boj.

Goldschmidtia Dammer. Orchidaceae. Nomen.

Golenkinianthe Koso-Poljansky (*Grammosciadium* DC.). Umbelliferae (III. 5). 1 N. temp. |✻.

Golionema S. Wats. ex O. Hoffm. Compositae (3). 1 Mexico.

Gomara Ruiz et Pav. (*Russellia EP.*). Scrophulariaceae (II. 4). 1 Peru.

Gomart *Bursera*.

Gombo, *Hibiscus esculentus* L.

Gomesa R. Br. Orchidaceae (II. 19). 8 Brazil. Cult. as Rodriguezias.

Gomesia La Llave. Compositae. Nomen.

Gomidesia Berg. (*Myrcia BH.*). Myrtaceae (1). 50 trop. Am., W.I. Ed. fr.

Gommier, *Bursera*, *Dacryodes*.

Gomortega Ruiz et Pav. Gomortegaceae. 1 S. Am. Shrub with opp. evergr. l. and racemes of fl., monochlamydeous, spirocyclic, ☿. P 7, A 2—3, G (2—3), with one pend. ov. in each loc. Drupe. Endosperm.

Gomortegaceae (*EP.*, Lauraceae p.p.? *BH.*). Dicots. (Archichl. Ranales). Only gen. Gomortega, *q.v.*

Gomphandra Wall. (*Stemonurus EP.*). Icacinaceae. 12 Indomal., Austr.

Gomphia Schreb. (*Ouratea* Aubl. *EP.*). Ochnaceae. 150 trop. Like Ochna, but sta. 10 only.

Gomphichis Lindl. Orchidaceae (II. 2). 5 Mts. of S. Am.

Gomphiluma Baill. (*Pouteria* p.p. *EP.*). Sapotaceae (1). 1 Brazil.

Gomphocalyx Baker. Rubiaceae (II. 10). 1 Madag.

Gomphocarpus R. Br. Asclepiadaceae (II. 1). 100 trop. and S. Afr., S. Am. *G. fruticosus* R. Br. (from Afr.) on shores of nearly all trop.

Gomphogyne Griff. Cucurbitaceae (1). 2 E. Ind.

Gompholobium Sm. Leguminosae (III. 2). 24 Austr.

Gomphostemma Wall. Labiatae (III). 25 Indomal., China.

Gomphostigma Turcz. Loganiaceae. 2 S. Afr.

Gomphrena L. Amarantaceae (3). 100 trop., subtrop.; herbs with cymose heads of fls.; ☿ with 5 hairy P-leaves and (5) sta. Cult. orn. fl.

Gomuti palm, *Arenga saccharifera* Labill.

Gonatanthus Klotzsch. Araceae (VI). 2 E. Indomal.

Gonatopus Hook. f. Araceae (1). 2 E. trop. Afr.
Gonatostylis Schlechter. Orchidaceae (II. 2). 1 New Caled.
Gongora Ruiz et Pav. (*Acropera* Lindl.). Orchidaceae (II. 13). 20 trop. Am. Epiph. with hanging fls. whose ovary is so bent that the labellum comes to stand above the column. The sepals and petals spring from the column (an argument for its axial nature). See Darwin, *Orchids*, p. 166. Cult. orn. fl.
Gongrodiscus Radlk. Sapindaceae (1). 2 New Caled.
Gongronema Decne. Asclepiadaceae (II. 3). 15 palaeotrop.
Gongrospermum Radlk. Sapindaceae (1). 1 Phil. Is.
Gongrothamnus Steetz (*Vernonia EP.*). Compositae (1). 3 trop. Afr.
Gongylocarpus Cham. et Schlecht. Onagraceae (2). 1 Mexico.
Gongylosperma King et Gamble. Asclepiadaceae (1). 1 Mal. Penins.
Gonianthes A. Rich. Rubiaceae (inc. sed.). 2 Cuba.
Goniocarpus Kon. = Haloragis Forst. (Halorag.)
Goniocaulon Cass. Compositae (11). 1 Indomal,
Goniogyna DC. = Heylandia DC. (Legum.).
Goniolimon Boiss. (*Statice* Tourn. *BH.*). Plumbaginaceae. 10 E. Eur., W. As.
Gonioma E. Mey. Apocynaceae (I. 3). 1 S. Afr.
Goniophlebium (Bl.) Presl = Polypodium L.
Goniopteris Presl = Dryopteris Adans.
Goniorrhachis Taub. Leguminosae (II. 3). 1 S.E. Brazil.
Gonioscypha Baker. Liliaceae (VII). 1 Himalaya.
Goniostachyum Small (*Lippia* p.p. *EP.*). Verbenaceae (1). 2 N.Am., W.I.
Goniothalamus Hook. f. et Thoms. Anonaceae (2). 45 trop. As.
Gonipia Rafin. = Gentiana Tourn. (Gentian.).
Gonocaryum Miq. Icacinaceae. 4 Malaya.
Gonocitrus Kurz. Rutaceae (inc. sed.). 1 Indomal.
Gonolobus Michx. Asclepiadaceae (II. 4). 80 Am.
Gonospermum Less. Compositae (7). 4 Canaries.
Gonostegia Turcz. = Pouzolzia Gaudich. (*BH.*). = Memorialis Buch.-Ham.
Gonyanera Korth. Rubiaceae (I. 7). 1 Sumatra.
Gonypetalum Ule. Dichapetalaceae. 2 Amazon valley.
Gonystilaceae (*EP.*; *Thymelaeaceae* p.p. *BH.*). Dicots. (Archichl. Malvales). Only gen. Gonystilus, *q.v.*
Gonystilus Teijsm. et Binn. Gonystilaceae. 7 Indomal. Shrubs with alt. entire exstip. l. and cymes of fls., ☿, reg. K, C 5—4, A ∞, $\underline{G}$ (5—3), each with 1 pend. ov. Berry. No endosperm.
Gonzalagunia Ruiz et Pav. (*Gonzalea BH.*). Rubi. (I. 7). 10 trop. Am., W.I.
Gonzalea Pers. (*cf.* last). Rubiaceae (I. 7). 10 trop. Am., W.I.
Goodallia Benth. Thymelaeaceae. 1 Brit. Guiana.
Goodenia Sm. Goodeniaceae. 100 Austr. Ovary 1-loc. above, often ± 2-loc. below.
Goodeniaceae (*EP.*, *BH.*). Dicots. (Sympet. Campanulatae; Campanales *BH.*). 13 gen., 300 sp., chiefly Austr. (esp. S.W.), a few N.Z., Polynes., and trop. coasts. Herbs and shrubs with rad. or alt. rarely opp. exstip. l. and no latex. Fls. ☿, ·|·, sol. in the leaf-axils or in cymes,

racemes, or spikes. K usu. 5, small; C (5); A 5, alt. with the petals, epipet. or not, with introrse sometimes syngenesious anthers; G (2), inf. or semi-inf. 1- or 2-loc.; ovules 1, 2, or ∞ in each usually ascending, anatr.; style simple with 'pollen-cup' close under the stigma. Into this the pollen is shed in the bud; it then closes up, leaving only a narrow opening. The style bends down to stand in the mouth of the almost horizontal fl., so that insect-visitors come in contact with the cup and dust themselves with a little of the powdery pollen. As the stigmatic lobes grow up in the cup they keep forcing fresh pollen into the narrow slit, and finally emerge by it themselves and then receive the pollen of younger fls. from insect-visitors. The mechanism should be carefully compared with that of Campanulaceae and Compositae. Fr. usu. caps., sometimes a nut or drupe. Embryo straight, in fleshy endosp.

The G. are very closely allied to Campanulaceae, differing chiefly in the absence of latex and the presence of the pollen-cup. They resemble Gentianaceae in a few points. *Chief genera:* Goodenia, Leschenaultia, Scaevola, Dampiera. [**BH. chars.** incl. those of Brunoniaceae.]

Goodenovieae (*BH.*) = Goodeniaceae.

Goodia Salisb. Leguminosae (III. 3). 2 S. Austr.

Good King Henry, *Chenopodium Bonus-Henricus* L.

Goodyera R. Br. Orchidaceae (II. 2). 40 N. temp., trop. As., New Caled., Mascarenes; *G. repens* R. Br. in Brit. Fl. as in Epipactis (Darwin, *Orchids*, p. 103).

Gooringia Williams (*Arenaria* p.p.). Carophyll. (I. 1). 1 Tibet.

Gooseberry, *Ribes Grossularia* L.; **American-** (W.I.), *Heterotrichum*; **Barbadoes-** (W.I.), *Peireskia aculeata* Mill.; **Cape-,** *Physalis*; **Otaheite-,** ditto; **-tomato,** ditto.

Goose-foot, *Chenopodium*; **-grass,** *Galium*, (Am.) *Eleusine indica.*

Gorceixia Baker. Compositae (1). 1 Rio de Janeiro.

Gordonia Ellis. Theaceae. 35 Indomal., China, N.Am. Seeds winged. The bark of *G. Lasianthus* L. (loblolly-bay, S. U.S.) is employed for tanning. Sta. opp. to petals.

Gorgoglossum F. C. Lehm. Orchidaceae (II. 13). 1 Colombia.

Gorgonidium Schott. Araceae (VII). 1 Malay Archipelago.

Gormania Britton ex Britton et Rose. Crassulaceae. 9 W. N.Am.

Gorse, *Ulex*; **needle-,** *Genista.*

Gorteria L. p.p. (p.p. = Berkheya Ehrh.). Compositae (10). 4 S. Afr.

Gosela Choisy. Scrophulariaceae (II. 7). 1 S. Afr.

Gossweilera Sp. Moore. Compositae (1). 1 Portuguese W. Afr.

Gossypianthus Hook. Amarantaceae (3). 2 Texas, Mexico.

Gossypium L. Malvaceae (4). 12 trop. and subtrop. Epicalyx of 3 l. G (5). Loculic. caps. The seeds are covered with long hairs forming the material known as cotton (*q.v.*). The cult. forms are apparently reducible to 3 sp., *G. barbadense* L. (trop. Am.), *G. arboreum* L. (Old World), and *G. herbaceum* L. (ditto). The cotton separates easily from the seed in the first sp., which is the Sea Island cotton of the U.S.; in Egypt, India, &c. the other sp. are most used. From the seeds an oil is obtained by crushing (cotton-seed oil), and the oil-cake left behind is largely used for feeding cattle, &c. The fls. are visited by bees and (in Am.) by humming-birds.

Gothofreda Vent. = Oxypetalum R. Br. (Asclep.).

Gouania Jacq. Rhamnaceae. 45 trop. and subtrop. Some have watch-spring tendrils. The stalks of some sp. contain saponin.

Goughia Wight = Daphniphyllum Blume (Euphorb.).

Goulardia Husnot (*Agropyrum* p.p.). Gramineae (12). 2 Europe.

Gouldia A. Gray. Rubiaceae (I. 7). 5 Hawaiian Is.

Goupia Aubl. Celastraceae. 2 Guiana.

Gourd, *Cucurbita*; **bitter-**, *Citrullus*; **bottle-**, *Lagenaria*; **snake-**, *Trichosanthes*.

Gourliea Gillies ex Hook. Leguminosae (III. 1). 1 temp. S. Am. Pod ed.

Goutweed, *Aegopodium Podagraria* L.

Govenia Lindl. Orchidaceae (II. 10). 18 Brazil to W.I.

Gowan, daisy.

Goyazia Taub. Gesneriaceae. 1 Brazil.

Grabowskia Schlechtd. Solanaceae (2). 6 S. Am.

Gracilis (Lat.), slender.

Graderia Benth. Scrophulariaceae (III. 2). 3 Afr.

Graeffea Seem. Tiliaceae. 1 Fiji.

Graellsia Boiss. Cruciferae (2). 1 Persia.

Graffenrieda DC. Melastomaceae (I). 18 trop. S. Am., W.I.

Graft-hybrid, *Cytisus*.

Grahamia Gill. Portulacaceae. 1 temp. S. Am.

Graines d'Avignon, *Rhamnus*; **grains of Paradise**, *Amomum*.

Gram, *Cicer*; **black** and **green**, *Phaseolus*; **horse**, *Dolichos*.

Grama or **gramma grass**, *Bouteloua*.

Gramerium Desv. (*Panicum* p.p. *EP.*). Gramineae (5). 1 Chili.

Gramineae (*EP.*, *BH.*). Monocots. (Glumiflorae; Glumaceae *BH.*). One of the largest orders of flg. pl., with about 450 gen. and 4500 sp. in all regions of the globe. In the temp. zones esp. they are a most important feature in the veg., forming prairies, steppes, &c. Most grasses are herbaceous with fibrous root, but a few, chiefly the bamboos (*q.v.*), reach a large size, even as much as 100 ft. Many are annual, but many perennial; the latter commonly branch largely from their lower nodes and thus often give rise to a tufted habit (as seen in many common sp.); many possess rhiz. The stem has well-marked nodes, composed chiefly of softer tissues. If a stem be bent downwards (as occurs when wheat is 'laid') these nodes recommence growth, growing more rapidly upon the lower side, so that the stem is once more brought to the vertical position. The stem is usu. hollow (exc. Zea, Saccharum, &c.) and circular in section. The l. are alt., and with few exceptions, in 2-ranked phyllotaxy; they have a sheathing base, the edges of the sheath overlapping one another upon the side of the stem opp. to the blade (*cf.* Cyperaceae); there is no petiole (exc. in a few bamboos, &c.), and at the junction of blade and sheath there is a little membranous outgrowth, the *ligule*, upon the upper side of the leaf. The blade is usu. linear. Many xero. grasses have grooves along the upper side of the l., with the stomata at the bases of the grooves; in most of these cases the

l. rolls up upwards in dry air, enclosing the stomata completely and checking transpiration; the lower surface, which thus becomes the outer, is covered with thick-walled cells and has no stomata. When the air again becomes moist the l. unrolls.

The infl. is complex; the unit of infl. is not the individual fl. but a *spikelet*, or small spike of fls. These are well seen in oats, where they are arranged in a panicle; in wheat the spikelets are sessile upon the main axis, forming a cpd. spike, usu. termed simply a spike; this is more clearly seen in rye-grass. Each of these spikelets consists of one or more (usu. not more than 5) fls. one above the other on opp. sides of a very short axis, the whole enclosed in one or two or more larger leaves at the base of the axis, the *glumes*. The first diagram gives a rough representation of the construction of a spikelet. The central line represents the axis (supposed elongated), which bears at the base usu. two leaves with nothing in their axils; these are the glumes. Above them stand one or more leaves, the *inferior paleae*, in whose axils occur fls. (sometimes aborted). Upon the axis of the fl., opp. to the inf. palea, stands another leaf, the *superior palea*. Between the paleae the fl. itself is enclosed. The sup. palea, being upon the same axis as the fl., is evidently its bracteole. Owing to the shortness of the floral axis, it appears to be in the axil of the inf. palea, or even upon the main axis of the spikelet. Above the sup. palea are two very small scales, the *lodicules*; they are opp. to the sup. palea (l in fig.) and insignificant in size. They are sometimes supposed to repres. two of the three l. of a reduced P, but it seems more probable that they really repres. a second bracteole and that the fl. is perfectly naked. The fl. itself has usu. 3 sta. with long filaments and versatile anthers, and 1 cpl. forming a 1-loc. ovary, with 1 basal erect anatr. ovule, and 1 or more (usu. 2) stigmas, much branched. This ovary has sometimes been regarded as formed of >1 cpl., but the suture of the post. side of the ovary (*cf.* Prunus) seems to point clearly to its being of 1 cpl. only. The two stigmas may then be regarded as developments of the lat. parts of the cpl. whilst the central part (which usu. forms the stigma) remains undeveloped; this also is the explanation of the two lodicules placed right and left of the proper position for an upper bracteole.

inf. palea - |
| - inf. palea
inf. palea - |
| - inf. palea
inner glume - |
| - outer glume

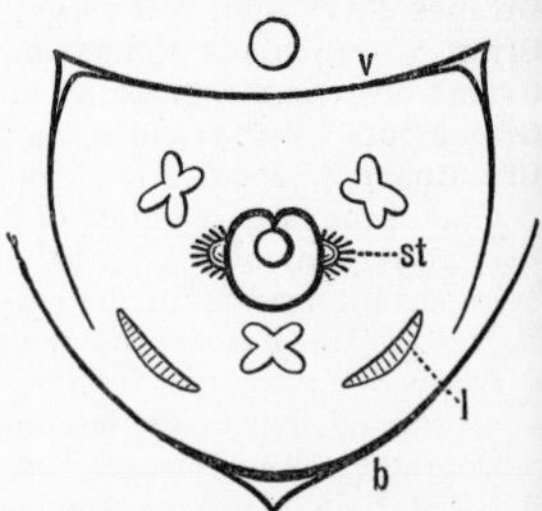

Floral diagram of a grass (after Eichler). b, inferior palea; v, superior palea; l, lodicule; st., stigma.

All the fls. in the spikelet are enclosed as a rule within the glumes until ready to open. Then the glumes separate, and the hygroscopic lodicules force apart the paleae of the fls. Most sp. in Eur. are anemoph. and protog.; the sta. grow very rapidly in warm weather and suspend the anthers clear of the paleae so that the loose powdery pollen is easily blown away and may be caught by the large stigma of another fl.

The fruit is a caryopsis, *i.e.* an achene whose pericarp is completely united to the seed-coat. Its construction can be well seen in maize (or wheat); at the broad end is the scar of the style, and on the under side at the pointed end is the embryo; on the upper side is the *hilum* or point where the ovule was attached to the wall of the cpl. (the form of this scar is important in classification); the bulk of the seed consists of floury endosp. The embryo is straight, with its one cot. (*scutellum*) completely enwrapping the radicle and plumule (this can be easily made out by dissecting soaked material). The radicle is towards the lower end of the fr. In germin. the cot. remains within the seed and extracts nourishment from the endosperm; afterwards it withers away. Most grass frs. are sufficiently light to be dispersed by wind, esp. as the paleae often remain attached to them and become dry and chaffy. Others have hooks. Self-burying arrangement in Stipa (*q.v.*), effected by aid of the *awn* (this term is applied to any long thread-like outgrowth of glume or palea). Many grasses, *e.g.* sp. of Poa and Festuca, are *viviparous*, esp. on mountains. The spikelets are replaced by leafy shoots with adv. roots at their bases. These drop off and grow upon the soil (*cf.* Agave, Allium, &c.).

From the economic point of view the G. are only rivalled in importance, if at all, by the Palmae and Leguminosae. The cereal grasses, *e.g.* Oryza, Triticum, Zea, Avena, Hordeum, &c. afford food to a large proportion of the earth's inhabitants (see Edible Products). Many grasses are valuable as fodder (*q.v.*) for domestic animals, or for hay. The bamboos (*q.v.*) supply many of the wants of the natives of trop. countries, Japan, &c. Many are used as sandbinders, &c.

Classification and chief genera (after Hackel): the G. show near relationship only to Cyperaceae and perhaps Juncaceae, and are easily distinguished from these either by their veg. or floral characters.

A. Spikelets 1-flowered without elongation of the axis beyond the fl., or 2-flowered with the lower fl. imperfect; without measurable internode between the individual glumes or paleae, and when ripe falling off from the stalk as a whole or together with certain parts of the axis of the spike.

a. Hilum point-like; spikelets not compressed lat., but usually dorsally compressed or cylindrical.

1. *Maydeae* (inf. palea and, when present, sup. palea thin and membranous; glumes firm, even leathery or cartilaginous, the lowest one the largest and overlapping the rest; spikelets usu. in racemes or spikes which become jointed when ripe; ♂ and ♀ spikelets in separate infls. or in separate parts of the same infl.); Euchlaena, Zea, Coix.
2. *Andropogoneae* (as I, but spikelets ☿, or ♂ and ♀ side by side in the same infl.): Saccharum, Andropogon, Sorghum.
3. *Zoysieae* (paleae membranous; glumes herbaceous, papery or leathery, the lowest usu. the largest; spikelets falling singly or in groups from an unjointed spike-axis): Zoysia.

4. *Tristegineae* (paleae membranous; glumes herbaceous or firm and papery, the lowest smaller or narrower than the rest; spikelets falling singly from the twigs of a panicle): Arundinella.
5. *Paniceae* (paleae usu. cartilaginous, leathery or papery; glumes more delicate, usu. herbaceous, the lowest usu. smaller; spikelets falling singly from the twigs of a panicle or unjointed spike-axis): Paspalum, Panicum, Setaria, Cenchrus, Pennisetum, Spinifex.

b. Hilum linear; spikelets lat. compressed.

6. *Oryzeae:* Zizania, Oryza, Lygeum, Leersia.

B. Spikelets 1—many-flowered; when 1-flowered often with a prolongation of the axis above the fl., their stalks usu. jointed above the glumes, so that they fall off leaving these on the axis; when 2- or more-flowered, always with distinct internodes between the fls.

a. Stem herbaceous annual. No petiole, or joint between blade and sheath.

7. *Phalarideae* (spikelets in panicles, spikelike panicles or racemes on distinct stalks—sometimes very short, not set in notches on the main axis; 1-flowered, with 4 glumes and 1-nerved sup. palea): Phalaris, Anthoxanthum.
8. *Agrostideae* (as 7, but spikelets with two or no glumes and 2-nerved sup. palea): Aristida, Stipa, Phleum, Alopecurus, Sporobolus, Polypogon, Agrostis, Calamagrostis, Ammophila, Apera, Lagurus.
9. *Aveneae* (infl. as 7, but spikelets 2—many-flowered; inf. paleae usu. shorter than glumes, with twisted awn upon the dorsal side, more rarely with no awn or with an awn upon the tip as 10, but then always with 2 almost opp. fls. and no prolongation of the axis beyond them): Holcus, Aira, Corynephorus, Deschampsia, Trisetum, Avena, Arrhenatherum, Danthonia.
10. *Festuceae* (as 9, but inf. palea usu. longer than glume, without awn or with untwisted awn at tip): Sesleria, Gynerium, Arundo, Phragmites, Eragrostis, Catabrosa, Melica, Briza, Dactylis, Cynosurus, Poa, Glyceria, Festuca, Bromus, Brachypodium.
11. *Chlorideae* (spikelets in 2 rows approximated to one another, forming a one-sided spike or raceme with unjointed axis): Cynodon, Spartina, Chloris, Bouteloua, Eleusine.
12. *Hordeeae* (spikelets in 2, or rarely more, opp. rows, forming a symmetrical, rarely one-sided, spike): Nardus, Lolium, Agropyrum, Secale, Triticum, Hordeum, Elymus.

b. Stem woody, at least below; leaf often petiolate, finally separating from its sheath by a joint.

13. *Bambuseae:* Arundinaria, Bambusa, Dendrocalamus.

Space will not permit of giving a key to the genera; the student should work through the commoner ones with a flora, or with Ward or Hutchinson's *British Grasses*.

Gramineous, relating to grasses, grass-like.
Grammadenia Benth. Myrsinaceae (II). 10 trop. Am., W.I.
Grammangis Reichb. f. Orchidaceae (II. 17). 2 Madag., Java.
Grammanthes DC. Crassulaceae. 1 S. Afr. L. opp.
Grammatocarpus Presl (*Scyphanthus EP.*). Loasaceae. 2 Chili.
Grammatophyllum Blume. Orchidaceae (II. 17). 5 Malaya. *G. speciosum* Bl. is about the largest known orchid.
Grammatotheca C. Presl (*Lobelia* p.p. *BH.*). Campanulaceae (III). 1 S. Afr., 1 Austr.
Grammica Lour. = Cuscuta L. (Convolv.).
Grammitis Sw. = Polypodium L.
Grammosciadium DC. (*Chaerophyllum* p.p. *BH.*). Umbelliferae (III. 8). 8 E. Medit.
Granadilla (Tour.) Rupp. = Passiflora L. p.p. (Passifl.).
Granadilla, *Passiflora quadrangularis* L.; **-tree** (W.I.), *Brya.*
Grandidiera Jaub. Flacourtiaceae (2). 1 Zanzibar.
Grandiflorus (Lat.), large fld.; **grandis** (Lat.), large.
Grangea Adans. Compositae (3). 2 palaeotrop.
Grangeria Comm. ex Juss. Rosaceae (VI). 3 Madag., Mauritius, Sundas.
Grantia Boiss. Compositae (4). 5 E. Medit.
Grape, *Vitis vinifera* L., &c.; **-fruit,** *Citrus decumana* Murr., var.; **-hyacinth,** *Muscari*; **seaside-, -tree, wild-** (W.I.), *Coccoloba.*
Graphephorum Desv. Gramineae (10). 1 N. Am.
Graphistemma Champ. ex Benth. et Hook. f. Asclep. (II. 1). 1 China.
Grapple plant, *Harpagophytum.*
Graptopetalum Rose. Crassulaceae. 1 Mexico.
Graptophyllum Nees. Acanthaceae (IV. B). 5 Austr., Polynesia. *G. hortense* Nees (*G. pictum* Griff.) cult. for its prettily marked l.
Grass, one of the Gramineae; **alkali-,** *Distichlis*; **arrow-,** *Triglochin*; **barley-,** *Hordeum*; **barnyard-,** *Panicum*; **beard-,** *Polypogon*; **bent-,** *Agrostis, Apera*; **Bermuda-,** *Cynodon*; **blue-,** see Kentucky blue; **brome-,** *Bromus*; **buffalo-,** *Buchloe*; **canary-,** *Phalaris*; **cat's tail-,** *Phleum*; **China-,** *Boehmeria*; **citronella-,** *Cymbopogon*; **cock's foot,** *Dactylis*; **cord-,** *Spartina*; **cotton-,** *Eriophorum*; **couch-,** *Agropyron*; **crab-** (Am.), *Panicum*; **darnel-,** *Lolium*; **ditch-** (Am.), *Ruppia*; **dog's tail-,** *Cynosurus*; **dog's tooth-,** *Cynodon*; **eel-,** *Zostera*; **esparto-,** *Lygeum, Stipa*; **false brome-,** *Brachypodium*; **false oat-,** *Arrhenatherum*; **feather-,** *Stipa*; **fescue-,** *Festuca*; **fiorin-,** *Agrostis*; **fowl-meadow-** (Am.), *Poa, Glyceria*; **fox-tail,** *Alopecurus*; **French rye,** *Arrhenatherum*; **gama-,** *Tripsacum*; **goose-,** *Galium*; **Geranium-,** *Andropogon*; **grama-,** *Tripsacum*; **Guinea-,** *Panicum*; **hair-,** *Deschampsia, Aira*; **hedgehog-** (Am.), *Cenchrus*; **herd's-** (Am.), *Phleum*; **holy-** (Am.), *Hierochloe*; **Indian-** (Am.), *Sorghum*; **kangaroo-,** *Anthistiria*; **Kentucky blue,** *Poa pratensis* L.; **knot-,** *Polygonum, Agropyron repens* Beauv., (Am.) *Paspalum distichum* L.; **lemon-,** *Cymbopogon*; **lyme-,** *Elymus*; **marram-,** *Ammophila*; **mat-,** *Nardus*; **Mauritius-,** *Panicum*; **meadow-,** *Poa*; **melic-,** *Melica*; **mesquite-** (Am.), *Bouteloua*; **millet-,** *Milium*; **oat-,** *Avena*; **-of Parnassus,** *Parnassia*; **Pampas-,** *Cortaderia*;

panic-, *Panicum*; **quake-**, *Briza*; **reed-**, *Phalaris*; **Rusa-**, *Cymbopogon*; **rush-** (Am.), *Vilfa*; **rye-**, *Lolium*; **scorpion-**, *Myosotis*; **scurvy-**, *Cochlearia*; **soft-**, *Holcus*; **sparrow-**, *Asparagus*; **sweet vernal-**, *Anthoxanthum*; **timothy-**, *Phleum*; **-tree**, *Xanthorrhoea*; **twitch-**, *Agropyron*; **wheat-**, *Agropyron*; **white bent-**, *Agrostis*; **whitlow-**, *Draba*; **-wrack**, *Zostera*.

Grass-cloth, Chinese, *Boehmeria*; **-hemp** (Austr.), *Agave rigida* Mill.

Gratiola (Rupp.) L. Scrophulariaceae (II. 6). 25 cosmop. Sta. 2. The dried plant of *G. officinalis* L. was formerly offic.

Gratwickia F. Muell. Compositae (4). 1 Austr.

Graveolens (Lat.), strongly scented.

Gravesia Naud. Melastomaceae (I). 20 Madag. Cult. orn. fl. Crossed with Cassebeeria they give the fancy 'Bertolonias.'

Gravisia Mez (*Aechmea* p.p. *BH.*). Bromeliaceae (4). 4 trop. Am., W.I.

Grayia Hook. et Arn. Chenopodiaceae (A). 2 W. U.S.

Greater celandine, *Chelidonium majus* L.

Greek valerian (Am.), *Polemonium*.

Green brier (Am.), *Smilax*; **-gram**, *Phaseolus Mungo* L.; **-heart**, *Nectandra Rodiaei* Hook.; **Kendal-**, *Genista*; **-manure**, *Leguminosae*; **-weed, dyer's**, *Genista*; **-withe** (W.I.), *Vanilla claviculata* Sw.

Greenea Wight et Arn. Rubiaceae (I. 3). 6 E. Indomal.

Greenella A. Gray. Compositae (3). 3 S.W. U.S.

Greeneocharis Guerke et Harms. Boraginaceae (IV. 2). 2 Pac. N. Am.

Greeniopsis Merrill. Rubiaceae (I. 5). 2 Phil. Is.

Greenmania Hieron. Compositae (5). 1 Colombia.

Gregarious, growing in company, all of one sp.

Greggia A. Gray. Cruciferae (4). 4 W. Am.

Greigia Regel. Bromeliaceae (4). 5 S. Am. Cult. orn. infl.

Grenacheria Mez. Myrsinaceae (II). 6 Malaya.

Grenadilla, *Passiflora quadrangularis* L.

Greslania Balansa. Gramineae (13). 3 New Caledonia.

Grevea Baill. Saxifragaceae (V). 1 Madag.

Grevellina Baill. (*Turraea* p.p. *EP.*). Meliaceae (III). 1 Madag.

Grevia L. = Grewia L. (Tiliaceae).

Grevillea R. Br. Proteaceae (II). 170 Austr. Trees and shrubs with racemose infls., 2 fls. in each axil. The style projects from the bud as a long loop, the stigma being held by the P until the pollen is shed upon it. Then the style straightens out, and the pollen may be removed; presently the female stage supervenes. Some yield useful timber, and *G. robusta* A. Cunn. (silky oak) and other sp. are now extensively employed as shade and timber trees in Ceylon and elsewhere.

Grewia L. Tiliaceae. 150 As., Afr., Austr., esp. trop.

Grewiella O. Ktze. (*Grewiopsis EP.*). Tiliaceae. 2 trop. Afr.

Grewiopsis De Wild. et Durand. Tiliaceae. 2 trop. Afr.

Greyia Hook. et Harv. Melianthaceae. 3 S. Afr.

Grias L. Lecythidaceae. 4 S. Am., W. Ind. *G. cauliflora* L., anchovy pear, cult. in the W.I.

Grielum L. Rosaceae (IV). 4 S. Afr.
Griffianthus Merrill (*Griffithia* Maingay). Anonaceae (I). 3 Phil. Is.
Griffinia Ker-Gawl. Amaryllidaceae (I). 8 Brazil.
Griffithella Warming. Podostemaceae. 1 W. Ghats of India. Plants with the general veg. structure of Dicraea, but remarkable for the extraordinary polymorphism of their shoots, which may be cup or wineglass shaped, creeping or erect, and of many different forms, shapes, and sizes (*cf.* Willis, *Ann. Perad.*, I., 1902, p. 364). They are of root nature.
Griffithia J. M. Black. Compositae (4). 1 S. Austr.
Griffithia Maingay. Anonaceae (1). 3 Malaya.
Griffithia Wight et Arn. = Randia Houst. (Rubiac.).
Griffithianthus Merrill. Anonaceae (1). 3 Phil. Is.
Griffonia Baill. (*Bandeiraea* Welw.). Legum. (II. 4). 3 W. trop. Afr.
Griffonia Hook. f. (*Acioa* Aubl.). Rosaceae (VI). 4 trop. Afr.
Grigri palm (W.I.), *Martinezia corallina* Mart.
Grimmeodendron Urb. Euphorbiaceae (A. II. 7). 2 W. Ind.
Grindelia Willd. Compositae (3). 35 Am.
Grisebachia Klotzsch (*Eremia* Don). Ericaceae (IV. 2). 25 S. Afr.
Grisebachiella Lorentz. Apocynaceae (II. 1). 1 Argentina.
Griselinia Forst. f. Cornaceae. 6 N.Z., S. Am.
Griselinia Scop. = Pterocarpus L. (Legum.).
Grisia Brongn. = Bikkia Reinw. p.p. (Rubi.).
Grislea L. Lythraceae. 1 trop. S. Am.
Grisollea Baill. Icacinaceae. 2 Madag., Seychelles.
Grobya Lindl. Orchidaceae (II. 17). 2 Brazil.
Gromwell, *Lithospermum*, *Mertensia*.
Grona Lour. Leguminosae (III. 10). 4 trop. As.
Gronophyllum Scheff. Palmaceae (IV. 1). 2 Malaya.
Gronovia Houst. ex L. Loasaceae. 2 trop. Am. A 5, no stds. G 1.
Grosourdya Reichb. f. Orchidaceae (II. 20). 3 Malay Archipelago.
Grossera Pax. Euphorbiaceae (A. II. 2). 4 trop. Afr.
Grossularia Tourn. ex Adans. (*Ribes* p.p.). Saxifrag. (VI). 40 N. Am.
Ground-cherry (Am.), *Physalis*; **-hemlock** (Am.), *Taxus*; **-ivy**, *Nepeta Glechoma* Benth.; **-laurel** (Am.), *Epigaea*; **-nut**, *Arachis*, *Voandzeia*, (Am.) *Apios*; **-pine**, *Ajuga Chamaepitys* Schreb., (Am.) *Lycopodium dendroideum* Michx.; **-pink** (Am.), *Phlox subulata* L.
Groundsel, *Senecio vulgaris* L.; **-tree** (Am.), *Baccharis*.
Growth, permanent change of form; for special cases see *Albizzia*, *Bamboos*, *Dendrocalamus*, *Dracaena*, *Eucalyptus*, *Sequoia*.
Grubbia Berg. Grubbiaceae. 3 S. Afr. Woody pl. with opp. leathery l. and small ☿ reg. fls. P 4, A 4+4, $\overline{G}$ (2), 2-loc. below while young, later 1-loc. with 2 pend. orthotr. ov. on central plac. Drupe. Oily endosp.
Grubbiaceae (*EP.*; *Santalaceae* p.p. *BH.*). Dicots. (Archichl. Santalales). Only gen. Grubbia, *q.v.*
Gruinalis (Lat.), crane's bill shaped.
Grumilea Gaertn. (*Psychotria* p.p. *BH.*). Rubiaceae (II. 5). 45 |✻.
Grundelia L., misprint for Gundelia.
Grusonia Hort. Nicolai ex K. Schum. = Opuntia Tourn. (Cact.).

Grypocarpha Greenman. Compositae (5). 1 Mexico.
Guaco, *Mikania amara* Willd.
Guadua Kunth (*Bambusa* p.p. *EP.*). Gramineae (13). 30 trop. Am.
Guaduella Franch. Gramineae (13). 4 trop. Afr.
Guaiacum Plum. ex L. Zygophyllaceae. 8 warm Am., W.I. *G. officinale* L. yields lignum-vitae wood, from which is also obtained the medicinal resin guaiacum.
Guamatela J. D. Smith. Rosaceae (III. 2). 1 C. Am.
Guamia Merrill. Anonaceae (1). 1 Phil. Is.
Guapira Aubl. Verbenaceae (inc. sed.). 1 Guiana.
Guapuronga, *Marlierea*.
Guar, *Cyamopsis*.
Guarana, *Paullinia Cupana* H. B. et K.
Guardiola Cerv. ex Humb. et Bonpl. Compositae (5). 5 S.W. U.S., Mexico.
Guarea Allem. ex L. Meliaceae (III). 100 trop. Am., Afr. The disc forms a gynophore, and the sta. are completely united into a tube.
Guatteria Ruiz et Pav. Anonaceae (1). 60 trop. Am. Berry stalked.
Guava, *Psidium*; **black-** (W.I.), *Guettarda argentea* Lam.
Guayule, *Parthenium argentatum* A. Gray.
Guaza, ganja.
Guazuma Plum. ex Adans. Sterculiaceae. 5 trop. Am.
Gueldenstaedtia Fisch. Leguminosae (III. 6). 10 Centr. As., China.
Guelder rose, *Viburnum Opulus* L.
Guepinia Bast. = Teesdalia R. Br. (Cruc.).
Guerkea K. Schum. Apocynaceae (II. 1). 2 trop. Afr.
Guernsey lily, *Nerine*.
Guettarda L. Rubiaceae (II. 2). 60 trop. all but 1 (*G. speciosa* L., which is common on trop. coasts) Am. Exalb. G 4—9-loc. Cots. o.
Guevina (*Gevuina*) Molina. Proteaceae (II). 1 Chili. Ed. nut.
Guichenotia J. Gay. Sterculiaceae. 5 W. Austr.
Guiera Adans. Combretaceae. 1 trop. Afr.
Guilandina L. = Caesalpinia L. (Legum.).
Guild, a group of pl. resembling one another ecologically.
Guilielma Mart. = Bactris Jacq. p.p. (Palm.).
Guillainia Vieill. (*Alpinia* p.p. *EP.*). Zingiberaceae (1). 2 W. Polynes.
Guilleminea H. B. et K. Amarantaceae (3). 3 warm Am.
Guillenia Greene. Cruciferae (1). 6 W. N. Am.
Guillonea Coss. Umbelliferae (III. 7). 2 Spain.
Guimauve, marsh mallow.
Guinea corn, *Sorghum vulgare* Pers.; **-grains**, *Amomum Melegueta* Rosc.; **-grass**, *Panicum maximum* Jacq.; **-hen's weed** (W.I.), *Petiveria*.
Guioa Cav. (*Cupania* p.p. *BH.*). Sapindaceae (1). 35 Indomal.
Guiraoa Coss. Cruciferae (2). 1 Spain.
Guizotia Cass. Compositae (5). 8 Afr. *G. abyssinica* Cass. (rantil or niger-seed) is cult. in India, &c, for its seeds, from which an oil is expressed.
Gulubia Becc. (*Kentia* p.p. *EP.*). Palmaceae (IV. 1). 2 New Guinea.
Gum, products of disintegration of internal tissues, exuding from stems, &c., swelling or dissolving in water, insoluble in alcohol or ether;

common in dry countries. Three chief classes: *arabin* (fully soluble), type *gum-arabic* (*Acacia Senegal* Willd.), *bassorin* (slightly soluble), type *gum-tragacanth* (*Astragalus gummifer* Labill.) and *cerasin* (swelling), type *cherry-gum* (*Prunus Cerasus* L.). *Cf.* above, and *Chloroxylon*, *Feronia*, *Piptadenia*, &c.; **-ammoniacum**, *Dorema*; **Angico-**, *Piptadenia*; **-arabic**, *Acacia Senegal* Willd.; **-benzoin**, *Styrax*; **blue-**, *Eucalyptus*; **chewing-**, *Achras Sapota* L.; **chicle-**, ditto; **-cistus**, *Cistus*; **-copal**, *cf.* Copal; **doctor's-** (W.I.), *Rhus Metopium* L.; **-elemi tree** (W.I.), *Dacryodes hexandra* Griseb.; **-euphorbium**, *Euphorbia resinifera* Berg. (Morocco); **-galbanum**, *Ferula*; **-guaiacum**, *Guaiacum*; **-kino**, *cf.* Kino; **-lac**, *cf.* Lac; **-ladanum**, *Cistus*; **-olibanum**, *Boswellia*; **-opopanax**, *Opopanax*; **-plant** (Am.) *Grindelia*; **-resins**, resins containing a mixture of gum and resin, *Boswellia* (frankincense), *Calophyllum*, *Convolvulus*, *Dorema*, *Ferula*, *Garcinia* (gamboge); **-sandarach**, *Tetraclinis*; **sweet-**, *Liquidambar*; **-tragacanth**, *Astragalus*; **-tree**, *Nyssa*, (W.I.) *Sapium*.

Gumbo, *Hibiscus esculentus* L.

Gumillea Ruiz et Pav. Cunoniac (?). 1 Peru. L. alt.

Gundelia (Tourn.) L. Compositae (10). 1 As. Min., Persia.

Gundlachia A. Gray. Compositae (3). 1 Cuba, St. Domingo.

Gundlea Steud. = Grumilea Gaertn. (Rubi.).

Gunnera L. Haloragidaceae. 40 S. Am., Costa Rica, N.Z., Tasm., Malaya, Polynes., Afr. Several are enormous herbs with l. several feet across. Fl. 2-merous. G 1-loc. Stem polystelic. In the leaf-axils are 'squamulae intravaginales' (*cf.* Potamogetonaceae). Cult. orn. fol.

Gunnia F. Muell. Aizoaceae (II). 2 S. and W. Austr.

Gunniopsis Pax (*Aizoon* p.p.). Aizoaceae (II). 1 S.E. Austr.

Gunny, *Corchorus*.

Gunpowder plant, *Pilea*.

Gurania Cogn. Cucurbitaceae (2). 75 trop. Am.

Guraniopsis Cogn. Cucurbitaceae (2). 1 Peru.

Gurjun balsam, *Dipterocarpus*.

Gussonea A. Rich. = Angraecum Bory p.p. (*BH.*) = Mystacidium Lindl. p.p.

Gustavia L. (*Japarandiba* Adans.). Lecythidaceae. 20 trop. Am. *G. augusta* L. is the stink-wood; the wood has a foetid smell.

Gutenbergia Sch. Bip. Compositae (I). 10 trop. Afr.

Guthriea Bolus. Achariaceae. 1 S. Afr.

Gutierrezia Lag. Compositae (3). 30 Am.

Gutta-jelutong, *Dyera*; **-percha**, a substance like rubber, but softening with heat, in latex, esp. of Sapotaceae; *cf. Bassia*, *Mimusops*, *Palaquium*, *Payena*; **-puteh**, *Palaquium*; **-rambong**, *Ficus*; **-sundek**, *Payena*.

Guttiferae (*EP.*; *BH.* excl. *Hypericaceae*, incl. *Quiinaceae*). Dicotyledons (Archichl. Parietales). 42 gen., 850 sp. chiefly trop. They are (exc. Hypericum) trees or shrubs with simple entire opp. exstip. l. Oil glands or passages are always present, often showing as translucent dots upon the l. The infl. is cymose, frequently umbellate. The fls. show considerable variety. The bracteoles are frequently close up to the calyx, and hardly to be distinguished from it. The axis is usu. convex, but exhibits many forms. The fl. may be cyclic or partly spiral, and is usu. reg., ☿, hypog. K imbricate; C imbr. or conv.; A ∞, free or united in various ways, frequently in bundles (usu. regarded as due to branching of originally simple papillae); very commonly the outer ones or even all are staminodial; G̲ usu. (5) or (3), multi- or 1-loc.; ovules ∞, few, or 1, anatr.; styles free or united. Fr. often capsular, sometimes a berry or drupe. Seed exalb. Many yield useful timber; the resins of Clusia, Garcinia, Calophyllum, &c., and the fr. of Garcinia and others are valuable.

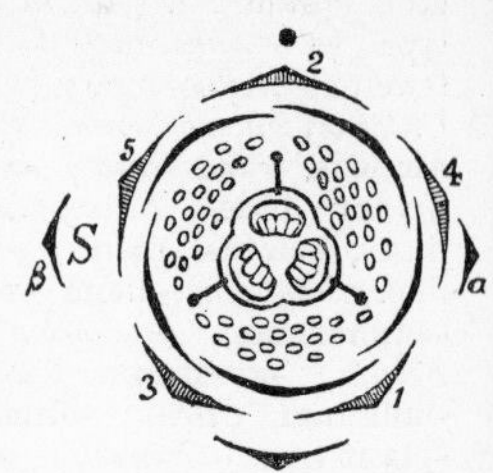

Floral diagram of Hypericum; after Eichler, ovary cut at base. *S* the "Schraubel" branch.

Classification and chief genera (after Engler): the G. are closely allied to Theaceae, the only constant distinction being the presence of oil-glands, and to Dipterocarpaceae, which are chiefly distinguished by their alt. stip. l. [**BH.** excl. Hypericoideae with Endodesmioideae as a separate fam.]

I. *KIELMEYEROIDEAE* (l. alt. or opp.; fls. usu. ☿, A ∞, style 1, G 3—5-loc.): Kielmeyera, Caraipa.

II. *HYPERICOIDEAE* (l. opp.; fl. ☿; sta. usu. ∞, usu. in 5 or 3—8 bundles before the petals; styles 3—5, usu. free; fr. a 1- or 3-loc. septi- or loculicidal caps., or indeh.; embryo usu. straight with not very thick cots.): Hypericum, Vismia.

III. *ENDODESMIOIDEAE* (sta. united into a tube above, in 5 bundles below; cpl. 1; drupe; cots. fleshy): Endodesmia (only genus).

IV. *CALOPHYLLOIDEAE* (l. opp.; fls. ☿ or ♂ ♀, A ∞ free or united at base, G 1—4 each with 2—1 ov.; fr. indeh.; cots. thick): Mesua, Mammea, Calophyllum.

V. *CLUSIOIDEAE* (1 opp.; fls. ☿ or ♂ ♀, A ∞ free or in groups; fr. various; cots. small): Clusia, Garcinia.

Guya Frapp. Flacourtiaceae (4). 1 Réunion.

Guyonia Naud. Melastomaceae (1). 2 trop. W. Afr.

Guzmania Ruiz et Pav. Bromeliaceae (1). 25 trop. Am., W.I. Epiph.

Gyminda Sarg. (*Myginda* Jacq.). Celastraceae. 2 Florida, W.I., C. Am.

Gymn-, gymno- (Gr. pref.), naked.

Gymnabicchia × G. Camus, &c. Orchidaceae. Hybrid, Gymnadenia—Habenaria (Bicchia).

Gymnacanthus Nees (*Sclerocalyx* Nees *BH.*). Acanth. (IV. A). 1 Mexico.

Gymnacranthera Warb. (*Myristica* p.p.). Myristicaceae. 12 Indomal.

Gymnadenia R. Br. (*Habenaria* p.p. *BH.*). Orchidaceae (II. 1). 20 N. temp. |✻.

Gymnadeniopsis Rydberg (*Platanthera* p.p. *EP.*). Orchidaceae (II. 1). 3 N. Am.

Gymnagathis Stapf. Melastomaceae (I). 1 S. China.
Gymnanacamptis × Aschers. et Graebn. Orchidaceae. Hybrid, Gymnadenia—Anacamptis.
Gymnandra Pall. = Lagotis Gaertn. (Scroph.).
Gymnanthemum Cass. = Vernonia Schreb. p.p. (Comp.).
Gymnanthera R. Br. Asclepiadaceae (I). 5 E. Indomal.
Gymnanthes Sw. Euphorbiaceae (A. II. 7). 12 trop. Am., W.I.
Gymnaplatanthera × G. Camus. Orchidaceae. Hybrid, Gymnadenia—Platanthera.
Gymnarrhena Desf. Compositae (4). 1 Medit., W. As.
Gymnartocarpus Boerlage. Moraceae (II). 1 Java.
Gymnema R. Br. Asclepiadaceae (II. 3). 40 W. Afr. to Austr. The leaves of *G. sylvestre* R. Br. contain gymnemic acid, and when chewed temporarily destroy the capacity of tasting sugar.
Gymnemopsis Constantin. Asclepiadaceae (II. 3). 1 Cochinchina.
Gymnigritella × G. Camus. Orchidaceae. Hybrid, Gymnadenia—Nigritella. 2 Eur.
Gymnobalanus Nees et Mart. = Ocotea Aubl. p.p. (Laur.).
Gymnocarpos Forsk. Caryophyllaceae (I. 4). 1 Canaries to India, used as fodder for camels.
Gymnochilus Blume. Orchidaceae (II. 2). 2 Mascarenes.
Gymnocladus Lam. Leguminosae (II. 7). 2 China and N. Am. Serial axillary buds. *G. canadensis* Lam. (Kentucky coffee tree) good timber.
Gymnocline Cass. = Chrysanthemum L. p.p. (Compos.).
Gymnocoronis DC. Compositae (2). 2 trop. Am.
Gymnodiscus Less. Compositae (8). 2 S. Afr.
Gymnogonum Parry (*Oxytheca* p.p.). Polygonaceae (I. 1). 1 N. Am.
Gymnogramma Desv. Polypodiaceae. 80, esp. trop. *G. leptophylla* Desv., an annual fern, in Jersey.
Gymnolaema Benth. Asclepiadaceae (I). 1 Kilimandjaro.
Gymnolaena Rydberg. Compositae (6). 4 Mexico.
Gymnolomia H. B. et K. Compositae (5). 25 N. and trop. Am.
Gymnopentzia Benth. Compositae (7). 2 S. Afr.
Gymnopetalum Arn. Cucurbitaceae (3). 10 Indomal.
Gymnopodium Rolfe. Polygonaceae (III. 1). 1 C. Am.
Gymnopogon Beauv. Gramineae (11). 10 Am., Ceylon.
Gymnopsis DC. = Gymnolomia H. B. et K. (Compos.).
Gymnopteris Bernh. Polypodiaceae. 15 warm Am., As.
Gymnoschoenus Nees (*Mesomelaena BH.*). Cyperaceae (II). 2 Austr.
Gymnosiphon Blume. Burmanniaceae. 20 trop.
Gymnosperma Less. Compositae (3). 1 Texas, Mexico.
Gymnospermae. One of the two great divisions of Spermaphyta or seed-plants, distinguished from Angiospermae by the fact that the cpls. are not so infolded or united as to form an ovary round the ovules; also the endosp. (female prothallus) is formed before fertilisation. The existing G. are divided into four great classes, Cycads, Ginkgoales, Conifers, and Gnetales. These differ very much from one another, so much so that it is by no means impossible that the Gymnosperms are polyphyletic. The Cycads traced backwards show a maximum in the Jurassic, decreasing until about the end of the

Eocene they had shrunk to their present size. They begin about the Permian period, about which time the great class of the Pteridospermae, or seed-bearing ferns (the bulk of what used to be regarded as true ferns in the coal-measures, &c.), was disappearing, and show considerable relationship to the latter. Some of the fossil forms have actual ☿ fls. with numerous sta., and it is quite possible that these are on the direct line of ascent to the Angiosperms. From what the Coniferae and Ginkgoales, which are first found about the beginning of the Permian, took their rise, is as yet quite uncertain, while we do not know enough about the Gnetaceae to draw many conclusions about them.

The fls. in most Cycads and Conifers take the form of cones, and whether each cone represents a fl. or an infl. has been much disputed. The sta. is of simple structure; in the Cycads there are several pollen-sacs, looking like the sporangia of Marattiaceae, on the lower side of a leaf-like organ; in the Conifers the sta. has usually fewer pollen-sacs and is more leaf-like, while in the Gnetaceae the anthers are sessile. The ovules are always naked in the sense of not being enclosed in an ovary formed of one or more hollow cpls., but they are usually protected in some way from the weather. Wind-pollination occurs.

In the Cycads a considerable mass of sporogenous tissue is formed in the ovule (mega-sporangium); one of the cells of this tissue gives rise to the embryo-sac (mega-spore). This behaviour is closely comparable to that of the higher Pteridophyta. In the embryo-sac the ♀ prothallus (endosperm) forms by cell-division, and archegonia in which the ova are contained develope at the micropylar end. The ovule is now mature and consists of an integument, nucellus, and embryo-sac and its contents.

In most Conifers the sporogenous tissue consists only of the cell which goes to form the embryo-sac. In the sac the same process goes on as in Cycads.

In Ephedra the phenomena are very similar to those in Conifers; in Gnetum several embryo-sacs are frequently formed, and the division of the nucleus of the sac gives rise, not to a prothallus as in the cases above described, but to a number of free nuclei lying on the wall of the sac. Those in the upper part remain free, and one or more of them being fertilised, produce pro-embryos. The lower part of the sac becomes septate into multinuclear compartments (in some sp.), which become uninucleate cells of the primary endosp. as a result of nuclear fusion; in these sp. the primary endosp. is constituted before fert. In Welwitschia it is constituted in a similar way.

The whole question of the relationships of the G. is one of much difficulty. (See Angiospermae, Chalazogamae, Pteridophyta, Cycadaceae, Coniferae, Ginkgo, and refer also to Coulter and Chamberlain, *Morphology of Gymnosperms*, Campbell's *Mosses and Ferns*, Nawaschin in *Mém. de l'Acad. des sc. de St-Pétersbourg*, XLII. 1894 (reviewed in *Bot. Centr.* 62, p. 324), and other papers referred to in the articles quoted.)

Gymnosporia Benth. et Hook. f. Celastraceae. 80 trop. and subtrop., esp. Afr. Many have branches modified into thorns.

Gymnostachys R. Br. Araceae (1). 1 E. Austr.
Gymnostachyum Nees (*Cryptophragmium* Nees *EP.*). Acanthaceae (IV. B). 25 trop. As.
Gymnostephium Less. Compositae (3). 6 S. Afr.
Gymnosteris Greene (*Gilia EP.*). Polemoniaceae. 1 N. Am.
Gymnostyles Juss. = Soliva Ruiz et Pav. (Comp.).
Gymnotheca Decne. (*Houttuynia EP.*). Saururaceae. 1 China.
Gymnotrix Beauv. = Pennisetum Pers. p.p. (Gramin.).
Gynandropsis DC. (*Pedicellaria* Schrank *EP.*). Capparidaceae (V). 15 trop. and subtrop. The seeds of *G. pentaphylla* DC. are used like mustard.
Gynandrous, A and G concrescent.
Gynerium Humb. et Bonpl. Gramineae (10). 3 trop. and warm temp. *G. argenteum* Nees (Pampas grass), *cf.* Cortaderia.
Gyno- (Gr. pref.), female; **-basic**, *Labiatae*, *Boraginaceae*; **-dioecism**, *Calamintha*, *Caryophyllaceae*, *Echium*, *Labiatae*, *Nepeta*, *Plantago*, *Satureia*, *Spergula*, *Thymus*; **-eceum**, the carpels, forming the ovary (*q.v.*); **-monoecism**, *Compositae*, *Labiatae*, &c.; **-phore**, an elongation of the recept. bearing cpls. only, *Anacardiaceae*, *Capparidaceae*, *Michelia*; **-stegium**, *Asclepiadaceae*; **-stemium**, *Aristolochiaceae*, *Stylidiaceae*.
Gynocardia R. Br. Flacourtiaceae (3). 1 India, *G. odorata* Br.; the seed yields Chaulmoogra oil, used medicinally in India. *Cf. Suppl.*
Gynochthodes Blume. Rubiaceae (II. 9). 3 Malay Archipelago.
Gynoglottis Smith. Orchidaceae (II. 3). 1 Sumatra.
Gynoon A. Juss. = Glochidion Forst. (Euph.).
Gynopachis Blume = Randia L. p.p. (Rubi.).
Gynopleura Cav. (*Malesherbia* p.p. *EP.*). Malesherbiaceae. 6 Chili.
Gynopogon Forst. (*Alyxia* R. Br.). Apocynaceae (I. 3). 50 Madag., Indomal.
Gynostemma Blume. Cucurbitaceae (4). 5 warm As., Polynes.
Gynotroches Blume. Rhizophoraceae. 2 Malaya.
Gynoxys Cass. Compositae (8). 20 Andes of trop.
Gynura Cass. Compositae (8). 40 trop. As. and Afr.
Gypothamnium Phil. (*Plazia EP.*). Compositae (12). 1 Chili.
Gypsocallis Salisb. = Erica Tourn. (Eric.).
Gypsophila L. Caryophyllaceae (II. 2). 55 Eur., As., esp. E. Medit. The fls. are shorter in the tube (class B) than most Silenoideae, and are visited by a greater variety of insects. Cult. orn. fl. (chalk plant).
Gypsy-wort, *Lycopus europaeus* L.
Gyranthera Pittier. Bombacaceae. 1 Panama.
Gyrate, curved into a circle.
Gyrinops Gaertn. Thymelaeaceae. 2 Indomal.
Gyrinopsis Decne. Thymelaeaceae. 1 Phil. Is.
Gyrocarpus Jacq. Hernandiaceae (Combretaceae *BH.*). 1 trop. formerly placed in Lauraceae, to which its sta. are very similar. The fr. is often mistaken for that of a Dipterocarp.
Gyrostachis Pers. (*Spiranthes* p.p.). Orchidaceae (II. 2). 10 Am.
Gyrostelma Fourn. Asclepiadaceae (II. 1). 1 Minas Geraes.
Gyrostemon Desf. Phytolaccaceae. 10 Austr.

Gyrotaenia Griseb. Urticaceae (1). 3 W.I.

H (fl. class), usu. zygomorphic fls. with tube 6—15 mm. long, suited to bees, *Aconitum*, *Anemone*, *Antirrhinum*, *Aquilegia*, *Labiatae*, *Leguminosae*, *Lotus*, *Primula*, *Trifolium*.

Haasia Nees = Dehaasia Blume (Laur.).

Haastia Hook. f. Compositae (3). 4 N.Z., growing closely together on the ground, and forming cushions (*cf.* Raoulia, Azorella).

Habenaria Willd. (*BH.* incl. *Bonatea* Willd., *Coeloglossum* Hartm., *Gymnadenia* R. Br., *Neotinea* Rchb. f., *Nigritella* Rich., *Platanthera* Rich., and other gen., making 500 sp. cosmop.). Orchidaceae (II. 1). 400 temp. and trop.; 5 in Brit., *H.* (*C.*) *viridis* R. Br. (frog-orchis), *H.* (*G.*) *conopsea* Benth. (scented orchis), *H.* (*P.*) *bifolia* R. Br. (butterfly orchis), &c. See Darwin's *Orchids*.

Habenella Small (*Habenaria* p.p.). Orchidaceae (II. 1). 1 N. Am.

Haberlea Frivald. Gesneriaceae (1). 1 Balkans.

Habit, general external appearance and impression.

Habitat, natural location.

Hablitzia Bieb. Chenopodiaceae (A). 1 Caucasus. Climbing shoot given off yearly from perenn. underground stem (*cf.* Bowiea); climbs by sensitive petioles.

Habracanthus Nees. Acanthaceae (IV. B). 4 Mexico to Colombia.

Habranthus Herb. = Hippeastrum Herb. (Amaryll.).

Habrosia Fenzl. Caryophyllaceae (I. 5). 1 W. As.

Habrothamnus Endl. = Cestrum L. p.p. (Solan.).

Habzelia A. DC. (*Xylopia BH.*). Anonaceae (4). 2 trop. As.

Hachettea Baill. Balanophoraceae. 1 New Caled.

Hackberry (Am.), *Celtis*.

Hackmatack (Am.), *Larix*.

Hacquetia Neck. Umbelliferae (II. 1). 1 C. Eur.

Haemacanthus Sp. Moore. Acanthaceae (IV. A). 1 Somaliland.

Haemadictyon Lindl. = Prestonia R. Br. p.p. (Apocyn.).

Haemanthus (Tourn.) L. Amaryllidaceae (1). 70 S. and trop. Afr. Fls. in cymose heads or umbels. Cult. orn. fl. (Cape tulip).

Haemaria Lindl. Orchidaceae (II. 2). 4 E. As., Malay Archipelago.

Haematocarpus Miers. Menispermaceae. 3 Himalaya, Khasia.

Haematostaphis Hook. f. Anacardiaceae (2). 2 W. Afr.

Haematoxylin, *Haematoxylon*.

Haematoxylon, L. Leguminosae (II. 7). 1 trop. Am., W.I., *H. campechianum* L. (logwood). Young foliage red. Thorns in the leaf-axils. The heart-wood contains haematoxylin and is used in dyeing.

Haemocharis Salisb. (*Laplacea BH.*). Theaceae. 15 Am., As.

Haemodoraceae (*EP.*; *BH.* include § VIII, IX, of *Liliaceae*, and part of III of *Amaryllidaceae*). Monocots. (Liliiflorae; Epigynae *BH.*). 10 gen., 40 sp., Austr., S. Afr., trop. Am. Herbs with panicled infl. of a number of cymes arranged in a racemose way (*cf.* Aesculus). Fl. reg. or transv. ·|· (*cf.* Anigozanthos), ☿, 3-merous; A 3, inserted on inner perianth-l., with intr. anthers; G (3), sup. or inf.; ovules few in each loc., semi-anatr.; stigma capitate. Capsule. *Chief genera:* Haemodorum, Lachnanthes, Wachendorfia. [**BH. chars.** incl. A 6 or 3, ovules sometimes ∞ anatr.]

Haemodorum Sm. Haemodoraceae. 17 Austr.
Haenianthus Griseb. (*Linociera BH.*). Oleaceae. 3 W.I.
Haenselera Boiss. ex DC. Compositae (13). 1 S. Spain.
Hagberry, *Prunus Avium* L.
Hagenbachia Nees et Mart. Haemodoraceae. 1 Brazil.
Hagenia J. J. Gmel. (*Brayera BH.*). Rosaceae (III. 5). 1 Abyssinia. The dried fls. (koso) are medic.
Hair, a cellular outgrowth of the epidermis, sometimes glandular, barbed, hooked, stinging, &c.; *cf.* Leaf for descriptive terms: **-bell**, *Campanula rotundifolia* L.; **-grass**, *Aira*, *Deschampsia*, (Am.) *Agrostis*, *Muhlenbergia*.
Hakea Schrad. Proteaceae (II). 100 Austr. Xero. with hard woody fr. The seedlings show transition stages (*cf.* Acacia) from entire l. to the much divided l. usu. in the genus.
Hakonechloa Makino (*Phragmites* p.p.). Gramineae (10). 1 cosmop.
Halacsya Doerfl. (*Zwackhia* p.p.). Boraginaceae (IV. 5). 1 Eur.
Halanthium C. Koch. Chenopodiaceae (B). 9 W. and C. As.
Halarchon Bunge. Chenopodiaceae (B). 1 Afghanistan.
Halconia Merrill. Tiliaceae. 2 Phil. Is.
Halenia Borckh. Gentianaceae (I). 25 As., Am.; alpine and arctic. Cleistogamic fls. frequent.
Halerpestes Greene (*Ranunculus* p.p.). Ranunculaceae (3). 3 N. Am.
Halesia L. Styracaceae. 4 Japan, China, and S.E. of N. Am. (*cf.* Epigaea, &c.). Snowdrop-tree, cult. orn. Fr. winged.
Halfordia F. Muell. Rutaceae (IV). 2 E. Austr., New Caled.
Halgania Gaudich. Boraginaceae (II). 10 Austr.
Halimium Spach = Helianthemum Tourn. (*BH.*) = Cistus L. 7 Medit.
Halimium Willd. Cistaceae. 30 N. temp., S. Am.
Halimocnemis C. A. Mey. Chenopodiaceae (B). 10 Cent. As.
Halimodendron Fisch. ex DC. Leguminosae (III. 6). 1 N. and W. As. on salt-steppes. Outer leaflets often thorny. Cult. orn.
Halimolobos Tausch. Cruciferae (inc. sed.). 12 Am.
Halimus L. = Atriplex L. (Chenopod.).
Halleria L. Scrophulariaceae (II. 4). 8 Afr., Madag.
Hallia Thunb. Leguminosae (III. 7). 6 S. Afr.
Hallieracantha Stapf (*Ptyssiglottis* p.p.). Acanth. (IV. B). 19 Mal. Arch.
Halmilla (Ceylon), *Berrya Ammonilla* Roxb.
Halo- (Gr. prefix), salt-; **-philous**, salt-loving; **-phytes**, the pl. of sea-coasts and salt-steppes, &c., where the presence of salt, by checking absorption, compels a reduction of transpiration, *Aster*, *Chenopodiaceae*, *Frankenia*, *Glaux*, *Halimodendron*, *Halogeton*, *Haloxylon*, *Nolana*, *Pedaliaceae*, *Pemphis*, *Plumbaginaceae*, *Reaumuria*, *Salicornia*, *Sesuvium*, *Spergularia*, *Statice*, *Suaeda*, *Tamaricaceae*, *Zygophyllaceae*.
Halocharis Moq. Chenopodiaceae (B). 4 W. As.
Halochloa Griseb. (*Monanthochloe EP.*). Gramineae (10). 1 Argentina.
Halocnemum Bieb. Chenopodiaceae (A). 1 Medit., C. As.
Halodule Endl. (*Diplanthera EP.*). Potamogetonaceae. 2 Indomal., Cuba.

Halogeton C. A. Mey. Chenopod. (B). 5 Medit., C. As. *H. sativus* Moq. (W. Medit.; barilla), formerly burnt for soda.

Halopegia K. Schum. (*Clinogyne* p.p. *BH.*). Marant. 4 palaeotrop.

Halopeplis Bunge. Chenopod. (A). 3 Medit., C. As.

Halophila Thou. Hydrocharid. 6 trop.

Halophyte, *cf.* **Halo-**.

Halophytum Spegazz. (*Tetragonia* p.p.). Chenopod. (A). 1 Patag.

Halopyrum Stapf. Gramin. (10). 1 coast of Ind. Ocean.

Haloragidaceae (*EP.*; *Halorageae* of *BH.* incl. *Callitrich.*, *Hippurid.*). Dicots. (Archichl. Myrtiflorae; Rosales *BH.*; pp. xxxix, li). 7/170 cosmop., esp. Austr. Land, marsh, or water herbs of various habits (*cf.* gen.), with great development of adv. r., opp., alt., or whorled usu. exstip. l., and inconspic. fls., sol. or in infl. Anatomy of interest. Fl. ☿ or ♂ ♀, usu. bracteolate, reg., epig., usu. 4-merous. P 4+4, or 4, or 0; A 4+4, obdipl., or fewer; $\overline{G}$ (1—4), multi-loc., usu. with 1 pend. anatr. ov. in each; styles free. Nut or drupe; embryo straight, in endosp. Related to Onagraceae, as reduced forms.

Classification and genera (Monogr. in *Pfl. R.*, 1905):

Fr. not a schizocarp, ov. 4—2-loc.; Loudonia (panicle), Haloragis (raceme, ☿, A 2-cyclic, usu. 4-merous), Meziella, Laurembergia (♂ ♀). Proserpinaca (3-merous). Fr. a schizocarp: Myriophyllum (ov. 4—2-loc.), Gunnera (ov. 1-loc.).

Haloragis Forst. Haloragid. 70 Austr., N.Z., Tasm., S.E. As.

Haloschoenus Nees = Rhynchospora Vahl p.p. (Cyper.).

Halostachys C. A. Mey. Chenopod. (A). 1 E. Eur., W. As. P (3).

Halotis Bunge = Halimocnemis C. A. Mey (Chenopod.).

Haloxylon Bunge. Chenopod. (B). 10 Medit., C. As. Steppe pl. of curious habit (fig. in *Nat. Pfl.*); twigs jointed, apparently leafless.

Hamadryas Comm. ex Juss. Ranunc. (3). 4 Antarctic Am. Dioecious.

Hamamelidaceae (*EP.*; *Hamamelideae* of *BH.* incl. *Myrothamn.*). Dicots. (Archichl. Rosales; pp. xxiii, li). 18/50, chiefly subtrop. (N. and S.), with very discontinuous distr. areas. ♄ with usu. alt., simple or palmate stip. l. Infl. racemose, often a spike or head, frequently with invol. of coloured br. Fl. ☿ or ♂ ♀, often apet., rarely naked, hypo-, peri-, or epi-gynous, usu. without a disc. K 4—5, usu. imbr.; C 4—5, open or valv., pets. often long and rolled up like a watch spring in bud; A 4—5 or rarely fewer; $\underline{G}$ to $\overline{G}$ (2), usu. median, rarely obliquely placed, 2-loc. with term. divided style; ovules 1 or more in each loc., pend., anatr., with ventral or lat. raphe. Caps. loculicid. or septic.; exocarp woody, endocarp horny. Embryo straight, endosp. Some yield useful timbers, resins, &c.

Classification and chief genera (after Niedenzu); closely allied to Cunoniaceae and thence to Saxifragaceae.

I. *BUCKLANDIOIDEAE* (ov. > 1 per loc.): (with C) Bucklandia, Rhodoleia; (without) Liquidambar, Altingia.

II. *HAMAMELIDOIDEAE* (ov. 1 per loc.): (sta. long, spikes) Parrotia, Fothergillia, Corylopsis; (sta. short; heads) Maingaya, Hamamelis, Sycopsis, Dicoryphe.

Hamamelis Gronov. ex L. Hamamelid. (11). 4 Chi., Jap., E.N. Am., incl. *H. virginiana* L. (N. Am., witch-hazel), cult. orn. shrub. It flowers in late autumn and ripens its fr. in the following year.

Hamaria Kunze. Rosaceae. Nomen.
Hamelia Jacq. Rubiaceae (I. 8). 15 Mexico to Paraguay., W.I.
Hamilcoa Prain. Euphorbiaceae (A. II. 7). 1 Cameroons, Guinea.
Hamiltonia Roxb. Rubiaceae (II. 6). 4 Indomal., China.
Hammatolobium Fenzl. Leguminosae (III. 7). 2 Medit.
Hamosa Medic. (*Astragalus* p.p.). Leguminosae (III. 6). 6 N. Am.
Hampea Schlechtd. Bombacaceae. 3 C. Am.
Hanabusaya Nakai. Campanulaceae (I. 1). 1 Corea.
Hanburia Seem. Cucurbitaceae (4). 1 Mexico. Fr. explosive.
Hancea Hemsl. Labiatae (inc. sed.). 5 China.
Hancockia Rolfe. Orchidaceae (II. 9). 1 China.
Hancornia Gomes. Apocynaceae (I. 1). 1 Brazil, *H. speciosa* Gomes, the Mangabeira rubber (*Kew Bull.* 1899, p. 185).
Handschia Pohl. Inc. sed. Nomen.
Hannafordia F. Muell. Sterculiaceae. 3 Austr.
Hannoa Planch. Simarubaceae. 4 trop. Afr.
Hansemannia K. Schum. Leguminosae (I. 1). 4 New Guinea.
Hansteinia Oerst. Acanthaceae (IV. B). 4 Mex., C. Am.
Hapaline Schott. Araceae (VI). 3 E. Indomal.
Hapalostephium D. Don ex Sweet = Crepis Vaill. (Comp.).
Hapaxanthic, with single flowering.
Haplanthodes O. Ktze. = Haplanthus Nees (Acanth.).
Haplanthus Nees. Acanthaceae (IV. B). 3 Indomal.
Haplocalymma Blake (*Viguiera* p.p.). Compositae (5). 1 Mexico.
Haplocarpha Less. (*Arctotis* p.p. *EP*.). Compositae (10). 4 Afr.
Haplochlamydeous, -stemonous, with one whorl of P or A.
Haplochorema K. Schum. Zingiberaceae (1). 6 Borneo.
Haploclathra Benth. Guttiferae (1). 2 N. Brazil. Wood red.
Haplocoelum Radlk. Sapindaceae (1). 2 Zanzibar.
Haplodypsis Baill. Palmaceae (IV. 1). 2 Madag.
Haploesthes A. Gray. Compositae (8). 1 California to Mexico.
Haplolophium Endl. (*Aplolophium*). Bignoniaceae (1). 3 Brazil.
Haplopappus Endl. (*Aplopappus*). Compositae (3). 125 W. Am.
Haplopetalon A. Gray. Rhizophoraceae. 3 Polynesia.
Haplophloga Baill. Palmaceae (IV. 1). 2 Madag., Masc.
Haplophyton A. DC. Apocynaceae (I. 3). 1 Arizona to Cuba.
Haplorhus Engl. Anacardiaceae (3). 1 Peru.
Haplostachys Hillebr. Labiatae (III). 3 Hawaiian Is.
Haplostephium Mart. ex DC. Compositae (1). 2 Minas Geraes.
Haplostichanthus F. Muell. Anonaceae (1). 1 Queensland.
Haptera, holdfasts of *Podostemaceae* and *Tristichaceae*.
Haptocarpum Ule. Capparidaceae (V). 1 E. Brazil.
Harbouria Coulter et Rose (*Thaspium* p.p.). Umbell (III. 5). 1 U.S.
Hard fern, *Blechnum*, *Lomaria*; **-hack** (Am.), *Spiraea*; **-wood tree** (W.I.), *Ixora ferrea* Benth.
Hardenbergia Benth. (*Kennedya* p.p. *EP*.). Leguminosae (III. 10). 15 Austr. Cult. orn. fl.
Hardwickia Roxb. Leguminosae (II. 2). 2 trop. As. Apet.
Hare bell, *Campanula rotundifolia* L.; **-'s ear**, *Bupleurum*; **-'s tail grass**, *Lagurus*.

Harfordia Greene et Perry (*Pterostegia* p.p.). Polygonaceae (I. 1). 2 California.
Hargasseria C. A. Mey. = Daphnopsis Mart. (Thymel.).
Haricot bean, *Phaseolus vulgaris* L.
Harina Buch.-Ham. = Wallichia Roxb. (Palmac.).
Hariota DC. (*Rhipsalis* p.p.). Cactaceae (III. 3). 2 S. Brazil.
Harmandia Pierre. Olacaceae. 1 W. Afr.
Harmandiella Costantin. Asclepiadaceae (II. 3). 1 Cochinchina.
Harmogia Schau. = Baeckea L. p.p. (Myrt.).
Harmsia K. Schum. Sterculiaceae. 2 trop. Afr.
Harmsiopanax Warb. (*Horsfieldia* Bl.). Araliaceae (2). 2 Malaya.
Haronga Thou. Guttiferae (II). 1 trop. Afr., Madag., Maur.
Harpachne Hochst. (*Eragrostis* p.p. *BH.*). Gramineae (10). 1 trop. Afr.
Harpagonella A. Gray. Boraginaceae (IV). 1 California.
Harpagophytum DC. Pedaliaceae. 4 S. Afr. *H. procumbens* DC. (grapple-plant) fr. is beset with large woody grapples about an inch long, pointed and barbed. It is thus suited to animal distribution, and is troublesome to wool growers (*cf.* Xanthium).
Harpalium Cass. = Helianthus L. (Comp.).
Harpalyce Moç. et Sesse ex DC. Leguminosae (III. 6). 6 trop. Am., W.I.
Harpanema Decne. in DC. Asclepiadaceae (I). 1 Madag.
Harpechloa Kunth. Gramineae (11). 2 S. Afr.
Harpephyllum Bernh. ex Krauss. Anacardiaceae (2). 1 S. Afr.
Harperella Rose (*Harperia* Rose). Umbelliferae (III. 5). 1 W. U.S.
Harperia Fitzgerald. Restionaceae. 1 Austr.
Harperia Rose. Umbelliferae (III. 5). 1 N. Am.
Harpochilus Nees. Acanthaceae (IV. B). 2 Brazil.
Harpullia Roxb. Sapindaceae (II). 25 palaeotrop.
Harrachia Jacq. f. = Crossandra Salisb. (Acanth.)
Harrimanella Coville (*Cassiope* p.p.). Ericaceae (II. 1). 2 boreal.
Harrisella Fawcett et Rendle (*Campylocentron* p.p.). Orchidaceae (II. 20). 1 W.I., Florida, Yucatan.
Harrisia Britton (*Cereus* p.p.). Cactaceae (III. 1). 18 W.I., warm Am.
Harrisonia R. Br. Simarubaceae. 4 trop. As. and Afr.
Hartia Dunn. Theaceae. 1 China.
Hartighsea A. Juss. = Dysoxylum Blume (Melia.).
Hartmannia DC. = Hemizonia p.p. (Comp.).
Hartmannia Spach = Oenothera L. (*BH.*) = Xylopleurum Spach.
Hartogia L. = Agathosma Willd. (Rut.).
Hartogia L. f. Celastraceae. 2 S. Afr., Madag.
Hart's tongue fern, *Phyllitis*, *Scolopendrium*.
Hartwegia Lindl. Orchidaceae (II. 6). 2 Centr. Am.
Hartwrightia A. Gray. Compositae (2). 1 Florida.
Harveya Hook. Scrophulariaceae (III. 2). 20 S. and trop. Afr. Some are root parasites, like Euphrasia.
Hashish, *Cannabis sativa* L.
Haselhoffia Lindau. Acanthaceae (IV. A). 2 W. trop. Afr.
Hasseanthus Rose (*Sedum* p.p.). Crassulaceae. 4 California.
Hasselquistia L. = Tordylium L. p.p. (Umbellif.).

Hasseltia H. B. et K. Flacourtiaceae (5). 5 Mexico, Andes.
Hasskarlia Baill. Euphorbiaceae (A. II. 2). 4 trop. Afr.
Hasslerella Chodat. Scrophulariaceae (III. 1). 1 Argentina.
Hassleropsis Chodat. Scrophulariaceae (II. 1). 1 Paraguay.
Hastate, with two pointed lobes projecting ⊥ at the base.
Hastingsia S. Wats. (*Schoenolirion EP.*). Liliaceae (III). 4 W. N.Am.
Hats, Panama, *Carludovica*.
Haulm, stem.
Haussknechtia Boiss. Umbelliferae (III. 6). 1 Persia.
Haussmannia F. Muell. Bignoniaceae (1). 1 Queensland.
Haustoria, the suckers of parasites.
Haustrum Nor. Inc. sed. Nomen.
Hauya (Moç. et Sesse ex) DC. Onagraceae (2). 8 C. Am., Mex., Calif.
Havardia Small (*Pithecolobium* p.p.). Leguminosae (I. 1). 1 N. Am.
Havetia H. B. et K. Guttiferae (V). 1 Colombia.
Havetiopsis Planch. et Triana. Guttiferae (V). 5 Amazon valley.
Havilandia Stapf. Boraginaceae (IV. 4). 1 Borneo.
Hawk-bit, *Leontodon*; **-'s beard**, *Crepis*; **-weed**, *Hieracium*.
Haworthia Duval. Liliaceae (III). 60 S. Afr. Xero. with fleshy l., similar in habit to Crassulaceae.
Hawthorn, *Crataegus*.
Haya Balf. f. Caryophyllaceae (I. 4). 1 Socotra.
Haylockia Herb. Amaryllidaceae (I). 2 temp. S. Am. Like Crocus, with fls. projecting from the soil.
Haynaldia Kanitz (*Lobelia* p.p. *EP.*). Campanulaceae (III). 4 Brazil.
Haynaldia Schur. (*Agropyron BH.*). Gramineae (12). 2 Medit.
Haynea Schumach. et Thoms. Urticaceae (inc. sed.). 1 trop. Afr.
Hazardia Greene (*Haplopappus EP.*). Compositae (3). 3 California.
Hazel nut, *Corylus*; **- withe**, *Hamamelis*.
Head, a mass of sessile fls. on a common recept., *Compositae*; **compound -**, *Echinops*; **cymose -**, *Dipsacaceae*, *Haemanthus*.
Headache-weed (W.I.), *Hedyosmum nutans* Sw.
Hearnia F. Muell. (*Aglaia* p.p. *EP.*). Meliaceae (II). 6 E. Indomal.
Heart pea (W.I.), *Cardiospermum*; **-'s ease**, *Viola*; **-wood**, the older wood of a tree trunk, in which no sap runs.
Heath, *Calluna*, *Erica*; **prickly**, *Pernettya*; **St. Dabeoc's -**, *Daboecia*; **sea -**, *Frankenia*.
Heather, *Calluna vulgaris* Salisb., *Erica*.
Heaven, tree of, *Ailanthus*.
Hebanthe Mart. (*Pfaffia EP.*). Amarantaceae (3). 20 trop. Am.
Hebecladus Miers. Solanaceae (2). 7 W. trop. S. Am.
Hebeclinium DC. = Eupatorium Tourn. p.p. (Comp.).
Hebecoccus Radlk. Sapindaceae (I). 1 Java.
Hebenstretia L. Scrophulariaceae (II. 7). 30 S. and trop. Afr. The corolla is slit open along the anterior side, and the style and sta. project through the slit.
Hebepetalum Benth. Linaceae. 2 trop. S. Am.
Heberdenia Banks (*Myrsine* p.p. *BH.*). Myrsinaceae (II). 2 Macronesia, Mexico.
Hebestigma Urb. Leguminosae (III. 6). 1 W.I.
Hebonga Radlk. Simarubaceae. 3 Phil. Is., Siam.

Hecastocleis A. Gray. Compositae (12). 1 Nevada.

Hechtia Klotzsch. Bromeliaceae (2). 30 C. Am., S.U.S. Cult. orn. infl.

Hecistopteris J. Sm. Polypodiaceae. 1 trop. Am.

Heckeldora Pierre. Meliaceae (III). 2 trop. Afr.

Heckelia K. Schum. Menispermaceae. 1 New Guinea.

Heckeria Kunth (*Piper* p.p. *EP.*). Piperaceae. 8 trop.

Hectorella Hook. f. Portulaceae. 1 N.Z.

Hecubaea DC. (*Helenium* p.p. *EP.*). Compositae (6). 1 Mexico.

Hedeoma Pers. Labiatae (VI). 30 Am.

Hedeomoides Briq. (*Pogogyne* p.p.). Labiatae (VI). 3 California.

Hedera Tourn. ex L. Araliaceae. 5 temp. |*. *H. Helix* L. (ivy) is a root climber. L. dimorphic, those on the climbing shoots lobed, those on the freely projecting shoots that bear the infl. not. The former form leaf-mosaics better. Fls. not very conspicuous, but coming out late in the year are largely visited for the freely exposed honey by flies and wasps.

Hederella Stapf (*Dissochaeta* p.p. *EP.*). Melastomac. (I). 4 Mal. Arch.

Hederopsis C. B. Clarke. Araliaceae (1). 1 Malay Peninsula.

Hedge-hog grass (Am.), *Cenchrus*; **-hyssop** (Am.), *Gratiola*; **-mustard**, *Sisymbrium*, (W.I.) *Chenopodium*; **-nettle** (Am.), *Stachys*; **-parsley**, *Caucalis*.

Hedona Lous. (*Lychnis* p.p.). Caryophyllaceae (II. 1). 1 Tibet.

Hedraeanthus A. DC. Campanulaceae (I). 12 S.E. Eur., Caucasus.

Hedraianthera F. Muell. Celastraceae. 1 E. Austr.

Hedwigia Sw. (*Tetragastris EP.*). Burseraceae. 3 trop. Am., W.I. *H. balsamifera* Sw. (Antilles) is known as pig's balsam, on account of a legend that wounded pigs rub against the trees to heal wounds with the resin.

Hedycapnos Planch. = Dicentra Bernh. (Papav.).

Hedycarya Forst. Monimiaceae. 20 Austr. to Fiji.

Hedychium Koen. Zingiberaceae (1). 50 trop. As., Madag. Rhizome often tuberous. The fl. has a long tube, at the end of which spring the narrow free parts of the petals and the larger staminodes and labellum. The stigma projects just beyond the anther. Cult. orn. fl.

Hedyosmum Sw. Chloranthaceae. 20 trop. Am.

Hedyotis L. (*Oldenlandia* p.p. *EP.*). Rubiaceae (I. 2). 120 trop.

Hedypnois Schreb. = Rhagadiolus Tourn.

Hedypnois (Tourn.) Scop. (*Leontodon BH.*). Compositae (13). 3 Medit.

Hedysarum (Tourn.) L. Leguminosae (III. 7), 100 N. temp.

Hedyscepe H. Wendl. et Drude (*Kentia* p.p. *EP.*). Palmaceae (IV. 1). 1 Lord Howe's Island.

Heeria Meissn. (*Anaphrenium* E. Mey. *BH.*). Anacardiaceae (3). 12 Afr.

Heeria Schlecht. (*Heterocentron EP.*). Melastomaceae (I). 6 C. Am. Some sta. attract insects, the others pollinate them (*cf.* Commelina).

Heimia Link et Otto (*Nesaea BH.*). Lythraceae. 2 trop. Am.

Heinsenia K. Schum. Rubiaceae (II. 1). 2 trop. Afr.

Heinsia DC. Rubiaceae (I. 8). 5 trop. Afr.
Heisteria Jacq. Olacaceae. 25 warm Am., W. Afr.
Hekistocarpa Hook. f. Rubiaceae (I. 2). 1 Nigeria.
Heladena A. Juss. Malpighiaceae (II). 5 Brazil, Argentina.
Helcia Lindl. (*Trichopilia BH.*). Orchidaceae (II. 19). 1 Panama.
Heldreichia Boiss. Cruciferae (2). 6 W. As.
Helenia L. = Helenium L.
Helenium L. Compositae (6). 30 W. Am.
Heleocharis (*Eleocharis*) R. Br. Cyperaceae (I). 90 cosmop.
Heleochloa Host. Gramineae (8). 8 N. palaeotemp.
Heleogiton Schult. = Scirpus L. (Cyper.).
Heleophylax Beauv. = Scirpus L. p.p. (Cyper.).
Helia Mart. (*Lisianthus BH.*). Gentianaceae (I). 7 trop. S. Am.
Heliamphora Benth. Sarraceniaceae. 1 Guiana, a pitcher plant (*cf.* Sarracenia).
Helianthella Torr. et Gray. Compositae (5). 15 W. U.S., Mexico.
Helianthemum Tourn. ex Hall. Cistaceae. 80 Eur., Medit., C. As. *H. vulgare* Gaertn. and 3 others in Brit. (rock-rose). Infl. a cincinnus. The fl. contains no honey and is homogamous, with sensitive sta., which move outwards when touched.
Helianthostylis Baill. Moraceae (II). 1 Amazon valley.
Helianthum Engelm. ex Britton (*Echinodorus EP.*). Alism. 3 N. Am.
Helianthus L. Compositae (5). 60 Am. Good for chars. of § 5. In *H. annuus* L. (sunflower) the number of fls. upon the head is often enormous and they show very regular spiral arrangement, probably due (largely) to pressure in the bud. Ray florets neuter. The seeds give oil. *H. tuberosus* L. (Jerusalem artichoke) has subterranean tuberous stems, like potatoes, with well marked 'eyes' (buds in axils of scale-l.).
Helichrysum Vaill. ex L. Compositae (4). 350 Eur., As., Afr., Austr.; 150 in S. Afr. Many xero. with hairy surface, decurrent, &c. The dried fl.-heads of some sp. are 'everlastings.'
Helicia Lour. Proteaceae (II). 40 Indomal., Japan to N. S. Wales.
Helicilla Moq. Chenopodiaceae (B). 1 China.
Helicodiceros Schott. Araceae (VII). 1 Corsica, Sardinia, *H. crinitus* Schott (*H. muscivorus* Engl.). The development of the pedate leaf is cymose; the later formed branches grow more slowly than the earlier. The name *muscivorus* is due to the number of flies captured; attracted by the foul smell of the infl. (*cf.* Arum) they collect inside the spathe in enormous numbers; it may often be seen tightly packed; when it withers the top closes and they are caught.
Heliconia L. Musaceae. 60 trop. Am. Fls. in cincinni; odd sep. post.
Helicophyllum Schott (*Eminium EP.*). Araceae (VII). 4 E. Medit.
Helicostylis Tréc. Moraceae (II). 2 Guiana, N. Brazil.
Helicteres Pluk. ex L. Sterculiaceae. 45 trop. (exc. Afr.). The fls. become zygomorphic if they happen to be in a horiz. position.
Helictonema Pierre. Celastraceae. 1 trop. Afr.
Helietta Tul. Rutaceae (IV). 4 trop. Am.
Heligme Blume = Parsonsia R. Br. (Apocyn.).

Helinus E. Mey. ex Endl. Rhamnaceae. 4 palaeotrop., S. Afr.
Helio- (Gr. pref.), sun-; **-trope,** *Heliotropium*; **-tropism,** irritability to light; **winter -trope,** *Petasites.*
Heliocarpus L. Tiliaceae. 10 Mexico to Paraguay. Dioec.; 4-merous.
Heliocarya Bunge. Boraginaceae (IV. 1). 1 Persia.
Heliocereus Britton et Rose (*Cereus* p.p.). Cactaceae (III. 1). 4 C. Am., Mex.
Heliophila Burm. f. ex L. Cruciferae (1). 80 S. Afr.
Heliophytum DC. = Heliotropium L. p.p. (Boragin.).
Heliopsis Pers. Compositae (5). 7 Am.
Heliosperma Reichb. (*Silene* p.p. *BH.*). Caryophyllaceae (II. 1). 5 Mountains of S. Eur.
Heliotropium (Tourn.) L. Boraginaceae (III). 220 trop. and temp. *H. peruvianum* L. (cherry pie) and others (heliotrope) cult. perf. fls.
Helipterum DC. Compositae (4). 50 Austr., S. Afr. Xero. with persistent invol. of white scaly bracts. Cult. orn. fl.; the dried flower-heads are sold as 'everlastings' (*cf.* Helichrysum, &c.).
Hellebore, *Helleborus*; **white -,** *Veratrum.*
Helleborine Tourn. ex Hall, Pers. = Serapias L. (Orchid.).
Helleborine Hill (*Epipactis* p.p.). Orchidaceae (II. 2). 10 N. temp.
Helleborine, *Epipactis.*
Helleborus (Tourn.) L. Ranunculaceae (2). 15 Eur., Medit.; 2 in Brit. (hellebore). Pl. woody below, each shoot from the stock taking several years to reach maturity and flower. Fl. protog., opening early in the year. Cpls. slightly coherent at base. In *H. niger* L. (Christmas rose) the P turns green after the fl. has been fert.
Hellenia Willd. = Alpinia L. (Zingib.).
Helleranthus Small (*Verbena* p.p.). Verbenaceae (1). 1 N. Am.
Hellwigia Warb. (*Alpinia* p.p.). Zingiberaceae (1). 1 New Guinea.
Helmholtzia F. Muell. Philydraceae. 2 E. Austr., Polynesia.
Helmia Kunth = Dioscorea L. p.p. (Dioscor.).
Helminthia Juss. = Picris L. p.p. (Comp.).
Helminthocarpum A. Rich. Leguminosae (III. 5). 1 Abyssinia.
Helminthostachys Kaulf. Ophioglossaceae. 1, *H. zeylanica* Hook. f., Ceylon, Himal. to Queensland. Rhiz. dorsiv. with 2-ranked l. on the upper side, and roots below, which do not bear any definite relation to the l. Sporangia peltate, on sporangiophores from the sides of the fertile spike. [Cf. Farmer and Freeman, in *Ann. of Bot.* XIII. 1899, p. 421; Lang on prothallus, do. XVI. 1902, p. 23.]
Helmontia Cogn. Cucurbitaceae (2). 2 Brazil, Guiana.
Helobieae. The 2nd order of Monocotyledons. *Cf.* p. ii.
Helodea Reichb. = Elodea Michx. (Hydrocharit.).
Helodrium (Cl.), a thicket formation.
Helogyne Nutt. Compositae (2). 2 Peru, Bolivia.
Helonias L. Liliaceae (1). 1 east N. Am. Cult. orn. fl.
Heloniopsis A. Gray. Liliaceae (1). 4 Japan, Formosa.
Helopus Trin. = Eriochloa H.B. et K. (Gram.).
Helosciadium Koch = Apium Tourn. p.p. (Umbellif.). 6 | ✻.
Helosis Rich. Balanophoraceae. 3 trop. Am.
Helwingia Willd. Cornaceae (Araliac. *BH.*). 3 Himal. to Japan.
Helxine L. = Polygonum Tourn. (*BH.*) = Fagopyrum Moench.

Helxine Reg. Urticaceae (4). 1 Corsica, Sardinia.
Hemandradenia Stapf. Connaraceae. 2 trop. Afr.
Hemarthria R. Br. (*Rottboellia* p.p. *EP.*). Gramin. (2). 8 warm |*.
Hemerocallis L. Liliaceae (III). 5 temp. Eur., As. Infl. a double bostryx. The fls. of *H. fulva* L. are self-sterile. Cult. orn. fl.
Hemi- (Gr. pref.), half, partial; **-cyclic**, part in spirals, part in whorls; **-parasite**, a facultative saprophyte, a parasite which can exist as a saprophyte; **-ptera**, bugs, &c.; **-tropous** (insects), with tongues of medium length, suited to fl.-classes B and B′.
Hemiandra R. Br. Labiatae (II). 3 S.W. Austr.
Hemiarrhena Benth. Scrophulariaceae (III. 3). 1 trop. Austr.
Hemiboea C. B. Clarke. Gesneriaceae (I). 3 China.
Hemicarex Benth. (*Kobresia* Willd., *Schoenoxiphium* Nees, *BH.*). Cyperaceae (III). 10 Himalaya, S. Afr.
Hemicarpha Nees et Arn. (*Scirpus* p.p. *BH.*). Cyper (I). 3 trop. and subtrop.
Hemicarpus F. Muell. = Trachymene Rudge (*BH.*) = Didiscus DC.
Hemichaena Benth. Scrophulariaceae (II. 4). 1 C. Am.
Hemichlaena Schrad. Cyperaceae (I). 3 S. Afr.
Hemichroa R. Br. Chenopodiaceae (A). 3 Austr.
Hemicrambe Webb. Cruciferae (2). 1 Morocco.
Hemicyclia Wight et Arn. Euphorbiaceae (A. I. 1). 10 Indomal.
Hemidesmus R. Br. Asclepiadaceae (I). 1 S. India.
Hemidia Rafin. Inc. sed. Nomen.
Hemidiodia K. Schum. (*Spermacoce* p.p.). Rubiaceae (II. 10). 1 Mexico to Brazil, Malay Archip.
Hemigenia R. Br. Labiatae (II). 25 Austr. L. in whorls of 3.
Hemiglochidion K. Schum. (*Phyllanthus* p.p.). Euphorbiaceae (A. I. 1). 4 New Guinea.
Hemigraphis Nees. Acanthaceae (IV. A). 25 trop. As.
Hemigyrosa Blume (*Guioa* p.p. *EP.*). Sapindaceae (I). 4 Indomal.
Hemihabenaria Finet (*Habenaria* p.p.). Orchid. (II. 1). 3 E. As.
Hemiheisteria Van Tiegh. (*Heisteria* p.p.). Olacaceae. 1 S. Am.
Hemilophia Franch. Cruciferae (2). 1 Yunnan.
Hemimeris L. f., Thunb. Scrophulariaceae (II. 2). 4 S. Afr.
Hemimeris Pers. = Alonsoa Ruiz et Pav. (Scroph.).
Hemionitis L. Polypodiaceae. 10 trop. Am. and As.
Hemiorchis Kurz. Zingiberaceae (I). 3 E. Indomal.
Hemiphora F. Muell. Verbenaceae (3). 1 W. Austr.
Hemiphragma Wall. Scrophulariaceae (III. 1). 1 Himalaya.
Hemiphylacus S. Wats. Liliaceae (III). 1 N. Mexico.
Hemipilia Lindl. Orchidaceae (II. 1). 5 Himal., China.
Hemipogon Decne. in DC. Asclepiadaceae (II. 1). 7 S. Am.
Hemisiphonia Urb. Scrophulariaceae (II. 6). 1 W. Indies.
Hemistemma Juss. ex Thou. = Hibbertia Andr. p.p. (Dillen.).
Hemistepta Bunge (*Saussurea* p.p.). Compositae (11). 1 E. As.
Hemistylus Benth. Urticaceae (4). 4 S. Am.
Hemitelia Br. Cyatheaceae. 75 trop. and S. temp. Tree-ferns.
Hemithrinax Hook. f. (*Thrinax* p.p. *EP.*). Palmaceae (I. 2). 1 Cuba.
Hemitria Rafin. Loranthaceae (inc. sed.). 1, habitat ?.
Hemizonella A. Gray. Compositae (5). 2 Pacif. U.S.

Hemizonia DC. Compositae (5). 25 west N. Am.

Hemizygia Briq. (*Ocimum* p.p. *BH.*). Labiatae (VII). 4 trop. and S. Afr.

Hemlock, *Conium maculatum* L.; **-spruce** (Am.), *Tsuga canadensis* Carr.; **water-**, *Cicuta virosa* L.

Hemp, *Cannabis*, *Moraceae*; **- agrimony**, *Eupatorium cannabinum* L.; **bastard - agrimony** (W.I.), *Ageratum conyzoides* L.; **Bombay -**, *Crotalaria juncea* L.; **bow-string -**, *Sansevieria zeylanica* Willd., &c.; **China -**, *Abutilon*; **Deccan -**, *Hibiscus cannabinus* L.; **Madras -**, *cf.* Bombay; **Manila -**, *Musa textilis* Née; **Mauritius -**, *Furcraea gigantea* Vent.; **-nettle**, *Galeopsis Tetrahit* L.; **New Zealand -**, *Phormium tenax* Forst.; **sisal -**, *Agave sisalana* Perrine; **sunn -**, *Crotalaria juncea* L.

Hemsleya Cogn. Cucurbitaceae (1). 8 S.E. As. Phils.

Hen-and-chickens, *Calendula officinalis* L., var.

Hen-bane, *Hyoscyamus niger* L.; **-bit**, *Lamium amplexicaule* L.

Henckelia Spreng. = Didymocarpus Wall. (Gesner.).

Henequen, *Agave fourcroydes* Lem.

Henicosanthum Becc. Anonaceae (1). 1 Borneo.

Henlea Griseb. Malpighiaceae. 1 Cuba.

Henleophytum Karst. (*Henlea* Griseb.). Malpighiaceae. 1 Cuba.

Henna, *Lawsonia inermis* L.

Hennecartia Poisson. Monimiaceae. 1 Paraguay, S. Braz.

Henonia Moq. Amarantaceae (1). 1 Madag.

Henoonia Griseb. Solanaceae (4) (Sapotaceae *BH.*). 1 Cuba.

Henophyton Coss. et Dur. Cruciferae (4). 1 Algeria.

Henosis Hook. f. (*Bulbophyllum* p.p.). Orchid. (II. 16). 1 Brazil.

Henricia Cass. Compositae (3). 1 Madag.

Henriettea DC. Melastomaceae (I). 12 trop. S. Am.

Henriettella Naud. Melastomaceae (I). 20 trop. Am., W.I.

Henriquezia Spruce ex Benth. Rubiaceae (I. 4). 5 N. Braz., Guiana.

Henrya Hemsl. Asclepiadaceae (II. 1). 1 Centr. China.

Henslowia Blume. Santalaceae. 20 Indomal., China.

Hensmania Fitzgerald (*Xerotes* p.p.). Liliaceae (III). 1 Austr.

Hepatica Dill. ex L. = Anemone L. p.p. (Ranunc.).

Heppiella Regel. Gesneriaceae (II). 10 trop. S. Am.

Heptacodium Rehder. Caprifoliaceae. 1 China.

Heptacyclum Engl. = Penianthus Miers p.p. (Menisp.). 1 trop. Afr.

Heptandrous, with 7 stamens.

Heptanthus Griseb. Compositae (5). 3 Cuba.

Heptapleurum Gaertn. (*Schefflera EP.*). Araliaceae (1). 70 palaeotrop.

Heracleum L. Umbelliferae (III. 6). 70 N. temp. and trop. Mts. (*H. Sphondylium* L., cow-parsnip, in Brit.).

Herb, a pl. with no woody part above ground; **- Christopher**, *Actaea spicata* L.; **- Bennett**, *Geum*; **- Paris**, *Paris quadrifolia* L.; **- Robert**, *Geranium Robertianum* L.; **-aceous** (l.). thin and green (stem), not woody above ground.

Herbarium, a collection of dried plants.

Herbertia Sweet (*Alophia EP.*). Iridaceae (II). 7 warm Am.

Hercules' Club (Am.), *Aralia spinosa* L.

Herderia Cass. Compositae (1). 3 trop. Afr.
Herd's grass (Am.), *Phleum pratense* L.
Heritiera (Dryand.) Ait. Sterculiaceae. 4 palaeotrop. coasts.
Herkogamous, ☿, but incapable of self-fertilisation.
Hermannia L. (*BH.* excl. *Mahernia* L.). Sterculiaceae. 150 trop. and sub-trop., chiefly Afr.
Hermaphrodite (fl.), with both stamens and carpels (functional).
Hermas L. Umbelliferae (I. 2). 5 S. Afr.
Hermbstaedtia Reichb. Amarantaceae (1). 10 trop. and S. Afr.
Hermesia Humb. et Bonpl. = Alchornea Sw. p.p. (Euph.).
Hermesias Loefl. (*Brownea BH.*). Legumin. (II. 3). 10 trop. Am , W.I.
Hermibicchia × G. Camus, Bergon, et A. Camus. Orchidaceae. Hybrid, Herminium—Gymnadenia (Bicchia).
Hermidium S. Wats. Nyctaginaceae. 1 S.W. U.S.
Herminiera Guill. et Perr. (*Aeschynomene* p.p. *EP.*). Leguminosae (III. 7). 1 trop. Afr., *H. elaphroxylon* G. et P. Wood light, used for floats, canoes, &c. *Cf.* with the development of aerenchyma seen in other marsh plants (Lycopus, Jussieua, &c.).
Herminium L. Orchidaceae (II. 1). 8 temp. Eur., As. (*H. Monorchis* R. Br., musk-orchis, in Brit.)
Hermione Salisb. = Narcissus Tourn. p.p. (Amaryll.).
Hermodactylus Tourn. ex Mill. Iridaceae (II). 1 Medit. G 1-loc.
Hernandia Plum. ex L. Hernandiaceae. 10 trop.
Hernandiaceae (*EP.*; *Lauraceae* p.p. *BH.*). Dicotyledons (Archichl. Ranales). 4 gen. 25 sp. trop. Shrubs or trees with alt. exstip. l., oil-cells, and cystoliths. Fl. ☿ or unisexual reg. P 4—10, A in whorl before outer P, $\bar{G}$ 1-loc., with 1 pend. anatr. ov. Fr. often winged. Embryo straight; endosperm O. *Chief genus:* Hernandia.
Herniaria (Tourn.) L. Caryophyllaceae (I. 4). 20 Medit., Eur., S. Afr. (*H. glabra* L., rupture-wort, in England.) Fl. apetalous.
Herpestis Gaertn. f. (*Bacopa EP.*). Scrophulariaceae (II. 6). 50 trop. and subtrop., chiefly Am.
Herpetacanthus Nees. Acanthaceae (IV. B). 5 Brazil.
Herpetica Cook et Collins, Rafin. (*Cassia* p.p.). Legum. (II. 5). 1 Porto Rico.
Herpetospermum Wall. Cucurbitaceae (3). 2 Himal., China.
Herpolirion Hook. f. Liliaceae (III). 1 N.Z., Tasm., S.E. Austr.
Herpysma Lindl. Orchidaceae (II. 2). 2 Himal., Phil. Is.
Herpyza Sauv. (*Teramnus EP.*). Leguminosae (III. 10). 1 Cuba.
Herrania Goudot (*Theobroma* p.p. *EP.*). Sterculiaceae. 5 trop. S. Am.
Herreria Ruiz et Pav. Liliaceae (II). 3 S. Am.
Herrickia Wooton et Standley. Compositae (3). 1 New Mexico.
Herschelia Lindl. (*Disa* p.p. *BH.*). Orchid. (II. 1). 6 S. and trop. Afr.
Hertia Neck. (*Othonnopsis* p.p. *B.H.*). Compos. (8). 8 W. As., S. Afr.
Herya Cordemoy. Celastraceae. 1 Bourbon.
Hesperaloe Engelm. Liliaceae (VI). 2 Texas, Mexico.
Hesperantha Ker-Gawl. Iridaceae (III). 25 S. and trop. Afr.
Hesperaster Cockerell (*Mentzelia* p.p.). Loasaceae. 10 N. Am.

Hesperastragalus A. A. Heller (*Astragalus* p.p.). Leguminosae (III. 6). 4 Calif.

Hesperelaea A. Gray. Oleaceae. 1 Lower California.

Hesperidanthus Rydberg (*Streptanthus* p.p.). Cruc. (1). 1 N. Am.

Hesperidium, the berry of Citrus, &c.

Hesperis L. Cruciferae (4). 25 Eur., Medit.; (1 Brit.). Orn. fl.

Hesperocallis A. Gray. Liliaceae (III). 1 Colorado desert.

Hesperochiron S. Wats. Hydrophyllaceae. 3 W. U.S.

Hesperochloa Rydberg (*Festuca* p.p.). Gramin. (10). 1 Rockies.

Hesperocnide Torr. Urticaceae (1). 3 California, Hawaiian Is.

Hesperodoria Greene (*Bigelowia* p.p.). Compos. (3). 2 W. U.S.

Hesperogenia Coulter et Rose. Umbelliferae (III. 4). 1 N. Am.

Hesperolinon Small (*Linum* p.p.). Linaceae. 10 California.

Hesperomannia A. Gray. Compositae (12). 3 Sandwich Is.

Hesperomecon Greene (*Meconella* Benth.). Papaver. (II). 10 Pac. N. Am.

Hesperomeles Lindl. = Osteomeles Lindl. (Ros.).

Hesperonia Standley (*Mirabilis* p.p.). Nyctaginaceae. 9 N. Am.

Hesperoschordum Lindl. = Brodiaea Sm. p.p. (Lili.).

Hesperoxalis Small (*Oxalis* p.p.). Oxalidaceae. 1 N.W. U.S.

Hesperoyucca Baker (*Yucca* p.p.). Liliaceae (VI). 1 Calif.

Hessea Herb. Amaryllidaceae (I). 10 S. Afr. Cult. orn. fl.

Hetaeria Blume. Orchidaceae (II. 2). 20 palaeotrop.

Heter, hetero- (Gr. pref.), diverse; **-carpous**, producing more than one kind of fr., *Aethionema*, *Calendula*, *Cardamine*, *Dimorphotheca*; **-chlamydeous**, with P l. of two kinds, K and C; **-cyclic**, with different numbers in different whorls; **-dromous** (aestivation), a right-hand-side fl. the reflection of a left, *Exacum*, *Marantaceae*, *Saintpaulia*; **-gamous**, heterostyled, or in *Compositae*, fls. of different sex in same head; **-merous**, whorls with different numbers of members; **-phylly**, polymorphic l., *Bryophyllum*, *Capsella*, *Dischidia*, *Liriodendron*, *Hedera* and other climbers, many epiphytes, insectivorous plants, and water-plants; **-spory**, presence of two kinds of spores, *Pteridophyta*; **-stylism**, occurrence of two or more kinds of pl. of the same sp., one with *e.g.* long sta. and short style, the other with short sta. and long style, or long, mid and short sta. and style, *Lythrum*, *Primula*, *Androsace*, *Boraginaceae*, *Bouvardia*, *Eichhornia*, *Erythroxylum*, *Fagopyrum*, *Hottonia*, *Lagerstroemia*, *Linum*, *Lythrum*, *Menyanthes*, *Mitchella*, *Oldenlandia*, *Oxalis*, *Pontederia*, *Primula*, *Psychotria*, *Pulmonaria*, *Rudgea*, *Statice*, *Turneraceae*.

Heterachaena Fres. (*Launaea* p.p. *EP.*). Compositae (13). 1 Arabia, Abyssinia.

Heterachne Benth. Gramineae (10). 2 N. Austr.

Heteracia Fisch. et Mey. Compositae (13). 1 W. As.

Heteradelphia Lindau. Acanthaceae (IV. A). 1 São Thome.

Heteranthelium Hochst. (*Agropyron* p.p. *BH.*). Gramineae (12). 1 W. As.

Heteranthera Ruiz et Pav. Pontederiaceae. 10 trop. and subtrop. Am., Afr. L. of two types—linear submerged and orbicular floating. Some have cleist. fls.

Heteranthia Nees et Mart. Scrophulariaceae (inc. sed.). 1 Brazil.

Heteranthoecia Stapf. Gramineae (5). 1 trop. Afr.
Heterapithmos Turcz. Inc. sed. 1 Brazil.
Heterixia Van Tiegh. (*Viscum* p.p.). Loranth. (II). 3 N.Z., Malaya.
Heterocarpus Phil. (*Cardamine* p.p. *BH.*). Crucif. (4). 1 Juan Fern.
Heterocaryum A. DC. = Echinospermum Sw. (*BH.*) = Lappula Moench.
Heterocentron Hook. et Arn. (*Heeria BH.*). Melastomaceae (I). 6 C. Am., Mex.
Heterochaenia A. DC. Campanulaceae (I). 1 Mascarenes.
Heterochaeta DC. = Aster Tourn. p.p. (Compos.).
Heterocodon Nutt. Campanulaceae (I). 1 W. N. Am.
Heterocoma DC. Compositae (1). 1 Brazil.
Heterodendron (um) Desf. Sapindaceae (I). 4 Austr.
Heteroderis Boiss. (*Crepis* p.p. *BH.*). Compositae (13). 2 W. As.
Heterodraba Greene (*Draba* p.p.). Cruciferae (4). 1 Calif.
Heterogaura Rothrock. Onagraceae (2). 1 California.
Heterolaena Sch.-Bip. = Eupatorium Tourn. p.p. (Compos.).
Heterolepis Cass. Compositae (4). 3 S. Afr.
Heteromeles M. Roem. (*Photinia* Lindl.). Rosac. (II). 2 Calif.
Heteromerae (*BH.*). The 2nd series of Gamopetalae.
Heteromma Benth. Compositae (3). 1 S. Afr. mts.
Heteromorpha Cham. et Schlechtd. Umbelliferae (III. 5). 3 Afr.
Heteronoma DC. = Arthrostema Ruiz et Pav. (Melastom.).
Heteropanax Seem. Araliaceae (1). 1 Fiji.
Heteropappus Less. Compositae (3). 5 China, Japan.
Heteropetalum Benth. Anonaceae (2). 1 N. Brazil.
Heterophragma DC. Bignoniaceae (2). 3 Indomal.
Heterophyllaea Hook. f. Rubiaceae (I. 5). 2 Bolivia, Argentina.
Heteropogon Pers. (*Andropogon* p.p. *EP.*). Gramin. (2). 5 trop.
Heteropsis Kunth. Araceae (I). 8 trop. S. Am.
Heteropteris H. B. et K. Malpighiaceae (1). 100 trop. Am., 1 in trop. Afr. Fr. a samara (*cf.* Acer, Banisteria).
Heteropyxis Harv. Inc. sed. (Myrt. ?, Lythr. ?). 2 S. Afr.
Heterosciadium Lange. Umbelliferae (III. 2). 1 Spain.
Heterosmilax Kunth. Liliaceae (XI). 5 E. As.
Heterospathe Scheff. Palmaceae (IV. 1). 10 Malay Archip.
Heterospermum Cav. Compositae (5). 10 Arizona to Argentina.
Heterostachys Ung. Sternb. Chenopodiaceae (A). 1 C. and S. Am.
Heterostemma Wight et Arn. Asclepiadaceae (II. 3). 25 Indomal.
Heterostemon Desf. Leguminosae (II. 3). 4 trop. Am.
Heterothalamus Less. Compositae (3). 6 S. Am.
Heterotheca Cass. Compositae (3). 5 W. U.S., Mexico.
Heterothrix Rydberg (*Streptanthus* p.p.). Cruciferae (1). 6 Am.
Heterotis Benth. = Dissotis Benth. (Melastom.).
Heterotoma Zucc. Campanulaceae (III). 6 Mexico. Cult. orn. fl.
Heterotrichum Bieb. = Saussurea DC. (Compos.).
Heterotrichum DC. Melastomaceae (I). 10 trop. Am., some ed. fr.
Heterotropa Morr. et Dcne. = Asarum L. p.p. (Aristoloch.).
Heuchera L. Saxifragaceae (1). 30 N. Am., sometimes apet.
Heuffelia Schur. = Avena L. p.p. (Gramin.).
Heurnia Spreng. (*Huernia* R. Br.) Asclep. (II. 3). 20 Afr.

Heurniopsis N.E. Br. (*Huerniopsis*). Asclep. (II. 3). 1 S. Afr.

Hevea Aubl. Euphorbiaceae (A. II. 3). 20 trop. Am. *H. brasiliensis* Müll.-Arg. is the source of the best caoutchouc (Para rubber), largely exported from Brazil. The tree was introduced into Ceylon and the east in 1876, and in the present century a very large industry has grown up in it. Sloping incisions, usu. in the form of a line or a basal V are made in the bark, and the latex flows from them. The wound is renewed at intervals of one or two days by shaving off a thin slice from the lower side, when there is a larger flow of milk than at first. The milk is usu. coagulated with the aid of enough acid to neutralise its alkalinity, and pressed into sheets or other forms, with or without smoking.

Hewardia Hook. Lili. (I). 1 Tasm.

Hewittia Wight et Arn. Convolvulaceae (I). 5 trop.

Hex- (Gr. pref.), six; **-androus**, with 6 sta., &c.

Hexadesmia Brongn. Orchid. (II. 6). 5 Brazil to Mexico and W.I.

Hexaglochin Nieuwland (*Triglochin* p.p.). Juncag. 1 U.S.

Hexaglottis Vent. Iridaceae (II). 3 Cape Colony.

Hexalectris Rafin. Orchidaceae (II. 7). 2 Mex., S. U.S.

Hexalobus A. DC. Anonaceae (3). 8 trop. Afr., Madag.

Hexaptera Hook. Cruciferae (I). 6 temp. S. Am. Fr. winged.

Hexapterella Urb. Burmanniaceae. 1 Lower Amazon.

Hexasepalum Bartl. ex DC. (*Diodia* p.p. *EP.*). Rubi. (II. 10). 1 Mex.

Hexatheca C. B. Clarke. Gesneriaceae (I). 1 Borneo.

Hexisea Lindl. Orchidaceae (II. 6). 5 Brazil to Mex. and W.I.

Heylandia DC. Leguminosae (III. 3). 1 S. India, Ceylon.

Heynea Roxb. (*Walsura* p.p. *EP.*). Meliaceae (III). 4 Indomal.

Heywoodia Sim. Euphorbiaceae (A. I. 1). 1 Cape Col. (Cape ebony).

Hians (Lat.), gaping.

Hibbertia Andr. (incl. *Candollea* Labill. 1806). Dilleniaceae. 100 Austr., New Caled. &c. Mostly ericoid or climbing shrubs. Some have phylloclades. Infl. dich., but often, by reduction, coming to look like a raceme. The sta. &c. vary much in number in different sp.

Hibernation, remaining quiescent during winter; *cf.* Bulbs, Corms, Rhizomes, Tubers, Water-plants, *Orchidaceae*, &c.

Hibiscadelphus Rock. Malvaceae (4). 3 Hawaiian Is.

Hibiscus L. (excl. *Abelmoschus* Medic.). Malvaceae (4). 160 trop. and subtrop. The 5 ante-sepalous sta. are repres. by teeth at the top of the stamen-tube. Several are cult., esp. *H. Rosa-sinensis* L. (shoe-flower, fls. showy), *H. Sabdariffa* L. (Rozelle, fr. for jelly, &c.), *H.* (*A.*) *esculentus* L. (Okra or Bandakai, mucilaginous young fr. in soups, &c.).

Hickory, *Carya*.

Hicksbeachia F. Muell. Proteaceae (II). 1 Austr.

Hicoria Rafin. = Carya Nutt. (Jugland.).

Hidalgoa La Llave. Compositae (5). 2 W.I., C. Am.

Hiemalis (Lat.), winter.

Hieracium (Tourn.) L. Compositae (13). 750 ✻, S. Afr., Andes; several in Brit. (hawk-weeds). Innumerable varieties have been raised by various botanists to specific rank (see *London Cat. of Brit. Plants*). Some are parthenogenetic.

Hiernia Sp. Moore. Scroph. (III. 2). Formerly Acanth. 1 Angola.
Hierobotana Briq. (*Verbena* p.p.). Verben. (1). 1 Colombia.
Hierochloë S. G. Gmel. Gramineae (7). 13 temp. and cold. 1 Brit.
Hieronima Allem. Euphorbiaceae (A. I. 1). 20 trop. Am., W.I.
Hieronymiella Pax. Amaryllidaceae (1). 1 Argentina.
Higginsia Pers. = Hoffmannia Sw. (Rubi.).
Higinbothamia Uline. Dioscoreaceae. 1 C. Am.
Hilairella Van Tiegh. Ochnaceae. 2 Brazil.
Hilaria H. B. et K. Gramineae (3). 5 C. Am. to S.W. U.S.
Hilbertia Thouin. Inc. sed. Nomen.
Hildebrandtia Vatke. Convolv. (1). 5 Afr. 2 seps. enlarged on fr.
Hillebrandia Oliv. Begon. 1 Hawaiian Is.
Hilleria Vell. (*Mohlana BH.*). Phytolacc. 4 trop. S. Am.
Hillia Jacq. Rubi. (I. 5). 5 Brazil to W.I. Epiph. shrubs. Fl. sol., term.
Hilum, the scar where stalk separates from the seed.
Himalayan spruce, *Picea Morinda* Link.
Himantandra F. von Muell., **Himantandraceae**, *cf.* Suppl.
Himantochilus T. Anders. Acanthaceae (IV. B). 6 Afr.
Himantoglossum Spreng. (*Orchis* p.p. *BH.*). Orchid. (II. 1). 2 Medit., mid-Eur.
Himantophyllum Spreng. = Clivia Lindl. p.p. (Amaryll.).
Himantostemma A. Gray. Asclepiadaceae (II. 4). 1 N. Am.
Himeranthus Endl. (*Jaborosa* p.p. *EP.*). Solanac. (2). 5 Argentina.
Hindsia Benth. Rubiaceae (I. 5). 7 trop. S. Am.
Hing (India), asafoetida, *Ferula*.
Hinterhubera Sch. Bip. 1855. Compositae (3). 3 Andes.
Hip, the fr. of *Rosa*.
Hippeastrum Herb. Amaryllidaceae (1). 75 trop. and subtrop. Am. Cult. orn. fl.
Hippeophyllum Schlechter (*Oberonia* p.p.). Orchid. (II. 4). 5 N.G., Celebes, Phil. Is.
Hippia L. Compositae (7). 4 S. Afr.
Hippia L. f. = Plagiocheilus Arn. (Comp.).
Hippia F. W. Schmidt = Gentiana Tourn. p.p. (Gent.).
Hippobromus Eckl. et Zeyh. Sapindaceae (II). 1 S. Afr.
Hippocastanaceae (*EP.*; *Sapindaceae* p.p. *BH.*). Dicots. (Archichl. Sapindales). Only genus Aesculus (*q.v.*).
Hippocastanum Tourn. ex Rupp. = Aesculus L. p.p. (Hippocast.).
Hippocratea L. Hippocrateaceae. 80 trop. Twining shrubs.
Hippocrateaceae (*EP.*; *Celastraceae* p.p. *BH.*). Dicots. (Archichl. Sapindales). 3 gen., 150 sp. trop. and subtrop. Shrubs, mostly lianes, with opp. or alt. simple l. Fls. in cymes, ☿, reg., with disc. K 5, C 5, A 3 (rarely 5, 4, 2), $\underline{G}$ (3), with 2—10 anatr. ov. in each loc. Berry or schizocarp. No endosp. *Genera:* Campylostemon, Hippocratea, Salacia.
Hippocrepis L. Leguminosae (III. 7). 12 Medit., Eur. *H. comosa* L. to Scotland. Fl. mechanism like Lotus. Useful fodders.
Hippodamia Decne. (*Solenophora BH.*). Gesner. (II). 3 Mex., Costa Rica.
Hippomane L. Euphorbiaceae (A. II. 7). 1 warm Am., W.I. (manchineel). Latex poisonous. A (2), G 6—9-loc. Drupe.
Hippomarathrum Hoffmg. et Link. Umbelliferae (III. 4). 12 Medit.

Hippophaë L. Elaeagnaceae. 2 N. temp. |*, *H. rhamnoides* L. (sea buckthorn) Brit. In the ♂ fl. the bracteoles form a hood over the sta. in wet weather; when the air is drier, they separate at the sides, and the pollen may be blown away.

Hipposelinum Britton et Rose (*Ligusticum* p.p.). Umb. (III. 5). 1 S. Eur.

Hippotis Ruiz et Pav. Rubiaceae (I. 7). 5 trop. S. Am.

Hippoxylon Rafin. = Oroxylum Vent. (Bignon.).

Hippuridaceae (*EP.*; *Haloragidaceae* p.p. *BH.*). Dicots. (Archichl. Myrtiflorae). Only genus Hippuris, *q.v.*

Hippuris L. Hippuridaceae. 1, *H. vulgaris* L. (mare's-tail) almost cosmop. A water plant, with creeping rhiz. and erect shoots, whose upper parts usu. project above the water. L. linear, in whorls, the submerged ones longer and more flaccid than the aerial. Fl. sessile in axil of l., ☿ (or sometimes ♀ on some stocks; *cf.* Labiatae), consisting of 1 epig. sta. and 1 cpl., with 1 pend. ov. and no integuments, and a slight seam representing the K; wind fertilised.

Hiptage Gaertn. Malpighiaceae (I). 10 Mauritius to China.

Hiraea Jacq. (*Mascagnia* Bert.). Malpighiaceae (I). 30 trop. Am.

Hircinus (Lat.), with goaty smell.

Hirpicium Cass. Compositae (10). 2 S. Afr.

Hirschia Baker. Compositae (4). 1 S. Arabia.

Hirsute, with long distinct hairs.

Hirtella L. Rosaceae (VI). 40 S. and Cent. Am., 1 Madag. Fl. ·|·, axis deeply hollowed on one side. The sta. and cpl. are not in the hollow, but on the other side of the surface of the axis.

Hirtus (Lat.), hirsute.

Hisingera Hellm. = Xylosma Forst. (Flac.).

Hispid, with rough bristly hairs.

Hispidella Barnad. ex Lam. Compositae (13). 1 Iberian Penins.

Histiopteris (Agardh) J. Sm. Polypodiaceae. 2 warm, and $\overline{*}$.

Hitchenia Wall. Zingiberaceae (I). 4 India.

Hitoa Nadeaud. Rubiaceae (II. 4). 1 Society Is.

Hladnikia Koch (*Pleurospermum* p.p. *BH.*). Umbell. (III. 4). 1 Adriatic.

Hoarea Sweet = Pelargonium L'Hérit. p.p. (Geran.).

Hoary, grey with fine pubescence.

Hobble-bush (Am.), *Viburnum*.

Hochstetteria DC. (*Dicoma* p.p. *EP.*). Compositae (12). 1 trop. Afr., Arabia.

Hockinia Gardn. Gentianaceae (I). 1 Rio de Janeiro.

Hodgkinsonia F. Muell. Rubiaceae (II. 3). 1 S.E. Austr.

Hodgsonia Hook. f. et Thoms. Cucurbitaceae (3). 2 Indomal.

Hodgsoniola F. Muell. Liliaceae (III). 1 S.W. Austr.

Hoeckia Engl. et Graebn. Valerianaceae. 1 China.

Hoehnelia Schweinf. Compositae (I). 1 E. Afr.

Hoelzelia Neck. = Swartzia Schreb. (Legum.).

Hoepfneria Vatke (*Abrus* p.p. *EP.*). Leguminosae (III. 9). 1 trop. Afr.

Hoffmannia Sw. Rubiaceae (I. 8). 24 trop. Am.

Hoffmanniella Schlechter. Compositae. Nomen. 1 trop. Afr.

Hoffmannseggia Cav. Leguminosae (II. 7). 20 S. Afr., S. Am.

Hofmeisterella Reichb. f. in Walp. Orchid. (II. 19). 1 Ecuador.
Hofmeisteria Walp. Compositae (2). 5 Calif. to Mexico.
Hog gum (W.I.), *Moronobea*; **false-** (W.I.), *Rhus Metopium* **L.**; **-plum,** *Spondias*; **-weed,** (W.I.), *Boerhaavia*; **poisoned -meat** or **weed** (W.I.), *Aristolochia grandiflora* Sw., (Am.) *Ambrosia artemisiaefolia* L.
Hohenackeria Fisch. et Mey. Umbelliferae (III. 5). 2 Medit., W. As.
Hohenbergia Schult. f. p.p. (*Aechmea* p.p. *BH.*). Bromeliaceae (4). 18 trop. Am., W.I.
Hoheria A. Cunn. Malvaceae (2). 3 New Zealand.
Hoitzia Juss. = Loeselia L. (Polemon.). 12 Am.
Holacantha A. Gray. Simarubaceae. 1 New Mexico.
Holalafia Stapf. Apocynaceae (II. 1). 1 Guinea.
Holarrhena R. Br. Apocynaceae (I. 3). 10 palaeotrop.
Holboellia Wall. Lardizabalaceae. 5 Himal., China.
Holcophacos Rydberg (*Astragalus* p.p.). Leguminosae (III. 6). 2 N. Am.
Holcus L. Gramineae (9). 8 Eur., N. and S. Afr. 2 in Brit., *H. mollis* L., and *H. lanatus* L., Yorkshire fog or soft-grass.
Holigarna Buch.-Ham. ex Roxb. Anacardiaceae (4). 5 Indomal.
Hollandaea F. Muell. Proteaceae (II). 2 E. Austr.
Hollisteria S. Wats. Polygonaceae (I. 1). 1 Calif.
Hollrungia K. Schum. Passifloraceae. 1 New Guinea.
Holly, *Ilex*; **-fern,** *Aspidium Lonchitis* Sw.; **-hock,** *Althaea*; **-oak** *Quercus Ilex* L.; **-rose** (W.I.), *Turnera*; **sea-,** *Eryngium*.
Holmbergia Hicken (*Chenopodium* p.p.). Chenopodiaceae (A). 1 Argent.
Holmia Börner = Cobresia Pers. p.p. (Cyper.).
Holmskioldia Retz. Verbenaceae (4). 4 Madag., trop. Afr., Himal.
Holo- (Gr. pref.), complete.
Holocalyx M. Micheli. Leguminosae (II. 9). 2 Brazil, Paraguay.
Holocarpa Baker (*Pentanisia EP.*). Rubiaceae (II. 1). 1 Madag.
Holocarpha Greene (*Hemizonia* p.p.). Compositae (5). 1 Calif.
Holochlamys Engl. Araceae (II). 3 New Guinea.
Holochloa Nutt. = Heuchera L. p.p. (Saxifrag.).
Holodictyum Maxon (*Asplenium* p.p.). Polypodiaceae. 2 Mexico.
Holodiscus Maxim (*Spiraea* p.p. *BH.*). Rosaceae (I. 3). 5 W. N.Am. Orn.
Holographis Nees. Acanthaceae (IV. B). 1 Mexico.
Hologyne Pfitzer (*Coelogyne* p.p.). Orchid. (II. 3). 2 Malay Archip.
Hololachna Ehrenb. Tamaricaceae. 2 C. As.
Holophyllum Less. = Athanasia L. p.p. (Comp.).
Holopleura Regel et Schmalh. Umbelliferae (inc. sed.). 1 Turkestan.
Holoptelea Planch. Ulmaceae. 1 Indomal.
Holoschoenus Link. = Scirpus L. p.p. (Cyper.).
Holostemma R. Br. Asclepiadaceae (II. 1). 3 Indomal., China.
Holosteum Dill. ex L. Caryophyllaceae (I. 1). 6 N. temp. |* (1 Brit.).
Holostigma Spach = Oenothera L. p.p. (*BH.*). = Chamissoa Link.
Holostylis Duch. Aristolochiaceae. 1 S. Centr. Brazil.
Holothrix L. C. Rich. Orchidaceae (II. 1). 25 Afr., trop. and S.

Holozonia Greene (*Lagophylla* p.p. *EP.*). Compositae (5). 1 N. Am.
Holstia Pax. Euphorbiaceae (A. II. 2). 2 trop. Afr.
Holubia Oliv. Pedaliaceae. 1 S. Afr.
Holy grass (Am.), *Hierochloe.*
Homalanthus A. Juss. Euphorbiaceae (A. II. 7). 20 Indomal., Polynes.
Homalium Jacq. Flacourtiaceae (9). 150 warm. After fert. the sepals or petals, or both, grow large and form wings (often hairy) to the fr.
Homalobus Nutt. ex Torr. et Gray (*Astragalus* p.p.). Leguminosae (III. 6). 10 N. Am.
Homalocalyx F. Muell. Myrtaceae (II. 2). 2 N.E. Austr.
Homalomena Schott. Araceae (V). 80 trop. As. and S. Am.
Homalopetalum Rolfe. Orchidaceae (II. 6). 1 Jamaica.
Homalosciadium Domin (*Hydrocotyle* p.p.). Umbellif. (I. 1). 1 Austr.
Homalostachys Boeck. (*Scleria* p.p. *EP.*). Cyperaceae (II). 1 China.
Homeria Vent. Iridaceae (II). 8 S. Afr. Bulbils in axils of lower l. Cult. orn. fl.
Homilacanthus Sp. Moore. Acanthaceae (IV. B). 1 E. trop. Afr.
Hominy, the meal of maize, *Zea Mays* L.
Homochaete Benth. Compositae (4). 1 S. Afr.
Homochroma DC. Compositae (3). 1 S. Afr.
Homogyne Cass. Compositae (8). 3 Mts. of Eur.
Homoianthus Bonpl. ex DC. = Perezia Lag. p.p. (Comp.).
Homoio-, **Homo-** (Gr. pref.), alike, similar; **-chlamydeous** (P), with l. of one kind only; **-dromous** (aestivation), all l. turned the same way, not to r. in one, to l. in another, fl.; **-gamous** (fl.) one in which sta. and stigma ripen together, and *cf. Compositae*; **-geneous**, uniform; **-logous**, equivalent by descent; **-morphous**, uniform in shape; **-nym**, the same specific name of the same pl., in another genus; **-plastic**, equivalent in structure and mode of origin, but of parallel, not common, descent; **-sporous**, with spores of one kind only, *Pteridophyta.*
Homolepis Chase (*Panicum* p.p.). Gramineae (5). 3 trop. S. Am.
Homonoia Lour. Euphorbiaceae (A. II. 2). 4 Indomal.
Homonoma Bello (*Nepsera EP.*). Melastomaceae (I). 1 Porto Rico.
Homopogon Stapf. Gramineae (2). 1 French Soudan.
Homoranthus A. Cunn. ex Schau. Myrtaceae (II. 2). 1 E. Austr.
Homozeugos Stapf. Gramineae (2). 2 W. Afr.
Honckenya Bartl. = Arenaria Rupp. (*BH.*) = Alsine Scop. p.p.
Honckenya Willd. Tiliaceae. 3 trop. W. Afr.
Honesty, *Lunaria biennis* Moench.
Honey, a sweet secretion formed (usu. in fl.) by nectaries; *cf.* especially Bee-flowers; **-dew**, *Acer*, *Tilia*; **-guides**, marks, &c. to show the way to the honey, *Myosotis*; **-leaves**, *Berberidaceae*, *Lardizabalaceae*, *Ranunculaceae*; **-locust**, *Gleditschia*; **-palm**, *Jubaea*; **sham-**, *Lopezia*, *Parnassia*; **-suckle**, *Lonicera*, (W.I.) *Desmodium*, *Tecoma*, (Austr.) *Banksia*; **- - French**, *Hedysarum.*
Hoodia Sweet. Asclepiadaceae (II. 3). 5 trop. and S. Afr. Cactus-like.
Hook-climbers, *cf.* Climbing Plants; **-s on fruit**, &c., aiding animal-dispersal, *cf. Agrimonia* (on receptacle), *Bidens* (pappus), *Cenchrus* (sterile spikelets), *Emex* (P), *Geum* (style), *Tragoceros* (C), *Triglochin* (cpl.), *Uncinia* (axis of origin), *Xanthium* (invol.).

Hookera Salisb. = Brodiaea Sm. (Lili.).
Hoop pine, *Araucaria*; **-tree** (W.I.), *Melia*; **-withe** (W.I.), *Colubrina*, *Rivina*.
Hoorebekia Cornelissen (*Aplopappus* p.p.). Compos. (3). 7 W. Am.
Hop, *Humulus Lupulus* L.
Hopea L. = Symplocos L. (Symploc.).
Hopea Roxb. Dipterocarpaceae. 50 Indomal.
Hopkinsia Fitzgerald. Restiaceae. 1 Austr.
Hoplestigma Pierre. Flacourtiaceae (2). 2 trop. Afr.
Hoplestigmataceae, a fam. sometimes made to contain the last.
Hoplophyllum DC. Compositae (1). 2 S. Afr.
Hoplophytum Beer (*Aechmea* p.p. *BH.*). Bromeliaceae (4). 8 Brazil.
Hoppea Willd. Gentianaceae (1). 2 India.
Hoppia Nees (*Bisboeckelera* O. Ktze.). Cyperaceae (11). 5 Brazil, Guiana.
Horaninovia Fisch. et Mey. Chenopodiaceae (B). 3 W. As.
Hordeum (Tourn.) L. Gramineae (12). 20 temp. 4 in Brit. (barley-grass). Spikelets in groups of 3 on the main axis, forming a dense spike. Each is 1-flowered when perfect, but commonly either the central or the two lat. fls. are aborted. The cult. barley is *H. vulgare* L. (*H. sativum* Pers.). The most common form is the var. *distichum* or 2-rowed barley, where the central fl. of each group is fertile, but 6-rowed barley (var. *hexastichum*), and 4-rowed barley or bere, are also grown. The last is the most hardy and is cult. as far as 70° N. (in Norway). *Cf.* Bews, *Grasses of the World.*
Horehound, *Marrubium vulgare* L.; **foetid -,** *Ballota nigra* L.; **white -,** *Marrubium vulgare* L.
Horkelia Cham. et Schlecht. (*Potentilla* p.p. *BH.*). Rosaceae (III. 2). 35 W. U.S.
Horkeliella Rydberg (*Horkelia* p.p.). Rosaceae (III. 2). 3 N. Am.
Hormidium Lindl. ex Heynh. (*Epidendrum* p.p. *EP.*). Orchidaceae (II. 6). 6 C. Am., Cuba.
Horminum Mill. = Salvia Tourn. p.p. (Labiat.).
Horminum (Tourn.) L. Labiatae (VI). 1 Mts. of S. Eur.
Hormogyne A. DC. (*Sideroxylon* p.p. *EP.*). Sapotaceae (1). 1 Austr.
Hornea Baker. Sapindaceae (1). 1 Mauritius.
Hornemannia Vahl. Ericaceae (III. 2). 2 Guiana, W.I.
Hornera Jungh. Inc. sed. 2 Japan.
Horn-beam, *Carpinus*; **-nut,** *Trapa*; **- of plenty,** *Fedia*; **-wort,** *Ceratophyllum*.
Hornschuchia Nees. Anonaceae (1). 2 Brazil.
Hornschuchia Spreng. Inc. sed. 1 Brazil.
Hornstedtia Retz (*Amomum* p.p. *BH.*). Zingiberaceae (1). 40 Indomal.
Hornungia Bernh. (*Gagea* p.p.). Liliaceae (IV). 20 Eur.
Horse Cassia (W.I.), *Cassia polyphylla* Jacq.; **-chestnut,** *Aesculus Hippocastanum* L.; **-gram,** *Dolichos biflorus* L.; **-hair, vegetable,** *Tillandsia*; **-mint** (Am.), *Monarda*; **-purslane** (W.I.), *Trianthema*; **-radish,** *Cochlearia Armoracia* L.; **-radish tree,** *Moringa pterygosperma* Gaertn.; **-tail,** *Equisetum*; **-wood** (W.I.), *Calliandra*.
Horsfieldia Bl. ex DC. (*Harmsiopanax EP.*). Araliaceae (2). 1 Java.
Horsfieldia Chifflot (*Monophyllaea* Reichb.). Gesner. (1). 1 Java.

Horsfieldia Willd. (*Myristica* p.p. *BH.*). Myristicaceae. 50 palaeotrop.
Horsfordia A. Gray (*Sida* p.p.). Malvaceae (2). 4 Mexico, Calif.
Hortensis (Lat.), of gardens.
Hortia Vand. Rutaceae (IV). 4 Brazil.
Horticulture, *cf.* Ornamental Plants.
Hortonia Wight. Monimiaceae. 3 Ceylon.
Hortus siccus, a herbarium, or collection of dried pl.
Hosackia Dougl. Leguminosae (III. 5). 30 W. N.Am.
Hosea Dennst. Inc. sed. 1 Indomal.
Hosea Ridley. Verbenaceae (4). 1 Penang.
Hosiea Hemsl. et E. H. Wilson (*Natsiatum* p.p.). Icacinaceae. 1 China.
Hoslundia Vahl. Labiatae (VII). 3 warm Afr.
Host (of parasite), the pl. on which it feeds.
Hosta Jacq. = Cornutia L. (Verben.).
Hosta Tratt. (*Funkia BH.*). Liliaceae (III). 5 Japan, China. *Cf.* Funkia.
Hoteia C. Morr. et Dcne. = Astilbe Buch.-Ham. (Saxifr.).
Hotnima A. Chevalier. Euphorbiaceae (A. II. 4). 1 trop. Afr.
Hottentot bread, *Testudinaria*; **-fig**, *Mesembryanthemum*.
Hottonia Boerh. ex L. Primulaceae. 2, one N. Am., the other, *H. palustris* L. (water-violet), W. As. and Eur. (incl. Brit.). Floating water pl. with finely-divided submerged l. The fls. project above the water; they are dimorphic like Primula.
Houlletia Brongn. Orchidaceae (II. 13). 5 trop. S. Am. Cult.
Hound's tongue, *Cynoglossum officinale* L.
Hounea Baill. Flacourtiaceae (6) (Passifl. *BH.*). 2 trop. Afr., Madag.
Houseleek, *Sempervivum*.
Houstonia Gronov. ex L. Rubiaceae (I. 2). 20 west N. Am. Fls. heterostyled as in Primula; similar differences in stigma and pollen.
Houttea Decne. (*Vanhouttea* p.p. *EP.*). Gesneriaceae (II). 3 Brazil.
Houttuynia Thunb. Saururaceae. 1 Himalaya to Japan. Parthenogenetic.
Hovea R. Br. Leguminosae (III. 3). 12 Austr.
Hovenia Thunb. Rhamnaceae. 1 Japan to Himal. Fr. axis ed.
Hoverdenia Nees in DC. Acanthaceae (IV. B). 1 Mexico.
Howardia Klotzsch = Aristolochia L. p.p. (Arist.).
Howea Becc. Palmae (IV). 2 Lord Howe's Island. Cult. orn.
Howellia A. Gray. Campanulaceae (III). 2 N. Am.
Howittia F. Muell. Malvaceae (2). 1 Austr.
Hoya R. Br. Asclepiadaceae (II. 3). 100 Indomal., Austr. Twiners and root-climbers with fleshy l. Cult. orn. fl. (wax-flower).
Hoyopsis Léveillé. Celastraceae. 1 China.
Hua Pierre et de Wild. Sterculiaceae. 2 trop. Afr.
Huanaca Cav. (*Azorella* p.p. *EP.*). Umbelliferae (I. 2). 6 S. Am., Austr., Tasm.
Huberia DC. Melastomaceae (I). 10 Brazil, Peru.
Huckleberry, *Gaylussacia*; **blue-**, *Vaccinium pennsylvanicum* Lam.
Hudsonia L. Cistaceae. 3 N. Am.
Huegelia Benth. = Gilia Ruiz et Pav. (Polemon.).

Huegelia R. Br. Inc. sed. Nomen.
Huernia (*Heurnia*) R. Br. Asclepiadaceae (II. 3). 20 S. and trop. Afr.
Huerniopsis N.E. Br. Asclepiadaceae (II. 3). 1 Cape Colony.
Huertea Ruiz et Pav. Staphyleaceae. 2 Peru, Cuba.
Hufelandia Nees (*Beilschmiedia* p.p. *BH.*). Lauraceae (II). 1 C. Am.
Hugeria Small (*Vaccinium* p.p.). Ericaceae (III. 1). 1 N. Am.
Hugonia L. Linaceae. 11 trop. |✱. The lower twigs of the infl. are modified into hooks for climbing.
Hulletia King. Moraceae (III). 2 Malay Peninsula.
Hulsea Torr. et A. Gray. Compositae (6). 6 W. U.S.
Humata Cav. Polypodiaceae. 20 palaeotrop.
Humbertia Lam. Convolvulaceae (I). 1 Madag.
Humble-bees, *cf.* Bee-flowers; **robbery by -,** *Aconitum*, *Delphinium*.
Humblotia Baill. Euphorbiaceae (A. I. 1). 1 Comoro Is.
Humboldtia Vahl (*Batschia* Vahl). Leguminosae (II. 3). 4 Ceylon and S. India. *H. laurifolia* Vahl is myrmecophilous. The non-flowering twigs are normal, but those that bear fls. have hollow obconical internodes. In each of these, at the top, opposite the l., is a slit leading to the cavity which is inhabited by ants.
Humea Sm. Compositae (4). 4 S. Austr.
Humifusus (Lat.), spreading on surface.
Humilis (Lat.), dwarf.
Humiria Jaume St. Hil. Humiriaceae. 3 trop. Am.
Humiriaceae (*EP.*, *BH.*). Dicots. (Archichl. Geraniales). 3 gen., 20 sp., trop. Am., Afr. Shrubs with alt. l. and ☿, reg. fls., 5-merous with 10—∞ sta. and cup-like disc. Ovules 1—2 per cpl. Drupe. *Chief genera:* Humiria, Saccoglottis.
Humming-bird flowers, *Abutilon*, *Erythrina*, *Marcgravia*.
Humulus L. Moraceae (IV). 2 N. temp. Perennial climbing herbs. Infl. cymose, dioec., the ♂ a much-branched pseudo-panicle, the ♀ a few-flowered pseudo-catkin with 2 fls. in the axil of each scale. Fl. protog., wind fert. Achene. *H. Lupulus* L. is the hop, largely cult.; the fr. catkin is used in brewing, &c.
Humus, decaying organic matter in the soil; *cf.* Saprophytes.
Hunga Panch. ex Guillaumin. Elaeocarpaceae. 1 New Caledonia.
Hunnemannia Sweet. Papaveraceae (II). 1 Mexico.
Hunteria Roxb. Apocynaceae (I. 3). 5 palaeotrop.
Huntleya Bateman (*Zygopetalum* p.p. *BH.*). Orchid. (II. 14). 2 trop. Am.
Huon pine, *Dacrydium Franklinii* Hook. f.
Hura L. Euphorbiaceae (A. II. 7). 2 trop. Am., W.I., incl. *H. crepitans* L., the sand box tree. Fr. with numerous hard woody cpls. Each, as the ripe fr. dries, tries to expand from the Δ shape to a U shape. Presently an explosion occurs and the seeds are shot out. The fr. used to be wired together and used as sand boxes before the era of blotting.paper.
Husemannia F. Muell. Menispermaceae. 1 N.E. Austr.
Husnotia Fourn. (*Ditassa* p.p. *EP.*). Asclepiadaceae (II. 1). 1 Brazil.
Hutchinsia R. Br. Cruciferae (4). 8 N. temp. (1 in Brit.).
Hutera Porta (*Coincya* p.p.). Cruciferae (3). 1 Spain.

Huthia Brand. Polemoniaceae. 2 Peru.
Huttonaea Harv. Orchidaceae (II. I). 3 S. Afr.
Huttonella T. Kirk (*Carmichaelia* p.p.). Legumin. (III. 6). 4 N.Z.
Huxleya Ewart. Verbenaceae (4). 1 N. Austr.
Hyacinth, *Hyacinthus*; **grape-,** *Muscari*; **wild-,** *Scilla nutans* Sm.
Hyacinthus (Tourn.) L. Liliaceae (V). 30 Medit., Afr. Many forms of hyacinth (derived from *H. orientalis* L.) are cult. orn. fl.
Hyalea Jaub. et Spach = Centaurea L. p.p. (Comp.).
Hyaline, transparent.
Hyalis D. Don ex Hook. et Arn. (*Plazia* p.p. *EP.*). Comp. (12). 4 S. Am.
Hyalocalyx Rolfe. Turneraceae. 2 Madag.
Hyalocystis Hallier f. Convolvulaceae (I). 1 trop. Afr.
Hyaloseris Griseb. Compositae (12). 2 Mts. of Argentina.
Hybanthus Jacq. (*Ionidium BH.*). Violaceae. 75 trop. and subtrop.
Hybophrynium K. Schum. Marantaceae. 1 Cameroons.
Hybosperma Urb. Rhamnaceae. 1 W.I.
Hybrid, a cross between two species; **graft-,** *Cytisus*.
Hydatella Diels. Centrolepidaceae. 2 W. Austr.
Hydathodes, pores through which the pl. excretes water.
Hydnocarpus Gaertn. Flacourtiaceae (3). 25 Indomal.
Hydnophytum Jack. Rubiaceae (II. 5). 40 E. As., New Guinea, Fiji, &c. Epiphytes with ant-inhabited tubers, like Myrmecodia (*q.v.*).
Hydnora Thunb. Hydnoraceae. 7 Afr.
Hydnoraceae (*EP.*; *Cytinaceae* p.p. *BH.*). Dicots. (Archichl. Aristolochiales). 2 gen. with 7 sp., Afr., S. Am. Parasites like Rafflesiaceae. Fls. ☿, reg. P (3—4) fleshy, A 3—4 epiphyllous, $\overline{G}$ (3) with parietal plac. and ∞ ov. Berry. Endosp. and perisperm. *Chief genus:* Hydnora.
Hydrangea Gronov. ex L. Saxifragaceae (III). 80 $\underline{*}$. Shrubs with opp. l., some climbing. Fls. in cymose corymbs, the outer (or in cult. forms all) neuter with petaloid calyx, giving conspicuousness to the infl. (*cf.* Compositae, Umbelliferae).
Hydrangeaceae (Warming) = Saxifragaceae (§ III).
Hydranthelium H. B. et K. Scrophulariaceae (II. 6). 2 trop. S. Am.
Hydrastis Ellis. Berberidaceae, sometimes in Ranunculaceae (I). 2, 1 in Japan, 1 in N. Am. (*H. canadensis* L., golden-seal, a tonic).
Hydrastylis Steud. = Sisyrinchium L. p.p. (Irid.).
Hydriastele H. Wendl. et Drude. Palmaceae (IV. 1). 2 Austr.
Hydrilla L. C. Rich. Hydrocharidaceae. 1 |*.
Hydro- (Gr. pref.), water-; **-chore,** pl. distributed by water; **-philous,** water pollinated, *Zostera*; **-phytes,** *cf.* Water-plants; **-phytium** (Cl.), a water-pl. formation; **-tropism,** irritability to presence of water.
Hydrobryum Endl. Podostemaceae. 5 India, Ceylon.
Hydrocaryaceae. A family sometimes made to include Trapa, usu. placed in Onagraceae.
Hydrocera Blume. Balsaminaceae. 1 Indomal.
Hydrocharideae (*BH.*) = Hydrocharitaceae.
Hydrocharis L. Hydrocharitaceae. 1 Eur. (incl. Brit.), As., *H. Morsus-ranae* L., the frog-bit, a rootless water-pl. with orbicular floating l. Fls. dioec., produced upon the surface. During summer the pl. multiplies by horizontal stolons, which form new pls. at the ends.

Large buds on stolons in autumn drop off, winter, sprout next year.

Hydrocharitaceae (*EP.*, *BH.*). Monocots. (Helobieae; Microspermae *BH.*; pp. iii, liv). 13/80 trop. and temp. water pl., §§ II and IV marine, usu. with ribbon-like submerged l., Hydrocharis, &c. with floating or subaerial l.; squamulae in axils, frequently serial buds. Infl. axillary, mon- or di-oec., ♀ usu. 1-fld., ♂ often > 1, enclosed at first in spathe of usu. 2 or more fused l. Fl. usu. reg., rarely ☿, 3-merous. P usu. in two heterochlam. whorls, A 1—5, innermost often stds.; $\overline{G}$ (2—15), 1-loc. with parietal plac. and ∞ ortho- to ana-tr. erect to pend. ov.; stigmas = cpls. Fr. irreg. dehisc. seeds ∞ exalb. *Classification and genera:*

Cpls. 6—15; plac. projecting far into loc.

I. *STRATIOTOIDEAE* (l. alt.): Boottia, Ottelia, Stratiotes, Hydromystria, Hydrocharis.

II. *THALASSIOIDEAE* (l. 2-ranked; marine): Enalus, Thalassia.

Cpls. 3, rarely 2, 4, 5; plac. slightly projecting.

III. *VALLISNERIOIDEAE* (heterochlam.): Blyxa, Vallisneria, Lagarosiphon, Hydrilla, Elodea.

IV. *HALOPHILOIDEAE* (homochlam.; marine): Halophila.

Hydrochloa Beauv. Gramin. (6). 1 S.E. U.S. Floating grass.

Hydrocleis Rich. Butom. 4 trop. S. Am., strikingly resembling Nymphaea or Limnanthemum. Cult. orn. fl.

Hydrocotyle (Tourn.) L. Umbell. (II. 1). 75 trop. and temp.; 1 Brit. *H. vulgaris* L. (white rot, pennywort), easily recognised among native U. by peltate l. L. stip. Mericarp 5-ribbed.

Hydrolea L. Hydrophyll. 20 warm. Some have axillary thorns (branches). L. alt. Styles 2; plac. large, spongy. Fl. self-fert.

Hydrolirion Léveillé. Hydrocharit. 1 Corea.

Hydrolythrum Hook. f. (*Rotala* p.p. *EP.*). Lythr. 1 Indomal.

Hydromystria G. F. W. Mey. (*Limnobium* p.p. *BH.*). Hydrocharit. (1). 3 trop. Am. L. floating. ♀ C 0. Plac. not projecting.

Hydropectis Rydberg (*Pectis* p.p.). Comp. (6). 1 Mex.

Hydrophylax L. f. Rubi. (II. 10). 3 coast of Ind. Oc. Fr. corky, indeh.

Hydrophyllaceae (*EP.*, *BH.*) Dicots. (Sympet. Tubiflorae; Polemoniales *BH.*; pp. xlv, liii). 18/250, cosmop. exc. Austr. Herbs or undershrubs with simple or cpd. radical, alt. or opp. exstip. l.; usu. hairy, sometimes glandular. Fls. scattered or in "boragoid" cincinni usu. with no bracteoles, ☿, reg., often blue, usu. 5-merous. K usu. (5), imbr., odd sep. post.; C (5), rotate, bell- or funnel-shaped, usu. imbr.; A usu. 5, epipet., alt. with pets., often with scale-like appendages at base; $\underline{G}$ (2), on disc or not, 1—2-loc. with 1—2 styles; ovules on each cpl. ∞—2, sessile or pend., anatr., often parietal. Fr. usu. a loculic. caps.; embryo small, in rich endosp. Fls. chiefly visited by bees; honey secreted below ovary, and protected by sta. appendages, which are frequently united to C, and in Hydrophyllum form tubes leading to honey. Fl. usu. protandrous. Many cult. orn. fl. *Chief genera:* Hydrophyllum, Nemophila, Phacelia, Nama, Hydrolea.

Hydrophyllum L. Hydrophyll. 7 N. Am. Fl. protandrous, with sta. appendages united to C, forming tubes to honey.

Hydropteridineae, see Filicineae Leptosp.

Hydropyrum Link = Zizania Gronov. (Gramin.).

Hydropyxis Rafin. Inc. sed. Nomen.
Hydrosme Schott (*Amorphophallus* p.p. *EP.*). Araceae (IV). 35 palaeotrop.
Hydrostachydaceae (*EP.*; *Podostemaceae* p.p. *BH.*). Dicots. Archichl. Rosales). Only genus Hydrostachys, *q.v.*
Hydrostachys Thou. Hydrostachydaceae. 10 Madag., Afr. Water pl. of the type of Podostemaceae, with spikes of dioecious naked fl., ♂ of 1 sta., ♀ of (2) cpls. and ∞ ovules. Capsule.
Hydrotaenia Lindl. (*Tigridia EP.*). Iridaceae (II). 3 Mex., Peru.
Hydrothrix Hook. f. Pontederiaceae. 1 Ceara.
Hydrotriche Zucc. Scrophulariaceae (II. 6). 1 Madag. Water pl. with dimorphic l.
Hyeronima Allem. Euphorbiaceae (A. I. 1). 12 trop. Am.
Hygea Hanst. Gesneriaceae (inc. sed.). 1 Chili.
Hygea Klotzsch. Asclepiadaceae (inc. sed.). 1 Guiana.
Hygrocharis Hochst. (*Nephrophyllum BH.*). Convolvul. (I). 1 Abyss.
Hygrochastic (fr.), one opening by water-absorption.
Hygrochilus Pfitz. (*Vanda* p.p.). Orchidaceae (II. 20). 1 Burma.
Hygrophila R. Br. Acanthaceae (IV. A). 40 trop., in marshes.
Hygrophytic, living with plentiful water supply.
Hygroryza Nees. Gramineae (6). 1 Indomal.
Hylaea, the upper regions of the Amazon valley.
Hyline Herb. Amaryllidaceae (I). 1 Brazil.
Hylium (Cl.), a forest formation.
Hylocereus Britton et Rose (*Cereus* p.p.). Cact. (III. 1). 20 C. Am., W.I., Fla.
Hylodendron Taub. Leguminosae (II. 3). 1 Gaboon.
Hylodium (Cl.), a dry open woodland.
Hylomecon Maxim. (*Stylophorum BH.*). Papaveraceae (II). 1 Japan.
Hylophila Lindl. Orchidaceae (II. 2). 3 Malaya, Phil. Is.
Hymenachne Beauv. = Panicum L. p.p. (Gram.).
Hymenaea L. Leguminosae (II. 3). 10 trop. Am. *H. Courbaril* L. (West Indian Locust) has buttress roots. The wood is valuable. From the stem exudes a resin (copal or anime) which is often found in lumps underground near the trees (*cf.* Agathis, Trachylobium); it is used in varnish, &c.
Hymenandra A. DC. ex Spach. Myrsinaceae (II). 1 Bengal, Assam.
Hymenanthera R. Br. in Tuckey. Violaceae. 4 E. Austr., N.Z., Norfolk I.
Hymenatherum Cass. (*Dysodia* p.p. *EP.*). Compositae (6). 15 warm Am.
Hymenella (Moç. et Sesse ex) DC. (*Alsine* p.p. *EP.*). Caryo. (I. 1). 1 Mexico.
Hymenocallis Salisb. Amaryllidaceae (I). 30 warm Am. The stipular appendages of the sta. are united into a tube, on the summit of which the filaments stand, and which surpasses the perianth in conspicuousness (*cf.* Eucharis). Cult. orn. fl.
Hymenocardia Wall. Euphorbiaceae (A. I. 1). 6 trop. Afr. and As.
Hymenocarpos Savi (*Circinus* Med.). Legumin. (III. 5). 1 Medit.
Hymenocharis Salisb. (*Ischnosiphon* p.p.). Marantaceae (II). 20 trop.
Hymenoclea Torr. et A. Gray. Compositae (5). 2 Texas to Calif.

Hymenocnemis Hook. f. Rubiaceae (II. 5). 1 Madag.

Hymenocrater Fisch. et Mey. Labiatae (VI). 9 W. As.

Hymenodictyon Wall. Rubiaceae (I. 5). 8 trop. Afr. and As.

Hymenolaena DC. = Pleurospermum Hoffm. p.p. (Umbell.).

Hymenolepis Cass. = Athanasia L. p.p. (Comp.).

Hymenolepis Kaulf. Polypodiaceae. 4 Indomal., Madag.

Hymenolobium Benth. Leguminosae (III. 8). 6 N. Brazil, Venezuela.

Hymenolophus Boerl. Apocynaceae (I. 3). 1 Sumatra.

Hymenonema Cass. Compositae (13). 2 Greece.

Hymenopappus L'Hérit. Compositae (6). 11 N. Am.

Hymenophyllaceae. Filicales Leptosporangiatae. 2 gen., 400 sp. trop. and temp. (filmy ferns), chiefly in damp woods. Stem very slender, often creeping; sometimes it bears roots, in other cases only root hairs. It grows more rapidly than the l., so that its leafless tip appears naked like a root. L. pinnate, filmy in texture (only one cell thick, except at the veins), with no stomata. The placenta is at the leaf-edge, a continuation of the vein; it bears sporangia and is surrounded by a cup-shaped indusium. Sporangia sessile, with oblique or transv. complete annulus, opening by a longitudinal fissure. The prothalli are capable of long life; in some they produce *gemmae* or buds on the margin, and may thus multiply veg. to a considerable extent. *Chief genera:* Hymenophyllum (indusium 2-valved), Trichomanes (indusium tubular or cup-like).

Hymenophyllum L. Hymenophyllaceae. 250 cosmop. 2 in Brit. (filmy ferns), *H. tunbridgense* Sm. and *H. peltatum* Desv.

Hymenophysa C. A. Mey. Cruciferae (inc. sed.). 2 Cent. As.

Hymenopogon Wall. Rubiaceae (I. 5). 2 Himal., Assam.

Hymenoptera, the bees, wasps, &c.; *cf.* Bee-flowers.

Hymenopyramis Wall. Verbenaceae (5). 1 India, Burma.

Hymenorchis Schlechter. Orchidaceae (II. 20). 7 N. Guinea, Java.

Hymenosicyos Chiov. Cucurbitaceae (2). 1 E. Afr.

Hymenosporum R. Br. ex F. Muell. Pittosporaceae. 1 E. Austr.

Hymenostegia Harms. (*Cynometra* p.p.). Leguminosae (II. 2). 3 trop. Afr.

Hymenostephium Benth. Compositae (5). 2 Mexico, Colombia.

Hymenothrix A. Gray (*Hymenopappus* p.p. *EP.*). Compos. (6). 2 Mex., Texas.

Hymenoxys Cass. (*Actinella* Nutt. p.p. *EP.*). Compositae (6). 17 Am.

Hyobanche L. Scrophulariaceae (III. 2). 2 S. Afr.

Hyophorbe Gaertn. Palmae (IV. 1). 3 Mascarenes.

Hyoscyamus (Tourn.) L. Solanaceae (2). 11 N. Afr., Eur., As. *H. niger* L. (henbane) in Brit., probably an escape, it having formerly been largely cult. as a narcotic. The fls. are in cincinni. The capsule stands erect enclosed in the calyx, and opens by a lid (censer-mechanism).

Hyoseris L. Compositae (13). 3 Medit.

Hyospathe Mart. Palmaceae (IV. 1). 4 trop. S. Am.

Hypargyrium Fourr. = Potentilla L. (Ros.).

Hyparrhenia Anderss. = Andropogon L. p.p. (Gram.). 60 warm, esp. Afr.

Hypecoum Tourn. ex L. Papaveraceae (I). 18 Medit., Cent. As. Fl. 2-merous throughout. The inner petals are 3-sect, and the middle lobe stands erect and encloses the sta. (*cf.* Eichler, *Blüthendiagramme*). In *H. procumbens* L. the pollen is shed in the bud into pockets on the inner surface of the inner petals, which close up before the stigma developes. When pressed by an insect the pockets open and dust it with pollen. The stigma only ripens after it has grown above the level of the pollen. Cult. orn. fl.

Hypelate P. Br. Sapindaceae (II). 1 W.I., Florida. White ironwood.

Hyperanthera Forsk. = Moringa Juss. (Moring.).

Hyperaspis Briquet. Labiatae (VII). 2 trop. Afr.

Hyperbaena Miers (*Pachygone BH.*). Menispermaceae. 12 trop. Am., W.I.

Hyperborean, northern.

Hypericaceae (Warming: Cistiflorae) = Hypericineae.

Hypericineae (*BH.*; *Guttiferae* p.p. *EP.*). Dicots. (Polypet., Guttiferales). *Cf.* Guttiferae (classification) for chars.

Hypericophyllum Steetz (*Jaumea* Pers.). Compositae (6). 5 trop. Afr.

Hypericopsis Boiss. (*Frankenia* p.p. *BH.*). Frankeniaceae. 1 Persia.

Hypericum Tourn. ex L. Guttiferae (II). 300 temp. (11 Brit., St John's wort, tutsan, &c.), nearly all perennial herbs with opp., often gland-dotted l. and cymes of fls., often forming pseudo-racemes or -umbels. Sta. ∞, united into 3 or 5 groups. Developmental study shows that each of these groups arises as a simple papilla, and afterwards branches; a comparison with other Guttiferae however shows that in H. we have more probably to do with a union of originally free sta. The fls. contain no honey, but offer abundant pollen, and the larger are frequently visited. They are homogamous, but the stigmas stick out through the sta. and there is thus a chance of a cross.

Hypertelis E. Mey. ex Fenzl (*Pharnaceum* p.p. *BH.*). Aizo. (I). 4 S. Afr.

Hypertrophy, excessive development of one part to loss of others.

Hyphaene Gaertn. Palmae (II). 15 warm Afr. (doum palms). The stem is frequently branched, a rare occurrence in Palms.

Hypo- (Gr. pref.), under; **-cotyl**, the part of the axis below the cotyledons in a seedling; **-crateriform**, salver-shaped; **-dermal**, beneath the epidermis; **-geal** (germination), with cotyledons below ground; **-gynous**, inserted below ovary on a convex receptacle.

Hypobathrum Blume. Rubiaceae (I. 8). 3 Malay Archipel.

Hypocalymma Endl. Myrtaceae (II. 1). 18 W. Austr.

Hypocalyptus Thunb. Leguminosae (III. 3). 1 S. Afr.

Hypochoeris L. Compositae (13). 60 N. temp. and S. Am. (3 Brit.).

Hypocoton Urb. Euphorbiaceae (A. II. 7). 1 S. Domingo.

Hypocylix Woloszczak. Chenopodiaceae (B). 1 Persia.

Hypocyrta Mart. Gesneriaceae (I). 12 Brazil, C. Am.

Hypodaphnis Stapf (*Ocotea* p.p.). Lauraceae (I). 1 trop. Afr.

Hypodematium A. Rich. (*Lissochilus BH.*). Rubiaceae (II. 10). 1 Nile.

Hypoderris Br. Polypodiaceae. 3 W. Ind., trop. Am.

Hypodiscus Nees. Restionaceae. 15 S. Afr.

Hypoestes Soland. Acanthaceae (IV. B). 85 palaeotrop., esp. Madag.

Hypogomphia Bunge. Labiatae (VI). 2 W. As.
Hypolaena R. Br. Restion. 2 Austr. G 1-loc., 1-ovuled.
Hypolepis Beauv. = Ficinia Schrad. (Cyper.).
Hypolepis Bernh. Polypodiaceae. 30 trop. and subtrop.
Hypolobus Fourn. Asclepiadaceae (II. 4). 1 E. Brazil.
Hypolytrum Rich. Cyperaceae (I). 30 trop. and subtrop.
Hypophyllanthus Regel (*Helicteres* p.p. *EP.*). Sterculiaceae (formerly Rutaceae). 1 Colombia.
Hypopitys Dill. ex Adans. = Monotropa L. p.p. (Pyrol.).
Hypoporum Nees = Scleria Berg. (Cyper.).
Hypoxis L. Amaryllidaceae (III). 80 trop. *Engl. Jb.*, 1914.
Hypsela Presl. Campanulaceae (III). 5 Andes.
Hypseocharis Remy. Oxalidaceae. 7 Andes.
Hypserpa Miers (*Limacia BH.*). Menispermaceae. 18 Indomal.
Hypsipodes Miq. Menispermaceae. 1 Java.
Hypsophila F. Muell. Celastraceae. 2 Austr.
Hypsophyllary leaves, bracts.
Hyptiandra Hook. f. Simarubaceae. 1 Queensland.
Hyptianthera Wight et Arn. Rubiaceae (I. 8). 1 N. India.
Hyptiodaphne Urb. (*Daphne* p.p.). Thymelaeaceae. 1 W.I.
Hyptis Jacq. Labiatae (VII). 300 warm Am., W.I.
Hyrtanandra Miq. = Pouzolzia Gaudich. (*BH.*). = Memorialis Buch.-Ham.
Hyssop, *Hyssopus officinalis* L.
Hyssopus (Tourn.) L. Labiatae (VI). 1 Eur., Medit., As., *H. officinalis* L., the hyssop, formerly used in medicine.
Hysterionica Willd. Compositae (3). 6 S. Brazil, Argentina.
Hysterophyta (Warming). The last cohort of Choripetalae.
Ianthe Salisb. (*Hypoxis* L.). Amaryllidaceae (III). 20 Afr.
Ibatia Decne. (*Lachnostoma BH.*). Asclepiadaceae (II. 4). 3 trop. Am.
Iberidella Boiss. (*Eunomia EP.*). Cruciferae (2). 10 Mts. E. Medit.
Iberis Dill. ex L. Cruciferae (2). 30 Eur., As. *I. amara* L. (candytuft), cult. orn. fl., a good example of the corymb. The outer petals of the fls. are longer than the rest, thus adding to the conspicuousness (*cf.* Umbelliferae).
Ibidium Salisb. (*Spiranthes* Rich.). Orchid. (II. 2). 20 N. temp.
Iboga J. Braun et K. Schum. (*Tabernanthe* Baill.). Apocynaceae (I. 3). 1 Cameroons.
Iboza N. E. Brown. Labiatae (VI). 12 S. and trop. Afr.
Icacina A. Juss. Icacinaceae. 5 trop. W. Afr.
Icacinaceae (*EP.*; *Olacineae* p.p. *BH.*). Dicots. (Archichl. Sapindales). 38 gen., 200 sp., trop. Trees and shrubs (often lianes) or rarely herbs, with alt. exstip. l., usu. entire and often leathery. Fls. in cpd. panicled infl., reg., usu. ☿. K (5) or (4), not enlarged when the fr. is ripe; C 5 or 4, rarely united, valvate or imbr.; A 5 or 4, alt. with petals, with usu. intr. anthers; disc rarely developed; $\underline{G}$ (3) or rarely (5) or (2), rarely multi-loc., usu. 1-loc. by abortion of the remaining cavities; ovules 2 per loc., pendulous from its apex, anatr., with dorsal raphe and micropyle facing upwards; funicle usu. thickened above the micropyle; style simple with 3 stigmas (or 5—2).

Fr. 1-loc., 1-seeded, usu. a drupe, sometimes a samara. Endosp. usu. present; embryo straight or curved. *Chief genera:* Lasianthera, Phytocrene.

Icacorea Aubl. = Ardisia Sw. p.p. (Myrsin.). 200 warm.

Icaque (W.I.), *Chrysobalanus Icaco* L.

Ice-plant, *Mesembryanthemum*.

Ichnanthus Beauv. Gramineae (5). 25 trop.

Ichnocarpus R. Br. Apocynaceae (II. 1). 6 Indomal.

Ichthyothere Mart. in Buchn. Compositae (5). 12 trop. S. Am.

Icianthus Greene (*Streptanthus* p.p.). Cruciferae (1). 3 W. U.S.

Icica Aubl. = Protium Burm. f. (Burs.).

Icma Phil. (*Baccharis* p.p. *EP.*). Compositae (12). 1 Chili.

Icomum Hua (*Aeolanthus* p.p. *EP.*). Labiatae (VII). 5 trop. Afr.

Icosandra Phil. Lauraceae (II). 1 Chili.

Idahoa A. Nelson et Macbride. Cruciferae (2). 1 W. U.S.

Idaneum O. Ktze. et Post = Adenium Roem. et Schult. (Apocyn.).

Idesia Maxim. Flacourtiaceae (4). 1 China, Japan.

Ifloga Cass. Compositae (4). 8 S. Afr., Medit.

Iguanura Blume. Palmaceae (IV. 1). 10 Malaya.

Ilang-ilang, *Cananga odorata* Hook. f.

Ildefonsia Gardn. Scrophulariaceae (II. 6). 1 trop. Brazil.

Ilex (Tourn.) L. Aquifoliaceae. 180 Cent. and S. Am., As., Afr., Austr., Eur. *I. Aquifolium* L., the holly, in Brit. Fls. dioecious, but in the ♀ the sterile sta. are so large that the fl. appears ☿. Truly ☿ fls. sometimes occur. *I. paraguensis* A. St Hil. is the Maté or Paraguay tea, largely used in S. Am. The l. contain caffeine; they are dried, broken up and used like tea.

Iliamna Greene (*Malva* p.p.). Malvaceae (2). 4 W. U.S.

Ilicineae (*BH.*) = Aquifoliaceae.

Illecebraceae (*BH.*; *Caryophyllaceae* p.p. *EP.*). Dicots. (Monochlam. Curvembryae). A fam. unnaturally divorced from its true relationships. Herbs, rarely shrubby, with l. usu. opp. entire, stip. Infl. usu. cymose, fl. usu. ☿, inconspic. P herbaceous or leathery, persistent (4—5), A 4—5, rarely more or less, opp. P; $\underline{G}$ 1-loc. style 1, rarely 2—3. Ovule 1, rarely 2, amphitr. or anatr. Endosp. Includes the last four groups of § I of Caryophyllaceae.

Illecebrum Rupp. ex L. Caryophyllaceae (I. 4). 1 W. Eur. (incl. Devon and Cornwall), Medit., W. Afr.

Illegitimate fertilisation, *Lythrum*, *Primula*.

Illicium L. Magnoliaceae. 20 Atl. N. Am., As. *I. verum* Hook. fil. (star-anise; China) is used for flavouring. There is a gradual transition in the spiral P from sepaloid to petaloid structure (*cf.* Nymphaea). The fr. is an aggregate of follicles.

Illigera Blume. Hernandiaceae (Combret. *BH.*). 10 palaeotrop.

Illipe Koenig, F. Muell. (*Bassia* p.p. *BH.*). Sapotaceae (1). 35 Indomal.

Ilyphilos Small (*Elatine* p.p.). Elatinaceae. 1 W. U.S. Wild rice.

Ilysanthes Rafin. Scrophulariaceae (II. 6). 25 trop. and subtrop.

Imantina Hook. f. (*Morinda* p.p. *EP.*). Rubiaceae (II. 9). 1 New Caled.

Imantophyllum Benth. et Hook. f. (*Imatophyllum* Hook.) = Clivia Lindl. p.p. (Amaryll.).

Imbricaria Comm. ex Juss. (*Mimusops* p.p. *EP.*). Sapotaceae (2). 7 palaeotrop.

Imbricate (aestivation, *q.v.*), overlapping.

Imhofia Herb. = Hessea Herb. p.p. (Amaryll.).

Immersed (venation), below surface.

Immobilis (Lat.), immoveable.

Immortelles, everlastings, *q.v.*

Imparipinnate (l.), pinnate with odd leaflet at end.

Impatiens Riv. ex L. Balsaminaceae. 340 trop. and temp. |*, esp. Mts. of India and Ceylon. *I. Noli-tangere* L., the touch-me-not, in Brit. The name is derived from the explosive fr., a caps. with fleshy pericarp; the outer layers of cells are highly turgid and thus a great strain is put upon the whole. Dehiscence is septifragal and is started by a touch when the fr. is ripe. The valves roll up inwards with violence (starting at the base) and the seeds are scattered in all directions. Many cult. orn. fl.

Imperata Cyrilli. Gramineae (2). 6 trop. and subtrop. *I. arundinacea* Cyrilli (lalang) is a very troublesome weed in Malaya.

Imperatoria (Tourn.) L. = Peucedanum Tourn. p.p. (Umbell.).

Imphee, *Sorghum vulgare* Pers., var.

Inaequale (Lat.), unequal.

Inarticulate, not jointed.

Incanus (Lat.), hoary-white.

Incarvillea Juss. Bignoniaceae (2). 5 E. and Cent. As. L. alt.

Incense, *Boswellia*, *Dacryodes*, *Styrax*.

Incertae sedis, of uncertain position. Numerous gen. here given are so described, usu. because their original descriptions leave much to the imagination, but sometimes because of real difficulty in placing them.

Incised (l.), notched at the margin.

Included, not projecting.

Incompletae (*BH.*) = Monochlamydeae.

Incomplete (fl.), wanting one or more kinds of organs.

Incumbent, *Cruciferae*.

Incurved, bending inwards.

Indefinite (growth), continuing till checked by the cold; (infl.), with the first axis not ending in a fl.

Indehiscent, not opening.

Indeterminate (infl.), indefinite.

Indian almond, *Terminalia Catappa* L.; **-bean** (Am.), *Catalpa*; **-butter tree**, *Bassia butyracea* Roxb.; **-chickweed** (Am.), *Mollugo*; **-copal**, *Vateria indica* L.; **-cork tree**, *Millingtonia hortensis* L. f.; **-corn**, *Zea Mays* L.; **-cress**, *Tropaeolum*; **-date**, *Tamarindus*; **-fig**, *Opuntia*; **-grass** (Am.), *Sorghum*; **-hemp**, *Cannabis sativa* L.; **-lilac**, *Melia*, *Lagerstroemia*; **-liquorice**, *Abrus precatorius* L.; **-madder**, *Rubia cordifolia* L.; **-mallow** (Am.), *Abutilon*; **-meal**, *Zea Mays* L.; **-millet**, *Panicum*; **-mulberry**, *Morinda citrifolia* L.; **-physic** (Am.), *Gillenia*; **-pink**, *Spigelia*; **-pipe** (Am.), *Monotropa*; **-redwood**, *Chickrassia tabularis* A. Juss.; **-rice**, *Zizania aquatica* L.; **-rubber**, *cf.* Rubber; **-shot**, *Canna*; **-tobacco** (Am.), *Lobelia inflata* L.; **-turnip** (Am.), *Arisaema*.

Indigenous, genuinely native.

Indigo, *Indigofera*; **China green -**, *Rhamnus chlorophora* Decne.; **Chinese -**, *Polygonum tinctorium* Ait.

Indigofera L. Leguminosae (III. 6). 350 warm. *I. leptostachya* DC., *tinctoria* L. and *Anil* L. furnish indigo. The plant is mown just before flowering, and soaked in water, whereby a yellowish solution is obtained. This on stirring and exposure to the air oxidises, and an insoluble precipitate of indigo is formed. The fls. are slightly explosive (*cf.* Genista).

Indokingia Hemsl. Araliaceae (I). 1 Seychelles.

Indomalaya, *cf.* Floral Regions, II (6) and (7).

Indovethia Boerlage. Ochnaceae (Violaceae *BH.*). 1 Borneo.

Induplicate (aestivation), leaf margins turned inwards; (vernation), *Palmae.*

Indusium, *Filicales*, *Pteridophyta.*

Inermis (Lat.), unarmed, thornless.

Inferae (*BH.*). The 1st series of Gamopetalae.

Inferior (ovary), enclosed in the receptacle.

Inflexed, bent inwards.

Inflorescence, the reproductive shoot, composed of, or bearing, a number of shoots of limited growth, termed flowers. Of two types, monopodial or *racemose*, where the first axis does not as a rule terminate in a fl., but grows steadily onwards; and sympodial or *cymose*, where the main axis soon terminates in a fl., and the growth is taken up by the lat. axes in succession. The typical *raceme* has an axis growing indefinitely up the middle, and successively younger fls. on lat. branches, *Cruciferae*, *Prunus*, *Ribes.* There are also the cpd. raceme or *panicle*, the raceme with sessile fls. or *spike*, with its var. the *catkin* or pendulous spike, the *corymb*, or raceme with all the fl. stalks elongating to the same level, *Iberis*, the *umbel*, which may be imagined as a corymb with all the fls. springing from one point, *Umbelliferae*, the *cpd. umbel*, the *head*, which is a common receptacle with the fls. arranged in a dense mass with the youngest to the centre, *Compositae*, the *cpd. head.* The cyme may be *mono-*, *di-* or *pleiochasial*, according as each branch bears upon itself 1, 2 or more branches; *cf.* dichasial cymes, &c. Many pl. possess mixed infls., with some branchings racemose, some cymose, *Aesculus*, *Betulaceae*, *Labiatae*, *Verbascum.*

Infundibuliform, funnel-shaped.

Inga Scop. Leguminosae (I. 1). 150 trop. and subtrop. Am., W.I.

Ingenhouzia (Moç. et Sesse ex) DC. Malvaceae (4). 2 Mexico.

Ink berry (W.I.), *Randia aculeata* L.; **- nut**, *Semecarpus Anacardium* L. f., *Terminalia.*

Innate (anther), joined to filament by its base.

Inobulbum Schlechter et Kränzlin (*Dendrobium* p.p.). Orchidaceae (II. 15). 2 New Caledonia.

Inocarpus Forst. Leguminosae (III. 8). 1 Malaya, Polynesia. Seed ed.

Inodes O. F. Cook (*Sabal* p.p.). Palmaceae (I. 2). 9 N. Am., W.I.

Inrolled leaf, *Capparidaceae*, *Empetrum.*

Insect powder, *Chrysanthemum.*

Insectivorous plants, pl. which capture insects, &c., by special apparatus, and absorb the resulting products, whether after a special fermentation, or as humus. About 400 spp. belonging to Droseraceae (*Aldrovanda*, *Dionaea*, *Drosera*, *Drosophyllum*, &c.), Cephalotaceae (*Cephalotus*), Lentibulariaceae (*Pinguicula*, *Utricularia*, &c.), Nepenthaceae (*Nepenthes*), and Sarraceniaceae (*Sarracenia*, &c.). *Cf.* gen. mentioned for details, and Darwin, *Insectivorous Plants*.
Insertion of leaves, mode of union with stem; *cf.* Leaf.
Insignis (Lat.), notable.
Insolation, exposure to sun.
Integrifolius (Lat.), simple-leafed.
Integuments, the coats of the ovule.
Inter- (Lat. pref.), between; **-calary** (growth), at a point between apex and base; **-cellular spaces**, air spaces in leaves, &c.; **-node**, the space between a leaf and the next above it; **-petiolar stipules**, *Rubiaceae*.
Interruptedly pinnate, with alt. large and small leaflets, *Rosaceae*.
Intrapetiolar stipules, *Rubiaceae*.
Introrse (anther), opening towards centre of fl.
Intruded, projecting forwards.
Intsia Thou. (*Afzelia* p.p.). Leguminosae (II. 3). 12 palaeotrop.
Inula L. Compositae (4). 100 Eur., As., Afr. (4 in Brit.). The root of *I. Helenium* L., the elecampane, is officinal.
Inulin, a carbohydrate.
Inulopsis O. Hoffm. (*Aplopappus* p.p.). Compositae (3). 1 S. Brazil.
Inversodicraea Engl. ex R. E. Fries. Podostemaceae. 15 trop. Afr.
Inverted flower, *Clitoria*, *Campanulaceae*, *Orchidaceae*.
Involucel, secondary involucre, *Umbelliferae*.
Involucre, a whorl of bracts, usu. in condensed infls., *Anemone*, *Compositae*, *Eranthis*, *Umbelliferae*.
Involute (vernation), margins rolled inwards.
Inyonia M. E. Jones. Compositae (inc. sed.). 1 N. Am.
Iochroma Benth. Solanaceae (II. 2). 15 trop. Am. *I. macrocalyx* Miers shows protection of the fl.-buds, as in Spathodea, by watery secretion between K and C. Cult. orn. fl.
Iodanthus Torr. et Gray. Cruciferae (2). 1 Atl. N. Am.
Iodes Blume. Icacinaceae. 6 trop. As., Afr., Madag.
Iodina Hook. et Arn. Santalaceae. 1 temp. S. Am.
Ionactis Greene (*Aster* p.p.). Compositae (3). 3 N. Am.
Ione Lindl. (*Bulbophyllum* p.p. *BH.*). Orchid. (II. 16). 5 Indomal.
Ionidium Vent. Violaceae. 50 trop. and subtrop. The roots of *I. Ipecacuanha* Vent. are used in medicine (white Ipecacuanha) in the same way as the true drug (Uragoga).
Ionopsidium Rchb. (*Cochlearia* p.p. *BH.*). 1 Portugal, *I. acaule* Rchb. with sol. fls. in the axils of radical leaves.
Ionopsis H. B. et K. Orchidaceae (II. 19). 10 trop. Am., epiphytes.
Ionoxalis Small (*Oxalis* p.p.). Oxalidaceae. 100 N. Am., W.I.
Iostephane Benth. Compositae (5). 2 Mexico.
Ipecacuanha Arruda = Psychotria L. (*BH.*) = Uragoga L.
Ipecacuanha, *Uragoga Ipecacuanha* Baill.; **bastard -** (W.I.), *Asclepias, curassavica* L.; **white -**, *Ionidium Ipecacuanha* Vent.

Iphigenia Kunth. Liliaceae (1). 10 Afr. and Madag. to N.Z.

Iphiona Cass. Compositae (4). 10 S. Afr. to Turkestan.

Ipnum Phil. (*Diplachne* p.p. *EP.*). Gramineae (10). 1 temp. S. Am.

Ipomoea L. (*BH.* incl. *Aniseia*, *Batatas*, *Calonyction* and *Exogonium* of Choisy, *Mina* Cerv., *Operculina* Silva Manso, *Pharbitis* Choisy, and *Quamoclit* Moench.). Convolvulaceae (I. 4). 400 trop. and warm temp., chiefly climbing herbs or shrubs; many cult. orn. fls. (*e.g. I. purpurea* Roth, the morning glory). *I. biloba* Forst. is a char. creeping pl. of trop. beaches. *I. Batatas* Lam. (*B. edulis* Choisy) is the sweet potato, largely cultivated in warm countries for its tubers, which are used like potatoes. *I.* (*Exogonium*) *Purga* Hayne is the jalap; its rhizome gives off turnip-like roots about the size of apples. Worm-eaten tubers are most valuable, as the non-resinous parts are eaten.

Ipomopsis Michx. = Gilia Ruiz et Pav. p.p. (Polemon.).

Ipsea Lindl. (*Pachystoma BH.*). Orchidaceae (II. 9). 3 trop. Afr. and As.

Iré rubber, *Funtumia elastica* Stapf.

Iresine P. Br. Amarantaceae (3). 40 Am., Afr.

Iriartea Ruiz et Pav. Palmae (IV. 1). 10 trop. Am. The stem is supported on aerial roots (*cf.* Pandanus). Some of the branches of these roots are thorny (*cf.* Acanthorhiza). In *I. ventricosa* Mart. (Paxiuba palm), the stem has a peculiar egg-like thickening about half-way up (*cf.* Bombacaceae, Jatropha).

Iriartella H. Wendl. (*Iriartea* p.p. *EP.*). Palmaceae (IV. 1). 1 Amazon.

Iridaceae (*EP.*, *BH.*). Monocotyledons (Liliiflorae; Epigynae *BH.*). 57 gen., 800 sp. trop. and temp.; the chief centres of distr. S. Afr. and trop. Am. Chiefly herbs with a sympodial tuber or rhizome below ground. L. usu. equitant in two ranks. Infl. term., cymose (1 fl. only in Crocoideae). Fl. ☿, reg. or ·|·. P 3+3, petaloid, united below into a long or short tube; A 3 (the outer whorl), with extr. anthers; $\overline{G}$ (3), 3-loc., with axile plac. (rarely 1-loc. with parietal plac.); style usu. trifid and frequently ± petaloid. Ovules usu. ∞, anatr. Loculic. caps. Embryo small, in hard endosp.

Classification and chief genera (after Pax):

I. *CROCOIDEAE* (fl. solitary, or several developed centrifugally round a central one; plant small; l. not exactly in ½ phyllotaxy): Crocus, Romulea.

II. *IRIDOIDEAE* (fls. numerous, in spathes, several in each, usu. reg.; stem distinct; l. equitant): Iris, Moraea, Tigridia, Sisyrinchium.

III. *IXIOIDEAE* (similar, but spathes 1-flowered; fl. often zygomorphic): Ixia, Tritonia, Gladiolus, Freesia.

Irideae (*BH.*) = Iridaceae.

Iris Tourn. ex L. Iridaceae (II). 200 N. temp. 2 in Brit., *I. Pseudacorus* L., the yellow flag, and *I. foetidissima* L, the gladdon. Many cult. orn. fl. Most have a sympodial rhiz. with equitant isobilat. l., and small cymes of fls. in spathes. P petaloid, the sepals usu. bending downwards at the outer ends; opp. to them and almost resting on them are the petaloid styles, under which are the sta. with their extr. anthers. Just above the anther, on the outer side of the style, is a little flap, whose upper surface is the stigma. Bees entering the fl. to get the honey secreted by the ovary rub off their pollen upon the stigma; going farther in they get fresh pollen; and when they come out close the stigma flap, which prevents self-fert. (*cf.* Viola). The flat seeds are suited to wind-distr. [Dykes, *The genus I.*, 1913.]

The dried rhiz. of *I. florentina* L. (Orris root) smells like violets, and is used in perfumery; 'essence of violets' is made from it.

Irlbachia Mart. (*Lisianthus BH.*). Gentianaceae (I). 3 trop. S. Am.

Irmischia Schlechtd. (*Metastelma BH.*). Asclepiad. (II. 1). 3 Mex., W.I.

Iron bark, *Eucalyptus*; **- shrub** (W.I.), *Sauvagesia erecta* L.; **- weed** (Am.), *Vernonia*; **- wood,** *Mesua*, &c., applied to different woods in different countries.

Irregular (fl.), one in which any whorl has members not all alike.

Irritability, sensitiveness to stimuli.

Irvingella VanTiegh. (*Irvingia* p.p.). Simarub. 10 trop. Afr. and As.

Irvingia Hook. f. Simarubaceae. 8 trop. Afr. and As. Butters from the seeds (cay-cay, dika, &c.).

Iryanthera Warb. (*Myristica* p.p. *BH.*). Myristicaceae. 8 N. trop. S. Am.

Isabelia Barb. Rodr. Orchidaceae (II. 6). 1 Brazil.

Isachne R. Br. Gramineae (5). 30 trop. and subtrop.

Isandra F. Muell. Solanaceae (inc. sed.). 1 Austr.

Isanthera Nees. Gesneriaceae (I). 3 Indomal.

Isanthus L. C. Rich. in Michx. Labiatae (I). 1 N. Am.

Isatis Tourn. ex L. Cruciferae (2). 50 Medit., Eur., As. *I. tinctoria* L. is the woad, largely used as a dye before the introduction of indigo. It is prepared by grinding the leaves to a paste and fermenting them. [*Nature*, 55, pp. 36, 79; 61, pp. 331, 563.]

Ischaemum L. Gramineae (2). 40 trop. and subtrop.

Ischarum Blume = Biarum Schott (Araceae). 8 Medit.

Ischnea F. Muell. Compositae (7). 1 New Guinea. Pappus 0.

Ischnocentrum Schlechter. Orchidaceae (II. *a*. III). 1 New Guinea.

Ischnochloa Hook. f. Gramineae (2). 1 N.W. Himalaya.

Ischnogyne Schlechter. Orchidaceae (II. 16). 1 Yunnan.

Ischnolepis Jumelle et Perrier. Asclepiadaceae (I). 1 Madag.

Ischnosiphon Koern. Marantaceae. 30 trop. Am. W.I.

Ischnostemma King et Gamble. Asclepiadaceae (II. 1). 1 Malaya.

Ischnurus Balf. f. Gramineae (12). 1 Socotra.

Iseilema Anderss. (*Anthistiria* p.p. *BH.*). Gramineae (2). 5 Indomal.

Isertia Schreb. Rubiaceae (I. 7). 10 S. Am.

Isidorea A. Rich. Rubiaceae (I. 1). 1 W.I.

Island floras, *cf.* Wallace, *Island Life*, Willis in *Ann. Bot.* 1916–21.

Ismene Salisb. = Hymenocallis Salisb. (Amaryllid.).

Isnardia L. = Ludwigia L. (Onagrac.). 4 N. Am., W.I.

Iso- (Gr. pref.), equal, especially in number; **-bilateral** (l.), with symmetrical internal structure, and edge to the light, *Acorus*, *Asphodelus*, *Eucalyptus*, *Gladiolus*, *Narthecium*; **-diametric,** of equal diameters; **-merous,** with equal numbers in every whorl; **-sporous,** with all spores alike; **-stemonous,** with sta. in one whorl, as many as P.

Isoberlinia Craib et Stapf. Leguminosae (II. 3). 2 Nigeria.

Isocarpha R. Br. Compositae (5). 5 Texas to Peru, W.I.
Isochilus R. Br. Orchidaceae (II. 6). 5 trop. Am., W.I.
Isochoriste Miq. Acanthaceae (IV. B). 2 Java, Angola.
Isocoma Nutt. (*Bigelowia* p.p.). Compositae (3). 10 N. Am.
Isodendrion A. Gray. Violaceae. 3 Hawaiian Is.
Isodesmia Gardn. Leguminosae (III. 7). 2 Brazil.
Isoetaceae. Isoetales. Only genus Isoetes (*q.v.*).
Isoetales. A class of Pteridophyta. Only fam. Isoetaceae.
Isoetes L. Isoetaceae. 50 temp. and trop. *I. lacustris* L. is the quill-wort of Brit. lakes, and *I. echinospora* Dur. is also found. Most are aquatics with short stout rhizomes and awl-shaped l., the habit being like that of Littorella, with which I. is frequently confused. The stem grows in thickness, but very slowly. The l. spread out at the base and sheath the stem. There are a number of roots, which branch dichotomously. Above the base of each l., on the inner side, is a large sporangium sunk in the tissue. The outer l. have micro-, the inner mega-, sporangia, whilst the innermost l. of all are usu. small and not sporangiferous. The sporangia are imperfectly chambered up by strands of tissue (*trabeculae*) running across them from front to back. The germination of the spores and the development of the embryo resemble the corresponding processes in Selaginella.

I. is frequently placed with Eusporangiate Filicales (see Campbell, *Mosses and Ferns*). It differs so much from other Pteridophyta that determination of its relationships is of great difficulty.

Isoetopsis Turcz. Compositae (7). 1 temp. Austr.
Isoglossa Oerst. Acanthaceae (IV. B). 30 Afr., Madag.
Isolepis R. Br. = Scirpus L. p.p. (Cyper.).
Isolobus A. DC. = Lobelia L. p.p. (Campan.).
Isoloma Decne. (*Kohleria* Regel). Gesneraceae (II). 40 trop. Am. Several sp. form runners above ground, thickly covered with scaly l.
Isolona Engl. Anonaceae (5). 15 trop. Afr., Madag.
Isomeris Nutt. Capparidaceae (V). 1 Calif.
Isonandra Wight. Sapotaceae (I). 10 Indomal. *Cf.* Palaquium.
Isonema R. Br. Apocynaceae (II. 2). 3 W. Afr.
Isopetalum Sweet = Pelargonium L'Hérit. p.p. (Geran.).
Isophyllum Hoffm. = Bupleurum Tourn. (Umbell.).
Isoplexis Lindl. (*Digitalis* p.p. *EP.*). Scrophulariaceae (III. 1). 2 Canaries, Madeira.
Isopogon R. Br. ex Knight. Proteaceae (I). 30 Austr.
Isoptera Scheff. ex Burck. Dipterocarpaceae. 1 Malay Arch.
Isopyrum L. Ranunculaceae (2). 20 N. temp.
Isostigma Less. Compositae (5). 10 Brazil, Argentina, on campos.
Isotoma Lindl. Campanulaceae (III). 8 Austr., W.I., Society Is.
Isotropis Benth. Leguminosae (III. 2). 10 Austr.
Ispaghul seed, *Plantago ovata* Forst.
Istle, ixtle, *Agave.*
Italian millet, *Setaria.*
Itatiaia Ule. Melastomaceae (I). 1 Itatiaia Mt. (near Rio).
Itea Gronov. ex L. Saxifragaceae (V). 6 E. As., Atl. N. Am.
Iteadaphne Blume. Lauraceae (II). 2 Java, Sumatra.
Itoa Hemsl. Flacourtiaceae (4). 1 China.

Iva L. Compositae (5). 15 N. and C. Am., W.I.
Ivesia Torr. et Gray (*Potentilla* p.p. *BH*). Rosac. (III. 2). 20 W. U.S.
Ivonia Vell. Inc. sed. 1 Brazil.
Ivory nut, - palm, vegetable -, *Phytelephas*.
Ivy, *Hedera Helix* L.; **ground-,** *Nepeta Glechoma* Benth.; **-leaved bell-flower,** *Wahlenbergia*; **-leaved toadflax,** *Linaria*; **poison-,** *Rhus Toxicodendron* L.
Ixanthus Griseb. Gentianaceae (I). 1 Canaries.
Ixerba A. Cunn. Saxifragaceae (V). 1 northern N.Z.
Ixia L. Iridaceae (III). 25 S. Afr. Cult. orn. fl.
Ixianthes Benth. Scrophulariaceae (II. 4). 1 S. Afr.
Ixiolaena Benth. Compositae (4). 5 Austr.
Ixiolirion Fisch. Amaryllidaceae (I). 2 W. As.
Ixodia R. Br. Compositae (4). 1 Victoria, S. Australia.
Ixonanthes Jack. Linaceae. 8 trop. As.
Ixophorus Schlechtd. (*Setaria* p.p. *BH.*). Gramineae (5). 2 Mexico.
Ixora L. Rubiaceae (II. 4). 200 trop. The fl. is commonly red with a long narrow tube, and probably butterfly-visited.
Ixorrhoea Fenzl. Boraginaceae (inc. sed.). 1 Argentina.
Jaborandi, *Pilocarpus pennatifolius* Lem.
Jaborosa Juss. Solanaceae (2). 10 Mexico, temp. S. Am.
Jaboticabá, *Myrciaria cauliflora* Berg., &c.
Jacaranda Juss. Bignoniaceae (2). 50 warm S. Am., W.I.
Jacaratia A. DC. (*Jaracatia* Marcgr.). Caricaceae. 6 trop. Am., Afr.
Jacea (Tourn.) L. = Centaurea L. p.p. (Comp.).
Jack, jak, *Artocarpus integrifolia* L.
Jackia Wall. Rubiaceae (I. 2). 1 Malaya.
Jacksonia R. Br. Leguminosae (III. 2). 40 Austr.
Jacobaea (Tourn.) L. = Senecio Tourn. (Comp.).
Jacobean lily, *Sprekelia formosissima* Herb.
Jacobinia Moric. Acanthaceae (IV. B). 25 trop. Am. Cult. orn. fl.
Jacob's ladder, *Polemonium*.
Jacquemontia Choisy. Convolvulaceae (I). 70 trop. Am., Afr., Sandw. Is.
Jacquinia L. Theophrastaceae. 10 warm Am., W.I.
Jaculator, *Acanthaceae*.
Jadunia Lindau. Acanthaceae (IV. B). 1 New Guinea.
Jaegeria H. B. et K. Compositae (5). 6 Mexico to Argentina.
Jaeschkea Kurz. Gentianaceae (I). 3 Himal.
Jagera Blume. Sapindaceae (I). 3 Malaya, Austr.
Jaggery, palm sugar, *Arenga*, *Borassus*, *Cocos*, &c.
Jalambica Rafin. (*Neurelmis* Rafin.). Comp. (inc. sed.). 1 Cuba?
Jalap, *Exogonium Purga* Benth.; **false -,** *Mirabilis Jalapa* L.
Jalapa Tourn. ex Adans. = Mirabilis L. (Nyctag.).
Jaliscoa S. Wats. Compositae (2). 1 Mexico.
Jamaica bark (W.I.), *Exostemma*; **- ebony,** *Brya Ebenus* DC.; **- quassia,** *Picraena*; **- sorrel,** *Hibiscus Sabdariffa* L.
Jambolana, Jambu, *Eugenia Jambolana* Lam.
Jambosa DC. (*Eugenia* p.p. *BH.*). Myrtaceae (I). 125 Indomal., Madag.

Jamesia Torr. et Gray. Saxifragaceae (III). 1 Rocky Mts.

Jamesonia Hook. et Grev. Polypodiaceae. 15 trop. Am.

Jamestown weed (Am.), *Datura Stramonium* L.

Janatsi, *Debregeasia edulis* Wedd.

Janipha H. B. et K. = Manihot Adans. (Euphorb.).

Jansenia Barb. Rodr. Orchidaceae (II. 19). 1 Brazil.

Jansonia Kippist. Leguminosae (III. 2). 1 W. Austr. L. opp.

Janusia A. Juss. Malpighiaceae (I). 10 warm Am.

Japan, Japanese, Aralia, *Fatsia*; **- cedar**, *Cryptomeria japonica* D. Don; **- climbing fern**, *Lygodium*; **- cloves**, *Lespedeza*; **- lacquer**, *Rhus vernicifera* DC.; **- laurel**, *Aucuba japonica* Thunb.; **- lilac**, *Syringa amurensis* Rupr.; **- pepper**, *Zanthoxylum piperitum* DC.; **- snow-flower**, *Deutzia*; **- wax**, *Rhus succedanea* L.

Japarandiba Adans. (*Gustavia* L.). Lecythidaceae. 20 trop. Am., W.I.

Jaracatia Marcgr. ex Endl. Caricaceae. 6 trop. Am.

Jarosse, *Lathyrus sativus* L.

Jarrah, *Eucalyptus marginata* Sm.

Jarul, *Lagerstroemia Flos-reginae* Retz. (India, Ceylon).

Jasione L. Campanulaceae (I). 5 Medit., Eur. *J. montana* L. (sheep's-bit scabious), in Brit. The fl. affords—like Phyteuma, but in a slightly different way—an intermediate step between Campanula and the Compositae, in the floral mechanism. The tube is formed by the anthers, which cohere at their base, while the petals spread out as soon as the bud opens.

Jasminaceae (Warming) = Oleaceae p.p.

Jasmine, *Jasminum*; **bastard -** (W.I.), *Cestrum*; **- box**, *Phillyrea*; **Cape -**, *Gardenia*; **Carolina -**, *Gelsemium*; **French -** (W.I.), *Calotropis*; **- tree** (W.I.), *Plumieria*.

Jasminum (Tourn.) L. Oleaceae. 200 trop. and subtrop. Erect or twining shrubs, often cult. perf. fls. (jasmine). The fr. is vertically constricted into two lobes.

Jasonia Cass. Compositae (4). 2 Medit.

Jateorhiza Miers. Menispermaceae. 2 trop. Afr. *J. Columba* Miers (*J. palmata* Miers) furnishes Radix Columba, used as a tonic.

Jatropha L. Euphorbiaceae (A. II. 3). 200 trop. and subtrop. *J. podagrica* Hook. is a xero. with egg-shaped swollen stem, consisting mainly of water-storing tissue; the l. fall in the dry season. The axis of the infl. is red, as well as the fls. The first branches of the dichasium end in ♀, the later in ♂ fls. (*cf.* Begonia).

Jatrorrhiza Prantl = Jateorhiza Miers (Menisp.).

Jaumea Pers. Compositae (6). 8 Am.

Jaundea Gilg. Connaraceae. 1 Cameroons.

Java almond, *Canarium commune* L.

Jeffersonia Bart. Berberidaceae. 2 N. Am., E. As.

Jehlia Rose (*Lopezia* p.p.). Onagraceae (2). 3 Mexico, C. Am.

Jenkinsonia Sweet = Pelargonium L'Hérit. p.p. (Geran.).

Jenmania Rolfe (*Rolfea* Zahlbr.). Orchid. (II. 7). 1 Guiana, W.I.

Jepsonia Small (*Saxifraga* p.p.). Saxifragaceae (I). 3 S. Calif.

Jerdonia Wight. Gesneriaceae (I). 1 S. India.

Jericho, rose of, *Anastatica hierochuntina* L.

Jerusalem artichoke, *Helianthus tuberosus* L.
Jessamine, Jasmine.
Jessenia Karst. Palmaceae (IV. 1). 3 Trinidad to Amazonas.
Jewel-weed (Am.), *Phlomis*.
Jew's mallow (W.I.), *Corchorus olitorius* L.
Jimson weed, Jamestown weed (Am.), *Datura Stramonium* L.
Jippi-jappa (Jamaica), *Carludovica*.
Joannegria Chiov. (*Negria*). Gramineae (11). 1 E. Afr.
Joannesia Vell. Euphorbiaceae (A. II. 3). 1 coast of Brazil; seed ed.; purgative; oil; good timber.
Jobinia Fourn. Asclepiadaceae (II. 3). 2 Brazil.
Job's tears, *Coix Lachryma* L.
Joe-pye-weed (Am.), *Eupatorium purpureum* L.
John Crow's nose (W.I.), *Phyllocoryne*.
John-go-to-bed-at-noon, *Tragopogon pratensis* L.
Johnsonia R. Br. Liliaceae (III). 3 S.W. Austr.
Johrenia DC. Umbelliferae (III. 6). 17 W. As.
Joint-grass (Am.), *Panicum distichum* L.
Joinvillea Gaudich. Flagellariaceae. 4 Malay Archipel., N. Cal.
Jolly, brown (W.I.), *Solanum Melongena* L.
Jollydora Pierre (*Connarus* p.p.). Connaraceae. 4 W. trop. Afr.
Jonesia Roxb. = Saraca L. (Legum.).
Jonesiella Rydberg (*Astragalus* p.p.). Legumin. (III. 6). 1 N. Am.
Jonquil, *Narcissus Jonquilla* L.
Jonquilla Haw. = Narcissus Tourn. p.p. (Amaryll.).
Joosia Karst. (*Ladenbergia BH.*). Rubiaceae (I. 5). 2 N. Andes.
Jordanian species, *cf.* Nomenclature.
Jorena Adans. Inc. sed. Nomen.
Josephia Wight. Orchidaceae (II. 3). 2 India, Ceylon.
Josephinia Vent. Pedaliaceae. 3 Indomal.
Jossinia Comm. = Eugenia L. p.p. (Myrt.).
Jouvea Fourn. Gramineae (12). 1 Mexico.
Jovellana Ruiz et Pav. (*Calceolaria* p.p.). Scrophulariaceae (II. 2). 6 Chili, N.Z.
Jowar (India), Guinea corn, *Sorghum vulgare* Pers.
Joyweed, *Telanthera*.
Juania Drude. Palmaceae (IV. 1). 1 Juan Fernandez.
Juanulloa Ruiz et Pav. Solanaceae (4). 10 trop. Am.
Jubaea H. B. et K. Palmae (IV. 2). 1 Chili, *J. spectabilis* H. B. et K., the Coquito-palm. Palm-honey is prepared by evaporation of the sap, and the tree is useful in other ways.
Jubelina A. Juss. Malpighiaceae (I). 3 Guiana, Nicaragua.
Jububa Bub. (*Zizyphus* p.p.). Rhamnaceae. 1 Medit.
Judas' bag, *Adansonia digitata* L.; **- tree**, *Cercis Siliquastrum* L.
Juglandaceae (*EP.*, *BH.*) Dicots. (Archichl. Juglandales; Unisex. *BH.*). 6 gen., 40 sp., N. temp., trop. As. Trees; alt. stip. l., with brown hairy winter buds; the buds arise rather high up in the leaf axils, and sometimes several appear in descending order. Infl. monoecious, the ♂ appearing as catkins on the twigs of the previous year, the ♀ as sessile fls. on the stems of the current year. P. typically 4-leaved, but often fewer by abortion. ♂ fl. with 3—40 sta. (more in the lower

fls.); ♀ fl. with epig. P; $\overline{G}$ (2), 1-loc., with 1 erect orthotr. ov.; style short with 2 stigmas. Wind-fert.; Juglans is chalazogamic. Drupe or nut; testa thin, seed exalb. *Chief genera:* Pterocarya (bracteoles ripening to wings), Juglans (not), Carya (P 0).

Juglandales, the 8th order of Dicots. Archichl.; p. x. **Juglandeae** (*BH.*) = Juglandaceae; **Juglandiflorae** (Warming), 3rd coh. Choripet.

Juglans L. Jugland. 12 ✻, Andes. *J. regia* L. (W. As., walnut), *J. cinerea* L. (Canada, U.S., butternut) and others useful. ♂ fl. adnate to br. and bracteoles, P 5—4—3—2, A to 20 in lowest fls., to 6 in upper. Drupe, with green fleshy exocarp, and hard endocarp (the shell). The "boats" into which the shell splits are not cpls.; the splitting is down the midribs. Within is seed with thin brown seed-coat, exalb. with basal radicle and two large cots., rendered irreg. in shape by presence of partial septa in ovary. Chalazogamic. Wood valued in cabinet-making, &c. The seeds yield an oil. Many var. cult. for fr. Many Tertiary fossils.

Jujuba Burm. = Zizyphus Adans. (Rhamn.).

Jujube, *Zizyphus vulgaris* Lam. (E. Medit.).

Juliana Reichb. = Choisya H. B. et K. (Rut.).

Juliania Schlechtd. Julian. 4 Mex., Peru.

Julianiaceae (*EP.*; *Anacard.* p.p. *BH.*). Dicots. (Archichl. Julianiales; pp. xiii, li). Trees or shrubs with alt. usu. pinnate exstip. l. and dioec. fls., ♂ ∞ in panicles, ♀ in fours at end of downward directed spike. ♂ P 6—8, A 6—8; ♀ naked, $\underline{G}$ 1-loc. with 1 ov. on cup-like funicle. Exalb. *Genera:* Juliania, Orthopterygium.

Julianiales, the tenth order of Dicots. Archichl.; p. xii.

Julocroton Mart. Euphorb. (A. II. 1). 35 trop. Am. Fls. in spikes, ♀ below.

Julostylis Thw. Malv. (4). 1 Ceylon. Seed reniform. A 10. $\underline{G}$ (2).

Jumellea Schlechter (*Angraecum* p.p.). Orchid. (II. 20). 25 Madag., Masc.

Juncaceae (*EP.*, *BH.*). Monocots. (Liliiflorae; Calycinae *BH.*; pp. vii, liv). 8/300 in damp and cold places, temp., arct., trop. Mts. Usu. creeping sympodial rhiz., one joint of the sympodium appearing above ground each year as a leafy shoot. The stem does not often lengthen above ground, except to bear infl.; l. usu. narrow, sometimes centric. Infl. usu. a crowded mass of fls. in cymes of various types, usu. monochas. Fl. usu. ☿, reg., wind-fert. P 3+3, usu. sepaloid, with odd l. of inner whorl post.; A 3+3 (or inner wanting), anthers dehisc. lat. or intr., pollen in tetrads; $\underline{G}$ (3), with axile or parietal plac. and ∞ or few anatr. ov.; style simple with 3 brush-like stigmas. Loculic. caps.; embryo straight, in starchy endosp. *Chief genera:* Prionium, Juncus, Luzula.

Juncaginaceae = Scheuchzeriaceae.

Juncago Tourn. = Triglochin L.

Juncea Briq. = Bupleurum L. p.p. (Umbell.).

Juncella F. Muell. (*Trithuria BH.*). Centrolep. 2 S. Austr., Tasm.

Juncellus C. B. Clark (*Cyperus* p.p. *EP.*). Cyper. (1). 10 warm.

Juncellus Griseb. = Cyperus L. p.p. (Cyper.).

Junceus (Lat.), rush-like.

Juncoides (Dill.) Adans. = Luzula DC. (Junc.).

Juncus (Tourn.) L. Junc. 225 cosmop., chiefly in cold or wet places, rare in trop. 18 (rushes) in Brit. Usu. low herbaceous pl. with sympodial rhiz. giving off one leafy shoot each year. The l. are of various types, with large sheathing bases. Some are flat and grass-like, others needle-like, and still others centric in structure and standing erect. The infl. is a dense head or panicle, of cymose construction (usu. rhipidia or drepania). In some sp. it appears to be lat. on a leaf-like cylindrical stem, but is really only pushed to one side by the bract of the infl. Fl. protog. and wind-fert.

Rushes are largely used for making baskets, chair bottoms, &c. *J. squarrosus* L. is common on hill pastures in Brit.; it is eaten by sheep and forms a valuable part of their fodder when grass is scarce.

June-berry (Am.), *Amelanchier*.

Jungia L. f. Compositae (12). 15 S. Am.

Jungle, low or thin forest.

Juniper, *Juniperus*.

Juniperus Tourn. ex L. Coniferae (Pinac. 42; see C. for genus characters). 30 ✻. The juniper, *J. communis L.* (Asia and Eur. incl. Brit.), and *J. Oxycedrus* L., &c. have needle l. throughout life; others, such as *J. Sabina* L., the savin (Eur. As.), have small l. closely appressed, as in Cupressus. Seedling forms of these are known (see Retinospora). The cone consists of 1—4 whorls of scales, one only being fertile, as a rule. In ripening the whole becomes a fleshy mass enclosing the hard seeds, and forming a good imitation of a true berry. The fruit is eaten by birds. That of *J. communis* is used in making gin. The wood of *J. virginiana* L. is the red cedar used for pencils; others also give useful timber.

Juno Tratt. = Iris L. p.p. (Irid.).

Junodia Pax. Euphorbiaceae (A. I. 1). 1 trop. Afr.

Jurinea Cass. Compositae (11). 50 Medit., Eur., As.

Juruasia Lindau. Acanthaceae (IV. B). 2 Amazonas.

Jussieua L. (*Jussiaea*). Onagraceae (I). 50 trop.; water and marsh plants. Aerating tissue is well developed (*cf.* Sonneratia, Sesbania). In *J. repens* L. (*J. diffusa* Forsk.), when growing in water, two forms of root develope, ordinary anchorage roots and erect spongy roots which grow upwards, often till they reach the surface of the water. The bulk of the tissue consists of aerenchyma. In *J. suffruticosa* L. (*J. salicifolia* H. B. et K.) there is an erect stem, whose lower part is covered with aerenchyma if growing in water (*cf.* Lycopus). If the plants be grown on land none of these phenomena appear. [Figs., &c., in Goebel's *Pflanzenbiol. Schild.* II. 256.]

Justenia Hiern. Rubiaceae (I. 2). 1 trop. Afr.

Justicia Houst. ex L. Acanthaceae (IV. B). 300 trop.

Jute, *Corchorus*; **China -**, *Abutilon Avicennae* Gaertn.

Kadsura Kaempf. ex Juss. Magnoliaceae. 8 trop. As., China, Japan. Fls. unisexual, spiral throughout. Climbing shrubs with no stipules.

Kadua Cham. et Schlecht. Rubiaceae (I. 2). 16 Hawaiian Is.

Kaempferia L. Zingiberaceae (I). 55 trop. As. and Afr. Cult. orn. fl.

Kaernbachia Schlechter. Cunoniaceae. 2 New Guinea.

Kaffir boom, *Erythrina*; **- bread**, *Encephalartos*; **- corn**, *Sorghum vulgare* Pers.; **- lily**, *Clivia*; **- thorn**, *Lycium*.

Kageneckia Ruiz et Pav. Rosaceae (I. 2). 3 Chili.

Kakosmanthus Hassk. (*Payena* p.p. *BH.*). Sapotaceae (1). 4 Malay Arch.
Kalaharia Baill. Verbenaceae (4). 2 trop. and S. Afr.
Kalanchoë Adans. Crassulaceae. 200 warm. Like Bryophyllum.
Kale, *Brassica oleracea* L. var.; **sea-**, *Crambe maritima* L.
Kalidium Moq. in DC. Chenopodiaceae (A). 4 S. Russia, W. As.
Kaliphora Hook. f. Cornaceae. 1 Madag.
Kallstroemia Scop. (*Tribulus* p.p.). Zygophyllaceae. 10 Am., Austr.
Kalmia L. Ericaceae (I. 3). 6 N. Am., Cuba. The anthers are held in pockets of the C, and the filaments are bent like bows when the fl. is open. An insect probing for honey releases them, and the anthers strike against him, loading him with pollen.
Kalmiella Small (*Kalmia* p.p.). Ericaceae (I. 3). 2 N. Am.
Kalopanax Miq. (*Acanthopanax BH.*). Araliaceae (1). 2 E. As.
Kalosanthes Haw. = Rochea DC. (Crass.).
Kalymopetalon Pohl. Inc. sed. Nomen.
Kampmannia Steud. Gramineae (inc. sed.). 1 N. Zealand.
Kanahia R. Br. Asclepiadaceae (II. 1). 3 E. Afr., Arabia.
Kandelia Wight et Arn. Rhizophoraceae. 1 trop. As.
Kangaroo apple, *Solanum aviculare* Forst.; **-grass**, *Anthistiria*; **-thorn**, *Acacia armata* R.Br.
Kania Schlechter. Saxifragaceae (III). 1 New Guinea.
Kaniata, *Mallotus*.
Kanimia Gardn. Compositae (2). 7 trop. S. Am.
Kapa cloth, *Broussonetia papyrifera* Vent.
Kapok *Eriodendron anfractuosum* DC., *Bombax*.
Karatas (Plum.) Mill. Bromeliaceae (4). 20 Mex.-Argent.
Karité, *Butyrospermum Parkii* Kotschy.
Karlea Pierre (*Maesopsis EP.*). Rhamnaceae (formerly in Styraceae and Sapotaceae). 1 trop. Afr.
Karpaton Rafin. Inc. sed. 1 N. Am.
Karri, *Eucalyptus diversicolor* F. Muell.
Karwinskia Zucc. Rhamnaceae. 3 warmer N. Am.
Katabolism, the breaking down of materials in the pl.
Katafa Costantin et Poiss. (*Cedrelopsis* Baill.). Meliaceae (1). (Authors place as new tribe of Celastraceae.) 1 Madag.
Kaufmannia Regel. = Cortusa L. p.p. (Primul.). 1 Turkestan.
Kaulfussia Blume (*Christensenia* Maxon). Marattiaceae. 2 S.E. As. The palmate l. has large pores below, due to tearing apart of guard cells of stomata. [Campbell in *Ann. Bzg.* 2. VII. 69.]
Kauri, **-copal**, *Agathis australis* Steud.
Kayea Wall. Guttiferae (IV). 12 Indomal.
Kedrostis Medic. Cucurbitaceae (2). 30 trop. Afr. and As.
Keel, *cf. Leguminosae*.
Keenania Hook. f. Rubiaceae (I. 7). 2 Indomal.
Keerlia A. Gray et Engelm. Compositae (3). 3 Texas, Mexico.
Kefersteinia Reichb. f. (*Zygopetalum BH.*). Orchid. (II. 14). 6 trop. S. Am.
Kegelia Reichb. f. Orchidaceae (II. 13). 1 Guiana.
Kei-apple, *Aberia* (*Doryalis*) *caffra* Harv. et Sond.
Keiria Bowdich. Oleaceae. 1 Madeira.

Keiskea Miq. Labiatae (VI). 1 Japan.
Keithia Benth. (*Hedeoma* p.p. *EP.*). Labiatae (VI). 9 trop. Am.
Keithia Spreng. Capparidaceae (inc. sed.). 1 Brazil.
Keitia Regel. Iridaceae (II). 1 Natal.
Kelleronia Schinz. Zygophyllaceae. 2 E. trop. Afr.
Kelloggia Torr. ex Benth. et Hook. f. Rubiaceae (II. 7). 1 W. N. Am.
Kelseya Rydberg (*Eriogynia* p.p.). Rosaceae (I. 1). 1 Montana.
Kendal green, *Genista tinctoria* L.
Kendrickia Hook. f. Melastomaceae (I). 1 Ceylon, S. India.
Kenguel seed, *Silybum Marianum* Gaertn.
Kennedya Vent. (incl. *Hardenbergia* Benth.). Leguminosae (III. 10). 15 Austr. The fls. of some are almost black. Cult. orn. fl.
Kenopleurum Candargy. Umbelliferae (III. 6). 1 Lesbos.
Kentia Blume. Palmae (IV. 1). 10 Moluccas to N.Z. (not in Austr.). Fls. in groups of 3 (2 male) on the spadix.
Kentiopsis Brongn. Palmaceae (IV. 1). 2 New Caledonia.
Kentranthus Neck. = Centranthus DC. (Valerian.).
Kentrochrosia Lauterb. et K. Schum. Apocynaceae (I. 3). 1 New Guinea.
Kentrophyllum Neck. = Carthamus L. (Comp.).
Kentrosphaera Volkens. Amarantaceae (2). 1 Kilimandjaro.
Keracia Calest. (*Hohenackeria* p.p.). Umbelliferae (III. 5). 1 W. Medit.
Keramanthus Hook. f. (*Adenia* p.p. *EP.*). Passifloraceae. 1 trop. Afr.
Keraselma Neck. = Euphorbia L. (Euph.).
Keratto, *Agave*.
Keraudrenia J. Gay. Sterculiaceae. 8 Austr., Madag.
Kerbera E. Fourn. (*Melinia EP.*). Asclepiadaceae (II. 1). 2 Braz., Urug.
Kerguelen cabbage, *Pringlea antiscorbutica* R. Br.
Kerinozoma Steud. Gramineae (12). 1 Java.
Kermadecia Brongn. et Gris. Proteaceae (II). 5 New Cal., E. Austr.
Kernera Medic. (*Cochlearia* L. p.p.). Cruciferae (2). 5 Mts. of S. Eur.
Kerneria Moench. = Bidens Tourn. p.p. (Comp.).
Kerria DC. Rosaceae (III). 1 E. As., *K. japonica* DC., often cult. orn. shrub.
Kerstingia K. Schum. Rubiaceae (II. 1). 1 Togoland.
Kerstingiella Harms. Leguminosae (III. 10). 1 Togoland. Geocarpic.
Keteleeria Carr. Coniferae (Pinac.; see C. for gen. char.). 4 China.
Keyserlingia Bunge ex Boiss. (*Sophora* p.p. *EP.*). Legum. (III. 1). 2 W. As.
Keysseria Lauterb. Compositae (3). 1 New Guinea.
Khas-khas, *Vetiveria zizanioides* Stapf.
Khat, *Catha edulis* Forsk.
Khaya A. Juss. Meliaceae (II). 8 trop. Afr.
Kibara Endl. Monimiaceae. 30 E. Indomal. A 5—8, G 7—26.
Kibessia DC. Melastomaceae (II). 16 Malaya.
Kickxia Blume. Apocynaceae (II. 1). 2 Java.
Kidney-bean, *Phaseolus vulgaris* L.; **-fern**, *Trichomanes*; **-vetch**, *Anthyllis vulneraria* L.
Kielmeyera Mart. Guttiferae (I). 18 S. Brazil, char. of campos.
Kigelia DC. Bignoniaceae (4). 3 warm Afr., Madag. The infls. are borne on old wood, hanging down on very long stalks. L. alt.

Kigelianthe Baill. Bignoniaceae (2). 2 Madag.
Kiggelaria L. Flacourtiaceae (3). 5 S. and trop. Afr. *K. Dregeana* Turcz. yields a good timber (Natal mahogany).
Kinepetalum Schlechter. Asclepiadaceae (II. 3). 1 Afr.
Kinetostigma Dammer. Palmaceae (IV. 1). 1 C. Am.
King-cup, *Caltha palustris* L.
Kingdonia Balf. f. et W. W. Smith. Ranunculaceae (3). 1 China.
Kingia R. Br. Liliaceae (III) (Junc. *BH.*). 1 W. Austr., a char. pl.
Kingiodendron Harms (*Hardwickia* p.p.). Leguminosae (II. 2). 1 Indomal.
Kingstonia Hook. f. et Thoms. Anonaceae (1). 1 Malay Peninsula
Kinia Rafin. Inc. sed. 1 Borneo.
Kinnikinnik (Am.), *Cornus sericea* L.
Kino, a resin-like substance, soluble in water, astringent, used medicinally and in tanning, *Butea*, *Eucalyptus*, *Pterocarpus*, &c.
Kirengeshoma Yatabe. Saxifragaceae (III). 1 Japan.
Kirganelia Juss. = Phyllanthus L. p.p. (Euph.).
Kirilowia Bunge. Chenopodiaceae (A). 1 Turkestan, Afghanistan.
Kirkia Oliv. Simarubaceae. 4 trop. and S. Afr.
Kissenia R. Br. ex T. Anders. Loasaceae. 1 Arabia, S. Afr.
Kissodendron Seem. (*Hedera* p.p. *BH.*). Araliaceae (1). 1 Austr., N.G.
Kitaibelia Willd. Malvaceae (1). 1 lower Danube. Cult. orn. fl.
Kitchingia Baker. Crassulaceae. 10 Madag.
Kitul (Ceylon), *Caryota urens* L.
Klaineanthus Pierre ex Prain. Euphorbiaceae (A. II. 6). 1 W. Afr.
Klainedoxa Pierre. Simarubaceae. 6 trop. Afr.
Klaprothia H. B. et K. Loasaceae. 1 N. trop. S. Am.
Klattia Baker. Iridaceae (II). 2 Cape Colony.
Kleinhovia L. Sterculiaceae. 1 trop. As.
Kleinia Jacq. = Porophyllum Vaill. (Comp.).
Kleinia L. = Senecio Tourn. (Comp.).
Klopstockia Karst. = Ceroxylon Humb. p.p. (Palm.).
Klossia Ridley. Rubiaceae (I. 2). 1 Malay Peninsula.
Klotzschia Cham. et Schlechtd. Umbelliferae (I. 2). 2 S. Brazil.
Klugia Schlechtd. Gesneriaceae (1). 4 trop. As., Am. Markedly anisophyllous, with heterodromous fls. (*cf.* Cassia, Saintpaulia).
Knappia Sm. = Mibora Adans. (Gram.).
Knapweed, *Centaurea Cyanus* L.
Knautia L. (*Scabiosa* p.p. *BH.*). Dipsaceae. 25 Medit., Eur.
Knawel, *Scleranthus annuus* L.
Knees, *cf. Taxodium.*
Kneiffia Spach (*Oenothera* p.p. *BH.*). Onagraceae (2). 10 temp. N. Am. Seeds long-stalked. Cult. orn. fl.
Knema Lour. (*Myristica* p.p. *BH.*). Myristicaceae. 40 Indomal.
Knesebeckia Klotzsch = Begonia L. p.p. (Begon.).
Knife-grass (W.I.), *Scleria latifolia* Sw.
Knightia R. Br. Proteaceae (II). 3 New Zealand, New Caled. *K. excelsa* R. Br. (rewa; N.Z.) furnishes a beautiful timber.
Kniphofia Moench. Lili. (III). 75 S. and E. Afr., Madag., cult. orn. fl. Bees sometimes force their way into fls. and are unable to return.
Knol-kohl, *Brassica oleracea* L., var.

Knotgrass, *Polygonum*, (Am.) *Paspalum distichum* L.; **-weed** (Am.) *Polygonum*.
Knowltonia Salisb. (*Anemone* p.p. *EP.*). Ranunculaceae (3). 6 S. Afr.
Knoxia L. Rubiaceae (II. 1). 9 Indomal.
Koanophyllon Arruda. Compositae (inc. sed.). 1 Peru.
Kobresia Willd. Cyperaceae (III). 30 N. temp. (1 Brit.).
Kochia Roth. Chenopodiaceae (A). 35 N. temp., Austr., S. Afr.
Kochiophyton Schlechter ex Cogn. (*Acacallis* Lindl.). Orchidaceae (II. 13). 1 Amazonas.
Koeberlinia Zucc. Capparidaceae (II) (Simarub. *BH.*). 1 Texas, Mexico. A leafless xerophyte with thorny twigs. *Cf.* next article.
Koeberliniaceae. Dicot. (Archichl. Parietales). A fam. made for the genus Koeberlinia (*q.v.*), now placed in Capparidaceae. See *Nat. Pfl.*
Koechlea Endl. (*Cirsium* p.p. *EP.*). Compositae (11). 1 Mt. Taurus.
Koehneola Urb. (*Tetranthus* p.p.). Compositae (5). 1 Cuba.
Koeleria Pers. Gramineae (10). 25 temp. (1 Brit.).
Koellensteinia Reichb. f. (*Aganisia* p.p. *BH.*). Orchid. (II. 14). 1 Colombia.
Koellia Moench. (*Pycnanthemum* Michx.). Labiatae (VI). 15 S. U.S.
Koellikeria Regel. Gesneriaceae (II). 1 Colombia.
Koelpinia Pall. Compositae (13). 3 N. Afr. to E. As.
Koelreuteria Laxm. Sapindaceae (II). 3 China. The capsule is large and bladdery and may be blown about by wind (*cf.* Colutea).
Koenigia L. (*Polygonum* p.p. *BH.*). Polygon. (I. 1). 1 Arctic, Himal.
Koernickea Klotzsch (*Paullinia* p.p. *EP.*). Sapindaceae (I). 1 Guiana.
Kohautia Cham. et Schlechtd. = Oldenlandia L. p.p. (Rubi.).
Kohleria Regel (*Isoloma BH.*). Gesner. (II). 40 trop. Am. Cult. orn. fl.
Kohlerianthus Fritsch (*Fluckigeria* p.p.). Gesneriaceae (I). 1 Bolivia.
Kohl-rabi, *Brassica oleracea* L., var.
Kokia Lewton (*Gossypium* p.p.). Malvaceae (4). 3 Hawaiian Is.
Kokoona Thw. Celastraceae. 3 Indomal.
Kola nut, *Cola acuminata* Schott. et Endl., *C. vera* K. Schum.
Kolkwitzia Graebn. Caprifoliaceae. 1 China.
Kolobochilus Lindau. Acanthaceae (IV. B). 2 Costa Rica.
Kolobopetalum Engl. Menispermaceae. 4 trop. Afr.
Kolowratia Presl (*Alpinia* p.p. *BH.*). Zingiberaceae (I). 1 Phil. Is.
Komaroffia O. Ktze. (*Nigella* p.p.). Ranunculaceae (2). 1 Turkestan.
Kompitsia Costantin et Galland. Asclepiadaceae (I). 1 Madag.
Koniga R. Br. = Alyssum Tourn. (*BH.*) = Lobularia Desv.
Koompassia Maingay (*Abauria* Becc.). Leguminosae (II. 5). 2 Malaya.
Koordersina O. Ktze. = Koordersiodendron Engl. (Anacard.).
Koordersiodendron Engl. Anacardiaceae (2). 1 Celebes.
Kopsia Blume. Apocynaceae (I. 3). 10 Indomal.
Korshinskia Lipsky. Umbelliferae (III. 5). 1 C. As.
Korthalsella Van Tiegh. (*Bifaria* p.p.). Loranthaceae (II). 20 Polynesia to Madag.
Korthalsia Blume. Palmae (III). 20 Indomal. Some, *e.g. K. horrida* Becc., are said to be myrmecophilous (*cf.* Cecropia), the ants living in the sheaths of the leaves.
Koslovia Lipsky (*Albertia* p.p.). Umbelliferae (III. 4). 1 Turkestan.

Kosmosiphon Lindau. Acanthaceae (IV. A). 1 trop. Afr.
Koso, *Brayera*, *Hagenia*.
Kosteletzkya C. Presl. Malvaceae (4). 8 ✻.
Kostyczewa Korshinsky. Leguminosae (III. 6). 1 Turkestan.
Kotchubaea Fisch. Rubiaceae (I. 8). 1 N. Brazil, Guiana.
Kraenzlinella O. Ktze. (*Otopetalum* Lehm. et Kränzl.). Orchidaceae (II. 16). 1 Ecuador.
Kralikia Coss. et Dur. Gramineae (12). 1 Algeria.
Krameria Loefl. Leguminosae (II. 6). 13 Mexico to Chili. Placed in Polygalaceae by *BH.*, but has a pet., not a sep., post. K and C 4—5; A 4, anthers opening by pores. Eichler, *Blüthendiag.* p. 522.
Krascheninikowia Coss. et Dur. = Stellaria L. p.p. (Caryophyll.).
Kraunhia Rafin. (*Wistaria* Nutt.). Leguminosae (III. 6). 4 E. As., E. N. Am.
Kraussia Harv. (*Tricalysia* p.p. *EP.*). Rubiaceae (I. 8). 3 trop. and S. Afr.
Kreysigia Reichb. Liliaceae (I). 1 S.E. Austr.
Krigia Schreb. Compositae (13). 6 N. Am.
Krokeria Moench. = Lotus L. p.p. (Legum.).
Krugella Pierre (*Pouteria* p.p. *EP.*). Sapotaceae (I). 1 Trinidad.
Krugia Urb. (*Marlierea* p.p.). Myrtaceae (I). 1 W.I.
Krugiodendron Urb. (*Ceanothus* p.p.). Rhamnaceae. 1 W.I.
Krynitzkia Fisch. et Mey. (*Cryptanthe EP.*). Boragin. (IV. 2). 45 W. Am.
Kugia Berl. Inc. sed. Nomen.
Kuhlhasseltia J. J. Smith. Orchidaceae (II. 2). 2 Malay Archip.
Kuhlia H. B. et K. (*Banara EP.*). Flacourtiaceae (5). 6 Am.
Kuhnia L. Compositae (2). 4 Arizona to Mexico.
Kuhnistera Lam. (*Petalostemon* Michx.). Leguminosae (III. 6). 20 N. Am.
Kumlienia Greene (*Oxygraphis EP.*). Ranunculaceae (3). 1 N.W. Am.
Kummeria Mart. (*Discophora* Miers). Icacinaceae. 2 Brazil, Guiana.
Kummerowia Schindler (*Lespedeza* p.p., *q.v.*). Legumin. (III. 7). 2 Japan.
Kumquat, *Citrus japonica* Thunb.
Kundmannia Scop. Umbelliferae (III. 5). 1 Medit., S. Eur.
Kunstleria Prain. Leguminosae (III. 8). 5 Malay Peninsula.
Kunthia Humb. et Bonpl. (*Chamaedorea* p.p. *BH.*). Palm. (IV. 1). 1 N.W. S. Am.
Kunzea Reichb. Myrtaceae (II. 1). 18 Austr.
Kunzmannia Klotzsch et Schomb. Rutaceae (inc. sed.). 1 Guiana.
Kurakkan (Ceylon), *Eleusine Coracana* Gaertn.
Kurdee seed, *Carthamus tinctorius* L.
Kurrimia Wall. Celastraceae. 8 Indomal.
Kurzamra O. Ktze. (*Soliera* Clos). Labiatae (VI). 1 Chili.
Kuschakewiczia Regel et Smirn. Boraginaceae (IV. 1). 1 Turkestan.
Kutchubaea Fisch. ex DC. Rubiaceae (I. 8). 1 N. Brazil, Guiana.
Kutira gum, *Cochlospermum*, *Sterculia*.
Kydia Roxb. Malvaceae (2). 2 India.
Kyllinga Rottb. Cyperaceae (I). 50 trop. and subtrop. Some have aromatic roots.

Kyrstenia Neck. (*Eupatorium* Tourn. p.p.). Compositae (2). 50 N. Am.

Labatia Sw. Sapotaceae (1). 6 trop. S. Am., W.I.

Labdanum, *Cistus creticus* L., *C. ladaniferus* L.

Labellum, *Canna, Marantaceae, Orchidaceae, Stylidiaceae, Zingiberaceae.*

Labiatae (*EP.*, *BH.*). Dicotyledons (Sympet. Tubiflorae; Lamiales *BH.*). 200 gen. 3000 sp., cosmop.; chief centre the Medit. region. Some small groups are localised in their distribution, *e.g.* § II. in Austr. and Tasmania, III. in India, Malaya, China, &c., VIII. in Centr. Am., whereas the large ones, such as I. and IV., are cosmop. Most L. are land-plants, and herbs or undershrubs, similar in habit and structure. Stem usu. square, with decussate simple exstip. l., often hairy and with epidermal glands secreting volatile oils, which give char. scents to many. A few marsh-plants (Mentha, Lycopus, &c.), a few climbers (Stenogyne sp., Scutellaria. &c.), and a few small trees (Hyptis sp.). Many xero. with reduced, sometimes infolded, l., hairiness, thick cuticles, &c., *e.g.* Rosmarinus.

The axis of the first order is not closed by a fl. but only those of later orders; thus the primary form of the infl. is racemose, and a simple raceme actually occurs in Scutellaria, &c. Usu. however a dichasial cyme, becoming cincinnal in its later branchings, occurs in the axil of each l. upon the upper part of the main axis. In Teucrium, Nepeta sp., &c., the construction of this cyme is easily seen; but in most L. it is closely 'condensed' into the axil, so that all the fls. are sessile; but it is easily seen that the central fl. opens first and then those on either side of it (see diagram). The two condensed cymes at each node overlap the leaf-axils and often form what looks like a whorl of fls.; this infl. is often called a *verticillaster* or false whorl.

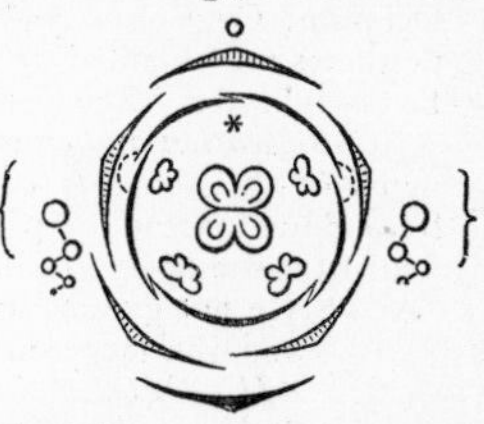

Floral diagram of Lamium album with indication of dich. double cincinnus at the sides. (After Eichler.) The asterisk represents the missing posterior sta.

Fl. ☿ or gynodioec., ·|·, hypog., 5-merous with suppression in some whorls. Usu. formula K (5), C (5), A 4, G̲ (2). K tubular, bell- or funnel-shaped, sometimes 2-lipped, persistent in fr.; C usu. 2-lipped with no clear indication of the individual petals; A 4, didynamous, or of nearly equal length, sometimes 2, epipet. with intr. anthers. G on a nectariferous disc (often developed on anterior side only), of (2) cpls. placed antero-post. Early in development a constriction appears in the ovary in the antero-post. line, dividing each cpl. into 2 loculi, so that the ovary becomes 4-loc. as it matures. Each of the 4 portions is nearly independent of the rest, and the style springs between them from the base of the ovary (*i.e.* is *gynobasic*); stigma 2-lobed. Placentae axile, each with 1 basal erect anatr. ovule with ventral raphe. Fr. usu. a group of 4 achenes or *nutlets*, each containing one seed; sometimes a drupe. Seed with no endosp. or very little; the radicle of the embryo points downwards (*cf.* Boraginaceae).

The fls. belong in general to classes H. and F. The 2-lipped C ensures that the visiting insect shall take a definite position in regard to the anthers and stigma whilst probing for the honey at the base of the fl. The lower lip acts as a flag to attract, and also as a landing-place, whilst the upper lip shelters the essential organs, which are usu. placed so as to touch the insect's back. The length of the C-tube varies very much, and with it the kind of visitors. Most Brit. sp. are bee fls., the long-tubed red fls. of Monarda &c. are butterfly fls., and a few sp. of Salvia &c. are humming-bird fls. The pollination-mech. is usu. simple; in Lamium, &c. the fl. is homogamous, the stigma merely projecting beyond the anthers so as to be touched first, but usu. the fl. is dichogamous (protandr.), often with movements of the essential organs, *e.g.* in Teucrium, &c. The lever-mechanism of Salvia is almost unique. Thymus, Origanum, and their allies, have nearly regular fls. visited by a more miscellaneous selection of insects. In many L., esp. § VI., interesting distrs. of sex appear, esp. gynodioecism.

A few disperse their fr. by aid of the persistent bladdery K, or by hooks formed from the K teeth. The stalks are often hygroscopic and move in such a way as to favour dispersal in wet weather.

Useful on account of their volatile oils; many, *e.g.* Thymus, Ocimum, Origanum, Salvia, &c., used as condiments. Oils and perfumes are obtained by distillation from Rosmarinus, Pogostemon, Lavandula, &c. Food products from Stachys sp.

Classification and chief genera (after Briquet, from whose account much of the above is condensed); closely allied to Verbenaceae; from Boraginaceae the position of the radicle sharply separates them, whilst the similarity to Scrophulariaceae, &c. is largely in minor chars.

A. Style not gynobasic. Nutlets with lateral-ventral attachment and usu. large surface of contact (often $>\frac{1}{2}$ as high as ovary).

I. *AJUGOIDEAE* (seed exalb.);

1. *Ajugeae* (corolla various; upper lip if present rarely concave; sta. 4 or 2; anther 2-loc.; nutlets ± wrinkled): Ajuga, Teucrium.

2. *Rosmarineae* (corolla strongly 2-lipped; upper lip very concave and arched; sta. 2; anthers 1-loc.; nutlets smooth): Rosmarinus (only genus).

II. *PROSTANTHEROIDEAE* (seed albuminous): Prostanthera.

B. Style perfectly gynobasic. Nutlets with basal attachment and usu. small surface of contact, rarely with ± basal-dorsal attachment.

III. *PRASIOIDEAE* (nutlet drupaceous with fleshy or very thick exocarp and hard endocarp): Stenogyne, Gomphostemma.

IV. *SCUTELLARIOIDEAE* (nutlet dry; seed ± transversal; embryo with curved radicle lying on one cot.): Scutellaria.

V. *LAVANDULOIDEAE* (nutlet dry; seed erect; embryo with short straight superior radicle; disc-lobes opp. to ovary-lobes; nutlets with ± distinct dorsal-basal attachment; sta. 4 included; anthers 1-loc. at tip through union of thecae): Lavandula (only genus).

VI. *STACHYDOIDEAE* (ditto, but disc-lobes, when distinct, alt. with ovary-lobes; nut with small basal attachment; sta. ascending or spreading and projecting straight forwards): Marrubium, Nepeta, Dracocephalum, Prunella, Phlomis, Galeopsis, Lamium, Ballota, Stachys, Salvia, Monarda, Ziziphora, Horminum, Calamintha, Satureia, Origanum, Thymus, Mentha, Pogostemon.

VII. *OCIMOIDEAE* (as VI., but sta. descending, lying upon under lip or enclosed by it): Hyptis, Ocimum.

VIII. *CATOPHERIOIDEAE* (nutlet dry; seed erect; embryo with curved radicle lying against the cotyledons): Catopheria.

Labiate (C), with projecting lip.

Labichea Gaudich. ex DC. Leguminosae (II. 5). 5 Austr.

Labidostelma Schlechter. Asclepiadaceae (II. 4). 1 Guatemala.

Labile, plastic.

Labisia Lindl. Myrsinaceae (II). 1 Malaya. Stem creeping.

Lablab Adans. (*Dolichos BH.*). Leguminosae (III. 10). 1 trop. Afr., *L. vulgaris* Sair, largely cult. in trop. for ed. pods.

Labordia Gaudich. Loganiaceae. 9 Hawaiian Is.

Labourdonnaisia Boj. Sapot. (1). 4 Mauritius, Madag. Natal Hard- [wood.

Labrador tea (Am.), *Ledum palustre* L.

Labramia A. DC. (*Mimusops* p.p. *EP.*). Sapotaceae (2). 1 Madag.

Laburnum L. Leguminosae (III. 3). 3 Eur., W. As. *L. vulgare* J. Presl, the common laburnum. The fl. has a simple Trifolium-mech. There is no free honey; bees pierce the swelling at the base of the vexillum (*cf.* Orchis). All parts are poisonous.

Lac, a resin formed as an excretion from the skin of the lac insect, living on *Butea*, *Croton*, *Ficus*, *Schleichera*, &c.

Lacaena Lindl. Orchidaceae (II. 13). 2 Mexico, C. Am. Cult. orn. fl.

Lacaitaea Brand (*Trichodesma* p.p.). Boragin. (IV. 1). 1 Sikkim.

Laccodiscus Radlk. (*Cupania* p.p. *BH.*). Sapindaceae (1). 1 trop. W. Afr.

Laccopetalum Ulbrich (*Anemone* p.p.). Ranunculaceae (3). 1 Peru.

Laccosperma G. Mann et H. Wendl. (*Ancistrophyllum* p.p.). Palmaceae (III). 1 W. Afr.

Lace-bark (W.I.), *Lagetta Lintearia* Lam.

Lacerate, deeply and irregularly divided.

Lachemilla Rydberg (*Alchemilla* p.p.). Rosaceae (III. 5). 15 N. Am.

Lachenalia Jacq. Liliaceae (V). 50 S. Afr. *L. tricolor* Jacq. a little bulbous plant with two leaves, cult. orn. fl.

Lachnaea L. Thymelaeaceae. 18 S. Afr.

Lachnagrostis Trin. = Deyeuxia Clar. (*BH.*) = Calamagrostis p.p.

Lachnanthes Ell. Haemodoraceae. 1 N. Am., *L. tinctoria* Ell., the paint-root. The roots yield red dye. *Orig. of Species*, 6th ed., p. 9.

Lachnastoma Korth. (*Coffea* p.p.). Rubiaceae (II. 4). 1 Java.

Lachnocapsa Balf. f. Cruciferae (4). 1 Socotra.

Lachnocaulon Kunth. Eriocaulaceae. 4 S.E. N.Am.

Lachnocephalus Turcz. (*Mallophora* p.p.). Verben. (3). 1 temp. W. Austr.

Lachnochloa Steud. Gramineae (inc. sed.). 1 Senegambia.

Lachnoloma Bunge. Cruciferae (1). 1 Turkestan.

Lachnophyllum Bunge. Comp. (3). 2 W. As.
Lachnorhiza (*Vernonia* p.p. *EP.*). Comp. (1). 2 Cuba. [pappus.
Lachnospermum Willd. Comp. (4). 1 S. Afr. Fr. glandular, with
Lachnostachys Hook. Verben. (3). 8 Austr. [stalked.
Lachnostoma H. B. et K. Asclep. (II. 4). 6 warm Am. Gynostemium
Lachnostylis Turcz. Euphorb. (A. I. 1). 1 Cape Col. Endosp. thin.
Laciala O. Ktze. (*Schizoptera EP.*). Comp. (5). 1 Ecuador.
Laciniaria Hill (*Liatris* Schreb.). Comp. (2). 25 N. Am.
Laciniate, divided into several long ± equal segments.
Lacis Schreb. Podostem. 1 Amazon.
Lacistema Sw. The only gen. of **Lacistemaceae** (*EP.*, *BH.*; Dicots. Archichl. Piperales; Monochl. Anom. *BH.*; pp. xi, liv). 16 trop. Am., W.I. Shrubs with distichous alt. l. with stips. deciduous or o. Fls. very small, ☿ or ♂ ♀, naked or with one whorl of P, and with concave disc. A 1, $\underline{G}$ (2—3) with parietal plac. and 1—2 pend. anatr. ov. on each. Caps. 1-seeded. Endosp. Closely allied to Piperac.
Lacmellia Karst. Apocyn. (I. 1). 1 trop. S. Am. Fr. ed.
Lacquer, Japan, *Rhus vernicifera* DC.
Lactoridaceae (*EP.*; *Piperaceae* p.p. *BH.*). Dicots. (Archichl. Ranales; pp. xix, liii). Only gen. **Lactoris** Phil., 1 Juan Fernandez, *L. fernandeziana* Phil., a shrub with alt. stip. l. and 3-merous fls. P 3, A 3 + 3, $\underline{G}$ 3 with pend. anatr. ov. Endosp. Highly endemic fam.
Lactuca (Tourn.) L. (excl. *Mulgedium*). Comp. (13). 100 $\underline{✱}$, chiefly N. temp. |✱, 4 Brit. *L. Scariola* L. (prickly lettuce), a compass pl. (*cf.* Silphium) in dry exposed places, spreading as a weed in the U.S.; *L. sativa* L. the lettuce. Fl. like Hieracium.
Lacuna, an open space in tissue; **lacustris** (Lat.), living in lakes.
Ladanium Spach = Cistus L. p.p. (Cist.).
Ladanum, *Cistus creticus* L. var. *villosus* L., *C. ladaniferus* L.
Ladanum Dill. ex L., S. F. Gray, O. Ktze. = Galeopsis Tourn. p.p.
Ladenbergia Klotzsch (incl. *Cascarilla*). Rubi. (I. 5). 40 S. Am. Bark astringent, containing alkaloids.
Lady-fern, *Athyrium Filix-femina* Roth.; **-'s fingers**, *Anthyllis vulneraria* L.; **-slipper orchid**, *Cypripedium*; **-thumb** (Am.), *Polygonum Persicaria* L.; **-tresses**, *Spiranthes autumnalis* Rich.
Ladyginia Lipsky. Umbell. (III. 6). 1 C. As. [with 8 pollinia.
Laelia Lindl. Orchid. (II. 6). 45 trop. Am., W. I. Like Cattleya, but
Laeliopsis Lindl. in Paxton = Epidendrum, &c. *BH.* = Laelia Lindl.
Laeliocattleya Rolfe. Hybrid Orchid, Laelia and Cattleya.
Laestadia Kunth. Comp. (3). 5 trop. Andes. No pappus. [dotted.
Laetia Loefl. Flacourt. (7). 10 trop. Am., W.I. L. often gland-
Laevigatus, laevis (Lat.), smooth.
Lafoensia Vand. Lythr. 12 trop. Am. Trees. 8—16-merous.
Lafuentia Lag. Scroph. (III. 1). 1 S. Spain. Woolly undershrub.
Lagarosiphon Harv. Hydrocharid. (III). 10 Afr., Madag., Ind. L. alt. ♂ fls. floating off. A 3, stds. usu. 3.
Lagascea Cav. Comp. (5). 10 C. Am., Braz. Heads cpd., 1-fld.
Lagenandra Dalz. Arac. (VII). 5 Ceylon, S. Ind.
Lagenanthus Gilg. Gentian. (I). 1 Colombia.
Lagenaria Ser. Cucurb. (3). 1 palaeotrop., *L. vulgaris* Ser. (calabash-cucumber, bottle-gourd). The woody outer pericarp makes a flask.

Lagenia E. Fourn. (*Araujia* p.p.). Asclepiadaceae (II. 1). 2 Brazil.
Lagenias E. Mey. (*Sebaea* p.p. *BH.*). Gentianaceae (I). 1 Cape Colony.
Lagenocarpus Nees. Cyperaceae (II). 20 trop. S. Am., Trinidad.
Lagenophora Cass. Compositae (3). 15 Japan to N.Z., Chili.
Lagerstroemia L. Lythraceae. 25 palaeotrop. Some heterostyled like Lythrum. Cult. orn. fl. trees. Some provide good timber.
Lagetta Juss. Thymelaeaceae. 3 W. Ind. *L. Lintearia* Lam. is the lace tree. Its bast-fibres on removal from the stem (by maceration, &c.) form a network used for making dresses, &c.
Laggera Sch.-Bip. ex Hochst. Compositae (4). 12 palaeotrop.
Lagoa Durand. Asclepiadaceae (II. 1). 1 Brazil.
Lagochilium Nees = Aphelandra R. Br. (Acanth.).
Lagochilus Bunge. Labiatae (VI). 15 W. As.
Lagoecia L. Umbelliferae (II. 2). 1 Medit. One of the usu. two loc. of the ovary is aborted.
Lagophylla Nutt. Compositae (5). 6 W. N. Am.
Lagos rubber, *Funtumia elastica* Stapf.
Lagoseris Hoffmgg. et Link = Crepis L. p.p. (Comp.).
Lagotis J. Gaertn. Scrophulariaceae (III. 1). 10 N. and C. As.
Laguna Cav. = Hibiscus L. (Malv.).
Lagunaria G. Don. Malvaceae (4). 1 E. Austr., Norfolk I., Howe I.
Laguncularia Gaertn. f. Combretaceae. 1 W. trop. Afr., Am. (mangrove).
Lagurus L. Gramineae (8). 1 Medit., *L. ovatus* L., cult. orn.
Lahia Hassk. (*Durio* p.p. *EP.*). Bombacaceae. 1 Borneo.
Lallemantia Fisch. et Mey. Labiatae (VI). 4 W. As.
Lamarchea Gaudich. Myrtaceae (II. 1). 1 W. Austr.
Lamarckia Moench. Gramineae (10). 1 Medit. Cult. orn.
Lamb-kill (Am.), *Kalmia angustifolia* L.; **-'s lettuce**, *Valerianella*, (Am.) *Fedia*; **-quarters**, *Chenopodium*.
Lambertia Sm. Proteaceae. 8 Austr.
Lamellisepalum Engl. Rhamnaceae. 1 trop. Afr.
Lamiacanthus O. Ktze. Acanthaceae (IV. A). 1 Java.
Lamiales (*BH.*). The 10th order of Gamopetalae.
Lamina, the blade of a l.
Lamium (Tourn.) L. Labiatae (VI). 40 Eur., As., extratrop. Afr. 5 in Brit., incl. *L. album* L. (white dead-nettle), *L. amplexicaule* L. (henbit), *L. purpureum* L. (purple dead-nettle) and *L. Galeobdolon* Crantz (yellow archangel). *L. album* has sympodial rhizomes and large white homogamous humble-bee fls. *L. amplexicaule* has cleist. fls. in spring and autumn; they look like ordinary buds with a small C, and are pollinated without opening.
Lamourouxia H. B. et K. Scrophulariaceae (III. 3). 20 trop. Am.
Lampaya Phil. Verbenaceae (I). 1 Chili.
Lampocarya R. Br. = Gahnia Forst. p.p. (Cyper.).
Lamprachaenium Benth. Compositae (1). 1 Indomal.
Lamprocaulos Mast. (*Elegia* p.p. *EP.*). Restionaceae. 2 S. Afr.
Lamprochlaenia Börner = Carex L. p.p. (Cyper.).
Lamprococcus Beer (*Aechmea* p.p. *BH.*). Bromeliaceae (4). 8 trop. Am. Cult. orn. infl.
Lamprodithyros Hassk. = Aneilema R. Br. p.p. (Commelin.).

Lamprolobium Benth. Leguminosae (III. 6). 1 Queensland.
Lamprospermum Klotzsch (*Matayba EP.*). Sapindaceae (1). 2 Guiana.
Lamprothamnus Hiern. Rubiaceae (II. 1). 1 Zanzibar.
Lamprothyrsus Pilger. Gramineae (9). 1 S. Am.
Lamprotis D. Don = Erica Tourn. p.p. (Eric.).
Lampsana (Tourn.) Rupp. = Lapsana L. (Comp.).
Lanaria Ait. Amaryllidaceae (III) (Haemodor. *BH.*). 1 S. Afr.
Lanatus (Lat.), woolly.
Lance, *Dendrocalamus*; **-wood,** *Duguetia*, *Oxandra*, *Tournefortia*, &c.
Lancea Hook. f. et Thoms. Scrophulariaceae (II. 6). 2 Tibet, China.
Lanceolate (l.), 3 times as long as broad, tapering gradually.
Landolphia Beauv. Apocynaceae (I. 1). 40 trop. and S. Afr. Several are lianes with curious hook tendrils like Strychnos. Fr. a large berry full of an acid pulp composed of the hair-structures on the seeds. Several, *e.g.* *L. Kirkii* Dyer, *L. comorensis* Benth. et Hook. f., &c., yield rubber, the coagulated latex. It is known in trade as African and Madagascar rubber.
Landtia Less. (*Arctotis* p.p. *EP.*). Compositae (10). 4 S. Afr., Abyss.
Landukia Planch. (*Vitis* p.p.). Vitaceae. 1 Java.
Lanessania Baill. Moraceae (II). 1 N. Brazil.
Langlassea H. Wolff. Umbelliferae (III. 6). 1 Mexico.
Langloisia Greene (*Gilia* p.p.). Polemoniaceae. 6 S.W. U.S.
Langsdorffia Mart. Balanophoraceae. 1 trop. Am. *L. hypogaea* Mart.
Lanium Lindl. (*Epidendrum* p.p. *EP.*). Orchidaceae (II. 6). 4 trop. Am.
Lankesteria Lindl. Acanthaceae (IV. A). 5 trop. W. Afr.
Lannea A. Rich (*Odina BH.*, *Calesium EP.*). Anacardiaceae (2). 15 palaeotrop.
Lanneoma Delile (*Lannea* p.p.). Anacardiaceae (2). 1 Abyss., E. Afr.
Lanose, lanuginose, woolly.
Lansbergia De Vriese = Trimezia Salisb. (Irid.).
Lansium Rumph. Meliaceae (III). 4 Indomal. *L. domesticum* Jack ed. fr.
Lantana L. Verbenaceae (1). 60 trop. and subtrop. Shrubs, often used for hedges. Some have ed. fr.
Lantanopsis Wright. Compositae (5). 3 Cuba, S. Domingo.
Lapageria Ruiz et Pav. Liliaceae (X). 1 Chili, *L. rosea* Ruiz et Pav., a climbing shrub with ed. fr., cult. orn. fl.
Lapatero (W.I.), *Copaifera officinalis* L.
Lapathum (Tourn.) Adans. = Rumex L. p.p. (Polygon.).
Lapeyrousia Pourr. Iridaceae (III). 50 S. Afr. to Abyss. Cult. orn. fl.
Laphamia A. Gray. Compositae (6). 15 S. U.S., Mexico.
Lapiedra Lag. Amaryllidaceae (1). 1 Spain.
Lapithea Griseb. (*Sabbatia BH.*). Gentian. (1). 1 Carolina to Texas.
Laplacea H. B. et K. (*Haemocharis EP.*). Theaceae. 25 trop. As., Am., W.I.
Laportea Gaudich. Urticaceae (1). 40 warm. Many sting violently.
Lappa (Tourn.) Rupp. = Arctium L. (Comp.).
Lappago Schreb. = Tragus Hall. (Gram.).
Lappula Moench. (*Echinospermum BH.*). Boragin. (IV. 2). 60 temp.
Lapsana L. Compositae (13). 9 N. temp. |*. *L. communis* L. (nipplewort) in Brit. The fls. are inconspicuous and pollinate themselves. There is no pappus.

Larch, *Larix*.
Laretia Gill. et Hook. Umbelliferae (I. 2). 1 Andes of Chili.
Laricopsis Kent. = Pseudolarix Gord. Coniferae (Pinac.).
Lardizabala Ruiz et Pav. Lardizabalaceae. 2 Chili. Tough fibre from the stems of *L. biternata* Ruiz et Pav.
Lardizabalaceae (*EP.*; *Berberidaceae* p.p. *BH.*). Dicots. (Archichl. Ranales). 7 gen. 15 sp. Himal. to Japan, Chili. Mostly climbing shrubs with palmate l. Fls. in racemes, usu. in the axils of the scale-l. at the bases of the branches, polygamous or diclinous. Usual formula P 3 + 3, A 3 + 3, $\underline{G}$ 3 or more. 2 whorls of small honey-leaves (see Ranunculaceae) often occur between P and A; sta. sometimes united; anthers extrorse; ovules ∞ in longitudinal rows on the lat. walls (cf. Nymphaeaceae), anatr. The fl. of either sex shows rudiments of the organs of the other sex. Berry. Embryo small and straight, in copious endosp. *Chief genera:* Decaisnea, Akebia, Lardizabala.
Larix Tourn. ex Adans. Coniferae (Pinac. 20; see C. for genus characters). 8 Eur., N. As., N. Am. The general chars. are those of Cedrus, but the l. are deciduous, and the cones ripen in a single year. *L. europaea* DC. (*L. decidua* Mill.) is the common larch, cult. on a large scale for its wood, bark (used in tanning) and turpentine (Venice t.). Others are also important, *e.g.* *L. americana* Michx. (tamarack).
Larkspur, *Delphinium*.
Larochea Pers. = Crassula Dill. p.p. (Crass.).
Larrea Cav. Zygophyllaceae. 4 subtrop. Am. Xerophytes. *L. mexicana* Moric. (Mexico, &c.) is the creosote plant, which forms a dense scrub-veg. and binds the drifting sand together. Its strong smell prevents it from being eaten by animals.
Larrea scrub, a scrub association char. by *Larrea mexicana* Moric.
Lasallea Greene (*Aster* p.p.). Compositae (3). 3 N. Am.
Lascadium Rafin. Inc. sed. 1 S. U.S.
Laseguea A. DC. Apocynaceae (II. 1). 10 trop. S. Am.
Laserpitium L. Umbelliferae (III. 7). 35 Eur., N. Afr., As.
Lasia Lour. Araceae (IV). 2 Indomal.
Lasiacis Hitchcock (*Panicum* p.p.). Gramineae (5). 6 N. Am.
Lasiadenia Benth. Thymelaeaceae. 1 Guiana.
Lasiagrostis Link = Stipa L. (Gram.).
Lasiandra DC. = Tibouchina Aubl. (Melast.).
Lasianthemum Klotzsch (*Talisia* p.p. *EP.*). Sapindaceae (I). 2 Guiana.
Lasianthera Beauv. Icacinaceae. 1 trop. W. Afr.
Lasianthus Jack. Rubiaceae (II. 5). 90 Indomal.
Lasiocarpus Liebm. Malpighiaceae (I). 1 Mexico.
Lasiochloa Kunth. Gramineae (10). 4 S. Afr.
Lasiocladus Boj. ex Nees. Acanthaceae (IV. B). 2 Madag.
Lasiococca Hook. f. Euphorbiaceae (A. II. 2). 1 Sikkim.
Lasiocoma Bolus. Compositae (8). 1 S. Afr.
Lasiocorys Benth. (*Leucas* p.p. *EP.*). Labiatae (VI). 7 Afr.
Lasiocroton Griseb. Euphorbiaceae (A. II. 2). 4 Jamaica, Cuba, &c.
Lasiodiscus Hook. f. Rhamnaceae. 5 trop. Afr., Madag.
Lasiopetalum Sm. Sterculiaceae. 25 Austr.

Lasiopogon Cass. Compositae (4). 3 S. Afr., Medit.
Lasiorrhiza Lag. = Leuceria Lag. p.p. (Comp.).
Lasiosiphon Fresen. (*Gnidia EP.*). Thymelaeaceae. 20 palaeotrop.
Lasiospermum Lag. Compositae (7). 3 S. Afr.
Lasiospora Cass. = Scorzonera Tourn. p.p. (Comp.).
Lasiostelma Benth. Asclepiadaceae (II. 3). 4 S. Afr.
Lasiostoma Schreb. = Strychnos L. (Logan.).
Lassa O. Ktze. = Pavonia Cav. (Malv.).
Lassonia Buchoz. Magnoliaceae. 2 China.
Lastarriaca Remy. Polygonaceae (I. 1). 2 Calif., Chili.
Lasthenia Cass. Compositae (6). 10 W. Am.
Lastrea Presl = Dryopteris Adans. (Polypod.).
Latace Phil. Liliaceae (IV). 1 Chili.
Latania Comm. ex Juss. Palmae (II). 3 E. Afr., Mascarenes.
Lateral branching, *cf.* Branch.
Latex, a milky fluid contained in special vessels or cells of the tissues, *Alismaceae*, *Apocynaceae*, *Araceae*, *Asclepiadaceae*, *Euphorbiaceae*, *Compositae* (Cichorieae), *Galactia*, *Moraceae*, *Sapotaceae*, &c. *Cf.* Guttapercha, Rubber, Balata; **laticiferous,** latex-bearing.
Lathraea L. Orobanchaceae. 5 temp. Eur., As. *L. Squamaria* L. in Brit. (tooth-wort) is a total parasite living upon the roots of hazel, beech, &c. It has a thick rhiz. bearing 4 rows of tooth-like scaly l. The fl. shoot comes above ground and bears a raceme of purplish fls., all bent round to the same side of the infl., protogynous. The scales upon the rhiz. are hollowed, each containing a branched cavity opening to the outside by a narrow slit at the base of the back of the l. This arises by a development similar to that which forms the chambers in the l. of Empetrum, Cassiope, &c. In the small lat. cavities opening out of the main one there are found peculiar glandular organs, resembling those of insectivorous plants. Small insects, &c. are often found in these leaves (*cf.* bladders of Utricularia, &c.) and it has been supposed that these organs absorb their proteids like the glands of Drosera, &c. This however is doubtful. *L. Clandestina* L. is parasitic upon willows. The capsule of L. splits explosively. [For details see Heinricher, *Die Schuppenwurz*, Stuttgart, 1908.]
Lathriogyna Eckl. et Zeyh. Leguminosae (III. 3). 1 S. Afr.
Lathrophytum Eichl. Balanophoraceae. 1 Rio de Janeiro.
Lathyrus (Tourn.). L. (incl. *Orobus* L.). Leguminosae (III. 9). 110 N. temp., and Mts. of trop. Afr. and S. Am. 10 in Brit. (pea), including *L. Aphaca* L. and *L. Nissolia* L. The former has large green stipules performing assim. functions, whilst the l. is transformed into a tendril; the latter has its petioles flattened into phyllodes and has no l. blade at all (see Acacia). *L. macrorrhizus* Wimm. has tuberous roots which may be eaten like potatoes. *L. sativus* L. (Jarosse) and *L. Cicera* L. are cult. in S. Eur. as fodder and are also eaten like chick-pea (Cicer). *L. odoratus* L. is the sweet-pea. The fl. is like that of Vicia; on the style is a tuft of hairs that brushes the pollen out of the apex of the keel, where it is shed by the anthers. *L. latifolius* (everlasting pea) also cult. orn. fl.
Lati- (Lat. pref.), broad; **-folius,** broad-leaved, &c. &c.
Latipes Kunth. Gramineae (3). 1 Senegal to Sind.

Latouchea Franch. Gentianaceae (I). 1 China.
Latouria Blume (*Dendrobium* p.p. *BH.*). Orchid. (II. 15). 1 New Guinea.
Latreillea DC. = Ichthyothere Mart. (Comp.).
Latrobea Meissn. Leguminosae (III. 2). 6 W. Austr.
Latua Phil. Solanaceae (2). 1 Chili.
Laubertia A. DC. Apocynaceae (II. 1). 2 Peru, Bolivia.
Laugeria Vahl (*Guettarda* p.p. *EP.*). Rubiaceae (II. 2). 2 W.I.
Launaea Cass. Compositae (13). 30 trop. and subtrop. *L. pinnatifida* Cass. a char. plant of sandy trop. beaches.
Lauraceae (*EP.*, *BH* incl. *Hernandiaceae*). Dicots. (Archichl. Ranales; Daphnales *BH.*). 40 gen. 1000 sp. trop. and subtrop.; chief centres of distr. S.E. As. and Brazil. Trees and shrubs with leathery evergr. alt. exstip. l. The tissues contain numerous oil-cavities. Cassytha is an interesting parasite. Infl. racemose, cymose, or mixed. Fl. actinom., apet., usu. 3-merous, ☿ or monoec. Formula usu. P_{2n}, A_{4n}, $\underline{G}_n$. P in two whorls, perig.; A perig. or epig., in 3 or 4 whorls, some of which are commonly reduced to stds.; anther usu. 4-loc. opening by valves (*cf.* Berberidaceae), usu. intr., but in many cases those of the third whorl extr. The axis is ± concave, and the ovary is free from it at the sides. $\underline{G}$ 1 (Payer, Baillon) or more probably 3 (Eichler), forming a 1-loc. ovary, with 1 pend. anatr. ov. Fr. a berry, often ± enclosed by the cup-like recept., which also becomes fleshy in these cases. Embryo straight; seed exalb. The position of the L. in the system is doubtful; they apparently form the connecting link between the Ranales (to the more typical fams. of which they are linked by Monimiaceae and Calycanthaceae) and the Thymelaeales. Important economic plants are found in nearly all the genera mentioned below. [See *Nat. Pfl.* and Mez. in *Bot. Jahresb.* 1889, p. 459, and *Bot. Centr.* 54, p. 275 (abstracts).]

Classification and chief genera (after Pax):

I. *PERSEOIDEAE* (anther 4-loc.): Cinnamomum, Persea, Sassafras, Litsea.

II. *LAUROIDEAE* (anther 2-loc.): Cryptocarya, Lindera, Laurus, Cassytha.

Laurel, *Laurus nobilis* L.; **Alexandrian -**, *Calophyllum Inophyllum* L.; **bay -**, *Laurus nobilis* L.; **cherry -**, *Prunus Laurocerasus* L.; **Japan -**, *Aucuba japonica* Thunb.; **Portugal -**, *Prunus lusitanica* L.; **sea-side -** (W. I.), *Phyllanthus*; **spurge-**, *Daphne Laureola* L.; **West Indian -** (W.I.), *Prunus occidentalis* Sw.
Laurelia Juss. Monimiaceae. 1 N.Z., 1 Chili. *L. Novae-Zealandiae* A. Cunn. supplies a useful timber. The frs. of *L. aromatica* Juss. are used as a spice under the name Peruvian nutmegs.
Laurembergia Berg. (*Serpicula* L.). Haloragidaceae. 20 trop. and subtrop.
Laurentia Michx. ex Adans. Campanulaceae (III). 10 Medit., S. Afr., N. Am.
Laurestinus (Am.), *Viburnum.*
Lauridia Eckl. et Zeyh. (*Elaeodendron BH.*). Celastraceae. 1 S. Afr.
Laurineae (*BH.*), Lauraceae.
Laurium (Cl.), a drain formation.

Laurocerasus (Tourn.), M. Roem. = Prunus L. p.p. (Ros.).

Laurophyllus Thunb. (*Botryceras BH.*). Anacardiaceae (3). 1 S. Afr.

Laurus (Tourn.) L. Lauraceae (11). 2, *L. nobilis* L. the true laurel or sweet bay, Medit. (l. aromatic, used in condiments, &c., berries in veterinary medicine), and *L. canariensis* Webb et Berth., Canaries and Madeira. Fls. unisexual by abortion.

Lautembergia Baill. (*Alchornea* p.p. *BH.*). Euph. (A. II. 2). 3 Madag.

Lauterbachia Perkins. Monimiaceae. 1 New Guinea.

Lavalleopsis Van Tiegh. Olacaceae. 3 W. trop. Afr.

Lavandula Tourn. ex L. Labiatae (V, *q.v.* for gen. char.). 20 Medit. to India. From *L. vera* DC. (lavender) is obtained oil of lavender, by distillation of the fls.; it is used in painting, and in the manufacture of lavender water. *L. Spica* Cav. and *L. Stoechas* L. are also used. The protandr. fls. are visited by bees and form a good source of honey.

Lavatera L. Malvaceae (2). 20 Medit., Austr., mid-As. *L. arborea* L., tree-mallow, on rocks on the Brit. coast.

Lavauxia Spach (*Oenothera* p.p. *BH.*). Onagraceae (2). 8 W. Am.

Lavender, *Lavandula vera* DC. &c.; **cotton-**, *Santalina*; **sea-**, *Statice.*

Lavenia Sw. = Adenostemma Forst. (Comp.).

Lavidia Phil. Compositae (12). 1 Patagonia.

Lavigeria Pierre (*Icacina* p.p.). Icacinaceae. 1 Cochinchina.

Lavoisiera DC. Melastomaceae (1). 50 Brazil.

Lavradia Vell. ex Vand. Ochnaceae. 6 Brazil.

Lawia Griff. ex Tul. Tristichaceae. 1 Ceylon to Bombay Ghats. Thallus of shoot nature, creeping, with endogenous shoots on upper side.

Lawsonia L. Lythraceae. 1 palaeotrop. *L. inermis* L. The powdered l. form the cosmetic, henna, used in the East to stain the finger-nails, &c., red.

Laxmannia R. Br. (*Bartlingia* F. Muell.). Liliaceae (III). 8 Austr.

Laxus (Lat.), loose.

Layia Hook. et Arn. Compositae (5). 14 W. N. Am. Cult. orn. fl.

Leader, top bud of a monopodial shoot, *Abies*.

Lead-tree (W.I.), *Leucaena glauca* Benth.; **-wort** (W.I.), *Plumbago*.

Leaf, a thin green expanded organ, borne on the stem at the nodes. The interior of an ordinary l. is made up of a mass of spongy green tissue (*mesophyll*), covered by an epidermis which contains *stomata* leading to the intercellular spaces in the interior, and whose outer wall is covered by a *cuticle* of waxy or corky nature. The vascular bundles that run through the l. and hold it outstretched are called the *veins* or *nerves*. The l. shows distinction into a *base* abutting on the stem and often bearing a pair of green or membranous expansions (*stipules*), and a *blade* or *lamina*, often with a stalk or *petiole* between. Such a l. has an upper or *ventral* surface, and a lower or *dorsal*, and is markedly *dorsiventral* in structure; it places itself ± horiz. in what is called its *fixed light position*. Others (*isobilateral*, *q.v.*) have symmetrical structure on both sides, and place themselves with their edges to the light (*phyllodes* (*q.v.*) also come into this category), and yet others (*centric*, *q.v.*) have symmetrical structure all round, and stand with their apices to the light. Many l. exhibit *sleep movements* at night, or movements during heat or dryness (*cf.* Movements). The fall of a l. is often effected by an *absciss-layer*, or stratum of cork which separates it from the stem, and then splits, leaving a *leaf-scar* upon the stem. L. with such a layer are called *articulate*, without, *non-articulate*.

Under other than mesophytic conditions such structure as just described shows many modifications; *cf.* Climbing Plants, Insectivorous Plants, Parasites, Saprophytes, Water Plants, Xerophytes. It is also modified for Storage (*q.v.*) of reserves, or for Vegetative Reproduction (*q.v.*).

In external form l. show very great variety, and the grouping of gen. into sp. is largely determined by this, so that it is necessary to understand the use of the technical terms employed in such work, before one can use a flora with any advantage. An outline of such terms and their use follows.

Descriptive Terms. The student should practise describing leafy shoots until expert in handling terminology, but there is no need to commit the terms to memory. At first he should describe in detail in the order given below, but afterwards try to render his descriptions short and pithy without sacrifice of essentials; this can only be well done by comparison with related forms to see what points are common to all.

L. as to phyllotaxy (*q.v.*) or arrangement may be *radical*, or on the subaerial stem (*cauline*); *whorled* (*verticillate*), *opposite* (and then *decussate* if each pair is ⊥ the next, *connate* if the two are concrescent as in Lonicera, *anisophyllous* if unequal in size or shape), or *alternate* (the phyllotaxy fraction may be given, or the number of ranks described by the terms *di-*, *tri-stichous*, &c.). With regard to *insertion* or mode of union with the stem the l. may be *petiolate* or *sessile* (*i.e.* with or without stalk respectively; the petiole is descr. like a stem), *auricled* (with two lobes of the blade overlapping the stem), *amplexicaul* (the lobes clasping the stem), *sheathing* (as in Grasses, the leaf-base forming a tube round the stem), *perfoliate* (the leaf united round the stem, as in Bupleurum), *decurrent* (continued by a wing on the stem, as in thistles), &c. It may bear a *ligule* or scale at the upper end of the leaf-base or sheath, as in Grasses. It may be *stipulate* or *exstipulate* (with or without stip. respectively); the shape, &c. of the stip. is described as if they were l. and they may be free or *adnate* (F in fig., concrescent with the leaf-base or petiole, as in rose), united to other stip., *inter-* or *intra-petiolar*, branched, &c. (see Rubiaceae), *ochreate* (sheathing, as in Polygonaceae), or modified in various ways. The *venation* (arrangement of the veins) may be *pinnate* or *palmate*; in the former case there is a *midrib* with lat. veins branching from it, in the latter several equal veins spread out in the l. like the ribs of a fan, from one point. The further ramification of the veins is descr. by *net-veined* (irreg. meshwork, as in most Dicots.), *parallel-veined* (meshes more or less rectangular, as in most Monocots.), *fork-veined* (veins forking into two, as in Ferns).

L. are divided into *simple* and *compound*, as the stalk bears one or several separate *leaflets*. In the latter case the leaflet is desc. as if it were a l., and the common stalk is called the *rachis*. If the leaflets spring from the sides of the rachis, as in the pea, the l. is *pinnate* (F), if all from one point *palmate* (E). If the leaflets of a pinnate l., as in many Acacias, are again pinnately cpd., the l. is *bipinnate*. A l. with 3 leaflets (as in clover) is *ternate* or *tri-foliolate*, with 3 ternate leaflets *biternate*. Pinnate l. may be *equally* (*pari-*) *pinnate* (with an even number of leaflets), *unequally* (*impari-*) *pinnate* (with an odd leaflet at the end), or *interruptedly pinnate* (large and small leaflets alt. as in many Rosaceae). A palmate l. with 5 or 7 leaflets is often called *digitate*. The leaflet may have stipule-like organs, or *stipels* (adjective *stipellate*).

The leaf may be *dorsiventral*, *isobilateral*, or *centric*, or replaced by a *phyllode*, *scale*, *pitcher*, or other organ.

The shape of the leaf-blade or leaflet itself, if simple, or the outline of a cpd. l., may be *needle-shaped* or *acicular* as in Pinus, *subulate* or awl-shaped, *tubular* as in onion, *linear* (long and narrow as in Grasses), *lanceolate* (about 3 times as long as broad, tapering gradually towards the tip; A in fig.), *ovate* (about twice as long as broad, and tapering towards the tip; B), *cordate* (similar, but heart-shaped at the base; C), *elliptical* (tapering equally to base and tip, and somewhat narrow), *oval* (do. but wider), *oblong* (sides ‖ for some distance, the ends tapering rapidly; F), *reniform* (kidney-shaped), *orbicular* (circular in outline; if the petiole is inserted at the middle of the blade, as in Tropaeolum, this leaf is termed *peltate*), *hastate* (with two pointed

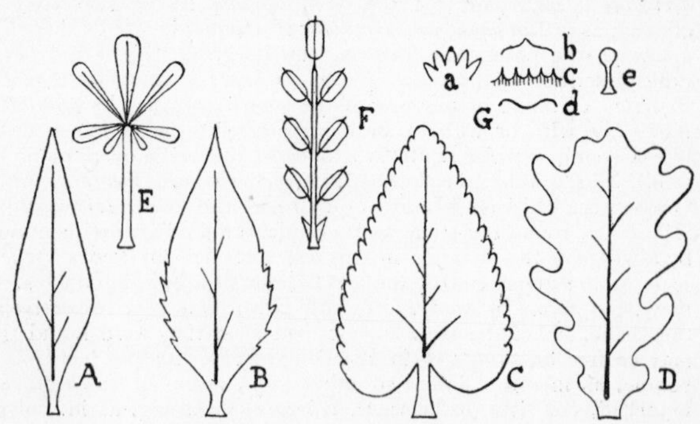

Forms of Leaves. A, subsessile, exstip., lanceolate with cuneate base, entire, acute. B, sessile, exstip., ovate, serrate below, entire above, acum. C, petiolate, exstip., cordate, crenate, obtuse. D, sessile, exstip., somewhat obovate, pinnatifid sinuate, obtuse. E, petiolate, exstip., palmate (digitate), with obtuse oblanceolate leaflets. F, impari-pinnate with triangular adnate stips.; leaflets shortly stalked, oblong, apiculate, the laterals oblique. G, *a*, plicate l. in section, *b*, mucronate apex, *c*, dentate spiny margin, *d*, retuse apex, *e*, glandular hair.

lobes sticking out horiz. at the base), *sagittate* (two lobes projecting towards the stem), *spatulate* (spoon-shaped, as in daisy), &c. If a l. be of lanceolate shape but the general tapering be towards the base, it is called *oblanceolate* (E); so also *obovate* or *obcordate*. If wedge-shaped, tapering to the base, it is *cuneate*. The l. may be *oblique* or *asymmetrical* (F), when the midrib divides it into unequal halves, as in Begonia.

The l. (or leaflet) may be *entire*, *i.e.* without notches in the margin (A), or *incised*; the margin may also be fringed or *fimbriate*, *cartilaginous*, *membranous*, wavy or *undulate* (as in holly), curled or *crisped* (as in sea-kale), *spiny* (G*c*), *glandular* (with sticky hairs or glands; G*e*), *ciliate* (with fine projecting hairs), &c. If the margin has small teeth pointing forwards, it is *serrate* (B), if pointing outwards, *dentate* (G*c*); if the teeth are rounded but the notches sharp, the margin is *crenate* (C), if both teeth and notches are rounded, it is *sinuate* (D). If the depth of the divisions is equal to ¼ the distance from midrib to margin, *i.e.* if the incisions are conspicuous in proportion to the size of the blade, other terms come into use. If the notching is from ¼ to ½ the depth, the l. is *-fid* (D), if ½ to ¾, *-partite*, if over ¾, *-sect*. Prefixes of *pinnati-* or *palmati-* are used before these terms to express the particular form of notching, which depends upon the venation. The portions into which the l. is thus divided are termed *lobes* or *segments*. Special terms are employed for such l. as mustard (*lyrate*, the end lobe very large), dandelion (*runcinate*, the lobes pointing backwards), hellebore (*pedate*), &c.

The apex may be *acute* (pointed; A), *obtuse* (blunt; C), *acuminate* (tapering in hollow curves to a long fine point; B), *emarginate* (notched), *retuse* (broadly do.; G*d*), *mucronate* (with large stiff point on nearly straight edge; G*b*), *apiculate* (do. with small point; F), *truncate* or *praemorse* (broad, straight end, as if bitten off), *cirrhose* (tendrilled).

The surface of the l., as of other parts, may be *glabrous* (without hairs), *pilose* (soft, scattered hairs), *downy* or *pubescent* (fine, soft hairs), *hairy* (coarser), *hispid* (rough, bristly), *tomentose* (with a cottony felt), *woolly*, *glandular-hairy*; *scabrous* (rough), *smooth*, *prickly*, *glaucous* (with bluish waxy gloss), *reticulate* (netted), *rugose* (ridged or wrinkled), *squarrose* (roughly scurfy), &c. Hairs may be *spreading* or *appressed* (flattened down), *simple* (unbranched), *glandular* (G*e*), *bifid*, *stellate* (like a starfish), *squamate* (scaly), &c.; prickles may be straight or curved, bent backwards (*retrorse*), &c. The l. may be *dotted* with oil-glands, or *variegated* in colour, green, red, &c.; frequent shades are *fulvous* (tawny), *rubiginose* (rust-coloured), &c. The texture may be *thin* or *herbaceous*, *coriaceous* (leathery), *succulent* or *fleshy*, *membranous* or *scarious* (thin, dry, not green, and flexible or stiff respectively), &c.

L. may be *evergreen* or *deciduous* (falling in winter); in this case *articulate* (cut off by special absciss layer and falling early), or *non-articulate* (hanging on to the stem, though dead, for an indefinite period, as in beech hedges, oak, &c.). The *vernation*, or folding in bud, is descr. like the aestivation of flower-buds (*q.v.*); the following terms are also used to describe the folding of the individual l., *conduplicate* (folded lengthwise as in oak), *plicate* (folded several times;

G*a*), *involute* (margins rolled inwards), *revolute* (outwards), *reclinate* (apex bent down to base), *convolute* (rolled spirally, as in Musa); conduplicate l. overlapping younger ones thus < < > >, as in Iris, are called *equitant*.

When a character is not accurately described by one of the terms given, but is rather half-way between two, both are used; thus a l. may be linear-lanceolate or ovate-cordate. *Sub*-, meaning 'nearly,' is often used as a prefix to adjectives, *e.g.* subsessile, subacute. As an example of the use of these technical terms, we quote from Lindley the descriptions of two leaves:

Lilac: leaves opposite, exstipulate, roundish-cordate, very acute, thin, smooth, rather longer than the linear channelled petiole.

Garden Strawberry: leaves all radical, ternate, dark-green, somewhat shining, very coarsely serrated; with strong parallel oblique veins, silky beneath; leaflets nearly sessile, roundish oblong, entire towards the base, shorter than the semi-cylindrical hairy petioles; stipules membranous, lanceolate, acuminate, half adnate.

For other details of leaf structure and modification, see Anisophylly, Bud, Climbing Plants, Concrescence, Dimorphism, Driptip, Insectivorous Plants, Parasites, Phyllodes, Phyllotaxy, Saprophytes, Stipule, Storage, Vegetative Reproduction, Water-plants, Xerophytes, and articles below.

Leaf, climbing, *cf.* Climbing Plants; **- colour**, *Amherstia*, *Brownea*, *Castilleja*, *Cinnamomum*, *Haematoxylon*, *Saraca*; **- cushion**, *Cactaceae*; **-cutting ants**, *Acacia*; **-fall** in dry season, *Bombax*, Caatingas, *Cochlospermum*; **- mosaic**, the fitting in of l. with one another to make the best use of light and air available, *Aesculus*, *Hedera*, *Tiliaceae*; **- movements**, cf. Movement.

Leandra Raddi. Melastomaceae (I). 200 trop. Am., W.I.

Leather-leaf (Am.), *Cassandra*; **- wood**, *Cyrilla*.

Leavenworthia Torr. Cruciferae (2). 4 Atl. N. Am.

Lebeckia Thunb. Leguminosae (III. 3). 25 S. Afr.

Lebetanthus Endl. Epacridaceae (1). 1 Fuegia, Patagonia.

Lebidiera Baill. = Cleistanthus Hook. f. (Euph.).

Lebidieropsis Muell.-Arg. (*Cleistanthus* p.p. *BH.*). Euphorbiaceae (A. I. 2). 1 Indomal.

Lecananthus Jack. Rubiaceae (I. 7). 3 Malaya.

Lecaniodiscus Planch. ex Benth. Sapindaceae (I). 2 trop. Afr

Lecanopteris Reinw. Polypodiaceae. 7 Malaya.

Lecanorchis Blume. Orchidaceae (II. 2). 4 Malaya, Japan.

Lecanosperma Rusby. Rubiaceae (I. 5). 1 Bolivia.

Lecanthus Wedd. Urticaceae (2). 1 Indomal., Abyssinia.

Lechea Kalm. ex L. Cistaceae. 15 N. and C. Am., W.I. Pets. 3 or O. [Ov. 2—3.

Lechlera Miq. Inc. sed. Nomen.

Lechuguilla, *Agave*.

Leciscium Gaertn. Myrtaceae (inc. sed.). Nomen.

Lecocarpus Decne. Compositae (5). 1 Galapagos.

Lecokia DC. Umbelliferae (III. 4). 1 Crete to Persia.

Lecomtea Pierre ex Van Tiegh. (*Harmandia* p.p.). Olac. 1 trop. Afr.

Lecomtedoxa Dubard (*Mimusops* p.p.). Sapotaceae (II). 3 Gaboon.

Lecontea A. Rich. (*Paederia* p.p. *EP.*). Rubiaceae (II. 6). 2 Madag.

Lecostemon (Moç. et Sesse ex) DC. Ros. (VI). 6 Braz. to Mex.
Lectandra J. J. Smith. Orchid. (II. a. III.). 5 Java, New Guinea.
Lecticula Barnhart (*Utricularia* p.p.). Lentibular. 1 E. U.S.
Lecythidaceae (*EP.*; *Myrt.* p.p. *BH.*). Dicots. (Archichl. Myrtiflorae; pp. xxxvii, lii). 18/150 trop. trees with l. bunched at ends of twigs, alt., simple, exstip. Fls. sol. or in racemose infl., ☿, reg. or C and A ·|·, perig. or epig., always with complete fusion of recept. and ovary. Usu. intra-staminal disc as well as one under C and A. K usu. 4—6, C, rarely (C), 4—6, imbr.; A ∞ in several whorls, sta. ± united at base, anther usu. versatile, bent inwards in bud. Sometimes A of remarkable appearance, owing to one-sided development of the union, and abortion of some anthers; in Napoleona outer whorl stdial. and petaloid. G (2—6) or more, multi-loc.; 1—∞ anatr. ov. in each, simple style. Berry or caps.; exalb.

Classification and chief genera:

Sta. very slightly united. Apet.

I. *FOETIDIOIDEAE:* Foetidia.

Sta. united ± high up.

II. *PLANCHONIOIDEAE* (berry with no lid; pets.): Barringtonia.

III. *NAPOLEONOIDEAE* (do.; no pets. Std. corolla): Napoleona.

IV. *LECYTHIDOIDEAE* (berry with lid, or lid-capsule; pets.): Lecythis, Couroupita, Bertholletia, Grias.

Lecythis Loefl. Lecythid. (IV). 45 trop. Am. Like Couroupita, but sta. of helmet sterile. Caps. with lid woody (monkey-pot; used with sugar to catch monkeys, which cannot withdraw the inserted hand). Oily seeds ed. (Sapucaia nuts).
Lecythopsis Schrank (*Couratari* p.p. *EP.*). Lecythid. (IV). 2 Braz.
Leda C. B. Clarke (*Leptostachya* p.p.). Acanth. (IV. B). 7 Malay Penins.
Ledebouriella H. Wolff (*Trinia* p.p.). Umbell. (III. 5). 1 Altai.
Ledenbergia Klotzsch ex Moq. (*Flueckigeria* O. K.). Phytolacc. 1 trop. S. Am., W.I.
Ledermannia Mildbr. et Burret. Tili. 1 Belg. Congo.
Ledermanniella Eng. Podostem. 1 Cameroons.
Ledothamnus Meissn. Eric. (I. 3). 1 Guiana. 5—6-merous.
Ledum Rupp. ex L. Eric. (I. 1). 6 N. temp. and arct. *L. palustre* L. circumpolar (used as tea in Labrador). L. rolled back (*cf.* Empetrum).
Leea Royen ex L. Vit. 60 palaeotrop. (A) in tube, united to C.
Leechee, *Litchi chinensis* Sonner. (Chi.). **Leek,** *Allium Porrum* L.
Leersia Soland. ex. Sw. Gramin. (6). 6 N. temp. and trop. Marsh grasses like Oryza, used as fodder in As. Glumes rudimentary. *L. oryzoides* Sw. (Eur.) has cleist. fls. (Darwin, *Forms of Fls.* 335).
Lefebvrea A. Rich. (*Peucedanum* p.p. *EP.*). Umbell. (III. 6). 4 trop. Afr.
Lefrovia Franch. Comp. (12). 1 Bolivia.
Legendrea Webb et Berth. (*Rivea* p.p. *EP.*). Convolv. (I. 4). 1 Canaries.
Legitimate pollination, *Lythrum*, *Primula.*
Legnephora Miers (*Pericampylus* p.p.). Menisperm. 2 New Guinea, N.E. Austr. K 3+3, C 3+3, A 3+3, G 3.
Legume, a fr. of one cpl., dehisc. on both sides, *Leguminosae.*
Leguminosae (*EP.*, *BH.*). Dicots. (Archichl. Rosales; pp. xxiii, li). The third largest fam. of flg. pl., with 600/12000, cosmop. Mimosoideae and Caesalpinioideae are mostly trop., Papilionatae largely temp. (abundant on steppes, &c.). (Cf. Taubert in *Nat. Pfl.*)

Living in every soil and climate they show great variety in habit—trees, shrubs, herbs, water-plants, xerophytes, climbers, &c. The roots of most exhibit peculiar *tubercles*—metamorphosed lat. roots containing peculiar bacterial organisms (Rhizobium sp.). Plants provided with these are able to take up much more atmospheric nitrogen. The plant appears actually to consume the 'bacteroids' which live in its cells, after they have stored up in themselves a considerable amount of nitrogenous material. Hence the value of the L. as a crop on poor soil, or as preceding wheat in the rotation of crops; for instead of impoverishing the soil they enrich it, either by the nitrogen contained in their roots and liberated as these decay, or by that of the whole pl. if ploughed in as 'green manure.'

Stem commonly erect; many climbers. Some, *e.g.* Vicia, climb by leaf-tendrils, some, *e.g.* Bauhinia, by stem-tendrils, some by hooks (modified in Caesalpinia, &c., emergences in Acacia, &c.), some by twining. Creeping stems, rooting at the nodes, also occur. Thorns, usu. modified branches (*e.g.* Gleditschia) or stipules (Acacia), are common. The stems of the erect trop. sp. often branch so that the branches run parallel and erect, and bear crowns of l. at the top. The stems of many lianes are peculiarly shaped, often flat, or corrugated in various ways, owing to peculiar growth in thickness.

L. usually alt., stip., and nearly always cpd. Many have very small l., *e.g.* Ulex, or scaly l. and flat stems, *e.g.* Carmichaelia. The stipules vary much in size, &c. (see Acacia, Lathyrus, Vicia). The l. usu. perform sleep-movements at night, some moving upwards, some downwards, or in other ways, but finally usu. placing the leaflet edgewise to the sky. In Mimosa and Neptunia the l. are sensitive to a touch and at once assume the sleep-position, recovering after a time. In *Desmodium gyrans* the lat. leaflets execute continuous spontaneous movements as long as the temperature is high enough.

Infl. apparently always racemose, but with variety; simple raceme very common, also panicle and spike. Dorsiventral racemes, resembling the cymes of Boraginaceae, also occur (*e.g.* Dalbergia). The fls. are regular (and then frequently polygamous) or irreg. (and then usu. ☿); recept. usu. convex or flat, so that at most the fl. is slightly perig. K developed in ascending order, usu. 5-merous, the odd (oldest) sepal anterior; the sepals ± united. C polypetalous, alt. with the K; aestivation valvate (Mimosoideae), ascending imbr. (Caesalpinioideae),

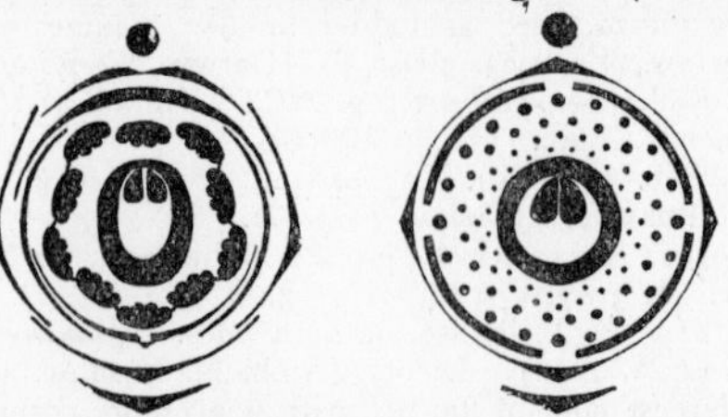

Floral diagrams of *Vicia Faba* (Papilionatae) and *Acacia latifolia* (Mimosoideae), after Eichler (modified).

or descending (Papilionatae). In many cases it is ·|· to a high degree, having a large petal posterior (vexillum or standard), two lateral (alae or wings), and two anterior ± joined to form a keel or carina. A typically of 10 sta., free or united into a tube; in the latter case the tenth sta. (the posterior one) often remains free, so as to leave a slit in the tube, only covered loosely by this sta. Many variations are found. In cases where a keel is present, the sta. are enclosed in it. G typically of one cpl. with its ventral side directly posterior; long style and terminal stigma. There are two rows of ovules (alt. with one another so as to stand in one vertical rank), anatr. or amphitr., ascending or pend.

Fertilisation (Papilionatae). The keel encloses the essential organs, protecting them from rain, &c. and rendering the fl. complex. Honey is secreted by the inner sides of the sta. near their base, and accumulates in the stamen-tube round the base of the ovary. The tenth sta. is free of the tube, and at the base, on either side of it, are two openings leading to the honey. The honey is thus concealed and at some depth, so that a clever insect with a tongue of moderate length is required. All this points to the P. being bee-flowers (class H), as in fact is the case. Insects alight upon the wings and depress them by their weight, whilst they probe for honey under the standard. The wings are always joined to the keel, usually by a protuberance in the former fitting into a suitable hollow in the latter, so that the keel is thus depressed likewise. This causes the emergence of the essential organs, the stigma usu. coming first, so that a fair chance of cross-fert. exists. Self-pollination usu. occurs when the insect flies off, leaving the keel to return to its former position.

"Four different types of structure may be distinguished (in Papilionatae) according to the manner in which the pollen is applied to the bee: (1) P. in which the sta. and stigma emerge from the carina and again return within it. They admit repeated visits; *e.g.* Trifolium, Onobrychis. (2) P. whose essential organs are confined under tension and explode. In these only one insect's visit is effective; *e.g.* Medicago, Genista, Ulex. (3) P. with a piston mechanism which squeezes the pollen in small quantities out of the apex of the carina, and not only permits but requires numerous insect visits; *e.g.* Lotus, Ononis, Lupinus. (4) P. with a brush of hairs upon the style which sweeps the pollen in small portions out of the apex of the carina. They for the most part require repeated insect visits; *e.g.* Lathyrus, Vicia." (Müller.) Cleistogamy is fairly common. In several cases the stigma in the unvisited fl. lies in the keel among the pollen, but it has been shown that it only becomes receptive (if young) when rubbed, so that autogamy does not necessarily occur. For the phenomenon of *enantiostyly* (right- and left-styled fls.) see Cassia. Some have fls. which after fertilisation bury themselves in the earth and there ripen their fruit; *e.g.* Arachis, Lathyrus, Trifolium, Vicia, Voandzeia, &c.

Fr. typically a *legume*, or pod opening by both sutures. In some the pod is constricted between the seeds, forming a *lomentum* which breaks up into indeh. one-seeded portions. The pods frequently open explosively, the valves twisting up spirally, *e.g.* in Ulex, Cytisus sp.,

&c. In Colutea, &c. they are inflated. Some are eaten by animals, but the seed-coats are hard enough to preserve the seeds from injury. Some have a coloured fleshy aril (Acacia sp., &c.). Still others have hooked pods, *e.g.* Medicago, Mimosa. The seed is exalb.; usu. large store of reserves in the cot.

Economically the L. are most important. The seeds of many sp. form important food-stuffs, *e.g.* of Arachis (see Edible Products for common names), Cajanus, Cicer, Dolichos, Glycine, Lathyrus, Lens, Lotus, Lupinus, Phaseolus, Pisum, Vicia, Voandzeia, &c. The pods of Ceratonia, Tamarindus, Phaseolus, Prosopis, &c. are also eaten. A great number are valuable as fodder, and known as artificial grasses, *e.g.* Trifolium, Medicago, Onobrychis, Lotus, Vicia, &c. Many trop. and subtrop. sp. yield valuable timber, *e.g.* Acacia, Albizzia, Dalbergia, Gleditschia, Hymenaea, Melanoxylon, Pericopsis, Pterocarpus, Robinia, Sophora, &c.; Crotalaria and others are sources of fibre; Acacia, Genista, Haematoxylon, Indigofera, &c. yield dyes; gums and resins are obtained from Acacia, Astragalus, Copaifera, Hymenaea, &c.; oil is expressed from the seeds of Arachis and Voandzeia; kino is obtained from Pterocarpus, and so on. See Economic Products and genera.

Classification and chief genera (after Taubert): nearly related to Rosaceae (espec. Chrysobalanoideae) and Connaraceae. Sometimes made a separate order, with the 3 divisions as fams.

The primary division is:

I. *MIMOSOIDEAE.* Fls. reg., C valvate.

II. *CAESALPINIOIDEAE.* Zygomorphic; corolla-aestivation imbricate-ascending.

III. *PAPILIONATAE.* Zygomorphic papilionaceous; corolla-aestivation imbricate-descending.

These are again subdivided as follows:

I. *MIMOSOIDEAE.*

A. Calyx valvate.

a. Sta. more than 10.

1. *Ingeae* (A united): Inga (l. once pinnate, G 1), Calliandra, Pithecolobium, Albizzia (l. twice pinnate, G 1, pod flat straight, not elastic).
2. *Acacieae* (A free): Acacia (only genus).

b. Sta. as many or twice as many as pets.

3. *Euminoseae* (anther glandless): Mimosa (pod compressed, flat).
4. *Adenanthereae* (anther in bud crowned by a gland; endosperm): Neptunia (head of fl. ♂ or neuter below), Prosopis.
5. *Piptadenieae* (do., no endosp.): Piptadenia, Entada.

B. Calyx imbricate.

6. *Parkieae*: Parkia (fls. in heads), Pentaclethra (spikes).

II. *CAESALPINIOIDEAE.*

A. Calyx in bud quite undivided or tubular below.

a. L. simple or one pair of leaflets. A 10 or less.

4. *Bauhinieae*: Cercis (fl. papilionate), Bauhinia (not so, l. of two equal lobes or parts).

b. L. once pinnate (exceptions). A ∞ or rarely 9—13.

9. *Swartzieae* (*Tounateae*): Swartzia (A ∞, C 1 or 0).
c. L. bipinnate, or once pinnate and then sta. 5.
1. *Dimorphandreae:* Dimorphandra (sta. 5 with 5 stds.).
B. Calyx in bud quite or very nearly polysepalous.
a. 2 anterior pets. modified to large glands, anthers opening by
6. *Kramerieae:* Krameria (only genus). [pores.
b. 2 anterior pets. developed or not, but not glandular.
L. some or all bipinnate.
7. *Eucaesalpinieae:* Gleditschia, Haematoxylon, Poinciana,
L. once pinnate. [Caesalpinia.
5. *Cassieae* (anthers basifixed, opening by term. pores): Cassia (no disc, C 5, l. paripinnate), Ceratonia (marked disc).
3. *Amherstieae* (dorsifixed, no pores; ovary adnate behind to torus): Hymenaea, Tamarindus, Vouapa, Amherstia.
8. *Sclerolobieae* (ovary free, ovules > 3): Sclerolobium.
2. *Cynometreae* (ovules 1 or 2): Copaiba (C 0, K 4, G stalked).

III. *PAPILIONATAE*.

A. Sta. free. [Baphia.
1. *Sophoreae* (l. pinnate): Myroxylon, Ormosia, Sophora,
2. *Podalyrieae* (simple or palmate): Anagyris, Baptisia, Po-
B. Sta. mon- or di-adelphous. [dalyria, Daviesia, Pultenaea.
a. Lomentum.
7. *Hedysareae:* Coronilla, Hedysarum, Onobrychis, Aeschynomene, Patagonium, Arachis, Zornia, Desmodium.
b. Legume or indeh. pod.
L. absent. Eremosparton (6, Galegeae).
L. present.
I. *L. or leaflet without stipels.*
(1) L. simple or palmate.
* Lf. with 3 entire leaflets.
3. *Genisteae* (shrubs): Bossiaea, Rafnia, Lotononis, Aspalathus, Crotalaria, Lupinus, Genista, Laburnum, Ulex, Cytisus.
6. *Galegeae* (herbs): Indigofera, Psoralea, Tephrosia, Robinia, Sesbania, Swainsona, Colutea, Astragalus, Oxytropis (cf.
** L. with 5 entire leaflets. [below).
5. *Loteae:* Anthyllis (pod indeh. or late dehisc.), Lotus.
*** L. with 3 toothed leaflets. [(A (9) + 1, C persistent).
4. *Trifolieae:* Ononis (A (10)), Medicago, Melilotus, Trifolium
(2) L. pinnate.
* Leafstalk ending in bristle or tendril.
9. *Vicieae:* Cicer, Vicia, Lens, Lathyrus, Pisum, Abrus.
** Leafstalk not ending so.
† Pod dehisc. in two valves.
§ Sta. filamentous.
10. *Phaseoleae* (ovary surrounded by disc): Clitoria, Glycine, Kennedya, Erythrina, Apios, Butea, Mucuna, Galactia, Canavalia, Rhynchosia, Eriosema, Phaseolus, Voandzeia,
6. *Galegeae* (no disc): as above. [Vigna, Dolichos.
§§ Some or all sta. broadened at apex.
5. *Loteae:* as above.
†† Pod indeh.

8. *Dalbergieae:* Dalbergia, Pterocarpus.
II. *Leaves or leaflets with stipels.*
10. *Phaseoleae:* (pod dehiscent) as before.
8. *Dalbergieae:* (pod indehiscent) as before.

Lehmanniella Gilg. Gentianaceae (1). 2 Colombia.

Leianthus Griseb. (*Lisianthus EP.*). Gentianaceae (1). 10 W.I., C. Am.

Leibergia Coulter et Rose. Umbelliferae (III. 5). 1 Idaho.

Leiboldia Schlecht. (*Vernonia* p.p.). Compositae (1). 4 N. Am.

Leichhardtia F. Muell. Menispermaceae. 1 N.E. Austr. A (3).

Leichtlinia H. Ross (*Agave* p.p. *EP.*). Amaryllidaceae (II). 1 Mexico.

Leidesia Muell.-Arg. in DC. Euphorbiaceae (A. II. 2). 1 S. Afr.

Leighia Cass. = Viguiera H.B. et K. (Comp.).

Leimanthium Willd. = Melanthium L. (Lili.).

Leiocarpodicraea Engl. (*Dicraea* p.p.). Podostemaceae. 3 trop. Afr.

Leiochilus Hook. (*Buseria EP.*). Rubiaceae (II. 4). 1 Madag.

Leioclusia Baill. Guttiferae (inc. sed.). 1 Madag.

Leiogyne K. Schum. (*Neves-Armondia EP.*). Bignoniaceae (1). 1 E. Brazil.

Leiophaca Lindau. Acanthaceae (IV. A). 1 trop. Afr.

Leiophyllum Hedw. f. Ericaceae (I. 3). 1 Atl. U.S.

Leioptyx Pierre ex De Wild. Meliaceae. 1 trop. Afr.

Leiostemon Rafin. (*Pentstemon* p.p.). Scrophular. (II. 4). 2 N.W. N. Am.

Leiothrix Ruhland (*Paepalanthus* p.p.). Eriocaulonaceae. 30 S. Am.

Leiothylax Wmg. (*Dicraea* p.p.). Podostemaceae. 5 trop. Afr.

Leiphaimos Cham. et Schlechtd. (*Voyria BH.*). Gentianaceae (1). 20 trop. Am. and Afr., W.I.

Leitgebia Eichl. Ochnaceae. 1 Brit. Guiana.

Leitneria Chapm. Leitneriaceae. 1 N. Am. Shrubs with spikes of dioecious fls. ♂ naked with 3—12 sta. ♀ with scaly P, 1 cpl. and long style. $\underline{G}$ 1-loc., with 1 amphitr. ov. Fr. drupaceous. Seed albuminous. Embryo straight. *Cf. Suppl.*

Leitneriaceae (*EP.*, *BH.*). Dicots. (Archichl. Leitneriales; Unisexuales *BH.*). Only genus Leitneria, *q.v.*

Leitneriales. The 7th order of Dicots. Archichlamydeae.

Leitnerieae (*BH.*) = Leitneriaceae.

Lemairea de Vriese. Goodeniaceae (inc. sed.). 1 Amboina.

Lemaireocereus Britton et Rose (Cereus p.p.). Cactaceae (III. 1). 13 trop. and subtrop. Am., W.I.

Lembertia Green (*Eatonella* p.p.). Compositae (6). 1 California.

Lemmonia A. Gray. Hydrophyllaceae. 1 California.

Lemna L. Lemnaceae. 6 cosmop.; 4 in Brit. (duckweed). The plant consists in most, *e.g. L. minor* L., of a flat green floating blade, the stem, which performs leaf-functions. From the under side hangs down a long adv. root, with well-marked root-cap, visible to the eye. No l. The stems are oval and slightly turned up at the ends, so that if two are placed near together in water, they will run against one another and adhere by the tips. In the post. portion on either side is a groove under the edge. In this arise branches which may either (as in *L. trisulca* L., &c.) remain in union with the parent shoot, or become detached and give rise to new plants. In autumn a number of these are formed ready to start growth next spring, whilst the mother pl. sink to the bottom. Fls. also borne in these grooves; spathe very reduced, with 2 ♂ fls. (each 1 sta.) and a ♀ (1 cpl.).

Lemnaceae (*EP.*, *BH.*). Monocots. (Spathiflorae; Nudiflorae *BH.*; pp. v, liv). 4/18, free-swimming perenn. water pl. with no l. (*cf.* description of Lemna). Fl. unisexual, monoec., naked; ♂ of 1 sta., ♀ of 1 cpl., with 1—6 basal, erect, orthotr. to anatr. ov. Endosp. slight. Often regarded as very reduced Araceae. *Chief genera:* Spirodela (shoots with several r.), Lemna (with 1 r.), Wolffia (no r.).

Lemnopsis Zipp. Podostem. (inc. sed.). 5 Malaya.

Lemon, *Citrus Medica* L., var. *Limonum*; **-grass**, *Cymbopogon citratus* Stapf; **-tree, bastard** (W.I.), *Fagara*; **water-**, *Passiflora laurifolia* L. (trop. Am.).

Lemonia Pers. = Watsonia Mill. (Irid.).

Lemurorchis Krzl. Orchid. (II. 17). 1 Madag.

Lencymmaea C. Presl. Inc. sed. 1 Burma.

Lendneria Minod (*Capraria* p.p.). Scroph. (III. 1). 2 warm Am.

Lennea Klotzsch. Legum. (III. 6). 2 Mex., C. Am. Style coiled.

Lennoa Lex. Lenno. 3 Centr. Mex. Sta. of two lengths.

Lennoaceae (*EP.*, *BH.*). Dicots. (Sympet. Ericales; pp. xli, lii). 3/5, S.W. U.S., Mex. Herbs, parasitic by r. on r. of Clematis, &c. Fl. ☿, reg., 5—∞-merous, with sta. in one whorl epipet. at throat of tube, anthers with slits; $\underline{G}$ (6—14) each with false septum and 2 ov. Dry drupe with 12—28 stones, enclosed in persistent K and C. Embryo spherical, undifferentiated; endosp. *Genera:* Pholisma, Ammobroma, Lennoa.

Lenophyllum Rose. Crassul. 4 Mex., Texas.

Lens (Tourn.) L. Legum. (III. 9). 6 Medit., W. As. *L. esculenta* Moench (*Ervum Lens* L.), the lentil, is a food pl. of great antiquity. The seeds furnish a flour. Close to Vicia, but ovules 2 only.

Lentibulariaceae (*EP.*, *BH.*). Dicots. (Sympet. Tubiflorae; Personales *BH.*; pp. xlvii, liii). 10/250 cosmop., all insectivorous (*cf.* Darwin, *Insectiv. Pl.*, and for details see gen.). Herbs, usu. of water or moist places, often without r. Infl. usu. a raceme or spike, or fls. sol. Fls. ☿, ·|·, 5-merous. K 2—5-lobed, the odd sep. post., often 2-lipped, persistent; C (5), 2-lipped, lower lip ± spurred; A 2 (anterior pair), epipet. with 1-loc. anthers; $\underline{G}$ (2), 1-loc. with free-central plac. and sessile 2-lobed stigma (post. lobe ± abortive); ovules ∞ or 2, anatr., often ± sunk in plac. Caps. with 2—4 valves and ∞ seeds, or 1-seeded indeh. Seed exalb. *Chief genera:* Pinguicula (K 5, fls. sol. on long stalks, land pl.), Genlisea (K 5, raceme, land), Polypompholyx (K 4, land), Utricularia (K 2, ovules ∞, land or water), Biovularia (K 2, ovules 2, water), Saccolaria.

Lenticel, a breathing pore in the bark, *Sambucus*.

Lenticular, lens-shaped; **lentiginose**, minutely dotted.

Lentil, *Lens esculenta* Moench (E. Medit.).

Lentiscus (Tourn.) L. = Pistacia L. (Anacard.).

Lenzia Phil. Amarant. (inc. sed., sometimes Portulac.). 1 Chile.

Leobordea Delile = Lotononis Eck. et Zeyh. p.p. (Legum.).

Leocereus Britton et Rose. Cact. (III. 1). 3 Bahia, Minas (Brazil).

Leochilus Knowles et Westc. (*Oncidium* p.p. *EP.*). Orchid. (II. 10). 16 trop. Am., W.I.

Leocus A. Chevalier. Labiat. (VII). 1 trop. Afr.

Leonia Ruiz et Pav. Violaceae. 2 Amazon valley. Placed by Martius in Myrsinaceae, by Meisner in a fam. Leoniaceae.
Leonotis R. Br. in Ait. Labiatae (VI). 15 trop. and S. Afr.
Leontice L. Berberidaceae. 12 N. temp. Stem base tuberous.
Leontochir Phil. Amaryllid. (III). 1 Chili. Plac. parietal.
Leontodon L. (incl. *Thrincia* Roth). Compositae (13). 45 temp., Eur., As.; 3 in Brit. (hawkbit). Very like Taraxacum. In *L. hirtus* L. the outer frs. have no pappus.
Leontonyx Cass. Compositae (4). 5 South Afr.
Leontopodium R. Br. Compositae (4). 10 Mts. of Eur., As. and S. Am. *L. alpinum* Cass. (Edelweiss) is a xero. growing in dense tufts, and covered with woolly hairs. The central florets are ♂, the style remaining, however, to act as pollen-presenter, though it has no stigmas. The outer florets are ♀.
Leonurus L. Labiatae (VI). 8 Eur., As., and trop. *L. Cardiaca* L. in Brit. (mother-wort).
Leopard's bane, *Doronicum*; **- wood**, *Brosimum Aubletii* Poepp.
Leopoldia Parl. = Muscari Mill. p.p. (Lili.).
Leopoldinia Mart. Palmae (IV. 1). 4 trop. Brazil. *L. Piassaba* Wallace yields the best Piassaba fibre (Wallace, *Amazon*, ch. IX).
Lepachys Rafin. (*Rudbeckia* L. p.p. *EP.*). Compositae (5). 4 N. Am. Cult. orn. fl.
Lepadanthus Ridl. Gesneriaceae (I). 1 Malay Peninsula.
Lepanthes Sw. Orchidaceae (II. 8). 60 trop. Am., W.I.
Lepargyrea Rafin. (*Shepherdia EP.*, *Elaeagnus BH.*). Elaeag. 3 N. Am.
Lepechinia Willd. Labiatae (VI). 4 Mexico.
Lepervenchea Cordemoy (*Angraecum* p.p.). Orchid. (II. 20). 1 Bourbon.
Lepidacanthus C. Presl. Acanthaceae (IV. B). 2 Brazil.
Lepidadenia Nees = Litsea Lam. (Laur.).
Lepidagathis Willd. Acanthaceae (IV. A). 80 trop.
Lepidaglaia Pierre (*Aglaia* p.p.). Meliaceae (II). 4 S.E. As.
Lepidella Van Tiegh. (*Lepidaria* p.p.). Loranthaceae. 4 Malay Arch.
Lepiderema Radlk. Sapindaceae (I). 1 New Guinea.
Lepidesmia Klatt. Compositae (2). 1 Cuba.
Lepidium L. Cruciferae (2). 100 cosmop. 5 Brit. (cress). *L. Sativum* L. (Orient) is the garden cress.
Lepidobolus Nees. Restionaceae. 3 S. Austr.
Lepidobotrys Engl. Linaceae. 1 trop. Afr.
Lepidocaryum Mart. Palmae (III). 5 N.W. Brazil.
Lepidoceras Hook. f. Loranthaceae (II). 1 Peru to Chiloe.
Lepidocroton Klotzsch. Menispermaceae (inc. sed.). 1 Guiana.
Lepidogyne Blume. Orchidaceae (II. 2). 1 Java.
Lepidolopha C. Winkler. Compositae (7). 1 Turkestan.
Lepidopetalum Blume (*Ratonia* p.p. *BH.*). Sapind. (I). 6 Malaya.
Lepidophyllum Cass. Compositae (3). 8 southern Andes.
Lepidopironia A. Rich. (*Tetrapogon EP.*). Gramineae (11). 1 Abyssinia.
Lepidoptera, butterflies and moths; *cf.* Butterfly Flowers, &c.
Lepidospartum A. Gray. Compositae (8). 3 S.W. U.S.

Lepidosperma Labill. Cyperaceae (11). 40 Austr., N.Z., trop. As. *L. gladiatum* Labill. is the sword-sedge, used to bind sand-dunes in Austr., and as a material for paper-making.
Lepidospora F. Muell. (*Schoenus* p.p. *EP.*). Cyperaceae (11). 1 Austr.
Lepidostemon Hook. f. et Thoms. Cruciferae (4). 1 E. Himalaya.
Lepidostephium Oliv. Compositae (7). 1 S. Afr.
Lepidote, with small scurfy scales.
Lepidotrichum Velen. et Bornm. Cruciferae (4). 1 Bulgaria.
Lepidoturus Baill. Euphorbiaceae (A. II. 2). 4 trop. Afr., Madag.
Lepigonum Wahlb. = Spergularia J. et C. Presl (Caryoph.).
Lepilaena J. Drum. et Harv. (*Althenia EP.*). Potamogeton. 3 Austr.
Lepinia Decne. Apocynaceae (I. 2). 2 Tahiti, Solomon Is.
Lepiniopsis Valeton. Apocynaceae (I. 2). 1 Ternate.
Lepionurus Blume. Opiliaceae. 2 E. Indomal.
Lepipogon Bertol. f. Rubiaceae (inc. sed.). 1 E. Afr.
Lepironia Rich. Cyperaceae (11). 1 Madag., trop. As., Austr., Polynes., *L. mucronata* Rich., cult. in China. The stems are beaten flat and woven into mats, sails (for junks), &c.
Lepisanthes Blume. Sapindaceae (1). 20 trop. As.
Lepismium Pfeiff. = Rhipsalis Gaertn. (Cact.).
Lepistemon Blume. Convolvulaceae (1). 5 Indomal.
Lepistemonopsis Dammer. Convolvulaceae (1). 1 Kilimandjaro.
Leptactinia Hook. f. Rubiaceae (I. 8). 8 trop. and S. Afr.
Leptadenia R. Br. Asclepiadaceae (II. 3). 15 trop. Afr., As.
Leptaleum DC. Cruciferae (4). 2 E. Medit., W. As.
Leptalix Rafin. = Fraxinus Tourn. (Oleac.).
Leptandra Nutt. = Veronica Tourn. (Scroph.).
Leptarrhena R. Br. Saxifragaceae (1). 1 Kamtschatka, Rocky Mts.
Leptasea Haw. (*Saxifraga* p.p.). Saxifragaceae (1). 12 N. temp.
Leptaspis R. Br. Gramineae (6). 5 palaeotrop.
Leptaulus Benth. Icacinaceae. 3 W. and C. trop. Afr.
Lepterica N.E. Br. Ericaceae (IV. 2). 1 S. Afr.
Leptilon Rafin. = Erigeron L. (Comp.). 20 Am., As.
Leptinella Cass. = Cotula Tourn. p.p. (Comp.).
Leptis E. Mey. ex Eckl. et Zeyh. = Lotononis Eckl. et Zeyh. p.p.
Leptobaea Benth. Gesneriaceae (1). 2 N. Bengal.
Leptocarpha DC. Compositae (5). 1 Chili.
Leptocarpus R. Br. Restionaceae. 12 S.E. As., Austr., Chili.
Leptocarydium Hochst. (*Triodia BH.*, *Diplachne* p.p. *EP.*). Gramineae (10). 1 S. Afr.
Leptocereus Britton et Rose (*Cereus* p.p.). Cactaceae (III. 1). 8 W.I.
Leptochilus Kaulf. Polypodiaceae. 65 trop. and subtrop.
Leptochlaena Spreng. (*Leptolaena* Thou.). Chlaenaceae. 6 Madag.
Leptochloa Beauv. Gramineae (11). 15 trop. and subtrop.
Leptoclinium Benth. Compositae (2). 1 Goyaz, Brazil.
Leptocodon Lem. Campanulaceae (1). 1 Himalaya. Pedicel of lat. fl. concrescent with axis of infl.
Leptocyamus Benth. = Glycine L. p.p. (Legum.).
Leptodactylon Hook. et Arn. (*Gilia* p.p.). Polemoniaceae. 6 N. Am.
Leptodermis Wall. Rubiaceae (II. 6). 12 Himalaya to Japan.
Leptoderris Dunn (*Derris* p.p.). Leguminosae (III. 8). 14 trop. Afr.

Leptodesmia Benth. Leguminosae (III. 7). 2 Madag., India.
Leptoglossis Benth. (*Salpiglossis* p.p. *EP.*). Solan. (5). 4 temp. S. Am.
Leptogonum Benth. Polygonaceae (III. 2). 1 S. Domingo.
Leptogramma J. Sm. = Dryopteris Adans. (Polypod.).
Leptolaelia × Mast. Orchid hybrid, Leptotes and Laelia.
Leptolaena Thou. Chlaenaceae. 6 Madagascar.
Leptolepia Mett. Polypodiaceae. 2 Austr., New Zealand.
Leptolepis Boeck. Cyperaceae (II). 1 Tibet.
Leptolobium Vog. = Sweetia Spreng. p.p. (Legum.).
Leptoloma Chase. Gramineae (5). 5 Austr.
Leptomeria R. Br. Santalaceae. 15 Austr.
Leptomischus Drake del Castillo. Rubiaceae (I. 2). 1 Tonquin.
Leptonema A. Juss. Euphorbiaceae (A. I. 1). 1 Madag.
Leptonychia Turcz. Sterculiaceae. 8 trop. Afr. and As.
Leptopharynx Rydberg (*Perityle* p.p.). Compositae (6). 12 N. Am.
Leptophoenix Becc. (*Nenga* p.p. *EP.*). Palmaceae (IV. 1). 3 New Guinea.
Leptophragma R. Br. Meliaceae (inc. sed.). 1 Austr.
Leptopoda Nutt. = Helenium L. p.p. (Comp.).
Leptopteris Presl. Osmundaceae. 7 New Guinea, Polynesia, N.Z.
Leptopyrum Reichb. (*Isopyrum BH.*). Ranunculaceae (2). 1 C. As.
Leptorhabdos Schrenk. Scrophulariaceae (III. 2). 4 C. and S. As.
Leptorhoeo C. B. Clarke. Commelinaceae. 1 Mexico to Brazil.
Leptorhynchus Less. Compositae (4). 8 temp. Austr.
Leptoscela Hook. f. Rubiaceae (I. 2). 1 E. Brazil.
Leptosiphonium F. Muell. (*Ruellia* p.p. *EP.*). Acanthaceae (IV. A). 1 New Guinea.
Leptosolena Presl (*Alpinia* p.p. *EP.*). Zingiberaceae (I). 1 Phil. Is.
Leptospermum Forst. Myrtaceae (II. 1). 25 Malaya, Austr., N.Z.
Leptosporangiatae (Filicales). See Filicales Leptosporangiatae.
Leptostachya Nees = Justicia L. p.p. (Acanth.).
Leptostylis Benth. Sapotaceae (I). 2 New Caledonia.
Leptosyne DC. (*Coreopsis* p.p. *EP.*). Compositae (5). 5 Calif., Mexico.
Leptotaenia Nutt. (*Ferula* p.p. *BH.*). Umbelliferae (III. 6). 12 N. Am.
Leptotes Lindl. (*Tetramicra* p.p. *BH.*). Orchid. (II. 6). 1 Brazil. Cult.
Leptothrium Kunth. Gramineae (3). 1 warm Am.
Leptothyrsa Hook. f. Rutaceae (I). 1 Amazon valley.
Leptovignea Börner = Carex p.p. (Cyper.).
Lepturella Stapf. Gramineae (12). 1 French Soudan.
Lepturopsis Steud. (*Rhytachne* p.p. *EP.*). Gramineae (2). 1 Guinea.
Lepturus R. Br. Gramineae (12). 4 trop. and subtrop. |*.
Lepuropetalon Ell. Saxifragaceae (I). 1 S. U.S., Chili.
Lepyrodia R. Br. Restionaceae. 7 Austr., New Zealand.
Lepyrodiclis Fenzl (*Arenaria* p.p. *BH.*). Caryophyll. (I. 1). 5 W. As.
Lerchea L. Rubiaceae (I. 2). 2 Malay Archipelago.
Leretia Vell. (*Mappia* p.p. *BH.*). Icacinaceae. 3 trop. Brazil.

Leria DC. = Chaptalia Vent. (Comp.).
Lescaillea Griseb. Compositae (6). 1 Cuba.
Leschenaultia R. Br. Goodeniaceae. 20 Austr. "In *L. formosa* R. Br., the insect's proboscis comes in contact with the lower lip of the pollen-cup (see fam.), opening it and dusting itself with pollen; in the next fl. it places this pollen on the stigmatic surface which lies outside the pollen-cup." (Müller.)
Lespedeza Michx. Leguminosae (III. 7). 60 temp. N. Am., As., and Mts. of trop. As., Austr. Fls. sometimes apetalous, and cleistogamic. *L. striata* Hook. et Arn. (Japanese clover; As.) is being spread over N. Am. by animal agency. It is a useful fodder-plant.
Lesquerella Wats. (*Vesicaria* p.p. *BH.*). Cruciferae (3). 50 Am.
Lessertia DC. Leguminosae (III. 6). 50 Afr.
Lessingia Cham. Compositae (3). 15 California.
Lestibudesia Thou. = Celosia L. p.p. (Amarant.).
Leto Phil. (*Brachyandra EP.*). Compositae (2). 1 Chili.
Lettsomia Roxb. Convolvulaceae (1). 20 warm As.
Lettuce, *Lactuca sativa* L.; **lamb's -**, *Valerianella*; **prickly -**, *Lactuca Scariola* L.; **- tree**, *Pisonia morindifolia* Br.; **water -**, *Pistia Stratiotes* L.
Leuc-, leuco- (Gr. pref.), white; **-anthous**, white flowered, &c.
Leucactinia Rydberg (*Pectis* p.p.). Compositae (6). 1 Mexico.
Leucadendron Berg. Proteaceae (1). 70 S. Afr. *L. argenteum* R. Br. (silver-tree) has l. covered with fine silky hairs, and may be used for painting upon. It has been nearly extirpated. Fl. like Protea. The P, when the fr. is ripe, splits into 4 segments, united round the stigma, and acts as a wing.
Leucadendron L. = Protea L. (Prot.).
Leucaena Benth. Leguminosae (I. 3). 12 warm Am., Polynesia.
Leucampyx A. Gray ex Benth. et Hook. f. Compos. (7). 1 S.W. U.S.
Leucanthemum (Tourn.) L. = Chrysanthemum Tourn. p.p. (Comp.).
Leucas Burm. Labiatae (VI). 70 trop. Afr., As.
Leucaster Choisy. Nyctaginaceae. 1 Brazil.
Leucelene Greene (*Aster* p.p.). Compositae (3). 6 N. Am.
Leuceres Calest. (*Endressia* p.p.). Umbelliferae (III. 5). 2 Spain.
Leuceria Lag. Compositae (12). 50 S. Am. Xerophytes.
Leuchtenbergia (Fisch.) Hook. Cactaceae (III. 1). 1 Mexico. See fam.
Leucobarleria Lindau. Acanthaceae (IV. B). 3 N.E. Afr., Arabia.
Leucocalantha Barb. Rodr. Bignoniaceae (inc. sed.). 1 Amazonas.
Leucocarpus D. Don. Scrophulariaceae (II. 4). 1 trop. Am.
Leucocodon Gardn. Rubiaceae (I. 7). 1 Ceylon.
Leucocoma Nieuwland (*Thalictrum* p.p.). Ranunculaceae (3). 1 N. Am.
Leucocoryne Lindl. Liliaceae (IV). 8 Chili. Cult. orn. fl.
Leucocrinum Nutt. ex A. Gray. Liliaceae (III). 1 W. U.S.
Leucocroton Griseb. Euphorbiaceae (A. II. 2). 5 Cuba, Haiti.
Leucogenes Beauverd. Compositae (4). 2 New Zealand.
Leucojum L. Amaryllidaceae (1). 10 S. Eur. (snow-flake).
Leucolaena R. Br. = Xanthosia Rudge p.p. (Umbell.).

Leucolena Ridley. Orchidaceae (II. 5). 1 Malay Peninsula.
Leucomeris D. Don. Compositae (12). 2 Nepal, Burma.
Leucomphalos Benth. Leguminosae (III. 1). 1 W. trop. Afr.
Leuconotis Jack. Apocynaceae (I. 1). 10 Malaya.
Leucopholis Gardn. Compositae (4). 3 S. Brazil.
Leucophrys Rendle (*Panicum* p.p.). Gramineae (5). 1 trop. Afr.
Leucophyllum Humb. et Bonpl. Scrophulariaceae (I. 1). 3 Texas, Mexico.
Leucopitys Nieuwland (*Pinus* p.p.). Coniferae (Pinaceae). 2 N. temp.
Leucopogon R. Br. (*Styphelia* Sol.). Epacridaceae (3). 130 Austr., Malaya.
Leucopsis Baker (*Aster* p.p. *EP.*). Compositae (3). 10 trop. Am.
Leucorchis Blume (*Didymoplexis BH.*). Orchidaceae (II. 2). 3 Indomal.
Leucosalpa Scott Elliot. Scrophulariaceae (III. 2). 1 Madag.
Leucosceptrum Sm. Labiatae (I). 2 Himalaya, China.
Leucosidea Eckl. et Zeyh. Rosaceae (III. 5). 1 S. Afr.
Leucosmia Benth. Thymelaeaceae. 4 Fiji.
Leucospermum R. Br. Proteaceae (I). 40 S. Afr.
Leucosphaera Gilg. Amarantaceae (2). 2 S.W. Afr.
Leucostegane Prain. Leguminosae (II. 3). 1 Dindings.
Leucostegia Presl = Davallia Sm. (Polypod.).
Leucosyke Zoll. et Morr. Urticaceae (3). 10 Malaya, Polynesia.
Leucosyris Greene (*Aster* p.p.). Compositae (3). 2 N. Am.
Leucothoë D. Don. Ericaceae (II. 1). 35 Am. Like Andromeda.
Leunisia Phil. Compositae (12). 1 Chili.
Leurocline Sp. Moore. Boraginaceae (IV. 5). 2 trop. Afr.
Leuzea DC. (*Centaurea* p.p. *EP.*). Compositae (11). 3 Medit.
Levenhookia R. Br. Stylidiaceae. 7 Austr. The labellum is shoe-shaped and at first embraces the column, but if touched it springs downwards.
Lever-wood, *Ostrya*.
Levieria Becc. Monimiaceae. 6 New Guinea, Queensland.
Levigatus (Lat.), smooth, slippery.
Levisticum Riv. ex L. Umbelliferae (III. 6). 2 Eur., W. As.
Levya Bur. ex Baill. Bignoniaceae (1). 1 Nicaragua.
Lewisia Pursh. Portulacaceae. 2 California. *L. rediviva* Pursh (bitter-root) with thick rhiz., fleshy roots and l., is very xero. Two years' drying will hardly kill it. K 4—8, C 8—16; A ∞.
Leycesteria Wall. Caprifoliaceae. 3 Himalaya, China.
Leyssera L. Compositae (4). 5 S. Afr,, Medit.
Lhotzkya Schau. Myrtaceae (II. 2). 10 Austr.
Liabum Adans. Compositae (8). 60 Am. and W. Ind.
Liane, a woody climber, *Ancistrocladus*, *Apocynaceae*, *Aristolochiaceae*, *Asclepiadaceae*, *Bignoniaceae*, *Hippocrateaceae*, *Landolphia*, *Leguminosae*, *Malpighiaceae*, &c. *Cf.* Climbing Plants.
Liatris Schreb. Compositae (2). 25 N. Am.
Libanotis Riv. ex Hall. = Seseli L. (*BH.*) = Athamanta L.
Liber, phloem.
Liberian coffee, *Coffea liberica* Hiern.

Libertia Spreng. Iridaceae (II). 8 Chili, Austr., N.Z. Cult. orn. fl.
Libocedrus Endl. Coniferae (Pinac. 37; see C. for gen. char.). 9, 2 in Chili, 2 in N.Z., 2 in New Guin., 1 each in Chi., Formosa, W. U.S. *L. Doniana* Endl. (N. Z.), *L. tetragona* Endl. (Chili) and *L. decurrens* Torr. (Calif., white cedar) yield valuable timber.
Licania Aubl. Rosaceae (VI). 45 S. Am.
Lichtensteinia Cham. et Schlechtd. Umbelliferae (III. 5). 7 S. Afr.
Licuala Thunb. Palmae (I. 2). 40 Indomal.
Lidbeckia Berg. Compositae (7). 3 S.W. Cape Colony.
Liebrechtsia Wildem. (*Vigna* p.p. *EP.*). Legumin. (III. 10). 6 trop. Afr.
Lietzia Regel. Gesneriaceae (II). 1 Brazil.
Lifago Schweinf. et Muschler. Compositae (4). 1 Algeria.
Life-history, the course of development and metamorphosis.
Ligea Poit. ex Tul. Podostemaceae. 5 Brazil, Guiana.
Ligeria Decne. = Sinningia Nees p.p. (Gesn.).
Light, effects of, see Physiological textbooks.
Lightfootia L'Herit. Campanulaceae (I). 45 Afr.
Lightia Schomb. Trigoniaceae. 2 Guiana, Amazon valley.
Lign-aloes, eagle-wood, *Aquilaria Agallocha* Roxb. (Burma).
Ligneus (Lat.), woody; **-ification**, becoming woody.
Lignum vitae, *Guaiacum officinale* L.
Ligularia Cass. (*Senecio* p.p. *BH.*). Compositae (8). 35 Eur., As.
Ligulate (C), strap-shaped, *Compositae*.
Ligule, a scale at upper end of leaf-sheath, *Gramineae*.
Liguliflorate, with ligulate flowers.
Ligusticella Coulter et Rose (*Ligusticum* p.p.). Umbelliferae (III. 5). 1 Colorado.
Ligusticum L. Umbelliferae (III. 5). 55 N. Hemisph., Chili, N.Z. *L. scoticum* L. (lovage) in Brit.; it is sometimes used as a pot-herb.
Ligustrum (Tourn.) L. Oleaceae. 40 Eur., Indomal., and esp. E. As. *L. vulgare* L. (privet) in Brit.
Lijndenia Zoll. et Morr. (*Memecylon* p.p. *BH.*). Melastom. (III). 1 Java.
Lilac, *Syringa vulgaris* L.; **Californian -**, *Ceanothus*; **Indian -**, *Melia Lagerstroemia*; **West Indian -**, *Melia*.
Lilaea Humb. et Bonpl. Scheuchzeriaceae (Naiad. *BH.*). 1 Rockies, Andes.
Liliaceae (*EP.*, *BH.*). Monocots. (Liliiflorae; Coronarieae *BH.*). One of the largest fams. of flowering plants; 250 gen., 3700 sp., cosmop.; the smaller groups often confined to definite floral regions. Most are herbs with sympodial rhiz. or bulbs; a few trop. and warm temp. forms, *e.g.* Yucca, Dracaena, &c., are shrubs or trees, often with an unusual mode of growth in thickness. Many are xero.; some, *e.g.* Aloe and Gasteria, are succulent; others, *e.g.* Phormium, have hard isobil. l.; others, *e.g.* Dasylirion, have tuberous stems and narrow l.; Bowiea only produces leafy shoots in the wet season. Smilax, Gloriosa, &c., are climbing pl., the former with peculiar stipular tendrils. Ruscus exhibits phylloclades.

Infl. most commonly racemose; fls. with no bracteoles; when the latter occur, the further branching from their axils usually takes a cymose form, especially that of a bostryx, as in Hemerocallis. The apparent umbels or heads of Allium, Agapanthus, &c. are really cymose. Sol. term. fls. occur in tulip, &c. Fls. usu. ☿, reg., pentacyclic, 3-merous (rarely 2, 4, or 5), hypog. P 3+3, free or united, petaloid or sometimes sepaloid; A 3+3 or fewer, rarely more, usually with introrse anthers; G (3) usu. sup., rarely inf. or semi-inf., 3-loc. with axile, or rarely 1-loc. with parietal plac.; ovules usu. ∞, in two rows in each loc., anatr. Fr. usu. capsular, loculic. or septic., sometimes a berry. Seed with straight or curved embryo, in abundant fleshy or cartilaginous, never floury, endosp.

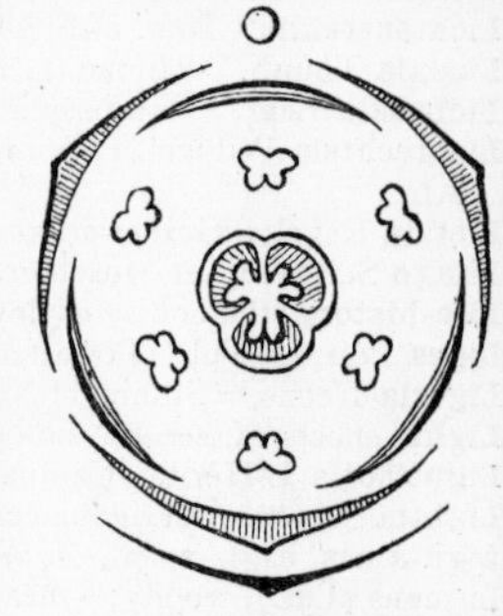

Diagram of Convallaria (after Eichler).

Fls. usu. insect-pollinated. Honey in Scilla, Allium, &c., is secreted by glands in the ovary-wall between the cpls.; in other cases by glands on the bases of the perianth-l. (see Müller's *Fert. of Fls.*). Yucca (*q.v.*) has a unique pollination-method.

Economically the L. are of no great value. The chief food plants are Allium and Asparagus; Phormium, Yucca, and Sansevieria yield useful fibre; Smilax, Urginea, Aloe, Colchicum, Veratrum, &c., are medicinal. Xanthorrhoea and Dracaena yield resins; Chlorogalum is used as soap. Many are favourite garden and greenhouse plants, *e.g.* Convallaria, Tulipa, Fritillaria, Lilium, Agapanthus, Kniphofia, Funkia, Hyacinthus, Gloriosa, and many more.

Classification and chief genera (after Engler): the L. are closely allied to Juncaceae; usu. they can be distinguished by their petaloid P, but many L. have a sepaloid P, *e.g.* Xanthorrhoea, Kingia, &c., and in these cases almost the only distinction is the absence in L. of the long thread-like twisted stigmas of J. *BH.* unite these genera, and some others, to Juncaceae, and place sub-fams. VIII and IX in Haemodoraceae. Warming splits up the family into Colchicaceae, Liliaceae, and Convallariaceae.

I. *MELANTHIOIDEAE* (rhiz., or bulb covered with scale-l. and with term. infl.; anthers extr. or intr.; caps. loculic. or septic.; fr. never a berry): Tofieldia, Narthecium, Veratrum, Gloriosa, Colchicum.

II. *HERRERIOIDEAE* (tuber, with climbing stem; l. in tufts; small-flowered racemes at base of these or in panicles at ends of twigs; septic. caps.): Herreria (only genus).

III. *ASPHODELOIDEAE* (rhiz. with radical l., rarely stem with crown of l. or leafy branched stem or bulb; infl. usu. term., a simple or cpd. raceme or spike; P or (P); anthers intr.; caps., rarely berry): Asphodelus, Chlorogalum, Bowiea, Funkia, Hemerocallis, Phormium, Kniphofia, Aloe, Gasteria, Haworthia, Aphyllanthes, Lomandra, Xanthorrhoea, Kingia.

IV. *ALLIOIDEAE* (bulb or short rhiz.; cymose umbel ± enclosed by two broad or rarely narrow l., sometimes joined; infl. rarely of 1 fl.): Agapanthus, Gagea, Allium, Brodiaea.

V. *LILIOIDEAE* (bulb; infl. term., racemose; P or (P); anthers intr.; caps. loculic., except in Calochortus): Lilium, Fritillaria, Tulipa, Scilla, Ornithogalum, Hyacinthus, Muscari.

VI. *DRACAENOIDEAE* (stem erect with leafy crown, except in Astelia; l. sometimes leathery, never fleshy; P free or united at base; anthers intr.; berry or caps.): Yucca, Dasylirion, Dracaena.

VII. *ASPARAGOIDEAE* (rhiz. subterranean, sympodial; berry): Asparagus, Ruscus, Polygonatum, Convallaria, Trillium.

VIII. *OPHIOPOGONOIDEAE* (short rhiz., sometimes with suckers, with narrow or lanceolate radical l.; P or (P); anthers intr. or semi-intr.; ovary sup. or ½-inf.; fr. with thin pericarp and 1—3 seeds with fleshy coats): Sansevieria, Ophiopogon.

IX. *ALETROIDEAE* (short rhiz. with narrow or lanceolate radical l.; (P); anthers semi-intr.; caps. loculic.; seeds ∞, with thin testa): Aletris (only genus).

X. *LUZURIAGOIDEAE* (shrubs or undershrubs with erect or climbing twigs; infl.-twigs usu. many-flowered, cymose, rarely 1-flowered, with scaly bract at base; both whorls of P alike or not; berry with spherical seeds): Luzuriaga, Lapageria.

XI. *SMILACOIDEAE* (climbing shrubs with net-veined l.; fls. small in axillary umbels or racemes or term. panicles; loc. with 1 or 2 orthotr. or semi-anatr. ovules): Smilax.

Liliago (Caesalp.) L. = Anthericum L. (Lili.).

Liliiflorae. The 9th order of Monocotyledons. *Cf.* p. vi.

Lilium Tourn. ex Linn. Liliaceae (V). 60 N. temp. Herbs with scaly bulbs, leafy stems and fls. in racemes. Honey secreted in long grooves at the bases of the P-leaves. The fls. of many sp. are visited by Lepidoptera. *L. Martagon* L. gives off its scent at night (*cf.* Oenothera). *L. bulbiferum* L. is reproduced veg. by bulbils in the leaf-axils. In most sp. with hanging fls. the caps. when ripe stands upwards, so that the seeds can only escape when it is shaken. Many sp. of lily cult. orn. fl.

Lilloa Speg. (*Synandrospadix EP.*). Araceae (VII). 1 Argentina.

Lily, *Lilium*, used of most *Liliaceae*, *Amaryllidaceae*, &c.; **arum -**, *Richardia africana* Kunth; **Bourbon -**, *Lilium candidum* L.; **Chinese sacred -**, *Narcissus*; **Jacobean -**, *Sprekelia formosissima* Herb.; **Kaffir -**, *Clivia*; **- of the valley**, *Convallaria majalis* L.; **queen -**, *Phaedranassa*; **spire -**, *Galtonia*; **swamp -**, *Zephyranthes*; **- thorn** (W.I.), *Catesbaea*; **water -**, *Nuphar*, *Nymphaea*.

Lima bean, *Phaseolus lunatus* L.

Limacia Lour. Menispermaceae. 10 E. Indomal.

Limaciopsis Engl. Menispermaceae. 1 trop. Afr.

Limatodes Lindl. (*Phajus* p.p. *BH.*). Orchidaceae (II. 9). 1 Burma. Crossed by *Preptanthe vestita* is the *Calanthe Veitchii* Hort.

Limb, the free portion of a concrescent corolla; one branch of a sympodium.

Lime, *Citrus Medica* L., var. *acida*, var. *Limetta*, *Tilia*; **- myrtle** (W.I.), *Triphasia*.

Limeum L. Phytolaccaceae (Aizoaceae *BH.*). 15 S. Afr. to India.

Limit of trees, either N. or S., or upwards in the Mts., beyond which they do not naturally occur.

Limivasculum Börner = Carex p.p. (Cyper.).

Limnanthaceae (*EP.*; *Geraniaceae* p.p. *BH.*). Dicot. (Archichl. Sapindales). A very small fam. (2 gen., 5 sp., N. Am.) sometimes united to Geraniaceae, but with the ovules as in ord. Sapindales. Herbs with exstip. alt. l. and reg. ☿ fls., 3—5-merous, with two whorls of sta. Ovary 3—5-loc., ovules 1 in each loc., ascending, the micropyle facing outwards and downwards. Fruit a schizocarp. Seeds exalbuminous. *Genera:* Limnanthes, Floerkea.

Limnanthemum S. P. Gmel. Gentianaceae (II). 20 trop. and temp. *L.* (*Villarsia*) *nymphaeoides* Hoffmgg. et Link, S. England, is a water-plant with habit of Nymphaea. The infl. appears to spring from the top of the leaf-stalk, but really the floating l. springs from the infl. axis. This is an advance upon the Nymphaea construction, as the materials going from l. to seeds have not to travel to the bottom of the pond and up again.

Limnanthes R. Br. Limnanthaceae. 4 Pacific N. Am.

Limnas Trin. Gramineae (8) 1 E. Siberia.

Limnia L. (*Claytonia* Gronov.). Portulacaceae. 10 N. Am.

Limnium (Cl.), a lake formation.

Limnobium Rich. (*Hydromystria* G. F. W. Mey., *Trianea* Karst.). Hydrocharitaceae. 3 Am. *L.* (*H.*) *stoloniferum* Griseb. (*T. bogotensis* Karst.), a small floating plant often cult. It reproduces veg. by 'runners' (*cf.* Hydrocharis). Its root-hairs are used to show circulation of protoplasm. Only the ♀ pl. is known in Eur.

Limnocharis Humb. et Bonpl. Butomaceae. 2 trop. S. Am., W.I.

Limnochloa Beauv. ex Lestib. = Eleocharis R. Br. (Cyper.).

Limnodium (Cl.), a salt marsh formation.

Limnophila R. Br. (*Ambulia* Lam. *EP.*). Scrophular. (II. 6). 30 palaeotrop.

Limnophyton Miq. Alismaceae. 2 palaeotrop.

Limnorchis Rydberg (*Habenaria* p.p.). Orchid. (II. 1). 24 N. Am., Eur.

Limnosipanea Hook. f. Rubiaceae (I. 3). 4 S. and C. Am.

Limodorum (Tourn.) L. Orchidaceae (II. 2). 1 S. Eur. A leafless saprophyte with no chlorophyll (*cf.* Epipogum). The 4 lat. sta. are sometimes fertile.

Limonia L. Rutaceae (V). 10 trop. Afr. and As. Some have thorns in the leaf-axils (l. of branch, as in Cactaceae). The fr. of *L. acidissima* L. is used in Japan as a substitute for soap.

Limoniastrum Moench. Plumbaginaceae. 3 Medit.

Limonium Tourn. ex Mill. = Statice L. (Plumbag.).

Limosella L. Scrophulariaceae (II. 6). 7 cosmop. *L. aquatica* L., mud-wort, in Brit. multiplies by runners.

Linaceae (*EP.*; *BH.* add *Erythroxylaceae*). Dicot. (Archichl. Geraniales). 9 gen., 150 sp., cosmop. Most are herbs and shrubs with alt. entire often stip. l. Infl. cymose, a dichasium or cincinnus, the latter usu. straightening out very much and looking like a raceme. Fl. ☿, reg., usu. 5-merous. K 5, quincuncial; C 5, imbr. or conv.;

A 5, 10 or more, often with stds., united at base into a ring; G (2—3—5), multi-loc., often with extra partitions projecting from the mid-ribs of the cpls., but not united to the axile plac.; ovules 1 or 2 per loc., pend., anatr., with the micropyle facing outwards and upwards. Septic. caps., or drupe. Embryo usu. straight, in fleshy endosp. Linum (flax, linseed) is economically important. *Chief genera:* Radiola, Linum, Hugonia. [**BH. chars.** incl. ov. 1-loc.]

Linaloa, *Bursera delpechiana* Poiss. (Mexico).

Linanthus Benth. (*Gilia* p.p.). Polemoniaceae. 55 N. Am.

Linaria Tourn. ex Mill. (*BH.* incl. *Cymbalaria* Medic., *Elatine* Rupp., *Elatinoides* Wettst.). Scrophulariaceae (II. 3). 100 ✻ and S. Am., chiefly extra-trop. 7 in Brit. (toad-flax), esp. *L. vulgaria* Mill. (yellow toad-flax). The pl. is a perennial, each year's growth arising from an adv. bud upon the summit of the root. The fl. is closed at the mouth; honey is secreted by the nectary at the base of the ovary and collects in the spur. The only visitors are the larger bees, which are able to open the fl., and whose tongues are long enough to reach the honey. Peloria of the fl. is frequent; a term. fl. appears upon the raceme and is symmetrical, with 5 spurs upon the C and a tubular mouth. Sometimes fls. of this type occur all down the raceme. Another interesting sp. is *L. Cymbalaria* Mill., the ivy-leaved toad-flax, found on walls in Brit. Before fert. the fls. are positively helio-tropic and stand erect; after it they become negatively heliotropic and bend downwards, seeking out the dark crannies in the substratum, where the seeds ripen.

Linariopsis Welw. Pedaliaceae. 1 trop. S.W. Afr.

Linconia L. Bruniaceae. 3 S. Afr.

Lindackeria Presl = Oncoba Forsk. (Flacourt.).

Lindauea Rendle. Acanthaceae (IV. B). 1 Somaliland.

Lindelofia Lehm. Boraginaceae (IV. 1). 15 N. Afr., As.

Linden, *Tilia*.

Lindenbergia Lehm. Scrophulariaceae (II. 6). 12 trop. As. and Afr.

Lindenia Benth. Rubiaceae (I. 3). 3 C. Am., Fiji, New Caledonia.

Lindera Thunb. Lauraceae (II). 80 sp. Japan to Java. *L. Benzoin* Meissn. has aromatic bark (antifebrile).

Lindernia All. (Vandellia L. *BH.*). Scrophular. (II. 6). 30 warm.

Lindheimera A. Gray et Engelm. Compositae (5). 1 Texas.

Lindleya H. B. et K. Rosaceae (I. 2). 1 Mexico.

Lindleyella Rydberg (*Lindleya* H. B. et K.). Rosaceae (I. 2). 2 N. Am.

Lindleyella Schlechter. Orchidaceae (II. 12). 1 W.I., Guiana.

Lindmania Mez. (*Cottendorfia* p.p.). Bromeliaceae (2). 5 S. Am.

Lindsaya Dryand. Polypodiaceae. 90 trop. and subtrop., exc. Afr.

Lineae (*BH.*) = Linaceae.

Linear (l.), long and narrow, as in grasses.

Lineate (dimin. lineolate), marked with (fine) lines.

Ling, *Calluna vulgaris* Salisb.

Lingelsheimia Pax. Euphorbiaceae (A. I. 1). 1 W. trop. Afr.

Linnaea Gronov. in L. (incl. *Abelia* R. Br.). Caprifoliaceae (III). 20 ✻, *L. borealis* L. in Scotland. Ovary covered with glandular hairs. Sta. 4, didynamous. Two loculi are ∞-ovulate and sterile, the other 1-ovulate and fertile. Some (Abelia) cult. orn. fl.; ed. fr.

Linnaeopsis Engl. Gesneriaceae (I). 1 trop. Afr.
Linnaeus' system, the artificial system, by which plants were divided into classes, &c. on purely artificial lines, by the number of stamens and cpls., &c.; **- species,** *cf.* Nomenclature.
Linocalyx Lindau. Acanthaceae (IV. B). 1 trop. Afr.
Linochilus Benth. = Diplostephium H. B. et K. (Comp.).
Linociera Sw. (*Mayepa* Aubl. *EP.*). Oleaceae. 50 trop., subtrop.
Linodendron Griseb. (*Lasiadenia BH.*). Thymelaeaceae. 4 Cuba.
Linospadix Becc. Palmaceae (IV. 1). 8 New Guinea, Austr.
Linostoma Wall. Thymelaeaceae. 2 Further India.
Linosyris Cass. = Aster Tourn. p.p.; **do.** Torr. et Gray = Bigelovia DC.
Linseed, Lint, *Linum usitatissimum* L.
Lintonia Stapf. Gramineae (9). 1 Brit. E. Afr.
Linum Tourn. ex L. Linaceae. 95 temp. and subtrop., esp. Medit. 4 in Brit., *L. catharticum* L. (purging flax), common, *L. usitatissimum* L. (common flax or linseed), an introduction, cult. in Ireland and elsewhere. Fls. in sympodial cincinni. Several are heterostyled (dimorphic), *e.g.* the common red one of gardens, *L. grandiflorum* Desf. Illegitimate pollination in this sp. produces absolutely no seed at all. The seed has a mucilaginous testa which swells on wetting. Flax is the fibre of *Linum usitatissimum* L., obtained by rotting off the softer tissues in water; linen is made from it. The shorter fibres form tow, and scraped linen lint. The seeds (linseed) yield an oil by pressure, and the remaining 'cake' (*cf.* Gossypium) is used for cattle-feeding, &c.
Lip, a projecting anterior part of an irregular corolla or calyx.
Liparia L. Leguminosae (III. 3). 4 S. Afr.
Liparis Rich. (*BH.* incl. *Cestichis* Thou.). Orchidaceae (II. 4). 100 trop. and temp. (1 in Brit., rare).
Liparophyllum Hook. f. Gentianaceae (II). 1 Tasm., New Zealand.
Lip-fern (Am.), *Cheilanthes.*
Lipocarpha R. Br. in Tuckey. Cyperaceae (I). 7 trop.
Lipochaeta DC. Compositae (5). 12 Hawaiian and Galapagos Is.
Lipostoma D. Don (*Coccocypselum BH.*). Rubiaceae (I. 2). 2 Brazil.
Lipozygis E. Mey. = Lotononis Eckl. et Zeyh. p.p. (Legum.).
Lippia Houst. ex L. Verbenaceae (I). 120 trop. Am., Afr. The l. of *L. citriodora* H. B. et K. yield an aromatic oil used in perfumery under the name Verbena-oil. Some have axillary thorns.
Liquidambar L. Hamamelidaceae. 4 Medit., As., N. Am. Fls. monoec., apet., the ♂ in upright spikes, the ♀ in heads on pend. stalks. The seeds are easily shaken out in strong winds. Storax (a fragrant balsam) is obtained from all, but chiefly from *L. orientalis* Mill. (As. min.). *L. styraciflua* L., sweet gum, N. Am.; wood useful (satin walnut).
Liquorice, *Glycyrrhiza glabra* L.; **Indian -, - vine** (W.I.), *Abrus.*
Lirayea Pierre (*Afromendoncia EP.*). Acanthaceae (II). 1 trop. Afr.
Liriodendron L. Magnoliaceae. 1 N. Am., *L. tulipifera* L., the tulip-tree, often cult. in parks. The l. is polymorphic. Fr. a samara; the aggregate of samaras upon the recept. looks like a pine-cone. The wood is useful (canary whitewood).
Liriope Lour. Liliaceae (VIII) (Haemodor. *BH.*). 2 E. As.

Liriosma Poepp. et Endl. Olacaceae. 15 trop. S. Am.
Lisaea Boiss. (*Caucalis* p.p. *BH.*). Umbelliferae (III. 2). 3 W. As.
Lisianthus L. Gentianaceae (I). 15 W.I., Cent. Am.
Lissanthe R. Br. (*Styphelia* p.p. *EP.*). Epacridaceae (3). 4 Austr.
Lissocarpa Benth. Styracaceae. 1 Brazil.
Lissochilus R. Br. Orchidaceae (II. 10). 60 warm Afr.
Listera R. Br. Orchidaceae (II. 2). 20 N. temp. *L. ovata* R. Br. (tway-blade) and *L. cordata* R. Br. in Brit. The labellum is bent downwards and forked into two. The rostellum on being touched ruptures violently and ejects a viscid fluid which cements the pollinia to the insect as in Epipactis (see Darwin, *Orchids*, p. 115).
Listia E. Mey. Leguminosae (III. 3). 1 S. Afr.
Listrostachys Reichb. f. (*Angraecum* p.p. *BH.*). Orchidaceae (II. 20). 25 warm Afr.
Litanthus Harv. Liliaceae (V). 1 S. Afr.
Litanum Nieuwland (*Talinum* p.p.). Portulacaceae. 1 N. Am.
Litchi Sonner. (*Nephelium* p.p. *BH.*). Sapindaceae (I). 1 China, *L. chinensis* Sonner. (litchi or leechee), cult. for ed. fr., a one-seeded nut with fleshy aril.
Literature: the following general works of reference may be mentioned, as providing further information upon the various subjects of this dictionary:

Admiralty *Manual of Scientific Enquiry.*
Bailey, L. H., *Universal Cyclopaedia of Horticulture.*
Baker, J. G., *Handbook of the Fern Allies.*
Bentham and Hooker, *Genera Plantarum.* London.
British *Pharmacopoeia.*
Britten and Holland, *Dict. of English Plant Names.*
Christensen, *Index Filicum.* Copenhagen, 1906.
Darwin, *Origin of Species*, *Naturalist's Voyage*, &c.
De Candolle, *Origin of Cultivated Plants*, Engl. ed.
De Dalla Torre and Harms, *Genera Siphonogamarum.*
De Vries, *The Mutation Theory*, Engl. ed.
Durand, *Index Generum Phanerogamarum.*
Eichler, *Blüthendiagramme.* Leipzig.
Engler, *Das Pflanzenreich.* Leipzig (in course of publication); *Syllabus der Vorlesungen.*
Engler and Prantl, *Die Natürlichen Pflanzenfamilien.* Second edition in course of publication. Leipzig.
Goebel, *Organography of Plants*, Engl. ed. Oxford.
Hooker and Jackson, *Index Kewensis*, and Supplements.
Jackson, *Dictionary of Botanical Terms.*
Kew: *Official Guides to the Museums.*
Knuth, *Handbook of Floral Pollination*, Engl. ed. Oxford.
Linnaeus, *Genera Plantarum.*
Sanders, *Encyclopaedia of Gardening.* London, 1912.
Schimper, *Geography of Plants*, Engl. ed. Oxford, 1903.
Stapf, *Index Londinensis*, Oxford, 1929 (in progress).
Strasburger, *Textbook of Botany.*
The *Treasury of Botany.* [&c.
Wallace, *Travels on the Amazon*, *Island Life*, *Malay Archipelago*,

Ward, *Trees*. Cambridge.
Warming, *Oecology of Plants*, Engl. ed. Oxford; *Systematic Botany*.
Watt, *Dictionary of the Economic Products of India*; *Commercial Products of India*, London, 1908.
Wiesner, *Die Rohstoffe des Pflanzenreichs*. Leipzig.
Willis, *Agriculture in the Tropics*. Cambridge, 1922.

Numerous more special works are mentioned under different heads throughout the book.

Lithobium Bong. Melastomaceae (I). 1 Minas Geraes.

Lithocardium L. = Cordia L. (Borag.).

Lithophragma Torr. et Gray (*Tellima* R. Br. p.p.). Saxifragaceae (I). 15 N. Am.

Lithophytum T. S. Brandegee. Solanaceae? 1 California.

Lithospermum (Tourn.) L. Boraginaceae (IV. 4). 50 temp.; 3 in Brit. (gromwell).

Lithraea Miers. Anacardiaceae (3). 3 S. Am.

Litobrochia Presl = Pteris L.

Litosanthes Blume. Rubiaceae (II. 5). 3 Malay Archipelago.

Litsea Lam. Lauraceae (II). 180 trop. As., Austr. L. and bark medicinal.

Littledalea Hemsl. Gramineae (10). 1 Tibet.

Littonia Hook. Liliaceae (I). 7 S. and trop. Afr. Like Gloriosa.

Littoralis (Lat.), growing on the beach.

Littorella Berg. Plantaginaceae. 2 sp., 1 in S. Am., and *L. lacustris* L. (shore-weed) in Eur. (incl. Brit.). This pl. exhibits two forms, one in water, another on land. The land form has a rosette of narrow l. about 3 cm. long, which spread out upon the ground and show distinct dorsiventral structure. Fls. in groups of 3, one ♂ on a long stalk between two sessile ♀, which are ripe before the sta. emerge from the former. Both sta. and style are very long and the fls. are wind-pollinated. Fr. a nut. The water form has much larger l. which grow erect and are cylindrical (centric) in form and internal structure; no fls. are produced, but the plant multiplies largely by runners. It is often mistaken for Isoetes.

Live-long, *Sedum*.

Liveus (Lat.), pale lead colour.

Livistona R. Br. Palmae (I. 2). 20 Indomal., Austr. Tall trees with fan leaves and panicles of ☿ fls. Fr. a berry.

Lizard's tail (Am.), *Saururus*.

Llagunoa Ruiz et Pav. Sapindaceae (II). 2 Andes.

Llanosia Blanco (*Ternstroemia* p.p.). Theaceae. 1 Phil. Is.

Llavea Lagasca. Polypodiaceae. 1 trop. Am.

Llavea Liebm. Inc. sed. 2 Mexico.

Lloydia Salisb. Liliaceae (V). 20 N. temp.; 1 on Snowdon.

Loasa Adans. Loasaceae. 100 Mexico and S. Am., chiefly Mts. of Chili and Peru. Several cult. orn. fl.; they possess stinging hairs. The fls. are generally yellow and face downwards. The nectaries, formed of combined stds. (see fam.), are large and conspicuous. The petals are boat-shaped and conceal the groups of sta.

Loasaceae (*EP.*, *BH.*). Dicotyledons (Archichl. Parietales; Passiflorales *BH.*). 13/250. Andine plants (*cf. Kissenia*), many cult. orn. fl.

Mostly herbs, frequently twining, with opp. or alt., rarely stip., l. The epidermis bears hairs of various kinds; esp. common are grapple-hairs and stinging-hairs. Fls. usu. in cymes, often sympodial, yellow (rarely white or red), ☿, usu. 5-merous. Receptacle deeply hollowed out, so that the fl. is epig. K 5, imbr.; C 5, free or united; A 5—∞. In the genera with ∞ sta. there is much difference as to the arrangement. In Mentzelia they are evenly distributed round the style, the outermost in some sp. being sterile. In other gen. it is the antesepalous sta. that are sterile, and in some, *e.g.* Loasa, Blumenbachia, 3 or more of the stds. are united to form a large coloured nectary, whose mouth is towards the centre of the fl. and partly obstructed by the other stds. $\overline{G}$ 1 or more commonly (3—5), with parietal plac.; ovules 1, several, or ∞, anatr., with one integument; style simple. Fr. various, often a caps., sometimes spirally twisted. Endosp. or not. *Chief genera:* Gronovia, Mentzelia, Loasa, Blumenbachia.

Loaseae (*BH.*) = Loasaceae.

Lobe (l.), portion of a divided (not cpd.) l. or stigma.

Lobelia Plum. ex L. Campanulaceae (III). 220 trop. and temp.; 2 in Brit., one in lakes (*L. Dortmanna* L.); several cult. orn. fl. The fl. (see fam.) is twisted upon its axis through 180°, and is ·|·. The anthers are syngenesious as in Compositae, and the style pushes through the tube thus formed, driving the pollen out at the top. Finally it emerges, the stigmas separate, and the ♀ stage begins. [See fam. and *cf.* Campanula, Phyteuma, Jasione and Compositae.]

Loblolly bay, *Gordonia Lasianthus* L.; **- pine,** *Pinus Taeda* L.; **- sweetwood** (W.I.), *Sciadophyllum*; **- tree** (W.I.), *Cupania*, *Pisonia*.

Lobogyne Schlechter. Orchidaceae (II. *a*. III). 2 New Guinea, Polynesia.

Lobostemon Lehm. Boraginaceae (IV. 5). 50 Afr.

Lobostephanus N.E. Br. (*Emicocarpus* p.p. *EP.*). Asclepiadaceae (II. 1). 1 S. Afr.

Lobularia Desv. (*Alyssum* p.p. *BH.*). Cruciferae (4). 4 Medit.

Locellate, divided into small compartments.

Lochia Balf. f. Caryophyllaceae (I. 4). 1 Socotra.

Lochmium (Cl.), a thicket formation.

Lochnera Reichb. (Vinca p.p. *BH.*). Apocynaceae (I. 3). 3 trop. *L. rosea* Reichb., one of the commonest trop. weeds.

Lockhartia Hook. Orchidaceae (II. 19). 30 trop. Am., W.I. No tubers; l. crowded together.

Loculament, loculus, a cavity in the ovary, usu. containing ovules; **loculicidal** (fr.), splitting down midrib of each cpl.

Locust, honey -, *Gleditschia*; **- tree,** *Robinia Pseudacacia* L. (W.I.), *Byrsonima*, *Hymenaea*.

Loddigesia Sims. Leguminosae (III. 3). 1 S. Afr.

Lodh bark, *Symplocos racemosa* Roxb. (India).

Lodhra Guill. = Symplocos Jacq. p.p. (Symploc.).

Lodicularia Beauv. = Hemarthria R. Br. (*BH.*). = Rottboellia L. f.

Lodicule, *Gramineae*.

Lodoicea Comm. Palmae (II). 1 Seychelles, *L. Sechellarum* Labill., the double coco-nut or Coco de mer. Dioec. The fr. is one of the largest known and takes 10 years to ripen. The nut is bilobed. The fr. used to be found floating before discovery of tree (*Treas. of Bot.*).

Loeflingia L. Caryoph. (I. 3). 6 Medit., C. As., N. Am.

Loeselia L. Polemon. 15 Calif. to Venezuela. Fl. ± ·|·.

Loesenera Harms. Legum. (II. 3). 1 W. trop. Afr.

Loewia Urb. Turner. 2 E. trop. Afr. [*Hered.*, Nov. 1916, p. 504.

Loganberry, a probable blackberry-raspberry hybrid, but *cf. Journ. of*

Logania R. Br. Logan. 25 Austr., N.Z. Sepal anterior.

Loganiaceae (*EP.*, *BH.*). Dicots. (Sympet. Contortae; Gentianales *BH.*; pp. xliii, liii). 35/550 trop., a few warm temp. Trees, shrubs, and herbs, with opp. or whorled simple stip. l.; stips. often much reduced. Many climbers. Infl. usu. cymose, various; fls. with br. and bracteoles, usu. reg., ☿, 4—5-merous with occasional increase in C and A. Disc small or absent. K (4—5), imbr.; C (4—5), valvate, imbr., or conv.; A 4—5, rarely 1, epipet.; G̲ (2), anteropost. rarely ½-inf., 2-loc. (rarely imperfectly so), 1-loc. or more-loc. with simple style and ov. usu. ∞, amphi- or ana-tr. Caps., usu. septicid., berry, or drupe; endosp. Nearly allied to Apocyn., Gentian., Solan., Scroph., Rubi.; *cf.* discussion in *Nat. Pfl.*, &c. *Chief genera:* Logania, Spigelia, Strychnos (no glandular hairs, l. 3—5-nerved, C valv., berry, seeds many), Fagraea, Buddleia, Desfontainea.

Logwood, Campeachy-, *Haematoxylon campechianum* L., *Ceanothus Chloroxylon* Nees; **bastard-** (W.I.), *Acacia Berteriana* Spreng.

Loheria Merrill. Myrsin. (II). 1 Phil. Is.

Loiseleuria Desv. Eric. (I. 3). 1 N. circumpolar, *L.* (*Azalea*) *procumbens* (L.) Desv. (Scot. Highlands, trailing Azalea). L. very wiry, rolled back at margins, reducing transpiration. Fl. reg., protog., opening soon after melting of snow. A 5, G 2—3-loc.

Lolium L. Gramin. (12). 8 Eur., N. Afr., temp. As. *L. perenne* L. (rye-grass) in Brit. Spikelets in 2-ranked spike, and placed edgewise (this distinguished subtribe *Lolieae* from *Leptureae*, to which Triticum and Hordeum belong). Valuable pasture and fodder.

Lomandra Labill. (*Xerotes BH.*). Lili. (III) (Junc. *BH.*). 35 Austr., New Caled., New Guinea. Dioec. P sepaloid, or inner petaloid.

Lomanthera Rafin. = Tetrazygia Rich. (Melastom.).

Lomaria Willd. = Blechnum L. (Polypod.).

Lomaspora DC. = Arabis L. (Crucif.).

Lomastelma Rafin. = Eugenia L. (Myrt.).

Lomatia R. Br. Prot. (II). 10 E. Austr., Tasm., Chile. Gynophore.

Lomatium Rafin. (*Peucedanum* p.p. *BH.*). Umbell. (III. 6). 60 W. [N. Am.

Lomatolepis Cass., Hook. f. = Launaea Cass. p.p. (Comp.).

Lomatophyllum Willd. Lili. (III). 3 Masc. Fr. fleshy, dehisc. Orn. fl.

Lomatozona Baker. Comp. (2). 1 Goyaz. L. opp. Pappus connate [at base.

Lombardy poplar, *Populus nigra* L., var. *pyramidalis* Spach.

Lomentose, like a lomentum, *Raphanus*; **lomentum**, a pod constricted between the seeds, breaking into 1-seeded portions, *Leguminosae*.

Lonas Adans. Comp. (7). 1 S.W. Medit.

Lonchanthera Less. ex Baker = Stenachaenium Benth. (Legum.).

Lonchitis Bubani = Serapias L. (Orchid.).

Lonchitis L. Polypod. 8 trop. Am. and Afr., Madag.

Lonchocarpus H. B. et K. Legum. (III. 8). 120 trop. Am., W.I., Afr., Austr.

Lonchomera Hook. f. et Thoms. (*Mezzettia* p.p.). Anonaceae (1). 1 Malay Peninsula.

Lonchophora Dur. Cruciferae (4). 1 N. Afr.

Lonchostephus Tul. Podostemaceae. 1 Amazon.

Lonchostoma Wikstr. Bruniaceae. 3 S. Afr.

London pride, *Saxifraga umbrosa* L.

Long and short shoots, *Berberis*, *Coniferae*, *Ginkgo*, *Phyllocladus*, *Pinus*.

Longan, *Nephelium Longana* Cambess.

Longetia Baill. Euphorbiaceae (A. I. 1). 6 New Caled.

Longi- (Lat. pref.), long.

Long-moss, *Tillandsia*.

Long-tongued insects, bees and Hymenoptera.

Lonicera L. Caprifoliaceae. 100 ✳. *L. Periclymenum* L. (honeysuckle or woodbine), and others, in Brit. Mostly erect shrubs, a few twining, with opp. frequently connate l. In the axils of many (*e.g. L. tatarica* L.) are serial buds, of which the lowest gives rise to the fls. usu. in pairs, the central fl. of the small dichasium not being developed. The fl. is frequently ·|·, and gives rise to a berry. In some the pair of fls. produces two independent berries, in others the berries fuse into one as they form. Some sp. exhibit the 'fusion' even earlier; and one finds two corollas seated upon what at first glance appears a single inf. ovary. Dissection shows that in most cases the two ovaries are side by side, free from one another, in a common hollow axis; in a few cases, however, the union is more complete. The fl. of the honeysuckle is visited chiefly by hawk-moths (at night). The fl. opens in the evening, the anthers having dehisced shortly before this. The style projects beyond the anthers. The fl. moves into a horiz. position at the same time. At first the style is bent downwards and the sta. form the alighting place for insects. Later on the style moves up to a horiz. position, the sta. shrivel and bend down, and this is complete by the second evening when the next crop of buds is opening. At the same time the fl. has changed from white to yellow. The length of the tube keeps out all but very long-tongued insects (class F).

Loofah, *Luffa cylindrica* M. Roem.

Looking glass tree, *Heritiera littoralis* Ait.

Loose pollen mechanism, *cf. Acanthus*, and *Bartsia*, *Borago*, *Calluna*, *Cyclamen*, *Erica*, *Ericaceae*, *Euphrasia*, *Galanthus*, *Melampyrum*, *Pedicularis*, *Scrophulariaceae*, *Solanum*.

Loosestrife, purple, *Lythrum*, **yellow**, *Lysimachia*.

Lopezia Cav. Onagraceae (2). 15 C. Am. Fl. ·|·. The two upper petals are bent upwards a little way from the base, and at the bend there seems to be a drop of honey. In reality this is a dry glossy piece of hard tissue; like the similar bodies in Parnassia it deceives flies. There are real nectaries at the base of the fl. There are two sta., of which the post. only is fertile; it is enclosed at first in the ant. one, which is a spoon-shaped petaloid std. In the early stage of the fl., the style is undeveloped and insects alight on the sta.; later the style grows out into the place first occupied by the sta., which now bends upwards out of the way. In *L. coronata* Andr., &c. there is an upward tension in the sta., a downward in the std., and an explosion occurs when an insect alights. Cult. orn. fl.

Lophacme Stapf. Gramineae (11). 1 S. Afr.

Lophactis Rafin. Compositae (inc. sed.). 1 N. Am.

Lophanthera A. Juss. Malpighiaceae (II). 3 Brazil. Carpophore.

Lophanthus Benth. Labiatae (VI). 2 C. As., China. Fl. stalk sometimes resupinate like that of Lobelia.

Lophatherum Brongn. Gramineae (10). 4 E. As.

Lophiocarpus Miq. (*Sagittaria* p.p. *BH.*). Alismaceae. 4 trop.

Lophiocarpus Turcz. Chenopodiaceae (inc. sed.). 2 S. Afr.

Lophiola Ker-Gawl. Amaryllidaceae (III). 1 Atl. N. Am.

Lophira Banks ex Gaertn. f. Ochnaceae. 2 trop. Afr. The fr. of *L. alata* Banks (African oak) has one sep. much, a second less, elongated. The seeds yield an oil on pressure; timber good.

Lophium (Cl.), a hill formation.

Lophocarpus Boeck. Cyperaceae (II). 1 Tonquin.

Lophocereus Britton et Rose (*Cereus* p.p.). Cactaceae (III. 1). 3 S.W. U.S.

Lophogyne Tul. Podostemaceae. 2 Rio de Janeiro.

Lopholaena DC. Compositae (8). 4 S. and trop. Afr.

Lopholepis Decne. Gramineae (3). 1 India.

Lophopappus Rusby. Compositae (12). 1 Bolivia.

Lophopetalum Wight ex Arn. Celastraceae. 12 Indomal.

Lophophora Coult. (*Anhalonium* p.p.). Cactaceae (III. 2). 1 N. Am.

Lophophyllum Griff. (*Peramphora* p.p. *EP.*). Menisperm. 1 Indomal.

Lophophytum Schott et Endl. Balanophoraceae. 4 trop. S. Am.

Lophopogon Hack. Gramineae (2). 1 India. Glume 3-toothed.

Lophopterys A. Juss. Malpighiaceae (I). 1 Guiana.

Lophopyxis Hook. f. Icacinaceae (formerly Euph.). 3 Malaya.

Lophoschoenus Stapf (*Cyclocampe* p.p.). Cyper. (II). 3 Seychelles, Borneo, New Caledonia.

Lophosciadium DC. Umbelliferae (III. 6). 5 S. Eur., W. As.

Lophospermum D. Don = Maurandia Orteg. p.p. (Scroph.).

Lophostachys Pohl. Acanthaceae (IV. A). 12 Brazil, Peru.

Lophostigma Radlk. Sapindaceae (I). 1 Bolivia.

Lophostoma Meissn. (*Linostoma BH.*). Thymelaeaceae. 3 Amazonas.

Lophotocarpus Durand (*Lophiocarpus* p.p.). Alismaceae. 2 trop.

Lopriorea Schinz. (*Psilotrichum* p.p.). Amarantaceae (2). 1 E. Afr.

Lopseed (Am.), *Phryma*.

Loquat, *Eriobotrya japonica* Lindl.

Loranthaceae (*EP.*, *BH.*). Dicots. (Archichl. Santalales; Achlamydosporae *BH.*). 30 gen., 520 sp., trop. and temp. The only genus in Brit. is Viscum, the mistletoe. An interesting fam. of parasites with green l. Mostly small semi-parasitic shrubs attached to their hosts by suckers or haustoria—usu. regarded as modified adv. roots. A few root in the earth, *e.g.* the W. Austr. Nuytsia, which grows into a small tree 30 feet high. Most are fairly omnivorous in their choice of hosts, but a few are restricted to one or two. Where the parasitic root joins the host, there is not uncommonly an outgrowth, often of considerable size and complicated in shape. The parasitic root often branches within the tissue of the host, as in mistletoe. The stem is sympodial, often dichasial, *e.g.* in Viscum, and the l. usu. evergr. and leathery.

Infl. cymose, the fls. usu. in little groups of 3 (or 2, by abortion of the central fl.). When the fls. are stalked, the bracts of the lateral fls. are always united to their stalks, up to the point of origin of the fl. (see Viscum and Loranthus). Infl. sometimes in spikes, with the fls. on the internodes as well as on the nodes.

The recept. is hollowed out, and the P springs from its margin. In the Loranthoideae there is below the P an outgrowth of the axis in the form of a small fringe—the *calyculus*. Some look upon it as a K, many as an outgrowth of the axis; and this is perhaps the safest view. P either sepaloid or petaloid. Fls. ☿ or unisexual. Sta. as many as, and (as in Proteaceae) united with, the P-leaves. The pollen is often developed in a great number of loculi, separate from one another, though often becoming continuous when mature. Ovary 1-loc., sunk in, and united with, the receptacle, the ovules not differentiated from the placenta. Embryo-sacs > one, curiously lengthened (*cf.* Casuarina). Fr. a pseudo-berry or -drupe, the fleshy part really the receptacle. Round the seed is a layer of viscin, a very sticky substance. [For full details of the many interesting features of this fam., the infl., fl., pollen, development and structure of ovule and embryo-sac, fruit, seed, germination, haustoria, &c., see Engler in *Nat. Pfl.* and papers by Wiesner in *Sitz. k. Akad.* Wien, CIII. 1894, and Keeble in *Trans. Linn. Soc.* V. 1896.]

Classification and chief genera (after Engler):

I. *LORANTHOIDEAE* (with calyculus): Struthanthus, Loranthus, Psittacanthus.

II. *VISCOIDEAE* (without calyc.): Arceuthobium, Viscum.

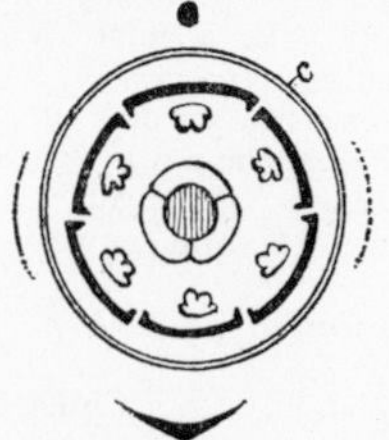

Diagram of Loranthus (after Eichler). *c*, calyculus.

Loranthus L. Loranthaceae (1). 350 | ✻ trop. and subtrop. Semi-parasites. ☿ or unisexual fls. in small cymes, the bracts adnate to the peduncles. Fr. like that of Viscum. See *Nat. Pfl.*, Eichler's *Blüthendiag.* and papers by Wiesner and Keeble (*cf.* fam.).

Lorate, loriform, strap-shaped.

Lords and ladies, *Arum maculatum* L.

Lorentea Lag. = Pectis L. p.p. (Comp.).

Lorentzia Griseb. (*Pascalia BH.*, *Wedelia* p.p. *EP.*). Compositae (5). 1 S. temp. Am.

Lorentzia Hieron. (*Ayenia* Loefl.). Sterculiaceae. 2 Argentina.

Loreya DC. Melastomaceae (I). 8 S. Am.
Loropetalum R. Br. Hamamelidaceae. 1 Khasias, S. China.
Lorostelma Fourn. Asclepiadaceae (II. 3). 1 Brazil.
Lortia Rendle. Euphorbiaceae (A. I. 8). 2 trop. Afr.
Lote fruit, *Zizyphus Lotus* Lam. (Medit.).
Lotononis Eckl. et Zeyh. Leguminosae (III. 3). 90 Afr., Medit.
Lotoxalis Small (*Oxalis* p.p.). Oxalidaceae. 15 N. Am.
Lotus (Tourn.) L. Leguminosae (III. 5). 15 temp. Eur., As., S. Afr., Austr. *L. corniculatus* L., bird's foot trefoil, and others, in Brit. The floral mechanism (class H) is typical of many of the fam. (*q.v.*). The keel is united above and below, leaving only a small opening at the apex. The pollen is shed in bud into the tip of the keel, and the filaments of five sta. thicken out below the anthers, together forming a piston, which, when the keel is depressed, forces the pollen out in a stream at the apex. The style is immersed in the pollen, but only becomes receptive on being rubbed, so that the fl. has a chance of cross-fert. The plant is useful for pasturage.
Lotus, *Zizyphus*; **-berry** (W.I.), *Byrsonima*; **sacred-,** *Nymphaea, Nelumbium.*
Loudonia Lindl. Haloragidaceae. 3 Austr.
Louisiana grass (Am.), *Paspalum platycaule* Poir.
Lourea Neck. Leguminosae (III. 7). 4 trop. As. and Austr.
Loureira Meissn. Inc. sed. 1 Cochinchina.
Lourya Baill. Liliaceae (VIII). 1 Cochinchina.
Lousewort, *Pedicularis.*
Louteridium S. Watson. Acanthaceae (IV. A). 2 C. Am.
Louvelia Jumelle et Perrier. Palmaceae (IV. 1). 1 Madag.
Lovage, *Ligusticum scoticum* L.
Love apple, *Lycopersicum esculentum* Mill.; **-grass** (Ceylon), *Andropogon aciculatus* Retz.; **-in a mist,** *Nigella*, (W.I.), *Passiflora foetida* L.; **-lies bleeding,** *Amaranthus.*
Lovoa Harms. Meliaceae (II). 5 trop. Afr.
Lovoma O. F. Cook (*Ptychosperma* p.p.). Palmaceae (IV. 1). 1 N. Austr.
Lowia Scortech. Musaceae. 2 Malaya.
Lowiara ×. Orchidaceae. Hybrid between Brassavola, Laelia, and Sophronitis.
Loxanthera Blume (*Loranthus* p.p. *BH.*). Loranth. (I). 2 Borneo, Java.
Loxocalyx Hemsl. Labiatae (VI). 1 China.
Loxocarpus R. Br. (*Didymocarpus* p.p.). Gesneriaceae (I). 3 Malaya.
Loxocarya R. Br. Restionaceae. 8 S.W. Austr.
Loxococcus H. Wendl. et Drude. Palmae (IV. 1). 1 Ceylon.
Loxodiscus Hook. f. Sapindaceae (II). 1 New Caledonia.
Loxogramme (Blume) Presl = Polypodium L. (Polypod.).
Loxonia Jack. Gesneriaceae (I). 1 Sumatra, Java.
Loxopterygium Hook. f. Anacardiaceae (3). 5 trop. S. Am.
Loxostemon Hook. f. et Thoms. Cruciferae (4). 2 Sikkim to Yunnan.
Loxostigma C. B. Clarke. Gesneriaceae (I). 2 Himalaya, China.
Loxostylis Spreng. ex Reichb. Anacardiaceae (3). 1 Cape Colony.
Loxothysanus Robinson (*Bahia* p.p.). Compositae (6). 2 Mexico.

Loxsoma Br. Hymenophyllaceae? 1 N.Z. It agrees with Trichomanes in the sorus, but differs widely in the veg. habit, which is that of Cyatheaceae, and is probably better placed in a separate fam.; *cf.* Gwynne-Vaughan, *Ann. Bot.* XIV. 1901, p. 71.

Loxsomaceae. Cf. Filicineae, and Loxsoma.

Lozanella Greenman. Ulmaceae. 1 Mexico.

Lubinia Comm. ex Vent. (*Lysimachia* p.p.). Primulaceae. 4 S. Afr., Masc. Is., Japan.

Lucaea Kunth = Arthraxon Beauv. (Gram.).

Lucens, lucidus (Lat.), with shining surface.

Lucerne, *Medicago sativa* L.

Lucilia Cass. Compositae (4). 25 S. Am.

Luciliopsis Wedd. Compositae (4). 2 Bolivia.

Lucinaea DC. Rubiaceae (I. 7). 10 Malaya.

Luculia Sweet. Rubiaceae (I. 5). 2 Himal., Khasias.

Lucuma Molina (excl. *Vitellaria* Gaertn. f.). Sapotaceae (I). 50 trop. Am. The fr. of *L. bifera* Molina is ed.

Lucya DC. Rubiaceae (I. 2). 1 W.I.

Ludia Comm. ex Juss. Flacourtiaceae (4). 2 E. Afr., Madag., Masc.

Ludovia Brongn. Cyclanthaceae. 2 trop. S. Am. ♂ fls. as in Carludovica, ♀ sunk to stigmas with rudimentary P. Climbers.

Ludovica Vieill. ex Guillaumin = Bikkia Reinw. (Rubi.).

Ludwigia L. Onagraceae (2). 20 cosmop.; 1 Brit.

Ludwigiantha Small (*Ludwigia* p.p.). Onagraceae (2). 1 N. Am.

Lueddemannia Reichb. f. (*Acineta* p.p. *EP.*). Orchid. (II. 13). 4 N. S. Am.

Luederitzia K. Schum. (*Pavonia* p.p.). Malvaceae (3). 2 S. Afr., Somaliland.

Luehea Willd. Tiliaceae. 18 trop. Am., W.I.

Luerssenia Kuhn. Polypodiaceae. 1 Sumatra.

Luffa (Tourn.) L. Cucurbitaceae (3). 7 trop. *L. cylindrica* M. Roem. (*L. aegyptiaca* Mill.) furnishes the loofah or bath sponge (the vascular bundle net of the pericarp). Fr. of most ed.

Lugonia Wedd. Asclepiadaceae (II. 1). 2 Peru, Bolivia.

Luina Benth. Compositae (8). 1 N.W. U.S.

Luisia Gaudich. Orchidaceae (II. 20). 15 trop. As. to Japan. Cult.

Lumnitzera Willd. Combretaceae. 2 palaeotrop., in mangrove (*q.v.*) swamps. Fr. floated by ocean currents.

Lunania Hook. Flacourtiaceae (7). 15 W.I., C. and S. Am. (K) in bud.

Lunaria Tourn. ex L. Cruciferae (2). 2 Eur. *L. biennis* Moench. (*L. annua L.*) is the honesty of gardens.

Lunasia Blanco. Rutaceae (I). 5 Malay Archipelago.

Lunate, half-moon-shaped.

Lundia DC. Bignoniaceae (I). 10 E. S. Am.

Lunellia Nieuwland. Scrophulariaceae (III. 1). 3 U.S.

Lung-wort, *Pulmonaria*, (Am.) *Mertensia*.

Lupin, *Lupinus*.

Lupinaster Buxb. = Trifolium Tourn. p.p. (Legum.).

Lupinus (Tourn.) L. Leguminosae (III. 3). 150 Am., Medit. Floral mechanism like Lotus. The fr. explodes, its valves twisting spirally. Several are cult. orn. fl., or used as fodder.

Lupsia Necker (*Galactites BH.*). Compositae (11). 3 Medit.

Luridus (Lat.), dingy brown or yellow.

Luteus (Lat.), yellow; **luteolus**, pale yellow; **lutescens** (Lat.), yellowish.

Luvunga Buch.-Ham. Rutaceae (V). 4 Indomal.

Luxembergia A. St Hil. Ochnaceae. 8 Brazil.

Luziola Juss. Gramineae (6). 6 Brazil to Alabama.

Luzonia Elmer. Leguminosae (III. 10). 1 Luzon.

Luzula DC. Juncaceae. 65 temp., chiefly Old World; 6 in Brit (wood-rush). Rhiz. as in Juncus; l. usu. flat.

Luzuriaga Ruiz et Pav. (*Enargea* Banks). Liliaceae (X). 7 S. Am., N.Z [to New Guin.

Lyallia Hook. f. Caryophyllaceae (I. 3). 1 Kerguelen.

Lycaste Lindl. Orchidaceae (II. 12). 30 trop. Am. Epiphytes. A chin is formed by an axial outgrowth from the column.

Lychniothyrsus Lindau. Acanthaceae (IV. A). 1 Brazil.

Lychnis (Tourn.) L. (*BH.* incl. *Agrostemma* L., *Githago* Adans., *Melandrium* Roehl, *Viscaria* Riv.). Caryophyllaceae (II. 1). 10 N. temp. |✻; 3 in Brit., incl. *L. Flos-cuculi* L. (ragged robin). Fls. protandrous, suited to bees and Lepidoptera. The fls. often show the sta. filled with a black or brown powder, instead of pollen; this is the spores of the fungus *Ustilago antherarum*, which are thus distributed from plant to plant, like pollen, by the visiting insects. [For *L. dioica* L. see Melandrium.]

Lychnodiscus Radlk. Sapindaceae (I). 5 W. Afr.

Lychnophora Mart. Compositae (1). 17 S. trop. Brazil.

Lychnophoriopsis Sch. Bip. Compositae (1). 2 Minas Geraes.

Lycium L. Solanaceae (2). 100 temp. Many have thorny twigs *L. afrum* L. (Kaffir thorn) is used for hedges in S. Afr. *L. barbarum* L. often cult. under the name tea-plant.

Lycomormium Reichb. f. Orchidaceae (II. 13). 1 Peru.

Lycopersicum Hill. (*Solanum* p.p. *EP.*). Solanaceae (2). 10 S. Am. *L. esculentum* Mill. (*Solanum Lycopersicum* L.) is the tomato or love-apple.

Lycopodiaceae. Lycopodiales, Eligulatae. 2 gen., 190 sp., trop. and temp. The fertilised ovum gives rise directly to the leafy plant; the embryo has a suspensor and a foot; and its upper part at first forms a tuber-like organ, the *protocorm*, from which the l. and stem develope. In P. the stem is short and unbranched, in L. long and much branched, bearing small simple l., and roots developed in acropetal succession. The sporangia are axillary, and form as a rule a dense terminal cone or strobilus. The spores are all of one kind and give rise on germ. to fairly large monoec. prothalli.

Classification and genera:

Small pl. with a few rad. l. and head of sphorophylls on leafless stalk: Phylloglossum.

Larger pl. with no rad. l. and sporophylls on leafy stalk: Lycopodium.

Lycopodiales. One of the main divisions of Pteridophyta. Mostly leafy plants, with well developed stems and small unbranched l. The sporophylls are usu. massed together into cones, recalling those of the Gymnosperms. Sporangia single at base of l. on upper side, or in axil, 1-loc. They are classified as follows.

A. *ELIGULATAE* (eligulate: spores all alike).
B. *LIGULATAE* (l. with ligules: spores of two kinds).

Lycopodium L. Lycopodiaceae. 185 trop. and temp.; 5 in Brit., chiefly in mountain districts (club-mosses). The commonest is *L. clavatum* L. (often called stag-horn moss); the others are *L. Selago* L., *L. alpinum* L., *L. annotinum* L., and *L. inundatum* L. All but the last are xero. evergr. pl. with hard wiry l. The stem branches frequently, apparently dichotomously, but in reality usu. in a monopodial manner. Upon it are borne the roots, which branch dichotomously, and are developed in acropetal succession. The l., narrow and unbranched, are usu. placed spirally upon the stem, but in some form four ranks, as in most Selaginellas. Many have veg. repr. by small bulbils in the l. axils. [Prothalli, see Bruchmann in *Bot. Zeit.* 1899, p. 6.]

Sporangia all alike in structure, containing spores of one kind only; placed upon the bases of l. which are usu. crowded together to form a terminal spike or strobilus. In *L. Selago* some or all of the sporangia are often replaced by small bulbils (*cf. Polygonum viviparum*, Allium sp., Globba, &c.).

Lycopsis L. Boraginaceae (IV. 3). 3 Eur., As. *L. arvensis* L., small bugloss, in Brit.

Lycopus Tourn. ex L. Labiatae (VI). 10 N. temp. *L. europaeus* L., gipsywort, in Brit.

Lycoris Herb. Amaryllidaceae (I). 4 Japan.

Lycoseris Cass. Compositae (12). 10 C. Am. to Peru.

Lycurus H. B. et K. Gramineae (8). 2 Mexico, New Mexico.

Lygeum L. Gramineae (6). 1 Medit., *L. Spartum* Loefl., one of the esparto-furnishing grasses (*cf.* Stipa and Ampelodesma).

Lyginia R. Br. Restionaceae. 1 S.W. Austr. (A).

Lygisma Hook. f. Asclepiadaceae (II. 3). 1 Burma.

Lygistum P. Br. = Manettia L. p.p. (Rubi.).

Lygodesmia D. Don. Compositae (13). 6 N. Am.

Lygodisodea Ruiz et Pav. (*Paederia* p.p. *EP.*). Rubi. (II. 6). 4 trop. Am.

Lygodium Sw. Schizaeaceae. 25 trop. and subtrop. Twining ferns. The stem remains comparatively undeveloped, but the l. has unlimited apical growth, and the long midrib twines around supports like the stem of the hop, bearing pinnae at intervals. The l. are borne on the stem in one dorsal row. The sporangia are in a double row on the back of the fertile pinnae, and each is surrounded by a cup-like indusium.

Lyme grass, *Elymus arenarius* L.

Lyonia Nutt. Ericaceae (II. 1). 16 E. As., N. Am., 1 circumpolar.

Lyonnetia Cass. = Anthemis Michx. p.p. (Comp.).

Lyonothamnus A. Gray. Rosaceae (inc. sed.). 1 California.

Lyonsia R. Br. Apocynaceae (II. 2). 15 Austr., New Guinea.

Lyperanthus R. Br. Orchidaceae (II. 2). 8 Austr., N. Z., New Caled.

Lyperia Benth. (*Chaenostoma* p.p. *EP.*). Scrophulariaceae (II. 5). 40 S. Afr., Canaries.

Lyrate (l.), divided with large term. lobe, as in mustard.

Lyrocarpa Hook. et Harv. Cruciferae (3). 2 California.

Lysias Salisb. (*Habenaria* p.p. *BH.*, *Platanthera* p.p. *EP.*). Orchidaceae (II. 1). 2 N. Am.

Lysicarpus F. Muell. Myrtaceae (II. 1). 1 Queensland.

Lysichiton Schott. Araceae (III). 1 temp. E. As.

Lysidice Hance. Leguminosae (II. 3). 1 S. China.

Lysiella Rydberg (*Habenaria* p.p.). Orchid. (II. 1). 1 N. Am.

Lysiloma Benth. Leguminosae (I. 1). 10 trop. Am., W.I.

Lysimachia (Tourn.) L. Primulaceae. 120 temp. and subtrop.; 4 in Brit. *L. vulgaris* L., yellow loosestrife, is said by Müller to occur in two forms, one in sunny places with large fls. suited to crossing, and one in shady spots with small self-fert. fls. *L. nemorum* L. (yellow pimpernel) and *L. Nummularia* L. (moneywort) also in Brit.

Lysimachiopsis A. A. Heller (*Lysimachia* p.p.). Primul. 4 Hawaiian Is.

Lysinema R. Br. Epacridaceae (2). 5 W. Austr.

Lysionotus D. Don. Gesneriaceae (1). 5 Himalaya, China.

Lysiosepalum F. Muell. Sterculiaceae. 2 W. Austr.

Lysiostyles Benth. Convolvulaceae (1). 1 Guiana.

Lysipomia H. B. et K. Campanulaceae (III). 7 Andes.

Lytanthus Wettst. (*Globularia* p.p.). Globular. 2 Canaries, Azores.

Lythraceae (*EP.*; *BH.* incl. *Olin.*, *Punic.*, *Sonnerat.*). Dicots. (Archichl. Myrtiflorae). 21 gen., 500 sp., all zones but frigid. Herbs, shrubs, or trees; l. usu. opp., entire, simple, with very small stipules or none. Fls. in racemes, panicles, or dichasial cymes, ☿, reg. or ·|·, usu. 4- or 6-merous. The axis ('calyx-tube') is hollow, generally tubular. The sepals are valvate, and frequently possess an epicalyx, formed, as in Potentilla, of combined stips. Petals crumpled in bud, sometimes absent. Sta. inserted (often very low down) on calyx-tube, typically twice as many as sepals, but sometimes fewer or ∞. $\underline{G}$ with simple style and usu. capitate stigma; 2—6-loc., at the base at least, rarely 1-loc. with parietal placenta. Ovules usu. ∞, anatr., ascending. The fls. of Lythrum (*q.v.*) and others are heterostyled. Dry fr., usu. capsular. No endosp. A few yield dyes (Lawsonia, &c.), or are medicinal. *Chief genera:* Peplis, Lythrum, Cuphea, Lagerstroemia.

Lythrum L. Lythraceae. 23 cosmop.; 2 in Brit., incl. *L. Salicaria* L. (purple loosestrife). The 6-merous fls. are sol. or in small axillary dichasia like Labiatae. Each has 12 sta. in two whorls of different length, and the style again is of different length to any of the sta. Three forms of fl. occur (*trimorphism*), each on a separate pl.; they are distinguished as long- mid- and short-styled fls. The diagram illustrates the arrangement of parts (S = stigma, A = anthers, B = base of fl.), as seen in side view. It is evident that an insect visiting the fls. will tend on the whole to transfer pollen from A_3 to S_3, A_2 to S_2, A_1 to S_1, rather than from sta. of one length to style of another, for it will enter these fls. in the same way and to the same depth. The sta. and style project so far that an insect can alight directly upon them. Darwin (*Forms of Flowers*) showed by a long series of experiments that the best results are obtained by pollinating S_3 from A_3, or S_1 from A_1, &c., *i.e.* by

S_3	A_3	A_3
A_2	S_2	A_2
A_1	A_1	S_1
B	B	B
long-styled	mid-styled	short-styled

crossing two plants. The number of seeds thus obtained is much greater and their fertility higher than if S_2 or S_1 be fertilised from A_3, or any other such union be made. Fertilisation of a stigma by sta. of corresponding length Darwin terms *legitimate*, by sta. of a different length *illegitimate*. The offspring of illegitimate fert. are few, and have the sterility and other sexual characters of hybrids. As in nearly all other heterostyled pl., the longer the sta. the larger the pollen grains, and the longer the style the larger the papillae of the stigma.

Maba Forst. Ebenaceae. 70 trop. and subtrop. The wood of some is used as a substitute for ebony. Fr. of some ed.

Mabea Aubl. Euphorbiaceae (A. II. 7). 30 trop. Am., Trinidad.

Mabee bark (W.I.), *Ceanothus reclinatus* L'Hérit.

Macadamia F. Muell. Proteaceae (II). 5 Austr. (nut-tree). Seeds ed.

Macairea DC. Melastomaceae (I). 20 trop. S. Am.

Macaranga Thou. Euphorbiaceae (A. II. 2). 225 palaeotrop. *M. caladifolia* Becc. has hollow peduncles inhabited by ants.

Macarisia Thou. Rhizophoraceae. 2 Madag.

Macarthuria Huegel ex Endl. Aizoaceae (I). 3 Austr., S.E. and S.W.

Macary butter (W.I.), *Picramnia Antidesma* Sw.

Macassar oil, *Cananga odorata* Hook. f.

Macaw bush (W.I.), *Solanum mammosum* L.; **-tree**, *Acrocomia*.

Macbridea Ell. ex Nutt. Labiatae (VI). 2 S.W. U.S.

Macchie, maqui, the copse association of Mediterranean coasts.

Macdougalia A. A. Heller. Compositae (6). 1 N. Am.

Mace, *Myristica fragrans* Houtt.; **-reed,** *Typha*.

Macfadyena A. DC. Bignoniaceae (I). 3 S. Am.

Macgregoria F. Muell. Stackhousiaceae. 1 E. Austr.

Macgregorianthus Merrill. Thymelaeaceae. 1 Luzon.

Machadoa Welw. ex Benth. et Hook. f. Passifloraceae. 1 trop. Afr.

Machaeranthera Nees (*Aster* p.p. *BH.*). Compositae (3). 45 N. Am.

Machaerium Pers. Leguminosae (III. 8). 65 trop. Am., W.I. Like Dalbergia. Many are lianes, climbing by sensitive lateral shoots, and provided with recurved stipular thorns. Some of the jacarandá timbers (rosewoods) are furnished by this gen. (*cf.* Dalbergia).

Machaerocarpus Small (*Damasonium* p.p.). Alism. 1 California.

Machaonia Humb. et Bonpl. Rubiaceae (II. 2). 12 trop. Am., W. I.

Machilus Nees. Lauraceae (I). 20 S.E. As. to Japan.

Mackay bean, *Entada scandens* Benth.

Mackaya Harv. (*Asystasia BH.*). Acanthaceae (IV. B). 1 S. Afr. Cult. orn. fl.

Mackinlaya F. Muell. Araliaceae (3). 2 Queensland.

Macleania Hook. Ericaceae (III. 2). 15 W. trop. Am. Cult. orn. fl.

Macleya Rchb. (*Bocconia* p.p.). Papaveraceae (II). 2 China, Japan. Cult. orn. fl.

Macludrania × André. Moraceae. Hybrid Maclura-Cudrania.

Maclura Nutt. Moraceae (I). 1 S. U.S., *M. aurantiaca* Nutt. (bow-wood or Osage orange). The tree bears thorns (branches). Fls. dioec., the ♂ in pseudo-racemes, the ♀ in pseudo-heads; individual fls. like Morus. After fert. each ♀ fl. produces an achene enclosed in the fleshy P, and at the same time the common recept. swells up into a fleshy mass, so that a large yellow multiple fr. is formed. The wood is used for bows, carriage-poles, &c. The l. are used for feeding silkworms. [*M. tinctoria* D. Don, &c. = Chlorophora.]

Macnabia Benth. Ericaceae (IV. 1). 1 S.W. Cape Colony.

Macnemaraea Willem. Inc. sed. 1 China.

Macodes Lindl. Orchidaceae (II. 2). 4 Malaya. Cult. orn. l.

Macomaria × Rolfe. Orchid hybrid, Macodes and Haemaria.

Macoubea Aubl. Inc. sed. 1 Guiana.

Macowania Oliv. Compositae (4). 2 S. Afr.

Macphersonia Blume. Sapindaceae (1). 5 trop. E. Afr., Madag.

Macqui berry, *Aristolochia Maqui* L'Hérit.

Macrachaenium Hook. f. Compositae (12). 1 Patagonia.

Macradenia R. Br. Orchidaceae (II. 19). 5 W.I., Guiana, C. Am.

Macranthera Torr. ex Benth. Scrophulariaceae (III. 2). 2 S. U.S.

Macranthisiphon Bur. Bignoniaceae (1). 1 Ecuador, Peru.

Macreightia A. DC. in DC. = Maba Forst. p.p. (Eben.).

Macro- (Gr. pref.), long, large; **-podous** (embryo), without cotyledons; **-sporangium**, that which holds **-spores**, the larger when there are two kinds, *Pteridophyta*.

Macrocalyx Costantin et Poisson. Malvaceae (4) 1 Madag.

Macrocalyx Miers. Rubiaceae (inc. sed.). Nomen.

Macrocarpaea Gilg (*Lisianthus BH.*). Gentian. (1). 10 Cuba, trop. S. Am.

Macrocarpium Nakai (*Cornus* p.p.). Cornaceae. 1 Japan.

Macrocentrum Hook. f. Melastomaceae (1). 3 Guiana, E. Brazil.

Macrochaetium Steud. (*Tetraria* p.p. *EP.*). Cyperaceae (II). 1 S. Afr.

Macrochordion de Vriese (*Aechmea* p.p. *BH.*). Bromeli. (4). 6 S. Am. Cult. orn. fl.

Macroclinidium Maxim. Compositae (12). 2 Japan.

Macroclinium Barb. Rodr. = Ornithocephalus Hook. p.p. (Orch.).

Macrocnemum P. Br. Rubiaceae (I. 5). 10 W.I., S. Am.

Macrococculus Becc. Menispermaceae. 1 New Guinea.

Macrodendron Taub. Cunoniaceae. 1 Rio de Janeiro.

Macrodiscus Bur. (*Distictis* Mart.). Bignoniaceae (1). 1 W.I.

Macrolobium Schreb. (*Vouapa* Aubl.). Legumin. (II. 3). 20 trop. Am., Afr.

Macrolotus Harms (*Argyrolobium* p.p. *EP.*). Legum. (III. 3). 1 trop. Afr.

Macromeria D. Don. Boraginaceae (IV. 4). 8 C. and S. Am.

Macropanax Miq. Araliaceae (1). 3 Sikkim to Java.

Macropelma K. Schum. Asclepiadaceae (1). 1 E. Afr.

Macropeplus Perkins. Monimiaceae. 1 E. Brazil.

Macropetalum Burch. ex Decne. Asclepiadaceae (II. 3). 2 Cape Colony.

Macrophloga Becc. (*Chrysalidocarpus* p.p.). Palm. (IV. 1). 1 Madag.

Macropidia J. Drumm. ex Harv. Amaryllidaceae (III). 1 W. Austr.

Macropiper Miq. (*Piper* p.p. *BH.*). Piperaceae. 6 Polynesia.

Macroplectrum Pfitz. (*Angraecum* p.p.). Orchidaceae (II. 20). 1 Madag., Masc. (*A. sesquipedale*, *q.v.*).

Macropodandra Gilg. Buxaceae. 1 trop. C. Afr.

Macropodium (R. Br. in) Ait. Cruciferae (4). 1 C. As.

Macropsychanthus Harms. Leguminosae (III. 10). 2 New Guinea, Phil. Is.
Macropteranthes F. Muell. Combretaceae. 4 N. Austr.
Macrorhamnus Baill. Rhamnaceae. 1 Madag.
Macrorhynchus Less. = Troximon Nutt. (Comp.).
Macrorungia C. B. Clarke. Acanthaceae (IV. B). 4 trop. and S. Afr.
Macroscepis H. B. et K. Asclepiadaceae (II. 1). 7 trop. Am.
Macrosepalum Regel et Schmalh. Crassulaceae. 1 Turkestan.
Macrosiphonia Muell.-Arg. Apocynaceae (II. 1). 10 trop. Am. Xero.
Macrosolen Blume = Loranthus L. p.p. (*BH.*) = Elytranthe Blume p.p.
Macrosphyra Hook. f. Rubiaceae (I. 8). 2 W. trop. Afr.
Macrostegia Nees in DC. Acanthaceae (IV. A). 1 Peru.
Macrostylis Bartl. et Wendl. Rutaceae (I). 10 S.W. Cape Colony.
Macrotomia DC. Boraginaceae (IV. 4). 8 Medit. to Himalaya.
Macrotorus Perkins (*Mollinedia* p.p.). Monimiaceae. 1 Rio de Janeiro.
Macrotropis DC. = Ormosia Jacks. (Legum.).
Macrozamia Miq. Cycadaceae, *q.v.* 15 Austr.
Macrozanonia Cogn. (*Zanonia* p.p.). Cucurbitaceae (I). 4 E. Indomal.
Maculatus (Lat.), spotted.
Mad-apple (W.I.), *Solanum Melongena* L.
Madagascar clove, *Ravensara aromatica* J. F. Gmel.; **-plum,** *Flacourtia*; **-rubber,** *Landolphia*, &c.
Madar fibre, *Calotropis gigantea* Ait.
Madarosperma Benth. Asclepiadaceae (II. 1). 1 Upper Amazon.
Maddenia Hook. f. et Thoms. Rosaceae (V). 4 Himalaya, China.
Madder, *Rubia tinctorum* L.; **field -,** *Sherardia arvensis* L.; **Indian -** (W.I.), *Oldenlandia umbellata* L.
Madia Molina. Compositae (5). 15 W. Am. *M. sativa* Mol. (madi, Chili; tarweed, U.S.), cult. for the oil from the seed.
Madras hemp, *Crotalaria juncea* L.
Madre de cacao (W.I.), *Erythrina umbrosa* H. B. et K.
Madronella Greene (*Monardella* p.p.). Labiatae (VI). 35 N. Am.
Maerua Forsk. Capparidaceae (II). 40 trop. Afr., As. The fr. is a berry, constricted between the seeds like a lomentum.
Maesa Forsk. Myrsinaceae (I). 105 trop., except Am.
Maesobotrya Benth. in Hook. Euphorbiaceae (A. I. 1). 18 trop. Afr.
Maesopsis Engl. Rhamnaceae. 2 trop. E. Afr.
Mafekingia Baill. (*Raphiacme EP.*). Asclepiadaceae (I). 1 S. Afr.
Mafootoo-withe (W.I.), *Entada scandens* Benth.
Maga Urb. (*Thespesia* p.p.). Malvaceae (4). 1 Porto Rico.
Magnistipula Engl. Rosaceae (VI). 3 trop. Afr.
Magnolia L. Magnoliaceae. 60 As., N. Am. (esp. trop.). Trees with sheathing stips. covering the bud, and term. fls. P petaloid, except sometimes the outermost l., and in whorls. Sta. and cpls. ∞, on a lengthened torus. Protogynous. Fr. an aggregate of follicles; each dehisces by its *dorsal* suture, and the seed dangles out of it on a long thread formed by the unravelling of the spiral vessels of the funicle. The outer integument of the ovule becomes fleshy as it ripens, and the seeds may thus be distr. by birds. Several cult. orn. fl.
Magnoliaceae (*EP.*; *BH.* incl. *Trochodendraceae*). Dicots. (Archichl. Ranales). 9 gen., 70 sp., trop. and subtrop. trees and shrubs (some

climbing). Oil passages in parenchyma. Alt. l., which in Magnolia, &c. have big stips. united to form a hood covering in bud all the younger l. As each l. expands it throws off the hood of the next older l. Fls. term. or axillary, usu. sol., ☿ or unisexual. P cyclic in Magnolia, &c., spiral in others; A, G spiral. P usu. petaloid; A ∞, hypog.; G usu. ∞, on long torus. Follicle, berry, or samara; seed album., endosp. not ruminate. Timber usu. good; Magnolia and Liriodendron cult. orn. fl.; *cf.* Illicium, &c. *Chief genera:* Magnolia, Liriodendron, Kadsura (climber), Schizandra (do.), Illicium (*cf.* Winteraceae), Drimys (do.), Michelia.

Magonia A. St. Hil. Sapind. (II). 2 Brazil. Disc of 2 post. lamellae.

Maguey, maguly, *Agave americana* L. (trop. Am.).

Magydaris Koch ex DC. Umbell. (III. 4). 2 Medit. Fr. bristly.

Mahafalia Jumelle et Perrier. Asclep. (II. 4). 1 Madag.

Mahernia L. (*Hermannia* p.p. *EP.*). Stercul. 80 Afr.

Mahea Pierre ex L., Planch. (*Mimusops* p.p.). Sapot. (I). 2 Masc., Natal.

Mahoberberis C. K. Schneider. Hybrid, Mahonia-Berberis.

Mahoe (W.I.), *Paritium, Thespesia, Hibiscus.*

Mahogany, strictly speaking the timber of *Swietenia Mahogoni* Jacq. (Honduras, &c.); now chiefly *Khaya senegalensis* A. Juss. (W. Afr.). Many others like these are also used, e.g. *Cedrela, Melia, Dysoxylum* and other Meliaceae, *Kiggelaria,* &c. Stone, *Timbers of Commerce*; Chaloner and Fleming, *The Mahogany Tree,* 1850.

Mahonia Nutt. (*Berberis* p.p.). Berberid. 50 *. Cult. orn. shrubs.

Mahua, Mahwa, *Bassia latifolia* Roxb. (Ind.).

Mahurea Aubl. Guttif. (I) (Ternstr. *BH.*). 5 trop. S. Am. L. alt. stip.

Mahya Cordem. (*Sphacele* p.p.). Labiat. (VI). 1 Bourbon.

Maianthemum (Weber in) Wigg. Lili. (VII). 3 N. temp. (incl. Brit.). Fl. 2-merous, protog., with 2 l. in middle of infl. axis.

Maidenhair fern, *Adiantum*; **-tree,** *Ginkgo biloba* L. (China).

Maidenia Rendle. Hydrocharit. ( ). 1 N.W. Austr.

Maieta Aubl. Melastom. (I). 8 trop. Am. Heterophyllous. Some have bladdery outgrowths of l., inhabited by ants (*cf.* Duroia). Fr. ed.

Maihuenia Phil. (*Opuntia* p.p.). Cact. (II). 5 Chile, Arg.

Maillardia Frapp. et Duch. Mor. (I). 1 Bourbon.

Maillea Parl. (*Phleum* p.p. *EP.*). Gramin. (8). 1 Medit. Is. A 2.

Maingaya Oliv. Hamamelid. 1 Penang, Perak.

Mairia Nees. Comp. (3). 10 Cape Col.

Mairella Léveillé = Phelypaea Tourn. p.p. (Orobanch.).

Maize, *Zea Mays* L.; **water-,** *Victoria regia* Lindl. (trop. S. Am.).

Majidea J. Kirk ex Oliv. (*Harpullia* p.p. *EP.*). Sapind. (II). 1 trop. Afr.

Majoe-bitter (W.I.), *Picramnia Antidesma* Sw.

Majorana (Tourn.) Rupp. (*Origanum* p.p. *BH.*). Labiat. (VI. 11). 6 E. Medit. Calyx-lips of 5 seps. and 1.

Majus (Lat.), greater.

Malabaila Hoffm. Umbell. (III. 6). 25 Medit., W. As.

Malabathris Rafin. = Otanthera Bl. (Melastom.).

Malacantha Pierre (*Chrysophyllum* p.p.). Sapot. (I). 5 W. trop. Afr.

Malacca Cane, *Calamus. Cf.* Ridley in *Straits Bull.* 1903.

Malache B. Vogel (*Pavonia* p.p.). Malv. (3). 3 warm Am., W.I.

Malachra L. Malv. (3). 6 warm Am., W.I. No epicalyx.

Malacocarpus Salm-Dyck (*Echinocactus* p.p.). Cact. (III. 1). 8 S. Braz., Uruguay. Stem not jointed; fls. apical in mass of hairs.

Malacochaete Nees = Scirpus Tourn. p.p. (Cyper.).

Malacolepis A. A. Heller (*Malacothrix* p.p.). Comp. (13). 1 Calif.

Malacomeles Dcne. (*Nagelia* Lindl.). Ros. (II). 2 Mex.

Malacomeris Nutt. = Malacothrix DC. (Comp.).

Malacophilous, fert. by snails.

Malacothamnus Greene (*Malvastrum* p.p.). Malv. (2). 10 N. Am.

Malacothrix DC. Comp. (13). 15 W. N. Am.

Malaisia Blanco. Mor. (I). 2 E. Indomal.

Malanea Aubl. Rubi. (II. 2). 12 trop. S. Am., W.I. Climbing shrubs.

Malanthos Stapf = Dissochaeta Blume (Melastom.).

Malaxis Soland. ex Sw. Orchid. (II. 4). 1 N. temp. (incl. Brit.), *M. paludosa* Sw. Fl. twisted through 360°, so that labellum again uppermost. Pollinia exposed by shrivelling of anther wall. Darwin, [*Orchids*, p. 130.

Malay apple, *Jambosa malaccensis* DC. (trop. As.).

Malcomia R. Br. (*Malcolmia* Spreng.). Crucif. (4). 35 Medit.

Male bamboo, *Dendrocalamus strictus* Nees; **-fl.**, with sta. only.

Malesherbia Ruiz et Pav. The only gen. of **Malesherbiaceae** (*EP.*; *Passiflor.* p.p. *BH.*) (Dicots. Archichl. Parietales; pp. xxxv, lii). 30 W. S. Am. Herbs or undershrubs with alt. often deeply lobed exstip. l., often very hairy. Racemes or cymes of ☿ reg. fls. K 5, C 5, imbr.; axis tubular, with central androphore bearing 5 sta. and $\underline{G}$ (3) with parietal plac. and ∞ anatr. ov.; styles 3—4 below apex of ov. Caps.; no aril. Differs from Passiflor. in having no aril, styles more deeply inserted and widely separated; from Turner. in no aril, in aestivation of C, and persistent recept.

Maliga Rafin. = Allium Tourn. (Lili.).

Malinvaudia Fourn. Asclep. (II. 4). 1 S. Brazil. C reticulate. Corona [double.

Mallea A. Juss. = Cipadessa Blume (Meli.).

Mallee (scrub), *Eucalyptus*, dwarf spp. like *E. dumosa* Cunn., &c.

Malleola J. J. Sm. et Schlechter (*Saccolabium* p.p.). Orchid. (II. 20). [18 Malaya.

Mallinoa Coult. Comp. (2). 1 Guatemala.

Mallophora Endl. Verben. (3). 1 W. Austr. Heads. Fls. 4-merous.

Mallostoma Karst. (*Arcythophyllum EP.*). Rubi. (I. 2). 15 trop. Am.

Mallota A. DC. = Tournefortia L. p.p. (Borag.).

Mallotonia Britton (*Tournefortia* p.p.). Borag. (III). 1 W.I., Fla., Mex.

Mallotopus Franch. et Sav. Comp. (8). 1 Japan. L. opp.

Mallotus Lour. Euphorb. (A. II. 2). 120 palaeotrop. The caps. of *M. philippinensis* Müll.-Arg. yields kamala dye.

Mallow, *Malva* and other Malvaceae; **marsh-**, *Althaea officinalis* L.; **musk-**, *Malva moschata* L., *Hibiscus*; **rose-**, *Hibiscus*; **tree-**, *Lava-* [*tera.*

Malmea Fries. Anon. (I). 1 Brazil.

Malope L. Malv. (I). 3 Medit. The 3 l. of the epicalyx are very large. Cpls. ∞, in vertical rows (see fam.). Cocci indeh. Cult. orn. fl.

Malortiea H. Wendl. (*Reinhardtia* p.p. *EP.*). Palm. (IV. 1). 4 C. Am.

Malosma Engl. = Rhus L. (Anacard.).

Malouetia A. DC. Apocyn. (II. 2). 15 S. Am., W.I., Afr.

Malperia Wats. Comp. (2). 1 Mex.

Malpighia Plum. ex L. Malpigh. (II). 30 trop. Am., W.I. Erect pl.; some with stinging hairs, some with cleist. fls.

Malpighiaceae (*EP.*, *BH.*). Dicots. (Archichl. Geraniales). 55 gen., 650 sp., trop., esp. S. Am. Shrubs or small trees, usu. climbing, forming a marked feature among the trop. lianes. Stem-anatomy peculiar. L. usu. opp., entire, stip., frequently gland-dotted; pl. usu. covered with peculiar branched unicellular hairs. Infl. racemose. Fl. ☿, obliquely ·|·. K (5), imbr., often with large glands at the base of (outside) the sepals; C 5, petals usually clawed, imbr.; A 5 + 5, obdiplost., often fewer, joined in a ring at the base; anthers opening intr. by longitudinal splits; G̲ (3), obliquely placed in the fl., 3-loc. with axile plac.; one ovule in each loc., pend., semi-anatr., with ventral raphe. Fr. typically a schizocarp breaking into 3 mericarps, but frequently one or more of the loc. abort. The mericarps are often winged, in some cases, *e.g.* Banisteria, like those of Acer. Seed exalbum.

Classification and chief genera (after Niedenzu):

I. *PYRAMIDOTORAE* (torus pyramidal; mericarps usually winged): Tetrapteris, Banisteria, Acridocarpus.

II. *PLANITORAE* (torus flat or concave; mericarps not winged): Malpighia, Bunchosia, Byrsonima.

Malt, barley steeped to start germ., and then kiln-dried.

Maltebrunia Kunth. Gramineae (6). 2 Madag., S. Afr.

Malus Tourn. ex L. = Pyrus Tourn. p.p. (Ros.).

Malva (Tourn.) L. (*BH.* excl. *Callirhoe* Nutt.). Malvaceae (2). 30 N. temp.; 3 in Brit. Fl. of the ordinary type of the fam., with ∞ cpls. Two Brit. sp. *M. sylvestris* L. and *M. rotundifolia* L. (large and small mallow) afford a contrast in floral mech., &c. Honey is secreted in little pockets in the recept., covered with hairs which exclude rain and very short-tongued insects. The large mallow is very protandr.; the sta. stand up at first in the middle of the fl., and afterwards bend outwards and downwards whilst the styles lengthen and occupy the original positions of the sta. The small mallow has much smaller fls., much less visited by insects; they go through stages similar to those described above, but at the end of the ♀ stage the styles bend downwards, twist in among the anthers and pollinate themselves.

The l. in autumn may usu. be seen covered with brown spots caused by the fungus *Puccinia malvacearum* (*cf.* Berberis).

Malvaceae (*EP.*; *B.H.* incl. *Bombacaceae*). Dicots. (Archichl. Malvales). 35 gen., 700 sp., trop. and temp. Herbs, shrubs, or trees, with alt. stip. l. Fls. sol. or in cpd. cymose infls. made up of cincinni, ☿, reg., usu. 5-merous. Epicalyx often present; probably an aggregation of bracteoles, but perhaps stipular like that of some Rosaceae (*q.v.*). K 5 or (5), valvate; C 5 conv., the petals usu. asymmetrlcal; A usu. ∞, owing to branching of the inner whorl of sta. (the outer is usu. absent), all united below into a tube which is joined to the petals and at first sight makes the C appear gamopetalous; the anthers are monothecous (*i.e.* each = half an anther), the pollen grains spiny. G̲ (1—∞) frequently (5), multi-loc., wiih axile placentae. In § I a division of the cpls. by horiz. transv. walls occurs, producing vertical rows of one-ovuled portions. Ovules 1—∞ in each cpl., anatr., usually ascending, sometimes pend. Malvaviscus has a berry, the rest of the order dry fr., either caps. or schizocarps. Embryo usually curved, surrounded by endosp. The fls. are generally protandr. (see Malva and Goethea). Gossypium (cotton), Hibiscus, and others are of economic value. Many are garden favourites. [**BH.** **chars**. incl. l. often palmately lobed or cpd.; A 5—∞, free or united, pollen smooth; endosp. little or none.]

Classification and chief genera (after Schumann):

A. Cpls. in vert. rows.
  1. *Malopeae:* Malope, Kitaibelia.

B. Cpls. in one plane.
  2. *Malveae* (schizocarp; styles as many as cpls.): Abutilon, Lavatera, Althaea, Malva, Anoda.
  3. *Ureneae* (schizocarp; styles twice as many as cpls.): Urena, Goethea, Pavonia.
  4. *Hibisceae* (capsule): Hibiscus, Gossypium.

Malvales. The 26th order (*EP.*) of Archichlamydeae. The 6th cohort (*BH.*) of Polypetalae. *Cf.* pp. xxx, l.

Malvastrum A. Gray. Malvaceae (2). 85 Am. and S. Afr.

Malvaviscus Dill. ex Adans. Malvaceae (3). 12 warm Am.

Mammea L. Guttiferae (IV). 1 W. Ind., *M. americana* L., cult. for ed. fr., the Mammee or St Domingo apricot. The fls. are used in preparing a liqueur (eau de Créole).

Mammee, *Mammea americana* L.; **- sapote,** *Lucuma mammosa* Gaertn. f.

Mammilla, *Cactaceae.*

Mammillaria Haw. (incl. *Anhalonium* Lem.). Cactaceae (III. 2). 200 trop. Am. Mostly small plants of very condensed form, often almost spherical in outline, with well-marked mammillae (see fam.). There is a division of the growing point into two in the course of formation of the mammilla, and the part at the base of the mammilla (*i.e.* in the axil) gives rise to the fl. The G elongates after fert. so that the tip of the long red berry is raised clear of the thorns. In some sp. veg. repr. and dispersal occurs by the mammillae breaking off and blowing about or adhering to animals, Fr. ed.

Mammoth tree, *Sequoia gigantea* Lindl. et Gord.

Man-of-the-earth (Am.), *Ipomoea pandurata* Meyer; **- orchis,** *Aceras anthropophora* R. Br.

Mana grass (Ceylon), *Cymbopogon confertiflorus* Stapf.

Managa Aubl. Inc. sed. 1 Guiana.

Manatu-grass (W.I.), *Thalassia.*

Manchineel, *Hippomane Mancinella* L.

Mancoa Wedd. Cruciferae (3). 1 Andes.

Mandevilla Lindl. Apocynaceae (II. 1). 45 trop. and subtrop. Am.

Mandioca, *Manihot Aipi* Pohl.

Mandragora (Tourn.) L. Solanaceae (2). 3 Medit. to Himal. (mandrake). For superstitions connected with this, *cf. Treas. of Bot.*

Mandrake, *Mandragora,* (Am.) *Podophyllum.*

Manettia Mutis. Rubiaceae (I. 5). 30 trop. Am., W.I.

Manfreda Salisb. (*Agave* p.p.). Amaryllidaceae (II). 20 N. Am.

Mangabeira rubber, *Hancornia speciosa* Gomez.

Mangel (mangold) wurzel, *Beta vulgaris* L. var.

Mangifera L. Anacardiaceae (I). 30 Indomal. *M. indica* L. is the mango, everywhere cult. in the trop. for its fr., a large drupe derived from the 1 cpl. of the fl. Numerous vars. occur.

Manglietia Blume (*Magnolia* p.p. *EP.*). Magnoliaceae. 3 Indomal.

Manglilla Juss. = Myrsine L. (*BH.*) = Rapanea Aubl.

Mango, *Mangifera indica* L.

Mangonia Schott. Araceae (VII). 1 Brazil.

Mangosteen, *Garcinia Mangostana* L.

Mangroves, the association of pl. of the muddy swamps at the mouths of rivers and elsewhere in the trop., over which the tide flows daily, leaving the mud bare at low water; chiefly |✻. Chief gen. *Rhizophora*; others are *Acanthus*, *Aegiceras*, *Avicennia*, *Bruguiera*, *Carapa*, *Ceriops*, *Conocarpus*, *Laguncularia*, *Kandelia*, *Lumnitzera*, *Scyphiphora*, *Sonneratia*, &c. Usu. much branched, with aerial roots, both flying buttress and pillar roots; aerating roots rise from the mud in *Avicennia*, *Bruguiera*, *Sonneratia*, &c. Many show viviparous germination.

Manicaria Gaertn. Palmaceae (IV. 1). 1 trop. Am., W.I.

Maniçoba rubber Gaertn., *Manihot Glaziovii* Muell.-Arg.

Manihot Tourn. ex Adans. Euphorbiaceae (A. II. 4). 150 S. Am. to Mexico. Shrubs and herbs with monoec. fls. *M. Glaziovii* Müll.-Arg. and other sp. show bud-protection well. The petiole of the young leaf curls upwards and inwards, so that the leaf is brought above the bud. *M. utilissima* Pohl is the bitter, *M. Aipi* Pohl (*M. palmata* Müll.-Arg.) the sweet cassava or mandioc; both are extensively cult. in the trop. for their large tuberous roots, which contain much starch, &c., and form a valuable food-stuff. The bitter cassava is the one usually cult.: its poisonous juice is squeezed out, and finally dissipated in the drying. The ground roots form mandioc or cassava meal, sometimes called Brazilian arrowroot. By a special mode of preparation, tapioca is prepared from the root. The poisonous juice, evaporated to a syrup and thus rendered harmless, forms an antiseptic, known as cassareep, used in preserving meat, &c. *M. Glaziovii* is the Ceara rubber; rubber is obtained by tapping the stem of the tree in the usual way. Several other sp. also yield rubber.

Manila copal, *Agathis Dammara* Rich.; **-elemi,** *Canarium commune* L.; **-hemp,** *Musa textilis* Née.

Maniltoa Scheff. Leguminosae (II. 2). 1 Colombia.

Manioca, *Manihot Aipi* Pohl.

Manisuris L. = Rottboellia L. f. (Gram.). 1 trop.

Manisuris Sw. Gramineae (2). 1 trop.

Manjack (W.I.), *Cordia macrophylla* L.

Manna D. Don = Alhagi Tourn. (Legum.).

Manna, *Alhagi*, *Tamarix*; **-grass** (Am.), *Glyceria*.

Mannia Hook. f. Simarubaceae. 1 trop. W. Afr.

Manniella Reichb. f. Orchidaceae (II. 2). 1 trop. Afr.

Manniophyton Muell.-Arg. Euphorbiaceae (A. II. 2). 1 trop. Afr. (C).

Manochlaenia Börner = Carex Dill. p.p. (Cyper.).

Manoelia Bowdich. Inc. sed. 1 Madeira.

Manotes Soland. ex Planch. Connaraceae. 7 trop. Afr.

Manothrix Miers. Apocynaceae (I. 1). 2 Brazil.

Mansoa DC. (*Cuspidaria BH.*). Bignoniaceae (1). 5 Brazil, Bolivia.
Mansonia J. R. Drumm. Sterculiaceae. 1 Burma.
Mantisia Sims. Zingiberaceae (1). 2 Indomal. *M. saltatoria* Sims (dancing girls) often cult. for its curious fls., borne on separate shoots from the rhiz. At the base is the K, then 3 broad pets., a curiously shaped labellum and 2 filamentous stds., and beyond all the fertile sta. and style.
Mantle leaf, *Platycerium.*
Manulea L. Scrophulariaceae (II. 5). 30 S. Afr.
Manzanita, *Arctostaphylos.*
Maoutia Wedd. Urticaceae (3). 10 trop. As. and Polynes. No P in the ♀ fl. *M. Puya* Wedd. yields good fibre.
Mapania Aubl. Cyperaceae (II). 45 trop.
Mapaniopsis C. B. Clarke. Cyperaceae (II). 1 N. Brazil.
Maple, *Acer*; **- sugar,** *Acer saccharum* Marshall.
Mapouria Aubl. (*Psychotria* p.p. *BH.*). Rubiaceae (II. 5). 80 trop.
Mappa A. Juss. = Macaranga Thou. p.p. (Euphorb.).
Mappia Jacq. Icacinaceae. 7 trop. As. and Am.
Maprounea Aubl. Euphorbiaceae (A. II. 7). 4 trop. Am., W. Afr.
Maqui, the copse association of the Medit. coasts.
Marah Kellogg (*Echinocystis* p.p.). Cucurbitaceae (4). 10 N. Am.
Marainophyllum Pohl. Inc. sed. Nomen.
Maranta Plum. ex L. Marantaceae. 30 trop. Am. The stds. β γ (see fam.) are present in many. The rhiz. of *M. arundinacea* L. furnishes West Indian arrowroot, prepared by grinding and washing to free the starch.
Marantaceae (*EP.*; *Scitamineae* p.p. *BH.*). Monocots (Scitamineae). 27 gen., 300 sp. trop., chiefly Am. Herbaceous perennials of various habit, resembling Zingiberaceae, but at once distinguishable by the presence of a swollen pulvinus or joint at the junction of petiole and leaf-blade. L. 2-ranked, sheathing; one side of the l. is larger than the other and is covered by it when the l. is rolled up in the bud. Fls. usu. upon the leafy shoots, in pairs in the axils of the bracts, either one pair or many (cymose, drepania). The fl. is asymmetric, but in each pair the one is complementary to the other (*i.e.* like its reflection in a glass). Fl. ☿, pentacyclic, 3-merous. P 3 + 3, clearly distinguished in most cases into calyx and corolla. As in the allied fams., the A is united to the C. There is one fertile sta., often petaloid, and round it various petaloid structures (*cf.* carefully Canna and Zingiberaceae). The labellum of Canna is represented by a hood-shaped l. covering the style (Kapuzenblatt). The staminode α is repres. by a more or less leathery or callous l. (Schwielenblatt); β and γ are not always present, but are petaloid when they do occur. The same views as to the morphology of these structures have been proposed as in the case

Floral diagram of *Maranta bicolor* (modified from Eichler). αβγ, staminodes; L., labellum (Kapuzenblatt).

of Canna *q.v.*). $\bar{G}$ (3), typically 3-loc. 3 ovuled, but commonly 2 of the loc. are abortive (as in fig.) and the third contains one ovule; ovule ana-campylo-tropous: style curved and at first enclosed in the 'Kapuzenblatt' or hood. The fl. often has an explosive mechanism. The pollen is shed upon the style, which remains held in the hood. Insects enter upon the staminode *a*, and in sucking honey (secreted by glands in the septa of the ovary) set free the style, which descends with a sudden shock, touching the insect's back and at the same time showering the pollen upon it (*cf.* Genista). Fr. usu. a loculic. caps. Embryo curved, in perisperm. Seed often arillate. Maranta and others furnish arrowroot, &c. *Chief genera:* Calathea, Maranta, Thalia.

Marantochloa Brong. ex Gris. Marantaceae. 1 Réunion.

Marasmodes DC. Compositae (7). 3 Cape Colony.

Marathrum Humb. et Bonpl. Podostemaceae. 8 trop. Am.

Marattia Sw. Marattiaceae (2). 30 trop. and N.Z. The synangium is oval and the compartments open by slits into a central space.

Marattiaceae. The only fam. of Filicales. Marattiales. 7/150 trop. and subtrop. Large ferns; stem stout usu. erect, rarely > 2′ long and seldom branched; strongly dorsiventral in Protomarattia and Christensenia. L., often very large, ovate, simply or compoundly pinnate, with circinate vernation. L.-base with stipular enlargements connected by transverse commissure. The r. arise at the growing point, one or more to each l., burrowing obliquely outwards.

Sori intramarginal on lower side of l., strictly circumscribed with no definite indusium. All have a simple series of sporangia radiately disposed round a central receptacle, linear or point-like as sorus is elongated or circular. The sporangia may be free from one another, or combined to form *synangia*. Spores all of one kind, though sometimes varying in shape, giving rise to monoec. prothalli like those of ordinary ferns, but large and capable of somewhat long life.

Classification and Genera:

Leaf ovate or pinnate; venation simple, dichotomous.

Sporangia separate: Angiopteris (l. compound pinnate), Macroglossum, Archangiopteris (ovate or once pinnate).

Synangia: Marattia (cpd. pinnate), Protomarattia, Danaea (simple or once pinnate).

Leaf palmate, with 5 nearly equal lobes; venation reticulate: Christensenia.

Cf. Bower, *Ferns*, ii, 95. Seward in *Linn. Jl.* 1922 (Hooker lecture).

Marcellia Baill. Amarantaceae (2). 2 trop. W. Afr.

Marcescent (P), one persisting withered round the fr.

Marcetia DC. Melastomaceae (1). 20 S. Am.

Marcgravia Plum. ex L. Marcgraviaceae. 45 trop. Am., climbing epiphytic shrubs, with two kinds of shoots—veg. with two-ranked sessile l. and clasping roots, and flg., with stalked l., spirally arranged, and ending in a cymose umbel of fls. The central fls. are abortive and their bracts are transformed into pocket-like coloured nectaries with stalks. The fertile fls. stand upside down, the infl. being pendulous, and humming-birds rub against them with their backs, while drinking honey.

Marcgraviaceae (*EP.*; *Ternstroem.* p.p. *BH.*). Dicots. (Archichl. Parietales). 5, 40, trop. Am. ♄, often epiph., with simple alt. exstip. l., usu. with pend. infls., bracts transformed into brightly coloured nectaries. Fls. ☿. K 4—5; C (4—5) or free, dropping as a cap; A 3—∞, or (3—∞) epipet.; G originally 1-loc. with parietal plac.; ovules ∞, anatr.; style simple. Capsule. Endosp. thin. *Chief genera:* Marcgravia, Norantea.
Marckea (*Markea*) Rich. Solanaceae (4). 5 trop. Am.
Marcuccia Becc. Anonaceae (1). 1 Borneo.
Mare's tail, *Hippuris vulgaris* L.
Marenteria Thou. (*Uvaria* p.p.). Anonaceae (1). 1 Madag.
Mareya Baill. Euphorbiaceae (A. II. 2). 3 trop. W. Afr.
Margaranthus Schlechtend. Solanaceae (2). 3 S.W. U.S., Mexico.
Margaretta Oliv. Asclepiadaceae (II. 1). 2 E. Afr.
Margaritopsis Wright in Sauv. Rubiaceae (II. 5). 1 Cuba.
Marginal (plac.), in single cpls., on the margins of the cpls.
Margosa, *Melia Azadirachta* L.
Margotia Boiss. (*Elaeoselinum* p.p. *BH.*). Umbellif. (III. 7). 1 W. Medit.
Margyricarpus Ruiz et Pav. Rosaceae (III. 5). 3 Andes.
Marialva Vaud. = Tovomita Aubl. (Guttif.).
Marianthus Hueg. Pittosporaceae. 16 Austr.
Marica Ker-Gawl. Iridaceae (II). 10 trop. Am., Afr. Cult. orn. fl.
Marigold, *Calendula officinalis* L., (W.I.) *Wedelia*; **African** or **French -,** *Tagetes*; **bur -,** *Bidens*; **corn -,** *Chrysanthemum segetum* L.; **marsh -,** *Caltha palustris* L.
Marila Sw. Guttiferae (I). 5 W.I. to Peru.
Marina Liebm. Leguminosae (III. 6). 1 Mexico.
Maripa Aubl. Convolvulaceae (I). 9 trop. Am.
Mariscus Gaertn. = Cyperus L. p.p. (Cyper.). 40 cosmop.
Maritimus (Lat.), belonging to the sea.
Marizia Gandoger = Daveaua Willk. (Comp.).
Marjoram, *Origanum vulgare* L., &c.
Markea (*Marckea*) Rich. Solanaceae (4). 5 trop. Am.
Markhamia Seem. (*Dolichandrone BH.*). Bignoniaceae (2). 6 Afr., As.
Marking nut, *Semecarpus*.
Marlea Roxb. (*Alangium* p.p. *EP.*). Alangiaceae. 20 Indomal.
Marlierea Cambess. Myrtaceae (I). 50 trop. S. Am. Fr. ed.
Marlieriopsis Kiaersk. (*Mitranthus* p.p. *EP.*). Myrtaceae (I). 1 S. Domingo.
Marlothia Engl. Rhamnaceae. 1 S. Afr.
Marlothiella H. Wolff. Umbelliferae (III. 5). 1 Namaqualand.
Marmalade plum (W.I.), *Lucuma mammosa* Gaertn.; **- tree,** *Vitellaria*.
Marmoratus (Lat.), with veins of colour.
Marquesia Gilg. Dipterocp. 3 trop. Afr.
Marram grass, *Ammophila arundinacea* Host.
Marrow, vegetable, *Cucurbita Pepo* L., var., *Blighia sapida* Kon.
Marrubium Tourn. ex L. Labiatae (VI). 30 Eur., N. Afr., temp. As. *M. vulgare* L., white horehound, in Brit., formerly officinal.
Marsdenia R. Br. Asclepiadaceae (II. 3). 100 trop. and subtrop.
Marsea Adans. = Conyza L. (Comp.).

Marsh betony, *Stachys palustris* L.; **-grass** (Am.), *Spartina*; **-mallow**, *Althaea officinalis* L.; **-marigold**, *Caltha palustris* L.; **-rosemary**, *Ledum*, (Am.) *Statice*.

Marshallia Schreb. Compositae (5). 5 S. U.S.

Marsilea L. Marsileaceae. 60 trop. and temp. Rhiz. bearing l. at the nodes, and roots on the lower side. L. petiolate with four lobes, resembling those of '4-leaved clover.' They 'sleep' at night like Oxalis. In some they are floating, on delicate petioles; others grow in shallow water, the l. standing erect. Some, *e.g. M. vestita* Hook. et Grev., vegetate during the wet season, and pass the dry in the form of sporocarps.

The sporocarp is a bean-like structure attached to the petiole of the l. by a stalk. It contains a number of sori, each forming a chamber reaching from the ventral to the dorsal edge of the sporocarp. In each sorus on the outer side is a placenta in the form of a ridge bearing micro-sporangia on its sides and mega-sporangia on the top. The latter contain one spore each. The sporocarp is very hard and may remain in water a long time without showing any effect. Ultimately however, or at once if the hard shell be injured, a swelling of the mucilaginous interior tissue bursts it. "As more water is absorbed, this gelatinous inner tissue continues to expand, and forms a long worm-shaped body to which are attached a number of sori, each surrounded by a sac-shaped indusium in which the sporangia are closely packed" (Campbell). The spores are finally set free by the dissolution both of indusium and sporangium wall. The prothalli are similar to those of Salviniaceae.

The sporocarps of some are eaten by the natives of Austr. (nardoo).

Marsileaceae. Filicales Leptosporangiatae. A fam. of 2 gen., 65 sp. trop. and temp. Mature pl. aquatic or amphibious with thin creeping stem, growing by an apical cell, and bearing l. at distinct nodes. L. circinate in vernation like those of ordinary ferns, but varying much in type (see gen.). Roots are formed from the lower side of the stem.

Sporangia in sporocarps, which are complex structures not homologous with those of Salviniaceae. Each is the equivalent of a leaf-segment and encloses several sori, the latter composed both of micro- and mega-sporangia. Each spore is furnished with an epispore of hardened frothy mucilage. The spores pass the winter (or dry season) inside the sporangia. The subsequent stages in the life history resemble those of Salviniaceae. See gen. for details.

Classification:

Leaf with 4-partite blade; sporocarp bean-shaped: Marsilea.
,, simple; sporocarp spherical : Pilularia.

Marsippospermum Desv. (*Rostkovia BH.*). Juncaceae. 3 S. Am., N.Z.

Marssonia Karst. (*Napeanthus BH.*). Gesneriaceae (1). 1 Trinidad, Venezuela.

Marsypianthus Mart. ex Benth. Labiatae (VII). 3 warm Am.

Marsypopetalum Scheff. Anonaceae (2). 1 Java.

Martagon lily, *Lilium Martagon* L.

Martha Fr. Muell. (*Posoqueria* p.p.). Rubiaceae (I. 8). 1 Brazil.

Marthella Urb. (*Gymnosiphon* p.p.). Burmanniaceae. 1 Trinidad.

Martia (*Martiusia*) Benth. Leguminosae (II. 5). 2 trop. S. Am.

Martinella Baill. Bignoniaceae (1). 3 N. trop. S. Am.

Martinella Leveillé. Cruciferae (inc. sed.). 1 China.

Martinezia Ruiz et Pav. Palmaceae (IV. 2). 7 W.I., trop. S. Am.

Martinia Vaniot (*Asteromaea* p.p. *EP.*). Compositae (3). 1 China.

Martiusia (*Martia*) Benth. Leguminosae (II. 5). 2 trop. S. Am.

Martretia Beille. Euphorbiaceae (A. I. 1). 1 trop. Afr.

Martynia Houst. ex L. (*BH.* incl. *Proboscidea* Schmid.). Martyniaceae. 1 Mexico. Fls. with sensitive stigmas like Mimulus. The fr. has 2 long curved horns, suited for animal-distr.

Martyniaceae (*EP.*; *Pedaliaceae* p.p. *BH.*). Dicots. (Sympet. Tubiflorae). 3 gen., with 10 sp., trop. and subtrop. Am., in dry or coast regions. Herbs, often with tuberous roots, with opp. or alt. l. and term. racemes of ☿, 5-merous, ⦂ fls. K (5); C (5); A 4 with a std., epipet., didynamous; $\underline{G}$ (2), 1-loc. with parietal plac., and ∞ or few anatr. ovules. Caps. loculic., the outer pericarp soft and falling off, the inner woody; it is rendered more or less 4-loc. by the union of the T-shaped placentae together and to the endocarp. The tissue at the top of the midrib of each cpl. also becomes woody and forms a projecting spur, usually hooked at the end or curved, and serving for animal distr. Seeds with little endosp. *Genera:* Martynia, Craniolaria, Proboscidea.

Marumia Blume. Melastomaceae (I). 15 Malaya.

Marupa Miers. Simarubaceae. 1 Brazil.

Maruta Cass. = Anthemis Mich. p.p. (Comp.).

Marvel of Peru, *Mirabilis Jalapa* L.

Maryland pink root, *Spigelia marilandica* L.

Mascagnia Bert. (*Hiraea BH.*). Malpighiaceae (I). 50 trop. Am.

Mascarenhasia A. DC. Apocynaceae (II. 1). 10 Madag., E. Afr. *M. elastica* K. Sch. yields rubber.

Maschalocephalus Gilg et K. Schum. Rapateaceae. 1 trop. Afr.

Maschalodesme K. Schum. et Lauterb. Rubiaceae (I. 7). 1 New Guinea.

Masdevallia Ruiz et Pav. Orchidaceae (II. 8). 120 trop. Am., Mexico. Petals small; sepals with long processes (Darwin, *Orchids*, p. 135).

Masked, personate.

Massangea F. Morren (*Caraguata* p.p. *BH.*). Bromeliaceae (1). 1 Colombia.

Masseranduba, *Mimusops elata* Allem.

Massia Bal. Gramineae (9). 1 Indomal.

Massoia Becc. Lauraceae (inc. sed.). 1 New Guinea.

Massonia Thunb. ex L. f. Liliaceae (V). 25 S. Afr.

Massowia C. Koch = Spathiphyllum Schott p.p. (Araceae).

Massulae, *cf. Azolla.*

Mastersia Benth. Leguminosae (III. 10). 3 Himalaya to Celebes.

Mastic, *Pistacia Lentiscus* L.; **American -**, *Schinus molle* L.; **- tree** (W.I.), *Bursera gummifera* L.

Mastixia Blume. Cornaceae. 25 Indomal.

Mat grass, *Nardus stricta* L.

Matayba Aubl. (*Ratonia* p.p. *BH.*). Sapindaceae (I). 36 warm Am.

Maté, *Ilex paraguensis* A. St Hil.

Matelea Aubl. Asclepiadaceae (II. 4). 6 trop. S. Am.
Mathewsia Hook. et Arn. Cruciferae (3). 4 Chili, Peru, Bolivia.
Mathurina Balf. f. Turneraceae. 1 Rodriguez.
Matico, *Piper angustifolium* Ruiz et Pav. (Peru).
Matisia Humb. et Bonpl. Bombacaceae. 10 Colombia, Guiana.
Matonia R. Br. Matoniaceae. 3 Borneo and Malay Penins. Herbs with creeping rhiz. and dichotomously branched l. Sori not numerous, of 6—10 radially arranged sporangia, on convex recept., with umbrella-like indusium. Annulus complete, closed, oblique. Cf. Filicales, Seward in *Phil. Trans.* B, 191, and Bower, *Ferns.*
Matoniaceae. Filicales Leptosporangiatae. Only genus Matonia, *q.v.*
Matricaria (Tourn.) L. Compositae (7). 50 S. Afr., Eur., Medit., W. As.; 2 in Brit. (wild chamomile or feverfew), incl. *M. Chamomilla* L. (officinal dried fls.). Pappus 0.
Matrimony vine (Am.), *Lycium.*
Mats, *cf. Andropogon, Bamboo, Cocos, Phoenix, Scirpus,* &c.
Matsumurella Makino (*Leonurus* p.p.). Labiatae (VI). 1 Japan.
Matsumuria Hemsl. (*Rehmannia* p.p.). Scrophulariaceae (III. 1), perhaps better Gesneriaceae. 1 Formosa.
Mattipal, *Ailanthus malabarica* DC. (India).
Matteuccia Todaro. Polypodiaceae. 3 N. temp.
Matthaea Blume. Monimiaceae. 15 Malay Archipelago.
Matthiola R. Br. Cruciferae (4). 50 Medit., Eur., S. Afr. 2 in Brit. (stock) on the coasts, incl. *M. incana* R. Br., the parent sp. of the garden stock.
Mattia Schult. = Rindera Pall. (Borag.).
Mattiastrum Brand (*Paracaryum* p.p.). Boraginaceae (IV. 1). 25 Medit.
Mauloutchia Warb. (*Myristica* p.p.). Myristicaceae. 1 Madag.
Maundia F. Muell. (*Triglochin* L. p.p.). Scheuchzer. 1 Austr.
Mauneia Thou. (*Ludia EP.*). Inc. sed. 1 Madag.
Maurandia Orteg. Scrophular. (II. 3). 6 warm Am., W.I. Leaf climbers with sensitive petioles. Cult. orn. fl.
Mauria Kunth. Anacardiaceae (3). 8 Andes.
Mauritia L. f. Palmae (III). 9 trop. Am., W. Ind. (Moriche, see Kingsley's *At Last*). They furnish wood, wine, fruit, fibre, &c.
Mauritius grass, *Panicum molle* Sw.; **-hemp,** *Furcraea gigantea* Vent.
Maurocenia L. (*Cassine* p.p.). Celastraceae. 1 S. Afr., *M. capensis* Sond. (Hottentot cherry).
Maw seed, opium seed.
Maxillaria Ruiz et Pav. Orchidaceae (II. 18). 110 trop. Am.
Maximiliania Mart. Palmae (IV. 2). 3 trop. S. Am., W.I.
Maximiliana Mart. et Schrank (*Cochlospermum* p.p.). Cochlosp. 13 trop.
Maximowiczia Cogn. Cucurbitaceae (2). 2 Mexico, S.W. U.S.
Maximus (Lat.), very large.
Maxwellia Baill. Bombacaceae. 1 New Caledonia.
May, *Crataegus*; **-apple** (Am.), *Podophyllum*; **-flower,** *Epigaea.*
Mayaca Aubl. Mayacaceae. 7 Am. Marsh herbs with alt. linear l. and sol. or umbellate fl., ☿, reg. 3-merous. A 3, $\underline{G}$ (3), 1-loc. with few orthotr. ov.; caps.

ayacaceae. Monocots. (Farinosae; Coronarieae *BH.*). Only gen. Mayaca, *q.v.*

ayepea Aubl. (*Linociera* Sw.). Oleaceae. 50 trop. and subtrop.

ayna Aubl. (*Oncoba* p.p. *BH.*). Flacourtiaceae (2). 8 trop. S. Am.

ayodendron Kurz. Bignoniaceae (2). 1 Burma.

aytenus Molina. Celastraceae. 75 S. Am., W.I.

azus Lour. Scrophulariaceae (II. 6). 10 China to Austr.

eadow beauty (Am.), *Rhexia*; **-crane's bill**, *Geranium pratense* L.; **-crocus**, *Colchicum autumnale* L.; **-grass**, *Poa*; **-rue**, *Thalictrum*; **-saffron**, *Colchicum autumnale* L.; **-sweet**, *Ulmaria palustris* Moench.

ealies (S. Afr.), Indian corn, *Zea Mays* L.

earnsia Merrill. Myrtaceae (II. 2). 1 Phil. Is.

echanisms, floral, *cf.* Floral Mechanisms.

echowia Schinz. Amarantaceae (2). 1 S.W. Afr.

ecomischus Coss. ex Benth. et Hook. f. Compositae (7). 1 Algeria.

econella Nutt. (*Platystigma* Benth.). Papaver. (II). 5 Pac. N. Am.

econopsis Vig. Papaveraceae (II). 40 N. temp. *M. cambrica* Vig., the Welsh poppy, in Brit. Cult. orn. fl.

ecopus Bennett. Leguminosae (III. 7). 1 Indomal.

ecranium Hook. f. Melastomaceae (I). 8 W.I.

edemia Princeps Gulielmus de Wurtemberg et A. Br. Palmaceae (II). 4 E. Afr.

edeola Gronov. ex L. Liliaceae (VII). 1 N. Am.

edial, central, middle.

edica Tourn. ex L. = Medicago Tourn. (Legum.).

edicago Tourn. ex L. Leguminosae (III. 4). 50 Eur., Medit., S. Afr.; 6 in Brit. (medick, nonsuch, burweed). The fl. has an explosive mech. like Genista (*q.v.*). The fr. is usu. twisted, often spirally coiled up into a ball or disc, and frequently provided with hooks enabling animal distr. *M. sativa* L. (lucerne or alfalfa), *M. lupulina* L., and others, are useful fodders.

edicosma Hook. f. Rutaceae (I). 1 E. Austr.

edinilla Gaudich. Melastomaceae (I). 150 palaeotrop.

edinillopsis Cogn. Melastomaceae (I). 2 Malaya.

ediocalcas J. J. Smith (*Cryptochilus* p.p. *EP.*). Orchid. (II. 5). 2 Mal.

editerranean region, the region round the Medit. Sea, including the Sahara, Egypt, N. Arabia to the Panjab, Asia Minor, the Balkans, Italy, and Spain.

edlar, *Pyrus germanica* Hook. f.

edulla, pith.

edusagyne Baker. Guttiferae (inc. sed.) (Ternstr. *BH.*). 1 Seychelles.

eehania Britton (*Cedronella* p.p.). Labiatae (VI). 1 E. U.S.

ega- (Gr. pref.), large; **-sporangium**, **-spore**, the larger when there are two kinds, *Pteridophyta*.

egabaria Pierre ex De Wild. Euphorbiaceae (A. I. 1). 2 trop. Afr.

egacarpaea DC. Cruciferae (2). 5 C. As., China. Sta. >6 in some.

egacaryon Boiss. Boraginaceae (IV. 5). 1 W. As.

egaclinium Lindl. Orchidaceae (II. 16). 20 trop. and subtrop. Afr. Cult.

Megadenia Maxim. Cruciferae (2). 1 China.
Megalachne Steud. Gramineae (10). 1 Juan Fernandez.
Megalochlamys Lindau. Acanthaceae (IV. B). 2 Afr.
Megalodonta Greene (*Bidens* p.p.). Compositae (5). 3 N. Am.
Megalopus K. Schum. Rubiaceae (II. 5). 1 Cameroons.
Megalostylis Sp. Moore. Euphorbiaceae (A. II. 2). 1 Upper Amazon
Megaphyllaea Hemsl. Meliaceae (III). 2 Perak.
Megapterium Spach (*Oenothera* p.p. *BH.*). Onagraceae (2). 3 Missouri valley. Cult. orn. fl.
Megarrhiza Torr. et Gray = Echinocystis Torr. p.p. (Cucurb.).
Megaskepasma Lindau. Acanthaceae (IV. B). 1 Venezuela.
Megastachya Beauv. = Eragrostis Beauv. p.p. (Gram.).
Megastigma Hook. f. Rutaceae (I). 2 Mexico, Guatemala.
Megastyles Schlechter. Orchidaceae (II. 2). 7 Indomal.
Megistostegium Hochr. (*Macrocalyx* Cost. et Poiss.). Malvaceae (4). 1 Madag.
Megistostigma Hook. f. Euphorbiaceae (A. II. 2). 1 Malacca.
Meibomia Heist. ex Adans. (*Desmodium* p.p.). Legumin. (III. 7). 6 Am
Meiocarpidium Engl. et Diels (*Uvaria* p.p.). Anonaceae (1). 2 W. Afr
Meiogyne Miq. (*Unona* p.p. *BH.*). Anonaceae (4). 5 trop. As.
Meionectes R. Br. Haloragidaceae. 1 S. Austr., Tasm.
Meiracyllium Reichb. f. Orchidaceae (II. 6). 2 Mexico.
Mela-, melano- (Gr. pref.), black.
Meladendron Molina. Solanaceae (inc. sed.). 1 Chili.
Melalema Hook. f. Compositae (8). 1 Patagonia.
Melaleuca L. Myrtaceae (II. 1). 100 Austr. 1 to India. The l. of *M. Leucadendron* L. (Austr., Indomal.) yield Cajeput oil. Sta. in antepe bundles. Several yield oil; timber useful.
Melampodium L. Compositae (5). 25 Am.
Melampyrum (Tourn.) L. Scrophulariaceae (III. 3). 35 N. temp 4 in Brit. (cow-wheat). Semi-parasites (see fam.). The fl. has loose-pollen mechanism; the 4 anthers lie close together and form a pollen-box; the filaments of the sta. are covered with sharp teeth
Melananthos Pohl. Inc. sed. Nomen.
Melananthus Walp. Solanaceae (5). 2 Brazil, C. Am.
Melancium Naud. Cucurbitaceae (2). 1 E. and S. Brazil.
Melandrium Roehl (*Lychnis* p.p. *BH.*). Caryophyllaceae (II. 1). 60 ⁎ S. Afr., S. Am. *M. rubrum* Garck. (*Lychnis dioica* L.) is dioec. and the ♀ pl. is stouter and coarser in growth than the ♂.
Melanobatus Greene (*Rubus* p.p.). Rosaceae (III. 2). 7 N. Am.
Melanocenchris Nees. Gramineae (11). 3 trop. As. and Afr.
Melanochyla Hook. f. Anacardiaceae (4). 4 Malaya.
Melanococca Blume. Rutaceae (inc. sed.). 1 New Guinea.
Melanodendron DC. Compositae (3). 1 St Helena. Tree.
Melanodiscus Radlk. Sapindaceae (1). 2 trop. Afr.
Melanophylla Baker. Cornaceae. 3 Madag.
Melanopsidium Cels. (*Billiottia* p.p. *BH.*). Rubi. (I. 8). 1 Rio de Janeiro.
Melanorrhoea Wall. Anacardiaceae (1). 6 Malaya. *M. usitata* Wall. (Theetsee) yields a valuable black varnish, obtained by tapping the stem; the sap turns black on exposure to air.

Melanosciadium Boissieu. Umbell. (III. 5). 1 China.
Melanoselinum Hoffm. (*Thapsia* p.p. *BH.*). Umbell. (III. 7). 2 Madeira.
Melanoseris Decne. = Lactuca Tourn. p.p. (Comp.).
Melanosinapis Schimp. et Spenn. = Brassica L. p.p. (Crucif.).
Melanosticta DC. = Hoffmannseggia Cav. (Legum.).
Melanotis Neck. Inc. sed. Nomen.
Melanoxylon Schott. Legum. (II. 8). 1 S.E. Brazil, *M. Brauna* Schott (brauna; timber useful).
Melanthera Rohr. Comp. (5). 30 Afr., Madag., Am., W.I.
Melanthesa Blume = Breynia Forst. (Euphorb.).
Melanthium Clayton ex L. Lili. (1). 5 N. Am. Lower fls. usu. ♂.
Melargyra Rafin. = Spergularia C. et J. Presl. (Caryoph.).
Melarhiza Kellogg = Wyethia Nutt. (Comp.).
Melascus Rafin. = Ipomoea L. (Convolv.).
Melasma Berg. Scroph. (III. 2). 25 trop., exc. Austr. C nearly reg.
Melasphaerula Ker-Gawl. Irid. (III). 1 Cape Col.
Melastoma Burm. ex L. Melastom. (1). 50 trop. and E. As. Sta. very unequal; connective of larger much produced. Fr. blackens mouth.
Melastomaceae (*EP.*, *BH.*). Dicots. (Archichl. Myrtiflorae; Myrtales, *BH.*; pp. xxxix, lii). 200/2500 trop. and subtrop. A very natural fam., usu. easy to recognise in veg. condition by the peculiar leaf-veining, &c. They exist under various conditions, and vary much in habit; herbs, shrubs, trees, with usu. erect stem, some climbing, usu. by r., some epiphytic, water, or marsh pl. Stem often 4-angled, l. usu. decussate, one much larger than other, the latter often withering as it grows older. L. usu. simple, the veins diverging from base and converging at apex, and ± the same size, with no true midrib. Phloem in pith. Many myrmecophilous (Tococa, Maieta, &c.).

Infl. cymose in great variety. Fl. usu. ☿, reg. or slightly ·|·, very char., easily recognised by the anther-appendages. Recept. or K-tube tubular or bell-shaped, usu. ± united with G, sometimes by longitudinal ribs only, often brightly coloured. K 4—5, C 4—5, usu. conv., perig. or epig., both usu. reg.; A often irreg., usu. twice pets., standing when mature in one whorl, bent down in bud with anthers between ov. and recept.; anther-loc. opening by common term. pore, connective developed in various ways and usu. provided with curious appendages, frequently of sickle-like form; G sup. or inf., usu. 4—5-loc. (1-loc. in Memecylon, &c.) with simple style and stigma, and ∞ anatr. ov. on axile plac. Berry or loculic. caps.; seed exalb., one cot. larger than other. A few yield colouring matters; many cult. orn. fl.

Classification and chief genera (after Krasser):

A. Fr. many-seeded. Embryo very small.
  I. *MELASTOMATOIDEAE* (ovules on slightly projecting plac. in inner angle of loc.): Tibouchina, Centradenia, Melastoma, Osbeckia, Rhexia, Monochaetum, Microlicia, Medinilla, Leandra, Tamonea (Miconia), Tococa, Maieta.
  II. *ASTRONIOIDEAE* (ov. on basal or parietal plac.): (caps.) Astronia and 2 more, (berry) Kibessia and 2 more.
B. Fr. a berry, 1—5-seeded. Embryo large.
  III. *MEMECYLOIDEAE*: Memecylon.

Meleagrinex Arruda. Inc. sed. (? = Sapindus Tourn.). 1 Brazil.
Melegueta pepper, *Amomum melegueta* Roscoe (trop. Afr.).

Mel-grass, *Ammophila arundinacea* Host. [flat. Epicalyx 3 large.
Melhania Forsk. Stercul. 45 Afr., As., Austr. A (5), stds. 5, pets. large,
Melia L. (excl. *Azadirachta*). Meli. (III). 15 palaeotrop. and subtrop. G to (8). Some useful for timber. *M. Azedarach* L. (beadtree) cult.
Meliaceae (*EP.*, *BH.* incl. § II of *Rutac.*). Dicots. (Archichl. Geraniales; pp. xxv, li). 40/600 warm. Mostly ♄, with usu. alt. exstip. pinnate l. without transparent dots, and cymose panicles of ☿ reg. fls. K (4—5) or 4—5, C usu. 4—5, rarely united, A 8—10 usu. united below into a tube, or sometimes completely united with anthers sessile on the tube; disc or not; G̲ 2—5-loc., rarely 1-loc. or > 5-loc., with style or not, and 1, 2, or more ov. in each loc., usu. pend. and anatr. with ventral raphe. Caps., berry, or drupe; seeds often winged, usu. with endosp. Many, *e.g.* Swietenia, Khaya, &c. (mahogany), Cedrela, &c. (cedars), yield valuable timber; the seeds of several are used as sources of oil, and others have ed. fr.

Classification and chief genera (after Engler): [Cedrela.

I. *CEDRELOIDEAE* (sta. free, seeds winged): Pteroxylon,

II. *SWIETENIOIDEAE* (sta. in a tube; seeds winged, loc. with > 2 ov.): Swietenia, Khaya, Soymida.

III. *MELIOIDEAE* (sta. in a tube, seeds not winged): Carapa, Xylocarpus, Melia, Azadirachta, Trichila, Guarea.

Meliadelpha Radlk. Meli. (inc. sed.). 2 Polyn., New Caled.
Melianthaceae (*EP.*; *Sapind.* p.p. *BH.*). Dicots. (Archichl. Sapindales; pp. xxix, li). 3/18 trop. and S. Afr. Trees and shrubs with alt. usu. stip. l., and racemes of ☿, ·|· fls. whose stalks twist through 180° at time of flg. K 5 or (5), sometimes 4 by union of two seps.; C 4—5; disc extra-staminal; A 5—4—10, free or united at base; G̲ (4—5), 4—5-loc. with one basal or many axile ov. in each; ov. erect or pend., anatr. with ventral or dorsal raphe according as they are erect or pend. Caps.; seed sometimes arillate; endosp. fleshy or horny. *Chief genus:* Melianthus.
Melianthus L. Melianth. 5 S. Afr. Post. sep. spurred or saccate. Ovules ∞. Fls. very rich in honey.
Melica L. Gramin. (10). 40 temp., exc. Austr.; 2 Brit. (melic-grass). Inf. palea 7—9-nerved. Lodicule 1. Cult. orn. fol.
Melic grass, *Melica*.
Melichlis Rafin. = Coryanthes Hook. (Orchid.).
Melichrus R. Br. (*Styphelia* p.p. *EP.*). Epacrid. (3). 2 Austr.
Melicocca L. Sapind. (I). 2 trop. Am., W.I. Anther extrorse. Fr. ed. *M. bijuga* L. (W.I.) for timber and fr. [merous.
Melicope Forst. Rut. (I. 1). 20 trop. As., warm Austr., N.Z. 4-
Melicytus Forst. Viol. 4 N.Z., Norfolk I. Fl. sub-reg. with no claws.
Mielientha Pierre. Opil. 1 Cambodia. [Ovules ∞ per plac. Berry.
Melilot, Melilotus. [3 Brit. (melilot). Bee-fls., much honey. Medic.
Melilotus Tourn. ex Hall. Legum. (III. 4). 20 temp. and sub-trop. |✱.
Melinia Decne. in DC. Asclep. (II. 1). 6 temp. S. Am.
Melinis Beauv. Gramin. (4). 3 trop. S. Am., Afr., Madag. Fodder.
Melioschinzia K. Schum. (*Chisocheton* p.p. *EP.*). Meli. (III). 1 New Guin.
Meliosma Blume. Sabi. 60 warm As., Am. 3 sta. reduced to double cups, 2 pets. usu. reduced to scales.

Melissa Tourn. ex L. Labiat. (VI. 11). 4 Eur., W. As. *M. officinalis* [L. (balm), cult.
Melitella Sommier. Comp. (13). 1 Malta.
Melittacanthus Sp. Moore. Acanth. (IV. B). 1 Madag.
Melittis L. Labiat. (VI. 4). 1 Eur. (incl. Brit.), *M. Melissophyllum* [L. (bastard-balm).
Mellera Sp. Moore. Acanth. (IV. A). 6 warm Afr.
Melleus (Lat.), of honey colour or taste.
Mellichampia A. Gray. Asclep. (II. 1). 1 Mex. C pink, corona [white.
Melliniella Harms. Legum. (III. 7). 1 W. trop. Afr.
Mellissia Hook. f. Solan. (2). 1 St Helena.
Melloa Bur. Bignon. (1). 2 Braz., Venezuela. Disc double.
Melo (Tourn.) L. = Cucumis Tourn. (Cucurb.).
Melocactus (Tourn.) Link et Otto. Cact. (III. 1). 30 W.I., trop. Am. Ribbed pl. like Cereus. Cephalium. Fls. produced at top.
Melocalamus Benth. Gramin. (13). 1 Burma. Seed fleshy.
Melocanna Trin. Gramin. (13). 2 Indomal. Berry; seed exalb., ed.
Melochia Dill. ex L. Stercul. 65 trop. A-tube short, pets. flat, deciduous; G 5-loc., 10-ovuled. **Do.** Rottb. Inc. sed. 1 Guiana.
Melodinus Forst. Apocyn. (I. 1). 30 Indomal. Scales in throat.
Melodorum Hook. f. et Thoms. Anon. (4). 40 trop. |✱. Usu. climb.
Melolobium Eckl. et. Zeyh. Legum. (III. 3). 25 S. Afr. K 2-lipped.
Melon, *Cucumis Melo* L.; **-cactus,** *Melocactus*; **-thick** (W.I.), *Melocactus*; **-, water,** *Citrullus vulgaris* Schrad; **-, white gourd,** *Benincasa cerifera* Savi.
Meloneura Rafin. = Utricularia L.
Melongena Tourn. ex Mill = Solanum Tourn. p.p. (Solan.).
Melosmon Rafin. (*Teucrium* p.p.). Labiat. (I). 5 Am., W.I.
Melosperma Benth. Scroph. (II. 6). 1 Chile. Seed large.
Melothria L. Cucurb. (2). 65 warm. Anther-loc. straight.
Membranous (l.), thin, dry, not green, flexible.
Memecylanthus Gilg et Schlechter. Caprifol. 1 New Caled.
Memecylon L. Melastom. (III). 130 palaeotrop. G 1-loc.
Memora Miers (*Adenocalymma* p.p. *BH.*). Bignon. (1). 20 S. Am.
Memorialis Buch.-Ham. (*Pouzolzia* p.p. *BH.*). Urtic. (3). 12 Indomal.
Menabea Baill. Asclep. (II. 2). 1 Madag.
Menadenium Rafin. (*Zygopetalum* p.p.). Orchid. (II. 14). 3 trop. S. Am.
Menais Loefl. Inc. sed. 1 S. Am.
Menaphronocalyx Pohl. Inc. sed. Nomen. [*Kew Bull.*, 1919, 407.
Mendoncia Vell. (*Mendozia* Ruiz et Pav.). Acanth. (II). 25 trop. Am.
Menepetalum Loes. Celastr. 6 New Caled.
Meniscium Schreb. = Dryopteris Adans. (Polypod.).
Menispermaceae (*EP.*, *BH.*). Dicots. (Archichl. Ranales; pp. xix, l). 65/350 warm. Mostly twining shrubs, herbs, or trees, a few erect, with alt. usu. simple, usu. exstip. l., usu. with serial axillary buds. Infl. racemose, with ultimate branching cymose. Fls. unisexual, usu. dioec., often ± caulifloral, rarely brightly coloured, usu. reg. Formula usu. K 3+3, C 3+3, A 3+3, $\underline{G}$ 3, but many exceptions. K and A often > 6; sometimes only 1 cpl., or more (to 32); A often ∞, or united, or in bundles. Stds. in ♀ fl. various, or 0. Ovules 2 per cpl., soon reduced to 1, ventral, pend., semi-anatr. Achene, sometimes drupaceous; endosp. or 0, sometimes ruminate. The fr. usu. curves in development, so that style is no longer term. Classification of the gen. is largely based on structure of

the seed. A few medicinal, on account of bitter principle in r. *Chief genera:* Chondrodendron, Tiliacora, Triclisia, Anamirta, Cosciniuin, Tinospora, Jateorhiza, Abuta, Hyperbaena, Hypserpa, Cocculus, Menispermum, Stephania, Cissampelos, Cyclea.

Menispermum (Tourn.) L. Menisperm. 2 temp. E. As., Atl. N. Am. (moonseed) (*cf.* Epigaea). K 4—10, spiral, C 6—9, A 12—24, [G 2—4.

Menkea Lehm. Crucif. (3). 3 Austr.

Menkenia Bub. = Lathyrus Tourn. p.p. (Legum.).

Menodora Humb. et Bonpl. Oleac. 18 warm Am., Afr. Caps.; seed [erect.

Menonvillea R. Br. ex DC. Crucif. (1). 4 Chile, Peru. Gynophore.

Mentha (Tourn.) L. Labiat. (VI. 11). 25 |✻. 6 Brit. (mint), incl. *M. piperita* L. (peppermint), *M. Pulegium* L. (pennyroyal). An oil used in medicine is distilled from the former. *M. viridis* L. (garden mint) cult. for flavouring. C sub-reg., 4-merous. A 4 equal.

Menthol, a substance extracted from oil of peppermint, &c.

Mentum, a chin, *cf. Orchidaceae.*

Mentzelia Plum. ex L. (*BH.* incl. *Eucnide*). Loas. 60 warm Am., W.I. No stinging hairs. In some, outer sta. sterile. G usu. (3).

Menyanthes (Tourn.) L. Gentian. (II). 1 N. temp. (incl. Brit.), *M. trifoliata* L. (buck or bog bean), a bog pl. with creeping rhiz. and alt. l. Fls. dimorphic heterost. (*cf.* Primula). Rhiz. bitter tonic.

Menziesia Sm. Eric. (I. 2). 7 N. temp. As., Am. *Cf.* Daboecia.

Meoschium Beauv. = Ischaemum L. p.p. (Gramin.).

Mephitidia Reinw. ex Blume = Lasianthus Jack (Rubi.).

Merathrepta Rafin. (*Danthonia* p.p.). Gramin. (9). 10 N. Am.

Meratia Loisel. = Calycanthus L. p.p. (Calycanth.).

Merciera A. DC. Campanul. (I. 1). 4 S. Afr. G 1-loc., ov. basal.

Merckia Fisch. (*Arenaria* p.p. *BH.*). Caryoph. 1 N.E. As., N.W. Am. G ± locular.

Mercurialis (Tourn.) L. Euphorb. (A II. 2). 8 Medit., Eur., E. As. 2 Brit. (mercury). L. opp. Dioec. Anemoph. C 0. A 8—20. [G (2). Veg. repr. by rhiz.

Mercury, *Mercurialis.*

Merendera Ram. Lili. (I). 10 Medit., Abyssin., Afghanist. Styles 3.

Meriandra Benth. Labiat. (VI. 7). 2 Himal., Abyssinia. [behind.

Meriania Sw. Melastom. (I). 30 W.I., trop. Am. Connective spurred

Mericarp, the one-seeded portion of a schizocarp, *Umbelliferae.*

Mericarpaea Boiss. Rubi. (II. 11). 1 W. As.

Meridional, southern.

Meringurus Murbeck. Gramin. (12). 1 Tunis.

Merinthopodium Donnell Smith. Solan. (4). 2 C. Am.

Merinthosorus Copeland (*Acrostichum* p.p.). Polypod. 1 Phil. Is.

Meriolix Rafin. (*Oenothera* p.p. *BH.*). Onagr. (2). 6 temp. N. Am. [Cult.

Merism, repetition of parts to form a symmetry or pattern.

Merismatic, meristematic, of dividing and growing cells.

Merismostigma Sp. Moore. Rubi. (II. 1). 1 New Caled.

Meristostylis Klotzsch (*Kalanchoë* p.p. *EP.*). Crassul. 3 trop. Afr [[Gentian. *BH.*]

Mermaid weed (Am.), *Proserpinaca.*

Merostachys Spreng. Gramin. (13). 12 S. Am. Climbing bamboos (*q.v.*)

Merostela Pierre. Meli. 2 Cochinchina. [70 warm

Merremia Dennst. (*Batatas*, *Convolvulus*, *Ipomoea* p.p.). Convolv. (1).

Merrillia Swingle. Rut. (V). 1 Malay Penins.

Merrittia Merrill (*Senecio* p.p.). Compositae (8). 1 Phil. Is.

Mertensia Roth. Boraginaceae (IV. 4). 30 N. temp. 1 in Brit., *M. maritima* S. F. Gray (gromwell), on sea-coasts.

Meryta Forst. Araliaceae (1). 15 New Caled., New Zealand, Polynesia.

Mesadenia Rafin. (*Senecio* p.p.). Compositae (8). 10 N. Am.

Mesanthemum Koern. Eriocaulonaceae. 4 Madag., trop. Afr.

Mescal, *Agave.*

Mesechites Muell.-Arg. = Echites L. (Apocyn.).

Mesembryanthemum Dill. ex L. Aizoaceae (II). 350 S. Afr. Xero. of the most pronounced kind with very succulent l., usu. closely packed together; the young l. stand face to face at the growing apex till well grown, and thus protect the young bud. In *M. obconellum* Haw. the pairs of l. are congenitally united into a fleshy body with a little slit in the centre. Several have thorns, sometimes fl.-stalks hardened after the fall of the fl., sometimes branches, as in *M. spinosum* L. (the leafy branches appear below these in the next year, in the same axils). Fls. usu. term. on the stems, sol. or in dichasia or cincinni. Outer sta. (due to branching) repres. by numerous petaloid stds., having the appearance of a C. The mature ovary is 5-loc. with parietal plac.; this peculiar feature is due to an excessive growth of the peripheral tissue during development, which gradually turns the loculi completely over (*cf.* Punica). Fr. a caps. which opens only in moist air, contrary to the usual wont of capsules. Some, *e.g.* *M. edule* L. (Hottentot fig), contain an ed. pulp. *M. crystallinum* L. is the ice-plant, so called because its l. are covered with small glistening bladder-shaped hairs.

Meso- (Gr. pref.), middle-; **-carp**, the middle part of a fr. wall; **-chil**, of a lip; **-phyll**, of a leaf; **-phytes**, average plants, suited to a fairly and continuously moist climate.

Mesochlaena R. Br. Polypodiaceae. 1 Malaya, Polynesia.

Mesogyne Engl. Moraceae (1). 2 trop. Afr.

Mesomelaena Nees (*Gymnoschoenus* Nees). Cyperaceae (II). 2 Austr.

Mesona Blume. Labiatae (VII). 3 E. Indomal.

Mesopanax R. Viguier = Schefflera, &c. p.p. (Aral.).

Mesoptera Hook. f. Rubiaceae (II. 1). 1 Malay Peninsula.

Mesoreanthus Greene (*Streptanthus* p.p.). Cruciferae (1). 1 Calif.

Mesosphaerum P. Br. = Hyptis Jacq. (Labi.).

Mesospinidium Reichb. f. (*Odontoglossum* p.p. *BH.*). Orchidaceae (II. 19). 4 C. Am. to Brazil.

Mespilodaphne Nees = Ocotea Aubl. p.p. (Laur.).

Mespilus (Tourn.) L. (*Pyrus* Tourn. p.p. *BH.*). Rosaceae (II). 40 N. temp. *M. germanica* L. is the medlar (ed. fr.). *M. Oxyacantha* Crantz, see Crataegus.

Mesquite grass, *Bouteloua*; **- tree,** *Prosopis juliflora* DC.

Messersmidia L. = Tournefortia L. (*BH.*). = Heliotropium L. (Borag.).

Mesua L. Guttiferae (IV). 3 trop. As. K, C 4. *M. ferrea* L. (Na or iron-wood) yields a valuable timber; its fls. are used in perfumery.

Metabolism, the chemical changes going on in the elaboration of food.

Metabolos Blume = Hedyotis L. (*BH.*) = Oldenlandia L. (Rubi.).

Metalasia R. Br. Compositae (4). 20 S. Afr. L. sometimes spirally twisted.

Metalepis Griseb. Asclepiadaceae (II. 4). 1 Cuba.

Metamorphosis, change of form and structure, whether ontogenetic as in *Astragalus*, *Geum*, or phylogenetic. [hollow.
Metanarthecium Maxim. Lili. (I). 2 Japan, Formosa. Filaments
Metaplexis R. Br. Asclepiadaceae (II. 1). 4 E. As.
Metaporana N. E. Brown. Convolvulaceae (I). 2 trop. Afr.
Metastelma R. Br. Asclepiadaceae (II. 1). 50 warm Am., W.I.
Metharme Phil. Zygophyllaceae. 1 Chili.
Metopium (P. Br.) Engl. Anacardiaceae (3). 3 W.I. Fla. 5-merous. Yields a purging resin (doctor gum) from the stem.
Metrodorea A. St Hil. (*Esenbeckia BH.*). Rutaceae (I). 5 Rio de Janeiro.
Metrosideros Banks. Myrtaceae (II. 2). 20 S. Afr., Sunda Is., Austr., Polynes. Some furnish useful timber.
Metroxylon Rottb. Palmae (III). 7 Siam to New Guinea. *M. Rumphii* Mart. and *M. laeve* Mart. are the sago palms, cult. in Malaya. Small trees whose stems die after producing their large term. monoec. infls. (*cf.* Corypha, &c.), but form rhiz. branches below. The fr. takes 3 years to ripen. The tree is cut down when the infl. appears, and the sago is obtained from the pith by crushing and washing.
Mettenia Griseb. Euphorbiaceae (A. II. 6). 2 Jamaica, Cuba.
Metteniusa Karst. Icacinaceae. 1 Colombia.
Metternichia Mikan. Solanaceae (4). 3 Brazil, Colombia.
Meu, *Meum athamanticum* Jacq.
Meum (Tourn.) Adans. Umbelliferae (III. 5). 1 Eur. (incl. Brit.), *M. athamanticum* Jacq. (meu or bald-money).
Mexican aloe, - fibre, *Agave*; **- poppy**, *Argemone mexicana* L.; **- rubber**, *Castilloa elastica* Cerv.; **- sunflower**, *Tithonia diversifolia* A. Gray; **- tea**, *Chenopodium anthelminticum* L.
Meyenia Nees (*Thunbergia* p.p. *BH.*). Acanthaceae (III). 1 Indomal.
Meyeria DC. = Calea L. p.p. (Comp.).
Mezereon, *Daphne Mezereum* L.
Mezia Schwacke. Malpighiaceae (I). 1 Minas Geraës.
Meziella Schindler. Haloragidaceae. 1 Austr.
Mezilaurus O. Ktze. (*Silvia* Allem). Lauraceae (II). 2 Brazil.
Mezoneurum Desf. Leguminosae (II. 7). 12 palaeotrop.
Mezzettia Becc. Anonaceae (I). 6 Malaya.
Mezzettiopsis Ridl. Anonaceae (I). 1 Borneo.
Mi, *Bassia longifolia* L.
Mibora Adans. Gramineae (8). 1 W. Eur. (incl. Brit.).
Michaelmas daisy, *Aster*.
Michauxia L'Hérit. Campanulaceae (I). 6 E. Medit. Fl. 7—10-merous throughout. Cult. orn. fl.
Michauxia Raeuschel. Inc. sed. 1, habitat?
Michelia L. Magnoliaceae. 25 trop. As., China. There is a gynophore between sta. and cpls. *M. Champaca* L. is cult. for its perfumed fl., used as offerings. Several yield useful timber.
Micheliella Briquet (*Collinsonia* p.p.). Labiatae (VI). 2 S.E. U.S.
Micholitzia N. E. Brown. Asclepiadaceae (II. 3). 1 India.
Michoxia Vell. Inc. sed. 1 Brazil.
Miconia Ruiz et Pav. (*Tamonea* Aubl.). Melastomaceae (I). 600 trop Am., W.I.

Micractis DC. Compositae (5). 1 Madagascar. No pappus.
Micradenia Miers = Dipladenia A. DC. (Apocyn.).
Micraea Miers = Ruellia L. p.p. (Acanth.). 1 Chili.
Micraira F. Muell. Gramineae (9). 1 Queensland.
Micrampelis Rafin. (*Sicyos* p.p.). Cucurbitaceae (4). 10 N. Am.
Micrandra Benth. in Hook. Euphorb. (A. II. 3). 6 Brazil, Venez.
Micranthemum Michx. Scrophulariaceae (II. 6). 16 warm Am.
Micranthes Haw. (*Saxifraga* p.p.). Saxifragaceae (I). 50 N. Am.
Micrantheum Desf. Euphorbiaceae (B. I). 2 Austr.
Micranthus Eckl. Iridaceae (III). 2 Cape Colony.
Micranthus Wendl. (*Phaylopsis BH.*). Acanthaceae (IV. A). 12 palaeotrop.
Micranthus (Lat.), small-flowered.
Micrargeria Benth. in DC. Scrophulariaceae (III. 2). 3 E. Afr., India.
Micrasepalum Urb. (*Borreria* p.p.). Rubiaceae (II. 10). 1 Cuba.
Micrechites Miq. Apocynaceae (II. 1). 5 E. Indomal.
Micrembryae (*BH.*). The 4th series of Incompletae.
Micro (Gr. pref.), small; **-millimetre**, $\frac{1}{1000}$ mm., denoted by μ; **-pyle**, the opening at the top of the ovule; **-sporangium**, **-spore**, **-sporophyll**, *Pteridophyta*, *Selaginella*.
Microbahia Cockerell (*Actinolepis* p.p.). Compositae (6). 1 Colorado.
Microbambus K. Schum. (*Guaduella* Franch.). Gramineae (13). 1 trop. Afr.
Microbignonia Kränzlin. Bignoniaceae (2). 1 Peru.
Microcachrys Hook. f. Coniferae (Taxac. 2; see C. for gen. chars.). 1 Tasm. Dioec. Fr.-scales fleshy, not united. Seed arillate.
Microcala Hoffmgg. et Link. Gentianaceae (I). 2, 1 Am., the other Medit. and W. Eur. (incl. south-west England and Ireland).
Microcalamus Franch. Gramineae (13). 5 trop. W. Afr.
Microcalamus Gamble = Bambusa Schreb. p.p. (Gram.).
Microcarpaea R. Br. Scrophulariaceae (II. 6). 1 E. As., Austr.
Microcasia Becc. (*Bucephalandra BH.*). Araceae (V). 2 Borneo.
Microcharis Benth. Leguminosae (III. 6). 4 trop. and S. Afr.
Microchloa R. Br. Gramineae (11). 4 Afr., one cosmotrop.
Microchonea Pierre. Apocynaceae (II. 2). 1 Cochinchina.
Microcitrus Swingle. Rutaceae (V). 4 Austr.
Microcnemum Ung.-Sternb. Chenopodiaceae (A). 1 Spain.
Micrococca Benth. Euphorbiaceae (A. II. 2). 10 trop. As., Afr.
Microcodon A. DC. Campanulaceae (I). 4 S. Afr.
Microcorys R. Br. Labiatae (II). 15 S.W. Austr.
Microcos Burm. ex L. = Grewia L. p.p. (Tili.).
Microcybe Turcz. Rutaceae (I). 3 Austr.
Microcycas A. DC. Cycadaceae (*q.v.*). 1 Cuba.
Microdactylon T. S. Brandegee. Asclepiadaceae (II. 1). 1 Mexico.
Microdesmis Hook. f. Euphorbiaceae (A. II. 5). 3 trop. Afr., As.
Microdon Choisy. Scrophulariaceae (II. 7) (Selag. *BH.*). 4 S. Afr.
Microdracoides Hua. Cyperaceae (III). 1 trop. Afr.
Microglossa DC. Compositae (3). 10 trop. As. and Afr.
Microgynoecium Hook. f. Chenopodiaceae (A). 1 Tibet.
Microkentia H. Wendl. ex Benth. et Hook. f. (*Cyphokentia* p.p. *EP.*). Palmaceae (IV. 1). 5 New Caledonia.

Microlaena R. Br. Gramineae (7). 5 Austr., New Zealand.
Microlecane Sch.-Bip. Compositae (5). 1 Abyssinia.
Microlepis Miq. Melastomaceae (1). 4 S. Brazil.
Microlespedeza Makino (*Lespedeza* p.p.). Legum. (III. 7). 2 Japan.
Microlicia D. Don. Melastomaceae (1). 100 trop. S. Am.
Microlobius Presl. Leguminosae (inc. sed.). 1 Mexico.
Microloma R. Br. Asclepiadaceae (II. 1). 8 S. Afr.
Microlonchoides Candargy (*Centaurea* p.p. *EP.*). Comp. (11). 1 Greece.
Microlonchus Cass. = Centaurea L. p.p. (Comp.).
Micromeles Decne. (*Pyrus* p.p.). Rosaceae (II). 10 N. temp.
Micromelum Blume. Rutaceae (V). 6 Indomal.
Micromeria Benth. Labiatae (VI). 130 cosmop. *M. Douglasii* Benth. (Calif., &c.) is the Yerba buena (medicinal).
Micromyrtus Benth. Myrtaceae (II. 2). 12 Austr.
Micronoma H. Wendl. Palmaceae (inc. sed.). Nomen.
Micronychia Oliv. Anacardiaceae (3). 1 Madagascar.
Microphacos Rydberg (*Astragalus* p.p.). Leguminosae (III. 6). 2 N. Am.
Micropholis Pierre = Sideroxylon Dill. (Sapot.).
Microphyes Phil. Caryophyllaceae (I. 3). 2 Chili.
Microphysa Naud. Melastomaceae (1). 2 Brazil, Peru.
Micropiper Miq. = Peperomia Ruiz et Pav. (Piper.).
Micropleura Lag. (*Centella* p.p. *EP.*). Umbelliferae (I. 1). 1 Chili.
Microplumeria Baill. Apocynaceae (I. 3). 1 Amazon valley.
Micropogon Spreng. Inc. sed. Nomen.
Micropora Hook. f. (*Hexapora* p.p.). Lauraceae (II). 1 Penang.
Micropsis DC. Compositae (4). 3 Chili, Arg., Uruguay.
Micropus L. Compositae (4). 5 W. As., Medit., N. Am.
Microrhamnus A. Gray. Rhamnaceae. 1 Mexico, Texas.
Microrhynchus Less. (*Launaea* p.p. *EP.*). Compositae (13). 20 Ind., Medit., S. Afr.
Microrphium C. B. Clarke. Gentianaceae (1). 1 Malay Peninsula.
Microsaccus Blume. Orchidaceae (II. 20). 4 Malaya.
Microschoenus C. B. Clarke. Cyperaceae (II). 1 W. Himalaya.
Microschwenkia Benth. (*Melananthus* p.p.). Solanaceae (5). 1 C. Am.
Microsciadium Boiss. Umbelliferae (III. 5). 1 Asia Minor.
Microsechium Naud. Cucurbitaceae (4). 2 Mexico.
Microselinum Andrz. Umbelliferae (inc. sed.). 1 Russia.
Microsemia Greene (*Streptanthus* p.p.). Cruciferae (1). 1 N. Am.
Microsemma Labill. Flacourtiaceae (inc. sed.). 1 New Caledonia.
Microseris D. Don. Compositae (13). 40 Am., Austr., N.Z.
Microspermae. The 11th order (*EP.*) of Monocots. The 1st series (*BH.*) of Monocots. *Cf.* pp. viii, liv.
Microspermum Lag. Compositae (6). 2 Mexico.
Microsplenium Hook. f. Caprifol. (= *Machaonia*, Rubiac., ?). 1 Mexico.
Microstachys A. Juss. = Sebastiania Spreng. p.p. (Euph.).
Microsteira Baker. Malpighiaceae (1). 7 Madag. Polygamous dioec.
Microstelma Baill. Asclepiadaceae (II. 4). 2 Mexico.
Microstemma R. Br. Asclepiadaceae (II. 3). 2 N.E. Austr.
Microstemon Engl. Anacardiaceae (3). 3 Malay Peninsula.
Microstephanus N.E. Br. (*Astephanus* *EP.*). Asclepiad. (II. 1). 1 E. Afr.

Microsteris Greene (*Collomia* p.p. *EP.*). Polemoniaceae. 9 W. Am.
Microstylis Nutt. Orchidaceae (II. 4). 150 As., Am. Fl. twisted through 360° (*cf.* Malaxis).
Microtatorchis Schlechter (*Taeniophyllum* p.p.). Orchidaceae (II. 20). 4 New Guinea, Fiji, New Caled.
Microtea Sw. Phytolaccaceae. 10 trop. Am., W.I. 5-merous.
Microtis R. Br. Orchidaceae (II. 2). 10 Australia, New Zealand.
Microtoena Prain (*Plectranthus* p.p.). Labiatae (VI). 6 Chi., Ind., Java.
Microtrichia DC. Compositae (3). 1 trop. Afr.
Microtropis Wall. Celastraceae. 12 Indomal.
Microula Benth. Boraginaceae (IV. 2). 2 Himalaya.
Middelbergia Schinz ex Pax = Cluytia Boerh. p.p. (Euph.).
Miersia Lindl. Liliaceae (IV). 2 Chili.
Miersiella Urb. (*Dictyostegia* p.p.). Burmanniaceae. 1 S.E. Brazil.
Miersiophyton Engl. (*Chasmanthera* p.p.). Menispermaceae. 1 trop. Afr.
Mignonette, *Reseda odorata* L.; **- tree**, *Lawsonia inermis* L.
Mihi, as authority to sp., accepted by author as the correct form.
Mikania Willd. Compositae (2). 175 trop., all but one (*M. scandens* Willd.) confined to Am. Twining herbs or shrubs, with opp. l.
Mildbraedia Pax. Euphorbiaceae (A. II. 5). 4 trop. Afr.
Mildbraediodendron Harms. Leguminosae (II. 9). 1 C. Afr.
Milfoil, *Achillea Millefolium* L.; **water -**, *Myriophyllum*.
Milicia Sim. Ulmaceae. 2 S.E. Afr.
Milium L. Gramineae (8). 6 N. temp. *M. effusum* L. (millet-grass) Brit. L.-blade turned over on itself (*cf.* Alstroemeria).
Miliusa Leschen. ex A. DC. Anonaceae (2). 25 Indomal.
Milk thistle, *Silybum Marianum* Gaertn.; **- tree**, *Brosimum Galactodendron* D. Don (Venezuela), *Mimusops elata* Allem. (Brazil); **- vetch** *Astragalus*; **- weed**, *Asclepias*; **- wort**, *Polygala vulgaris* L.; **sea - -**, *Glaux maritima* L.
Milla Cav. Liliaceae (IV). 1 Mexico.
Millefolium Tourn. = Achillea L. p.p. (Comp.).
Milleria Houst. ex L. Compositae (5). 1 C. Am., Mexico.
Millet, *Panicum*, *Sorghum*, &c.; **bulrush -**, *Pennisetum typhoideum* Rich.; **- grass**, *Milium*; **great -**, *Sorghum vulgare* Pers.; **Indian -**, *Panicum miliaceum* L.; **Italian -**, *Setaria italica* Beauv.; **little -**, *Panicum miliare* Lamk.; **pearl -**, *Pennisetum typhoideum* Rich.; **Samoa -**, *Panicum*; **spiked -**, *cf.* pearl.
Millettia Wight et Arn. Leguminosae (III. 6). 120 trop. and subtrop. |*.
Milligania Hook. f. Liliaceae (VI). 4 Tasmania.
Millingtonia L. f. Bignoniaceae (I). 1 Burma.
Millotia Cass. Compositae (4). 2 temp. Austr.
Millspaughia Robinson. Polygonaceae (III. 1). 2 C. Am.
Milnea Roxb. = Aglaia Lour. (Meli.).
Miltianthus Bunge. Zygophyllaceae. 1 Afghanistan.
Miltonia Lindl. Orchidaceae (II. 19). 20 trop. Am. Epiphytes.
Miltonioda ×. Orchidaceae. Hybrid, Miltonia-Cochlioda.
Milula Prain. Liliaceae (inc. sed.). 1 E. Himalaya.
Mimela Phil. (*Leuceria* p.p. *EP.*). Compositae (12). 1 Chili.

Mimetanthe Greene (*Mimulus* p.p. *BH.*). Scrophular. (II. 6). 1 S.W. N. Am.

Mimetes Salisb. Proteaceae (I). 15 S. Afr.

Mimophytum Greenman. Boraginaceae (IV. 1). 1 Mexico.

Mimosa L. Leguminosae (I. 5). 400 trop. and subtrop. Am., a few in Afr. and As. *M. pudica* L. (sensitive plant) is now a common trop. weed and is cult. in hothouses. Mainly herbs and undershrubs, frequently with stipular thorns. *M. pudica* has a bipinnate l. with four secondary petioles. It is exceedingly sensitive, and a touch or shake will make it move rapidly into the position which it assumes at night. The leaflets move upwards in pairs, closing against one another, the secondary petioles close up against one another and the main petiole drops through about 60°. After a short time the movements are slowly reversed. They are effected by the aid of a *pulvinus* or swollen joint at each point of movement. Each pulvinus can be made to work independently of the rest by gentle stimulation, and the propagation of the stimulus from pulvinus to pulvinus may also be seen. The ribs of the fr. are frequently thorny and are usu. dropped on dehiscence. **M. bark**, bark of Acacias used for tanning.

Mimulopsis Schweinf. Acanthaceae (IV. A). 15 trop. Afr., Madag.

Mimulus L. Scrophulariaceae (II. 6). 80 cosmop. *M. luteus* L. (yellow monkey-flower) nat. in Brit. *M. moschatus* Dougl. is the common musk-plant of cottage windows. Insects entering the fl. touch first the stigma, which is sensitive to contact and closes up (*cf.* Martynia). Cult. orn. fl.

Mimusops L. Sapotaceae (2). 65 trop. *M. Balata* Crueg. (*M. globosa* Gaertn.; Guiana) yields a gutta-percha (balata). *M. elata* Allem. is the Brazilian milk tree or Masseranduba. The timber is hard and durable, the fr. edible, "but strangest of all is the vegetable milk, which exudes in abundance when the bark is cut; it has about the consistence of thick cream." (Wallace, *Amazon*, ch. II.) It is used as milk, and for glue.

Mina Cerv. (*Ipomoea* L. p.p. *BH.*, *Quamoclit EP.*). Convolvulaceae (I). 2 Mexico. Cult. orn. fl.

Minaea Lojacono (*Bivonaea* p.p. *EP.*, *Thlaspi* p.p. *BH.*). Cruciferae (2). 2 Italy, Spain.

Minkelersia Mart. et Gal. Leguminosae (III. 10). 3 Mexico.

Minquartia Aubl. Olacaceae (Bignon. *BH.*). 1 Guiana.

Mint, *Mentha*, esp. *M. viridis* L.; **cat-**, *Nepeta cataria* L.; **pepper-**, *Mentha piperita* L., (Am.) *Mirabilis*.

Minuartia L. = Arenaria Rupp. p.p. (*BH.*) = Alsine p.p. (Caryo.).

Minuria DC. Compositae (3). 4 Austr.

Minuriella Tate. Compositae (3). 1 Austr.

Minurothamnus DC. Compositae (4). 1 Cape Colony.

Mionandra Griseb. Malpighiaceae (II). 2 Argentina.

Miquelia Meissn. Icacinaceae. 6 Indomal.

Mirabilis Riv. ex L. (*BH.* excl. *Oxybaphus* L'Hérit.). Nyctaginaceae (I). 25 trop. Am. At the base of the fl. is an involucre of 5 l. resembling a K; it is really the bracts of a 3-fld. dich. cyme, of which in most only the central fl. is developed. In some, however, *e.g.* *M. coccinea* Benth. et Hook. f., the invol. encloses > 1 fl. The fl.

opens in the evening and is protog. (in *M. Jalapa* L. and other sp.), with ultimate autogamy on withering. The invol. often forms a parachute on the fr. The tuberous roots of *M. Jalapa* L. (false jalap, four-o'clock, marvel of Peru) were formerly used as jalap.

Mirasolia Sch.-Bip. (*Tithonia* p.p. *EP.*, *Gymnolomia* p.p. *BH.*). Compositae (5). 2 Mexico, C. Am.

Mirbelia Sm. Leguminosae (III. 2). 16 Austr.

Mirtana Pierre (*Anamirta* p.p.). Menispermaceae. 1 Cochinchina.

Misanteca (*Miscanteca*) Cham. et Schlechtd. Lauraceae (II). 4 trop. Am., W.I. (A).

Miscanthus Anderss. Gramineae (2). 10 S. and E. As.

Miscellaneous useful products may be roughly grouped into such things as beads (*Abrus*), cork (*Quercus*), teasels (*Dipsacus*), vegetable ivory *Phytelephas*), weights (*Abrus*, &c.). *Cf.* these heads.

Mischobulbum Schlechter (*Tainia* p.p.). Orchidaceae (II. 9). 5 N.G.

Mischocarpus Blume (*Ratonia* p.p. *BH.*). Sapindaceae (I). 12 Indomal.

Mischocodon Radlk. Sapindaceae (I). 1 New Guinea.

Mischodon Thw. Euphorbiaceae (A. I. 1). 1 Ceylon, S. India.

Mischophloeus Scheff. Palmaceae (IV. 1). 1 Ternate.

Miscolobium Vog. = Dalbergia L. (Legum.).

Missiessya Gaudich. = Leucosyke Zoll. (Urtic.).

Mission grass, *Stenotaphrum*.

Mistletoe, *Viscum*, esp. *V. album* L., *Loranthaceae*, (Am.) *Phoradendron*.

Mistus, mixtus (Lat.), cross-bred between forms of a sp.

Mitchella L. Rubiaceae (II. 7). 2 N. Am. (*M. repens* L.) and Japan. Dimorphic heterostyled. The fls. are in pairs with united ovaries. Occasionally K and C also fuse and give a double ovary surmounted by a 10-lobed K and C (*cf.* Lonicera).

Mitella Tourn. ex L. Saxifragaceae (I). 10 N. Am., Japan. The inconspic. greenish fls. stand in unilateral racemes.

Mitellastra Howell (*Mitella* p.p.). Saxifragaceae (I). 1 N.W. N. Am.

Mitolepis Balf. f. Asclepiadaceae (I). 1 Socotra.

Mitophyllum Greene (*Streptanthus* p.p.). Cruciferae (I). 1 Calif.

Mitostemma Mast. Passifloraceae. 2 Brazil, Guiana.

Mitostigma Decne. in DC. Asclepiadaceae (II. 1). 6 S. Am.

Mitozus Miers (*Echites* R. Br. p.p.). Apocynaceae (II. 1). 20 S. Am.

Mitracarpum Zucc. Rubiaceae (II. 10). 15 S. Am., Afr.

Mitragyna Korth. Rubiaceae (I. 6). 12 trop. As., Afr.

Mitranthes Berg (*Calyptranthes BH.*). Myrtaceae (I). 4 trop. Am., W.I.

Mitraria Cav. Gesneriaceae (I). 1 Chili.

Mitrasacme Labill. Loganiaceae. 28 Austr., N.Z., trop. As.

Mitrastemma (*Mitrastemon*) Makino. Rafflesiaceae. 1 Japan.

Mitratheca K. Schum. Rubiaceae (I. 2). 1 trop. Afr.

Mitre-flower, *Mitraria*; **-wort** (Am.), *Mitreola*.

Mitreola L. Loganiaceae. 4 Am., Indomal., Austr.

Mitrephora Hook. f. et Thoms. Anonaceae (2). 25 trop. As.

Mitriostigma Hochst. (*Randia* p.p. *EP.*). Rubiaceae (I. 8). 3 trop. and S. Afr.

Mixed (infl.), partly racemose, partly cymose, *Aesculus*, *Betulaceae*, *Ceratostigma*, *Labiatae*, *Morina*, *Statice*, *Verbascum*.

Miyoshia Makino (*Protolirion* Ridl.). Liliaceae (1). 1 Japan.
Mnassea Vell. Inc. sed. 1 Brazil.
Mnemion Spach = Viola Tourn. (Viol.).
Mniochloa Chase (*Digitaria* p.p.). Gramineae (5). 2 Cuba.
Mniodes A. Gray. Compositae (4). 2 Peru.
Mniopsis Mart. Podostemaceae. 4 Brazil.
Mniothamnus Niedenzu (*Berzelia* p.p.). Bruniaceae. 1 S. Afr.
Moa, *Bassia latifolia* Roxb.
Moccasin flower (Am.), *Cypripedium.*
Mocinna Cerv. ex La Llave. Caricaceae. 1 Mexico.
Mocker nut (Am.), *Carya tomentosa* Nutt.
Mock-orange (Am.), *Philadelphus.*
Mocquerysia Hua. Flacourtiaceae (10). 1 trop. W. Afr.
Modecca Lam. (*Adenia* Forsk. *EP.*). Passifloraceae. 50 palaeotrop.
Modiola Moench. Malvaceae (2). 1 Am., S. Afr. (?).
Modiolastrum K. Schum. (*Modiola* Moench). Malvac. (2). 1 S. Am.
Moehringia L. (*Arenaria* p.p. *BH.*). Caryophyllaceae (I. 1). 20 N. temp.
Moenchia Ehrh. (*Cerastium* p.p. *BH.*). Caryophyllaceae (I. 1). 5 Eur., Medit.
Moerenhoutia Blume. Orchidaceae (II. 2). 2 Polynesia.
Moghania Jaume St Hil. (*Flemingia* Roxb.). Legum. (III. 10). 20 palaeotrop.
Mogiphanes Mart. (*Alternanthera* p.p. *EP.*). Amarantaceae (3). 12 trop. Am.
Mogorium Juss. = Jasminum Tourn. (Oleac.).
Mohadenium Pax. Euphorbiaceae (A. II. 8). 1 E. Afr.
Mohavea A. Gray. Scrophulariaceae (II. 3). 2 S.W. U.S.
Mohlana Mart. Phytolaccaceae. 2 S. Am., trop. Afr., Madag.
Mohria Sw. Schizaeaceae. 3 trop. and S. Afr. Sporangia on under side of ordinary l., margins turned back over them (*cf.* Pteris).
Moldenhauera Schrad. Leguminosae (II. 7). 3 Brazil, Venezuela.
Molina Ruiz et Pav. = Baccharis L. (Comp.).
Molinaea Comm. ex Juss. (*Cupania* p.p. *BH.*). Sapindaceae (1). 8 Madagascar, Mascarene Is.
Molineria Parl. (*Aira* p.p. *BH.*). Gramineae (9). 3 W. and S. Eur., As. Min.
Molineriella Rouy (*Aira* p.p.). Gramineae (9). 1 Medit.
Molinia Schrank. Gramineae (10). 5 Eur. (incl. Brit.), As. *M. caerulea* Moench, char. of wet grass moors.
Mollera O. Hoffm. Compositae (4). 2 trop. Afr.
Mollia Mart. Tiliaceae. 7 trop. S. Am.
Mollinedia Ruiz et Pav. Monimiaceae. 70 trop. Am.
Mollis (Lat.), soft, pubescent.
Mollugo L. Aizoaceae (1). 15 trop., and N. Am.
Molopanthera Turcz. Rubiaceae (I. 5). 1 E. Brazil.
Molospermum Koch. Umbelliferae (III. 2). 1 W. Medit.
Moltkia Lehm. Boraginaceae (IV. 4). 6 Himalaya to Medit.
Moluccella L. Labiatae (VI). 2 Medit.
Moly, *Allium Moly* L.
Mombin, *Spondias.*

Momisia F. G. Dietr. = Celtis Tourn. p.p. (Ulm.).
Momordica (Tourn.) L. Cucurbitaceae (3). 65 palaeotrop.
Monachanthus Lindl. = Catasetum Rich. (Orchid.).
Monachochlamys Baker. Acanthaceae (II). 1 Madag.
Monachosorum Kunze. Polypodiaceae. 2 E. warm As.
Monachyron Parl. (*Tricholaena* p.p.). Gramineae (5). 1 Cape Verde Is.
Monactinocephalus Klatt (*Inula* p.p. *EP.*). Compositae (4). 1 S. Afr.
Monactis H. B. et K. Compositae (5). 2 trop. S. Am.
Monadelphanthus Karet (*Capirona* p.p. *EP.*). Rubi. (I. 4). 1 Colombia, Peru.
Monadelphous (A), concrescent in one bundle.
Monadenia Lindl. (*Disa* p.p. *BH.*). Orchidaceae (II. 1). 12 Cape Col.
Monadenium Pax. Euphorbiaceae (A. II. 8). 20 trop. Afr.
Monandrous, with one sta.
Monanthes Haw. Crassulaceae. 10 Morocco, Canaries. Cult. orn. pl.
Monanthochloe Engelm. Gramineae (10). 2 warm Am., W.I.
Monanthotaxis Baill. Anonaceae (1). 1 Congo.
Monarda L. Labiatae (VI). 20 N. Am. Sta. 2. Fl. protandrous, visited by bees (and humming-birds in the red sp.). The l. of some are used medicinally in the form of tea (Oswego-tea).
Monardella Benth. Labiatae (VI). 25 W. N. Am.
Monarrhenus Cass. Compositae (4). 3 Madagascar, Mascarene Is.
Monarthrocarpus Merrill (*Desmodium* p.p.). Leguminosae (III. 7). 1 Phil. Is.
Monechma Hochst. (*Justicia* p.p.). Acanthaceae (IV. B). 50 trop. Afr.
Monelasum Van Tiegh. = Ouratea Aubl. (Ochn.).
Monelytrum Hack. Gramineae (3). 1 S.W. Afr.
Monenteles Labill. = Pterocaulon Ell. (Comp.).
Monerma Beauv. (*Psilurus* p.p. *BH.*). Gramineae (12). 3 warm |✻.
Moneses Salisb. (*Pyrola* p.p.). Pyrolaceae. 1 boreal and arctic.
Money wort, *Lysimachia Nummularia* L.; **Cornish - -**, *Sibthorpia europaea* L.
Moniliform, like a row of beads.
Monimia Thou. Monimiaceae. 4 Madag., Mascarenes.
Monimiaceae (*EP.*, *BH.*). Dicots. (Archichl. Ranales; Micrembryae *BH.*). 30 gen., 200 sp., chiefly S. trop., and esp. in the 'oceanic' floral regions (Madag., Austr., Polynes.). Shrubs and trees, with leathery evergr. l., often resiniferous with aromatic scent, usu. opp., exstip. Fls. sol. or in cymes., perigynous, commonly unisexual, reg.; often the two sexes differ in the hollowing of the axis. Frequently the bud opens by throwing off the outer ends of the P-leaves as a sort of lid. P 4—∞, simple, or 0; A ∞ or few, the anthers intr. or extr., opening by slits or valves; $\underline{G}$. usu. ∞, sometimes few or 1, each with 1 usu. basal erect anatr. ovule. Fr. of achenes, often ± enclosed in or borne on a fleshy recept. Embryo straight, in copious endosp. The fam. forms a connecting link between Lauraceae and the other Ranales, being closely allied on one side to L., on the other to Calycanthaceae. *Chief genera:* Hedycaria, Peumus, Tambourissa, Laurelia.
Monixus Finet (*Angraecum* p.p.). Orchid. (II. 20). 8 trop. Afr., Madag.
Monizia Lowe = Thapsia L. (*BH.*) = Melanoselinum Hoffm.

Monkey apple (W.I.), *Anona palustris* L.; **-bread,** *Adansonia digitata* L.; **-flower,** *Mimulus luteus* L.; **-pot,** *Lecythis*; **-puzzle,** *Araucaria imbricata* Cav.

Monkshood, *Aconitum.*

Monnieria L. Rutaceae (I). 2 trop. S. Am.

Monnina Ruiz et Pav. Polygalaceae. 75 Mexico to Chili. One of the two cpls. is usu. rudimentary. Fr. indehiscent.

Mono- (Gr. pref.), one; **-carpellary,** of 1 cpl.; **-carpic,** once-fruiting, *Agave*, *Corypha*, &c.; **-chasial cyme,** one in which each successive branch bears one branch upon itself, and of four types, *bostryx*, *cincinnus*, *drepanium*, *rhipidium*, *q.v.*; **-chlamydeous,** with one whorl of P; **-clinous,** hermaphrodite; **-ecious,** with ♂ and ♀ fls. on the same pl.; **-graph,** a systematic account of a group; **-petalous,** sympetalous; **-podial branching, -podium,** where the same growing point continues in a straight line from year to year, and forms branches in regular succession, *Coniferae*, *Paris*, *Pothos*; **-spermous,** one-seeded; **-symmetrical,** zygomorphic; **-thecal,** *Malvaceae*; **-tocous,** fruiting once only; **-typic** (genus), with one species.

Monocarpia Miq. Anonaceae (I). 2 trop. As.

Monocera Jack = Elaeocarpus Burm. p.p. (Elaeocarp.).

Monochaete Doell. Gramineae (II). 1 Brazil.

Monochaetum Naud. Melastomaceae (I). 30 W. trop. Am. A dimorphous. The style, at first bent down., moves slowly up till horiz.

Monochasma Maxim ex Franch. et Sav. Scroph. (III. 3). 1 Japan, China.

Monochilus Fisch. et Mey. Verbenaceae (I). 1 Brazil.

Monochilus Wall. ex Lindl. = Zeuxine Lindl. (Orchid.).

Monochlamydeae (*BH.*). One of the chief divisions of Dicots.

Monochoria C. Presl. Pontederiaceae. 4 E. Afr. to Austr.

Monococcus F. Muell. Phytolaccaceae. 1 Austr., New Caled.

Monocosmia Fenzl. Portulacaceae. 1 Chili.

Monocostus K. Schum. Zingiberaceae (II). 1 Peru.

Monocotyledones. One of the two great divisions of Angiospermae. Their classification is less difficult than that of the Dicotyledons, and a comparison should be made of the ways in which it is done in the various systems.

On the origin of M., one of the great unsolved problems in phylogeny, *cf.* Seward, *Geological History*, in *Ann. of Bot.* X, 1896, p. 205; Miss Sargant, *Theory of origin of M.*, in *do.* XVII, 1903, p. 1, and esp. review by Bancroft, in *New Phytol.* 13, 1914, p. 285.

Monodora Dun. Anonaceae (5). 10 trop. Afr., Madag. Berry with woody epicarp. Seeds of *M. Myristica* Dun. sometimes used as nutmegs.

Monogramma Schk. Polypodiaceae. 15 trop. and subtrop.

Monolena Triana. Melastomaceae (I). 4 trop. S. and C. Am. Cult. orn. fl.

Monolepis Schrad. Chenopodiaceae (A). 3 N. Am.

Monolopia DC. Compositae (6). 5 Calif.

Monomeria Lindl. Orchidaceae (II. 16). 2 Nepal, Burma.

Monoon Miq. = Polyalthia Blume p.p. (Anon.).

Monopetalanthus Harms. Leguminosae (II. 2). 2 trop. Afr.
Monophrynium K. Schum. (*Phrynium* p.p.). Marantaceae. 2 Phil. Is.
Monophyllaea R. Br. Gesneriaceae (I). 7 Malay Archipelago.
Monophyllanthe K. Schum. Marantaceae. 1 French Guiana.
Monoporandra Thw. Dipterocarpaceae. 2 Ceylon.
Monoporus A. DC. (*Ardisia* p.p.). Myrsinaceae (II). 6 Madagascar.
Monopsis Salisb. (*Lobelia* p.p. *BH.*). Campanul. (III). 9 S. Afr., Abyss.
Monopteryx Spruce. Leguminosae (III. 1). 2 Amazon valley.
Monoptilon Torr. et Gray. Compositae (3). 1 California, Utah.
Monopyle Moritz ex B. et H. f. Gesneriaceae (II). 6 C. Am. to Peru.
Monopyrena Spegazzini. Verbenaceae (I). 1 Patagonia.
Monosepalum Schlechter (*Bulbophyllum* p.p.). Orchidaceae (II. 16). 3 New Guinea.
Monosis DC. = Vernonia Schreb. p.p. (Comp.).
Monostachya Merrill. Gramineae (10). 1 Luzon.
Monostemma Turcz. (*Sarcostemma* p.p.). Asclepiad. (II. 1). 1 S. Afr.
Monotagma K. Schum. (*Ischnosiphon* p.p.). Marant. 8 trop. and S. Am.
Monotaxis Brongn. Euphorbiaceae (B. II). 7 Austr.
Monotes A. DC. Dipterocarpaceae. 15 trop. Afr.
Monothecium Hochst. Acanthaceae (IV. B). 3 palaeotrop.
Monotoca R. Br. Epacridaceae (3). 6 Austr.
Monotropa L. (incl. *Hypopitys* Dill.). Pyrolaceae. 3 N. temp. *M. Hypopitys* Walt. (yellow bird's-nest), in fir, birch and beech woods in Brit., a yellowish saprophyte with scaly l. and a short term. raceme of fls. Below the soil is found a very much branched root system, the roots being covered with a superficial mycorhiza by whose aid absorption takes place. Buds are formed adv. upon the roots and lengthen into the flowering shoots.
Monotropeae (*BH.*; *Pyrolaceae* p.p. *EP.*). Dicots. (Gamopet. Ericales). A fam. containing the saprophytic Pyrolaceae only.
Monotropsis Schwein. ex Ell. = Schweinitzia Ell. (Pyrol.).
Monoxalis Small (*Oxalis* p.p.). Oxalidaceae. 1 N. Am.
Monsonia L. Geraniaceae. 30 Afr., As. A 15 in 5 bundles.
Monstera Adans. Arac. (II). 30 trop. Am., W.I. Climbing shrubs with pinnatifid l., full of round holes. When very young the l. is entire; then the tissue between the veins ceases to grow rapidly, becomes dry and tears away, thus leaving holes between the ribs; at the edge the marginal part usually breaks, and thus the outermost hole gives rise to a notch in the l., which becomes pinnated. Beginning as a climber the pl. usu. ends as an epiph. with aerial roots to the soil. Fls. ☿. The fr. of *M. deliciosa* Liebm. is ed.
Monstrosities, marked aberrant variations suddenly appearing.
Montagnaea DC. = Montanoa Cerv. (*BH.*) = Eriocoma H. B. et K. (Comp.).
Montanoa Cerv. Compositae (5). 25 Mexico to Colombia. Cult. orn. fl.
Montanus (Lat.), mountain.
Montbretia DC. = Tritonia Ker-Gawl p.p. (Irid.).
Monterey cypress, *Cupressus macrocarpa* Hartn.
Montezuma (Moç. et Sesse ex) DC. Bombacaceae. 1 Mexico.

Montia Mich. ex L. Portulacaceae. 1 cosmop. *M. fontana* L. (blinks), an annual herb, usu. in wet places, with small cymes of fls. In bad weather or when submerged they become cleistogamic. The stalk moves like that of Claytonia, and the fr. explodes in the same way. Eaten as salad. [Am. authors incl. *Claytonia* p.p.]

Montinia Thunb. Saxifragaceae (v). 1 S. Afr.

Montiopsis O. Ktze. Portulacaceae. 1 Bolivia.

Montolivaea Reichb. f. (*Habenaria* p.p.). Orchid. (II. 1). 1 Abyssinia.

Montrichardia Crueg. Araceae (IV). 2 trop. Am., W.I.

Montrouziera Planch. ex Planch. et Triana. Guttif. (v). 3 New Caled.

Monttea C. Gay. Scrophulariaceae (II. 6). 3 Chili.

Moonia Arn. (*Chrysogonum* p.p. *BH.*). Compositae (5). 5 Indomal.

Moonseed, *Menispermum*; **-wort,** *Botrychium*.

Moorea Lemaire (*Cortaderia* p.p.). Gramineae (10). 5 S. Am.

Moorea (*Neomoorea*) Rolfe. Orchidaceae (II. 13). 1 S. Am.

Moquilea Aubl. Rosaceae (VI). 20 S. and C. Am. Some apet.

Moquinia DC. Compositae (12). 10 S. Am. Dioecious shrubs.

Mora Schomb. ex Benth. = Dimorphandra Schott (Legum.).

Moraceae (*EP.*; *Urticaceae* p.p. *BH.*). Dicots. (Archichl. Urticales). 55 gen., 800 sp., trop. and subtrop., a few temp. Most are trees or shrubs with stip. l., and with latex. [See Ficus, Cecropia, Maclura, Humulus.] Infl. cymose, usu. in the form of (pseudo-) racemes, spikes, umbels or heads (*cf.* Urticaceae, and paper there cited). Fls. unisexual. P usu. 4 or (4), persistent; A in ♂ = l. and opp. to P, bent inwards or straight in the bud, not exploding like those of Urticaceae; G in ♀ of (2) cpls. of which one is usu. aborted all but the style; ovary 1-loc. sup. to inf.; ovule 1, pend., with micropyle facing upwards, or rarely basal and erect. Fr. an achene or drupe-like; but commonly a multiple fr. arises by union of the frs. of different fls., often complicated by addition of the fleshy common recept. (see Morus, Ficus, Artocarpus). Seed with or without endosp.; embryo usu. curved. Many yield useful fruits, *e.g.* Morus, Artocarpus, Ficus, Brosimum, &c.; other important economic plants are Broussonetia (paper), Castilloa (rubber), Brosimum (milk), Ficus (caoutchouc, lac, timber, &c.), Cannabis (hemp, ganja), Humulus (hop) and others.

Classification and chief genera (after Engler):

I. *MOROIDEAE* (sta. incurved in bud; ovule apical, ana- or amphi-tr.; l. folded in bud; stipules small and not leaving an amplexicaul scar on falling): Morus, Maclura, Broussonetia, Dorstenia.

II. *ARTOCARPOIDEAE* (sta. straight; ovule as in I.; l. convolute; stipules leaving an amplexicaul scar): Artocarpus, Castilloa, Antiaris, Brosimum, Ficus.

III. *CONOCEPHALOIDEAE* (sta. straight; ovule at base or apex, orthotr. or slightly curved; l. &c., as in II.): Cecropia.

IV. *CANNABOIDEAE* (sta. short and straight; ovule apical, anatr.; achene; endosp.; herbs with free stipules): Humulus, Cannabis.

Moraea Mill. ex L. Iridaceae (II). 90 Afr., Masc. The outer integument of the ovule becomes fleshy as it ripens. Cult. orn. fl.

Morass weed (W.I.), *Ceratophyllum*.
Morelia A. Rich. Rubiaceae (I. 8). 1 trop. Afr.
Morella Lour. (*Myrica* p.p.). Myricaceae. 4 U.S.
Morenia Ruiz et Pav. (*Chamaedorea* p.p. *BH.*). Palm. (IV. 1). 5 Andes.
Moreton Bay chestnut, *Castanospermum australe* A. Cunn.
Morettia DC. Cruciferae (4). 4 Arabia to Morocco.
Morgania R. Br. Scrophulariaceae (II. 6), 4 Austr.
Moricandia DC. Cruciferae (4). 10 Medit.
Moriche, *Mauritia*.
Moriera Boiss. (*Aethionema* p.p. *EP.*). Cruciferae (2). 7 W. As.
Morierina Vieill. Rubiaceae (I. 1). 2 New Caled. (A).
Morina Tourn. ex L. Dipsacaceae. 10 E. Eur., As. Infl. like Labiatae.
Morinda L. Rubiaceae (II. 9). 45 sp. trop. Fls. in heads; the ovaries united. Several yield dye-stuffs.
Morindopsis Hook. f. Rubiaceae (I. 8). 1 Burma.
Moringa Burm. The only genus of Moringaceae. 3 Medit., India. Trees with deciduous l.; fls. in racemes, ·|·, 5-merous. P, A+A on cupule-like disc; G on gynophore, 1-loc. with 3 parietal plac. Capsule pod-like. Seeds winged, exalbum. *M. oleifera* Lam. cult. for the oil (ben-oil) obtained from the seeds.
Moringaceae (*EP.*, *BH.*). Dicotyledons (Archichl. Rhoeadales). Only genus Moringa (*q.v.*). It forms a connecting link to the Rosales (Leguminosae). *BH.* place it as an anomalous fam. at the end of Disciflorae.
Moringeae (*BH.*) = Moringaceae.
Morisia J. Gay. Cruciferae (2). 1 Sardinia, Corsica.
Morisonia L. Capparidaceae (II). 4 W.I., S. Am.
Moritzia DC. ex Meissn. Boraginaceae (IV. 4). 4 trop. S. Am.
Morkillia Rose et Painter (*Chitonia* p.p.). Zygophyllaceae. 2 Mex.
Mormodes Lindl. Orchidaceae (II. 11). 20 trop. Am. Fl. complex; the column is bent to one side, the labellum to the other. The pollinia, with their viscid disc, are violently shot out if an insect touches the articulation of anther to column. See Darwin's *Orchids* p. 208. *Cf.* Catasetum and Cycnoches, allied genera. Cult. orn. fl.
Mormolyce Fenzl. Orchidaceae (II. 18). 1 Mexico. Cult. orn. fl.
Morning glory, *Ipomoea purpurea* Roth.
Morocarpus Sieb. et Zucc. = Debregeasia Gaudich. (Urtic.).
Morongia Britton (*Schrankia* p.p.). Leguminosae (I. 3). 6 Am.
Moronobea Aubl. Guttiferae (V). 4 Guiana, N. Brazil.
Morphaea Nor. Inc. sed. Nomen.
Morphin, an alkaloid from opium.
Morphixia Ker-Gawl. = Ixia L. p.p. (Irid.).
Morphology, the comparative study of form and structure; *cf. Cactaceae, Euphorbia.*
-morphous (suff.), -shaped.
Morrenia Lindl. Asclepiadaceae (II. 1). 2 Argentina.
Mortonia A. Gray. Celastraceae. 4 N. Am.
Morus (Tourn.) L. Moraceae (I). 12 N. temp. Fls. monoec. or dioec., the ♂ in catkins, the ♀ in pseudo-spikes, wind-pollinated. Each ovary gives an achene enclosed in the P whose l. become completely

united and fleshy. The whole mass of frs. thus produced on the one spike is closely packed together, giving a multiple fr. like a blackberry (Rubus), but of very different morphological nature. The fr. (mulberry) is edible. The leaves of *M. alba* L. (white mulberry), *M. nigra* L. (black mulberry), and others are used for feeding silkworms.

Morysia Cass. = Athanasia L. (Comp.).

Moscharia Ruiz et Pav. Compositae (12). 1 Chili.

Moschatel, *Adoxa Moschatellina* L.

Moschopsis Phil. Calyceraceae. 2 Chili, Patagonia.

Moschosma Reichb. Labiatae (VII). 6 palaeotrop.

Moschoxylum A. Juss. = Trichilia P. Br. p.p. (Meli.).

Mosenodendron R. Fries. (*Hornschuchia* p.p. *EP.*). Anonac. (1). 1 Brazil.

Mosla Buch.-Ham. (*Hedeoma* p.p. *BH.*). Labiatae (VI). 8 Himal. to Japan.

Mosquitoxylum Krug. et Urb. Anacardiaceae (3). 1 Jamaica. Mosquito wood.

Moss campion, *Silene acaulis* L.; **club-, staghorn-**, *Lycopodium*; **long-, Spanish-**, *Tillandsia*; **-pink** (Am.), *Polemonium subulata* L.

Mostuea Didr. Loganiaceae. 10 trop. Afr., Madag., S. Am.

Motandra A. DC. Apocynaceae (II. 1). 5 W. Afr.

Moth flowers (class F), *Angraecum*, *Calystegia*, *Lilium*, *Lonicera*, *Oenothera*, *Paradisea*, *Silene*, *Yucca*.

Motherwellia F. Muell. (*Aralia* p.p. *EP.*). Araliaceae (2). 1 N.E. Austr.

Motherwort, *Leonurus Cardiaca L.*

Moullava Adans. Gentianaceae (inc. sed.). Nomen.

Moulmein cedar, *Cedrela Toona* Roxb.

Moultonia Balf. f. et W. W. Smith. Gesneriaceae (I). 1 Borneo.

Moultonianthus Merrill. Euphorbiaceae (A. II. 5). 1 Sarawak.

Mountain ash, *Pyrus Aucuparia* Ehrh.; **-damson** (W.I.), *Simaruba*; **-everlasting**, *Antennaria dioica* Gaertn.; **-grape** (W.I.), *Guettarda*, *Coccoloba*; **-papaw**, *Carica candamarcensis* Hook.; **-plum** (W.I.), *Ximenia*; **-sorrel** (Am.), *Oxyria*.

Mountnorrisia Szysz. (*Anneslea* Wall.). Theaceae. 2 Indomal.

Mourera Aubl. Podostemaceae. 3 Guiana, Brazil.

Mouriria Juss. Melastomaceae (III). 40 trop. Am., W.I.

Mouse-ear (Am.), *Myosotis*; **--chickweed**, *Cerastium*; **-tail**, *Myosurus minimus* L.

Moutabea Aubl. Polygalaceae. 5 trop. S. Am.

Movement, carpotropic (of fl. stalk after fert.) and **gamotropic** (before fert.), *Aristolochia*, *Cardamine*, *Coronilla*, *Delphinium*, *Oxalis*, *Primula*, *Veronica*; **flower-**, *Anagallis*, *Bellis*, *Calandrinia*, *Papaver*, *Tragopogon*; **leaf-**, *Biophytum*, *Desmodium*, *Mimosa*, *Neptunia*; **shoot-**, *cf.* Nutation; **sleep-**, *Leguminosae*, *Oxalis*, &c.; **stamen-**, *Berberis*, *Portulaca*, *Sparmannia*, and *cf.* Dichogamy, which is usu. accompanied by movement of sta.

Moya Griseb. (*Gymnosporia* p.p. *EP.*). Celastraceae. 3 Argentina.

Msuata O. Hoffm. Compositae (1). 1 Congo.

Mucilage, a gummy secretion, frequent in water pl. and on seeds of *Anthemis*, *Barleria*, *Blepharis*, *Brassica*, *Collomia*, *Crossandra*, *Linum*, *Plantago*, *Ruellia*, &c. *Cf. Ophiopogon*.

Mucro, a sharp term. point; *cf.* Leaf, fig. G, *b*.

Mucuna Adans. Leguminosae (III. 10). 35 trop. and subtrop. Some have stinging hairs on the pods. *M. pruriens* DC. is the cowage or cowitch, a var. of which is the Florida velvet bean, a useful fodder.

Mudwort, *Limosella aquatica* L.

Mudar fibre, *Calotropis gigantea* Ait.

Muehlbergella Feer (*Wahlenbergia* Schrad.). Campanul. (I. 1). 1 Cauc.

Muehlenbeckia Meissn. Polygonaceae (III. 1). 15 Austr. to S. Am. *M. platyclados* Meissn. has flat green phylloclades with transv. bands at the nodes, and green l. which drop early. Fls. polyg. or dioec.

Muehlenbergia Schreb. Gramineae (8). 80 N. Am., Andes, Japan, Himal. Some are useful fodder-grasses.

Muellera L. f. (*Coublandia* Aubl.). Leguminosae (III. 8). 2 trop. Am.

Muellerargia Cogn. Cucurbitaceae (2). 1 Timor.

Mug-wort, *Galium*, (Am.) *Artemisia*.

Muilla S. Wats. Lili. (IV). 3 Calif., Mex. Rootstock with fibrous [covering.

Mukia Arn. = Melothria L. p.p. (Cucurb.).

Mulberry, *Morus*; **-fig**, *Ficus Sycomorus* L.; **Indian -**, *Morinda citrifolia* L.

Mulgedium Cass. (*Lactuca BH.*). Compositae (13). 22 N. temp.

Mulinum Pers. Umbelliferae (I. 2). 20 char. pl. of southern Andes.

Mullein, *Verbascum*.

Multi- (Lat. pref.), many; **-farious**, many ranked; **-jugate**, with many pairs; **-parous**, pleiochasial; **-partite**, much cut; **-ple fr.**, the product of several fls., combined into one fr., *Artocarpus*, *Broussonetia*, *Ficus*, *Maclura*, *Moraceae*, *Morus*, *Platanus*.

Multiovulatae Aquaticae and **M. Terrestres** (*BH.*). The 2nd and 3rd series of Incompletae.

Mumeazalea Makino (*Azaleastrum* p.p.). Ericaceae (I. 2). 1 Japan.

Munbya Pomel (*Psoralea* p.p. *EP.*). Leguminosae (III. 6). 2 Algeria.

Mundtia (*Mundia*) H. B. et K. Polygalaceae. 1 S. Afr.

Mundulea Benth. Leguminosae (III. 6). 12 trop. Afr., Madag., Ceylon, S. Ind.

Mung (India), green gram, *Phaseolus Mungo* L.

Munroa Torr. Gramineae (10). 3 S. U.S., Argentina.

Munronia Wight. Meliaceae (III). 7 Ceylon to China.

Muntingia Plum. ex L. Elaeocarpaceae. 3 trop. S. Am., W.I.

Muralis (Lat.), growing on walls.

Muraltia Neck. Polygalaceae. 45 S. Afr.

Muretia Boiss. Umbelliferae (III. 5). 3 Medit. Pets. yellow, inrolled.

Muricaria Desv. Cruciferae (2). 1 N. Afr.

Muricate (dim. **muriculate**), rough with short firm outgrowths.

Muricauda Small (*Arum* p.p.). Araceae (VII). 1 Atl. N. Am.

Murraya Koen. ex L. Rutaceae (V). 5 Indomal. The timber is useful, and the l. are used in curries.

Murtonia Craib. Leguminosae (between III. 7 and III. 10). 1 Burma.

Musa L. Musaceae. 80 palaeotrop. Large herbs (to 10 ft.) with rhiz. and 'false' aerial stems (see fam.). The infl. springs from rhiz. and emerges at the top of the aerial 'stem.' Fls. ∞, in the axils of leathery, often reddish-coloured bracts, the fruit-forming ♀ flrs. at the base of the infl. The sepals and two ant. petals are joined into a tube, the post. petal is free; there are 5 fertile sta., except in *M. Ensete* J. F. Gmel. where the post. sta. is also fertile; the ovary is 3-loc., with ∞ anatr. ovules. Fr. a longish berry. Seeds with mealy perisperm. *M. paradisiaca* L., the plantain, with its subsp. *M. sapientum* L., the banana, is one of the most important food-plants, and is everywhere cult. in the trop. and subtrop., yielding much more food per acre than even the potato. The cult. forms are

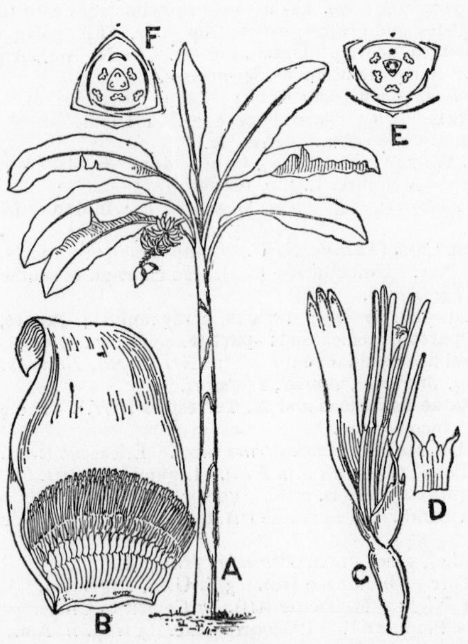

A. Banana (*Musa paradisiaca*, subsp. *sapientum*) in fruit; the fruits are seen on the lower portion of the peduncle, the upper which bore male flowers is bare, at the extreme end a few spathes remain; much reduced. B. Single spathe with a large number of flowers crowded in its axil, reduced.

C. Male flower of *M. Ensete*. The posterior median petal is on the right, the remaining five perianth-leaves are represented by the larger strap-shaped trifid limb on the left; the lateral members of the inner whorl are not represented in the incision of the limb.

D. Upper portion of perianth-limb of *M. Cavendishii* shewing five lobes, the two smaller representing the lateral members of the inner whorl.

E. Floral diagram of a bisexual flower of *Musa*.

F. Floral diagram of *Heliconia metallica*.

A, after Redouté. B, C, from *Botanical Magazine*. D, after K. Schumann.
E, F, after Eichler.

propagated entirely from the rhiz. and produce no seeds (*cf. Citrus*). About 200 different forms are in cult., and some other sp. are occasionally employed. There is a vast trade, esp. to the U.S., from C. Am., Jamaica, Canaries, &c. In Venezuela, &c. alcohol is prepared. The dried fr. are ground to form plantain-meal. The stalk of the infl. of *M. Ensete* (Abyss.) is cooked and eaten. The leaf-stalks of *M. textilis* Née (Philippines, &c.) furnish a useful fibre, known as Manila hemp or abaca. [For details of economic uses, &c., see *Kew Bulletin*, Aug. 1894.] *Cf.* Supplement.

Musaceae (*EP.*; *Scitamineae* p.p. *BH.*). Monocots. (Scitamineae). 6 gen., 150 sp. trop. They are (except Ravenala) gigantic herbs with usu. freely branching rhiz. from which the l. spring; the sheaths of the l. are rolled round one another below, and form what looks like an aerial stem, attaining in the banana some yards in height. The l. is large and oval, with a stout midrib, and parallel veins running from it to the edge; it is rolled up in bud. The edge is easily torn between the bundles, as they do not join in the same way as in a Dicot.; and so the wind and rain soon reduce the l. to a very ragged condition. Fls. in cymes or racemes with large brightly coloured bracts or spathes; usu. ☿, exc. Musa, and ·|·, but nearer to the usual type of Monocotyledonous fl. than those of other Scitamineae. P 3+3, free or united in various ways, both whorls petaloid; A 3+2, the post. sta. repres. by a std.; $\overline{G}$ (3), 3-loc., with 1—∞ ov. in each loc. Berry, caps., or schizocarp. Seed with straight embyro and mealy perisperm. Fls. rich in honey, and visited by bees and birds. Musa is an important economic genus.

Classification and genera: closely related to the other Scitamineae (joined by *BH.*), less closely to Liliiflorae and Orchids.

I. *MUSOIDEAE* (l. alt., fl. collateral, post. P leaf free): Musa.

II. *STRELITZIOIDEAE* (l. in 2 ranks, fl. in cymes, K free): Ravenala, Strelitzia, Heliconia.

III. *LOWIOIDEAE* (l. in 2 ranks, fl. in panicles from rhiz., K tubular): Lowia, Orchidantha.

Musanga C. Sm. ex R. Br. Moraceae (III). 1 Congo.

Muscadinia Small (*Vitis* p.p.). Vitaceae. 2 N. Am., W.I.

Muscari Tourn. ex Mill. Liliaceae (V). 40 Medit., Eur., As. *M. racemosum* Mill. (grape-hyacinth) in Brit. Collateral buds in axils. Upper fls. of the raceme neuter, giving extra conspicuousness to the infl. (*cf. Centaurea Cyanus*).

Muscaria Haw. = Saxifraga Tourn. p.p. (Saxifr.).

Muschleria Sp. Moore. Compositae (I). 1 Angola.

Museniopsis Coulter et Rose. Umbelliferae (III. 5). 10 Mex., W. U.S.

Musenium Nutt. (*Musineum* Rafin.). Umbell. (III. 4). 3 N. Am.

Musgravea F. Muell. Proteaceae (II). 1 Queensland.

Muskit, *cf.* Mesquite.

Musk mallow, *Malva moschata* L., *Hibiscus*; **-melon**, *Cucumis Melo* L.; **-orchis**, *Herminium Monorchis* R. Br.; **-plant**, *Mimulus moschatus* Dougl.; **-thistle**, *Carduus nutans* L.

Musquash root (Am.), *Cicuta maculata* L.

Mussaenda Burm. ex L. Rubiaceae (I. 7). 60 palaeotrop. One sepal is large, leafy, and brightly coloured, and helps to make the fl. conspicuous (*cf.* Euphorbia, Salvia).

Mussaendopsis Baill. Rubiaceae (I. 5). 1 Malaya.

Mussatia Bur. (*Bignonia* p.p.). Bignoniaceae (1). 1 Guiana.

Musschia Dum. Campanulaceae (I. 1). 2 Madeira. The capsule opens by many transv. slits between the ribs. Cult. orn. fl.

Mustard, *Brassica nigra* Koch, *Sinapis*; **hedge -,** *Sisymbrium officinale* Scop.; **treacle -,** *Erysimum cheiranthoides* L.; **- tree,** *Salvadora persica* L.

Mutabilis (Lat.), changeable (in colour, &c.).

Mutant, form arising by mutation; *cf.* de Vries, *Mutation Theory*.

Muticous, blunt.

Mutisia L. f. Compositae (12). 55 S. Am. Many climbers (a rare habit in C.) with ends of leaf-midribs prolonged into tendrils. All are shrubby with large heads of fls. Shows well chars. of § 12.

Mutumocarpon Pohl. Inc. sed. Nomen.

Myagrum (Tourn.) L. Cruciferae (2). 1 Medit., mid-Eur.

Myall (Austr.), *Acacia homalophylla* A. Cunn.

Myanthus Lindl. = Catasetum Rich. (Orchid.).

Mycelium, *Rafflesiaceae.*

Mycetia Reinw. (*Adenosacme BH.*). Rubiaceae (I. 7). 7 Indomal.

Mycorhiza, a fungus whose hyphae replace root-hairs in absorption (*cf.* Saprophytes), *Botrychium*, *Epipogum*, *Neottia*, *Orchidaceae.*

Myginda Jacq. Celastraceae. 15 trop. Am., W.I.

Myodocarpus Brongn. et Gris. Araliaceae (2). 12 New Caledonia.

Myonima Comm. ex Juss. Rubiaceae (II. 4). 5 Mauritius, Bourbon.

Myopordon Boiss. Compositae (11). 2 Persia.

Myoporaceae (*EP.*, *BH.*). Dicots. (Sympet. Tubiflorae; Lamiales *BH.*). 5 gen., 100 sp. chiefly Austr. and neighbouring Is. (1 in each of following:—Sandw. Is., E. As., Mauritius, Afr., W.I.). Most are trees or shrubs, with alt. or opp. entire exstip. l., often covered with woolly or glandular hairs, frequently very reduced in size. Fls. sol., or in cymose groups, axillary, ☿, reg., or ·|·. K (5), C (5), A 4, didynamous; anther loculi confluent; G (2), 2-loc. or by segmentation 3—10-loc., in the former case with 1—8, in the latter with 1, pend. anatr. ovule in each loc. Drupe. Endosperm. *Chief genera:* Pholidia, Myoporum.

Myoporineae (*BH.*) = Myoporaceae.

Myoporum Banks et Soland. Myoporaceae. 25 Austr., E. As., Sandw. Is., Mauritius. *M. laetum* Forst. f. (N.Z.) yields useful timber.

Myoschilos Ruiz et Pav. Santalaceae. 1 Chili.

Myoseris Link = Pterotheca Cass. (Comp.).

Myosotidium Hook. Boraginaceae (IV. 1). 1 sp. Chatham Is.

Myosotis L. Boraginaceae (IV. 4). 35 sp. |✻ temp. 8 in Brit. (scorpion-grass, forget-me-not). The corolla-mouth is nearly closed by scales, and in some there is a coloured ring at the entrance forming a honey guide (see Life of Sprengel, in *Nat. Science*, Apr. 1893). The colour of the C changes as it grows older (see fam.).

Myosurandra Baill. Hamamelidaceae. 1 Madagascar.

Myosurus L. Ranunculaceae (3). 7 temp. *M. minimus* L. (mousetail) in Brit. Recept. much elongated.

Myracrodruon Allem. = Astronium Jacq. p.p. (Anac.). [Ov. ∞ per loc.
Myrceugenia Berg. (*Myrtus* p.p. *BH.*). Myrt. (I). 15 temp. S. Am.
Myrcia DC. ex Guill. Myrt. (I). 500 trop. S. Am., W.I. Ov. 2 per
Myrcialeucas Roj. Myrt. (I). 1 Arg. [loc. K free or slightly united.
Myrcianthes Berg. = Myrtus L. (*BH.*) = Eugenia p.p.
Myrciaria Berg. (*Eugenia* p.p. *BH.*). Myrt. (I). 65 trop. S. Am., W.I. Like Eugenia, but ov. 2 per loc. Fr. ed. (jaboticabá, &c.).
Myriactis Less. Comp. (3). 4 Phil. Is. to Persia. No pappus.
Myrialepis Becc. (*Plectocomiopsis* p.p.). Palm. (III. 2). 1 Perak.
Myrianthemum Gilg. Melastom. (I). 1 W. trop. Afr.
Myrianthus Beauv. Mor. (III). 12 trop. Afr.
Myriaspora DC. Melastom. (I). 2 trop. S. Am. Cauliforal. Calyptra.
Myrica L. The only gen. of **Myricaceae** (*EP.*, *BH.*). Dicots. (Archichl. Myricales; Unisexuales *BH.*; pp. xi, liv). 45 temp. and subtrop. with exstip. usu. simple l., and fls. in short catkins, achlam. The ♂ has usu. 2 bracteoles and 4 (2—16) sta.; the ♀ 2—4 bracteoles and (2) cpls. with 1 erect orthotr. ov. Drupe or nut, the exocarp secreting wax. Exalb. *M. Gale* L. (sweet gale, bog myrtle) in bogs in Brit.; l. with resinous smell. *M. cerifera* L. (N. Am., wax-myrtle, bay-berry), &c. are sources of wax; the fr. are boiled.
Myricales, the 5th order of Dicots. Archichl.; p. x.
Myricaria Desv. Tamaric. 10 N. temp. |✱. (A) obdipl. G (3).
Myriocarpa Benth. Urtic. (3). 8 trop. Am. Fls. ∞, in catkins.
Myriocephalus Benth. Comp. (4). 8 temp. Austr. Head 1-fld., cpd.
Myrioneuron R. Br. Rubi. (I. 7). 8 E. Indomal. Heads nodding.
Myriophyllum Ponted. ex L. Haloragid. 40 cosmop.; 2 in Brit. (water milfoil). Submerged water pl. with usu. whorled much divided l., borne on shoots that spring from the rhiz.-like creeping stems. Land forms occasionally produced in some. Infl. above water; fls. wind-fert. Hibernation by winter buds as in Utricularia. *Cf.* Arber,
Myriopteron Griff. Asclep. (I). 1 E. Indomal. [*Water Pl.*
Myriostachya Hook. f. Gramin. (10). 1 Indomal. [pappus.
Myripnois Bunge. Comp. (12). 3 N. China. Dioec. Fr. glandular with
Myristica L. Myristic. 85 palaeotrop. Trees with evergr. l. Berry splits by both sutures, disclosing a large seed—nutmeg—with a branched red aril—mace—around it. The ordinary nutmeg is the seed of *M. fragrans* Houtt. (*moschata* Thunb.), of the Moluccas.
Myristicaceae (*EP.*, *BH.*). Dicots. (Archichl. Ranales; Micrembryae *BH.*; pp. xix, liii). 18/275 trop., esp. As. ♄ with simple evergr. exstip. l., with oil cells, and racemes of dioec. reg. fls., usu. 3-merous. P (3), simple (*cf.* Monodora); A (3—18), extr.; $\underline{G}$ 1, with 1 basal anatr. ov. Fleshy dehisc. fr. Aril. Ruminate endosp. Oils and spices are obtained from Myristica, &c. *Chief genera:* Myristica,
Myrmechis Blume. Orchid. (II. 2). 3 Java to Japan. [Virola.
Myrmecodia Jack. Rubi. (II. 5). 25 E. Indomal. Epiph. with leafy stems. The base forms a large tuber, fastened by adv. r., composed of a mass of tissue, chiefly cork, penetrated by numerous communicating galleries and chambers, inhabited by ants. In germin. the hypocotyl swells into a small tuber, in which a phellogen appears, forming cork on the inner side; other phellogens appear later, increasing the number of passages, for the cork falls out. The

pl. may be called myrmecophilous, but it is doubtful if the ants perform any service to it. *Cf.* Acacia, and Myrmecophily. [trop. S. Am.

Myrmecophila Rolfe (*Schomburgkia* p.p.). Orchid. (II. 6). 7 C. and

Myrmecophily, symbiosis with ants; *cf.* Acacia, and Bombacaceae, Cecropia, Clerodendron, Cuviera, Duroia, Humboldtia, Hydnophytum, Korthalsia, Macaranga, Maieta, Myrmecodia, Nauclea, Rubiaceae, Triplaris. Ridley in *Ann. Bot.* 24, p. 457.

Myrmedoma Becc. Rubi. (II. 5). 1 New Guinea. Epiph.

Myrmephytum Becc. Rubi. (II. 5). 2 Celebes, Phil. Is. Epiph.

Myrmidone Mart. Melastom. (I). 3 trop. S. Am. Heterophyllous.

Myrobalans (gall-nuts), astringent fr. used for tanning and in medicine; **emblic-**, *Phyllanthus Emblica* L.; **chebulic-**, *Terminalia Chebula*

Myrobalanus Gaertn. = Terminalia L. p.p. (Combret.). [Retz.

Myrocarpus Allem. Legum. (III. 1). 3 S. Braz., Paraguay. L. translucent-dotted. Yield a balsam like balsam of Peru.

Myrodendron Spreng. = Humiria Aubl. (Humir.). [Am., W.I.

Myrodia Sw. (*Quararibea* p.p. *EP.*). Bombac. (Stercul. *BH.*). 8 trop.

Myrosma L. f. Marant. 8 S. and C. Am. [Fr. winged, indeh.

Myrospermum Jacq. Legum. (III. 1). 1 trop. Am., W.I. L. dotted.

Myrothamnaceae (*EP.*, *Hamamelid.* p.p. *BH.*). Dicots. (Archichl. Rosales; pp. xxiii, li). Only genus **Myrothamnus** Welw., 2 Afr., Madag. Xero. shrubs with opp. stip. l. and spikes of dioec. reg. achlam. fls.; ♂ of 4—8 sta. free or united; ♀ of $\underline{G}$ (4—3), multiloc. with short thick style and flattened lobed stigma; ovules ∞ anatr. Septic. caps. Endosp.

Myroxylon J. et G. Forst. (*Xylosma* Forst. f.). Flacourt. (4). 60 warm, exc. Afr. Usu. dioec. Often axillary thorns. Seps. ± united.

Myroxylon L. f. (*Toluifera* L.). Legum. (III. 1). 8 trop. S. Am. L. translucent-dotted. Fr. winged, indeh. *M. Pereirae* Klotzsch yields the medicinal balsam of Peru, *M. toluifera* H. B. et K. the

Myrrh, *Commiphora*, *Myrrhis*. [balsam of Tolu.

Myrrha Mitch. Umbell. (inc. sed). Nomen.

Myrrhidendron Coulter et Rose. Umbell. (III. 6). 1 Costa Rica.

Myrrhidium DC., Eckl. et Zeyh. = Pelargonium L'Herit. p.p. (Geran.).

Myrrhinium Schott. Myrt. (I). 3 warm S. Am. A 4—8. Ed. fr.

Myrrhis (Tourn.) L. Umbell. (III. 2). 2 Eur., W. As., Chile. *M. odorata* Scop. (Brit., sweet cicely, myrrh, pot-herb). Ribs 3-angled.

Myrsinaceae (*EP.*, *BH.* incl. *Theophrast.*). Dicots. (Sympet. Primulales; pp. xli, lii). 35/1000, trop. and subtrop., S. Afr., N.Z. ♄ with alt. exstip. l., often rosetted; usu. leathery, entire, with resin-passages usu. visible to naked eye or lens. Fls. in racemose infls., with 2 bracteoles, ☿ or unisexual, reg., 4—5-merous. K (5) or 5; C (5); A 5, epipet., opp. to pets., intr., the stds. in ♀ fl. often almost as large as sta., stds. rarely present in ♂; $\underline{G}$, rarely semi-inf., 1-loc. plac. basal or free-central with ∞ or rarely few ov., ½-anatr. or ½-campylotr. sunk in plac. tissue, style and stigma simple. Most ov. usu. abort as fr. ripens. Drupe or berry; embryo straight or slightly curved, endosp. fleshy or horny.

Classification and chief genera (after Mez): close to Primul. (distinguished by habit and fr.), Sapot. (chambered ovary, latex), Theophrast. (extr. anther, usu. stds.). [Monograph in *Pfl. R.* 1901.]

I. *MAESOIDEAE* (G $\frac{1}{2}$-inf.; fr. many-seeded): Maesa (only gen.).
II. *MYRSINOIDEAE* (G; fr. 1-seeded)
1. *Ardisieae* (ov. usu. many in many rows, rarely few): Aegiceras (anther-loc. transv. septate), Ardisia (sta. free).
2. *Myrsineae* (ov. usu. few, in one row): (infl. elongated, loose) Oncostemon, Embelia (polypet.); (infl. dense, short-stalked, ± umbellate) Rapanea, &c.

Myrsine L. (excl. *Rapanea*). Myrsin. (II. 2). 7 Azores, Afr. to China.
Myrsiphyllum Willd. = Asparagus Tourn. p.p. (Lili.).
Myrstiphyllum P. Br. = Psychotria L. p.p. (Rubi.).
Myrtaceae (*EP.*; *BH.* incl. *Lecythid.*). Dicots. (Archichl. Myrtiflorae; Myrtales *BH.*; pp. xxxix, lii). 90/2800 warm; chief centres Austr. (§ II) and trop. Am. (§ I). Trees and shrubs, varying from small creepers to the giant Eucalyptus; oil glands in l., bicollateral bundles, phloem in pith. L. usu. opp., exstip., evergr., usu. entire. Fls usu. in cymes, ☿, reg., perig. or epig., usu. with 2 bracteoles at base; Recept. ± hollow and united to G; in § II. 1 the union is not very complete, but in the rest it is so, and the fl. is epig. K 4—5 or (4—5), sometimes thrown off unopened as a lid, usu. quincuncial with second l. post.; C 4—5, imbr., pets. often nearly circular; A ∞, free or in bundles, rarely definite, usu. bent inwards in bud, connective often with glands above; $\overline{G}$ (or $\frac{1}{2}$-inf.) ∞—1-loc. with usu. 2—∞ anatr. or campylotr. ov. in each, style (usu. long) and stigma simple, plac. usu. axile, rarely parietal. Berry, drupe, caps., or nut; no endosp. Wood usu. hard; several yield useful timber. Eucalyptus gives timber, kino, oil, Eugenia cloves, &c. Many have ed. fr.

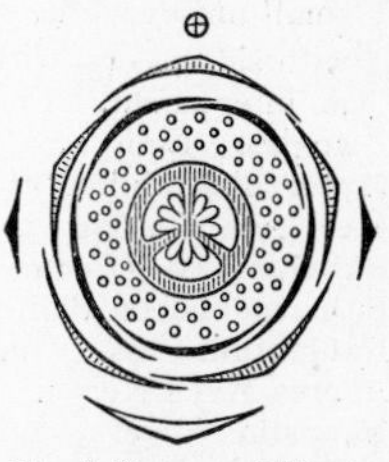
Floral diagram of *Myrtus communis* (after Eichler).

Classification and chief genera: distinguished from all other Myrtiflorae by oil glands.
I. *MYRTOIDEAE* (berry, rarely drupe; l. always opp.):
1. *Myrteae:* Myrtus, Psidium, Pimenta, Myrcia, Calyptranthes, Eugenia, Myrciaria, Jambosa, Syzygium.
II. *LEPTOSPERMOIDEAE* (dry fr.; l. opp. or alt.):
1. *Leptospermeae* (G multiloc., at least when yonng): [loculic. caps., embryo straight, anth. versatile] Metrosideros (pets. with narrow base, A free, plac. central, many seeds), Tristania (do.; A in bundles opp. pets.), Eucalyptus (pets. with broad base, united, falling as a cap; K-teeth inconspic. or 0), Leptospermum, Callistemon (sta. much exceeding C, free, K deciduous), Melaleuca (do. but sta. in bundles opp. pets., ov. ∞ per loc.), Baeckea.
2. *Chamaelaucieae* (1-loc.; 1-seeded nut): Calycothrix, Chamaelaucium, Darwinia, Verticordia.

Myrtales (*BH.*), p. li. **Myrtiflorae** (*EP.*), 29th order, Archichl., p. xxxvi.
Myrtella F. Muell. (*Baeckea* p.p. *EP.*). Myrt. (II. 1). 2 New Guinea.
Myrteola Berg. (*Myrtus* p.p. *BH.*). Myrt. (I). 8 S. Am. Ed. fr.
Myrtillocactus Console (*Cereus* p.p.). Cact. (III. 1). 4 Mex., Guatem.

Myrtle, *Myrtus communis* L.; **bog -**, *Myrica Gale* L.; **- scrub**, (Austr.) *Banksia*, (Tasm.) *Fagus* (*Nothofagus*) *Cunninghamii* Hook.; **- tree**, *Nothofagus*; **wax -**, *Myrica cerifera* L.; **willow -**, *Agonis*.
Myrtopsis Engl. Rutaceae (1). 1 New Caledonia.
Myrtopsis O. Hoffm. = Eugenia L. p.p. (Myrt.).
Myrtus (Tourn.) L. (*BH.* incl. *Ugni* Turcz.). Myrtaceae (1). 70 trop. and subtrop. *M. communis* L. (myrtle, W. As.) long nat. in Eur. Cult. orn. shrubs.
Mystacidium Lindl. Orchidaceae (II. 20). 35 Afr. Cult. orn. fl.
Mystropetalon Harv. Balanophoraceae. 2 S. Afr.
Mystroxylon Eckl. et Zeyh. (*Elaeodendron* Jacq.). Celastraceae. 15 trop. and S. Afr., Madag.
Myxopyrum Blume. Oleaceae. 7 Indomal. Twiners.
Myzodendraceae (*EP.*; *Santalaceae* p.p. *BH.*). Dicots. (Archichl. Santalales). Only genus Myzodendron.
Myzodendron (Banks) Soland. Myzodendraceae. 10 Chili, Patagonia. Semi-parasitic green shrubs, like Loranthaceae, with alt. l. and very small unisexual fls. ♂ naked, of 2- 3- 1 sta.; ♀ with P (?) concrescent with sides, $\overline{G}$ (3) with 3 stigmas and axile plac., bearing 3 ovules with no integument. Fr. with 3 angles or wings and feather-like hairs in angles. Endosp.
Myzorrhiza Phil. (*Aphyllon* Mitch.). Orobanchaceae. 10 Am.
Na (Ceylon), *Mesua ferrea* L.
Nabalus Cass. (*Prenanthes* Vaill.). Compositae (13). 5 N. Am.
Nabiasodendron Pitard (*Gordonia* p.p.). Theaceae. 9 Indomal.
Nablonium Cass. Compositae (4). 1 Tasmania.
Nacrea Aven Nelson. Compositae (4). 1 Wyoming.
Naegelia Regel (*Smithiantha EP.*). Gesneriaceae (II). 6 Mexico. They form subterranean runners, covered with scaly l. Cult. orn. fl.
Nageia Gaertn. = Podocarpus L'Hérit. (Conif.).
Nagelia Lindl. (*Cotoneaster* p.p. *BH.*). Rosaceae (II). 2 Mexico.
Naiadaceae (*EP.*; *Naiadeae BH.* incl. *Potamogetonaceae*, *Naiadaceae*, *Aponogetonaceae*, *Juncaginaceae*). Monocot. (Helobieae). Only genus Najas (*q.v.*).
Naiadeae (*BH.*; *cf. Naiadaceea*). Monocots. (Apocarpae). 16 gen., 150 sp. cosmop. Water or marsh herbs, with rad., alt., opp., or whorled l. and small fls. in racemose infl. ☿ or unisexual. P 0 or 1—6, A 1—6, rarely connate, G 1—6, rarely slightly connate, style short, ov. 2—∞, very rarely 1, micropyle downwards. Dry fr.: seed exalbum. For genera cf. fams. mentioned above.
Naiocrene Rydberg (*Claytonia* p.p.). Portulaceae. 1 N. Am.
Najas L. Naiadaceae. 35 cosmop.; 2 in Brit. Freshwater annuals, submerged, with slender stems and opp. usu. toothed linear l. Fls. unisexual; ♂ a single anther, term. on the axis and 1- or 4-loc. enclosed in two sheathing Ps. ♀ fl. $\underline{G}$ 1 naked or surrounded by a perianth-like organ. Pollination occurs under water as in Zostera, but the pollen is spherical. Ovule 1, anatr. term. on the axis. Embryo straight; no endosp. *Cf.* Arber, *Water Plants*.
Naked (fl.), without P.
Nama L. Hydrophyllaceae. 40 Am., Hawaiian Is.
Namation Brand (*Nama* p.p.). Scrophulariaceae (II. 6). 1 Mexico.

Namatium (Cl.), a brook formation.
Nananthera DC. Compositae (7). 1 Corsica.
Nandina Thunb. Berberidaceae. 1, *N. domestica* Thunb., China, Japan. P (incl. 2 whorls of honey l.) in 9 whorls, showing more petaloid structure as they near the centre. Cult. orn. fl.
Nannoglottis Maxim. Compositae (8). 1 N. China.
Nannorrhops H. Wendl. Palmaceae (I. 2). 1 N.W. India, Persia.
Nanny berry, *Viburnum*.
Nanochilus K. Schum. (*Hedychium* p.p.). Zingiber. (1). 2 Mal. Arch.
Nanocnide Blume. Urticaceae (1). 2 Japan, Corea.
Nanodea Banks. Santalaceae. 1 S. temp. S. Am.
Nanolirion Benth. Liliaceae (III). 1 S. Afr.
Nanophyton Less. Chenopodiaceae (B). 1 W. As.
Nanostelma Baill. Asclepiadaceae (II. 1). 1 Congo.
Nanothamnus T. Thoms. Compositae (4). 1 Bombay.
Nanus (Lat.), dwarf.
Napaea L. Malvaceae (2). 1 N. Am. Dioec. Fibre from bark.
Napeanthus Gardn. Gesneriaceae (1). 8 trop. Am.
Napiform, turnip-shaped.
Napoleona Beauv. Lecythidaceae. 12 W. trop. Afr. The fl. resembles that of Passiflora, owing to the corona of stds. G 5—20-loc. Berry.
Naravelia DC. (*Clematis* p.p.). Ranunculaceae (3). 4 Indomal.
Narcissus (Tourn.) L. Amaryllidaceae (1). 40 Eur., Medit., As. Several cult. orn. fl., *e.g.* *N. Pseudo-Narcissus* L., the daffodil, *N. poeticus* L., the poet's Narcissus, *N. Jonquilla* L., the jonquil, *N. Tazetta* L., and others. Corona well developed, free from the A (see fam.).
Narcotics, sleep-producing drugs, *Cannabis*, *Hyoscyamus*, *Papaver*.
Nard grass, *Nardus stricta* L.
Nardoo, *Marsilea*.
Nardophyllum Hook. et Arn. Compositae (3). 10 Andes.
Nardosmia Cass. = Petasites Tourn. (Comp.).
Nardostachys DC. Valerianaceae. 2 Himal. *N. Jatamansi* DC., the spikenard, has very fragrant rhizomes.
Narduroides Rouy (*Nardurus* p.p.). Gramineae (10). 1 France.
Nardurus Reichb. = Festuca Tourn. p.p. (Gram.). 6 W. Eur. to India.
Nardus Linn. Gramineae (12). 1 Eur., W. As., *N. stricta* L., the nard or mat-grass, common on the drier grass moors in Brit. Infl. markedly unilateral (unusu. in § 12).
Naregamia Wight et Arn. Meliaceae (III). 1 India.
Nargedia Bedd. Rubiaceae (I. 8). 1 Ceylon.
Narras, *Acanthosicyos horrida* Welw.
Narthecium Moehr. Liliaceae (1). 4 N. temp.; *N. ossifragum* Huds. (bog-asphodel), in Brit. It has a sympodial rhiz. and isobil. l. The fl. is conspicuous, but contains no honey (class Po).
Narthex Falc. = Ferula Tourn. [*N. asafoetida* Falc. = F. Narthex].
Narvalina Cass. Compositae (5). 2 W.I., S. Am.
Naseberry, *Achras Sapota* L.
Nashia Millspaugh. Verbenaceae (1). 3 W.I. L. used as tea.
Nasonia Lindl. (*Centropetalum BH.*). Orchid. (II. 20). 3 Colombia.
Nassauvia Comm. ex Juss. Compositae (12). 50 Andes.
Nassella E. Desv. (*Oryzopsis* p.p. *BH.*). Gramineae (8). 10 Andes.

Nasturtium L. Cruciferae (2). 50 cosmop.; 4 in Brit., including *N. officinale* R. Br., the water-cress. In the perennial sp. buds arise at the base of the year's shoot, and take root while still attached to the parent. The adv. roots are said to arise exogenously.
Nasturtium (of gardens), *Tropaeolum*.
Nastus Dioscorides ex Lunell. Gramineae (5). 1 N. Am.
Nastus Juss. Gramineae (13). 3 Mascarene Is.
Natans (Lat.), swimming (under water).
Nathusia Hochst. (*Schrebera* Roxb.). Oleaceae. 5 Afr., India.
Natsiatopsis S. Kurz. Icacinaceae. 1 Burma.
Natsiatum Buch.-Ham. Icacinaceae. 1 Himalaya.
Natural history, ecology; **-order**, a group of several allied families, *e.g. Ranales, Rosales*; **-selection**, survival of the fittest; **-system**, that which tries to classify plants according to their relationships.
Naturalisation, establishment in a new country; **naturalised weeds**, *Ageratum*, *Cactaceae*, *Cynara*, *Eichhornia*, *Elodea*, *Galinsoga*, *Lactuca*, *Mimosa*, *Opuntia*, *Tithonia*, *Xanthium*.
Nauclea L. Rubiaceae (I. 6). 50 trop. As., Polynes. Fls. in spherical heads. *N. lanceolata* Blume (*N. purpurea* Roxb.) has hollow swollen portions of stem, below infls., inhabited by ants (*cf.* Acacia).
Naudinia Planch. et Lind. Rutaceae (I). 1 Colombia. (C).
Naudiniella Krasser (*Astronia* p.p.). Melastom. (II). 6 Polyn.
Naumannia Warb. (*Riedelia* p.p. *EP.*). Zingiberaceae (I). 1 N.G.
Naumburgia Moench (*Lysimachia* p.p. *BH.*). Primul. 1 N. temp.
Nautilocalyx Linden = Episcia Mart. p.p. (Gesn.).
Nautonia Decne. Asclepiadaceae (II. 1). 1 S. Brazil.
Navarretia Ruiz et Pav. (*Gilia* p.p.). Polemoniaceae. 50 Am., esp. N.
Navia Schult. f. (*Dyckia* p.p. *B.H.*). Bromeliaceae (2). 2 trop. S. Am.
Navicular, boat-shaped.
Naxiandra Krasser. Melastomaceae (III). 4 Malaya.
Neactelis Rafin. Compositae (inc. sed.). 1 N. Am.
Nealchornea Huber. Euphorbiaceae (A. II. 2). 1 Upper Amazon.
Nearctic, American arctic.
Nebelia Neck. (*Raspalia* Brongn. *EP.*). Bruniaceae. 6 S. Afr.
Necepsia Prain. Euphorbiaceae (A. II. 2). 1 trop. Afr.
Neckia Korth. Ochnaceae (Violaceae *BH.*). 6 Indomal.
Neck-lace tree, *Ormosia*; **-weed** (Am.), *Veronica peregrina* L.
Nectandra Roland. Lauraceae (I). 70 trop. and S. subtrop. Am. *N. Rodiaei* Hook. (greenheart) and others good timber.
Nectarine, *Prunus persica* Stokes, var.
Nectaripetalum Pohl. Inc. sed. Nomen.
Nectaropetalum Engl. Linaceae. 2 trop. Afr.
Nectary, a honey-secreting gland, usu. floral, *Aconitum*, *Alisma*, *Allium*, *Aquilegia*, *Berberidaceae*, *Borago*, *Campanulaceae*, *Compositae*, *Delphinium*, *Eranthis*, *Labiatae*, *Leguminosae*, *Marcgravia*, *Nigella*, *Norantea*, *Ranunculaceae*, *Tilia*, sometimes **extra-floral**, *Aleurites*, *Convolvulaceae*, *Prunus*, *Triumfetta*, *Turneraceae*, *Viola*; **sham-**, *Lopezia*, *Parnassia*.
Nectouxia H. B. et K. Solanaceae (2). 1 Mexico.
Neea Ruiz et Pav. Nyctaginaceae. 30 trop. S. Am., W.I. The l. o *N. theifera* Oerst. (caparrosa) are used as tea, and yield a black dye

Needhamia R. Br. Epacridaceae (3). 1 W. Austr.
Needle, Adam's, *Yucca*; **double -.** *Coniferae, Sciadopitys*; **- gorse,** *Genista*; **- leaf,** *Coniferae, Xerophytes.*
Neem, nim, *Melia Azadirachta* L. (*Azadirachta indica* A. Juss.).
Neeragrostis Bush (*Poa* p.p.). Gramineae (10). 2 Am.
Neesia Blume. Bombacaceae. 7 Malaya.
Negretia Ruiz et Pav. = Mucuna Adans. (Legum.).
Negria Chiov. = Joannegria Chiov. (Gram.).
Negria F. Muell. Gesneriaceae (1). 1 Lord Howe I.
Negundo Moench (*Acer* p.p. *EP.*, *q.v.*). Aceraceae. 4 N. temp.
Neillia D. Don. Rosaceae (I. 1). 3 Himal., S. China.
Neja D. Don = Hysterionica Willd. (Comp.).
Nelitris Spreng. = Decaspermum Forst. (Myrt.).
Nelsia Schinz (*Sericocoma* p.p.). Amarantaceae (2). 1 S. trop. Afr.
Nelsonia R. Br. Acanthaceae (1). 1 palaeotrop.
Nelumbium Juss. Nymphaeaceae (1). 2, *N. luteum* Willd., Pennsylvania to Colombia, and *N. speciosum* Willd. (*N. nuciferum* Gaertn.), As. and N.E. Austr. The latter sometimes supposed to be the sacred Lotus, no longer found in the Nile, is sacred in India, Tibet, China, and was introduced to Egypt about 500 B.C. (*cf.* Nymphaea). Both are marsh plants; the fls., which are very large and handsome, and the big peltate slightly hairy l., stand above the water and do not float upon it. The rhiz. bears 'triads' of leaves; after a long internode comes a scaly-l. on the lower side, then one on the upper side, immediately followed by a foliage-l. with ochreate stipule, then a long internode again, and so on. This peculiar leaf-arrangement is quite unique. From the axil of the second scale-l. springs the fl., from that of the foliage-l. a branch. The fl. has no bracteoles. The first P-leaf is ant., the second post., then follow 2 lat.; these 4 are sometimes regarded as a K. They are followed by numerous petals and sta., acyclically arranged. In the centre of the fl. stands the obconical G, a large number of cpls. embedded separately in the top of the swollen recept. Each contains 1 pend. ovule. The recept. becomes dry and very light, and the achenes separate from it, as the fruit ripens. It breaks off bodily from the stalk and floats about until decay sets free the fruits, which sink to the bottom of the pond. There is no endosp. or perisperm. The seeds of *N. speciosum* are used as food in Cashmere, &c.
Nelumbo (Tourn.) Adans. = Nelumbium Juss. (Nymph.).
Nemacaulis Nutt. Polygonaceae (I. 1). 1 California.
Nemacladus Nutt. Campanulaceae (II). 3 Calif., Mexico.
Nemastylis Nutt. Iridaceae (II). 10 Am. Cult. orn. fl.
Nematanthera Miq. (*Piper* p.p. *BH.*). Piperaceae. 2 Guiana.
Nematanthus Schrad. Gesneriaceae (1). 6 Brazil.
Nematolepis Turcz. Rutaceae (1). 2 W. Austr.
Nematopogon Bureau et K. Schum. (*Digomphia* p.p.). Bignoniaceae (2). 2 Brazil, Guiana.
Nematosciadium H. Wolff. Umbelliferae (III. 4). 1 Mexico.
Nematostylis Hook. f. Rubiaceae (II. 1). 1 Madag.
Nemesia Vent. Scrophulariaceae (II. 3). 50 S. Afr. Cult. orn. fl.
Nemexia Rafin. (*Smilax* p.p.). Liliaceae (XI). 10 U.S.

Nemopanthus Rafin. Aquifoliaceae. 1 N.E. Am.
Nemophila Nutt. Hydrophyllaceae. 30 N. Am., often cult. orn. fl.
Nemoralis (Lat.), living in woods.
Nemuaron Baill. Monimiaceae. 2 New Caledonia.
Nenax Gaertn. Rubiaceae (II. 7). 6 S. Afr.
Nenga H. Wendl. et Drude. Palmaceae (IV. 1). 12 Malaya.
Nengella Becc. (*Nenga* p.p. *EP*.). Palmaceae (IV. 1). 2 Malaya.
Nenuphar Link = Nuphar Sm. (Nymph.).
Neo- (Gr. pref.), new.
Neobaronia Baker (*Phylloxylon* Baill.). Leguminosae (III. 8). 2 Madagascar. Timber hard.
Neobeckia Greene (*Nasturtium* p.p.). Cruciferae (2). 1 N. Am.
Neobenthamia Rolfe. Orchidaceae (II. 5). 1 Zanzibar.
Neobertiera Wernham. Rubiaceae (I. 8). 1 Brit. Guiana.
Neobiondia Pampan. Phytolaccaceae. 1 China.
Neobolusia Schlechter (*Brachycorythis* p.p.). Orchidaceae (II. 1). 1 S. Afr.
Neoboutonia Muell.-Arg. Euphorbiaceae (A. II. 2). 4 trop. Afr.
Neobrittonia Hochr. (*Sida* p.p.). Malvaceae (2). 1 Mexico.
Neobuchia Urban. Bombacaceae. 1 W.I.
Neocastela Small (*Castela* p.p.). Simarubaceae. 1 S. Domingo.
Neocentema Schinz (*Centema* p.p.). Amarantaceae (2). 2 E. Afr.
Neocheiropteris Christ. Polypodiaceae. 1 Yunnan.
Neochevaliera A. Chevalier et Beille. Euph. (A. I. 1). 1 Congo.
Neoclia Nor. Inc. sed. Nomen.
Neocogniauxia Schlechter. Orchidaceae (II. 6). 2 W.I.
Neocollettia Hemsl. Leguminosae (III. 7). 1 Burma.
Neocouma Pierre (*Tabernaemontana* p.p.). Apocyn. (I. 1). 1 Brazil.
Neocracca O. Ktze. (*Cracca* p.p.). Leguminosae (III. 6). 1 Bolivia.
Neodeutzia Small (*Deutzia* p.p.). Saxifragaceae (III). 2 Mexico.
Neodielsia Harms. Leguminosae (III. 6). 1 China.
Neodonnellia Rose (*Donnellia* Clarke). Commelinaceae. 1 C. Am.
Neodregia C. H. Wright. Liliaceae (I). 1 S. Afr.
Neodryas Reichb. f. Orchidaceae (II. 19). 2 trop. S. Am.
Neodypsis Baill. Palmaceae (IV. 1). 2 Madag.
Neoglaziovia Mez (*Dyckia* p.p.). Bromeliaceae (4). 2 Brazil.
Neogoetzea Pax. Euphorbiaceae (A. I. 2). 1 trop. Afr.
Neogoezea Hemsl. Umbelliferae (III. 4). 3 Mexico.
Neogyna Reichb. f. (*Coelogyne* p.p. *BH*.). Orchid. (II. 3). 1 Himal.
Neohallia Hemsl. Acanthaceae (IV. B). 1 S. Mexico.
Neojatropha Pax (*Jatropha* p.p.). Euphorb. (A. II. 3). 2 E. trop. Afr.
Neojobertia Baill. Bignoniaceae (1). 1 Piauhy to Pernambuco.
Neojunghuhnia Koorders. Ericaceae (III. 2). 1 New Guinea.
Neokoehleria Schlechter. Orchidaceae (II. 19). 2 Peru.
Neolacis Wedd. in DC. = Apinagia Tul. (Podost.).
Neolauchea Kränzl. Orchidaceae (II. 6). 1, habitat?
Neolehmannia Kränzl. Orchidaceae (II. 6). 2 Ecuador, Peru.
Neolindenia Baill. (*Louteridium* p.p. *EP*.). Acanth. (IV. A). 1 Mex.
Neolindleya Kränzl. (*Platanthera* p.p.). Orchid. (II. 1). 1 N.E. As.
Neolitsea Merrill (*Litsea* p.p.). Lauraceae (1). 10 Indomal.
Neoluederitzia Schinz. Zygophyllaceae. 1 S.W. Afr.

Neomacfadyena Baill. Bignoniaceae (I). I Cuba.
Neomanniophyton Pax et K. Hoffm. Euphorbiaceae (A. II. 2). 12 W. Afr.
Neomazaea Urb. (*Rondeletia* p.p.). Rubiaceae (I. 3). I W.I.
Neomezia Votsch (*Deherainia* p.p.). Theophrastaceae. I W.I.
Neomoorea (*Moorea*) Rolfe. Orchidaceae (II. 13). I Andes.
Neomuellera Briquet. Labiatae (VII). 2 S.W. Afr.
Neonauclea Merrill=Nauclea L. (Rubi.).
Neonelsonia Coulter et Rose. Umbelliferae (III. 4). 2 Mexico.
Neonicholsonia Dammer. Palmaceae (IV. 1). 2 C. Am.
Neopatersonia Schönland. Liliaceae (V). I Cape Colony.
Neophloga Baill. (*Hyophorbe* p.p.). Palmaceae (IV. I). 7 Madag.
Neopieris Britton (*Andromeda* p.p.). Ericaceae (II. I). 2 E. N. Am.
Neopringlea S. Wats. (*Llavea* Liebm.). Celastraceae? Simarubaceae? I Mexico.
Neopycnocoma Pax. Euphorbiaceae (A. II. 2). I Spanish Guinea.
Neorautanenia Schinz. Leguminosae (III. 10). I trop. Afr.
Neoroepera Muell.-Arg. Euphorbiaceae (A. I. I). 2 Queensland.
Neosabicea Wernham. Rubiaceae (I. 7). I Colombia.
Neoschimpera Hemsl. Rubiaceae (II. 5). I Seychelles.
Neoschumannia Schlechter. Asclepiadaceae (inc. sed.). I trop. Afr.
Neosciadium Domin (*Hydrocotyle* p.p.). Umbellif. (I. I). I Austr.
Neoscortechia O. Ktze., **Neoscortechinia** Pax=Scortechinia Hook. f. (Euph.).
Neosilvia Pax (*Silvia* Allem.). Lauraceae (II). 2 Brazil.
Neosloetiopsis Engl. (*Sloetiopsis* p.p.). Morac. (I). I Cameroons.
Neosparton Griseb. Verbenaceae (I). 2 temp. S. Am.
Neostapfia Davy. Gramineae (10). I N. Am.
Neostyphonia Shafer (*Styphonia* p.p.). Anacard. (3). I Calif.
Neothorelia Gagnep. Capparidaceae (II). I Laos.
Neotinea Rchb. f. (*Habenaria* p.p. *BH.*). Orchidaceae (II. I). I Medit., W. Eur.
Neotreleasia Rose. Commelinaceae. 3 N. Am.
Neotropical, New World tropical.
Neottia L. Orchidaceae (II. 2). 3 temp. Eur. and As.; *N. Nidus-avis* Rich. (bird's-nest orchis) in Brit. is a leafless saprophyte, the rhiz. giving off a number of roots which form a nest-like mass in the humus, with endotropic mycorhiza. The older roots may throw off their caps and form shoots (*cf.* Anthurium). Fl. as in Listera (Darwin's *Orchids*, p. 125).
Neotuerckheimia Donnell-Smith. Bignoniaceae (4). I Guatemala.
Neotysonia Dalle Torre et Harms. Compositae (4). I Austr.
Neourbania Fawcett et Rendle. Orchidaceae (II. 6). I Jamaica.
Neowashingtonia Sudw. (*Washingtonia* p.p.). Palm. (I. 2). 5 N. Am.
Nepenthaceae (*EP.*, *BH.*). Dicots. (Archichl. Sarraceniales; Multiovulatae Terrestres *BH.*). Only genus Nepenthes (*q.v.*).
Nepenthandra Sp. Moore. Euphorbiaceae (A. II. 5). I Burma.
Nepenthes L. Nepenthaceae. 60 palaeotrop. (pitcher plants). Most are herbs growing in boggy places and climbing by aid of tendrils, prolongations of the leaf-midribs. The end of the tendril developes as a rule into a pitcher, with a lid projecting over the mouth, but not

closing it except in the young state. The pitcher developes by an invagination of the upper surface of the tip of the l.; the tip takes no part in the development, and the lid grows out below it. The edge of the pitcher is curved inwards; at the entrance are numerous honey-glands, and for some distance below it are other glands, sunk in little pits on the inner surface. Insects attracted by the honey (or by the bright colour) gradually work their way downwards among the glands, and presently get upon the slippery lower part and ultimately into the water at the bottom of the pitcher, where they are drowned. The plant absorbs the products of their decay.

Many are epiphytic. In *N. ampullaria* Jack there are two kinds of l. (*cf.* Cephalotus), some with tendrils and no pitchers; others, as stalked pitchers arranged in a radical rosette.

Fls. dioec., reg., in racemes or with the secondary branching cincinnal; no bracts. P 2+2; in the ♂ fl. sta. (4—16) in a column; in the ♀ fl. G (4), 4-loc.; ovules ∞, anatr., in many rows. Capsule leathery, loculic. Seeds light with long hair-like processes at the ends; embryo straight, in fleshy endosp. Many sp. and hybrids cult. [See Goebel's *Pflanzenbiol. Sch.*, Macfarlane in *Ann. of Bot.* III. and VII., and *cf.* Sarracenia, Cephalotus.]

Nepeta Riv. ex L. (excl. *Glechoma* L.). Labiat. (VI). 150 N. |✻. *N. Glechoma* Benth. (ground-ivy) and *N. Cataria* L. (cat-mint) in Brit. Fls. gynodioecious.

Nephelaphyllum Blume. Orchidaceae (II. *a.* II). 6 E. As.

Nephelium L. (excl. *Litchi* Sonner.). Sapindaceae (I). 25 Indomal. *N. lappaceum* L. (rambutan) cult. ed. fr. *N. Longana* Cambess. (longan) and others also used. [*N. Litchi* Cambess, see Litchi.]

Nephelochloa Boiss. Gramineae (10). 1 W. As.

Nephradenia Decne. Asclepiadaceae (II. 3). 5 Braz. to Mex.

Nephrocarpus Dammer. Palmaceae (IV. 1). 1 New Caled.

Nephrocarya Candargy. Boraginaceae (IV. 3). 1 Greece.

Nephrodium Rich. = Dryopteris Adans. p.p. (Polypod.).

Nephrolepis Schott. Polypodiaceae. 18 trop., and Japan, N.Z. They produce runners like strawberry, but not axillary, which root and give new pl.

Nephropetalum Robinson et Greenman. Sterculiaceae. 1 N. Am.

Nephrophyllidium Gilg (*Menyanthes* p.p. *BH.*, *Fauria* p.p. *EP.*). Gentianaceae (II). 1 N.W. Am., Japan.

Nephrophyllum A. Rich. Convolvulaceae (I). 1 Abyssinia.

Nephrosperma Balf. f. Palmaceae (IV. 1). 1 Seychelles.

Nephrostigma Griff. Anonaceae (inc. sed.). Nomen.

Nephthytis Schott. Araceae (IV). 4 trop. W. Afr.

Nepsera Naud. Melastomaceae (I). 1 trop. S. Am., W.I.

Neptunia Lour. Leguminosae (I. 4). 10 trop. and subtrop. *N. oleracea* Lour. has a floating stem, rooting at the nodes, and covered by aerenchyma. The l. are sensitive like those of Mimosa. Fls. in heads, the lower ♂, or neuter with petaloid stds.

Neraudia Gaudich. Urticaceae (3). 3 Hawaiian Is.

Neriacanthus Benth. Acanthaceae (IV. B). 1 Jamaica.

Neriandra A. DC. = Skytanthus Meyen (Apocyn.).

Nerine Herb. Amaryllidaceae (I). 15 Cape Colony. Cult. orn. fl.

Nerisyrenia Greene (*Greggia EP.*). Cruciferae (4). 2 W. N. Am.
Nerium L. Apocynaceae (II. 1). 3 Medit. to Japan. *N. Oleander* L. (oleander) has pits on the lower surface of the evergr. l., in which the stomata are sunk (several in each) and covered with hairs, reducing transpiration. Fls. suited to long-tongued moths.
Nerophila Naud. Melastomaceae (I). 1 Senegambia.
Nertera Banks et Soland. Rubiaceae (II. 7). 10 Andes, N.Z., Austr., Sandw. Is., Malaya.
Nerve (l.), the vascular bundles which run through it.
Nervilia Comm. ex Gaudich. (*Pogonia* p.p. *BH.*). Orchidaceae (II. 2). 25 trop. and subtrop. |*.
Nesaea Comm. ex Juss. Lythraceae. 50 Afr., Austr., As., N. Am.
Nesiota Hook. f. Rhamnaceae. 1 St Helena.
Neslia Desv. Cruciferae (4). 1 Eur., N. As., Medit.
Nesodoxa Calest. (*Eremopanax* p.p.). Araliaceae (1). 1 New Caled.
Nesodraba Greene (*Draba* p.p.). Cruciferae (4). 4 W. N. Am.
Nesogenes A. DC. Verbenaceae (3). 4 Rodrigues, Polynesia.
Nesogordonia Baill. Inc. sed. 1 Madag.
Nesothamnus Rydberg (*Perityle* p.p.). Compos. (6). 1 Lower Calif.
Nestlera Spreng. Compositae (4). 10 Cape Colony.
Nettle, *Urtica*; **dead -**, *Lamium*; **devil** or **fever -**, *Laportea*; **hemp -**, *Galeopsis*; **Nilgiri -**, *Girardinia*; **Spanish -** (W.I.), *Bidens*; **- tree**, *Celtis*, (W.I.) *Pilea*.
Nettoa Baill. Tiliaceae. 1 Austr.
Net-veined, with irreg. network of veins, most Dicots.
Neuburgia Blume. Apocynaceae (I. 1). 1 Malaya.
Neumannia A. Rich. (*Aphloia BH.*). Flacourtiaceae (4). 4 Madag., E. Afr.
Neuracanthus Nees. Acanthaceae (IV. A). 10 palaeotrop.
Neurachne R. Br. Gramineae (3). 3 Austr.
Neurada L. Rosaceae (IV). 1 Medit. to Indian desert.
Neurocalyx Hook. Rubiaceae (I. 2). 6 Ceylon, Borneo.
Neurocarpaea P. Br. (*Pentas* p.p.). Rubiaceae (I. 2). 3 Afr., Madag.
Neurocarpum Desv. = Clitoria L. p.p. (Legum.).
Neurolaena R. Br. Compositae (8). 2 W.I., trop. Am.
Neurolobium Baill. Apocynaceae (I. 3). 1 Brazil.
Neuroloma Andrz. ex DC. = Parrya R. Br. (Crucif.).
Neuropeltis Wall. Convolvulaceae (1). 4 trop. As. and Afr.
Neurosoria Mett. Polypodiaceae. 1 trop. Austr.
Neurotheca Salisb. ex B. et H. f. Gentian. (1). 5 trop. Afr., S. Am.
Neustanthus Benth. = Pueraria DC. p.p. (Legum.).
Neuter, without fertile sporophylls, *Centaurea*, *Hydrangea*, *Muscari*, *Viburnum*.
Neuwiedia Blume. Orchidaceae (I. 1). 6 E. Indomal.
Nevesarmondia K. Schum. (*Pithecoctenium* p.p.). Bignoniaceae (1). 1 Brazil.
Neviusia A. Gray. Rosaceae (III. 1). 1 Alabama.
Newberrya Torr. Pyrolaceae. 2 Oregon, Washington.
Newbouldia Seem. Bignoniaceae (2). 3 trop. W. Afr.
Newcastlia F. Muell. Verbenaceae (3). 7 trop. Austr.
New Jersey tea, *Ceanothus*.

Newtonia Baill. Leguminosae (I. 4). 2 trop. W. Afr.

Newtonia O. Hoffm. (*Antunesia BH.*, *Gongrothamnus EP.*). Compositae (8). 1 Angola.

New Zealand flax, hemp, *Phormium tenax* Forsk.; **- - daisy bush,** *Oleandra*; **- - holly,** *Osmanthus*; **- - pincushion,** *Raoulia*; **- - spinach,** *Tetragonia expansa* Murr.

Neyraudia Hook. f. Gramineae (10). 1 trop. As., Afr., Madag.

Ngai camphor, *Blumea balsamifera* DC.

Nicandra Adans. Solanaceae (1). 1 Peru, *N. physaloides* Gaertn. Ov. divided in an irreg. way by plac. Berry nearly juiceless and with ∞ seeds, enclosed in the enlarged K. Cult. orn. fl.

Nicker bean, *Caesalpinia bonducella* Flem., *Entada.*

Niclouxia Battandier. Compositae (4). 1 S.W. Sahara.

Nicobar breadfruit, *Pandanus Leram* Jones.

Nicodemia Tenore. Loganiaceae. 3 Madagascar, Mascarene Is.

Nicolasia Sp. Moore. Compositae (4). 3 S.W. trop. Afr.

Nicolletia A. Gray. Compositae (6). 2 S.W. U.S.

Nicolsonia DC. = Desmodium Desv. p.p. (Legum.).

Nicoteba Lindau (*Justicia* p.p.). Acanthaceae (IV. B). 5 palaeotrop.

Nicotiana L. Solanaceae (4). 45 Am., Polynes., 1 Austr. *N. Tabacum* L., cult. in warm countries, esp. U.S., Cuba, Sumatra, Egypt, Brazil, etc., is the tobacco, grown as an annual crop; the l. are gathered, hung up and slowly dried, then packed in heaps and fermented slightly. Different varieties are grown, and usu. in different places, for cigar, cigarette, and pipe tobacco. *N. rustica* L. and others are also used.

Nidorella Cass. Compositae (3). 30 Abyssinia to S. Afr.

Nidularium Lem. (*Karatas BH.*). Bromeliaceae (4). 15 Brazil.

Niebuhria DC. (*Maerua* p.p. *EP.*). Capparidaceae (II). 12 trop. As., Afr.

Niederleinia Hieron. Frankeniaceae. 3 temp. S. Am.

Niedzwedzkia B. Fedtschenko = Sesamum L. p.p. (Pedal.).

Niemeyera F. Muell. Sapotaceae (1). 1 trop. E. Austr.

Nierembergia Ruiz et Pav. Solanaceae (4). 20 trop. and subtrop. Am.

Nietneria Klotzsch et R. Schomb. Liliaceae (1). 1 Brit. Guiana.

Nigella (Tourn.) L. Ranunculaceae (2). 16 Medit., Eur., often cult. orn. fl. (love-in-a-mist, devil-in-a-bush). Annuals. Alt. with the K is an invol. of 5 l. Within the coloured K are 5—8 nectaries, pocket-like structures with lids which prevent small insects from reaching the honey. The cpls. are more or less completely united but have separate styles; they give a caps. fr. Fl. protandrous.

Niger (Lat.), black.

Niger seed, *Guizotia abyssinica* Cass.

Night-flowering cactus, *Cereus grandiflorus* Mill., &c.

Nightshade, *Solanum*; **deadly -,** *Atropa Belladonna* L.; **enchanter's -,** *Circaea lutetiana* L.

Nigrescens, nigricans (Lat.), blackish.

Nigribicchia × E. G. Camus, Beyer, et R. Camus. Orchidaceae. Hybrid Nigritella-Habenaria (Bicchia).

Nigritella Rich. (*Habenaria* p.p. *BH.*). Orchidaceae (II. 1). 1 Mts. of Eur.

Nilgiri nettle, *Girardinia heterophylla* Decne.
Nim, neem, *Azadirachta indica* A. Juss. (*Melia Azadirachta* L.).
Nimble Will (Am.), *Muehlenbergia diffusa* Schreb.
Niopo tree (W.I.), *Piptadenia*.
Nipa Thunb. Palmae (VI). 1 palaeotrop., *N. fruticans* Thunb., a low-growing palm with monoec. infl. Fr. woody, combined into a dense head; each contains one seed. It grows in brackish water and is very char. upon trop. coasts. [See Phytelephas.]
Niphaea Lindl. Gesneriaceae (II). 2 Guatemala, Cuba.
Niphobolus Kaulf. = Cyclophorus Desv. (Polypod.).
Nipplewort, *Lapsana communis* L.
Nirarathamnos Balf. f. Umbelliferae (III. 5). 1 Socotra.
Nirwamia Rafin. Euphorbiaceae (inc. sed.). 1 Japan.
Nisa Noronha = Homalium Jacq. p.p. (Flac.).
Nissolia Jacq. Leguminosae (III. 7). 7 trop. and subtrop. Am.
Nitidus (Lat.), lustrous, smooth and shining.
Nitraria L. Zygophyllaceae. 3 palaeotrop.
Nitrophila S. Wats. Chenopodiaceae (A). 1 W. N. Am.
Nivalis (Lat.), growing near snow; **niveus** (Lat.), snow-white.
Nivenia R. Br. (*Paranomus* p.p. *EP.*). Proteaceae (I). 18 S. Afr.
Nivenia Vent. (*Aristea BH.*). Iridaceae (II). 2 S. Afr. Cult. orn. fl.
Noaea Moq. in DC. Chenopodiaceae (B). 7 W. As.
Noccaea Moench (*Hutchinsia* p.p. *EP.*). Cruciferae (4). 2 Alps.
Node, the joint where a leaf springs from the stem.
Nodocarpaea A. Gray. Rubiaceae (II. 10). 1 Cuba.
No-eye pea (W.I.), *Cajanus indicus* Spreng.
Noisettia H. B. et K. Violaceae. 1 Brazil, Peru, Guiana.
Nolana L. Nolanaceae. 20 Chili, Peru. Many are shore plants with fleshy l.
Nolanaceae (*EP.*; *Convolvulaceae* p.p. *BH.*). Dicots. (Sympet. Tubiflorae). 5 gen., 50 sp., W. coast of S. Am. Herbs or low shrubs with simple l., often covered with glandular hairs. The l. in the veg. region are alt., but in the infl. portion they become paired in the same way as in Solanaceae (*q.v.*). Many are sea-shore plants with fleshy l. Fls. sol. in the leaf-axils, ☿, reg. K (5); C (5); A 5, alt. with petals; $\underline{G}$ typically 5, only united in Alona, usu. free and divided by irreg. longitudinal constrictions into 5 or 10 portions standing in a row, or by longitudinal and transv. constrictions into 10—30 portions in 2 or 3 rows. The fr. consists of a corresponding number of 1—7-seeded nutlets. Style 1. Seed album. *Genera:* Nolana, Alona, Dolia.
Nolina Michx. Liliaceae (VI). 25 S.W. N. Am. Xero. Cult.
Nolletia Cass. Compositae (3). 4 Morocco, S. Afr.
Noltea Reichb. Rhamnaceae. 1 S. Afr. Cult. orn. shrub.
Nomaphila Blume (*Hygrophila* p.p. *EP.*). Acanth. (IV. A). 8 palaeotrop.
Nomenclature (with esp. reference to classification). The unit in classification is the *species*, which was described by A. L. de Jussieu as "the perennial succession of similar individuals perpetuated by generation." All marsh marigolds (*Caltha palustris*) form one sp., or all pl. of Indian corn (*Zea Mays*) or coconut (*Cocos nucifera*). But exactly to

define a sp. is impossible. Each man in practice arrives at his own conception somewhere between (or at) the extremes usu. called Linnean and Jordanian sp. *Draba* (*Erophila*) *verna* for example (Linnean) is distinguished from other D. by absence of petiole and oblong-elliptical pod, but Jordan, studying the sp. in great detail, split it into a great number of forms, to which he gave specific rank, when he found that each one continued to breed true. These were distinguished by "small" characters, such as differences in hairiness, fruit-shape, leaf-form, &c. *Cf.* Jordan, *Diagnoses d'espèces nouv. ou méconnues*, Paris, 1864, Rosen in *Bot. Zeit.* 1889, p. 565.

The most popular conception of sp., and the one used in this book, and in most floras and other botanical books, is the Linnean, or somewhere near to it, *e.g.* as used by Sir J. D. Hooker, or Dr A. Engler. The many forms into which a wide ranging sp. can be divided are classed, the larger and more important as *subspecies*, the smaller as *varieties*, *subvarieties*, and *forms*. Publication of a sp., by sale or public distribution of printed matter or indelible autographs, consists in the giving of a Latin description of the sp. sufficient to distinguish it from its congeners, and of a name (Latin or Latinised) by which it may be recognised. The name of the author is then appended (often in abbreviated form, *cf.* Abbreviations), and publication is complete. A sp. for example may be *viscosa* (sticky) Jones, or *gigas* (giant) Klein.

The next stage above sp. is *genus* or group of sp., with possible intermediates of *subgenus*, *section* and *subsection*; and again the difficulty crops up as to the comprehensiveness of the group. What one may consider as a subgenus, or even a section, another may regard as a genus. The great thing is to find a group of sp. clearly marked off by two or three distinct chars. from all other groups. Such a genus as the roses (*Rosa*), the buttercups (*Ranunculus*), the bananas (*Musa*), the pineapples (*Ananas*) or the figs (*Ficus*) is unmistakeable, and is still defined as it was defined by Tournefort or Linnaeus. But in such a case as *Andropogon*, *Cereus*, *Eugenia*, *Loranthus*, *Myristica*, *Oenothera*, the genus is not so clearly marked off, and does not, throughout its members, retain a few well-marked chars. constantly, so that a large number of botanists prefer to split it into other smaller genera. Some of those mentioned are often recognised as composed of 5 to 20 genera.

Genera are grouped into *families* (*e.g.* Ranunculaceae), these into *orders* (*e.g.* Ranales), *classes* (*e.g.* Dicotyledoneae), and *divisions* (*e.g.* Siphonogama). But subdivision is usu. necessary here, so that the list of possible headings ultimately runs:

Div., Subdiv., Class, Subclass, Order, Suborder, Fam., Subfam., Tribe, Subtribe, Gen., Subgen., Sect., Subsect., Sp., Subsp., Var., Subvar., Form.

To every plant is given a binomial appellation, the first half being the gen., the second the sp., *e.g. Ranunculus acris*. To complete the identification the name of the author of this name must be appended, in this case Linnaeus (L.), as there might be another plant with the same name given by someone else.

The essential points to aim at are fixity of names, and the avoidance of confusion, but in very many cases these are yet to be arrived at.

A group of any rank can bear only one valid name—the oldest. But to apply this rule rigidly would allow almost no fixity. For flowering plants and ferns it is therefore agreed to go back only to the first edition (1753) of Linnaeus' *Species Plantarum*, and the descriptions in his *Genera Plantarum*, edit. 5, 1754. Further, there are a large number of genera whose current names are not the oldest, but are so familiar that a change would cause confusion, so that it has been agreed, for instance, that *Welwitschia* shall retain that name and not be termed *Tumboa*, though the latter was first bestowed, and the same in a great number of other instances.

When a name given to a genus by a pre-Linnean author is taken over by Linnaeus or a subsequent author, it is thus indicated:

Mercurialis (Tourn.) L. (named by T., accepted by L.).

When a name was given, but not published, by a botanist, and subsequently published by another, it is shown thus:

Leersia Soland. ex Sw. (given by Solander, in MS., and published by Swartz).

When a name is published by a man writing in someone else's publication, it is indicated by 'in,' *e.g.* L. C. Rich. in Michx. means given by Richard in Michaux's Flora.

When a sp. is transferred from one gen. to another, it retains its specific name if possible (*i.e.* usu. if the new gen. does not already contain a sp. with the same name), and the author of the first may be indicated in brackets, *e.g. Cheiranthus tristis* L. may become *Matthiola tristis* (L.).

Genera and species that are merged in others become *synonyms*, of which there are vast numbers. This book contains very many generic synonyms, indicated thus:

Acrocarpidium Miq. = Peperomia Ruiz et Pav.

But a synonym may at any time be revived, so that it is not customary to use names from the list of synonyms to designate new gen. or sp.

When a genus is merged in another, the fact is often signified by the letters p.p. (*pro parte*), to indicate that it only forms a portion of the larger genus, often a subgenus or a section.

The symbol × is used to designate a *hybrid* (cross of two species) or *mule* (cross of two divisions of one sp.).

Generic and specific names as published are collected in the *Kew Index*, to which a supplement is published every 5 years. At first the names were divided into valid and synonyms, but now all are published without any editorial expression of opinion. In de Dalla Torre and Harms' *Genera Siphonogamarum* is a list of generic names and synonyms pretty much as accepted by Engler. In this book I have placed all genera as accepted by Linnaeus, Bentham-Hooker, or Engler-Prantl, and all subsequent genera, whether usu. considered synonyms or not.

For details see Briquet, *Règles Internationales de la nomenclature botanique*, Jena, 1912; Asa Gray, *Structural Botany*, ch. X.

Nomocharis Franch. Liliaceae (V). 15 S.E. As.

Non-articulate, not cut off by an absciss-layer.

Nonatelia Aubl. = Palicourea Aubl. (Rubi.).

Nonnea Medic. Boraginaceae (IV. 3). 30 Medit.
Nonsuch, *Medicago*; **-e so pretty,** *Saxifraga umbrosa* L.
Noogoora burr (Austr.), *Xanthium.*
Nopalea Salm-Dyck. Cact. (II). 7 C. Am., W.I. Similar to Opuntia. Upon *N. coccinellifera* Salm-Dyck the cochineal insect (*Coccus cacti*) is cult., chiefly in the Canaries, &c. It has no thorns.
Norantea Aubl. Marcgraviaceae. 40 trop. Am., W.I. All fls. are fertile, and have saccate nectariferous bracts. Resembles Philodendrum in habit.
Norfolk Island pine, *Araucaria excelsa* R. Br.
Normanbya F. Muell. = Ptychosperma Labill. (Palm.).
Normandia Hook. f. Rubiaceae (II. 7). 1 New Caled.
Noronhia Stadm. Oleaceae. 3 Madag., Timor.
Norrisia Gardn. Loganiaceae. 2 Malaya.
Northea Hook. f. Sapotaceae (2). 1 Seychelles.
Northern fern, *Blechnum boreale* Sw.; **- glacial zone, zone of cold winters, of hot summers,** *cf.* Zones of Vegetation.
Norway spruce, *Picea excelsa* Link.
Norysca Spach = Hypericum Tourn. p.p. (Guttif.).
Nosema Prain. Labiatae (inc. sed.). 3 S.E. As.
Notanthera G. Don = Loranthus L. p.p. (*BH.*) = Phrygilanthus.
Notaphoebe Blume ex Pax (*Alseodaphne BH.*). Lauraceae (I). 40 Indomal., Am., W.I.
Notelaea Vent. Oleaceae. 6 Austr., N.Z. Hard timber.
Nothites Cass. = Stevia Cav. (Comp.).
Nothocalais Greene (*Microseris* p.p. *EP.*). Compos. (13). 2 N. and C. Am.
Nothocestrum A. Gray. Solanaceae (2). 4 Hawaiian Is.
Nothochilus Radlk. Scrophulariaceae (III. 2). 1 Brazil.
Nothochlaena R. Br. Polypodiaceae. 50 trop. and temp.
Nothofagus Blume (*Fagus* p.p. *BH.*). Fagaceae (I). 12 S. temp., exc. Afr. *N. Cunninghami* Oerst. (myrtle tree), good timber.
Nothoholcus Nash (*Holcus* p.p.). Gramineae (9). 8 temp. |✻.
Notholaena R. Br. = Nothochlaena R. Br. (Polypod.).
Notholcus Nash ex Hitchcock = Nothoholcus Nash (Gram.).
Nothopanax Miq., Seem. (*Panax BH.*). Araliaceae (I). 12 ✻̄.
Nothopegia Blume. Anacardiaceae (4). 3 Indomal.
Nothophlebia Standley. Rubiaceae (I. 7). 1 Costa Rica.
Nothoprotium Miq. Burseraceae. 1 Sumatra.
Nothosaerua Wight. Amarantaceae (2). 1 trop. Afr. and As.
Nothoscordum Kunth. Liliaceae (IV). 30 Am. (P). Adv. embryos form by budding of nucellus round embryo-sac (*cf.* Funkia).
Nothosmyrnium Miq. Umbelliferae (III. 4). 1 Japan.
Nothospondias Engl. Anacardiaceae (2). 1 Cameroons.
Noticastrum DC. = Aster Tourn. p.p. (Comp.).
Notobuxus Oliv. Buxaceae. 1 Natal.
Notoceras R. Br. in Ait. Cruciferae (4). 2 Medit.
Notochaete Benth. Labiatae (VI). 1 Himalaya.
Notochloe Domin (*Triodia* p.p.). Gramineae (10). 1 New S. Wales.
Notodon Urb. Leguminosae (III. 6). 1 W.I.
Notonerium Benth. Apocynaceae (I. 2). 1 S. Austr.

Notonia DC. (*Senecio* p.p. *EP.*). Compositae (8). 12 palaeotrop.
Notopora Hook. f. Ericaceae (III. 2). 1 Brit. Guiana.
Notoptera Urb. Compositae (5). 6 trop. Am., W.I.
Notopterygium Boissieu. Umbelliferae (III. 2). 2 China.
Notorhizal, *Cruciferae*.
Notosceptrum Benth. Liliaceae (III). 8 S. and trop. Afr.
Notospartium Hook. f. Leguminosae (III. 6). 1 N.Z.
Notothixos Oliv. Loranthaceae (II). 6 Indomal.
Notothlaspi Hook. f. Cruciferae (I). 3 N.Z.
Nototribe (fl.), with essential organs striking a visitor's back.
Nototriche Turcz. (*Malvastrum* A. Gray). Malvaceae (2). 75 S. Am.
Nototrichium Hillebrand. Amarantaceae (2). 3 Hawaiian Is.
Notylia Lindl. Orchidaceae (II. 19). 24 trop. Am. Cult. orn. fl.
Nouelia Franch. Compositae (12). 1 S.W. China.
Nouettea Pierre. Apocynaceae (II. 1). 1 Cochinchina.
Noyera Tréc. (*Perebea* p.p.). Moraceae (II). 1 Guiana.
Nucellus, the mass of the ovular tissue.
Nucularia Battand. Chenopodiaceae (B). 1 S. Oran.
Nuculiferae (Warming). The 6th cohort of Sympetalae.
Nudiflorae (*BH.*). The 5th series of Monocotyledons.
Nudiflorus (Lat.), with naked fl.
Nuphar Sibth. et Sm. Nymphaeaceae (III). 7 N. temp. and cold. *N. luteum* Sibth. et Sm. (yellow water-lily or brandy-bottle) in Brit. Veg. habit of Nymphaea (*q.v.*). The fl. projects a little above the water, and is fully hypog. At the base of the peduncle is a rudimentary bract. There are 5 large coloured outer P leaves, quincuncial, the fourth anterior; within are the 'petals,' 13 in number arranged in a 5/13 spiral. Then follow ∞ sta., the outer 13 alt. with the petals, the next 13 with them, and so on in a spiral. $\underline{G}$ (10—16), multiloc. Stigmas, ovules, &c., as in Nymphaea. Fr. a large berry; it breaks off from the stalk and splits up into separate cpls. The seeds have no aril like Nymphaea, but the slimy pericarp contains bubbles: the seeds are set free by its decay, and sink.
Nut, a dry indeh. fr., the product of > 1 cpl.; **Areca -**, *Areca*; **Australian chest-**, *Castanospermum australe* A. Cunn.; **Bambarra ground -**, *Voandzeia subterranea* Thou.; **betel -**, *Areca Catechu* L.; **bladder -**, *Staphylea*; **Brazil -**, *Bertholletia excelsa* Humb. et Bonpl.; **bread -**, *Brosimum*; **butter -**, *Caryocar nuciferum* L.; **candle -**, *Aleurites triloba* Forst.; **cashew -**, *Anacardium occidentale* L.; **chest-**, *Castanea vulgaris* Lam.; **cob-**, *Corylus*; **coco-**, *Cocos nucifera* L.; **cola-**, *Cola vera* K. Schum.; **coquilla -**, *Attalea funifera* Mart.; **earth -**, *Arachis hypogaea* L., *Conopodium denudatum* Koch; **- grass**, *Cyperus*; **ground -**, *Arachis hypogaea* L.; **hazel -**, *Corylus Avellana* L.; **hog -**, *Spondias*; **horn -**, *Trapa*; **horse-chest-**, *Aesculus Hippocastanum* L.; **ivory -**, *Phytelephas*; **kola -**, see cola; **marking -**, *Semecarpus*; **pea-**, *Arachis hypogaea* L.; **pistachio -**, *Pistachia vera* L.; **pecan -**, *Carya*; **physic -**, *Jatropha Curcas* L.; **- rush** (Am.), *Scleria*; **Sapucaia -**, *Lecythis*; **Souari -**, *Caryocar nuciferum* L.; **- tree** (Austr.), *Macadamia*.
Nutans (Lat.), nodding.
Nutation, lateral swaying of tip of a growing organ.

Nutlets, *Labiatae* (fr.).
Nutmeg, *Myristica fragrans* Houtt., *Monodora Myristica* Dun.; **Brazilian -**, *Cryptocarya*; **calabash -**, *Monodora Myristica* Dun.; **- grass** (Am.), *Cyperus rotundus* L.; **Peruvian -**, *Laurelia aromatica* Juss.
Nuttallia DC. = Nemopanthes Rafin. (Aquifol.).
Nuttallia Rafin. = Mentzelia Plum. p.p. (Loas.).
Nuttallia Torr. et Gray. Rosaceae (v). 1 N.W. Am. Like Prunus, but with 5 free cpls.
Nuxia Comm. ex Lam. Loganiaceae. 20 Afr., Madag.
Nuytsia R. Br. Loranthaceae (1). 1 W. Austr., a small tree, doubtfully parasitic on roots. Cotyledons 3. L. alt.
Nyctaginaceae (*EP.*, *BH.*). Dicots. (Archichl. Centrospermae; Curvembryae *BH.*). 20 gen., 160 sp., mostly trop. and esp. Am. Trees, shrubs or herbs with opp. (often unequal) l. and no stips. Fls. in cymes, ☿ or unisexual, and with much variety. At the base of the fls. are usu. several bracts, often large and coloured. In Bougainvillaea 3 large conspicuous bracts enclose a group of 3 fls. In Abronia the number of bracts and fls. is larger, while in Mirabilis there is only one fl. and the involucre resembles a calyx. P usu. (5), petaloid, persistent upon the ripe fr.; usu. the upper part drops away and the fr. remains in the lower part, which is termed the *anthocarp*, and may become glandular, or form an umbrella-like wing, or otherwise serve for seed-dispersal. A typically 5, alt. with the P, but often 3, 8, 10 or other numbers, or raised to 20 or 30 by branching; filaments often of unequal length; $\underline{G}$ 1, with long style and 1 basal erect ana-campylotr. ov. Achene enclosed in the P. The N. are of slight economic value; see Mirabilis, Neea, &c. *Chief genera:* Mirabilis, Bougainvillaea, Pisonia, Neea, Reichenbachia.
Nyctagineae (*BH.*) = Nyctaginaceae.
Nyctaginia Choisy. Nyctaginaceae. 1 Texas, Mexico.
Nyctago Juss. = Mirabilis L. p.p. (Nyct.).
Nyctanthes L. Oleaceae. 1 Indomal.
Nycterinia D. Don = Zaluzianskya F. W. Schmidt (Scroph.).
Nycterium Vent. = Solanum Tourn. p.p. (Sol.).
Nycticalos Teijsm. et Binnend. Bignoniaceae (1). 2 Malaya.
Nyctocereus Britton et Rose (*Cereus* p.p.). Cactaceae (III. 1). 5 Mexico, Nicaragua.
Nyctophyla Zipp. Inc. sed. 1 Timor.
Nymania K. Schum. Euphorbiaceae (A. I. 1). 1 New Guinea.
Nymania S. O. Lindb. Meliaceae (III). 1 S. Afr.
Nymphaea (Tourn.) L. (*Castalia* Salisb.). Nymphaeaceae (III). 40 trop. and temp. *N. alba* L. (white water-lily) in Brit. Many cult., *e.g. N. Lotus* L. considered to be the original sacred lotus of Egypt (see Nelumbium). They grow in shallow water. There is a stout creeping rhiz.; at the tip it is bent up, and bears stip. l. and fls. on long stalks. The peduncle occupies the position of one of the l. of the spiral, and there is no bract at its base. The l. is large and floats on the surface; it is nearly circular, entire, and leathery, with stomata, cuticle and palisade tissue on the upper side.

Fl. ☿, reg., acyclic; floats on the surface. The 4 outermost floral l. exhibit a peculiar aestivation, the ant. being entirely outside, the post.

inside the lat. l. Most authors regard them as K, but Caspary (Eichler, *Blütendiagr.*, II. 184) regards the anterior l. as bract adnate to peduncle (*cf.* Solanaceae), the lats. as bracteoles, the post. as a true sep. C ∞, 4 outer alt. with K, 4 inner with these; each of the 8 begins a spiral of pets., usu. 4 in each, alt. approximately with one another and the outer 8, and showing gradual transition to the 50—100 sta. which continue the spirals. K hypog., C and A inserted up sides of G (10—20)-loc. with sessile stigmas on upper surface, and ∞ ovules scattered over the whole carpellary surface (*cf.* Butomus). Fr. a large berry; ∞ seeds, each with spongy aril entangling air bubbles; the seeds float up on dehisc. of fr., and float about till the aril decays. Perisperm round endosp. proper. N. was the original sacred Lotus of Egypt; Nelumbium (*q.v.*) was introduced about 500 B.C. (Conard, *The Waterlilies*, Washington, 1905).

Nymphaeaceae (*EP.*, *BH.*). Dicots. (Archichl. Ranales; pp. xvii, l). 8/50 trop. and temp. Water or marsh pl., usu. with rhiz., aerial, floating, or submerged l., and sol. usu. large fls. of great variety of pattern (described in detail under gen., *q.v.*). Cabomba with completely free cpls. agrees best with other Ranales, whilst great modification, espec. in G, shows in the other groups. Nelumbium is still apocp., though cpls. connected by torus. The rest are syncp., sup. in Nuphar, semi-inf. in Nymphaea, inf. in Victoria. Much variety in $\underline{P}$ (*cf.* Cabomba and Nuphar); K often 4; A usu. ∞ (6—∞); $\underline{G}$ to $\overline{G}$ 3—∞, free or united, each with 1—∞ anatr. ov. on inner surface. Fr. berry-like; seed with endosp. and perisperm, or none, often arillate. (*Cf.* Eichler, *Blütendiagr.*, Arber, *Water Plants*, Conard, [*The Waterlilies*.)

Classification and genera:

I. *NELUMBONOIDEAE* (exalb.; cpls. free in obconical recept.): Nelumbium (only gen.).

II. *CABOMBOIDEAE* (endosp. and perisperm; cpls. free): Cabomba (A 3—6), Brasenia (A ∞).

III. *NYMPHAEOIDEAE* (do.; cpls. united); Victoria (pl. spiny), Euryale (do.), Nymphaea (K 4 inf.), Nuphar (K 5 or more inf., A inf.), Barclaya.

Nymphaeola Heist. = Hydrocharis L. (Hydrocharit.).

Nymphoides Hill, Medic. (*Limnanthemum* S. G. Gmel.). Gentian. (II). 20 trop. and temp.

Nymphona Bubani = Nuphar Sm. (Nymph.).

Nyrophylla Neck. Laur. Nomen.

Nyssa Gronov. ex L. Nyss. 7 N. Am., Himal., Chi. to Java. *N. sylvatica* Marsh, &c. (N. Am., tupelo, pepperidge, sour or cotton gum-tree, ogeechee lime) yield timber and ed. fr. Style usu. simple.

Nyssaceae (*EP.*; *Cornaceae* p.p. *Nat. Pfl.* and *BH.*). Dicots. (Archichl. Myrtiflorae; pp. xxxix, lii). 3/10 E. As., E. N. Am. (*cf.* Epigaea, &c.). Trees or shrubs with alt. exstip. l., and ♂ fls. in heads, racemes, or umbels, ♀ sol. Recept. flat or hollow; KC 5 or more or 0; A twice as many or more or less; $\overline{G}$, 1-loc. (in Davidia 6—10-loc.) with 1 sol. pend. anatr. ov. in each loc. Usu. drupe; endosp. Near to Combret.; Davidia peculiar. *Genera:* Nyssa, Camptotheca, Davidia.

Nyssanthes R. Br. Amarant. (2). 2 Austr. P 4, two inner smaller.

Nyssopsis O. Ktze. = Camptotheca Decne. (Nyss.).

Oak, *Quercus*; **American turkey -,** *Quercus obtusiloba*; **Ceylon -,** *Schleichera trijuga* Willd.; **cork -,** *Quercus Suber* L.; **Dominica -,** *Ilex sideroxyloides* Griseb.; **- fern,** *Dryopteris Linneana* C. Chr.; **forest -,** *Casuarina*; **dyer's -,** *Quercus tinctoria* Bartr.; **live -,** *Quercus virginiana* Mill. and other evergr. sp.; **patana -** (Ceylon), *Careya arborea* Roxb.; **holly -,** *Quercus Ilex* L.; **Quebec -,** *Quercus alba* L.; **she -,** *Casuarina*; **silky -,** *Grevillea*; **Turkey -,** *Quercus Cerris* L.; **white -,** *Quercus alba* L.

Oakesia S. Wats. (*Uvularia EP.*). Liliaceae (1). 2 N. Am.

Oakesiella Small (*Uvularia* p.p.). Liliaceae (1). 3 N. Am.

Oat, *Avena sativa* L.; **- grass,** *Avena fatua* L., &c.; **side -,** *Bouteloua.*

Oaxacania Robinson et Greenman. Compositae (2). 1 Mexico.

Ob- (Lat. pref.), inverted; **-diplostemonous** (sta.), in two whorls, the outer opp. to the pets., *Burseraceae*, *Caryophyllaceae*, *Crassulaceae*, *Oxalidaceae*, *Saxifragaceae*, *Zygophyllaceae*; **-lanceolate, -lique, -long, -ovate,** &c., see Leaf; **-solete,** aborted.

Obbea Hook. f. Rubiaceae (II. 2). 1 Hawaiian Is.

Obeliscaria Cass. = Lepachys Rafin. (*BH.*). = Rudbeckia L. p.p.

Oberonia Lindl. Orchidaceae (II. 4). 100 palaeotrop. Fl. minute.

Obetia Gaudich. Urticaceae (1). 2 Madagascar, Bourbon.

Obione Gaertn. = Atriplex L. p.p. (Chenop.).

Obolaria L. Gentianaceae (1). 1 N. Am. Saprophyte (*cf.* Bartonia) of a purplish green colour with scaly l.

Occidentalis (Lat.), western.

Oceanium (Cl.), an ocean formation.

Oceanorus Small (*Amianthium* A. Gray). Liliaceae (1). 1 N. Am.

Ochagavia Phil. Bromeliaceae (4). 1 Juan Fernandez.

Ochanostachys Mast. Olacaceae. 1 Malay Peninsula, Borneo.

Ochlandra Thw Gramineae (13). 12 India, Ceylon, Madag.

Ochna L. Ochnaceae. 90 trop. As., Afr., Cape Col. K coloured. Cpls. 3—15, free below, but with a common style. After fert. the style falls and each cpl. gives a drupe, while the recept. becomes fleshy under them. The l. shows veining well.

Ochnaceae (*EP.*; *BH.* place *Sauvagesia*, &c. in Violaceae). Dicots. (Archichl. Parietales; Geranialer *BH.*). 20 gen., 400 sp., trop. Most are trees or shrubs with alt. usu. simple stip. l. and panicles, racemes or cymes (Sauvagesia, &c.) of ☿, usu. reg. fls. K 5, free or united at base, imbr.; C 5, rarely 10, contorted; A 5, 10, or ∞, hypog. or on an elongated axis; $\underline{G}$ (2—5), rarely (10—15), often free below with common style (*cf.* Apocynaceae). Ovules 1—2—∞ in each cpl., erect or rarely pend., always with ventral raphe. The axis swells and becomes fleshy under the fr., which is usually a cluster of drupes, but sometimes a berry or capsule. Endosp. or not. *Chief genera:* Ochna, Gomphia, Sauvagesia.

Ochocoa Pierre (*Scyphocephalium EP.*). Myristicaceae. 1 trop. Afr.

Ochra, *Hibiscus esculentus* L.

Ochradenus Delile. Resedaceae. 5 S. Medit.

Ochrea, ocrea, sheathing stipule, *Polygonaceae.*

Ochrocarpus Thou. Guttiferae (IV). 20 palaeotrop.

Ochroma Sw. Bombacaceae. 1 trop. S. Am., W.I., *O. Lagopus* Sw. (balsa, corkwood). Wood very light. Seeds embedded in hairs.
Ochronerium Baill. Apocynaceae (II. 1). 1 Madagascar.
Ochropteris J. Sm. Polypodiaceae. 1 Madagascar, Mascarene Is.
Ochrosia Juss. Apocynaceae (I. 3). 15 palaeotrop.
Ochthocharis Blume. Melastomaceae (I). 8 Malaya.
Ochthocosmus Benth. (*Phyllocosmus* Klotzsch). Lin. 3 trop. Am., Afr.
Ochthodium DC. Cruciferae (2). 1 W. As.
Ocimum L. Labiatae (VII). 60 sp. trop. and warm temp. *O. Basilicum* L. is the basil, sacred in the Hindu religion (tulsi).
Oclemena Greene (*Aster* L. p.p.). Compositae (3). 2 N. Am.
Ocotea Aubl. Lauraceae (I). 230 trop. and subtrop. *O. bullata* E. Mey. (S. Afr.) yields a useful timber (stinkwood).
Ocotilla, *Fouquieria splendens* Engelm.
Ocrearia Small (*Saxifraga* p.p.). Saxifragaceae (I). 1 W. N. Am.
Octadesmia Benth. Orchidaceae (II. 6). 3 Jamaica, S. Domingo.
Octarrhena Thw. = Phreatia Lindl. (Orchid.).
Octas Jack. Inc. sed. 1 Malaya.
Octella Rafin. = Melastoma L., &c., p.p. (Melast.).
Octoceras Bunge. Cruciferae (4). 1 W. As.
Octodon Thonn. (*Borreria* p.p. *EP.*). Rubiaceae (II. 10). 2 trop. Afr
Octoknema Pierre. Olacaceae. 4 trop. Afr. *Cf.* Supplement.
Octolepis Oliv. Thymelaeaceae, once Flacourtiaceae. 4 W. Afr.
Octolobus Welw. Sterculiaceae. 1 Angola.
Octomelis Miq. Datiscaceae. 2 Malay Archipelago.
Octomeria R. Br. Orchidaceae (II. 8). 15 Brazil to W.I.
Octopleura Griseb. (*Ossaea* p.p. *EP.*). Melastom. (I). 5 trop. Am., W.I.
Octotheca R. Viguier. Araliaceae (I). 1 New Caledonia.
Octotropis Bedd. Rubiaceae (II. 1). 1 Travancore.
Odacmis Rafin. Inc. sed. 1 N. Am.
Odina Roxb. (*Calesium* Adans.). Anacardiaceae (2). 15 trop. Afr., As.
Odonia Bertol. (*Galactia* P. Br.). Leguminosae (III. 10). 8 trop. Am.
Odont-, odonto- (Gr. pref.), tooth.
Odontadenia Benth. Apocynaceae (II. 1). 20 trop. S. Am.
Odontandra Willd. ex Roem. et Schult. (*Trichilia* p.p. *BH.*). Meliaceae (III). 4 trop. S. Am.
Odontanthera Wight. Asclepiadaceae (inc. sed.). Nomen.
Odontarrhena C. A. Mey. = Alyssum Tourn. p.p. (Crucif.).
Odontelytrum Hack. Gramineae (5). 1 trop. Afr.
Odontioda × Rolfe. Orchidaceae. Hybrid, Odontoglossum-Cochlioda.
Odontites (Riv.) Hall (*Bartsia BH.*). Scrophulariaceae (III. 3). 20 Medit., S. Eur., W. As. Semiparasites (see fam.).
Odontocarya Miers. Menispermaceae. 6 trop. S. Am., W.I.
Odontochilus Blume. Orchidaceae (II. 2). 10 Indomal, Polynesia.
Odontocidium ×. Orchidaceae. Hybrid, Odontoglossum-Oncidium.
Odontocyclus Turcz. Cruciferae (inc. sed.). 1 Kurile Is.
Odontoglossum H. B. et K. Orchidaceae (II. 19). 100 Mts. of trop. Am. Epiphytes. Many cult. orn. fl. Many hybrids.
Odontonema Nees (*Thyrsacanthus BH.*). Acanthaceae (IV. B). 25 trop. Am.

Odontonemella Lindau (*Eranthemum* p.p.). Acanth. (IV. B). 2 Indo-mal.
Odontonia × Rolfe. Orchidaceae. Hybrid, Odontoglossum-Miltonia.
Odontonychia Small (*Siphonychia* p.p.). Caryoph. (I. 4). 2 N. Am.
Odontosoria (Presl) Fée. Polypodiaceae. 20 trop. and subtrop., exc. Afr.
Odontospermum Neck. (incl. *Asteriscus* Moench). Compositae (4). 12 Medit. *O.* (*A.*) *pygmaeum* O. Hoffm. is a xero. whose fr.-heads close in dry weather (*cf.* Anastatica, Mesembryanthemum); the seeds only escape in damp weather suitable for germination.
Odontostelma Rendle (*Schizoglossum EP.*). Asclep. (II. 1). 1 Angola.
Odontostomum Torr. Liliaceae (III) (Haemodor. *BH.*). 1 California.
Odontotecoma Bur. et K. Schum. (*Tecoma* p.p.). Bignoniaceae (2). 1 Brazil.
Odontychium K. Schum. (*Hedychium* p.p.). Zingiber (1). 1 Mal. Pen.
Odostemon Rafin. (*Berberis* p.p.). Berberidaceae. 12 N. Am.
Odyendea Engl. (*Quassia* p.p.). Simarubaceae. 2 trop. Afr. (K).
Oeceoclades Lindl. = Saccolabium Blume (Orchid.).
Oecology, ecology.
Oecopetalum Greenman et C. H. Thompson. Icacinaceae. 1 Mexico.
Oedematopus Planch. et Triana (*Havetiopsis BH.*). Guttiferae (V). 6 Amazon valley.
Oedera L. Compositae (7). 4 Cape Colony.
Oegroe Phil. Compositae (inc. sed.). 1 Chili.
Oenanthe (Tourn.) L. Umbelliferae (III. 5). 35 N. temp. |✻. 7 in Brit. (water drop-wort).
Oenocarpus Mart. Palmaceae (IV. 1). 8 N. S. Am.
Oenone Tul. (*Ligea* Tul.). Podostemaceae. 25 Guiana, Brazil.
Oenosciadium Pomel (*Oenanthe* p.p. *EP.*). Umbellif. (III. 5). 1 N. Afr.
Oenothera L. (*BH.* incl. *Godetia* Spach, *Onagra* Tourn., *Xylopleurum* Spach). Onagr. (2). 50 Am., W.I. *O.* (*Onagra*) *biennis* L. (evening primrose), &c., cult. orn. fl. The fls. of *O. biennis* emit scent at evening and are visited by nocturnal moths, to which they are suited by the long tubes.
Oenotheraceae (Warming) = Onagraceae.
Oenotheridium Reiche (*Godetia* p.p.). Onagraceae (2). 1 Chili.
Oeonia (*Aeonia*) Lindl. Orchidaceae (II. 20). 5 Mascarene Is.
Oeoniella Schlechter (*Epidendrum* p.p.). Orchid. (II. 6). 2 Madag., Masc.
Ofaiston Rafin. Chenopodiaceae (B). 1 W. As.
Officinalis (Lat.), medicinal.
Offset, a short runner, bending up at the end, *Agave*, *Sempervivum*.
Oftia Adans. Myoporaceae. 2 S. Afr.
Ogeechee lime (Am.), *Nyssa*.
Oianthus Benth. Asclepiadaceae (II. 3). 3 India.
-oides (Gr. suff.), -like.
Oil occurs in plants in two forms, the *fixed oils*, or non-nitrogenous reserves in seeds, and the *volatile oils*, which give the perfume to many fls. and l. The former are obtained by pressure, the latter by distillation. Fixed oils from *Aleurites*, *Arachis* (groundnut), *Argania*,

Barringtonia, *Brassica* (rape, colza), *Calophyllum*, *Carya*, *Cocos* (coconut), *Corylus*, *Croton*, *Elaeis* (palm oil), *Eruca*, *Fagus*, *Ginkgo*, *Glycine* (soja, soy), *Gossypium* (cottonseed), *Guizotia* (nigerseed), *Helianthus*, *Juglans* (walnut), *Linum* (linseed), *Melia*, *Moringa*, *Olea* (olive), *Papaver*, *Polygala*, *Ricinus* (castor), *Sapium*, *Schleichera*, *Sesamum* (gingelly), *Theobroma* (cacao-butter), *Tilia*, *Vateria*, &c., &c. Some of these are drying oils, like linseed, and used in painting, some remain fluid, some are solid or fatty, esp. in Europe. More solid fatty bodies are obtained from *Bassia*, *Butyrospermum*, *Caryocar*, *Pentadesma*, &c. Volatile oils from *Acacia*, *Backhousia*, *Calamintha*, *Cananga*, *Cinnamomum* (cinnamon), *Citrus* (lemon, &c.), *Cymbopogon* (citronella, geranium, lemongrass), *Dictamnus*, *Eucalyptus*, *Eugenia* (clove), *Gaultheria* (wintergreen), *Jasminum*, *Labiatae*, *Lavandula* (lavender), *Lippia*, *Melaleuca*, *Mentha* (peppermint), *Nardostachys* (spikenard), *Origanum*, *Pelargonium*, *Pogostemon* (patchouli), *Reseda*, *Rosa*, *Rosemarinus*, *Santalum* (sandalwood), *Sassafras*, *Thymus*, *Viola*, &c., &c.

Andiroba -, *Carapa*; **argan -**, *Argania*; **bay -**, *Laurus*; **ben -**, *Moringa*; **bergamot -**, *Citrus*; **birch -**, *Betula*; **cajeput -**, *Melaleuca*; **camphor -**, *Cinnamomum*; **caraway -**, *Carum*; **castor -**, *Ricinus*; **chaulmoogra -**, *Gynocardia*; **citron -**, *Citrus*; **citronella -**, *Cymbopogon*; **clove -**, *Eugenia*; **coconut -**, *Cocos*; **cohune -**, *Attalea*; **colza -**, *Brassica*; **cottonseed -**, *Gossypium*; **croton -**, *Croton*; **cumin -**, *Cuminum*; **Florence** (fine olive) **-**, *Olea*; **geranium -**, *Pelargonium*, *Cymbopogon*; **gingelly -**, *Sesamum*; **groundnut -**, *Arachis*; **hempseed -**, *Linum*; **illupi -**, *Bassia*; **jasmine -**, *Jasminum*; **juniper -**, *Juniperus*; **kekuna -**, *Aleurites*; **khus-khus -**, *Vetiveria*; **lavender -**, *Lavandula*; **lemon -**, *Citrus*; **lemongrass -**, *Cymbopogon*; **linseed -**, *Linum*; **Macassar -**, *Cananga*; **margosa -**, *Azadirachta*; **marjoram -**, *Origanum*; **mustard -**, *Brassica*; **neroli -**, *Citrus*; **nim -**, *Azadirachta*; **olive -**, *Olea*; **palm -**, *Elaeis*; **patchouli -**, *Pogostemon*; **peanut -**, *Arachis*; **pimento -**, *Pimenta*; **poppy -**, *Papaver*; **rantil -**, *Guizotia*; **rape -**, *Brassica*; **rosemary -**, *Rosmarinus*; **rue -**, *Ruta*; **rusa -**, *Cymbopogon*; **sandalwood -**, *Santalum*; **sanderswood -**, *Santalum*; **sassafras -**, *Sassafras*; **savin -**, *Juniperus*; **sunflower -**, *Helianthus*; **thyme -**, *Thymus*; **tonquin -**, *Dipteryx*; **turpentine -**, *Pinus*, &c.; **verbena -**, *Lippia*; **walnut -**, *Juglans*; **wintergreen -**, *Gaultheria*; **wood -**, *Dipterocarpus*, *Aleurites*; **- glands** or passages, *Guttiferae*, *Lauraceae*, *Monimiaceae*, *Myrtaceae*.

Oilapetalum Pohl. Inc. sed. Nomen.

Oionychion Nieuwland (*Viola* p.p.). Violaceae. 1 N. Am.

Oiospermum Less. Compositae (1). 1 Bahia.

Oistonema Schlechter. Asclepiadaceae (II. 3). 1 Borneo.

Okenia Schlecht. et Cham. Nyctaginaceae. 3 S. Mexico.

Okra, *Hibiscus esculentus* L.

Ola (Ceylon), *Borassus*, *Corypha*, &c.

Olacaceae (*EP.*; *Olacineae* p.p. *BH.*). Dicots. (Archichl. Santalales). 25 gen., 120 sp., trop. Most are shrubs or trees with alt. entire l. and small ☿ reg. fls. There is a distinct K, resembling the calyculus of Loranthaceae, but probably not equivalent to it. C 4—6; A as many or 2 or 3 times as many; G partly sunk in the disc, or free, 2—5-loc. at base, 1-loc. above, with free plac. and 1 ovule hanging down into each loc. (occasionally 1-loc. 1-ovuled). Drupe or nut, one-seeded. Seed with testa and endosp. *Chief genera:* Ximenia, Olax.

Olacales (*BH.*). The 8th order of Polypetalae.

Olacineae (*BH.*, *Olacaceae+Icacinaceae EP.*). Trees and shrubs with usu. alt. l. and axillary infl. of ☿ or unisexual reg. fls. K, C (4—5—6), A 4—10, rarely 12, G free or partly in disc, (3—5), 1- or multi-loc. with few ovules. Drupe 1-seeded. Endosp.

Olax L. Olacaceae. 35 palaeotrop.

Oldenburgia Less. Compositae (12). 3 Cape Colony.

Oldenlandia L. (incl. *Hedyotis* L.). Rubiaceae (I. 2). 180 warm. Some are heterostyled (dimorphic).

Oldfieldia Hook. Euphorbiaceae (A. I. 1). 1 trop. W. Afr., *O. africana* Benth. et Hook. f., the African oak. Good timber.

Old maid (W.I.), *Vinca rosea* L.; **-man**, *Artemisia Abrotanum* L.; **- -'s beard**, *Tillandsia*; **- - cactus**, *Cereus senilis* Salm-Dyck; **-woman's bitter** (W.I.), *Picramnia*; **-witch grass** (Am.), *Panicum capillare* L.

Olea (Tourn.) L. Oleac. 35 Medit., Afr., Indomal., Austr., N.Z., Polynes. *O. europaea* L. (olive), cult. in Medit. region from early ages. The wild form has thorny twigs and a small fr., the cult. form (var. *sativa* DC.) is smooth and has a large drupe with oily flesh. The oil is obtained by bruising and pressing the fruit. Several yield good timber, *e.g.* the olive, *O. laurifolia* Lem. (S. Afr.; black ironwood), &c.

Oleaceae (*EP.*, *BH.*). Dicots. (Sympet. Contortae; Gentianales *BH.*). 21 gen., 400 sp., trop. and warm temp., esp. E. Ind. Shrubs and trees usu. with opp. l., which are exstip., simple or pinnate, often entire. Serial accessory buds occur in the leaf-axils of many sp. (*e.g.* Syringa) in both flg. and veg. parts. The infl. is racemose or cymose, often bracteolate. Fls. ☿, rarely unisexual, reg., 2—6-merous, sometimes poly- or a-petalous (Fraxinus, &c.). K typically (4), valvate; C (4) valvate or imbr., rarely conv.; A 2, epipet. usu. transv. placed, and alt. with cpls.; no disc; G (2); stigma 2-lobed on simple style; ov. 2-loc. with 2 anatr. ov. in each loc. Berry, drupe, or caps., or schizocarp, with 1—4 seeds. Endosp. or none, embryo straight. Olea, Fraxinus, &c., are of economic value.

Oleander, *Nerium Oleander* L.

Oleandra Cav. Polypodiaceae. 10 trop.

Olearia Moench. Compositae (3). 90 Austr., N.Z., New Guinea. Replaces Aster, and closely resembles it, but all trees or shrubs.

Oleaster, *Elaeagnus*, *Olea*.

Oleiferus (Lat.), oil-bearing.

Oleine, *Cocos*.

Oleoxylon Roxb. Dipterocarpaceae. 1 Burma.

Oleraceus (Lat.), esculent.

Olibanum, *Boswellia Carteri* Birdw., &c.

Oligandra Less. Compositae (4). 3 trop. S. Am.

Oliganthes Cass. Compositae (1). 8 trop. Am.

Oligarrhena R. Br. Epacridaceae (3). 1 W. Austr.

Oligo- (Gr. pref.), few; **-merous**, with fewer members in whorl.
Oligobotrya Baker. Liliaceae (VII). 1 China.
Oligocarpus Less. Compositae (9). 3 S. Afr.
Oligocladus Chodat et Wilczek. Umbelliferae (III. 6). 1 Argentina.
Oligodora DC. (*Athanasia* p.p. *EP.*). Compositae (4). 1 S. Afr.
Oligogynium Engl. (*Nephthytis* p.p. *BH.*). Araceae (IV). 3 W. Afr.
Oligolobos Gagnep. Hydrocharidaceae. 2 China, Indochina.
Oligomeris Cambess. Resedaceae. 5 Africa, India, S.W. U.S.
Oligonema S. Wats. Compositae (3). 1 Mexico.
Oligoneuron Small (*Solidago* p.p.). Compositae (3). 4 N. Am.
Oligosporus Cass. = Artemisia L. p.p. (Comp.).
Oligostemon Benth. (*Duparquetia EP.*). Leguminosae (II. 5). 1 W. Afr.
Oligothrix DC. Compositae (8). 2 trop. and S. Afr.
Olinia Thunb. Oliniaceae. 6 Afr. Shrubs with opp. entire l. and panicles of ☿ fls. K, C, A 4—5, $\overline{G}$ (3—5), 3—5-loc. each with 2—3 ovules; short style. Drupe; no endosp.
Oliniaceae (*EP.*; *Lythraceae* p.p. *BH.*). Dicots. (Archichl. Thymelaeales). Only genus Olinia (*q.v.*).
Olisbea DC. (*Mouriria BH.*). Melastomaceae (III). 4 Brazil, W.I.
Olivaea Sch.-Bip. Compositae (6). 1 Mexico.
Olive, *Olea europaea* L.
Oliveranthus (*Oliverella*) Rose. Crassulaceae. 1 Mexico.
Oliveria Vent. Umbelliferae (III. 5). 1 W. As.
Oliveriana Reichb. f. (*Trichopilia BH.*). Orchid. (II. 19). 1 Colombia.
Olmedia Ruiz et Pav. Moraceae (II). 6 trop. Am.
Olmediella Baill. Flacourt. (4), formerly Morac. 2 Brazil?
Olmediophaena Karst. Moraceae (II). 1 Colombia.
Olneya A. Gray. Leguminosae (III. 6). 1 California to Mexico.
Olostyla DC. Rubiaceae (II. 9). 1 New Caledonia.
Olympusa Klotzsch. Asclepiadaceae (inc. sed.). 1 Guiana. Nomen.
Olyra L. Gramineae (5). 20 trop. Am., Afr.
Omania Sp. Moore. Scrophulariaceae (III. 3). 1 Arabia.
Ombrophile, a pl. which can, **-phobe**, which cannot, stand long continued rain.
Ombrophytum Poepp. Balanophoraceae. 2 Peru.
Omphacomeria A. DC. Santalaceae. 2 Austr.
Omphalea L. Euphorbiaceae (A. II. 7). 10 trop. Am., As., Madag.
Omphalobium Gaertn. = Connarus L. (Connar.).
Omphalocarpum Beauv. Sapotaceae (I). 5 trop. W. Afr.
Omphalodes Tourn. ex Moench. Boraginaceae (IV. 1). 24 Eur., As., Mexico. The borders of the achenes are inrolled.
Omphalogonus Baill. Asclepiadaceae (I). 1 Zanzibar.
Omphalogramma Franch. (*Primula* p.p.). Primul. 4 Himal., China.
Omphalopappus O. Hoffm. Compositae (5). 1 Angola.
Omphalophthalmum Karst. Asclepiadaceae (II. 4). 1 Colombia.
Omphalopus Naud. Melastomaceae (I). 2 Java, Sumatra.
Omphalothrix Maxim. Scrophulariaceae (III. 3). 1 N.E. As.
Onagra (Tourn.) Adans. (*Oenothera* L. p.p. *BH.*). Onagraceae (2). 8 N. Am., incl. *O. biennis* Scop., the evening primrose.

Onagraceae (*EP.*, *BH.*). Dicots. (Archichl. Myrtiflorae; Myrtales *BH.*; pp. xxxix, lii). 40/500, temp. and trop. Most are perenn. herbs, a few shrubs or trees, with alt., opp., or whorled l., usu. simple, rarely stip. Fls. sol. in axils, or in spikes, racemes, or panicles, ☿, reg. or ·|·, usu. 4-merous (2—5). Axis usu. prolonged beyond ovary into a calyx-tube. K 4, valvate; C 4, rarely 0, usu. conv.; A 4+4, or 4—2—1, pollen grains with 3 exits; $\overline{G}$ (4), 4-loc., or $\frac{1}{2}$-inf. 2-loc., with axile plac. and ∞—1 anatr. ov.; septa commonly imperfect below; style simple, stigmas 1 or more. Fls. often very protandr., suited to bees or Lepidoptera; *cf.* Lopezia. Fr. usu. a loculic. caps., sometimes nut or berry; endosp. little or 0. Many cult. orn. fl.

Classification and chief genera (after Engler):

1. *Trapeae* (G $\frac{1}{2}$-inf., 2-loc.; fr. thorny): Trapa.
2. *Oenothereae* ($\overline{G}$ 4—1-loc.): Epilobium, Jussieua, Ludwigia, Oenothera, Clarkia, Fuchsia, Lopezia, Circaea.

Oncidioda ×. Orchid hybrid, Oncidium-Cochlioda.

Oncidium Sw. Orchid. (II. 19). 350 warm Am., W.I. Epiph. Some have flat tubers which collect humus, some fleshy l. Cult. orn. fl.

Oncinocalyx F. Muell. Verben. (4). 1 Austr.

Oncinotis Benth. Apocyn. (II. 1). 15 trop. and S. Afr., Madag.

Oncoba Forsk. Flacourt. (2). 30 trop. Am., Afr., Madag. Fr. not winged.

Oncocalamus Mann et H. Wendl. Palm. (III. 2). 1 W. Afr. Climber.

Oncocarpus A. Gray (*Semecarpus* p.p. *EP.*). Anacard. (4). 3 New Guin., Fiji, Phil. Is.

Oncodostigma Diels. Anon. (2). 1 New Guin.

Oncosperma Blume. Palm. (IV. 1). 8 Indomal. Very thorny.

Oncostemma K. Schum. Asclep. (II. 3). 1 S. Thomé (W. Afr.).

Oncostemon A. Juss. Myrsin. (II. 2). 60 Madag., Masc. Largest genus endemic to islands only.

Oncotheca Baill. Aquifol.? Eben.? 1 New Caled.

Oncus Lour. = Tiliacora Colebr. (Menisp.) (formerly Dioscor.).

Ondetia Benth. Comp. (4). 1 S.W. Afr.

Ongokea Pierre. Olac. 2 Gaboon, Cameroons.

Onion, *Allium Cepa* L. **Onites** Rafin. = Origanum Tourn. (Labiat.).

Onix Medic. = Astragalus Tourn. p.p. (Legum.).

Onixotis Rafin. = Xylobium Lindl. (*BH.*) = Dipidax Laws. (*EP.*).

Onobroma Gaertn. = Carduncellus Adans. (Comp.).

Onobrychis L. Legum. (III. 7). 100 Eur., Medit., As. Fl. mech. like Trifolium. Petiole persistent. Ovules collat. *O. sativa* Lam. (sainfoin) good fodder.

Onoclea L. Polypod. 1 N. Am., N. As.

Ononis L. Legum. (III. 4). 75 Medit., Eur. (3 Brit., rest-harrow). Lat. branches sometimes thorny. Rarely > 3 leaflets. Fl. mech. between Lotus and Trifolium. At first upper edges of keel cohere, and pollen is squeezed out at tip; then anthers emerge as in Trif.

Onopix Rafin. Comp. (inc. sed.). 2 Louisiana.

Onopordon L. Comp. (11). 20 Eur., N. Afr., W. As. *O. Acanthium* L. (cotton thistle) Brit. L. decurrent. Invol. brs. thorny.

Onoseris DC. Comp. (12). 25 S. Am., Mex.

Onosma L. Boragin. (IV. 4). 80 Medit., Himal. R. of *O. echioides* L. yields dye (orsanette).

Onosmodium Michx. Boragin. (IV. 4). 7 N. Am.

Ontogeny, development of the individual.

Onuris Phil. Cruciferae (4). 6 Chili, Patagonia.
Onychium Kaulf. Polypodiaceae. 6 trop. and subtrop.
Onychosepalum Steud. Restionaceae. 1 S.W. Austr.
Oocarpon Micheli. Onagraceae (2). 1 Brazil, Guiana, Cuba.
Ooclinium DC. = Eupatorium Tourn. p.p. (Comp.).
Oonopsis Greene (*Aplopappus* p.p.). Compositae (3). 6 N. Am.
Oophyte, gametophyte, *Pteridophyta*; **-sphere**, ovum.
Open (aestivation), l. not even meeting by their edges.
Opercularia Gaertn. Rubiaceae (II. 7). 14 Austr.
Operculina Silva Manso (*Ipomoea* p.p. *BH.*). Convolvulaceae (I). 20 trop. Am., As. *O. turpethum* Silva Manso yields a drug.
Operculum (Lat.), a lid.
Ophelia D. Don = Swertia L. p.p. (Gentian.).
Ophio- (Gr. pref.), snake.
Ophiobotrys Gilg. Flacourtiaceae (7). 1 Cameroons.
Ophiocaryon Schomb. Sabiaceae. 1 Guiana (snakeseed).
Ophiocaulon Hook. f. (*Adenia* p.p. *EP.*). Passifloraceae. 6 Afr.
Ophioglossaceae. Filicales Ophioglossales. 3 gen., 50 sp., trop., temp. Small herbs, some trop. sp. epiphytic; there is a root-stock or rhiz. bearing roots in acropetal succession, and giving off l. which project above the soil. The l. bases are usu. fleshy and fit closely together, concealing the stem. The l. splits into a dorsal and a ventral part, the former being the 'sterile' green blade, the latter the 'fertile' sporangiferous spike, often much branched and containing the sporangia sunk in its tissues. The spores are all of one kind and give rise to subterranean colourless prothalli, living saprophytically. *Genera:* Ophioglossum (sporangia sessile, in two rows, forming a narrow close spike), Botrychium (sporangia in small crested clusters forming a long loose spike), Helminthostachys (sporangia peltate, borne on sporangiophores which arise from the two sides of the fertile spike). [Lang in *Ann. Bot.* 1902, p. 23.]
Ophioglossales. The 3rd order of Filicales (*q.v.*). Only fam. Ophioglossaceae.
Ophioglossum L. Ophioglossaceae. 30 trop. and temp. *O. vulgatum* L., adder's-tongue, in Brit. The l. are developed very slowly, one appearing above the soil each year. Adv. buds are formed on the roots and thus the pl. multiplies veg. The sporangiferous spike is usu. unbranched, except in *O. palmatum* L., where "instead of a single spike there are a number arranged in two rows along the sides of the upper part of the petiole and the base of the lamina." (This sp. and *O. pendulum* L. are epiphytic.) The roots most often arise in relation to the l., one at the base of each; commonly unbranched.
Ophione Schott. Araceae (IV). 1 Colombia.
Ophiopogon Ker-Gawl. Liliaceae (VIII) (Haemod. *BH.*). 5 Japan, China. The mucilaginous tubers of *O. japonicus* Ker-Gawl. are ed.
Ophiorrhiza L. Rubiaceae (I. 2). 80 Indomal.
Ophiorrhiziphyllum Kurz. Acanthaceae (1). 1 Burma.
Ophioxylon L. = Rauwolfia Plum. (Apocyn.).
Ophiurus Gaertn. f. Gramineae (2). 70 trop.
Ophryococcus Oerst. Rubiaceae (I. 7). 1 Nicaragua.
Ophryosporus Meyen. Compositae (2). 15 trop. and subtrop. Am.

Ophrys L. Orchidaceae (II. 1). 30 Eur., W. As., N. Afr. (*O. apifera* Huds., bee-orchis, *O. aranifera* Huds., spider-orchis, *O. muscifera* Huds., fly-orchis, in Brit.). Terrestrial herbs with habit and fl. chars. of Orchis. *O. apifera* is one of the few self-fert. orchids. If the pollinia are not removed by insects (as in Orchis) they drop out of the anther and dangle on their long caudicles in front of the stigma, against which they get blown or knocked (see Darwin).

Ophthalmoblapton Allem. Euphorbiaceae (A. II. 7). 4 Brazil.

Opicrina Rafin. Compositae (inc. sed.). 2 N. Am.

Opilia Roxb. Opiliaceae. 6 palaeotrop. Fl. ☿, heterochlam., with seam-like K. G with one ov. without integument. Parasitic.

Opiliaceae (*EP.*; *Olacineae* p.p. *BH.*). Dicots. (Archichl. Santalales). Chief genus Opilia, *q.v.*

Opisthocentra Hook. f. Melastomaceae (I). 1 N. Brazil.

Opium, *Papaver somniferum* L.

Opizia J. et C. Presl. Gramineae (11). 1 Mexico.

Oplismenus Beauv. Gramineae (5). 15 trop. and subtrop.

Oplotheca Nutt. = Froelichia Moench (Amarant.).

Opocunonia Schlechter. Cunoniaceae. 4 New Guinea.

Opopanax Koch. Umbelliferae (III. 6). 4 Medit. Gum opopanax, used in perfumery, is obtained from incisions in the roots.

Opopanax, gum -, *Opopanax*.

Oporanthus Herb. = Sternbergia Waldst. et Kit. p.p. (Amaryll.).

Opposite (l.), two at a node, at angle 180°; **-ifolius**, with opp. l.

-opsis (Gr. suff.), -like.

Opulus Tourn. ex L. = Viburnum L. p.p. (Caprifol.).

Opulaster Medic. (*Neillia BH.*, *Physocarpus EP.*). Ros. (I. 1). 20 N. Am.

Opuntia Tourn. ex Mill. Cactaceae (II). 250 Am. Some have become troublesome weeds in Austr., &c. Fleshy stemmed, usu. with small fleshy l., which drop off very early (see fam.). In *O. subulata* Engelm. the l. are large and do a good deal of assimilation. Some, *e.g. O. Stapeliae* DC., have mammilla-like cushions; *O. brasiliensis* Haw. has the main stem cylindrical and the lat. ones flat; most have all the stems flattened, *e.g. O. vulgaris* Mill. (prickly pear), *O. Ficus-indica* Mill. (Indian fig), &c. (see Goebel's *Pflanzenbiol. Sch.* I. p. 73 seq.). The l. of the lat. shoots usu. form groups of thorns, but in *O. diademata* Lem. are ribbon-like and scaly. Many are veg. propagated by the detachment of branches, *e.g. O. fragilis* Haw., which rarely flowers at all. The fr. of prickly pear, &c. are ed.; some are used for hedge-making, others as food for cochineal-insects (see Nopalea). [For *O. coccinellifera* Steud. see Nopalea.]

Opuntiales. The 28th order of Archichlamydeae. *Cf.* p. xxxvi.

Orache, *Atriplex*.

Orange, *Citrus Aurantium* L.; **-grass** (Am.), *Hypericum Sarothra* Michx.; **Jamaica mandarin -**, *Glycosmis*; **mandarin -**, *Citrus nobilis* Lour.; **osage -**, *Maclura aurantiaca* Nutt.; **-root** (Am.), *Hydrastis*; **wild -** (W.I.), *Drypetes*.

Orania Zippel. Palmae (IV. 1). 5 Malay Archipelago.

Orbea Haw. = Stapelia L. p.p. (Asclep.).

Orbicular (l.), circular in outline.

Orbignya Mart. ex Endl. Palmae (IV. 2). 7 Brazil, Bolivia.
Orbinda Nor. Inc. sed. Nomen.
Orchadocarpa Ridl. Gesneriaceae (I). 1 Malay Peninsula.
Orchard grass (Am.), *Dactylis glomerata* L.
Orchiaceras × E. G. Camus. Orchidaceae. Hybrid, Orchis-Aceras.
Orchicoeloglossum × Aschers. et Graebn. Orchid. Hybrid, Orchis-Coeloglossum.
Orchidaceae (*EP.*, *BH.*). Monocots. (Microspermae). 450 gen., 7500 sp., cosmop., abundant in trop., rare in arctic regions. They agree in some general features of habit, &c., *e.g.* they are all perennial herbs, but differ widely in detail, owing to the diversity of conditions in which they exist—land-plants, epiphytes, saprophytes, &c. Within the trop. they form an important feature of the veg., living chiefly as epiphytes. Most temp. zone forms are terrestrial.

The plant as a whole may be built up in one of three ways, (1) a monopodium, the main axis growing steadily on, year after year, and bearing the fls. on lat. branches; (2) an *acranthous* sympodium, the main axis being composed of annual portions of successive axes, each of which begins with scale l. and *ends* in an infl.; (3) a *pleuranthous* sympodium, where the infls. are borne on *lateral* axes, the shoot which for the current year continues the main axis stopping short at the end of its growing period, and not ending in an infl. These types of construction are used in classification (see below).

The saprophytes are few; they have no green l.; below the soil, in the humus, is a fleshy rhiz., with (Neottia) or without roots. It is much branched, and does part or all of the work of absorption. Mycorhiza occurs in most or all. The terrestrial forms are all sympodial, and have usu. a rhiz.; each annual shoot bends up into the leafy shoot of the current year. Many being xero., and all perenn., it becomes a necessity that there should be a storage reservoir to last over the non-veg. period of the year. In a great many this takes the form of a thickened internode of the stem: in many again, among which the Brit. orchids are included, the bud for the next year's growth, *i.e.* the next part of the sympodium, is laid down at the base of the stem, and from it is developed a thick and fleshy adv. root, forming a large tuber, which lasts over the winter.

Coming lastly to the epiphytes, abundant in the trop., we find great variety. [See Schimper, *Die epiphytische Vegetation Amerikas*.] They are mostly sympodial, but the few monopodial O. also belong to this group. The exceedingly light seeds and the xero. habit of many O. fit them to become epiph. The roots of the epiph. forms are of interest. In the first place, to fasten the pl. to its support there are 'clinging' roots, insensitive to gravity, but negatively heliotropic. The niche between the pl. and its support and the network formed by the roots act as reservoirs for humus, and into this project 'absorbing' roots, branches from the others; these are usu., Schimper asserts, negatively geotropic. Finally the true aerial roots hang down in long festoons. The outer layers of cells (the epidermis and *velamen*) are dead and perforated, and act as a sponge to absorb water trickling over them. Their internal tissue is green (as may be seen on wetting a root) and assimilates. During the dry season a great proportion of the O. drop their l. (though they may flower), and 'hibernate' in the condition of fleshy *pseudobulbs*. One pseudobulb, which is a thickened stem-internode, is usu. formed each year. In this, water and other reserves are stored. Those epiphytes which do not form these tubers have fleshy l. which serve the same end; the fleshy leaved orchids, *e.g.* Vanilla, have usu. a very feebly developed velamen. Some monopodial forms have no green l. at all, assimilating either by the surface of the stem, or by the long dangling aerial roots (Polyrrhiza, &c.).

The infls. are racemose, very often spikes, which look like racemes, the long inf. ovary resembling a stalk. The fl. is ·|· and departs from the ordinary Monocot. type. There are two chief divisions of O., with different fls., the *Monandrae* and *Pleonandrae*, with 1 and 2 sta. respectively; the great majority are monandrous. P in 2 whorls, epig., petaloid. The post. petal is usu. larger than the rest, and is termed the *labellum*; by the twisting (*resupination*) of the ovary through 180° it comes round to the ant. side of the fl. and forms a landing place for insects. In many O. its structure is exceedingly complex. The essential organs of the fl. are all comprised in a central structure by which the O. can be recognised at a glance, viz. the *column*, which consists in the simpler cases of the combined style and sta. (to use the old-fashioned expression; in reality it is very probably an outgrowth of the axis, bearing the anthers and stigmas at the top). In the monandrous forms the column exhibits one anther and two fertile stigmas (often ± confluent), together with a special organ, the *rostellum*, which repres. the third stigma. The single anther is the ant. one of the outer whorl (if we imagine the fl. of O. derived from a typical 3-merous fl.); the other two of this whorl are entirely absent, and also all those of the inner whorl, though in some genera, *e.g.* Orchis, the ant. two are repres. by stds. upon the sides of the column. The two fertile stigmas are the post. pair, and the third (ant.) is repres. by the rostellum (in using the terms ant. and post., the resupination is supposed not to have occurred).

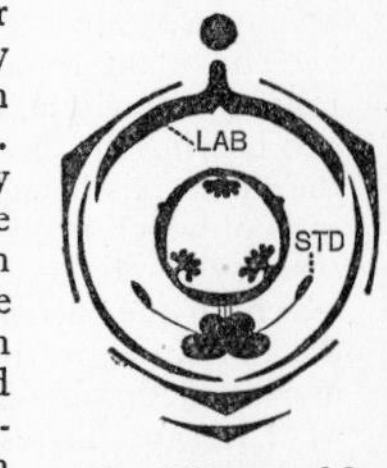

Floral diagram of Orchis, before resupination (after Eichler, modified); LAB = labellum, STD = staminode.

The various organs face the labellum, and, in the fl. of a simple O., *e.g.* Orchis, can easily be made out. A little above the base are the two stigmas, then above these a projecting point, the rostellum, and above this again, and behind it, forming the apex of the column, is the anther, which shows two lobes. Each is occupied by a *pollinium*, or mass of pollen. Under the microscope the grains of pollen are seen to be tied together in packets by elastic threads; these unite at the base of the pollinium and form a cord, the *caudicle*, which runs down into, and is attached to part of the rostellum.

The simple construction found in Orchis, &c., as thus described, is replaced by much more complex arrangements in many. The labellum itself may be rendered very complex, by the addition of spurs and other outgrowths; often outgrowths of the summit of the receptacle take place, displacing some of the organs, thus for example in Drymoda and others, the labellum and the sepals on either side of it are carried forward on an axial protuberance in such a way that the sepals appear to spring from the labellum, the axial growth (*chin*) appearing like the basal part of this organ. Some of these constructions are very complex. Several are described in connection with the genera to which they belong.

Similarly the column shows great variety in structure (refer as above). One point may be mentioned specially as of importance in classification. In the simple case of Orchis, &c., described above, the *base* of the anther loculi is against the rostellum; such cases are called *basitonic*; in others it is the apex that is next the rostellum (Oncidium, &c.), and these are *acrotonic.*

[Diandrae. So far only monandrous forms have been considered. In Cypripedium and its allies the column has 2 anthers, no rostellum, and a simple stigma, composed of the 3 carpellary stigmas. The two sta. belong to the inner whorl, and the sta. which in Monandrae is fertile, is here repres. by a large std. The stigma is not sticky, but the pollen is, and it is not combined into pollinia.]

The ovary is inf. in all O., uniloc. with 3 parietal plac. (exc. Apostasia), and ∞ ovules, which do not develope until fert. of the fl. occurs.

The adaptations of orchid flowers to *fertilisation* by insects are endless, and many very complicated. Reference must be made to text-books for the details. No student should omit to read Darwin's *Fertilisation of Orchids*, at least the first two and the last chapters. In it will be found accounts of the mech. of most of the common gen. A few general points only can be mentioned here; in the description of the individual gen. other details are given. Very few secrete free honey; in most cases the insect has to bite into or drill the tissue for the juice therein contained; this tissue is usu. part of the labellum—often a spur at the base—or the basal part of the column. The pollinia are removed as a rule when the insect is going out of the fl. In most cases the insect in entering displaces the rostellum or some portion of it, and thereby exposes and comes into contact with a sticky mass (due to disorganisation of cells formerly living). This becomes cemented to the insect while it is drilling for honey, and as the insect goes out again it takes with it the viscid lump, together with the pollinia, either merely glued to it, or attached by caudicles. In many cases the pollinia are in such a position that when the insect enters the next fl. they will touch the stigmas. In others this is not so, *e.g.* Orchis, where the anthers and stigma are far apart on the column, and in such cases the pollinia, on getting out of the anther, execute a hygroscopic movement which brings them into the proper position on the insect's body to strike the stigmas. Such is the general principle of the orchid mechanism, but the variety in detail is endless. Many fls. have the most extraordinary structure, *e.g.* Coryanthes, Stanhopea, Vanda, &c. See under gen.

The *fruit* is a caps., containing usu. a gigantic number of exceedingly small and light seeds, which are well suited to wind distr. (hence, among other causes, the epiph. habit of so many).

The O. are favourites in horticulture, and very many gen. are cult.

There are many generic hybrids; the names of most of those as yet produced, *e.g.* Orchicoeloglossum, Phaiocalanthe, Zygocolax, are included in this book. Vanilla is the only orchid of economic importance.

Classification and chief genera (after Pfitzer):

I. *PLEONANDRAE* (two stamens).

1. Apostasieae: Apostasia.
2. Cypripedileae: Cypripedium.

II. *MONANDRAE* (one stamen).

a. *Basitonae* (basitonic, anther not falling off):

1. Ophrydeae: Ophrys, Orchis, Habenaria, Disa.

b. *Acrotonae* (acrotonic, anther usually falling easily):

α. ACRANTHAE (acranthous sympodial):

I. **Convolutae** (l. convolute in bud, with no distinction between blade and sheath):

2. Neottieae: Vanilla, Epipactis, Neottia.

II. **Articulatae** (as I., but with a joint between blade and sheath):

3. Coelogyneae: Coelogyne, Pholidota.

III. **Duplicatae** (l. folded in bud):

4. Liparideae: Liparis, Corallorhiza.
5. Polystachyeae: Galeandra.
6. Laelieae: Epidendrum, Cattleya, Laelia.
7. Sobralieae: Sobralia.
8. Pleurothallidieae: Masdevallia, Pleurothallis.

β. PLEURANTHAE (pleuranthous sympodial):

I. **Convolutae** (l. convolute in bud):

9. Phajeae: Phajus, Calanthe.
10. Cyrtopodieae: Lissochilus.
11. Cataseteae: Mormodes, Catasetum.
12. Lycasteae: Lycaste.
13. Gongoreae: Coryanthes, Stanhopea, Gongora.
14. Zygopetaleae: Zygopetalum.

II. **Duplicatae** (l. folded in bud):

1. *Sympodiales* (sympodial).

15. Dendrobieae: Dendrobium, Eria.
16. Bolbophylleae: Drymoda, Bolbophyllum.
17. Cymbidieae: Cymbidium.
18. Maxillarieae: Maxillaria, Scuticaria.
19. Oncidieae: Ada, Odontoglossum, Oncidium.

2. *Monopodiales* (monopodial).

20. Sarcantheae: Phalaenopsis, Vanda, Angraecum, Polyrrhiza, Aerides.

Orchidantha N. E. Br. (*Lowia* Hook. f.). Musaceae (III). 2 Malaya.

Orchideae (*BH.*) = Orchidaceae.

Orchidotypus Kränzlin. Orchidaceae (II. 8). 1 Peru.

Orchid-tree, *Amherstia nobilis* Wall.

Orchigymnadenia × E. G. Camus. Orchid. Hybrid, Orchis-Gymnadenia.

Orchis (Tourn.) L. (*BH.* incl. *Anacamptis* Rich., *Himantoglossum* Spreng.). Orchidaceae (II. 1). 70 Eur., temp. As., N. Afr., Am.

(10 Brit., incl. *O. mascula* L., early purple orchis, and *O. maculata* L., spotted orchis.) Sympodial perennials forming one tuber each year (see fam.). The fls. stand in a dense spike and have curious mech. for insect fert. The anther is basitonic and well above the stigmas. The rostellum has an outer firm pouch, inside which is the viscid substance to which are firmly attached the caudicles of the pollinia. An insect entering the fl. probes the spur of the labellum and its back comes into contact with the rostellum and depresses the pouch, causing the viscid substance to adhere to the insect. The tissue of the spur has to be drilled for honey, and while this is being done the cement rapidly sets, so that, as the insect leaves the fl., it takes with it the pollinia, standing upright on their caudicles. If they remained in this position they would never touch the stigmas of another fl., but as soon as the caudicles are exposed to air, they contract on the side towards the base of the fl. (*i.e.* towards the insect's head) and move the pollinia downwards from ! to –. In this position, when the insect enters another fl., they pass under the rostellum and strike the stigmas. [See Darwin's *Orchids* for details.]

Orchis, *Orchis*, any terrestrial member of Orchidaceae; **bee -**, *Ophrys apifera* Huds.; **bird's nest -**, *Neottia*; **butterfly -**, *Habenaria*, *Oncidium*; **dove -**, *Peristeria*; **early purple -**, *Orchis mascula* L.; **fly -**, *Ophrys muscifera* Huds.; **frog -**, *Habenaria* (*Coeloglossum*) *viridis* R. Br.; **lady's slipper -**, *Cypripedium*; **man -**, *Aceras anthropophora* R. Br.; **musk -**, *Herminium Monorchis* R. Br.; **scented -**, *Gymnadenia conopsea* R. Br.; **spider -**, *Ophrys aranifera* Huds.; **spotted -**, *Orchis maculata* L.

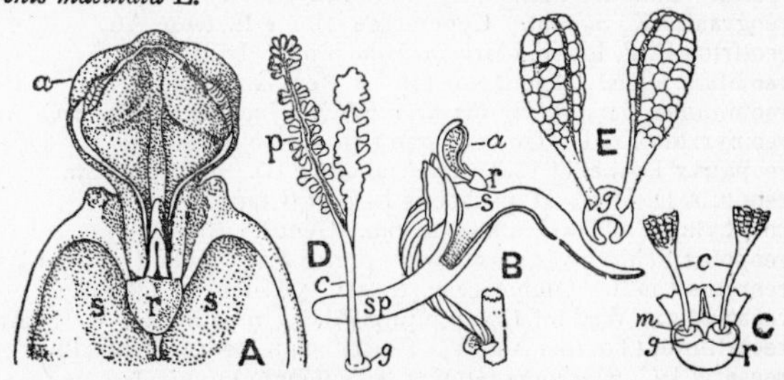

A—D. *Orchis mascula* (Purple Orchis). A. Front view of anther and top of column; *a*, anther; *s*, *s*, pair of stigmatic surfaces, one on each side of the rostellum, *r*. The pollen-sacs have split lengthwise, exposing the pollinia in the upper portion. On either side of the anther is a blunt outgrowth representing a sterile stamen. B. Dissection of flower, side view, showing part of lip and the spur (*sp*) and the relation of rostellum (*r*) and stigma (*s*) to entrance of spur. C. Base of pair of pollinia, front view; *c*, caudicles; *r*, rostellum; *g*, gland; *m*, membranous disc. D. Single pollinium, the pollen-containing portion separated, showing arrangement of packets of pollen on the two main axes.
E. Pollinia of *O. pyramidalis* attached to a common gland (*g*).

All enlarged. A, D, from original drawing by Fr. Bauer. B, C, E, after Darwin.

Orchiserapias × E. G. Camus. Orchidaceae. Hybrid, Orchis-Serapias.
Orcuttia Vasey. Gramineae (10). 1 California.

Ordeal bark, *Erythrophloeum*; **-bean**, *Physostigma*.
Oreacanthus Benth. Acanthaceae (IV. B). 1 Cameroons.
Oreanthes Benth. Ericaceae (III. 2). 1 Ecuador.
Oregon cedar, *Chamaecyparis Lawsoniana* Parl.
Oreinotinus Oerst. = Viburnum L. p.p. (Caprif.).
Oreiostachys Gamble. Gramineae (13). 1 Java.
Oreo- (Gr. pref.), mountain.
Oreobambos K. Schum. Gramineae (13). 1 E. Afr.
Oreobatus Rydberg (*Rubus* p.p.). Rosaceae (III. 2). 2 N. Am.
Oreobliton Dur. et Moq. Chenopodiaceae (A). 1 Algeria.
Oreobolus R. Br. Cyperaceae (II). 3 S. Am., Austr., N.Z., Polynesia.
Oreocallis Small (*Leucothoë* p.p.). Ericaceae (II. 1). 1 N.W. U.S.
Oreocarya Greene (*Krynitzkia* p.p.). Boraginaceae (IV. 2). 20 Pac. N. Am.
Oreocereus Riccob. (*Pilocereus* p.p.). Cactaceae (III. 1). 1 Boliv.
Oreocharis Benth. Gesneriaceae (I). 8 China, Japan.
Oreochloa Link. Gramineae (10). 2 S. Eur.
Oreochrysum Rydberg (*Aplopappus* p.p.). Compositae (3). 1 N. Am.
Oreocnida Miq. = Villebrunea Gaudich. (Urtic.).
Oreodaphne Nees et Mart. = Ocotea Aubl. p.p. (Laur.).
Oreodoxa Willd. Palmae (IV. 1). 6 trop. Am., W.I. Monoec.; fls. in groups of 3, a ♀ between two ♂. *O. oleracea* Mart. is the cabbage palm; the young head of l. is cut out and eaten. The fr. yields an oil, and a form of sago is obtained from the stem (see Metroxylon). The l. are used for thatch, &c. *O. regia* H. B. et K. is the royal palm. Both are extensively used for avenues.
Oreograstis K. Schum. Cyperaceae (I). 1 E. trop. Afr.
Oreolirion E. P. Bickn. (*Sisyrinchium* p.p.). Iridaceae (II). 2 N. Am.
Oreomitra Diels. Anonaceae (2). 1 New Guinea.
Oreomunnea Oerst. (*Engelhardtia BH.*). Juglandaceae. 1 C. Am.
Oreomyrrhis Endl. Umbelliferae (III. 4). 6 S. temp.
Oreopanax Decne. et Planch. Araliaceae (I). 80 trop. Am.
Oreophila D. Don = Hypochoeris L. p.p. (Comp.).
Oreophylax Endl. = Gentiana L. p.p. (Gent.).
Oreopolus Schlecht. (*Cruckshankia* p.p. *EP.*). Rubi. (I. 2). 1 Andes.
Oreorchis Lindl. Orchidaceae (II. 5). 5 Himalaya to Japan.
Oreosciadium Wedd. (*Apium* p.p. *EP.*). Umbellif. (III. 5). 5 Andes.
Oreoselinum (Tourn.) Adans. = Peucedanum Tourn. (Umbel.).
Oreoseris DC. = Gerbera Gronov. p.p. (Comp.).
Oreosolen Hook. f. Scrophulariaceae (III. 1). 2 Himalaya.
Oreosphacus Phil. Labiatae (VI). 1 Chili.
Oreostemma Greene (*Aster* p.p.). Compositae (3). 4 N. Am.
Oreostylidium Berggr. Stylidiaceae. 1 New Zealand.
Oreosyce Hook. f. Cucurbitaceae (2). 6 W. trop. Afr.
Oreothyrsus Lindau. Acanthaceae (IV. B). 2 New Guinea.
Oreoxis Rafin. (*Cymopterus* p.p.). Umbellif. (III. 5). 1 Colorado.
Oresitrophe Bunge. Saxifragaceae (I). 1 China.
Orestia Ridl. Orchidaceae (II. 4). 1 St Thomas I., W. Afr.
Orgadium (Cl.), an open woodland formation.
Organs, the parts of a plant regarded as performing functions.
Orias Dode. Lythraceae. 1 Cochinchina.

Oricia Pierre. Rutaceae (IV). 3 trop. Afr.
Orientale (Lat.), eastern.
Orientation, definite position with regard to stimuli.
Origanum Tourn. ex L. Labiatae (VI). 7 Eur., Medit. *O. vulgare* L. (marjoram) in Brit., used as a flavouring herb. *O. Majorana* L. yields oil of marjoram by distillation.
Orites R. Br. Proteaceae (II). 6 temp. E. Austr.
Oritrephes Ridl. Melastomaceae (I). 5 Malay Peninsula.
Orixa Thunb. (*Celastrus* p.p. *BH.*). Rutaceae (I). 1 Japan.
Orlaya Hoffm. (*Daucus* p.p. *BH.*). Umbelliferae (III. 2). 1 Medit.
Orleanisia Barb. Rodr. Orchidaceae (II. 6). 1 Brazil.
Ormocarpum Beauv. (Diphaca Lour.). Leguminosae (III. 7). 10 trop. and subtrop. |✻.
Ormosciadium Boiss. Umbelliferae (III. 6). 1 W. As.
Ormosia Jacks. Leguminosae (III. 1). 25 trop. The seeds of *O. dasycarpa* Jacks. (bead or necklace tree) show the same red and black surface as *Abrus precatorius*.
Ornamental plants, whether cult. for fl., fr. or l., or as ornamental shrubs or trees, are very numerous, and cannot be listed. Against most important genera thus employed are placed such notes as "cult. orn. fl." So far as the cold zones are concerned they may be roughly classified into *hardy* pl., which will stand the winter out of doors, *half-hardy*, which require protection during winter, or if annual to be germinated under glass and planted out, *cool house* plants from warmer climates than England, *succulent house* plants from dry climates, and *stove* plants from hot moist trop. climates. Or in another way, they may be grouped into ornamental trees, shrubs, and herbs, with the minor groups of water-plants, climbers, &c.
Ornanthes Rafin. = Fraxinus Tourn. (Olea.).
Ornithidium Salisb. Orchidaceae (II. 18). 25 trop. Am., W.I. Cult.
Ornitho- (Gr. pref.), bird ; **-phily**, fert. by birds.
Ornithobaea Parish. Gesneriaceae (I). 4 S.E. As.
Ornithocarpa Rose. Cruciferae (3). 1 Mexico.
Ornithocephalus Hook. Orchidaceae (II. 19). 20 trop. Am., W.I.
Ornithochilus Wall. ex Lindl. Orchidaceae (II. 20). 2 E. As.
Ornithogalum (Tourn.) L. Liliaceae (V). 90 temp. |✻. *O. umbellatum* L. (star-of-Bethlehem) in Brit.
Ornithoglossum Salisb. Liliaceae (I). 2 S. Afr.
Ornithophora Barb. Rodr. (*Sigmatostalix* p.p. *EP.*). Orchidaceae (II. 19). 1 Brazil.
Ornithopus L. Leguminosae (III. 7). 8 Medit., W. As., trop. Afr., S. Brazil. *O. perpusillus* L. in Brit. (bird's foot). *O. sativus* Brot. (seradella, serratella) affords good fodder.
Ornithostaphylos Small (*Arctostaphylos* p.p.). Ericaceae (II. 3). 1 Lower California.
Ornithoxanthum Link = Gagea Salisb. (Lili.).
Ornitrophe Comm. ex Juss. = Schmidelia L. (*BH.*) = Allophylus L.
Ornus Neck. = Fraxinus Tourn. (Olea.).
Orobanchaceae (*EP.*, *BH.*). Dicots. (Sympet. Tubiflorae ; Personales *BH.*). 12 gen., 140 sp., chiefly N. temp. |✻; a few Am. and trop. All are parasitic herbs with little or no chlorophyll, attached by

suckers formed upon their roots to the roots of other plants (the seeds of Orobanche only germinate when in contact with a root of a host). For details see genera. Infl. term., a raceme or spike (exc. Phelipaea, which has a sol. term. fl.). Fl. ☿, ·|·. K (2—5) hypog., C (5), imbr., 2-lipped; A 4, didynamous, epipet.; anthers opening longitudinally; G usu. (2), rarely (3), 1-loc. Placentae parietal, often T-shaped in section or branched; ovules ∞, anatr.; style 1. Loculic. caps.; seeds small, with minute undifferentiated embryo in oily endosp. *Chief genera:* Orobanche, Christisonia, Lathraea, Phelipaea.

Orobanche (Tourn.) L. Orobanchaceae. 90 temp. and subtrop.; 7 in Brit. (broom-rape). Parasitic by their roots upon the roots of other pl.; no green tissue. *O. ramosa* L. is common on hemp. *O. major* L. (*O. elatior* Sutton) on Centaurea, &c. (in Brit.), *O. minor* Sutton on clover. Some are confined to one host, *e.g.* *O. Hederae* Duby to ivy, others are more general in their attacks.

Orobus (Tourn.) L. = Lathyrus Tourn. p.p. (Legum.).

Orochaenactis Coville (*Chaenactis* p.p.). Compositae (6). 1 Calif.

Orogenia S. Wats. Umbelliferae (III. 4). 2 W. N. Am.

Orontium L. Araceae (III). 1 Atl. N. Am. Aquatic.

Oropetium Trin. Gramineae (12). 6 India, Afr.

Orophaca Britton (*Astragalus* p.p.). Leguminosae (III. 6). 3 N. Am.

Orophea Blume. Anonaceae (2). 32 Indomal.

Orophochilus Lindau. Acanthaceae (IV. A). 1 Peru.

Orophytium (Cl.), a subalpine plant formation.

Oroxylon Vent. Bignoniaceae (1). 1 Indomal.

Orphanidesia Boiss. et Bal. Ericaceae (II. 1). 1 W. As.

Orphium E. Mey. Gentianaceae (1). 1 Cape Colony.

Orpine, *Sedum Telephium* L.

Orris root, *Iris florentina* L.

Ortega L. Caryophyllaceae (I. 3). 2 Spain, Italy.

Ortgiesia Regel. Bromeliaceae (4). 8 trop. Am.

Orthaea Klotzsch (*Thibaudia* p.p. *EP.*). Ericaceae (III. 2). 1 Peru.

Orthantha Kerner. Scrophulariaceae (III. 3). 3 Eur., W. As.

Orthanthera Wight. Asclepiadaceae (II. 3). 4 Afr., India.

Orthechites Urb. (*Echites* p.p.). Apocynaceae (II. 1). 1 Jamaica.

Ortho- (Gr. pref.), upright, straight; **-plocous,** *Cruciferae*; **-stichies,** straight ranks; **-tropous** (ov.), in a straight line with the funicle; **-tropic,** placing itself in line with the stimulus.

Orthocarpus Nutt. Scrophulariaceae (III. 3). 30 W. Am.

Orthoceras R. Br. Orchidaceae (II. 2). 1 S.E. Austr., New Zealand.

Orthoclada Beauv. Gramineae (10). 1 trop. Am. L. petiolate.

Orthogoneuron Gilg. Melastomaceae (I). 1 trop. Afr.

Orthogynium Baill. Menispermaceae. 1 Madagascar.

Orthopappus Gleason (*Elephantopus* p.p.). Compos. (1). 1 trop. Am.

Orthopenthea Rolfe. Orchidaceae (II. 1). 10 S. Afr.

Orthophytum Beer (*Prantleia* *EP.*, *Pitcairnia* *BH.*). Bromeliaceae (4). 2 C. Brazil.

Orthopogon R. Br. = Oplismenus Beauv. (Gram.).

Orthopterygium Hemsl. (*Juliania* p.p.). Julianiaceae. 1 Peru.

Orthorrhiza Stapf (*Chorispora* p.p.). Cruciferae (4). 1 Persia.

Orthosia Decne. (*Vincetoxicum* Moench *BH.*, *Cynanchum* L. p.p. *EP.*). Asclepiadaceae (II. 1). 12 S. Am.
Orthosiphon Benth. Labiatae (VII). 50 Indomal., trop. Afr.
Orthostemon Berg. (*Feijoa* p.p. *BH.*). Myrtaceae (I). 1 subtrop. S. Am.
Orthostemon R. Br. (*Canscora* p.p.). Gentianaceae (I). 1 trop. Afr.
Orthotactus Nees=Dianthera Gronov. (*BH.*)=Justicia L.
Orthrosanthus Sweet. Iridaceae (II). 7 Austr., S. Am. to Mexico.
Orumbella Coulter et Rose (*Ligusticum* p.p.). Umbelliferae (III. 5). 1 Alaska.
Orychophragmus Bunge (*Moricandia* p.p. *BH.*). Crucif. (4). 2 China.
Oryctanthus Eichl. (*Loranthus* p.p. *BH.*). Loranth. (I). 10 trop. Am.
Oryctes S. Wats. Solanaceae (2). 1 Nevada.
Orygia Forsk. Aizoacae (I). 1 Afr. to Mysore.
Oryza L. Gramineae (6). 6 trop., incl. *O. sativa* L. (rice), one of the chief food plants of the world, an annual, wild in Indomal., S. Am. The cult. rices are probably derived polyphyletically from some of these. The main kinds are hill and swamp rice, the former chiefly grown by wild tribes. Swamp rice is chiefly cult. in Bengal, S. India, S.E. As., Japan, China and S. Am., and occurs in ∞ vars. It is cult. in shallow water till nearly ripe, when the water is drained off. The grain in the husk is known as paddy.
Oryzopsis Michx. Gramineae (8). 15 N. temp.
Osage orange, *Maclura aurantiaca* Nutt.
Osbeckia L. Melastomaceae (I). 50 palaeotrop.
Osbornia F. Muell. Myrtaceae (II. 1). 1 N.E. Austr.
Oschatzia Walp. (*Azorella* p.p. *BH.*). Umbelliferae (I. 1). 2 Austr.
Oserya Tul. et Wedd. Podostemaceae. 5 Brazil to Mexico.
Osier, *Salix viminalis* L.
Osmanthus Lour. Oleaceae. 10 E. and S. As., Polynes., N. Am. *O. fragrans* Lour. (*Olea fragrans* Thunb.), often cult., has ed. fr., and its l. are used to perfume tea.
Osmelia Thw. Flacourtiaceae (7). 8 Indomal.
Osmia Sch.-Bip. (*Eupatorium* p.p.). Compositae (2). 3 N. Am.
Osmites L. Compositae (4). 6 Cape Colony.
Osmitopsis Cass. Compositae (4). 1 Cape Colony.
Osmohydrophora Barb. Rodr. Bignoniaceae (I). 1 Amazonas.
Osmorhiza Rafin. Umbelliferae (III. 2). 15 As., Am.
Osmoxylon Miq. Araliaceae (I). 2 Malay Archipelago.
Osmunda L. Osmundaceae. 10 temp. and trop. *O. regalis* L. (royal fern) in Brit. has a root-stock sometimes a foot high, like the stem of a tree fern, bearing scale l. below the soil and ordinary l. above. The fronds are large (1—10 feet); the lower pinnae are veg., the upper are repr. only and form a sort of panicle. They are densely covered with sori, which have no indusium and have a peculiar annulus consisting of a round group of cells at one side of the apex. The sporangium dehisces longitudinally. Other sp. have the fertile pinnae on the lower part of the l., others again have separate veg. and repr. l.
Osmundaceae. Filicales Leptosporangiatae. 2 gen., 12 sp., trop. and temp. Short-stemmed ferns, with naked sori. The sporangia are

shortly stalked and have an annulus, consisting of a roundish group of cells at one side of the apex; they open by a longitudinal fissure. *Genera:* Osmunda (sori on special pinnae), Todea (sori on backs of ordinary pinnae).

Ossaea DC. Melastomaceae (I). 55 trop. Am., W.I.

Ostenia Buchenau. Butomaceae. 1 Uruguay.

Osteocarpum F. Muell. (*Threlkeldia BH.*). Chenopod. (A). 5 Austr.

Osteocarpus Phil. (*Alona* p.p.). Nolanaceae. 4 Chili.

Osteomeles Lindl. Rosaceae (II). 10 Andes, Polynesia.

Osteophloeum Warb. (*Myristica* p.p.). Myristic. 1 Amazonas.

Osteospermum L. Compositae (9). 40 S. Afr.

Osterdamia Neck=Zoysia Willd. (Gram.).

Ostiolate, with a mouth.

Ostodes Blume. Euphorbiaceae (A. II. 5). 12 Indomal.

Ostrearia Baill. ex Niedenzu. Hamamelidaceae. 1 Queensland.

Ostrich fern, *Matteuccia Struthiopteris*.

Ostrowskia Regel. Campanulaceae (I). 1 Turkestan.

Ostrya Mich. ex L. Betulaceae. 4 N. temp. Like Carpinus. *O. virginica* Willd. (lever-wood) furnishes a hard wood.

Ostryocarpus Hook. f. Leguminosae (III. 8). 3 trop. W. Afr.

Ostryoderris Dunn. Leguminosae (III. 8). 3 trop. W. Afr.

Ostryopsis Decne. Betul. 2 E. Mongolia, China. Dwarf shrub. A 4—6.

Oswego tea, *Monarda*.

Osyricera Blume. Orchidaceae (II. 16). 2 Java, New Guinea.

Osyridicarpos A. DC. Santalaceae. 3 Abyssinia to S. Afr.

Osyris L. Santalaceae. 7 |✻.

Otacanthus Lindl. Scrophular. (II. 6), (*Acanth. BH.*). 2 Brazil.

Otaheite apple (W.I.), *Eugenia malaccensis* L.; **-gooseberry** (W.I.), *Phyllanthus distichus* Muell.-Arg.

Otanthera Blume. Melastomaceae (I). 10 Malaya, trop. Austr.

Othake Rafin. (*Gaillardia BH.*). Compositae (6). 6 S.W. U.S., Mexico.

Otherodendron Makino (*Elaeodendron* p.p.). Celastraceae. 1 Japan.

Othonna L. Compositae (8). 80 S. Afr. Xero. with swollen roots and often fleshy l.

Othonnopsis Jaub. et Spach (*Hertia EP.*). Compos. (8). 8 Afr., W. As.

Otiophora Zucc. Rubiaceae (II. 7). 5 Madag., trop. Afr.

Otocalyx T. S. Brandegee (inc. sed.). 1 Mexico.

Otochilus Lindl. Orchidaceae (II. 3). 4 Himalaya, Burma.

Otochlamys DC. Compositae (7). 1 Cape Colony.

Otomeria Benth. Rubiaceae (I. 2). 7 trop. Afr., Madag.

Otonephelium Radlk. (*Nephelium* p.p. *BH.*). Sapindac. (I). 1 Malabar.

Otopappus Benth. (*Zexmenia* p.p. *EP.*). Compositae (5). 6 C. Am.

Otopetalum Miq. Apocynaceae (I. 1). 1 Java.

Otopetalum F. C. Lehm. et Kränzl. Orchidaceae (II. 16). 1 Ecuador.

Otophora Blume. Sapindaceae (I). 12 trop. As.

Otoptera DC (*Vigna* p.p. *BH.*). Leguminosae (III. 10). 1 S. Afr.

Otostegia Benth. Labiatae (VI). 10 W. As., Abyssinia.

Otoxalis Small (*Oxalis* p.p.). Oxalidaceae. 1 Guatemala.

Ottelia Pers. Hydrocharidaceae. 15 trop. and subtrop.

Otto of rose, *Rosa*.

Ottoa H. B. et K. Umbelliferae (III. 4). 1 Mexico.
Ottonia Spreng. = Piper L. p.p. (Pip.).
Ottoschulzia Urb. (*Poraqueiba* p.p.). Icacinaceae. 3 W.I.
Oubanguia Baill. Tiliaceae. 5 trop. Afr.
Oudemansia Miq. = Helicteres Pluk. (Stercul.).
Ougeinia Benth. Leguminosae (III. 7). 1 India.
Ouratea Aubl. (*Gomphia BH.*). Ochnaceae. 200 trop.
Ourisia Comm. ex Juss. Scrophulariaceae (III. 1). 20 Am., N.Z.
Ourouparia Aubl. (*Uncaria* Schreb.). Rubiaceae (I. 6). 30 trop., esp. As.
Outea Aubl. = Macrolobium Schreb. (Legum.).
Outfit for collecting, *cf.* Collecting.
Ouvirandra Thou. = Aponogeton Thunb. (Apon.).
Oval (l.), widish, tapering equally to base and tip.
Ovary, the hollow chamber formed by the infolded sporophylls, in which the ovules are borne on thickened *placentae* or cushions. It may be *superior* (on apex of torus above sta.) or *inferior* (sunk in torus below sta.) or intermediate, *apocarpous* (free cpls.) or *syncarpous* (united), in spirals or whorled, radial or ·|· in symmetry. It may be *unilocular* (1-chambered), or *bi- tri- locular*, &c. (often simply called *multiloc.*). The imaginary joins of the cpls. are called the *sutures* (ventral if at the centre), and the midrib of the cpl. is called the dorsal suture. The placenta may bear one, two or more rows of ovules, or one or two ovules only. The partitions of the ovary are called the *septa*, and false septa, chambering it into more loc. than normal, are found in *Astragalus*, *Cruciferae*, *Gaylussacia*, *Linum*, &c.

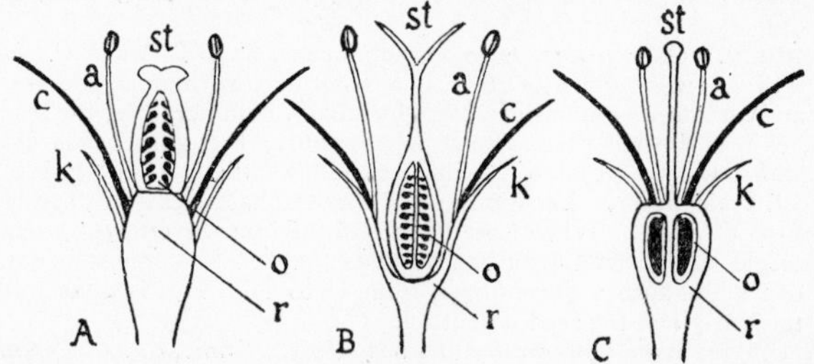

Diagrammatic longitudinal Sections of Flowers, to show types of receptacle, ovary, stigma, &c. A, hypogynous flower with unilocular ovary, parietal placentation, and numerous ascending anatropous ovules with raphe downwards; stigma sessile, bilobed. B, perigynous flower with multi-locular ovary, axile placentation, and numerous horizontal anatropous ovules with raphe upwards; style with bifid stigma. C, epigynous flower with multi-locular ovary, apical placentation, and solitary pendulous anatropous ovules with ventral raphe; style long with capitate stigma. *r*, receptacle; *k*, calyx; *c*, corolla; *a*, stamens; *o*, ovary; *st*, stigma.

The style, if present, may be long or short, cylindrical, filiform, ribbed, &c.; it may be terminal, lateral, or basal. The stigma or stigmas may be sessile or on a style, simple (and then often capitate or head-like), lobed, -fid, radiate, &c.

The ovule may be sessile or stalked (on a *funicle*); erect, ascending, horizontal, or pendulous. It may be *ortho-* or *atropous* (in a line with stalk, micropyle away from the latter), *anatropous* (reversed, and attached to stalk along side), *amphitropous* (stalk attached to middle of ovule), or *campylotropous* (ovule itself curved into U shape).

Ovate (l.), about twice as long as broad, tapering to the tip.

Overlook (W.I.), *Canavalia ensiformis* DC.

Ovidia Meissn. Thymelaeaceae. 4 Chili.

Ovieda L. = Clerodendron L. (Verben.).

Ovoid, solid oval.

Ovule, the possible future seed, *cf.* Ovary.

Ovuliferous scale, *cf. Coniferae.*

Ovum, the ♀ sexual cell, *Angiospermae*, *Pteridophyta.*

Owataria Matsumura. Guttiferae (v). 1 Formosa.

Owenia F. Muell. Meliaceae (III). 5 Austr.

Oxalidaceae (*EP.*; *Geraniaceae* p.p. *BH.*). Dicots. (Archichl. Geraniales). 7 gen., 850 sp., mostly trop. and subtrop. Most are perennial herbs with alt. often cpd. exstip. l. and large fls., usu. in cymes, ☿, reg. K 5, imbr., persistent; C 5, twisted or imbr., free or slightly united; A 10, obdiplost. (*i.e.* the outer whorl opp. to the petals, the inner to the sepals, and thus the cpls. opp. to the petals, instead of to the sepals, as in diplostemonous fls. with two whorls of sta. in proper alternation), united below, with introrse anthers; $\underline{G}$ (5), with free styles, 5-loc., with axile plac.; ovules in 1 or 2 rows in each loc., or few, anatr., with micropyle facing upwards and outwards. Capsule or berry; embryo straight, in fleshy endosp. *Chief genera:* Oxalis, Biophytum, Averrhoa. Closely allied to Geraniaceae. The chief difference is in the fruit.

Oxalis L. Oxalidaceae. 800 cosmop. chiefly S. Afr., Am. *O. Acetosella* L. (wood-sorrel) in Brit. is a small herb with monopodial rhiz. and ternate l., which sleep at night and in cold weather, the leaflets bending downwards. The fl. is protandr.; the stalk bends downwards and the fl. closes in dull or cold weather. Cleistogamic fls. (*cf.* Viola) occur. Loculic. caps. The seed has a fleshy aril springing from the base. When ripe the cells of the inner layers are extremely turgid, and a small disturbance causes the aril to turn inside out, as one might turn a glove-finger, from U to ∩. This is done instantaneously and the seed is shot off.

Many have bulbous or tuberous stems. Some, *e.g. O. bupleurifolia* A. St Hil., have phyllodes in place of the ordinary l. (*cf.* Acacia). Fls. sol. or in cymose infls. Many exhibit trimorphic heterostyled fls. (see Darwin, *Forms of Fls.*); there are three stocks of pl., one bearing fls. with long styles, and mid- and short-length sta., the others with mid or short styles and correspondingly long and short or long and mid sta. (*cf.* Lythrum). Some produce axillary bulbils; others repr. veg. by underground offshoots. The tubers of *O. Deppei* Lodd. (S. Am., Mex.), and others, are used as food.

Oxandra A. Rich. (*Bocagea* p.p. *BH.*). Anonaceae (1). 7 trop. Am. Wood useful.

Oxera Labill. Verbenaceae (4). 15 New Caled.

Oxeye-daisy, *Chrysanthemum Leucanthemum* L.; **oxlip**, *Primula elatior* Hill.

Oxodium (Cl.), a humus marsh formation.
Oxyacantha Medic. = Crataegus Tourn. (*BH.*). = Mespilus L.
Oxyanthus DC. Rubiaceae (I. 8). 20 Afr.
Oxybaphus L'Hérit. (*Mirabilis* p.p. *EP.*). Nyctaginaceae. 20 W. Am., Himal.
Oxychloe Phil. (*Distichia* p.p.). Juncaceae. 2 Bolivia, N. Chili.
Oxycoccus Tourn. ex Adans. = Vaccinium L. *O. palustris* Pers. = V. Oxycoccus.
Oxydendrum DC. Ericaceae (II. 1). 1 E. U.S. (sorrel tree, sourwood).
Oxygonum Burch. Polygonaceae (II. 2). 10 trop. E. and S. Afr.
Oxygraphis Bunge. Ranunculaceae (3). 9 N. temp. As., Am.
Oxygyne Schlechter. Burmanniaceae. 1 trop. Afr.
Oxylobium Andr. (*Callistachys* Vent.). Leguminosae (III. 2). 30 Austr.
Oxylobus Moç. ex DC. (*Ageratum* p.p.) Compositae (2). 3 Mexico.
Oxymeris DC. (*Leandra* p.p. *EP.*). Melastomaceae (I). 95 S. Am.
Oxymitra Hook. f. et Thoms. Anonaceae (4). 50 palaeotrop.
Oxyosmyles Spegazz. Boraginaceae (II). 1 Argentina.
Oxypappus Benth. Compositae (6). 2 Mexico.
Oxypetalum R. Br. Asclepiadaceae (II. 1). 90 Brazil, Mexico, W.I.
Oxyphyllum Phil. Compositae (12). 1 Chili.
Oxypolis Rafin. (*Peucedanum* p.p.). Umbelliferae (III. 6). 1 N. Am.
Oxypteryx Greene (*Asclepias* p.p.). Asclepiadaceae (II. 1). 1 N. Am.
Oxyrhynchus T. S. Brandegee. Leguminosae (III. 10). 1 Mexico.
Oxyria Hill. Polygonaceae (I. 2). 1 N. Arctic and subarctic (*O. digyna* Hill in Brit. alpine). Like Rumex, but dimerous, and with branching of the outer sta.
Oxys Tourn. ex Adans. = Oxalis L. (Oxal.).
Oxyspora DC. Melastomaceae (I). 15 Indomal.
Oxystelma R. Br. Asclepiadaceae (II. 1). 10 trop. and subtrop.
Oxystemon Planch. et Triana (*Clusia* p.p. *BH.*). Guttif. (V). 1 Colombia.
Oxystigma Harms (*Hardwickia* p.p.). Leguminosae (II. 2). 2 Cameroons.
Oxystylis Torr. et Frém. (*Wislizenia* p.p. *EP.*). Capparidaceae (V). 1 California.
Oxytenanthera Munro. Gramineae (13). 20 trop. As. and Afr.
Oxytenia Nutt. Compositae (5). 1 Colorado, California.
Oxytheca Nutt. Polygonaceae (I. 1). 6 California, Chili.
Oxythece Miq. (*Lucuma* p.p. *BH.*). Sapotaceae (I). 2 N. Brazil.
Oxytropis DC. Leguminosae (III. 6). 100 N. temp.; 2 in Brit.
Oyedaea DC. Compositae (5). 15 trop. Am.
Oyster plant, *Tragopogon porrifolius* L.
Ozomelis Rafin. (*Mitella BH.*). Saxifragaceae (I). 9 N. Am.
Ozothamnus R. Br. = Helichrysum Vaill. p.p. (Comp.).
Pachidendron Haw. = Aloe Tourn. p.p. (Lili.).
Pachira Aubl. (*Bombax* p.p. *EP.*). Bombacaceae. 4 trop. Am.
Pachistima Rafin. Celastraceae. 2 N. Am.
Pachites Lindl. Orchidaceae (II. 1). 2 S. Afr.
Pachyanthus Rich. Melastomaceae (I). 7 Colombia, Cuba.
Pachy- (Gr. pref.); thick; **-carpous**, with thick pericarp, &c.
Pachycarpus E. Mey. (*Gomphocarpus* R. Br. p.p.). Asclep. (II. 1). 20 S. Afr.
Pachycentria Blume. Melastomaceae (I). 12 Malay Archipelago.

Pachycereus Britton et Rose (*Cereus* p.p.). Cact. (III. 1). 10 C. Am.

Pachychlamys Dyer (*Shorea* p.p.). Dipterocp. 5 Malaya.

Pachycladon Hook. f. Crucif. (4). 1 Mts. of N.Z.

Pachycornia Hook. f. Chenopod. (A). 1 Austr. Like Salicornia.

Pachydiscus Gilg et Schlechter. Caprifol. 1 New Caledonia.

Pachyelasma Harms (*Stachyothyrsus* p.p.). Legum. (II. 7). 1 W. Afr.

Pachygone Miers. Menisperm. 12 E. Indomal. Exalb.

Pachylaena D. Don ex Hook. et Arn. Comp. (12). 1 Chilean Andes.

Pachylepis Brongn., Benth. =Callitris Vent. p.p. (Conif.).

Pachylobium Benth. =Dioclea H.B. et K. (Legum.).

Pachylobus G. Don (*Canarium* p.p. *BH.*). Burser. 15 trop. Afr., W.I. L. pinnate. 3-merous. Resins. Some have ed. fr.

Pachyloma DC. (*Comolia* pp., *Urodesmium*). Melastom. (1). 2 Braz. Connective with auricles in front, appendages behind.

Pachylophus Spach (*Oenothera* p.p. *BH.*). Onagr. (2). 12 W. U.S.

Pachymeria Benth. =Meriania Sw. p.p. (Melastom.). [thick below.

Pachynema R. Br. ex DC. Dillen. 3 N. Austr. Phylloclades. Sta.

Pachynocarpus Hook. f. Dipterocp. 4 Malaya. Fr. united to K.

Pachyphyllum H. B. et K. Orchid. (II. 20). 20 Andes. L. fleshy.

Pachyphytum Link, Klotzsch et Otto (*Cotyledon* p.p. *BH.*). Crassul

Pachyplectron Schlechter. Orchid. (II. 2). 2 New Caled. [8 Mex.

Pachypodanthium Engl. et Diels (*Uvaria* p.p.). Anon. (1). 2 W. Afr.

Pachypodium Lindl. Apocyn. (II. 1). 10 S. Afr., Madag. *Ann. Bot*

Pachypodium Nutt. ex Torr. et Gray = Thelypodium Endl. [1912, 929

Pachypterygium Bunge. Crucif. (2). 3 W. C. As. Fr. margin thick

Pachyrhizus Rich. ex DC. Legum. (III. 10). 2 trop., tall twining herbs, cult. for the ed. tuberous root (yam-bean).

Pachyrhynchus DC. Comp. (4). 1 S. Afr. Fr. glandular with pappus

Pachysandra Michx. Bux. 4 E. As., Alleghanies (*cf.* Epigaea).

Pachystachys Nees (*Jacobinia* p.p. *BH.*). Acanth. (IV. B). 6 trop

Pachystela Pierre (*Sideroxylon* p.p.). Sapot. (1). 8 trop. Afr. [Am., W.I

Pachystemon Blume (*Macaranga BH.*). Euphorb. (A. II. 2). 6 Indomal. Anther 3-loc. G 4—6-loc. L. peltate.

Pachystigma Hochst. (*Fadogia BH.*). Rubi. (II. 1). 15 warm Afr.

Pachystima Rafin. Celastr. 3 N. Am. G ½-inf. [Afr

Pachystoma Reichb. f. (*Ancistrochilus* Rolfe). Orchid. (II. 9). 3 trop

Pachystoma Blume. Orchid. (II. 9). 8 Indomal. No l.; subterr. tubers

Pachystroma (Klotzsch) Muell.-Arg. Euphorb. (A. II. 4). 1 S. Braz

Pachystylus K. Schum. Rubi. (II. 4). 1 New Guinea. [able l. form

Pachytrophe Bur. Mor. (1). 2 Madag. G oblique, style excentric. Vari

Pacouria Aubl. =Landolphia Beauv. (Apocyn.).

Pacourina Aubl. Comp. (1). 1 trop. S. Am. Aquatic. Head sessile

Padauk, *Pterocarpus macrocarpus* Kurz. (Burma). [Ed.

Padbruggea Miq. (*Millettia* p.p.). Legum. (III. 6). 2 Malay Pen., Java

Paddy, rice in the husk, *Oryza sativa* L. (trop. As.).

Padus L. = Prunus Tourn. p.p. (Ros.). [whorled

Paederia L. Rubi. (II. 6). 40 trop. Climbing shrubs. L. sometime

Paederota L. (*Veronica* p.p. *EP.*). Scroph. (III. 1). 5 N. temp.

Paeonia (Tourn.) L. Ranuncul. (1). 15 Eur., As., W.N. Am. *P. officinalis* L. (paeony) has tuberous r., large fls. with much honey, sligh cohesion of cpls., follicle with red seeds, protog. fls. closing at night

Paeony, *Paeonia*. Harding, *The Book of the Peony*.
Paepalanthus Mart. Eriocaulaceae. 215 warm S. Am., W.I.
Paesia St Hil. Polypodiaceae. 7 trop. Am., E. As., N.Z.
Pagaea Griseb. in DC. Gentianaceae (I). 6 Guiana, N. Brazil.
Pagamea Aubl. Rubiaceae (II. 5) (Logan. *BH*.). 8 Brazil, Guiana.
Pagerea Pierre. Inc. sed. 1 Cochinchina.
Pagetia F. Muell. Rutaceae (I). 1 Queensland.
Pahudia Miq. Leguminosae (II. 3). 3 Malay Archip. Good timber.
Paigle, cowslip, *Primula veris* Lehm.
Paina de seda, *Chorisia speciosa* St. Hil.
Paint brush, -ed cup, -ed lady, *Castilleja*; **-root,** *Lachnanthes*.
Paivaea Berg. Myrtaceae (I). 1 São Paulo.
Paivaeusa Welw. Euphorbiaceae (A. I. 1) (Burser. *BH*.). 1 W. Afr.
Pajanelia DC. Bignoniaceae (2). 1 Indomal.
Palaearctic, old world arctic; **-obotany**, fossil botany; **-o-tropical**, old world tropical.
Palafoxia Lag. Compositae (6). 7 E. and S.E. U.S.
Palaquium Blanco (*Dichopsis* Thw.). Sapotaceae (I). 65 Indomal. *P. Gutta* Burck was formerly the chief source of gutta-percha, but it is now extinct exc. in cult., and gutta is obtained from other sp. and from *Payena Leerii*, &c. The trees are cut down or ringed and the milky latex coagulates, forming gutta percha (*cf.* Rubber).
Palas, *Butea frondosa* Roxb.
Palava Juss. (*Palaua* Cav.). Malvaceae (I). 5 Chili, Peru.
Pale, palea, palet, *cf. Gramineae*.
Palenia Phil. (*Heterothalamus* p.p. *EP*.). Compositae (3). 1 Chili.
Paliavana Vell. ex Vand. Gesneriaceae (II). 2 Brazil.
Palicourea Aubl. Rubiaceae (II. 5). 120 trop. Am., W.I.
Palimbia Bess. (*Peucedanum* p.p. *BH*.). Umbellif. (III. 6). 1 Russia.
Palisander, wood of Brazilian sp. of *Dalbergia*, *Jacaranda*, *Machaerium*, &c.
Palisota Reichb. Commelinaceae. 25 trop. W. Afr. Cult. orn. fl.
Palissya Baill. (*Alchornea* p.p. *BH*.). Euphorb. (A. II. 2). 1 Madag.
Paliurus Tourn. ex Mill. Rhamnaceae. 2, one, *P. aculeatus* Lam. (Christ's thorn, cf. Zizyphus), S. Eur. to China; one China, Japan. The former has stipular thorns, one straight, the other recurved; the latter has both thorns straight. The fr. has a horizontal wing, developed at the base of the style after fert.
Pallasia Klotzsch. Rubiaceae (I. 3). 1 Guiana.
Pallenis Cass. Compositae (4). 1 Medit.
Pallens (Lat.), pale coloured.
Palm, one of the *Palmae*; **Assai -**, *Euterpe*; **betelnut -**, *Areca*; **cabbage -**, *Oreodoxa*; **- cabbage**, *Cocos*, &c.; **carnauba -**, *Copernicia*; **coconut -**, *Cocos nucifera* L.; **cohune -**, *Attalea*; **coquito -**, *Jubaea*; **date -**, *Phoenix dactylifera* L.; **doum -**, *Hyphaene*; **gomuti -**, *Arenga*; **- honey**, *Jubaea*; **ivory -**, *Phytelephas*; **macaw -**, *Acrocomia*; **oil -**, *Elaeis*; **palmetto -**, *Sabal*; **Palmirah** or **Palmyra -**, *Borassus*; **paxiuba -**, *Iriartea*; **peach -**, *Bactris*; **piassaba -**, *Attalea*, *Leopoldinia*; **royal -**, *Oreodoxa*; **sago -**, *Metroxylon*; **- sugar**, *Arenga*, *Borassus*, *Cocos*, *Caryota*, &c.; **thatch -**, *Sabal*, *Thrinax*, &c.; **toddy -**, *Caryota*; **wax -**, *Ceroxylon*, *Copernicia*; **wine -**, *Raphia*.

Palmae (*EP.*, *BH.*). Monocots. (Principes; Calycinae *BH.*). 200 gen., 1500 sp. trop. and subtrop.; most of the gen. well localised in the various floral regions, the chief exceptions being *Cocos nucifera*, *Elaeis guineensis* and *Raphia vinifera*. The palms form a char. feature of trop. veg. The veg. habit is familiar—a crown of l. at the end of an unbranched stem (Hyphaene is branched). The stem exhibits various forms; some palms, *e.g.* Nipa, Phytelephas, have a short rhiz. or stock bearing 'radical' leaves and often branching below ground; some, *e.g.* Geonoma, Calamus, Desmoncus, have a thin reed-like stem with long internodes (the two latter are climbers); others again have a tall stem with a crown of l. at the top. The stem is often covered with the remains of old leaf-sheaths, or is thorny. Its height may reach 150 feet in some, and it grows slowly in thickness. At the base the stem is usu. conically thickened or provided with buttress roots; this gives the necessary mechanical rigidity. The stems of Cocos and other palms are curved instead of straight; this appears to be due to reaction to light.

The l. is very characteristic; the only closely similar l. is that of Carludovica, though those of Cycads and some tree ferns have a superficial likeness. Some have palmate (fan) l., some pinnate (feather) l., but this structure arises by a development unlike that which gives rise to these forms in Dicots. and more like that in Araceae. The l. is usu. very large, and at the base of the petiole is a sheath, which makes a firmer attachment to the stem than a mere articulation. The sheath contains many bundles of fibres, which remain after the decay of the softer tissues. The pinnae are folded where they meet the main stalk of the l., sometimes upwards (*induplicate*, V in section), sometimes downwards (*reduplicate*, Λ in section); these chars. are important in classification. The l. emerges from the bud in an almost vertical line and thus escapes excessive radiation and transpiration. The palms are pronounced sun-plants, and show xero. chars. in their l. The leaf-surface is glossy with a thick cuticle, and is rarely arranged ⊥ to the incident rays. Often the l. is corrugated, or placed at an angle by the twisting or upward slope of the stalk; sometimes the leaflets slope upwards, and so on.

Infl. usu. very large and much branched. In Corypha and others it is term., its production being a mark of the end of the life of the plant (*cf.* Agave), but usu. it is axillary; sometimes in the axils of the current l., sometimes lower on the stem. The branching is racemose and the fls. are often embedded in the axis; the whole is often termed a *spadix*. It is enclosed in a spathe of several l. and emerges when the fls. are ready to open. Some are diœc., some monœc., in the latter case often with the fls. in groups (small dichasia) of 3, one ♀ between two ♂.

The fl. has usu. the formula P 3+3, A 3+3, $\underline{G}$ 3 or (3). P homochlam., varying in texture. G (3) 1-loc. or 3-loc., with 3 or sometimes 1, anatr. ovules (rarely semi-anatr., or orthotr.). Some are wind-pollinated, others are entomoph.

Fr. a berry or drupe; in the latter case the endocarp usu. united to the seed. Fr. in § III covered with dry woody scales. Endosperm large; in date, vegetable ivory, &c., it is very hard, the non-nitrogenous storage-material taking the form of cellulose, deposited upon the cell walls. In germ. the cot. lengthens and pushes out the radicle, and then the plumule grows out of the sheathing cotyledon.

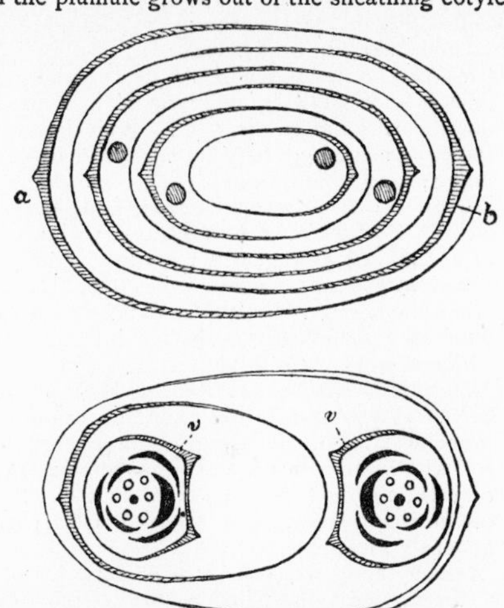

Diagrams of Raphia (after Eichler). Above, the arrangement of the last branches of infl. *a*, *b*, two of the sterile sheathing bracts, above them bracts with branches in their axils, a little out of the median line. Below, arrangement of the flowers on branches of upper figure: bracts 2-ranked; each fl. has a 2-keeled bracteole *v*.

Economically, the P. are very important, furnishing many of the necessaries of life in the tropics, &c. Many have ed. fr. or seed, *e.g.* date (Phoenix) and coco-nut (Cocos); the stems contain much starch as reserve food, esp. in those sp. which save up for a great terminal infl., *e.g.* Metroxylon (sago), Caryota, &c.; the rush of sap to the infl., esp. in the cases just mentioned, is great; and by tapping the stem great quantities of sugar-containing fluid may be obtained and utilised, either directly as a source of sugar or indirectly to make intoxicating drinks by fermentation. The bud of l. at the top of the stem is sometimes used as cabbage, but of course its removal kills the tree. The stems are used in building, but do not yield plank-timber; the l. in thatching and basket-making, and for hats, mats, &c.; the fibres of the leaf-sheaths or sometimes of the pericarp (*e.g.* Cocos) are used for ropes, &c.; other P. furnish oil from the seed (*e.g.* Elaeis, Cocos), wax (Copernicia), vegetable ivory (Phytelephas, &c.), betel-nuts (Areca), &c. [Cf. Baillon, *Hist. des Pl.* XIII. 283.]

Classification and chief genera (after Drude):

A. Perianth 6-partite, enclosing the fruit after fertilisation.

I. *CORYPHOIDEAE* (spadix loosely branched, often a prolix panicle; fls. single or in long rows flowering from above;

cpls. 3, or loosely united, separating after fert.; berry; fan or feather l., induplicate):

1. *Phoeniceae* (feather l.): Phoenix.
2. *Sabaleae* (fan l.): Chamaerops, Rhapis, Corypha, Livistona, Sabal, Copernicia.

II. *BORASSOIDEAE* (spadix simple or little branched with thick cylindrical twigs; fls. markedly diclinous dimorphic, invested with bracts, the ♂ in 1—∞ cincinni in grooves of the twigs; cpls. (3), fully united, producing a one-seeded drupe; fan l., induplicate):

1. *Borasseae*: Hyphaene, Borassus, Lodoicea.

III. *LEPIDOCARYOIDEAE* (spadix branched once or more in a 2-ranked arrangement; fls. in cincinni or 2-ranked spikes with bracts and bracteoles round them; cpls. (3), fast united, covered with scales; fr. 1-seeded, covered with hard scales; feather or fan l., reduplicate):

1. *Mauritieae* (fan l.): Mauritia.
2. *Metroxyleae* (feather l.): Raphia, Metroxylon, Calamus.

IV. *CEROXYLOIDEAE* (spadix simple or one or several times branched; fls. diclinous, usu. dimorphic; when dioec. sol. with rudimentary bracts, when monoec. usu. in cymes of 3 fls., 2 being ♂ and 1 ♀, or rarely ∞ ♂ and 1 at the end of the row being ♀; cpls. (3), 3- 2- 1-loc.; fruit smooth, not scaly; feather l.):

1. *Areceae* (berry fr.): Caryota, Arenga, Leopoldinia, Iriartea, Ceroxylon, Chamaedorea, Oreodoxa, Euterpe, Kentia, Areca.
2. *Cocoeae* (drupe fr.): Elaeis, Attalea, Cocos, Bactris, Desmoncus.

B. Perianth rudimentary in ♂ or ♀. Fruit in dense heads.

V. *PHYTELEPHANTOIDEAE* (♂ fl. with ∞ free sta.; ♀ with P; endosp. ivory-like): Phytelephas (only gen.).

VI. *NIPOIDEAE* (♂ with (3) sta.; ♀ naked; woody endocarp): Nipa (only gen.).

For further details of P. see *Nat. Pfl.*, Seemann's *History of the Palms*, and *Treas. of Bot.*

Palmate, divided, and arranged like the leaves of a fan.

Palmatifid, -partite, -sect, palmately divided to $\frac{1}{4}$—$\frac{1}{2}$, $\frac{1}{2}$—$\frac{3}{4}$, over $\frac{3}{4}$ of the depth.

Palmerella A. Gray. Campanulaceae (III). 2 Mexico, California.

Palmeria F. Muell. Monimiaceae. 7 Austr., New Guinea, Celebes.

Palmetto, *Sabal*, *Thrinax*; **small -**, *Carludovica*.

Palmiet, *Prionium Palmita* E. Mey.

Palmirah, Palmyra palm, *Borassus flabellifer* L.

Palmiste, *Oreodoxa*.

Palmorchis Barb. Rodr. (*Sobralia* p.p. *EP*.). Orchid. (II. 7). 2 Brazil.

Palmstruckia Sond. Cruciferae (I). 1 S. Afr.

Palovea Aubl. Leguminosae (II. 3). 1 French Guiana.

Palta, avocado, *Persea gratissima* Gaertn. f.

Paltonium Presl. Polypodiaceae. 2 trop. Am., China.

Paludose, palustris (Lat.), of marshes.

Palumbina Reichb. f. (*Oncidium* p.p. *BH.*). Orchid. (II. 19). 1 Guatem.

Pamburus Swingle. Rutaceae (v.). 1 India.

Pampas, the grassy plains of S. temp. Am.; **-grass**, *Cortaderia argentea* Stapf.

Pampelmousse, shaddock, *Citrus decumana* Murr.

Pamphalea DC. Compositae (12). 5 temp. S. Am.

Pamphilia Mart. Styracaceae. 3 Brazil.

Panama hats, *Carludovica*; **-rubber**, *Castilloa elastica* Cerv., &c.

Panargyrus Lag. = Nassauvia Juss. p.p. (Comp.).

Panax Linn. (*BH.* incl. *Cheirodendron* Nutt., *Nothopanax* Seem.). Aral. (2). 6 trop. and E. As., N. Am. Ginseng from *P. Ginseng.*

Pancheria Brongn. et Gris. Cunoniaceae. 18 New Caled.

Pancovia Willd. (*Erioglossum BH.*). Sapindaceae (1). 3 trop. W. Afr.

Pancratium Dill. ex L. Amaryllidaceae (1). 12 Medit., trop. As.

Panda Pierre. Pandaceae. 1 trop. W. Afr. Fl. cyclic, dioec., heterochlam. $\underline{G}$ (3), each with one pend. orthotr. ov. Drupe with 3 one-seeded chambers.

Pandaceae (*EP.*). Dicots. (Archichl. Pandales). Only gen. Panda, *q.v.*

Pandales. The 22nd. order of Dicots. Archichl. Only fam. Pandaceae.

Pandanaceae (*EP.*, *BH.*). Monocots. (Pandanales; Nudiflorae *BH.*). 3 gen., 225 sp., char. pl. of the Old World tropics, but a few warm temp. Mostly sea-coast or marsh pl. with tall stems supported upon aerial roots, frequently branched; buds are found in all axils, and the branching appears dichotomous; some are climbers. The aerial roots have marked root-caps of membranous texture. L. in 3-ranked phyllotaxy, but stem usu. twisted so that they appear to run in well-marked spirals, whence the name of screw-pines. L. parallel-veined, long, and narrow, with open sheath and usu. thorny margin; generally sharply bent downwards at the middle, and corrugated like a palm l.

Infl. term., with a few bract-like l. at the base going gradually over into the foliage l., usu. a racemose spadix with neither bracts nor bracteoles to the individual fls., which are somewhat difficult to make out. The ♂ fls. in sp. of Freycinetia have a rudimentary G, but in the rest of the fam. they have not. The floral axis of the ♂ fl. bears a number of sta., arranged in a raceme or umbel-like manner upon it. The G in the ♀ fl. of ∞ cpls. in a ring, 1-loc. or ∞-loc., the union being ± complete, or it may be reduced, even to 1 cpl., or to a row of cpls. arranged transv. Stigmas sessile. Ovules anatr. Berry or multi-loc. drupe, often containing hollow spaces which aid it in swimming. Seed with oily endosp. The plants yield thatch, &c. *Genera:* Sararanga (infl. paniculate; fls. pedicelled; drupe), Freycinetia (infl. capitulate or spicate; fls. sessile; berry), Pandanus (infl. as last; fls. sessile; drupe).

Pandanales. The 1st order of Monocots. *Cf.* p. ii.

Pandaneae (*BH.*) = Pandanaceae.

Pandanophyllum Hassk. = Mapania Aubl. p.p. (Cyper.).

Pandanus Rumph. ex L. f. Pandanaceae. 180 palaeotrop. (screw-pines). Trees with flying-buttress roots. Fls. in large heads, enclosed in spathes. ♂ of ∞ sta., arranged in various ways upon the axis, ♀ of 1—∞ cpls., free or united. Each gives a drupe containing as many seeds as cpls. Seeds album. The pericarp is rich in fibres. The fr. of some are cooked and eaten, *e.g. P. leram* Jones, the Nicobar bread-fruit. The l. of many are used for weaving, *e.g. P. tectorius* Sol., which is cult. in Java. Several have sweetly scented fls. or l. which are used for ornament and otherwise in the East.

Panderia Fisch. et Mey. Chenopodiaceae (A). 1 Syria, Persia.

Pandiaka Moq., Benth. et Hook. f. (*Achyranthes* p.p. *EP.*). Amarantaceae (2). 10 trop. Afr.

Pandorea Spach (*Tecoma* p.p. *BH.*). Bignoniaceae (2). 6 E. Indo-mal.

Pandurate, fiddle-shaped.

Paneion Lunell (*Poa* p.p.). Gramineae (10). 12 N. Am.

Pangium Reinw. Flacourtiaceae (3). 2 Malay Archip. The seeds of *P. edule* Reinw. are eaten after long soaking to dissipate the hydrocyanic acid which they, like all parts, contain (Treub in *Ann. Buit.* XIII. 1).

Panic grass (Am.), *Panicum*.

Panicle, a compound raceme, *Avena*.

Panicularia Fabr. (*Glyceria* p.p.). Gramineae (10). 20 Am.

Panicum L. Gramineae (5). 500 trop. and warm temp. The spikelets are 1- or 2-flowered. Many P., known as millets, are important cereals, extensively cult. in India, S. Eur., &c., *e.g. P. miliaceum* L., the common millet, *P. miliare* Lamk., the little millet, and other minor sp. Many are important fodder plants, *e.g. P. maximum* Jacq. (trop.; Guinea grass), *P. molle* Sw. (trop. Am.; Mauritius grass), *P. Crus-galli* L. (Am., nat. in Brit.; the barnyard grass of the U.S.), *P. sanguinale* L. and others (crab or panic grasses of U.S.). Many are distributed by animals, for the joints of the stem will grow after passing the alimentary canal.

Panisea Lindl. Orchidaceae (II. 16). 2 Himalaya, Khasias.

Pannosus (Lat.), felt-like.

Panopsis Salisb. Proteaceae (II). 8 trop. Am.

Pansy, *Viola tricolor* L., &c.

Pantacantha Spegazz. Solanaceae (4). 1 Patagonia.

Pantathera Phil. Gramineae (10). 1 Juan Fernandez.

Pantlingia Prain (*Stigmatodactylus* p.p. *EP.*). Orchid. (II. 2). 1 Himal.

Panurea Spruce ex B. et H. f. Leguminosae (III. 1). 1 N. Brazil.

Papain, **papaw**, *Carica Papaya* L.

Papaver Tourn. ex L. Papaveraceae (II). 110 Eur., As., Am., S. Afr., Austr. *P. Rhoeas* L. and 3 others (poppy) in Brit. The fls. nod in bud, not by their own weight, but by more rapid growth of one side of the stalk. Ovary crowned by a sessile rayed stigma, each lobe of which stands over a placenta instead of as usual over a midrib. This is commonly explained by supposing each actual ray of the stigma to be formed of one half of each of two adjacent stigmas. The fl. of most contains no honey, and is homogamous; both cross- and self-pollination usually occur with insect visits. Fr. a round caps., opening by pores under the eaves of the roof formed by the dry stigmas, so that the seeds are protected from rain and can only escape when the capsule is shaken by strong winds or other agencies (censer mechanism, *cf.*

Aconitum). *P. somniferum* L. is the opium poppy; the drug is obtained by cutting notches in the half ripened capsules, from which the latex exudes and hardens. The seeds of this and other sp. yield an oil on pressure.

Papaveraceae (*EP.*, *BH.*). Dicots. (Archichl. Rhoeadales; Parietales *BH.*). 28 gen., 600 sp., chiefly N. temp. Most are herbs with alt. l., and §§ I. and II. contain latex. Corydalis and Fumaria are climbers, Bocconia a shrub. Fls. sol. or in racemes, or in dichasia with cincinnal tendency, reg. or irreg., ☿, hypog. (exc. Eschscholtzia). K 2 (united in Eschscholtzia), caducous; C 2+2, rolled or crumpled in bud (see Hypecoum); A 4 or ∞ or 2 (see sub-fams.); in the last case each sta. branches into 3 parts (see fig.), the centre one bearing an entire anther, the lat. ones each half an anther; G̲ (2—∞), 1-loc. with parietal plac., which in Papaver, &c. project into the loc. Ovules generally ∞, anatr. or slightly campylotr. Fr. a septic. caps., or one opening by pores, or a nut; seeds with oily endosp., and small embryo. The fls. are mostly large and conspicuous, but many contain no honey and are visited by pollen-seeking insects; they are often protandr. Those of sub-fam. III. are irreg., and adapted to bees in a way somewhat like that found in Leguminosae. The order is of little economic value; see Papaver.

Floral diagram of *Corydalis cava* (after Eichler).

Classification and chief genera:

I. *HYPECOIDEAE* (petals without spur; sta. 4; cpls. 2): Hypecoum.

II. *PAPAVEROIDEAE* (as I., but sta. ∞; cpls. 2—∞): Eschscholtzia, Chelidonium, Glaucium, Papaver.

III. *FUMARIOIDEAE* (petals with spur; sta. 2, each branched into 3): Dicentra, Corydalis, Fumaria.

Many authors split off III. as a separate fam., Fumariaceae.

Papaya Tourn. ex L. = Carica L. (Caric.).

Papayaceae = Caricaceae.

Paper is made from fine fibre that is entirely (or almost) composed of cellulose. The best is made of cotton and linen rags; and cf. *Bamboo*, *Borassus*, *Broussonetia*, *Fatsia*, *Hedychium*, *Lepidosperma*, *Stipa*, *Streblus*, *Zea*, &c. *Adansonia*, *Coniferae* (the wood, pulped), *Corchorus*, *Crotalaria*, *Musa* (*textilis*), straw, &c. are also used.

Paphia Seem. (*Agapetes BH.*). Ericaceae (III. 2). 1 Fiji. Cult. orn.

Paphinia Lindl. (*Lycaste* p.p. *BH.*). Orchidaceae (II. 12). 2 Guiana.

Paphiopedilum Pfitz. (*Cypripedium* p.p.). Orchidaceae (I. 2). 50 trop. As., Am.

Papilionanthe Schlechter (*Vanda* p.p.). Orchidaceae (II. 20). 1 Indomal.

Papilionatae, a subfamily of Leguminosae.

Papiliopsis E. Morr. ex Cogn. et Marchal (*Oncidium* p.p.). Orchidaceae (II. 19). 1 S. Am.

Pappea Eckl. et Zeyh. Sapindaceae (1). 4 trop. and S. Afr. *P. capensis* E. et Z. is the 'wilde preume' of S. Afr., with ed. fr.; oil is obtained from the seeds, and the timber is useful.

Pappea Sond. et Harv. (*Choritaenia* Benth.). Umbell. (III. 6). 1 S. Afr.

Papperitzia Reichb. f. Orchidaceae (II. 19). 1 Mexico.

Pappophorum Schreb. Gramineae (10). 20 trop. and subtrop.

Pappostyles Pierre. Styracaceae. 1 trop. Afr.

Pappothrix A. Gray, Rydberg (*Laphamia* p.p.). Comp. (6). 3 S.W. U.S.

Pappus, the tuft of hairs, bristles, &c., repres. K, *Compos.*, *Valer.*

Papualthia Diels (*Goniothalamus* p.p.). Anonaceae (2). 8 New Guinea.

Papyrus Willd. = Cyperus Mich. *P. antiquorum* Willd. = C. Papyrus.

Para- (Gr. pref.), beside.

Para rubber, *Hevea brasiliensis* Muell.-Arg., &c.

Parabaena Miers. Menispermaceae. 10 Indomal.

Parabarium Pierre (*Echites* p.p.). Apocynaceae (II. 1). 10 Cochin-china.

Parabarleria Baill. (*Barleria* p.p.). Acanth. (IV. A). 1 E. trop. Afr.

Parabignonia Bur. (*Tecoma* p.p.). Bignoniaceae (2). 1 Bahia.

Paraboea C. B. Clarke (*Didymocarpus* p.p.). Gesner. (1). 15 Malaya.

Parabouchetia Baill. Solanaceae (4). 1 Brazil.

Paracaryum Boiss. Boraginaceae (IV. 1). 35 Medit., C. As.

Paracelsia Zoll. Euphorbiaceae (B. II). 1 Malay Archipelago.

Paracephaelis Baill. Rubiaceae (I. 6). 1 Madagascar.

Parachute mechanism, *cf.* Dispersal.

Paracolea Baill. Bignoniaceae (4). 1 Madagascar.

Paracorolla, appendage of a corolla, corona.

Paracroton Miq. Euphorbiaceae (A. II. 5). 1 W. Java.

Paradaniella Rolfe. Leguminosae (II. 3). 1 trop. Afr.

Paradisanthus Reichb. f. Orchidaceae (II. 13). 1 Bahia.

Paradise, grains of, *Amomum Melegueta* Roscoe.

Paradisia Mazzuc. Liliaceae (III). 1 Mts. of Eur.

Paradolichandra Hassler. Bignoniaceae (2). 1 Paraguay.

Paradombeya Stapf. Bombacaceae. 2 E. As.

Paragenipa Baill. Rubiaceae (inc. sed.). 1 trop. Afr.

Paragonia Bur. (*Bignonia* p.p. *BH.*). Bignoniaceae (1). 1 Brazil.

Paragophytum K. Schum. Rubiaceae (II. 1). 1 Cameroons.

Paraguay tea, *Ilex paraguensis* A. St Hil.

Parajaeschkea Burkill. Gentianaceae (1). 1 Sikkim.

Paralamium Dunn. Labiatae (VI). 1 Yunnan.

Parallel descent, that which results in similar structure, though the plants be not descended from an immediate common ancestor, *e.g.* l. of *Selaginella* and mosses.

Paralstonia Baill. Apocynaceae (I. 3). 1 Phil. Is.

Paralyxia Baill. Apocynaceae (I. 3). 1 Guiana.

Paramansoa Baill. Bignoniaceae (1). 1 Venezuela.

Parameria Benth. Apocynaceae (II. 1). 5 Malaya. Some yield rubber.

Paramignya Wight. Rutaceae (V). 6 Indomal.

Paramo, the alpine region of the N. Andes; *Espeletia.*
Paranephelium Miq. Sapindaceae (I). 4 S.E. As.
Paranomus Salisb. (*Nivenia* p.p. *BH.*). Proteaceae (I. 2). 12 S. Afr.
Paraphlomis Prain (*Phlomis* p.p.). Labiatae (VI). 3 E. Indomal.
Parapodium E. Mey. Asclepiadaceae (II. I). 3 S. Afr.
Parartocarpus Baill. Moraceae (II). 5 Malaya.
Parascopolia Baill. Solanaceae (inc. sed.). 1 Mexico.
Parashorea Kurz (*Shorea* p.p. *BH.*). Dipterocarpaceae. 3 S.E. As.
Parasia Rafin. (*Belmontia* p.p.). Gentian. (I). 6 trop. and S. Afr.
Parasites, pl. which draw all (*total*), or some (*partial*), of their food from other pl. (*hosts*) by special organs termed *suckers* or *haustoria.* Total p. have not green tissue, partials have, as they draw only unelaborated food. Total: *Balanophoraceae*, *Cassytha*, *Cuscuta*, *Hydnoraceae*, *Lathraea*, *Lennoaceae*, *Orobanche*, *Rafflesiaceae*; partial: *Loranthaceae*, *Myzodendraceae*, *Santalaceae*, *Scrophulariaceae* (Rhinanthus group, § III. 2 and 3). *Cf.* Schimper, *Plant Geography*, or Hemsley in *Linn. Soc. Journ.* XXXI.
Parasol pine, *Sciadopitys verticillata* Sieb. et Zucc.
Paraspalathus Presl = Aspalathus L. (Legum.).
Parasponia Miq. Ulmaceae. 2 Java, Polynesia.
Parastemon A. DC. Rosaceae (VI). 2 Malay Peninsula, Borneo.
Parastichy, a secondary spiral in phyllotaxy.
Parastranthus G. Don = Lobelia L. (Campan.).
Parastrephia Nutt. Compositae (3). 1 Peru.
Parasystasia Baill. (*Barleria* p.p.). Acanthaceae (IV. B). 1 Somali.
Paratephrosia Domin. Leguminosae (III. 6). 1 C. Austr.
Paratheria Griseb. (*Chamaeraphis EP.*). Gramineae (5). 1 W.I., S. Am.
Parathesis Hook. f. Myrsinaceae (II). 20 Cuba, trop. Am.
Paratrophis Blume. Moraceae (I). 7 N.Z., Polynesia.
Paratropia DC. = Heptapleurum Gaertn. (*BH.*) = Schefflera Forst.
Paravallaris Pierre. Apocynaceae (II. 2). 1 Cochinchina.
Pardalopetalum Hallier = Paphiopedilum Pfitz. p.p. (Orchid.).
Pareira brava, *Chondodendron tomentosum* Ruiz et Pav.; **-, false**, *Cissampelos Pareira* L.; **- root, white**, *Abuta rufescens* Aubl.
Parentucellia Viv. (*Bartsia* p.p. *BH.*). Scrophular. (III. 3). 2 W. Medit.
Pareugenia Turrill. Myrtaceae (I). 1 Fiji.
Pariana Aubl. Gramineae (12). 10 trop. S. Am.
Parietal (plac.), on the walls of a 1-loc. ovary; *cf.* diagram of *Gesneriaceae*, *Orchidaceae*, &c.
Parietales. The 27th order (*EP.*) of Archichlamydeae. The 2nd cohort (*BH.*) of Polypetalae. *Cf.* pp. xxx, l.
Parietaria (Tourn.) L. Urticaceae. 7 temp. and trop. (*P. officinalis* L., pellitory, in Brit.). Fls. mostly ☿ (unlike most of the fam.), in little cymes in the l. axils. According to Eichler the first fl. is ♀, the bulk of the cyme ☿, and the last fls. ♂. The ☿ fls. are exceedingly protog., the style protruding from the bud; the sta. develope later, exploding when ripe like those of the nettle, but by this time the stigma is incapable of fert., and usu. the style has dropped off, so that at first glance the fl. looks as if ♂.
Parinarium Aubl. Rosaceae (VI). 60 trop. Some have ed. seed.

Paripon Voigt. Palmae (inc. sed.). 1, habitat?

Paris (Rupp.) L. Liliaceae (VII). 20 N. palaeotemp. *P. quadrifolia* L. (herb-Paris) in Brit. Monopodial rhiz. and aerial stem with whorl of 4 or more net-veined l.; the aerial stems are formed, not annually, but at irreg. periods. P. 4- (or more) merous, as well as the other whorls; in herb-Paris the sepals alt. with the foliage-l. The fls. of this sp. are very protog., and colour and scent attract flies.

Parishella A. Gray. Campanulaceae (II). 1 California.

Parishia Hook. f. Anacardiaceae (3). 5 Burma, Malay Peninsula.

Paripinnate, pinnate with an even number of leaflets.

Paritium A. Juss. = Hibiscus L. (Malv.).

Park-land, savannah, open grassy country with patches of forest or copse.

Parkeriaceae, *cf.* Filicales, Leptosporangiatae.

Parkia R. Br. Leguminosae (I. 6). 20 trop. Fls. in heads, of which either the upper or lower fls. are male or neuter. The seeds of *P. africana* R. Br. are eaten in Afr.

Parkinsonia Plum. ex L. Leguminosae (II. 7). 4 trop. and subtrop.

Parlatorea Barb. Rodr. (*Gomesa* R. Br. p.p.). Orchid. (II. 19). 1 Brazil.

Parlatoria Boiss. Cruciferae (2). 2 W. As.

Parmena Greene (*Rubus* p.p.). Rosaceae (III. 2). 5 N. Am., E. As.

Parmentiera DC. Bignoniaceae (4). 2 C. Am. *P. cerifera* Seem., used as fodder, has caulifloral fr. which look like candles.

Parn grass (W.I.), *Panicum molle* Sw.

Parnassia (Tourn.) L. Saxifragaceae (I). 45 N. temp., chiefly in mountain bogs; 1 in Brit.—*P. palustris* L. (grass of Parnassus). Floral axis hollowed out and united to the base of the ovary. K 5; C 5; A 5, and alt. with them 5 stds.; G (4) or half-inf., 1-loc., with large projecting parietal plac. The fl. (class A) is protandr., the anthers in turn dehiscing just above the pistil and then moving outwards. Stds. opp. to the petals. Each has a solid nectar-secreting base, and ends above in a candelabra-like structure, each twig of which is terminated by a yellow knob, glistening in the sun and looking like a drop of honey. Flies are deceived by this appearance, and have been seen licking the knobs. [See Eichler's *Blüthendiag.* and Mrs Arber in *Ann. Bot.* XXVII. p. 491.]

Parnassus grass, *Parnassia palustris* L.

Parochetus Buch.-Ham. Leguminosae (III. 4). 1 Mts. of trop. As. and Afr. It has cleistogamic and open fls.

Parolinia Webb. Cruciferae (4). 1 Canaries.

Paronychia (Tourn.) L. Caryophyllaceae (I. 4). 40 cosmop. The small axillary fls. are concealed by the stipules.

Paronychiaceae. See Caryophyllaceae (I. 4).

Paropsia Nor. ex Thou. Flacourtiaceae (6). 15 trop. and subtrop. |✻.

Paropsiopsis Engl. Flacourtiaceae (6). 6 W. Afr.

Parosela Cav. (*Dalea* p.p.). Leguminosae (III. 6). 50 Am.

Parquetina Baill. Asclepiadaceae (I). 1 Gaboon.

Parrot weed (W.I.), *Bocconia frutescens* L.; **-'s bill**, *Clianthus*.

Parrotia C. A. Mey. Hamamelidaceae. 1 Persia. Fl. ☿, apet.

Parrotiopsis Schneider (*Fothergilla* p.p. *EP.*). Hamamel. 1 W. Him.

Parrya R. Br. Cruciferae (4). 10 N. temp. As., N. Am.

Parryella Torr. et Gray. Leguminosae (III. 6). 1 warm N. Am.

Parsley, *Petroselinum sativum* Hoffm.; **-fern**, *Cryptogramma crispa* R. Br.; **fool's -**, *Aethusa Cynapium* L.; **hedge -**, *Caucalis*; **- piert**, *Alchemilla*, (W.I.) *Petroselinum*.

Parsnip, *Pastinaca sativa* L.; **cow -**, *Heracleum Sphondylium* L.; **water -**, *Sium*.

Parsonsia R. Br. Apocynaceae (II. 2). 10 Malaya, Austr., Polynes., N.Z.

Parthenice A. Gray. Compositae (5). 1 Colorado to Mexico.

Parthenium L. Compositae (5). 10 Am., W.I. Br. attached to fr.

Parthenocarpy, production of fr. without fert.; **P.-genesis**, development of ovum to embryo without fert., *Alchemilla*, *Antennaria*, *Hieracium*, *Houttuynia*, *Wikstroemia*.

Parthenocissus Planch. (*Quinaria* Rafin.). Vitaceae. 10 temp. As., Am. *P. tricuspidata* Planch. and *P. quinquefolia* Planch. are the Virginia creepers.

Partial, used in sense opposed to general or total, *cf.* Parasites.

Partim (Lat.), partly.

Partridge berry (Am.), *Gaultheria procumbens* L., *Mitchella repens* L.; **- pea** (Am.), *Cassia Chamaecrista* L.

Parvatia Decne. Lardizabalaceae. 2 Khasias, China.

Parviflorus (Lat.), small-flowered.

Pasaccardoa O. Ktze. (*Phyllactinia* Benth.). Comp. (12). 1 trop. Afr.

Pasania Oerst. (*Quercus* p.p.). Fagaceae. 150 Malaya, Polynesia. Some have 3 ♀ fls. in the cupule.

Pascalia Orteg. (*Wedelia EP.*). Compositae (5). 1 Chili.

Paschanthus Burch. (*Modecca* p.p. *BH.*). Passifloraceae. 1 S. Afr.

Pascual, growing in pastures.

Pasithea D. Don. Liliaceae (III). 1 Chili.

Paspalum L. Gramineae (5). 250 trop., and temp. Am., where they form a large proportion of the pasture of the Campos, Pampas, &c. Good fodder. *P. scrobiculatum* L. (Kodo millet) cult. in India.

Pasque flower, *Anemone Pulsatilla* L.

Passerina L. Thymelaeaceae. 4 S. Afr. G 1-loc. C 0.

Passiflora L. (*BH.* excl. *Tacsonia* Juss.). Passifloraceae. 400 chiefly Am.; a few in As. and Austr., 1 in Madag. Climbing pl. with axillary tendrils. Some have curious bilobed l. (crescentic or swallow-tailed in shape), the centre lobe not developing. At the base of the leaf-stalk there are usu. extra-floral nectaries. The fls. spring from the same axils as the tendrils, sol. or in small cymes; the bract is usu. 'adnate' to the peduncle. The recept. is hollowed into a cup, bearing on its margin 5 sepals, 5 petals, and a number of effigurations of the axis—thread-like petaloid bodies, forming a dense mass (the corona) round the central androphore, at whose apex is borne the ovary. Five sta. spring from the androphore at the base of the ovary, and are bent downwards at first; afterwards the styles bend down also. Honey is secreted at the base of the androphore. Fr. a berry; seed enveloped in a fleshy aril. Many passion-flowers cult. orn. fl. Several have ed. fr., *e.g.* *P. quadrangularis* L., the Granadilla (trop. Am.), *P. maliformis* L., the sweet calabash (W. Ind.), *P. laurifolia* L., the water-lemon, *P. edulis* Sims (passion fruit), &c.

Passifloraceae (*EP.*; *BH.* incl. *Achariaceae*, *Caricaceae*, *Malesherbiaceae*). Dicots. (Archichl. Parietales; Passiflorales *BH.*). 12 gen., 580 sp. trop. and warm temp. Shrubs and herbs, mostly climbers with axillary tendrils, and with alt. stip. l. Fls. ☿ or unisexual, reg. Recept. of various shapes, often hollowed and frequently with a central andro- or gyno-phore; usu. term. by outgrowths, often of petaloid or staminodial appearance, forming the *corona*. K 3—5; C 3—5 or 0: A 3—5; $\underline{G}$ (3), 1-loc. with parietal plac. and several or ∞ anatr. ov.; style 1, simple or branched, or 3—5 separate styles. Caps. or berry. Seed with fleshy aril and endosp. *Chief genera:* Modecca, Passiflora. [**BH. chars.** incl. those of fams. mentioned, all somewhat rare.]

Passiflorales (*BH.*). The 13th order of Polypetalae.

Passion-flower, - fruit, *Passiflora.*

Pastinaca L. Umbelliferae (III. 6). 15 N. temp. |❋. *P. sativa* L. is the parsnip, a biennial, often cult. for ed. root.

Pasture, *cf.* Fodder.

Patabea Aubl. = Psychotria L. (Rubi.).

Patagonium Schrank (*Adesmia BH.*). Leguminosae (III. 7). 100 warm S. Am.

Patagonula L. Boraginaceae (I). 2 Brazil, Argentina. Good timber.

Patana oak (Ceylon), *Careya arborea* Roxb.

Patascoya Urb. (*Taonabo* p.p.). Theaceae. 1 Colombia.

Patchouli, *Pogostemon Patchouly* Pellet.

Patens (Lat.), spreading.

Patersonia R. Br. Iridaceae (II). 20 Austr., Tasmania.

Pathfinders, honey guides, *Myosotis.*

Patience (Am.), *Rumex Patientia* L.

Patima Aubl. Rubiaceae (I. 7). 1 Guiana.

Patosia Buchen. (*Rostkovia* p.p.). Juncaceae. 1 Chili.

Patrinia Juss. Valerianaceae. 13 E. As.

Patrisia Rich. (*Ryania* Vahl). Flacourtiaceae (7). 10 N. S. Am.

Pattalias S. Wats. (*Melinis* p.p.). Asclep. (II. 1). 2 Mexico, S.W. U.S.

Patulous, slightly spreading.

Pauciflorus (Lat.), few-flowered.

Pauladolphia Börner = Rumex p.p. (Polygon.).

Pauletia Cav. = Bauhinia L. p.p. (Legum.).

Paullinia L. Sapindaceae (I). 120 warm Am., 1 Madag., Afr. Lianes with watch-spring tendrils. Caps. often winged. *P. Cupana* H. B. et K. (guarana) cult. in Brazil; seeds used like cacao.

Paulowilhelmia Hochst. Acanthaceae (IV. A). 5 trop. Afr. Seeds often with toothed scales, spreading when wetted.

Paulownia Sieb. et Zucc. Scrophulariaceae (II. 4). 5 Chi., Jap. Trees (rare in S.). *P. imperialis* S. et Z. often cult. in parks.

Paulseniella Briquet. Labiatae (VI). 1 Pamirs.

Pauridia Harv. Haemodoraceae. 1 Cape Colony.

Pauridiantha Hook. f. Rubiaceae (I. 7). 2 trop. W. Afr.

Paurolepis Sp. Moore. Compositae (I). 1 Rhodesia.

Paurotis O. F. Cook. Palmae (I. 2). 1 Bahamas.

Pausandra Radlk. Euphorbiaceae (A. II. 5). 4 trop. S. Am.

Pausinystalia Pierre ex Beille (*Corynanthe* p.p.). Rubiaceae (I. 5). 3 trop. W. Afr.

Pavetta L. Rubiaceae (II. 4). 90 palaeotrop. The l. of many have little warts inhabited by bacterial colonies (Zimmermann in *Prings. Jahrb.* XXXVII. 1901, p. 1).
Pavia Boerh. = Aesculus L. (Hippocast.).
Pavieasia Pierre (*Sapindus* p.p.). Sapindaceae (I). 1 Tonquin.
Pavonia Cav. Malvaceae (3). 70 trop. and subtrop. There are 5 cpls. and 10 styles, 5 of these corresponding to cpls. which abort in development. The cpls. are hooked in fr.
Pavonia Ruiz et Pav. = Laurelia Juss. (Monim.).
Pawpaw (Am.), *Asimina triloba* Dun.
Paxia Gilg. Connaraceae. 2 W. Afr.
Paxiodendron Engl. = Xymalos Baill. (Laur.). 1 E. Afr.
Paxiuba palm, *Iriartea.*
Payena A. DC. Sapotaceae (I). 20 Malaya. *P. Leerii* Kurz yields a good gutta percha (see Palaquium), known as gutta sundek.
Payera Baill. Rubiaceae (I. 2). 1 Madag.
Paypayrola Aubl. Violaceae. 7 trop. S. Am. Tree. (A).
Pea, *Lathyrus*, *Pisum*; **blackeyed -** (W.I.), *Dolichos*; **chick -**, *Cicer arietinum* L.; **Congo -** (W.I.), *Cajanus indicus* Spreng.; **cow -**, *Vigna sinensis* Endl.; **dry -**, Congo -; **- flower** (W.I.), *Centrosema*, *Clitoria*; **everlasting -**, *Lathyrus latifolius* L.; **- nut**, *Arachis hypogaea* L.; **sweet -**, *Lathyrus odoratus* L.
Peach, *Prunus persica* Stokes; **- palm**, *Bactris*; **- wood**, *Caesalpinia.*
Peacock flower, *Caesalpinia pulcherrima* Sw.
Pear, *Pyrus communis* L.; **alligator -**, **avocado -**, **aguacate -**, *Persea gratissima* Gaertn. f.; **anchovy -**, *Grias cauliflora* L.; **prickly -**, *Opuntia*; **wooden -**, *Xylomelum.*
Pearcea Regel (*Isoloma BH.*). Gesneriaceae (II). 1 Ecuador.
Pearl millet, *Pennisetum typhoideum* Rich.; **-wort**, *Sagina.*
Pearsonia Dümmer (*Lotononis* p.p.). Leguminosae (III. 3). 11 S. Afr.
Pecan nut, *Carya.*
Pechuel-Loeschea O. Hoffm. Compositae (4). 1 W. Afr.
Peckia Vell. (*Cybianthus* Mart.). Myrsin. (II). 3 Brazil, Bolivia.
Peckoltia Fourn. Asclepiadaceae (II. 4). 1 Brazil.
Pectiantia Rafin. (*Mitella* p.p.). Saxifragaceae (I). 4 N. Am.
Pectinaria Cordem. 1899 (*Angraecum* p.p.). Orchidaceae (II. 20). 1 Madagascar, Mascarene Is.
Pectinaria Hack. (*Eremochloa* Buese). Gramineae (2). 6 E. Indomal.
Pectinaria Haw. Asclepiadaceae (II. 3). 4 S. Afr.
Pectinate, comb-like.
Pectinella J. M. Black (*Cymodocea* p.p.). Potamogeton. 1 S. coast Austr.
Pectis L. Compositae (6). 60 Arizona to Brazil.
Pectocarya DC. ex Meissn. Boraginaceae (IV. 1). 5 Pacif. Am.
Pedaliaceae (*EP.*; *BH.* incl. *Martyniaceae*). Dicots. (Sympet. Tubiflorae; Personales *BH.*). 14 gen., 45 sp., trop. and S. Afr., Madag., Indomal., mostly shore and desert plants. Herbs or rarely shrubs with opp. l. and glandular hairs. Fls. sol. or in cymes (usu. 3-flowered), with glands (metamorphosed fls.) at the base of the stalks, ☿, ·|·. K (5); C (5); A 4, didynamous, with a post. std.; $\underline{G}$ (2) [$\overline{G}$ in Trapella], with long style and 2 stigmas, 2—4-loc. or apparently 1-loc., often with

false septa; ovules 1—∞ per loc., on axile plac. Caps. or nut, often with hooks. Embryo straight; endosp. thin. Sesamum is economically important. *Chief genera:* Pedalium, Sesamum, Harpagophytum. [**BH. chars.** include Martyniaceae. The chief distinctions from M. lie in the placentation, the fruit, calyx, and glandular hairs.]

Pedalineae (*BH.*) = Pedaliaceae.

Pedaliophyton Engl. Pedaliaceae. 1 trop. Afr.

Pedalis (Lat.), a foot long or high.

Pedalium Royen ex L. Pedaliaceae. 1 trop. Afr., As., Madag.

Pedate (l.), *Helleborus*, *Sauromatum*.

Peddiea Harv. in Hook. Thymelaeaceae. 7 S. and trop. Afr.

Pedicel, stalk of single fl. in a group.

Pedicellaria Schrank (*Gynandropsis* DC.). Capparidaceae (v). 15 trop. and subtrop.

Pedicularis (Tourn.) L. Scrophulariaceae (III. 3). 275 ✻, S. Am., esp. on Mts.; 2 in Brit., *P. palustris* L. and *P. sylvatica* L. (lousewort). Semi-parasites with loose-pollen fls., fert. by humble-bees, &c.

Pedilanthus Neck. Euphorbiaceae (A. II. 8). 15 trop. Am., W.I.

Pedilochilus Schlechter. Orchidaceae (II. 16). 15 New Guinea.

Pediophytium (Cl.), an upland plant formation.

Peduncle, stalk of a group of fls., or of a single fl.

Peepul (pipul), *Ficus religiosa* L.

Peganum L. Zygophyllaceae (Rutaceae, *BH.*). 4 sp. Medit., As., N. Am. The seeds of *P. Harmala* L. yield turkey-red.

Pegia Colebr. (*Tapiria BH.*). Anacardiaceae (2). 1 E. Himalaya.

Peglera Bolus. Rhizophoraceae. 1 S. Afr.

Pegolettia Cass. Compositae (4). 5 S. Afr. to Java.

Peireskia Steud. = Pereskia Plum. (Cact.).

Peixotoa A. Juss. Malpighiaceae (I). 15 Brazil.

Pekoe, *cf. Thea*.

Pelagium (Cl.), a surface sea formation.

Pelagodendron Seem. Rubiaceae (I. 8). 1 Fiji.

Pelargonium L'Hérit. Geraniaceae. 250, chiefly S. Afr., a few Medit., Austr. Many vars. and hybrids cult. orn. fl. and l., of which one is the so-called Geranium of greenhouses, &c. In many the base of the stem is tuberous. An oil, used as a substitute for otto of roses, is distilled in Algeria from *P. odoratissimum* Ait.

Pelatantheria Ridl. Orchidaceae (II. 20). 3 S.E. As.

Pelea A. Gray (*Melicope* p.p. *BH.*). Rutaceae (I). 22 Polyn., Madag.

Pelecyphora Ehrenb. Cactaceae (III. 2). 2 Mexico.

Pelexia (Poit.) L. C. Rich. Orchidaceae (II. 2). 10 trop. Am., W.I.

Pelican flower, *Aristolochia*.

Peliosanthes Andr. Liliaceae (VIII) (Haemod. *BH.*). 10 Indomal.

Peliostomum E. Mey. Scrophulariaceae (I. 2). 6 S. and trop. Afr.

Pellacalyx Korth. Rhizophoraceae. 4 Malay Archipelago.

Pellaea Link. Polypodiaceae. 70 trop. and subtrop.

Pelletiera A. St Hil. (*Asterolinon BH.*). Primul. 1 S. Am.

Pelliciera Planch. et Triana. Theaceae. 1 Panama.

Pellionia Gaudich. Urticaceae. 15 trop. and E. As., Polynes. *P. umbellata* Wedd. has the br. of the ♂ fls. united to form an invol.

Pellitory, *Parietaria*.

Pellucid, transparent.
Pelma Finet. Orchidaceae (II. 16). 2 New Caled., New Guinea.
Peloria, sudden development of actinom. symmetry in a normally ·|· fl., *Linaria*, *Scrophulariaceae*.
Pelozia Rose. Onagraceae (2). 2 Calif., Mexico.
Peltandra Rafin. Araceae (V). 2 Atl. N. Am.
Peltanthera Benth. Loganiaceae. 1 Peru.
Peltaria Jacq. Cruciferae (2). 3 S.E. Eur., Medit.
Peltate (l.), ± circular, with petiole inserted near the centre of blade, *Nelumbium*, *Tropaeolum*.
Pelticalyx Griff. Anonaceae (inc. sed.). 1 Indomal.
Peltiphyllum Engl. (*Saxifraga* p.p.). Saxifrag. (1). 1 Calif.
Peltobryon Klotzsch = Piper L. p.p. (Pip.).
Peltodon Pohl. Labiatae (VII). 4 Brazil, Paraguay.
Peltogyne Vogel. Leguminosae (II. 3). 5 trop. Brazil. Timber, dye.
Peltophorum Walp. Leguminosae (II. 7). 8 trop.
Peltostegia Turcz. Inc. sed. 1 Brazil.
Peltostigma Walp. Rutaceae (1). 1 Jamaica.
Pelucha S. Wats. Compositae (4). 1 Lower Calif.
Pemphis Forst. Lythraceae. 1, *P. acidula* Forst., on paleotrop. coasts, esp. on beaches that are washing away.
Penaea L. Penaeaceae. 10 Cape Colony.
Penaeaceae (*EP.*; *BH.* incl. *Geissolomaceae*). Dicots. (Archichl. Myrtiflorae; Daphnales *BH.*). 5 gen., 25 sp., S.W. Cape Col. Shrubby xero. of ericoid habit, with opp. evergr. l. Fls. axillary, sol. or in pairs, the br. often coloured. Fl. ☿, reg., 4-merous. Recept. hollow, tubular. No petals. Ovary 4-loc.; style simple. Ov. 2 in each loc., anatr. Caps. No endosp. *Chief genera:* Penaea, Sarcocolla.
Penang lawyer, *Licuala acutifida* Mart.
Pencil cedar, *Juniperus virginiana* L.; **-flower**, *Stylosanthes*.
Pendulous, drooping; **-shoots**, *Amherstia*, *Brownea*, *Carpinus*, *Saraca*.
Penianthus Miers. Menispermaceae. 2 W. trop. Afr.
Penicillaria Willd. = Pennisetum Rich. p.p. (Gram.).
Penicillate, brush-shaped.
Peniocereus Britton et Rose (*Cereus* p.p.). Cact. (III. 1). 1 S. W. U.S., Mex.
Pennantia Forst. Icacinaceae. 4 Austr., N.Z., Norfolk I.
Pennilabium J. J. Smith (*Saccolabium* p.p.). Orchidaceae (II. 20). 3 Malay Archipelago.
Pennisetum Rich. Gramineae (5). 50 trop. and subtrop. Afr., S. Eur., As., Am. Involucre as in Cenchrus. *P. typhoideum* Rich., the bulrush, spiked, or pearl millet, is extensively cult. in India.
Penny cress, *Thlaspi*; **-royal**, *Mentha Pulegium* L.; **-wort**, *Cotyledon umbilicus* L., *Hydrocotyle vulgaris* L.
Penta- (Gr., pref.), five; **-cyclic**, **-merous**, **-gynous**, &c.
Pentabothra Hook. f. Asclepiadaceae (II. 1). 1 Assam.
Pentacaena Bartl. Caryophyllaceae (I. 4). 5 Pac. Am.
Pentacarpaea Hiern. Rubiaceae (I. 2). 1 trop. Afr.
Pentace Hassk. Tiliaceae. 10 Malaya, Burma.
Pentaceras Hook. f. Rutaceae (1). 1 E. Austr.

Pentachaeta Nutt. Compositae (3). 6 Calif.
Pentachondra R. Br. Epacridaceae (3). 4 Victoria, Tasm., N.Z.
Pentaclethra Benth. Leguminosae (I. 6). 3 trop. Am. and Afr.
Pentacme A. DC. (*Shorea* p.p. *BH.*). Dipterocarp. 3 Malay, Burma.
Pentacyphus Schlechter. Asclepiadaceae (II. 1). 1 Peru.
Pentadesma Sabine. Guttiferae (V). 4 W. trop. Afr., incl. *P. butyracea* Sabine, the tallow or butter tree. The fr. yields a greasy juice used as butter.
Pentadiplandra Baill. Tiliaceae. 1 Congo.
Pentadynamis R. Br. Leguminosae (III. 3). 1 S. Austr.
Pentagonia Benth. Rubiaceae (I. 7). 8 trop. Am.
Pentaloba Lour. = Alsodeia Thou. (*BH.*) = Rinorea Aubl. (Viol.).
Pentaloncha Hook. f. Rubiaceae (I. 7). 1 W. trop. Afr.
Pentameris Beauv. = Danthonia DC. p.p. (Gram.). 5 S. Afr.
Pentanema Cass. = Vicoa Cass. (*BH.*) = Inula L. p.p. (Comp.).
Pentanisia Harv. Rubiaceae (II. 1). 8 Afr., Madag.
Pentanopsis Rendle. Rubiaceae (I. 2). 1 Somaliland.
Pentanura Blume. Asclepiadaceae (I). 1 Sumatra.
Pentapanax Seem. Araliaceae (2). 10 Indomal., S. Am.
Pentapeltis Bunge (*Xanthosia BH.*). Umbellif. (I. 1). 1 W. Austr.
Pentapera Klotzsch (*Erica* p.p. *EP.*). Ericaceae (IV. 1). 1 Sicily.
Pentapetes L. Sterculiaceae. 1 Indomal.
Pentaphalangium Warb. Guttiferae (V). 4 New Guinea.
Pentaphragma Wall. Campanulaceae (I). 8 Indomal.
Pentaphylacaceae (*EP.*; *Ternstroemiaceae* p.p. *BH.*). Dicots. (Archichl. Sapindales). Only gen. Pentaphylax (*q.v.*).
Pentaphylax Gardn. et Champ. Pentaphylacaceae. 2 China, Malaya. Shrubs with alt. leathery l. and small ☿, reg., 5-merous, isomerous fls. in racemes below l. $\underline{G}$ (5), each with 2 pend. ov. Caps. Endosp. slight.
Pentapleura Handel-Mazzetti. Labiatae (VI). 1 Kurdistan.
Pentapogon R. Br. Gramineae (8). 1 Victoria, Tasmania.
Pentaptera Roxb. = Terminalia L. p.p. (Combret.).
Pentapterygium Klotzsch. Ericaceae (III. 2). 5 E. Himal., Khasia, Malay Peninsula. Fr. a five-winged berry.
Pentaptilon Pritzel (*Catosperma* Benth.). Goodeniaceae. 1 Austr.
Pentapyxis Hook. f. Caprifoliaceae. 1 Himalaya.
Pentarhaphia Lindl. Gesneraceae (II). 20 trop. Am., W.I.
Pentarrhaphis H. B. et K. Gramineae (11). 2 Mexico to Colombia.
Pentarrhinum E. Mey. Asclepiadaceae (II. 1). 4 Afr.
Pentas Benth. Rubiaceae (I. 2). 20 Afr., Madag. Cult. orn. fl.
Pentasachme Wall. ex Wight. Asclepiadaceae (II. 3). 3 E. As.
Pentaschistis Stapf (*Danthonia* p.p.). Gramineae (9). 40 Afr., Madag.
Pentascyphus Radlk. Sapindaceae (I). 1 French Guiana.
Pentaspadon Hook. f. Anacardiaceae (3). 2 Sumatra.
Pentasticha Turcz. (*Fuirena* p.p. *BH.*). Cyperaceae (I). 1 Madag., trop. Afr.
Pentatrichia Klatt (*Inula* p.p. *EP.*). Compositae (4). 1 S. W. Afr.
Pentatropis R. Br. Asclepiadaceae (II. 1). 8 palaeotrop.
Penthea Lindl. = Disa Berg. (Orchid.).
Pentheriella O. Hoffm. et Muschler. Compositae (3). 1 S. Afr.

Penthorum Gronov. ex L. Saxifrag. (1). 3 N.E. Am., Chi., Japan.
Pentochna Van Tiegh. (*Ochna* p.p.). Ochnaceae. 1 Congo.
Pentodon Hochst. (*Oldenlandia* p.p. *EP.*). Rubi. (I. 2). 5 trop. Afr., S. U.S.
Pentopetia Decne. Asclepiadaceae (1). 7 Madag., Natal.
Pentopetiopsis Costantin et Galland. Asclepiadaceae (1). 1 Madag.
Pentstemon Mitch. Scrophulariaceae (II. 4). 100 N. Am., E. As. Several cult. orn. fl. Post. sta. repres. by a large std. which is bent down to the lower side of the C (*cf.* Scrophularia).
Pentstemonacanthus Nees. Acanthaceae (IV. A). 1 Minas Geraes.
Pentzia Thunb. Compositae (7). 10 S. Afr.
Peperomia Ruiz et Pav. Piperaceae. 500 trop. and subtrop., esp. Am. Many are epiph. with creeping stems, adv. roots and fleshy l. (water-tissue under the upper epidermis). Fls. ☿, with 2 sta., arranged in term. spikes, which may, as in Piper, give rise to a sympodium. (See *Ann. Bot.* XX. p. 395, and XXI. p. 139.)
Peplidium Delile. Scrophulariaceae (II. 6). 2 palaeotrop.
Peplis L. Lythraceae. 3, wet places, N. temp. *P. Portula* L. in Brit., a little annual herb, very like *Montia fontana* with minute hexamerous fls. Self-fert. by the bending inwards of the sta. over the stigma. Fr. biloc. (the partition does not come up to the very apex) with many seeds, but indeh. When submerged the pl. has a more etiolated structure and becomes perennial.
Peplonia Decne. Asclepiadaceae (II. 1). 2 Brazil.
Pepo (Tourn.) L. = Cucurbita Tourn. (Cucurb.).
Pepo, the fruit of Cucurbitaceae.
Peponia Naud. Cucurbitaceae (3). 25 Afr., Madag.
Peponium Engl. (*Peponia* Naud.). Cucurbitaceae (3). 10 Afr., Madag.
Peponopsis Naud. Cucurbitaceae (3). 1 trop. Am.
Pepper, *Piper*; **African** - (W.I.), *Xylopia*; **betel** -, *Piper Betle* L.; **Cayenne** -, *Capsicum annuum* L.; - **bush** (Am.), *Clethra*; - **elder** (W.I.), *Peperomia*, &c.; - **grass** (Am., W.I.), *Lepidium*; **Guinea** - (W.I.), *Xylopia*, *Capsicum*; **Japan** -, *Zanthoxylum*; **Melegueta** -, *Amomum*; -**mint**, *Mentha piperita* L.; **negro** - (W.I.), *Xylopia*; **red** -, *Cayenne*; - **rod** (W.I.), *Croton humilis* L.; - **root** (Am.), *Dentaria*; - **tree**, *Schinus Molle* L.; **wall** -, *Sedum acre* L.; **water** -, *Elatine Hydropiper* L., &c.; -**wort** (Am.), *Lepidium*.
Pepperidge, *Nyssa*.
Pera Mutis. Euphorbiaceae (A. II. 2). 20 trop. Am., W.I.
Peracarpa Hook. f. et Thoms. Campanulaceae (1). 1 Himalaya.
Perama Aubl. Rubiaceae (II. 10). 6 trop. S. Am., W.I.
Peramium Salisb. (*Goodyera* p.p.). Orchidaceae (II. 2). 2 N. Am.
Peranema Don. Polypodiaceae. 1 India.
Peraphyllum Nutt. ex Torr. et Gray (*Amelanchier* p.p.). Rosaceae (II). 1 N.W. Am.
Peraphora Miers (*Lophophyllum* p.p. *BH.*). Menisp. 1 Himal., Khasias.
Percurrent, extending throughout entire length.
Perdicium L. = Gerbera Gronov. et Trixis R. Br. (Comp.).
Perebea Aubl. Moraceae (II). 10 trop. Am.
Pereilema J. et C. Presl. Gramineae (8). 3 trop. Am.

Perenideboles Goyena. Acanthaceae (IV. B). 1 Nicaragua.

Perennial, living for more than two years.

Pereskia Plum. ex L. Cactaceae (I). 18 trop. Am., W.I. Leafy plants (see fam.). Some, *e.g. P. aculeata* Mill., climb like Rubus with recurved thorns.

Pereskiopsis Britton et Rose (*Opuntia* et *Pereskia* p.p.). Cactaceae (I). 12 trop. Am.

Perezia Lag. Compositae (12). 75 Texas to Patagonia.

Pereziopsis Coulter. Compositae (12). 1 Guatemala.

Perfoliate (l.), united round the stem, *Baptisia*, *Bupleurum*.

Perforate, pierced through, or with translucent dots.

Perfumes, *Acacia*, *Acorus*, *Andropogon*, *Citrus*, *Curcuma*, *Dipteryx*, *Iris*, *Mesua*, *Michelia*, *Osmanthus*, *Pandanus*, *Plumieria*, *Pogostemon*, *Polyanthes*, *Rosa*, *Thymus*, &c., &c.

Pergamena Finet. Orchidaceae (II. 4). 1 Japan.

Pergularia L. Asclepiadaceae (II. 3). 15 Afr. and trop. As.

Peri- (Gr. pref.), around; **-anth**, see below; **-carp**, the fruit wall; **-chylous**, with aqueous tissue round the green tissue; **-derm**, bark; **-gone**, perianth; **-gyny**, *cf.* Ovary; **-sperm**, nutrient tissue round the embryo, derived from the nucellus, *Aizoaceae*, *Canna*, *Caryophyllaceae*, *Nymphaeaceae*, *Phytolaccaceae*, *Piperaceae*.

Periandra Mart. ex Benth. Leguminosae (III. 10). 6 Brazil.

Perianth, the outer covering of the fl., composed of non-reproductive l., usu. divided into an outer greenish whorl, the K, and an inner, coloured, the C. Concrescence is frequent, and the petals may be aborted (only recognisable for certain when many closely related forms possess them), thus giving an *apetalous* fl. Fl. with perianth, *chlamydeous*, without, *naked* or *achlamydeous*; with one whorl, *haplo-* or *mono-chlamydeous* or '*incomplete*' (*apetalous* if the phenomenon is due to suppression of C), with two whorls, *di-* or *diplo-chlamydeous* or '*complete*.' P with l. of one kind only (*tepals*) *homo-chlamydeous*, of two kinds (*sepals* forming a *calyx*, and *petals* a *corolla*), *heterochlamydeous*.

The P (K, C) may be *hypo-*, *peri-*, or *epi-gynous*; of free organs (*poly-phyllous*, *-sepalous*, *-petalous*) or concrescent (*gamo-phyllous*, *-sepalous*, *gamo-* or *sym-petalous*); in the latter case the concrescent part or *tube* bears the free *lobes*, *teeth*, or *segments* together forming the *limb*. It may also be *regular* (*actinomorphic*) or *irregular* (*zygomorphic*, or *asymmetrical*). If it fall as the bud opens, it is *caducous*, just after fert., *deciduous*; if it remain unwithered round the fr., *persistent*; withered, *marcescent*; enlarged, as in Physalis, *accrescent*.

A homochlam. P may be *sepaloid* (looking like a K in colour and texture) or *petaloid* (like a C). The aestivation is described in the terms given under Aestivation.

The sepals are commonly leafy and green, but sometimes ± woody (some Myrtaceae, &c.), or brightly coloured (Clerodendron, some Ranunculaceae, &c.). In many epig. fls. they are much reduced, *e.g.* in Umbelliferae and Rubiaceae. In Compositae they are frequently repres. by a *pappus* of hair or bristles. If concrescent, the K is described by the terms given for the C. In Malvaceae, some Rosaceae (*e.g.* Potentilla) and Lythraceae there is an *epicalyx* of apparent stipular nature (see also Dipsaceae).

The petals are usu. of some other colour than green, and of delicate texture. They may be narrowed at the base, as in wallflower, into a *claw* (*unguiculate*), fringed with hair-like teeth, as in pinks (*fimbriate*), *bi-fid*, *tri-fid*, &c. (*cf.* l.), or divided into several long segments (*laciniate*); they may be *spurred* (with long hollow projection, as in Viola), *saccate* or *gibbous* (with projecting broad pouch), *scaphoid* (boat-shaped, as in Loasa), &c. The general form of the sympetalous corolla may be *tubular*, *funnel-shaped*, *urceolate* (urn-shaped), *campanulate* (bell-shaped as in Canterbury bells), *rotate* (wheel-shaped with little or no tube, as in Veronica), *salver-shaped* (ditto, but with long tubular portion, as in primrose), *spurred*, *saccate*, *gibbous*, *ventricose* (swollen out all round in the basal part); if irreg., it may be *labiate* or *bilabiate* (with two projecting lips, as in Labiatae), *personate* (labiate, mouth closed by projecting lobe, as in Antirrhinum, &c.), *helmet-shaped*, *ligulate* (strap-shaped, as in dandelion, &c.), &c.

The shape, texture, &c. of the individual sepals, petals, calyx-lobes, corolla-lobes, are described as if they were leaves.

Perianthomega Bur. (*Bignonia* p.p.). Bignon. (1). 1 C. Brazil.

Perianthostelma Baill. Asclepiadaceae (II. 1). 3 trop. Afr.

Periblema DC. (*Boutonia* DC. *EP.*). Acanthaceae (IV. A). 1 Madag.

Periblepharis Van Tiegh. (*Luxemburgia* p.p.). Ochn. 1 Brazil.

Pericampylus Miers. Menispermaceae. 6 E. Indomal.

Perichasma Miers (*Stephania* p.p. *BH.*). Menispermaceae. 1 trop. W. Afr.

Perichlaena Baill. Bignoniaceae (2). 1 Madag.

Periclymenum Tourn. ex Rupp. = Lonicera L. p.p. (Caprifol.).

Pericome A. Gray. Compositae (6). 2 S. U.S., Mexico.

Pericopsis Thw. Leguminosae (III. 1). 1 Ceylon, yielding a pretty cabinet wood (nedun).

Perictenia Miers (*Odontadenia* p.p. *EP.*). Apocyn. (II. 1). 1 Peru.

Peridiscus Benth. Flacourtiaceae (inc. sed.). 1 Braz., Venezuela.

Periestes Baill. Acanthaceae (IV. B). 2 Madagascar, Comoros.

Perilla Linn. Labiatae (VI). 3 India to Japan.

Perillula Maxim. Labiatae (VI). 1 Japan.

Perilomia H. B. et K. Labiatae (VI). 8 Chili to Mexico.

Perinerion Baill. (*Baissea* A. DC. p.p.). Apocyn. (II. 1). 1 Angola.

Periodicity, usu. correlated with periodicity in climate, *e.g.* winter and summer, wet and dry, or hot and cool seasons. And *cf. Agave*, *Fagus*, &c.

Periomphale Baill. Gesneriaceae (inc. sed.). 2 New Caledonia.

Peripeplus Pierre. Rubiaceae (II. 5). 1 Gaboon.

Periphragmos Ruiz et Pav. (*Cantua* Juss.). Polemon. 2 Andes.

Periploca Tourn. ex L. Asclepiadaceae (I). 12 temp. |✻, trop. Afr.

Peripterygia Loes. (*Pterocelastrus* p.p.). Celastr. 1 New Caled.

Peristeria Hook. Orchidaceae (II. 13). 5 C. Am., incl. *P. elata* Hook. (dove orchid). Cult. orn. fl.

Peristethium Van Tiegh. (*Loranthus* p.p.). Loranth. (I). 1 Andes.

Peristrophe Nees. Acanthaceae (IV. B). 15 palaeowarm.

Peristylus Blume (*Habenaria* p.p.). Orchidaceae (II. 1). 80 warm |✻.

Perithrix Pierre (*Batesanthus EP.*). Asclepiad. (I). 1 Cameroons.

Peritoma DC. = Cleome L. (Cappar.).

Perityle Benth. Compositae (6). 15 S.W. U.S., Mexico.
Periwinkle, *Vinca.*
Perizoma Miers (*Salpichroa* p.p.). Solanaceae (2). 1 S. E. U.S.
Pernambuco rubber, *Hancornia speciosa* Gomes.
Pernettya Gaudich. Ericaceae (II. 2). 30 S. Am., Mexico, Tasm., N.Z.
Pernettyopsis King et Gamble. Ericaceae (II. 2). 2 Malay Penins.
Peronema Jack. Verbenaceae (5). 1 Malay Archipelago.
Perotis Ait. Gramineae (3). 5 palaeowarm. Glumes awned.
Perotriche Cass. Compositae (4). 1 S. Cape Colony.
Perovskia Karel. Labiatae (VI). 4 W. As.
Perpusillus (Lat.), very small.
Perralderia Coss. (*Grantia BH.*). Compositae (4). 2 N. W. Afr.
Perriera Courchet. Simarubaceae. 1 Madagascar.
Perrieranthus Hochr. Malvaceae (4). 1 Madag.
Perrierophytum Hochr. Malvaceae (4). 1 Madag.
Perrottetia H. B. et K. Celastraceae. 10 Mexico, C. Am., Polynesia.
Persea Plum. ex L. Lauraceae (1). 20 trop. The fr. of *P. gratissima* Gaertn. f. (aguacate, avocado, alligator pear, palta) is ed.
Persian berries, yellow berries, *Rhamnus infectoria* L.; **-insect powder,** *Chrysanthemum roseum* Adam.; **-lilac,** *Melia Azedarach* L.
Persica (Tourn.) Mill. = Prunus L. (Ros.).
Persicaria (Tourn.) L. (*Polygonum* p.p.). Polygonaceae (II. 2). 75 N. Am., W.I., trop. S. Am.
Persimmon, *Diospyros virginiana* L., *D. Kaki* L. f., &c.
Persistent (P, K, C), remaining unwithered round the fl., *Corylaceae, Fagaceae, Physalis.*
Personales (*BH.*). The 9th order of Gamopetalae.
Personatae (Warming). The 5th order of Sympetalae.
Personate (C), labiate, mouth closed by projecting lobe, *Antirrhinum.*
Persoonia Sm. Proteaceae (1). 60 Austr., N.Z.
Pertusate, with slits.
Pertya Sch.-Bip. Compositae (12). 5 Japan to Afghanistan.
Peru, balsam of, *Myroxylon Pereirae* Klotzsch; **- bark,** *Cinchona*; **marvel of -,** *Mirabilis*; **-vian nutmeg,** *Laurelia.*
Perularia Lindl. (*Habenaria* p.p. *BH.*). Orchid. (II. 1). 1 N. Am., As.
Pervillaea Decne. Asclepiadaceae (II. 3). 1 Madag.
Perymenium Schrad. Compositae (5). 25 C. Am.
Pescatoria Rchb. f. (*Zygopetalum* p.p. *BH.*). Orchidaceae (II. 14). 10 Colombia. Cult. orn. fl.
Peschiera A. DC. = Tabernaemontana Plum. (Apocyn.).
Pessopteris Underwood (*Polypodium* p.p.). Polypod. 1 trop. Am.
Pestallozzia Zoll. et Morr. = Gynostemma Blume (Cucurb.).
Petagnia Guss. Umbelliferae (III. 2). 1 Sicily.
Petal, a l. of the C, usu. coloured; **-ody,** change of sta. to pet.; **-oid,** petal-like; **-omania,** abnormal increase of petals.
Petalacte D. Don. Compositae (4). 1 W. Cape Colony.
Petalactella N. E. Br. Compositae (4). 1 S. Afr.
Petalidium Nees (*EP.* excl. *Pseudobarleria*). Acanth. (IV. A). 1 Indomal.
Petalinia Becc. (*Ochanostachys* p.p. *EP.*). Olacaceae. 1 Banka.

Petalodiscus Baill. (*Savia BH.*). Euphorbiaceae (A. I. 1). 5 Madag.
Petalolophus K. Schum. Anonaceae (4). 1 New Guinea.
Petalonema Gilg. Melastomaceae (1). 1 trop. E. Afr.
Petalonyx A. Gray. Loasaceae. 4 Mexico, S.W. U.S.
Petalostelma Fourn. Asclepiadaceae (II. 3). 1 Brazil.
Petalostemma R. Br. = Glossonema Decne. p.p. (Asclep.). 1 Abyss.
Petalostemon Michx. (*Kuhnistera EP.*). Legumin. (III. 6). 25 N. Am.
Petalostigma F. Muell. Euphorbiaceae (A. I. 1). 3 E. Austr.
Petalostylis R. Br. Leguminosae (II. 5). 1 Austr.
Petasites (Tourn.) L. Compositae (8). 15 N. temp. *P. officinalis* Moench (butter-bur) in Brit. spreads largely by rhiz. It is dioecious (*cf.* Tussilago, its close ally). The ♂ head has about 30 fls. with the usual mech. of Compositae, the style acting as pollen-presenter, though the ovary is not fertile. Occasionally a few ☿ fls. are found. The ♀ head consists of about 150 ♀ fls. surrounding 1—3 ♂ fls. Only the male fls. secrete honey. *P. fragrans* Presl (winter heliotrope) cult. perf. fls., which appear in Feb.
Petastoma Miers (*Bignonia* p.p. *BH.*). Bignoniaceae (1). 8 trop. Am.
Peteria A. Gray. Leguminosae (III. 6). 1 New Mexico.
Petermannia F. Muell. Dioscoreaceae. 1 New S. Wales.
Petersia Welw. Lecythidaceae. 2 W. trop. Afr.
Petersianthus Merrill (*Petersia* Welw.). Lecythid. 3 Afr., Phil. I.
Petesia P. Br. = Rondeletia L. (Rubi.).
Petesioides Jacq. (*Wallenia* Sw.). Myrsinaceae (II). 4 W.I.
Petiole, leafstalk; **sensitive -**, *cf.* Climbing Plants.
Petitia Jacq. Verbenaceae (4). 4 Mexico, W.I.
Petitmenginia Bonati. Scrophulariaceae (III. 2). 1 Cambogia.
Petiveria Plum. ex L. Phytolaccaceae. 2 warm Am., W.I.
Petlomelia Nieuwland (*Fraxinus* p.p.). Oleaceae. 1 N. Am.
Petraeus (Lat.), growing on rocks; **petrium** (Cl.), a rock formation; **-odium** (Cl.), a boulder field formation.
Petraeovitex Oliv. Verbenaceae (5). 3 Malay Archipelago.
Petrea Houst. ex L. Verbenaceae (1). 12 trop. Am., W. Ind. Cult. orn. fl., climber.
Petrobium R. Br. Compositae (5). 1 St Helena.
Petrocallis R. Br. (*Draba* p.p. *BH.*). Cruciferae (2). 1 Mts. S. Eur.
Petrocarya Schreb. = Parinarium Aubl. (Ros.).
Petrocodon Hance. Gesneriaceae (1). 1 China.
Petrocoptis A. Br. (*Lychnis* p.p. *BH.*). Caryophyll. (II. 1). 2 Pyrenees.
Petrocosmea Oliv. Gesneriaceae (1). 3 China.
Petrollinia Chiov. (*Inula* p.p.). Compositae (4). 1 E. trop. Afr.
Petromecon Green (*Eschscholtzia* p.p.). Papaver. (II). 2 Calif.
Petronia Barb. Rodr. (*Promenaea* p.p. *EP.*). Orchid. (II. β. II). 1 Braz.
Petrophila R. Br. Proteaceae (1). 35 Austr.
Petrophyes Webb et Berth. = Monanthes Haw. (Crassul.).
Petrophyton Rydberg (*Spiraea* p.p.). Rosaceae (I. 1). 5 N. Am.
Petrosavia Becc. Liliaceae (1). 1 Borneo.
Petroselinum Hoffm. (*Carum* p.p. *BH.*). Umbelliferae (III. 5). 5 Eur., Medit. *P. sativum* Hoffm. is the parsley, cult. as condiment.

Petrosimonia Bunge. Chenopodiaceae (B). 7 Greece to C. As.

Petrusia Baill. Olacaceae. 1 Madagascar.

Petteria C. Presl. Leguminosae (III. 3). 1 S.E. Eur.

Petty whin, *Genista anglica* L.

Petunga DC. Rubiaceae (I. 8). 6 E. Indomal.

Petunia Juss. Solanaceae (4). 25 S. and warm N. Am. *P. violacea* Lindl. and others often cult. orn. fl.

Peucedanum (Tourn.) L. (*BH.* incl. *Anethum* Tourn., *Pastinaca* L.). Umbelliferae (III. 6). 180 Eur., As., Afr., Am.; 4 in Brit. *P. sativum* Benth. et Hook. f. (parsnip), *cf.* Pastinaca. *P.* (*A.*) *graveolens* Benth. et Hook. f. (Medit.) is the dill; fr. a condiment; *P. officinale* L. (Brit.) is the sulphur-root used in veterinary practice; *P. Ostruthium* Koch (Brit.) is also used.

Peucephyllum A. Gray. Compositae (8). 1 S.W. U.S.

Peumus Molina. Monimiaceae. 1 Chili, *P. Boldus* Molina, the Boldo. Wood hard; bark yields dye; fr. ed.

Peutalis Rafin. = Polygonum Tourn. (Polyg.).

Peyrousea DC. Compositae (7). 1 Cape.

Pezisicarpus Vernet. Apocynaceae (II. 1). 1 Siam.

Pfaffia Mart. Amarantaceae (3). 20 warm S. Am.

Pfeiffera Salm-Dyck (*Rhipsalis* p.p.). Cact. (III. 3). 1 S. Braz.

Phaca L. (*Astragalus* p.p.). Leguminosae (III. 6). 60 N. Am.

Phacelia Juss. (incl. *Cosmanthus* Nolte, *Eutoca* R. Br., *Whitlavia* Harv.). Hydrophyllaceae. 120 N. Am., Andes, often cult. orn. fl. The fl. is a bee-flower with honey secreted below the ovary and guarded by stipule-like flaps at the base of the sta. The large-flowered sp. are highly protandrous. The anther as it dehisces turns inside out.

Phacellanthus Sieb. et Zucc. Orobanchaceae. 1 Japan.

Phacellaria Benth. Santalaceae. 4 S.E. As.

Phacellothrix F. Muell. Compositae (4). 1 E. trop. Austr.

Phacelophrynium K. Schum. (*Phrynium* p.p.). Marantaceae. 6 Malaya.

Phacopsis Rydberg (*Astragalus* p.p.). Legum. (III. 6). 2 N. Am.

Phaeanthus Hook. f. et Thoms. Anonaceae (2). 7 Malaya.

Phaecasium Cass. (*Crepis* p.p. *EP.*). Compositae (13). 3 Eur., W. As.

Phaedranassa Herb. Amaryllidaceae (1). 4 Andes.

Phaedranthus Miers (*Bignonia* p.p. *BH.*). Bignoniaceae (1). 1 Mex.

Phaenixopus Cass. = Lactuca Tourn. p.p. (Comp.).

Phaenocoma D. Don. Compositae (4). 1 Cape Colony. Cult. orn. fl.

Phaenogams, Phanerogams, *Spermaphyta*.

Phaenohoffmannia O. Ktze. (*Pleiospora* Harv.). Leguminosae (III. 3). 1 S. Afr.

Phaenology, study of the periodic phenomena of vegetation.

Phaenopyrum M. Roem. = Crataegus Tourn. (*BH.*) = Cotoneaster Rupp.

Phaenosperma Munro ex Benth. Gramineae (4). 1 China.

Phaeocephalus Sp. Moore. Compositae (7). 1 Cape Colony.

Phaeomeria Lindl. (*Amomum* p.p. *BH.*). Zingiber. (1). 25 Indomal.

Phaeoneuron Gilg. Melastomaceae (1). 4 trop. Afr.

Phaeopappus Boiss. = Centaurea L. p.p. (Comp.).

Phaeoptilum Radlk. Nyctaginaceae. 1 S. Afr.
Phaeospheriona Hassk. (*Athyrocarpus BH.*). Commelin. 4 trop. Am.
Phaeostemma Fourn. Asclepiadaceae (II. 4). 2 Brazil.
Phagnalon Cass. Compositae (4). 20 Canaries to Himalaya.
Phaiocalanthe × Rolfe. Orchidaceae. Hybrid, Phaius-Calanthe.
Phaiocymbidium ×. Orchidaceae. Hybrid, Phaius-Cymbidium.
Phaius Lour. (*Phajus* Hassk.). Orchidaceae (II. 9). 16 trop. As., Malaya, Austr., &c. Terrestrial.
Phalacraea DC. = Piqueria Cav. (Comp.).
Phalacrocarpum Willk. (*Chrysanthemum* p.p. *BH.*). Comp. (7). 1 Spain.
Phalacroderis DC. (*Rodigia EP.*). Compositae (13). 1 Aegean.
Phalacrodiscus Less. = Chrysanthemum Tourn. p.p. (Comp.).
Phalacroseris A. Gray. Compositae (13). 1 California.
Phalaenopsis Blume. Orchidaceae (II. 20). 40 Indomal. Epiph. with flattened aerial roots.
Phalangium (Tourn.) Adans. = Anthericum L. p.p. (Lili.).
Phalaris L. Gram. (7). 20 N. and S. temp. *P. canariensis* L. (canary grass) seeds are used for cage-birds. *P. arundinacea* L. (reed-grass) is common in Brit.
Phaleria Jack. Thymelaeaceae. 12 Indomal.
Phanera Lour. = Bauhinia L. p.p. (Legum.).
Phanerogamae, see Spermaphyta.
Phanerophlebia Presl. Polypodiaceae. 10 trop. Am.
Phania DC. Compositae (2). 3 W.I.
Phanopyrum Nash (*Panicum* p.p.). Gramineae (5). 1 N. Am.
Pharbitis Choisy (*Ipomoea* p.p. *BH.*). Convolvulaceae (1). 60 trop. and subtrop. Cult. orn. fl.
Pharetranthus F. W. Klatt (*Coreopsis* p.p. *EP.*). Comp. (5). 1 Phil.
Pharmacosycea Miq. = Ficus Tourn. p.p. (Mor.).
Pharnaceum L. Aizoaceae (1). 16 S. Afr.
Pharus P. Br. Gramineae (6). 5 trop. Am.
Phaseolus (Tourn.) L. Leguminosae (III. 10). 160 trop. and warm temp. Fl. mech. like Vicia, but complicated by the spiral coiling of the keel with the inclosed style. *P. multiflorus* Willd. (Mexico) is the scarlet-runner, *P. vulgaris* L. the French or kidney bean, *P. lunatus* L. the Lima or duffin bean similarly used in the trop., *P. acutifolius* A. Gray the tepary of the S.W. U.S., *P. Mungo* L. (*P. Max* L.) the 'green gram' of India, used like kidney beans, or roasted, and as horse food. The var. *radiatus* of the last, with darker beans (black gram), is a highly valued pulse and horse food in India.
Phaulanthus Ridl. (*Anerincleistus* p.p.). Melastomaceae (1). 6 Malay Peninsula, Assam.
Phaulothamnus A. Gray. Phytolaccaceae. 1 North Mexico.
Phaylopsis Willd. (*Micranthus EP.*). Acanthaceae (IV. A). 12 palaeotrop.
Pheasant's eye, *Adonis autumnalis* L.
Phebalium Vent. Rutaceae (1). 35 Austr., N.Z.
Phegopteris Fée = Dryopteris Adans. (Polypod.).
Phellandrium (Tourn.). L. = Oenanthe Tourn. p.p. (Umbellif.).

Phelypaea Tourn. ex L. Orobanchaceae. 2 Cent. As.
Phelline Labill. Aquifoliaceae. 12 New Caledonia.
Phellium (Cl.), a rock field formation.
Phellodendron Rupr. Rutaceae (IV). 4 E. temp. As.
Phellogen, formative tissue of cork (bark).
Phellolophium Baker. Umbelliferae (III. 5). 1 Madag.
Phellopterus Benth. in B. et H. f. = Glehnia F. Schmidt (Umb.).
Phellopterus Nutt. (*Cymopterus* Rafin. p.p.). Umbelliferae (III. 6). 4 E. As., W. N.Am.
Phenax Wedd. Urticaceae (3). 12 trop. Am., W.I.
Pherosphaera Archer (*Dacrydium* p.p.). Coniferae (Taxaceae 1; see C. for gen. chars.). 1 Austr., 1 Tasmania. Shrubs.
Pherotrichis Decne. Asclepiadaceae (II. 4). 2 Mexico.
Phialacanthus Benth. Acanthaceae (IV. B). 1 E. Bengal.
Phialanthus Griseb. Rubiaceae (II. 3). 4 W.I.
Phialocarpus Deflers. Cucurbitaceae (2). 1 Arabia.
Phialodiscus Radlk. (*Blighia* p.p.). Sapindaceae (I). 5 trop. Afr.
Philactis Schrad. Compositae (5). 2 Mexico.
Philadelphus (Riv.) L. Saxifragaceae (III). 50 N. temp. Shrubs with opp. l.; the buds arise closely protected by the l.-bases through which in many they have to break. Fls. conspicuous, strongly scented, protogynous. Sta. 20—40; ovary inf., usu. 4-loc. Several sp. cult. orn. fl. shrub (Syringa).
Philastrea Pierre. Sterculiaceae. 1 Cambodia.
Philbornea Hallier (*Durandea* p.p.). Linaceae. 2 Borneo.
Philesia Comm. ex Juss. Liliaceae (X). 1 S. Chili, a much-branched shrub with petioled, 1-nerved, rolled-back l., not easily recognised as a Monocot.
Philgamia Baill. Malpighiaceae (inc. sed.). 1 Madag.
Philibertella Vail. (*Philibertia* p.p.). Asclep. (II. 1). 30 Am., W.I.
Philibertia H. B. et K. Asclepiadaceae (II. 1). 35 Am., W.I.
Philippia Klotzsch. Ericaceae (IV. 2). 20 S. Afr., Madag., Masc.
Philippiella Spegazz. Caryophyllaceae (I. 4). 1 Patagonia.
Phillipsia Rolfe (*Satanocrater* p.p. *EP.*). Acanthaceae (IV. A). 1 Somaliland.
Phillyrea L. Oleaceae. 6 Medit.
Phillyrophyllum O. Hoffm. Compositae (4). 1 Kalahari desert.
Philodendron Schott. Araceae (V). 250 warm Am., W.I. Usu. shrubs, usu. climbing, often epiph., with both clasping roots and aerial roots reaching the soil (see fam.). The latter sometimes twine as they descend. The pinnation of the l. is due to a delayed development of the portions between the ribs, and not to a process such as occurs in Monstera (*q.v.*). Monoecious.
Philodice Mart. Eriocaulonaceae. 2 Brazil.
Philoglossa DC. Compositae (5). 2 Peru, Ecuador.
Philogyne Salisb. = Narcissus Tourn. p.p. (Amaryll.).
Philonotion Schott. Araceae (V). 1 Amazonas.
Philotheca Rudge. Rutaceae (I). 5 Austr.
Philotria Rafin. (*Elodea* p.p.). Hydrocharidaceae. 5 N. Am.
-philous (Gr. suff.), loving, dwelling in.
Philoxerus R. Br. (*Iresine* p.p. *EP.*). Amarant. (3). 10 trop. exc. As.

Philydraceae (*EP.*, *BH.*). Monocots. (Farinosae; Coronarieae *BH.*; pp. vii, liv). 3/4 Indomal., Austr. Herbs with 2-ranked sheathing narrow l., and fls. in spikes, ☿, ·|·*P* homochlam., outer 1 + (2) post., inner 2 anter. only developed; A 1, anter.; $\underline{G}$ (3), with 1 style, axile or parietal plac., and ∞ anatr. ov. Caps.; endosp. *Genera:* Philydrum (sta. free), Helmholtzia, Pritzelia (sta. on P).

Philydrum Banks. Philydr. 1 E. As., Malay Arch., Aust.

Philyra Klotzsch (*Argithamnia* p.p.). Euphorb. (A. II. 2). 1 S. Braz., Paraguay.

Philyrophyllum O. Hoffm. Comp. (4). 1 Kalahari desert.

Phinaea Benth. Gesner. (II). 4 Colombia. G $\frac{1}{2}$-inf.

Phippsia R. Br. Gramin (8). 1 arctic.

Phitopis Hook. f. Rubi. (I. 3). 1 Peru. Densely hairy tree.

Phlebanthia Reichb. Caryoph. (inc. sed.). Nomen.

Phlebocalymna Griff. ex Miers (*Gonocaryum EP.*). Olac. 4 E. Indomal.

Phlebocarya R. Br. Amaryllid. (III; Haem. *BH.*). 3 W. Austr. G 1-loc.

Phlebochiton Wall. (*Tapiria BH.*, *Pegia EP.*). Anacard. (2). 2 S.E. As.

Phlebodium (R. Br.) J. Smith (*Polypodium* p.p.). Polypod. 10 warm.

Phlebolithis Gaertn. Sapot. (inc. sed.). 1, habitat?

Phlebotaenia Griseb. (*Polygala* p.p. *EP.*). Polygal. 3 Cuba, P. Rico.

Phleum L. Gramin. (8). 10 N. temp., S. Am. Inf. palea shorter than awned glume. *P. pratense* L. (Brit., timothy grass) valuable fodder.

Phloem, the outer part of the vascular bundle, carrying prepared food.

Phloga Nor. ex Thou. Palm. (IV. 1). 4 Madag. L. with whorled pinnae.

Phlogacanthus Nees. Acanth. (IV. B). 15 Indomal. A 2. Cult. orn. fl.

Phlogella Baill. Palm. (IV. 1). 1 Comoros.

Phlomis L. Labiat. (VI. 4). 70 N. palaeotemp. The helmet-like upper lip of fl. is raised by a visiting insect. Style branches differ.

Phlox L. Polemon. 60 N. Am., Siberia. Sta. inserted at unequal height. Cult. orn. fl.

Phoberos Lour. = Scolopia Schreb. (Flacourt.).

Phocea Seem. = Macaranga Thou. (Euphorb.). 1 New Caled.

Phoebanthus Blake (*Helianthella* p.p.). Comp. (5). 2 N. Am.

Phoebe Nees. Laur. (I). 60 Indomal., trop. Am., W.I.

Phoenicanthemum Blume = Loranthus L. p.p. (Loranth.).

Phoenicaulis Nutt. (*Cheiranthus* p.p. *BH.*). Crucif. (3). 2 Pac. Am.

Phoeniceus (Lat.), scarlet.

Phoenicophorium H. Wendl. (*Stevensonia BH.*). Palm. (IV. 1). 1 Seychelles.

Phoenicospermum Miq. (*Sloanea* p.p. *EP.*). Elaeocarp. 1 Java.

Phoenix L. Palm. (I. 1). 12 warm Afr., As., incl. *P. dactylifera* L. (date, N. Afr., S.W. As.). Columnar stem covered with old l.-bases; l. pinnate. Dioec.; ♀ spadix fert. by hanging a ♂ over it. Berry; usu. 1 cpl. only ripens; seeds with hard cellulose endosp. Yields fr., wine, sugar (*cf.* Cocos), &c. Hats, mats, thatch, &c. from leaves.

Pholacilia Griseb. = Trichilia L. (Meli.).

Pholidia R. Br. Myopor. 60 Austr.

Pholidocarpus Blume. Palm. (II). 3 Malay Arch. Fr. papillose, hairy.

Pholidostachys H. Wendl. Palm. (IV. 1). 1 Costa Rica.

Pholidota Lindl. Orchid. (II. 3). 30 Indomal., China.

Pholisma Nutt. ex Hook. Lenno. 1 Calif. In sandy ground. Spike.

Phoradendron Nutt. Loranth. (II). 125 Am., W.I. Trelease, *P.*, 1916.

Phormium Forst. Lili. (III). 2 N.Z., Norfolk I. L. isobilat. The l. of *P. tenax* Forst. furnishes N.Z. flax. Cult. orn. pl.

Phornothamnus Baker. Melastomaceae (I). 1 Madag.
-phorus (suff.), stalk, bearer (bearing).
Photinia Lindl. Rosaceae (II). 30 S.E. As., N. Am.
Photinopteris J. Sm. Polypodiaceae. 1 Malaya, Phil. Is.
Phoxanthus Benth. (*Ophiocaryon EP.*). Sabiaceae. 1 Amazonas.
Phragmites Trin. Gramineae (10). 3, 1 Argentine, 1 trop. As. and 1 cosmop. (incl. Brit.), *P. communis* L. the common reed. It forms floating fens at the Danube mouth. It has a creeping rhiz. and tall upright stem with a dense panicle of spikelets. The lowest fl. of the spikelet is ♂, the rest ☿. A few cm. above the leaf-sheath are three transverse dents in the l. (Teufelsbiss); these are due to pressure at the time when the rolled up blade is still in the sheaths of older l.
Phragmopedilum Rolfe. Orchidaceae (I. 2). 12 trop. Am.
Phreatia Lindl. Orchidaceae (II. 15). 75 Indomal.
Phretium (Cl.), a tank formation.
Phrissocarpus Miers (*Tabernaemontana* p.p.). Apocynaceae (I. 3). 1 S. Am.
Phrodus Miers. Solanaceae (2). 4 Chili.
Phryganocydia Mart. (*Macfadyena BH.*). Bignoniaceae (1). 1 E. S. Am.
Phrygilanthus Eichl. (*Loranthus* p.p. *BH.*). Loranthaceae (I). 20 S. Am., E. Austr.
Phrygiobureaua O. Ktze. = Phryganocydia Mart. (Bignon.).
Phryma L. Phrymaceae. 1 E. As., N. Am. Herb with opp. l. and small axillary fls., ·|·. Cpl. 1 with one erect orthotr. ov.
Phrymaceae (*EP.*; *Verbenaceae* p.p. *BH.*). Dicots. (Sympet. Tubiflorae). Only gen. Phryma, *q.v.*; the chief distinction from Verbenaceae is the erect orthotr. ovule; no transitions between this and other V.
Phrynium Loefl. Marantaceae. 30 Indomal., trop. Afr. Aril.
Phtheirospermum Bunge. Scrophulariaceae (III. 3). 4 E. As.
Phthirusa Mart. (*Loranthus* p.p. *BH.*). Loranth. (1). 35 trop. Am.
Phuodendron Graebn. Valerianaceae. 1 Brazil.
Phuopsis Benth. et Hook. f. Rubiaceae (II. 11). 1 Caucasus.
Phycella Lindl. = Hippeastrum Herb. p.p. (Amaryll.).
Phygelius E. Mey. Scrophulariaceae (II. 4). 2 S. Afr. Cult. orn. fl.
Phyla Lour. (*Lippia* p.p.). Verbenaceae (1). 6 N. Am.
Phylacium Bennett. Leguminosae (III. 7). 1 Malay Archipelago.
Phylica L. Rhamnaceae. 70 S. Afr., Madag., &c. Mostly xero. shrubs, often of heath-like habit with l. rolled back (*cf.* Empetrum).
Phyllacantha Hook. f. Rubiaceae (I. 8). 1 Cuba.
Phyllachne Forst. Stylidiaceae. 9 Tasm., N.Z., S. Am.
Phyllactinia Benth. (*Pasaccardoa EP.*). Compositae (12). 1 trop. Afr.
Phyllactis Pers. (*Valeriana* p.p. *EP.*). Valerian. 25 Mexico, S. Am.
Phyllagathis Blume. Melastomaceae (I). 5 S.E. As.
Phyllanthera Blume. Asclepiadaceae (I). 2 Malay Penins., Java.
Phyllanthodendron Hemsl. (*Phyllanthus* p.p. *EP.*). Euphorbiaceae (A. I. 1). 2 Siam.
Phyllanthus L. Euphorbiaceae (A. I. 1). 500 temp. and trop., exc. Eur. and N. As. The trop. Am. § *Xylophylla* has flat green phylloclades bearing fls. on the margins. The ultimate shoots in § *Euphyllanthus* look like pinnate l. In *P. cyclanthera* Baill. the ♂ fl. has its 3 sta. united into a synandrium with ring-like anther at top.

Phyllarthron DC. Bignoniaceae (4). 6 Madag., Mascarenes. The l. is reduced to a jointed winged petiole.

Phyllepidum Rafin. Amarantaceae (inc. sed.). Gen. dubium. 1 N. Am.

Phyllis L. Rubiaceae (II. 7). 1 Canaries, Madeira.

Phyllitis Ludwig. Polypodiaceae. 10 trop. and subtrop.

Phyllo- (Gr. pref.), **-phyllous** (suff.), leaf; **-clade**, a stem structure usu. ± flattened and serving l. purposes, *Asparagus*, *Baccharis*, *Bossiaea*, *Carmichaelia*, *Hibbertia*, *Lathyrus*, *Lemna*, *Muehlenbeckia*, *Phyllanthus*, *Phyllocladus*, *Ruscus*, *Semele*; **-de**, a petiole flattened and green, taking over l.-functions, *Acacia*, *Oxalis*; **-dy**, change of fl. organs to l.; **-me**, a leaf structure; **-taxy**, the arrangement of the l. upon the stem. It follows definite rules, esp. in flowering-plants, though it varies within certain narrow limits. The l. may be several at each node (in *whorls*), or two (usu. *opposite*), or one (*alternate*). When the stem is so short that the l., as in the primrose or dandelion, are all crowded together and spring from the level of the ground, they are said to be '*radical.*' In the first two cases the l. at one node usu. stand above the gaps at the node below. In the case of alt. l. there is found to be a fairly constant angle between each l. and the next one above it, *e.g.* in Plantago (fig.) this angle is $\frac{3}{8}$ of the whole circumference measured the nearest way. This fraction $\frac{3}{8}$ represents the phyllotaxy. Twisting excepted the l. will stand in 8 vertical rows, each divided from the next by $\frac{1}{8}$ of the circumference. Leaf 2 will be $\frac{3}{8}$, 3 will be $\frac{6}{8}$, 4 will be $\frac{9}{8}$, 5 will be $\frac{12}{8}$, 6 will be $\frac{15}{8}$, 7 will be $\frac{18}{8}$, 8 will be $\frac{21}{8}$, and 9 will be $\frac{24}{8}$, of the circumference from leaf 1, *i.e.* immediately over it, and three turns of the spiral above it. Hence the rule for determining phyllotaxy: start from any l. A and draw a spiral round the stem, passing by the nearest way through all consecutive l. to the l. B exactly above A; then the number of l. from A to B is the denominator, the number of turns of the spiral the numerator, of the fraction representing the phyllotaxy.

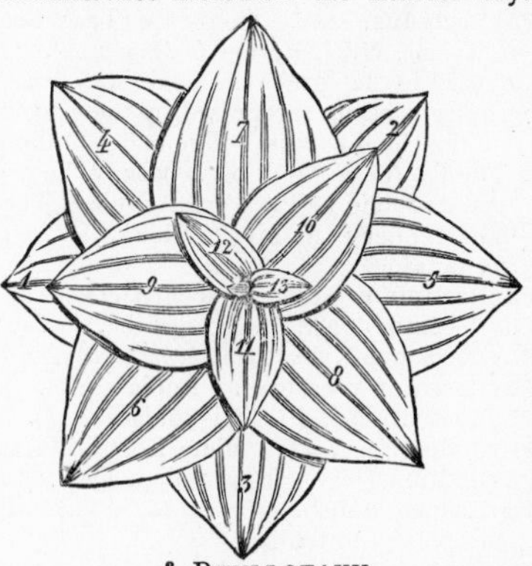

$\frac{3}{8}$ PHYLLOTAXY.

In Gramineae the phyllotaxy is $\frac{1}{2}$, *i.e.* alt. on opp. sides of the stem, in Cyperaceae $\frac{1}{3}$. Nearly all other actual arrangements are terms of the continued fraction starting from $\frac{1}{2}$, $\frac{1}{3}$. If we add the numerators together to make a new numerator, and treat the denominators in the same way, we get the next arrangement $\frac{2}{5}$. This with $\frac{1}{3}$ gives $\frac{3}{8}$, and then $\frac{5}{13}$ and so on. It is rare to find a stem that shows the phyllotaxy very clearly; usually in the course of growth more or less twisting occurs (*cf.* Pandanaceae). The benefit of the phyllotaxy is that the leaves are spread out to occupy the available space to advantage.

Phyllotaxies of these types give shoots of radial symmetry; there are also bilateral arrangements, esp. upon horizontal shoots. Sometimes the dorsiventrality is attained by the twisting of the leaf-stalks from the positions in which they arose, but more commonly there is a more or less two-ranked (*distichous*) phyllotaxy, the l. arising upon the sides of the axis, and merely having to twist at their bases to place themselves horizontally; *e.g.* in the yew (Taxus), lime (Tilia), Abies, Anona, Betulaceae, Pinus, Ulmus, &c.

In other plants, again, alterations of phyllotaxy occur for which no explanation can be given; *e.g.* in Baptisia, Eucalyptus, Nolanaceae, Quisqualis, Solanaceae, Thelygonum, &c.

Phylloboea Benth. Gesneriaceae (1). 2 Further India, China.

Phyllobotrium Muell.-Arg. Flacourtiaceae (10). 3 W. Afr.

Phyllocactus Link. (*EP.* incl. *Epiphyllum* p.p.). Cactaceae (III. 1). 25 warm Am., W.I., often epiphytic. Flat-stemmed plants (see fam.).

Phyllocalyx Berg. = Eugenia Mich. p.p. (Myrt.).

Phyllocarpus Riedel ex Endl. Leguminosae (II. 8). 1 Rio de Janeiro.

Phyllochlamys Bur. in DC. Moraceae (1). 1 Indomal.

Phyllocladus Rich. Coniferae (Taxaceae, 6; see C. for gen. char.). 6 Tasm., N.Z., Borneo (celery pine). The 'short shoots' are represented by flat green leaf-like structures—phylloclades—whose stem-nature is easily recognized by their position in the axils of the scale l. on the 'long shoots.' The edges of the phylloclades also bear scales. The fls. (mon- or di-oec.) occupy the position of phylloclades. Each cpl. has one axillary erect ovule. The seed has a small basal aril. The timber is useful: the bark of *P. trichomanoides* D. Don is used for tanning.

Phylloclinium Baill. Flacourtiaceae (10). 1 Congo.

Phyllocomos Mast. Restionaceae. 1 S. Afr.

Phyllocosmus Klotzsch (*Ochthocosmus EP.*). Linaceae. 5 trop. Am., Afr.

Phyllocrater Wernham. Rubiaceae (I. 2). 1 Borneo.

Phylloctenium Baill. Bignoniaceae (4). 1 Madag.

Phyllodes Lour. = Phrynium Loefl. (Marant.).

Phyllodium Desv. = Desmodium Desv. (Legum.).

Phyllodoce Salisb. (*Bryanthus BH.*). Ericaceae (I. 3). 10 N. circumpolar and temp.

Phylloglossum Kunze. Lycopodiaceae. 1 Austr. and N.Z., *P. Drummondii* Kunze. The embryo forms a protocorm (see fam.), which produces a crown of sterile l. and a short unbranched stem, bearing at its apex a single cone of sporangia, like the cone of Lycopodium. "At the end of the growing season a new protocorm is formed. This arises directly from the apex of the old one where no strobilus is developed, but in the latter case grows out upon a sort of peduncle from near the base of one of the l." (Campbell). Prothallus subterranean. [*Cf. Ann. Bot.* 1910, p. 335 and 1919, p. 485.]

Phyllogonum Coville. Hydnoraceae. 1 California.

Phyllomelia Griseb. Rubiaceae (II. 4). 1 Cuba.

Phyllonoma Willd. ex Schult. Saxifrag. (v). 6 trop. Am. Mts. $\overline{G}$.
Phyllophiorrhiza O. Ktze. = Ophiorhizophyllum S. Kurz (Acan.).
Phyllopodium Benth. Scrophulariaceae (II. 5). 15 S. Afr.
Phyllorhachis Trimen. Gramineae (5). 1 Angola.
Phylloscirpus C. B. Clarke. Cyperaceae (I). 1 Argentina.
Phyllosma Bolus. Rutaceae (I). 1 S. Afr.
Phyllospadix Hook. Potamogetonaceae. 2 W. coast N. Am., Japan. Dioecious.
Phyllostachys Sieb. et Zucc. Gramineae (13). 25 Japan to Himalaya. The stripped stems are Whangee canes.
Phyllostegia Benth. Labiatae (III). 17 Hawaii, Tahiti.
Phyllostylon Capanema ex B. et H. f. Ulmaceae. 1 Rio, 1 Paraguay, 1 Cuba. Good timber.
Phyllota Benth. Leguminosae (III. 2). 10 Austr.
Phyllotrichum Thorel ex Lecomte. Sapind. (inc. sed.). 1 S.E. As.
Phylloxera, the root and leaf louse of the vine (Vitis).
Phylloxylon Baill. Leguminosae (III. 8). 2 Madag., Mauritius.
Phylogeny, line of descent from other forms.
Phylon (Gr.), line of descent.
Phymaspermum Less. Compositae (7). 5 Cape Colony.
Phymatidium Lindl. Orchidaceae (II. 19). 2 Brazil.
Phymatocarpus F. Muell. Myrtaceae (II. 1). 2 W. Austr.
Phymatodes Presl = Polypodium L. (Polypod.).
Physacanthus Benth. Acanthaceae (IV. A). 3 W. trop. Afr.
Physaliastrum Makino (*Chamaesaracha* p.p.). Solan. (2). 2 Japan.
Physalidium Fenzl. Cruciferae (2). 1 Persia.
Physalis L. Solanaceae (2). 50 cosmop. The berry of *P. Alkekengi* L. (winter cherry) is edible, also that of *P. peruviana* L. (strawberry or gooseberry tomato, or cape gooseberry). It is enclosed in the bladdery persistent calyx, which becomes red.
Physaria A. Gray. Cruciferae (3). 6 Pac. N. Am.
Physedra Hook. f. Cucurbitaceae (3). 5 trop. W. Afr.
Physena Nor. ex Thou. Flacourtiaceae (inc. sed.). 2 Madag.
Physic-nut, *Jatropha Curcas* L.
Physocalymma Pohl. Lythraceae. 1 trop. S. Am. Timber valuable.
Physocalyx Pohl. Scrophulariaceae (III. 2). 2 Brazil.
Physocarpus Maxim. (**-pa** Rafin.) (*Neillia BH.*). Rosaceae (I. 1). 5 N. Am., N.E. As. G usu. 5. Fr. 2-valved. Cult. orn. shrub.
Physocaulis Tausch (*Chaerophyllum* p.p. *BH.*). Umbelliferae (III. 2). 1 Medit.
Physochlaina G. Don. Solanaceae (2). 5 C. As.
Physodium Presl. Sterculiaceae. 2 Mexico.
Physoleucas Jaub. et Spach (*Leucas* p.p. *BH.*). Labi. (VI). 1 Arabia.
Physolobium Benth. = Kennedya Vent. p.p. (Legum.).
Physopodium Desv. Lythraceae. 1 Bourbon.
Physopsis Turcz. Verbenaceae (3). 1 W. Austr.
Physoptychis Boiss. (*Vesicaria BH.*). Cruciferae (4). 1 Persia.
Physorrhynchus Hook. Cruciferae (2). 2 Persia, Afghanistan.
Physosiphon Lindl. Orchidaceae (II. 8). 5 trop. Am. Cult. orn. fl.
Physospermum Cusson. Umbelliferae (III. 4). 5 Eur.
Physostegia Benth. Labiatae (VI). 5 N. Am.

Physostelma Wight. Asclepiadaceae (II. 3). 2 Malaya.

Physostemon Mart. (*Cleome* p.p. *BH.*). Capparid. (V). 4 trop. S. Am.

Physostigma Balf. Leguminosae (III. 10). 2 trop. Afr. The keel is spurred. *P. venenosum* Balf. is the ordeal bean of Calabar.

Physotrichia Hiern. Umbelliferae (III. 5). 6 trop. Afr.

Physurus L. C. Rich. Orchidaceae (II. 2). 35 warm As., Am., W.I.

Phyt-, Phyto- (Gr. pref.), plant-; **-logy**, botany.

Phytelephas Ruiz et Pav. Palmae (V). 4 trop. Am. Like Nipa, widely different from other palms; with affinities to Pandanaceae and Cyclanthaceae. Short-stemmed with large pinnate rad. l., and dioec. infls. ♂ infl. a sausage-shaped spadix; the fl. has an irreg. P and ∞ sta. with long filaments. ♀ spadix simple with spathe of several l., and about 6 fls.; the fl. has an irreg. P (an outer whorl of 3 and inner of 5—10 longer l.), numerous stds. and usu. a 5-loc. ov. with long style and stigmas. Each fl. gives a berry, and the actual fr. consists of 6 or more of these united together. The outer coat is hard, with woody protuberances. Each partial fr. contains several seeds; the endosp. (cellulose) is very hard (vegetable-ivory) and is used for turning into billiard balls, &c. [Compare this fr. with Pandanus and Carludovica.]

Phyteuma L. Campanulaceae (I. 1). 45 Medit., Eur., As. *P. orbiculare* L. and *P. spicatum* L. (rampion) in Brit. Fl. mech. interesting (see fam.). The fls. are small, and massed together in heads. A tube is formed by the coherence of the tips of the long thin petals, within which the anthers are held. The style pushes up through this and drives the pollen gradually out at the end, where it is exposed to insects. Finally the style emerges, the stigmas open and the petals separate and fall back. [Compare with Campanula, Jasione and Compositae.]

Phytocrene Wall. Icacinaceae. 7 Indomal. Twining shrubs with very large vessels in the stem. If the stem be cut a quantity of water escapes, which is drunk by the Malabar natives. Fls. dioec.

Phytolacca Tourn. ex L. (incl. *Pircunia* Bert.). Phytolaccaceae. 26 trop. and subtrop. Herbs with fleshy roots, or shrubs or trees. Fls. reg.; P 5, A 10→30, G 7—16 or (7—16); in the latter case fr. a berry, in the former an aggregate of achenes or drupes.

Phytolaccaceae (*EP.*, *BH.*). Dicots. (Archichl. Centrospermae; Curvembryae *BH.*). 22 gen., 120 sp., chiefly trop. Am. and S. Afr. Herbs, shrubs, or trees, with racemose or cymose infls. of regular inconspic. ☿ fls. P 4—5, A 4—5 or more (to ∞), $\underline{G}$, rarely G, 1—∞ or (1—∞), ovules 1 in each cpl., amphi- or campylo-tropous. Drupe or nut, rarely capsule. Seed with perisperm, often arillate. The fls. exhibit great variety in structure, owing to branching of sta. and different numbers and arrangements of cpls. *Chief genera:* Seguiera, Rivina, Phytolacca.

Phytosalpinx Lunell = Lycopus Tourn. (Labi.).

Piaranthus R. Br. Asclepiadaceae (II. 3). 12 S. Afr.

Piassaba fibre, *Attalea funifera* Mart. (Bahia), *Leopoldinia Piassaba* Wallace.

Picardaea Urb. Rubiaceae (I. 1). 1 Haiti.

Picconia DC. (*Notelaea* p.p.). Oleaceae. 1 Canaries, Madeira.

Picea Link. *Synonymy: P. vulgaris* Link (*Pinus Abies* L.) = P. excelsa Link; *P. canadensis* Link = Tsuga canadensis; *P. Pinsapo* Loud. = Abies Pinsapo; *P. rubra* A. Dietr. = P. nigra Link.

Coniferae (Pinaceae 13; see C. for gen. char.). 35 *. Long shoots only with needle l. Fls. single. Cones ripening in one year. *P. excelsa* Link, the Norway spruce or spruce-fir, found in Eur. from the Pyrenees to 68° N., furnishes valuable wood, resin, and turpentine. *P. alba* Link (silver fir, N. Am.), *P. Morinda* Link (Himalayan spruce), and others are also valuable.

Pichleria Stapf et Wettst. Umbelliferae (III. 5). 2 Persia.

Pichonia Pierre (*Epiluma* p.p. *EP.*). Sapotaceae (I). 2 New Caled.

Pickerel weed (Am.), *Pontederia.*

Pickeringia Nutt. ex Torr. et Gray. Legumin. (III. 2). 1 Calif.

Picotee, var. of carnation, *Dianthus Caryophyllus* L.

Picradenia Hook. (*Actinella* p.p.). Compositae (6). 20 N. Am.

Picradeniopsis Rydberg (*Bahia* p.p.). Compositae (6). 1 N. Am.

Picraena Lindl. (*Picrasma* p.p. *EP.*). Simarubaceae. 2 W.I., Brazil.

Picralima Pierre. Apocynaceae (I. 3). 1 Gaboon.

Picramnia Sw. Simarubaceae. 30 trop. Am., W.I.

Picrasma Blume. Simarubaceae. 8 trop. and subtrop. The bitter wood and bark are used as a substitute for quassia.

Picrella Baill. Simarubaceae. 1 Mexico.

Picridium Desf. (*Reichardia EP.*). Compositae (13). 10 Medit.

Picris Linn. Compositae (13). 36 Medit., W. As., Abyss. 2 in Brit.

Picrocardia Radlk. Simarubaceae. 1 New Caled.

Picrodendron Planch. Simarubaceae. 1 W.I.

Picrolemma Hook. f. Simarubaceae. 1 Amazonas.

Picrorrhiza Royle ex Benth. Scrophulariaceae (III. 1). 1 Himal.

Picrosia D. Don. Compositae (13). 1 warm S. Am.

Pictetia DC. Leguminosae (III. 7). 6 W.I., Mexico.

Pictus (Lat.), coloured.

Piddingtonia A. DC. = Pratia Gaudich. (Campan.).

Pierardia Roxb. = Baccaurea Lour. p.p. (Euph.).

Pieris D. Don (*Lyonia* p.p. *EP.*). Ericaceae (II. 1). 10 N. Am., E. As.

Pierrea Hance. Dipterocarpaceae. 1 Malaya.

Pierreanthus Bonati = Delpya Pierre (Scroph.).

Pierreodendron Engl. Simarubaceae. 1 trop. Afr.

Pierrina Engl. Scytopetalaceae. 2 trop. Afr.

Pig lily (Afr.), *Zantedeschia*; **- nut** (Am.), *Carya porcina* Nutt., (W.I.) *Omphalea*; **- weed** (Am.), *Chenopodium*; **-'s balsam**, *Hedwigia.*

Pigafettia Becc. Palmae (III). 3 Malay Archipelago.

Pigea DC. = Ionidium Vent. (*BH.*). = Hybanthus Jacq. (Viol.).

Pigeon berry (Am.), *Phytolacca*; **-pea**, *Cajanus indicus* Spreng.

Pignons, ed. seeds of *Pinus Pinea* L.

Pilea Lindl. Urticaceae (2). 140 trop., cult. (artillery plant), so called from the puffs of pollen ejected by the exploding sta. (*cf.* Urtica).

Pileanthus Labill. Myrtaceae (II. 2). 3 W. Austr.

Pileostegia Hook. f. et Thoms. Saxifragaceae (III). 1 S.E. As.

Pileus Ramirez. Passifloraceae. 1 Mexico.

Pilewort, *Ranunculus Ficaria* L.

Piliferous, hair-bearing.

Piliocalyx Brongn. et Gris. Myrtaceae (I). 4 New Caledonia.
Pillansia L. Bolus. Iridaceae (III). 1 S. Afr.
Pillar roots, *cf.* Aerial roots.
Pillwort, *Pilularia.*
Pilocarpus Vahl. Rutaceae (I). 12 trop. Am., W.I. The leaves of *P. pennatifolius* Lem. are the officinal 'folia Jaborandi.'
Pilocereus Lem. (*Cereus* p.p. *BH.*). Cactaceae (III. 1). 50 Mex., S. Am.
Pilogyne Schrad. = Melothria L. p.p. (Cucurb.).
Pilophyllum Schlechter (*Chrysoglossum* p.p.). Orchidaceae (II. *a.* 11). 2 Java, New Guinea.
Pilose, with soft scattered hairs.
Pilosella (Rupp.) Sch.-Bip. = Hieracium Tourn. p.p. (Comp.).
Pilosperma Planch. et Triana. Guttiferae (V). 1 Colombia.
Pilostigma Costantin. Asclepiadaceae (II. 1). 1 Indochina.
Pilostyles Guill. (*Apodanthes* p.p. *BH.*). Rafflesiaceae. 8 S. Am. to W. As. Parasites on Leguminosae.
Pilouratea Van Tiegh. (*Gomphia* p.p.). Ochnaceae. 2 Brazil.
Pilularia L. Marsiliaceae. 6 N. and S. temp. *P. globulifera* L., the pill-wort, on the margins of lakes in Brit. Creeping rhiz. bearing roots on the lower surface and linear erect l. on the upper. The pea-shaped sporocarp, borne on the ventral side of a l.-stalk, has a hard outer coat and consists of four sori, each containing micro- and mega-sporangia. Life history like Marsilia.
Pilumna Lindl. = Trichopilia Lindl. (Orchid.).
Pimelandra A. DC. (*Ardisia* p.p.). Myrsinaceae (II). 7 Indomal.
Pimelea Banks et Soland. Thymelaeaceae. 80 Austr., Tasm., N.Z., Timor. Fls. in heads, protandrous. Cult. orn. fl.
Pimeleodendron Hassk. Euphorbiaceae (A. II. 7). 6 Malaya.
Pimenta Lindl. Myrtaceae (I). 5 trop. Am., W.I. The unripe fr. of *P. officinalis* Lindl., rapidly dried, form allspice.
Pimentelea Wedd. Rubiaceae (I. 5). 1 Peru.
Pimento, *Pimenta officinalis* Lindl.
Pimia Seem. Sterculiaceae. 1 Fiji.
Pimpernel, *Anagallis arvensis* L.; **yellow** -, *Lysimachia nemorum.*
Pimpinella (Riv.) L. Umbelliferae (III. 5). 110 | ✻ exc. Austr. 2 in Brit., incl. *P. Saxifraga* L. (burnet-saxifrage). *P. Anisum* L. (Medit., anise), fr. (aniseed) are used in flavouring.
Pin-eyed (in Primula, &c.), long-styled.
Pinaceae, see *Coniferae.*
Pinanga Blume. Palmae (IV. 1). 50 Indomal.
Pinaropappus Less. Compositae (13). 3 Texas, Mexico.
Pinarophyllon T. S. Brandegee. Rubiaceae (I. 8). 1 Mexico.
Pinaster, *Pinus Pinaster* Ait.
Pinckneya Michx. Rubiaceae (I. 1). 1 S. U.S. Cinchonin in bark.
Pindarea Barb. Rodr. Palmae (IV. 2). 2 Brazil.
Pinder (W.I.), ground nut, *Arachis hypogaea* L.
Pine, *Pinus*; **-apple**, *Ananas sativus* Schult.; **Bhotan -**, **blue -**, *Pinus excelsa* Wall.; **Bunya-Bunya -**, *Araucaria Bidwilli* Hook.; **celery -**, *Phyllocladus*; **cluster -**, *Pinus Pinaster* Ait.; **Corsican -**, *Pinus Laricio* Poir.; **cypress -**, *Callitris*; **digger -**, *Pinus Sabiniana* Dougl.; **frank-**

incense -, *Pinus Taeda* L.; **golden -**, *Pseudolarix*; **hoop -**, *Araucaria Cunninghamii* Ait.; **huon -**, *Dacrydium Franklinii* Hook. f.; **loblolly -**, *Pinus Taeda* L.; **Norfolk Island -**, *Araucaria excelsa* R. Br.; **Oregon -**, *Pseudotsuga Douglasii* Carr.; **parasol -**, *Sciadopitys*; **pitch -**, *Pinus palustris* Mill., &c.; **-sap** (Am.), *Monotropa*; **screw -**, *Pandanus*; **stone -**, *Pinus Pinea* L.; **sugar -**, *Pinus Lambertiana* Dougl.; **Weymouth -**, *Pinus Strobus* L.; **wild -** (W.I.), *Tillandsia*; **yellow -**, *Pinus echinata* Mill.

Pineda Ruiz et Pav. (*Banara* p.p. *BH.*). Flacourt. (5). 3 N.W. S. Am.

Pinelea Lindl. (*Restrepia* p.p. *EP.*). Orchid. (II. 8). 1 Brazil.

Pinellia Tenore. Araceae (VII). 6 Japan, China. Cult.

Piney varnish, *Vateria indica* L.

Pingerin, pinguin (W.I.), *Bromelia Pinguin* L.

Pinguicula Tourn. ex L. Lentibulariaceae. 30 N. extra-trop., Andes, Antarctic zone; 3 in Brit. (butterwort), incl. *P. vulgaris* L. It has a rhiz. with a rosette of rad. l. arranged in $\frac{3}{8}$ phyllotaxy. The l. are covered with glands, some sessile, some on stalks, secreting a sticky fluid to which small insects adhere. Rain washes them against the edge of the l., which is slightly upturned: when stimulated by the presence of proteid bodies it rolls over upon itself and encloses them, and then the sessile glands secrete a ferment, digest the prey, and absorb the products, after which the l. unrolls again. *P. lusitanica* L. is found on the western shores of Brit. and is one of a few sp. which have migrated thus far up the Atl. coasts (common in Portugal).

Pinillosia Ossa in DC. Compositae (5). 2 Cuba.

Pink, *Dianthus*, esp. *D. monspessulanus* L.; **Cheddar -**, *D. caesius* Sm.; **Chinese -**, *D. chinensis* L.; **clove -**, *D. caryophyllus* L.

Pinna, leaflet of a pinnate l.; **pinnate**, cpd., leaflets on either side of stalk, like a feather; **pinnati-fid, -partite, -sect**, pinnately notched to $\frac{1}{4}$—$\frac{1}{2}$, $\frac{1}{2}$—$\frac{3}{4}$, $>\frac{3}{4}$ depth.

Pintoa C. Gay. Zygophyllaceae. 1 Chili.

Pinus (Tourn.) L. *Synonymy: P. Abies* L. (*P. excelsa* Lam.) = Picea excelsa; *P. alba* Ait. = Picea alba; *P. balsamea* L. = Abies balsamea; *P. Cedrus* L. = Cedrus Libani; *P. Douglasii* Lamb. = Pseudotsuga Douglasii; *P. Larix* L. = Larix europaea; *P. maritima* Lam. = P. Pinaster; *P. nigra* Ait. = Picea nigra; *P. Picea* L. = Abies pectinata.

Coniferae (Pinaceae 18: see C. for gen. chars.). 100 N. temp. and on Mts. in the N. trop. Evergr., resinous trees with both long and short shoots (see Coniferae). If a tree be examined in winter the main axes will be found each with a group of buds at the end, one term., the rest lat., covered with resinous scale l. Each gives rise in spring to a 'long shoot' or shoot of unlimited growth; the term. bud continues the main axis of all, forming a year's growth before branching in a similar way again. The large branches thus form rough whorls marking each year's growth. On the stem of a long shoot no green l. are directly borne, but only scales, first the bud scales above mentioned and then others in whose axils arise the 'short shoots,' or shoots of limited growth. Each of these has a few scale l. at the base of a very short stem and ends with 2 or more green l. of needle shape. When there are two, their upper flat sides face one another. These needle l. exhibit xero. characters; they are thick in proportion to surface exposed, they have a very stout epidermis with a hypoderm of thick walled tissue under it, and the stomata are placed at the bottom of deep pits; the intercellular spaces too are very small.

The fls. take the form of the familiar cones, the ♂ grouped together in spikes. Each fl., whether ♂ or ♀, occupies the position of a short shoot and is of limited growth—an axis with a few scale-l. below bearing a number of sporophylls. In the ♂ there are many sta., each with two pollen-sacs on the under side; the pollen is loose and powdery, and each grain has two bladdery expansions of the cuticle helping it to float in the air. In the ♀, the cpls. are very small, but the ovuliferous scales, which show at the outside of the cone, are very large, and each bears two ovules at its base, with the micropyles facing the axis. The ♀ cones take 2 to 3 years before the seeds are ripe. In May of the first year, the first stage may be seen—young cones, about 1 cm. long, in the position of short shoots near the tip of the lengthening axis. The ovules are not ripe for fert. In June (the time varies from year to year according to season) pollination takes place. The ♂ cones shed their pollen in great quantities, so that in a pine forest the air is often full of it (if it rain, the phenomenon of 'showers of sulphur' may occur), and the wind carries it about. At the same time the ovuliferous scales spread apart. If a grain fall between two of them it slips down to the micropyle of an ovule, where it becomes held by the sticky fluid then exuding. After a short time the ♀ cones close up again. The pollen grain is brought into contact with the nucellus by the drying up of the mucilage; it forms a short pollen-tube, and then a resting period comes on. Next year in May or June the ♀ cone has become a fat green body about 3 cm. long, with the ovules ready for fert.; the pollen-tubes now recommence growth and reach the ova. Then in the third year the cone is mature—a hard woody cone containing the seeds between the scales. Each seed contains an embryo with a whorl of cots., embedded in rich endosp., and has a hard testa. To the end of this is attached a thin membranous wing, derived from the ovuliferous scale. In dry weather the cone opens and the seeds are blown away. In germ. the seed is lifted up above the earth by the growing plant and the cots. remain inside the testa till the reserves are exhausted. They are green whilst in the seed, though in darkness—an exception to the rule that chlorophyll requires light for its formation. During the first year no short shoots are formed, and the seedling has green l. borne directly on the main stem.

The pines are amongst the most valuable of all plants and are cultivated on an enormous scale, chiefly for their timber, which is easily worked, and resinous products. The resin renders the timber very resistent to decay, &c. Some of the more important sp. will now be mentioned. (*Cf.* also under Pine.)

I. *PINASTER* Endl. Visible part of fruit scale more or less pyramidal with central boss.

§ 1. *Pinea* (short shoot with 2 or rarely 1 needles): 20 sp. *P. sylvestris* L., the Scotch fir, the only Brit. sp., occurs in Eur. to 68° N., in Asia to 66° N., and as far south as Spain and Italy (alpine). The wood (yellow deal) is largely used in the arts; turpentine is obtained by tapping the tree.

The resin exudes and is distilled; the distillate is oil of turpentine, the remainder rosin. Tar and pitch are correspondingly the products of destructive distillation in closed chambers. *P. Pumilio* Haenke (*P. montana* Mill.) is a shrubby decumbent sp., Pyrenees to Caucasus. *P. Pinea* L. (Medit.), the stone pine, furnishes edible seeds ('pignons'). *P. Laricio* Poir. (S. Eur.) is the Corsican pine. *P. Pinaster* Ait., the cluster pine or pinaster (Medit.), is a valuable tree. It grows well near the sea, and large areas of the Landes of S. France are planted with it. It furnishes much of the turpentine &c. in use. *P. echinata* Mill. the short leaved or yellow pine is a valuable N. Am. sp. *P. longifolia* Roxb. (Himal.) is tapped for resin.

§ 2. *Taeda* (needles 3, triangular in section): 16 sp. *P. Taeda* L. (loblolly or frankincense pine, southern U.S.) yields turpentine. *P. palustris* Mill. (*P. australis* Michx.) (pitch-pine, U.S.) yields timber and turpentine. Other sp., *e.g. P. ponderosa* Dougl. and *P. rigida* Mill., are also known by the name of pitch-pine.

II. *STROBUS* Spach. Visible part of fruit scale with terminal boss. Needles usually 5 in each short shoot. 20 sp.

§ 1. *Eustrobus* (cones hanging, seeds winged): *P. Strobus* L., the Weymouth or white pine (East N. Am.), a timber tree; *P. Lambertiana* Dougl., the giant sugar pine of the W. U.S.; *P. excelsa* Wall., the Bhotan or blue pine (E. India).

§ 2. *Cembra* (cones erect or drooping, seeds not winged); *P. Cembra* L. the Siberian cedar (Alps, Carpathians, Ural, Siber.) has ed. seeds and valuable wood; *P. flexilis* James (N. Am.) &c. [For further details see *Nat. Pfl.*, Veitch's *Manual of Coniferae*, *European pine timbers* in Kew Bull. 1915, p. 265, Sargent, *Manual of Timbers of N. Am.*, *&c.*]

Pinweed, *Lechea.*

Pinxter-fl. (Am.), *Azalea nudiflora* L.

Pionandra Miers = Cyphomandra Mart. (Solan.).

Pionocarpus Blake (*Helianthella* p.p.). Compositae (5). 1 Mexico.

Piper L. (*BH.* incl. *Chavica* Miq.). Piperaceae. 700 trop. mostly climbing shrubs (peppers). Fls. in sympodial spikes, the bracts closely appressed to the axis. Fr. a berry. That of *P. nigrum* L., gathered before ripe and dried, forms a black peppercorn; or if the outside be removed by maceration, a white one. Pepper is chiefly cult. in Malaya. *P. Cubeba* L. f. is the cubebs, *P. Betle* L. the betel pepper (see Areca). See *Treas. of Bot.*

Piperaceae (*EP.*, *BH.* incl. *Saururaceae* and *Lactoridaceae*). Dicots. (Archichl. Piperales; Micrembryae *BH.*). 7 gen. with 1150 sp. trop. Pl. of simple organisation. Herbs or shrubs with simple usu. alt. l. with or without stipules; the l. have a pungent taste. Fls. naked, in spikes. A 1—10, $\underline{G}$ (1—4), 1-loc. with 1 basal orthotr. ov. Seeds with dense perisperm round the endosp.; embryo small. The stem-anatomy is interesting. Piper is economically useful. *Chief genera:* Piper, Peperomia. [**BH. chars.** incl. those of S. and L., esp. parietal plac., and > 1 ov.]

Piperales. The 2nd order of Archichlamydeae.

Piperia Rydberg (*Habenaria* p.p.). Orchidaceae (II. 1). 10 N. Am.
Pipe vine (Am.), *Aristolochia Sipho* L'Hérit.; **-wort**, *Elatine*, *Eriocaulon*.
Piptadenia Benth. Leguminosae (I. 5). 45 trop., esp. Am. *P. rigida* Benth. (Brazil) yields Angico gum, used like gum-arabic.
Piptanthocereus Riccob. (*Cereus* p.p.). Cactaceae (III. 1). 10 Argentina to Mexico.
Piptanthus Sweet. Leguminosae (III. 2). 2 Himalaya, China.
Piptatherum Beauv. = Oryzopsis Michx. p.p. (Gram.)
Piptocalyx Oliv. ex Benth. Monimiaceae. 1 New S. Wales.
Piptocalyx Torr. (*Krynitzkia* p.p. *BH.*, *Greeneocharis* p.p. *EP.*). Boraginaceae (IV. 2). 2 Pac. N. Am.
Piptocarpha R. Br. Compositae (1). 30 trop. Am.
Piptocelus C. Presl. Inc. sed. 1 Ecuador.
Piptochaetium J. Presl (*Oryzopsis* p.p. *BH.*). Gramin. (8). 10 temp. S. Am.
Piptocoma Cass. Compositae (1). 1 S. Domingo.
Piptolepis Sch.-Bip. Compositae (1). 8 Minas Geraës.
Piptoptera Bunge. Chenopodiaceae (B). 1 Turkestan.
Piptosaccos Turcz. Inc. sed. 1 Malaya.
Piptospatha N. E. Br. Araceae (V). 8 Malaya.
Piptostigma Oliv. Anonaceae (2). 6 W. Afr.
Piptothrix A. Gray. Compositae (2). 3 Mexico.
Pipturus Wedd. Urticaceae (3). 8 Mascarenes to Australia.
Pipul (peepul) *Ficus religiosa* L.
Piqueria Cav. Compositae (2). 15 Bolivia to Mexico.
Piranhea Baill. Euphorbiaceae (A. I. 1). 1 Brazil.
Piratinera Aubl. = Brosimum Sw. (Morac.)
Pircunia Bert. = Phytolacca L. (Phytol.)
Pirea Durand (*Dictyosperma* p.p.). Cruciferae (2). 1 W. As.
Pirigara Aubl. = Gustavia L. (Lecythid.)
Piriqueta Aubl. Turneraceae. 25 warm Am., Afr., Madag.
Pirola Neck. = Pyrola Tourn. (Pyrol.)
Pirolaceae = Pyrolaceae.
Pironneauella O. Ktze. = Streptocalyx Beer. (Bromel.)
Pironneava Gaudich. (*Aechmea* p.p. *BH.*). Bromel. (4). 1 Rio de Janeiro.
Pirus Hall. = Pyrus Tourn. (Ros.)
Pisang, *Musa paradisiaca* L.
Piscaria Piper (*Eremocarpus BH.*). Euphorb. (A. II. 1). 1 N.W. U.S.
Piscidia L. Leguminosae (III. 8). 1 Florida, Mexico, W.I.
Pisiform, pea-shaped.
Pisonia Plum. ex L. Nyctaginaceae. 60 warm. Fls. usu. unisexual. The anthocarp is glandular and is one of the few fr. which are able to cling to feathers. On Keeling Island they adhere to herons in such quantities as sometimes to cripple them.
Pisoniella Heimerl (*Pisonia* p.p.). Nyctaginaceae. 1 warm Am.
Pisoniella Standley (*Boerhaavia* p.p.). Nyctagin. 2 warm Am.
Pisosperma Sond. Cucurbitaceae (2). 1 S. Afr.
Pistachio nut, *Pistacia vera* L.
Pistacia L. Anacardiaceae (3). 5 Medit., E. As., Mexico. Fls. dioec., apet. or naked. Drupe. *P. Terebinthus* L. yields Chian turpentine, *P. Lentiscus* L. mastic. Fr. of *P. vera* L. (pistachio nuts) ed.
Pistaciopsis Engl. Sapindaceae (II). 3 trop. Afr.

Pistia L. Araceae (VIII). 1 trop. and subtrop., *P. Stratiotes* L., a floating water-plant, rarely anchored by its roots, and often blown about by wind. It is of sympodial structure, but the internodes remain short and bear a rosette of large l.; these sleep at night, moving upwards from the nearly horiz. day position. The continuation shoots of the sympodium are axillary, but beside each l. arises a stolon which grows out along the water and gives rise to a new pl. The infl. is small and monoec.; above is a whorl of ♂ fls., each with a synandrium of 2 sta.; below is a ♀ fl. of 1 cpl. Both are naked. P. is a link between Lemnaceae and Araceae (*q.v.*). *Cf.* Arber, *Water Plants*.

Pistil, the whole G in syncarpous fl., each cpl. in apocarpous; **-late fl.**, ♀; **-lode**, an aborted pistil.

Piston mechanism, *Campanulaceae*, *Compositae*, *Leguminosae*.

Pistorinia DC. = Cotyledon Tourn. p.p. (Crass.).

Pisum (Tourn.) Linn. Leguminosae (III. 9). 6 Medit. W. As., incl. *P. sativum* L. (pea). The fl. mech. resembles Lathyrus.

Pita, *Agave*.

Pitavia Molina. Rutaceae (I). 1 Chili.

Pitcairnia L'Hérit. Bromel. (3). 175 trop. Am., W.I. Most are terrestrial; many form stolons at the base. Cult. orn. infl.

Pitch, Canada, *Tsuga canadensis* Carr.; **-pine**, *Pinus palustris* Mill., &c.

Pitcher-plant, an insectivorous pl. (*q.v.*) catching insects in pitchers, *Cephalotus*, *Darlingtonia*, *Heliamphora*, *Nepenthes*, *Sarracenia*. *Cf.* also *Dischidia*.

Pith tree, *Aeschynomene aspera* L.

Pithecoctenium Mart. ex DC. Bignoniaceae (I). 20 Brazil to Mex.

Pithecolobium Mart. Leguminosae (I. 1). 120 trop. Stipules often thorny. Fr. often coiled like Medicago. *P. Saman* Benth. (trop. S. Am.) is the rain tree, so called because of a legend that it was always raining under its branches. The ejections of juice by the cicadas are responsible for this (*cf.* Acer, Andira). It shows sleep movement of l. well.

Pithecoseris Mart. Compositae (I). 1 N. Brazil.

Pithocarpa Lindl. Compositae (4). 1 W. Austr.

Pittiera Cogn. Cucurbitaceae (3). 3 C. Am.

Pittierella Schlechter. Orchidaceae (II. 18). 1 Costa Rica.

Pittoniotis Griseb. = Antirrhoea Comm. (Rubi.)

Pittosporaceae (*EP.*, *BH.*). Dicotyledons (Archichl. Rosales; Polygalinae *BH.*). 9 gen. 200 sp., confined (exc. Pittosporum) to Austr. Trees or shrubs, often climbing, with alt., leathery, evergr., usu. entire, exstip. l. Resin is present in large quantity in passages at the outer side of the bast. Fls. ☿, reg., 5-merous; sta. hypog.; cpls. 2 or more, forming a 1-loc. or multi-loc. ovary with parietal or axile plac., and 2-ranked ∞ anatr. ov.; style simple. Caps. or berry with album. seeds. *Chief genera:* Pittosporum, Billardiera, Sollya. The relationships are very obscure (see *Nat. Pfl.*).

Pittosporopsis Craib. Icacinaceae. 1 Burma.

Pittosporum Banks. Pittosporaceae. 70 trop. and subtrop. |*. The seeds of some are sticky. Some yield useful timber.

Pituranthos Viv. Umbelliferae (III. 5). 10 Afr., W. As.

Pituri, *Duboisia Hopwoodi*, F. Muell. (W. Austr.)

Pityopus J. K. Small (*Monotropa* p.p.). Pyrolaceae. 1 Oregon.
Pityranthe Thw. Tiliaceae. 1 Ceylon.
Pityrodia R. Br. Verbenaceae (3). 15 Austr.
Piuttia Mattei (*Thalictrum* p.p.). Ranunculaceae (3). 1 Himalaya.
Placea Miers. Amaryllidaceae (1). 3 Chili.
Placenta, see Ovary; *Butomaceae*, *Cabomba*.
Placocarpa Hook. f. Rubiaceae (II. 3). 1 Mexico.
Placodiscus Radlk. Sapindaceae (1). 3 trop. Afr.
Placolobium Miq. Leguminosae (inc. sed.). 1 Sumatra.
Placopoda Balf. f. Rubiaceae (I. 2). 1 Socotra.
Placus Lour. = Blumea DC. (Comp.)
Pladera Soland. = Canscora Lam. (Gentian.)
Plaesiantha Hook. f. (*Pellacalyx EP.*). Rhizophoraceae. 1 Borneo.
Plagianthus Forst. Malvaceae (2). 10 Austr., N.Z. *P. betulinus* A. Cunn. (N.Z.; lace-bark) good timber.
Plagio- (Gr. pref.), oblique; **-tropic**, placing itself ⊥ the stimulus.
Plagiobasis Schrenk. Compositae (11). 2 W. As.
Plagiobothrys Fisch. et Mey. Boraginaceae (IV. 2). 15 Pac. Am.
Plagiocarpus Benth. Leguminosae (III. 6). 1 trop. Austr.
Plagiocaryum Willd. Inc. sed. 1 Brazil.
Plagiocheilus Arn. Compositae (7). 7 S. Am.
Plagiogyria Kunze. Polypodiaceae. 11 E. As., Am.
Plagiolirion Baker (*Elisena EP.*). Amaryllidaceae (1). 1 Colombia.
Plagiolophus Greenman. Compositae (5). 1 Yucatan.
Plagiopteron Griff. Flacourtiaceae (inc. sed.). 1 Further India.
Plagioscyphus Radlk. Sapindaceae (1). 1 Madagascar.
Plagiosetum Benth. Gramineae (5). 1 Austr.
Plagiosiphon Harms. Leguminosae (II. 2). 1 trop. Afr.
Plagiospermum Oliv. Rosaceae (II?) (Celastr. *BH.*). 1 N. China.
Plagiostachys Ridl. (*Alpinia* p.p.). Zingiberaceae (1). 15 Malaya.
Plagiostyles Pierre. Euphorbiaceae (A. I. 7). 1 trop. Afr.
Plagius L'Hérit. = Chrysanthemum Tourn. p.p. (Comp.)
Planaltoa Taubert. Compositae (2). 1 C. Brazil.
Planchonella Van Tiegh. Ochnaceae. 1 Peru.
Planchonia Blume. Lecythidaceae. 4 Malay Archipelago.
Plane tree, *Platanus orientalis* L.; (Scotland) sycamore.
Planera J. F. Gmel. Ulmaceae. 1 S. U.S., a useful timber tree.
Planodes Greene (*Cardamine* p.p.). Cruciferae (2). 1 temp., subtrop.
Planotia Munro. Gramineae (13). 5 trop. S. Am.
Plant formations, associations, societies, descending grades of communities of plants found associated together on land with similar ecological characters. The *sand-dune formation*, *e.g.*, is split (in England) into associations of *strand-plants*, of *marram grass*, and *fixed dunes*, and these again into societies. *Cf.* Tansley, *Types of British Vegetation*, Cambridge, 1911; **-s and insects**, *cf.* Flowers; **insectivorous-**, *cf.* Insectivorous; **ornamental-**, *cf.* Ornamental.

Plantaginaceae (*EP.*, *BH.*). Dicots. (Sympet. Plantaginales). 3 gen., 200 sp. cosmop. (See genera.) Annual or perennial herbs; l. without distinction into stalk and blade, exstip. Fls. usu. in heads or spikes, inconspic., usu. ☿, reg., without bracteoles, wind- or partly insect-fert. K (4), diagonally placed; C usu. (4), membranous; A 4, with very long filaments and versatile anthers containing much powdery pollen; G usu. (2), 2-loc., with 1—∞ semi-anatr. ov. on axile plac. Fr. a membranous caps., opening with a lid cut off by a peripheral dehiscence, or sometimes, a nut surrounded by the persistent calyx. Embryo straight, in fleshy endosp. *Genera:* Plantago, Littorella, Bougueria. See P. and L. for details. The relationships of the P. are difficult to make out. The fl. is usu. regarded as derived from a 5-merous type in the same way as that of Veronica, and most authors agree in regarding the P. as degraded forms allied to Scrophulariaceae, Labiatae, &c. The wind-pollination of the flr. is also an evidence of this.

Plantaginales. The 7th order of Sympetalae; p. xlvi.

Plantagineae. (*BH.*) = Plantaginaceae.

Plantago (Tourn.) L. Plantaginaceae. 200 cosmop.; 5 in Brit., good illustrations of the gen. *P. major* L. (greater plantain) is a perennial with a thick root and a rosette of large erect l., in whose axils arise the infls. (spikes). Fl. protog., the stigmas protruding from the bud; the sta. appear later. Wind-pollination is the rule, but insects sometimes visit them for pollen. The fruit-spikes are often given as food to cage-birds. *P. media* L. (hoary plantain) shows similar general features, but the l. lie flat on the ground (hence it is a troublesome weed); they exhibit the 3/8 phyllotaxy (*q.v.*) very clearly. The fl. is more conspicuous than *P. major* and has a pleasant scent, and though primarily wind-pollinated, is largely visited for pollen. It is sometimes gynodioec. (*cf.* Labiatae). *P. lanceolata* L. (rib-wort plantain) has narrow erect l., and fls., also gynodioec. *P. Coronopus* L. (buck's-horn plantain) is xero. with hairy l., growing in sandy places. Many S. Am. sp. show marked xero. characters—dense tufting, small hairy l., often grooved on the lower surface (*cf.* Ericaceae), &c. *P. maritima* L. (the sea-side plantain) has linear fleshy l.; it is found at high levels in the Scottish Mts., though rarely in the intermediate regions.

The seeds of many swell up when wetted and become mucilaginous (*cf.* Linum). Those of *P. Psyllium* L. (Medit.) are used in silk and cotton manufacture; they have also been used in medicine.

If the young growing infl. be vigorously shaken, when left to itself it droops and only becomes erect again after some time. The strain stretches the young cell walls beyond their limit of elasticity.

Plantain, *Musa paradisiaca* L. (in India &c., incl. *Musa Sapientum* L., the banana), *Plantago*; **bastard-** (W.I.), *Heliconia*; **water-,** *Alisma Plantago* L.

Platanaceae (*EP.*, *BH.*). Dicots. (Archichl. Rosales; Unisexuales *BH.*). Only gen. Platanus (*q.v.*). Relationships obscure.

Platanthera Rich. (*Habenaria* p.p. *BH.*). Orchid. (II. 1). 80 N. temp., trop.

Platanus (Tourn.) L. Platanaceae. 5 N. temp., incl. the plane-tree, *P. orientalis* L. The bark scales off every year, leaving a smooth surface. The axillary bud is developed under the base of the petiole, which fits over it like an extinguisher. The stipules are united round the stem. Fls. monoec. in pend. heads, wind-fert. K, C 4 or 3, A 4 or 3, opp. sepals, G 4 or 3; ovules orthotr., pend. Multiple fr., each cpl. giving a caryopsis, often winged. Seed album. The wood of the plane is useful, and also that of the buttonwood of N. Am. *P. occidentalis* L.

Platea Blume. Icacinaceae. 6 Malay Archipelago.
Plateilema Cockerell (*Actinella EP.*). Compositae (6). 1 Mexico.
Plathymenia Benth. Leguminosae (I. 5). 2 Brazil. Good timber.
Platonia Mart. Guttiferae (V). 1 trop. Brazil. Fr. ed.
Platorheedia Roj. (*Platonia* p.p.). Myrtaceae. 2 Argentina.
Platostoma Beauv. Labiatae (VII). 4 trop. As., Afr.
Platy- (Gr. pref.), broad-; **-carpous**, broad-fruited, &c., &c.
Platycalyx N.E. Br. Ericaceae (IV. 2). 1 S. Afr.
Platycarpha Less. Compositae (10). 3 S.W. Afr.
Platycarpum Humb. et Bonpl. Rubiaceae (I. 4). 1 Venezuela.
Platycarya Sieb. et Zucc. Juglandaceae. 1 Japan, N. China.
Platycelyphium Harms. Leguminosae (III. 1). 1 trop. Afr.
Platycentrum Klotzsch = Begonia L. p.p. (Begon.).
Platycentrum Naud. Melastomaceae (I). 1 Guiana.
Platycerium Desv. Polypodiaceae. 15 Afr., Malaya, Austr. (stag-horn ferns), epiph., or on steep rock surfaces. The rhiz. is short and bears alt. l. of two kinds. The young l. are protected by hairs. Of the two kinds of l., the one stands ± erect (the 'mantle' l.), the other is pend., usu. much branched, and bears the sporangia in irreg. areas on its lower surface. Assimilation is chiefly carried on by the pend. l. Two types of mantle l. occur, repres. in *P. grande* J. Sm. and *P. bifurcatum* C. Chr. In the former the base of the l., which is unbranched, clings closely to the supporting trunk, whilst the upper part spreads out and makes a niche in which humus collects; in this the roots ramify and absorb food. In the latter the whole of the mantle l. clings to the support, and the only humus-supply is that furnished by the decay of old mantle l. and perhaps of the tree bark; it grows in great colonies, owing to adv. budding from the r. In both the bases of the l. are fleshy. Cult. orn. Bower, *Ferns*, iii, 232.
Platychaeta Boiss. = Pulicaria Gaertn. p.p. (Comp.).
Platyclinis Benth. Orchidaceae (II. 3). 15 Indomal. Cult. orn. fl.
Platycodon A. DC. Campanulaceae (I. 1). 1 E. As. Cult. orn. fl.
Platycoryne Reichb. f. Orchidaceae (II. 1). 10 trop. Afr., Madag.
Platycrater Sieb. et Zucc. Saxifragaceae (III). 1 Japan.
Platycyamus Benth. Leguminosae (III. 10). 1 Brazil.
Platydesma H. Mann. Rutaceae (I). 4 Hawaiian Is.
Platygyna Mercier. Euphorbiaceae (A. II. 2). 1 Cuba.
Platykeleba N.E. Br. Asclepiadaceae (II. 1). 1 Madag.
Platylepis Kunth = Ascolepis Nees (Cyper.).
Platylepis A. Rich. Orchidaceae (II. 2). 12 warm Afr., Madag., Masc.
Platylobium Sm. Leguminosae (III. 3). 3 Austr. Pods flat.
Platylophus D. Don. Cunoniaceae. 1 S. Afr.
Platymerium Bartl. ex DC. (*Hypobathrum EP.*). Rubi. (I. 8). 1 Phil. Is.
Platymiscium Vog. Leguminosae (III. 8). 16 trop. Am. Good timber.
Platymitrium Warb. (*Dobera* p.p. *EP.*). Bixaceae. 1 C. trop. Afr.
Platymitra Boerl. Anonaceae (2). 1 Java.
Platyosprion Maxim. (*Sophora* p.p. *EP.*). Leguminosae (III. 1). 1 Jap.
Platypholis Maxim. Orobanchaceae. 1 Bonin Is. (Japan).
Platypodium Vog. Leguminosae (III. 8). 2 Brazil.
Platypus Small et Nash. Orchidaceae (II. 10). 1 N. Am.

Platyrrhiza Barb. Rodr. (*Zygostates* p.p. *EP.*). Orchidaceae (II. 19). 1 Brazil.
Platysace Bunge. Umbelliferae (I. 1). 3 Austr.
Platyschkuhria Rydberg (*Bahia* p.p.). Compositae (6). 2 N. Am.
Platysepalum Welw. ex Baker. Leguminosae (III. 6). 12 W. trop. Afr.
Platyspermum Hook. Cruciferae (2). 1 Oregon.
Platystachys C. Koch = Tillandsia L. p.p. (Bromel.).
Platystele Schlechter. Orchidaceae (II. 8). 1 Costa Rica.
Platystemma Wall. Gesneriaceae (I). 1 Himalaya.
Platystemon Benth. Papaveraceae (II). 60 W.N. Am. L. in apparent whorls (see fam.).
Platystigma Benth. (*Meconella* Nutt.). Papaveraceae (II). 3 California, Oregon. L. as in Platystemon.
Platystigma R. Br. Euphorbiaceae (inc. sed.). 1 India.
Platytaenia Kuhn. Polypodiaceae. 1 Malaya, Polynesia.
Platytheca Steetz. Tremandraceae. 1 W. Austr.
Platytinospora Diels in Engl. Menispermaceae. 1 W. trop. Afr.
Plazia Ruiz et Pav. Compositae (12). 8 S. Andes, Argentina.
Plecosorus Fée. Polypodiaceae. 3 trop. Am.
Plecospermum Tréc. Moraceae (I). 1 Indomal.
Plectaneia Thou. Apocynaceae (I. 3). 5 Madag.
Plectis O. F. Cook. Palmae (IV. 1). 1 C. Am.
Plectocomia Mart. et Blume. Palmae (III). 6 E. Indomal. Climbers like Calamus with hooked l.
Plectocomiopsis Benth. Palmae (III). 5 Malaya.
Plectranthus L'Hérit. Labiatae (VII). 110 palaeotrop., E. As.
Plectritis DC. (*Valerianella* p.p. *BH.*). Valerianaceae. 8 U.S., Chili.
Plectrocarpa Gillies. Zygophyllaceae. 1 temp. S. Am.
Plectronia L. Rubiaceae (II. 1). 100 palaeotrop. Some have axillary thorns.
Plectrophora H. C. Focke (*Comparettia BH.*). Orchid. (II. 19). 2 Guiana.
Pleea L. C. Rich. in Michx. Liliaceae (I). 1 S.E. U.S.
Pleiadelphia Stapf. Gramin. (2). 1 Portuguese Congo.
Pleio-, pleo- (Gr. pref.), several; **-chasial cyme**, one in which each successive branch bears > 2 fls.; **-mery**, with more whorls than normal.
Pleiocardia Greene (*Streptanthus* p.p.). Cruciferae (1). 10 Calif.
Pleiocarpa Benth. Apocynaceae (I. 2). 10 W. Afr.
Pleiocarpidia K. Schum. (*Aulacodiscus BH.*). Rubi. (I. 7). 1 Malaya.
Pleioceras Baill. Apocynaceae (II. 2). 3 W. trop. Afr.
Pleiochiton Naud. ex A. Gray. Melastomaceae (7). 7 S. Brazil.
Pleiococca F. Muell. Rutaceae (I). 1 E. Austr.
Pleiogynium Engl. Anacardiaceae (2). 1 Queensland.
Pleiomeris A. DC. (*Myrsine* p.p. *BH.*). Myrsinaceae (II). 1 Canaries, Madeira.
Pleione D. Don (*Coelogyne* p.p. *BH.*). Orchidaceae (II. 3). 15 Indomal. Cult.
Pleiospora Harv. Leguminosae (III. 3). 6 S. Afr.
Pleiostachya K. Schum. (*Ischnosiphon* p.p.). Marant. 2 Ecuador, C. Am.

Pleiotaenia Coulter et Rose (*Polytaenia* DC.). Umbelliferae (III. 6). 1 N. Am.
Pleiotaxis Steetz. Compositae (12). 10 trop. Afr.
Plenckia Reissek. Celastraceae. 1 Brazil.
Plenus (Lat.), full.
Pleodendron Van Tiegh. (*Cinnamodendron* p.p.). Winteranaceae. 1 W.I.
Pleodiporochna Van Tiegh. (*Ochna* p.p.). 1 trop. Afr.
Pleogyne Miers. Menispermaceae. 1 trop. E. Austr.
Pleomele Salisb. (*Dracaena* p.p.). Liliaceae (VI). 100 palaeotrop.
Pleonotoma Miers (*Bignonia* p.p.). Bignoniaceae (I). 6 Brazil.
Pleopeltis Humb. et Bonpl. = Polypodium L. (Polypod.).
Pleopetalum Van Tiegh. (*Ochna* p.p.). Ochnaceae. 4 Indomal.
Pleouratea Van Tiegh. (*Gomphia* p.p.). Ochnaceae. 1 Brazil.
Plerandra A. Gray. Araliaceae (1). 6 New Guinea to Fiji.
Plerandropsis R. Viguier. Araliaceae (1). 1 Tonquin.
Pleroma D. Don = Tibouchina Aubl. p.p. (Melast.).
Plesiatropha Pierre ex Hutchinson = Mildbraedia Pax (Euph.).
Plesmonium Schott. Araceae (IV). 1 N. India.
Plethadenia Urb. Rutaceae (I). 1 S. Domingo.
Plethiandra Hook. f. Melastomaceae (II). 4 Borneo.
Pleur-, pleuro- (Gr. pref.), side-; **-anthous**, *Orchidaceae*; **-rhizal**, *Cruciferae*.
Pleurandra Labill. = Hibbertia Andr. p.p. (Dillen.).
Pleurandropsis Baill. (*Asterolasia* p.p. *BH.*). Rutac. (I). 1 W. Austr.
Pleuranthium Benth. (*Epidendrum* p.p. *EP.*). Orchid. (II. 6). 1 Cuba.
Pleuranthodes Weberb. (*Gouania* p.p.). Rhamnaceae. 2 Hawaiian Is.
Pleuricospora A. Gray. Pyrolaceae. 2 California.
Pleurisanthes Baill. Icacinaceae. 1 French Guiana.
Pleuroblepharis Baill. Acanthaceae (IV. B). 1 Madag.
Pleuroblepharon Kunze. Orchidaceae. Nomen.
Pleurobotryum Barb. Rodr. (*Pleurothallis* p.p.). Orch. (II. 8). 1 Braz.
Pleurocalyptus Brongn. et Gris. Myrtaceae (II. 1). 1 New Caled.
Pleurocarpaea Benth. Compositae (1). 1 trop. Austr.
Pleurocoffea Baill. Rubiaceae (II. 4). 1 Madag.
Pleurogyna Eschsch. ex Cham. et Schlechtd. Gentianaceae (I). 7 N. temp. and cold.
Pleuropetalum Hook. f. Amarantaceae (I). 2 C. Am., Galapagos.
Pleurophora D. Don. Lythraceae. 6 S. Am.
Pleurophragma Rydberg (*Thelypodium* p.p.). Crucif. (I). 3 N. Am.
Pleurophyllum Hook. f. Compositae (3). 3 S. islands off N.Z.
Pleuropogon R. Br. Gramineae (10). 3 N. temp. and polar.
Pleuropterantha Franch. Amarantaceae (2). (Chenop. *BH.*) 1 Somaliland.
Pleuropterygium Gross. (*Polygonum* p.p.). Polygonaceae (II. 2). 3 Japan, Saghalien.
Pleuroridgea Van Tiegh. (*Ochna* p.p.). Ochnaceae. 5 trop. Afr.
Pleurosorus Fée. Polypodiaceae. 3 Spain, Chili, N.Z.
Pleurospermum Hoffm. Umbelliferae (III. 4). 25 N. As., E. Eur.
Pleurostachys Brongn. (*Rhynchospora* p.p. *EP.*). Cyper. (II). 30 S. Am.

Pleurostelma Baill. Asclepiadaceae (II. 1). 1 Madag.
Pleurostelma Schlechter (*Schlechterella EP.*). Asclep. (1). 1 E. Afr.
Pleurostemon Raf. Inc. sed. 1 N. Am.
Pleurostylis Wight et Arn. Celastraceae. 2 S. Afr. to India.
Pleurothallis R. Br. Orchidaceae (II. 8). 500 trop. Am., W.I.
Pleurothyrium Nees. Lauraceae (1). 1 Peru.
Plicate (vernation), folded several times.
Plicouratea Van Tiegh. (*Gomphia* p.p.). Ochnaceae. 8 Brazil.
Plinthus Fenzl. Aizoaceae (II). 2 Cape Colony.
Pliogynopsis O. Ktze. (*Pleiogynium* Engl.). Anacard. (2). 1 N.E. Austr.
Plocama Ait. Rubiaceae (II. 7). 1 Canaries.
Plocaniophyllon T. S. Brandegee. Rubiaceae (I. 8). 1 Mexico.
Plocoglottis Blume. Orchidaceae (II. 9). 10 Malay Archipelago.
Plocosperma Benth. Loganiaceae. 2 Guatemala, Mexico.
Pluchea Cass. Compositae (4). 30 trop. and subtrop.
Plukenetia L. Euphorbiaceae (A. II. 2). 8 warm Am.
Plum, *Prunus domestica* L.; **coco-**, *Chrysobalanus*; **date-**, *Diospyros Kaki* L. f.; **hog-**, *Spondias*; **Madagascar-**, *Flacourtia*; **marmalade-** (W.I.), *Lucuma mammosa* Gaertn. f.; **sapodilla-**, *Achras Sapota* L.; **tamarind-**, *Dialium indum* L.; **-tree, seaside** (W.I.), *Ximenia*.
Plumbagella Spach (*Plumbago* p.p. *BH.*). Plumbaginaceae. 1 E. As.
Plumbaginaceae (*EP.*, *BH.*). Dicots. (Sympet. Plumbaginales; Primulales *BH.*). 10 gen., 280 sp. cosmop., but esp. on salt steppes and sea-coast. Perennial herbs or shrubs with narrow l., on whose surface water glands occur, or sometimes chalk glands (*cf.* Saxifraga). Infl. of various types, racemose and cymose (see Plumbago, Ceratostigma, Statice, Armeria), bracteolate. Fls. reg., ☿, 5-merous, the odd sepal post. K persistent, C often nearly polypetalous, conv., A 5, epipet. and opp. the petals, $\underline{G}$ (5), 1-loc., with basal placenta, and one anatr. ov., whose stalk curves up to the top of the loc. and causes the micropyle to be directed upwards. Styles or stigmas 5. Nut; embryo straight, in floury endosp. The fam. is distinguished from Primulaceae by the ovary and styles. *Chief genera:* Plumbago, Ceratostigma, Acantholimon, Armeria, Statice, Limoniastrum.
Plumbaginales. The 3rd order of Dicots. Sympetalae.
Plumbago Tourn. ex L. Plumbaginaceae. 10 cosmop. Racemose infl. K with glandular hairs, aiding seed-dispersal.
Plumbeus (Lat.), lead-coloured.
Plumeria Tourn. ex L. Apocynaceae (I. 3). 45 warm Am. Several cult. orn. perf. fls. (offered in Buddhist temples), esp. *P. acutifolia* Poir (temple tree, frangipani).
Plummera A. Gray. Compositae (6). 1 Arizona.
Plumose, feathered.
Plumule, the stem bud of the embryo pl. in the seed.
Pluri- (Lat. pref.), many-.
Pneumatophore, erect root with aerenchyma; *cf.* Mangroves.
Pneumonanthe Gleditsch (*Gentiana* p.p.). Gentian. (1). 25 N. Am.
Po (fl.-class), fls. offering pollen only to visitors, *Anemone*, *Hypericum*, *Papaver*, *Rosa*, *Thalictrum*, *Verbascum*.

Poa L. Gramineae (10). 200 cosmop.; 8 in Brit. (meadow grass). Many are useful pasture-grasses.
Poacynum Baill. (*Apocynum* p.p.). Apocynaceae (II. 1). 1 Centr. As. L. alt.
Poaephyllum Ridley (*Agrostophyllum* p.p.). Orchid. (II. 4). 4 Malaya.
Poagrostis Stapf. Gramineae (9). 1 S. Afr.
Pochota Goyena. Bombacaceae. 1 Nicaragua.
Pockwood tree (W.I.), Guaiacum.
Pocockia Ser. = Trigonella L. p.p. (Legum.).
Podachaenium Benth. (*Ferdinanda* p.p. *EP.*). Compositae (5). 1 C. Am. Cult. orn. l.
Podadenia Thw. Euphorbiaceae (A. II. 2). 2 Ceylon, Java.
Podagrostis Scribner et Merrill (*Agrostis* p.p.). Gramineae (8). 1 Alaska to Oregon.
Podalyria Lam. Leguminosae (III. 2). 20 S. Afr.
Podandra Baill. Asclepiadaceae (II. 1). 1 Bolivia.
Podandria Rolfe (*Habenaria* p.p. *EP.*). Orchidaceae (II. 1). 1 trop. Afr.
Podanthes Haw. (*Stapelia* p.p.). Asclepiadaceae (II. 3). 8 S. Afr.
Podanthum Boiss. (*Phyteuma* p.p.). Campanulaceae (I. 1). 50 Medit.
Podanthus Lag. Compositae (5). 2 Chili, Argentina.
Podistera S. Wats. (*Cymopterus* p.p.). Umbelliferae (III. 5). 1 N. Am.
Podo- (Gr. pref.), stalk.
Podocarpus (L'Hérit.) Pers. Coniferae (Taxac. 5; see C. for gen. chars.). 60 E. As. and S. temp. and trop. Dioec.; ♀ peculiar. There are usu. three pairs of scales, decussate. One of the middle pair projects above all the rest, bearing an anatr. ov. The other 5 are sometimes united to form the so-called recept. The fr. usu. consists of a fleshy mass (the 'recept.') bearing an arillate seed. In some the sterile scales do not become fleshy. Timber valuable.
Podochilus Blume. Orchidaceae (II. *a*. III). 12 Indomal. Epiphytes.
Podochrea Fourr. = Astragalus L. p.p. (Legum.).
Podochrosia Baill. Apocynaceae (I. 3). 1 New Caledonia.
Podococcus G. Mann et H. Wendl. Palmae (IV. 1). 1 W. trop. Afr.
Podocoma Cass. Compositae (3). 7 Austr., S. Am.
Podogynium Taub. Leguminosae (II. 2). 1 E. trop. Afr.
Podolasia N.E. Br. Araceae (IV). 1 Malaya.
Podolepis Labill. Compositae (4). 15 Austr.
Podolobium R. Br. = Oxylobium Andr. (Legum.).
Podonephelium Baill. Sapindaceae (I). 2 New Caledonia.
Podoon Baill. Phytolaccaceae. 1 Yunnan.
Podopetalum F. Muell. Leguminosae (III. 1). 1 Queensland.
Podophania Baill. Compositae (2). 1 Mexico.
Podophorus Phil. Gramineae (8). 1 Juan Fernandez.
Podophyllum L. Berberidaceae. 5 N. temp. (May apple). In *P. peltatum* L. the rhiz. sends up yearly a shoot bearing two large peltate l., which hang down when young like a closed umbrella. A drug is prepared from the rhiz. Fr. a berry, whose flesh consists chiefly of the plac. which grows up round the seeds (wrongly termed aril).
Podopogon Ehrenb. Inc. sed. Nomen.
Podopterus Humb. et Bonpl. Polygonaceae (III. 1). 1 Mexico.

Podorungia Baill. Acanthaceae (IV. B). 1 Madag.
Podosciadium A. Gray (*Eulophus* p.p. *EP.*). Umbelliferae (III. 5). 2 Calif.
Podosemum Desv. = Muehlenbergia Schreb. p.p. (Gram.).
Podosperma Labill. = Podotheca Cass. (Comp.).
Podospermum DC. = Scorzonera L. p.p. (Comp.).
Podostelma K. Schum. Asclepiadaceae (II. 1). 1 Abyssinia.
Podostemma Greene (*Asclepias* p.p.). Asclepiad. (II. 1). 6 N. Am.
Podostemaceae (*EP.* and *BH.* incl. *Tristichaceae*). Dicotyledons (Archichl. Rosales; Multiovulatae aquaticae *BH.*). 22 gen., 100 sp. trop. A remarkable fam. of plants living only in rushing water, and growing only on rocks in rivers. The morphology of the veg. organs is extremely varied and complex. The seeds are shed on the rocks during the drier season of the year, and germinate when the rains cause them to be submerged. The primary axis is usu. small, and from the base there buds out a green *thallus*, usu. of adv. root nature. In Podostemon, &c. it is ± filamentous, creeping on the rock, and attached to it by hairs or exogenous projections termed *haptera*. In Dicraea it is ± freely swimming and often ribbon-like or sea-weed-like. In Hydrobryum it is ± flattened, creeping, lichen-like. Other complications occur in Castelnavia and others. From the thallus in most cases endogenous secondary shoots arise, and remain veg. (l. alt., simple or much divided) till the latter part of the rainy season, when they form fls. which open when exposed by the fall of the water. The plants die after shedding their seed, unless an early rise of water occurs. Their outer tissues are usually very siliceous. Fls. simple, ☿, reg. or not, naked, enclosed in a spathe, hypog. A 1–2–∞, $\underline{G}$ usu. (2) 2-loc. with thick axile plac. Ovules ∞ (exc. Farmeria), anatr. Caps.; exalbum. seeds. The more dorsiventral the veg. organs, the more dorsiventral in general is the fl., the phenomenon showing progressively in A, G, fr., seed, and embryo. *Chief genera:* Rhyncholacis, Mourera, Podostemon, Dicraea, Hydrobryum, Castelnavia. [For full details see Willis in *Ann. Perad.* I, 1902 and literature there quoted.]
Podostemon Tul. Podostemaceae. 12 trop. and subtrop.
Podostigma Ell. Asclepiadaceae (II. 1). 1 S.E. U.S.
Podotheca Cass. Compositae (4). 5 temp. Austr.
Podranea Sprague (*Tecoma* p.p.). Bignoniaceae (2). 2 warm Afr.
Poecilandra Tul. Ochnaceae. 1 Guiana, N. Brazil.
Poecilanthe Benth. Leguminosae (III. 6). 3 Brazil.
Poecilochroma Miers. Solanaceae (2). 8 Peru, Ecuador.
Poeciloneuron Bedd. Guttiferae (IV). 2 S. India.
Poecilopteris Presl = Leptochilus Kaulf.
Poecilostachys Hack. Gramineae (10). 12 Madag., E. Afr.
Poederiopsis Rusby (*Paederia* p.p.). Rubiaceae (II. 6). 1 Boliv.
Poeppigia C. Presl. Leguminosae (II. 8). 1 trop. Am., W.I.
Poga Pierre. Rhizophoraceae. 1 Gaboon.
Poggea Guerke. Flacourtiaceae (2). 2 W. trop. Afr.
Poggeophyton Pax. Euphorbiaceae (A. II. 2). 1 W. trop. Afr.
Pogochloa Sp. Moore. Gramineae (10). 1 Matto Grosso.
Pogocybe Pierre. Leguminosae (II. 7). 1 Cochinchina.
Pogogyne Benth. Labiatae (VI). 3 California.

-pogon (Gr. suff.), a beard of hairs.
Pogonanthera Blume. Melastomaceae (I). 8 Malaya.
Pogonanthus Montr. Inc. sed. 1 New Caled.
Pogonarthria Stapf. Gramineae (10). 2 trop. and S. Afr.
Pogonatherum Beauv. Gramineae (2). 2 India to Japan. Sta. 2.
Pogonia Andr. = Myoporum Banks et Soland. (Myopor.).
Pogonia Juss. Orchidaceae (II. 2). 5 E. As.
Pogoniopsis Reichb. f. Orchidaceae (II. 2). 1 Brazil.
Pogonophora Miers. Euphorbiaceae (A. II. 5). 2 Guiana, Brazil.
Pogonopus Klotzsch. Rubiaceae (I. 1). 3 S. and C. Am.
Pogonotrophe Miq. = Ficus Tourn. p.p. (Mor.).
Pogopetalum Benth. = Emmotum Desv. (Icacin.).
Pogostemon Desf. Labiatae (VI). 35 Indomal. *P. Patchouly* Pellet yields the well-known perfume by distillation.
Poicilla Griseb. Asclepiadaceae (II. 4). 1 Cuba.
Poicillopsis Schlechter (*Poicilla* p.p.). Asclepiadaceae (II. 4). 5 S. Domingo.
Poikilacanthus Lindau (*Adhatoda* p.p.). Acanth. (IV. B). 4 S. Am.
Poikilospermum Zipp. ex Miq. Urticaceae (3). 1 Amboina.
Poinciana Tourn. ex Linn. Leguminosae (II. 7). 3 trop. Afr., Madag., As. *P. regia* Boj. cult. orn. flg. tree (flamboyante). Endosp.
Poinsettia R. Grah. = Euphorbia L. p.p. (Euph.).
Poiretia Vent. Leguminosae (III. 7). 5 trop. Am.
Poison, *Acokanthera*, *Aconitum*, *Antiaris*, *Erythrophloeum*, *Physostigma*, *Strychnos*, *Toxicodendrum*, &c.; **-berry** (W.I.), *Cestrum*; **bikh-**, *Aconitum*; **curare-**, *Strychnos toxifera* Schomb.; **-dogwood** (Am.), *Rhus venenata* DC.; **-hemlock** (Am.), *Conium*; **-ivy**, *Rhus Toxicodendron* L.; **-oak**, *Rhus*; **-sumach** (Am.), *Rhus*; **wourali-** *Strychnos*.
Poissonia Baill. (*Coursetia* p.p.). Leguminosae (III. 6). 1 Peru.
Poitaea Vent. Leguminosae (III. 6). 5 W.I.
Poium (Cl.), a meadow formation.
Poivrea Comm. ex Thou. = Combretum L. (Combr.)
Pokeweed, Phytolacca.
Polakia Stapf. Labiatae (VI). 1 Persia.
Polakowskia Pittier. Cucurbitaceae (4). 1 Costa Rica.
Polanisia Rafin. (*Cleome* p.p. *BH.*). Capparid. (V). 30 trop., subtrop.
Polemannia Eckl. et Zeyh. Umbelliferae (III. 5). 2 S. Afr.
Polemoniaceae (*EP.*, *BH.*). Dicots. (Sympet. Tubiflorae; Polemoniales *BH.*). 12 gen., 300 sp., chiefly N. Am.; a few in Chili, Peru, Eur., N. As. Herbs (rarely shrubby below), glabrous or shortly hairy, with usu. opp. exstip. l. Fls. in cymes (sometimes condensed into involucrate heads), ☿, reg. or slightly ·|·, with or without bracteoles. K (5), valvate or imbr., persistent; C (5), bell- funnel- or plate-shaped, usu. conv.; A 5, epipet., alt. with petals; $\underline{G}$ (3) or rarely (2—5), on a disc, multiloc., with simple style ± lobed at tip. Ovules 1—∞ in each loc., anatr., sessile. Fr. usu. a loculic. caps. Embryo straight, in endosp. *Chief genera:* Cobaea, Cantua, Phlox, Collomia, Gilia, Polemonium (mostly favourite border plants).
Polemoniales (*BH.*). The 8th order of Gamopetalae.
Polemoniella A. A. Heller (*Polemonium* p.p.). Polemon. 1 N. Am.

Polemonium (Tourn.) L. Polemoniaceae. 30 N. temp., Chili. *P. caeruleum* L. (Jacob's ladder) in Brit.

Polianthes L. Amaryllidaceae (II). 15 C. Am. *P. tuberosa* L. (tuberose) cult. for scented fls.

Poliomintha A. Gray (*Hedeoma* p.p. *EP.*). Labiatae (VI). 5 S.W. N. Am.

Poliothyrsis Oliv. Flacourtiaceae (4). 1 China.

Polish wheat, *Triticum polonicum* L.

Politus (Lat.), polished.

Polium Tourn. ex L. = Teucrium Tourn. p.p. (Labiat.).

Pollards, *Salix,* &c.

Pollen, the microspores of fl. pl.; **- as food for insects,** *cf.* Po; **- cup,** *Goodeniaceae*; **- dimorphism,** *Faramea*; **- sac,** *cf. Cucurbitaceae.*

Pollia Thunb. Commelinaceae. 16 palaeotrop.

Pollichia (Soland. in) Ait. Caryophyll. (I. 4). 2 trop. and S. Afr.

Pollination, the placing of pollen upon the stigma or ovule, may be effected by wind, animals, or water, and may be cross or self-fert. *Wind-pollinated* fls. (class W) show abundance of pollen, ripening simultaneously, dry and incoherent, freely accessible to the wind (catkins, pend. sta., explosive anthers, &c.); large much-branched stigmas to catch it; often flowering before the l. appear, &c.; *Artemisia, Betulaceae, Calluna, Carex, Casuarina, Coniferae, Corylus, Cycadaceae, Cyperaceae, Elaeagnaceae, Empetrum, Fraxinus, Gramineae, Humulus, Juglandaceae, Juncaceae, Littorella, Mercurialis, Myrothamnaceae, Platanus, Potamogeton, Quercus, Rumex, Sparganium, Spinacia, Thalictrum, Triglochin, Typhaceae, Ulmaceae, Urticaceae, Zea. Pollination by animals* is usu. by insects; the most important are Coleoptera (beetles), very short tongued, Diptera (flies), mostly short tongued, but the Syrphidae or hover-flies long tongued and clever at finding concealed honey, Hymenoptera (ants, wasps, bees, &c.) all short tongued but the bees, and Lepidoptera (butterflies and moths) all long tongued. Other animals are very rarely employed; bats in *Freycinetia. Cf.* Flower classes, Floral Mechanisms. *Pollination by water* in *Ceratophyllum, Enhalus, Najas, Ruppia, Vallisneria, Zannichellia, Zostera,* &c.; **legitimate and illegitimate,** *Lythrum, Primula.*

Pollinia Trin. Gramineae (2). 40 warm |✻.

Pollinium, a number of pollen-grains united into a mass (a definite number of masses per anther), *Asclepiad., Orchid.*

Polpoda C. Presl. Phytolaccaceae (Aizoaceae *BH.*). 1 S. Afr.

Poly- (Gr. pref.), **many-**; **-adelphous, -androus,** &c.; **-carpic,** fruiting many times; **-embryony,** formation of > 1 embryo in an ovule; **-gamy,** ☿, ♂, and ♀ fls. in various combinations on one or more pl. *Anacardium, Euonymus, Fraxinus, Rhus*; **-morphism** (*cf.* Dimorphism), *Catasetum, Compositae, Cycnoches, Griffithella, Liriodendron*; **-phyly,** origin from several stocks; **-pody,** *Polypodium.*

Polyachyrus Lag. Compositae (12). 12 Peru, Chili.

Polyactidium DC. = Erigeron L. p.p. (Comp.).

Polyactium Eckl. et Zeyh. = Pelargonium L'Hérit. p.p. (Geran.).

Polyadenia Nees (*Lindera* p.p. *BH.*). Lauraceae (II). 3 S.E. As.

Polyadoa Stapf (*Carpodinus* p.p.). Apocynaceae (I. 3). 2 W. Afr.

Polyalthia Blume. Anonaceae (1). 70 palaeotrop.

Polyandrococos Barb. Rodr. (*Diplothemium* p.p.). Palm. (IV. 2). 3 Braz.

Polyaster Hook. f. Rutaceae (1). 2 Mexico.

Polybotrya Humb. et Bonpl. Polypodiaceae. 30 warm Am., As., Polyn.

Polycardia Juss. Celastraceae. 5 Madag.

Polycarena Benth. Scrophulariaceae (II. 5). 12 S. and trop. Afr.

Polycarpaea Lam. Caryophyllaceae (I. 3). 30 cosmop.

Polycarpicae (Warming). The 8th order of Choripetalae.

Polycarpon Loefl. Caryophyllaceae (I. 3). 7 cosmop. *P. tetraphyllum* L. (polycarp or allseed) in Brit.

Polycephalium Engl. Icacinaceae. 2 trop. Afr.

Polyceratocarpus Engl. et Diels. Anonaceae (4). 1 Usambara.

Polychaetia Less. = Nestlera Spreng. (Comp.).

Polychilos Breda, Kuhl, et Hasselt (*Phalaenopsis* p.p. *BH.*) Orchidaceae (II. 20). 1 Burma.

Polyclathra Bertol. Cucurbitaceae (inc. sed.). 1 Guatemala.

Polycline Oliv. Compositae (4). 2 E. trop. Afr.

Polycnemum L. Chenopodiaceae (A). 5 Eur., Medit. Structure of the fr. curious, a ridge developing at its apex after fert.

Polyctenium Greene (*Smelowskia* p.p.). Cruciferae (4). 3 N.W. U.S.

Polycycnis Reichb. f. Orchidaceae (II. 13). 3 Guiana to C. Am.

Polydragma Hook. f. Euphorbiaceae (A. II. 2). 1 Perak.

Polygala (Tourn.) L. Polygalaceae. 475 cosmop. exc. N.Z., Polynes., and Arctic zone. A few have stipular thorns. *P. vulgaris* L. (milkwort), in Brit. The fls. owe their conspicuousness to the two coloured sepals; they occur in three colours, red, white, and blue, usu. on different plants but sometimes on the same. The essential organs in most sp. are contained in the keel and emerge from it, as in Leguminosae, when it is depressed by a visiting insect. *P. Senega* L. (Senega snake-root) in N. Am. is medicinal.

Polygalaceae (*EP.*, *BH.*). Dicots. (Archichl. Geraniales; Polygalinae *BH.*). 10 gen., 700 sp., cosmop. exc. N.Z., Polynes., and Arctic zone. Herbs, shrubs, or small trees with simple entire alt. opp. or whorled usu. exstip. l.; the stipules when present are usu. thorny or scaly. Infl. a raceme, spike, or panicle, with bracts and bracteoles. Flr. diplochlam., medially ·|·. K usu. 5, rarely (5), the 2 inner sepals (*alae*) often large and petaloid; C 5, rarely all present usu. only 3—the lowest and two upper—± joined to sta.-tube, the median ant. petal keel-like and often with a term. brush; A in two 5-merous whorls, usu. only 8, or 7, 5, 4 or 3, usu. united below into an open tube; $\underline{G}$ (5—2), usu. (2), antero-post., 2-loc. with 1 anatr. pend. ov. in each loc. (rarely 1-loc. with ∞ ov.). Caps. nut or drupe. Endosp. or not. The fl. mech., like the structure, resembles that found in many Leguminosae (*cf.* Krameria). *Chief genera:* Polygala, Securidaca, Xanthophyllum. For floral diagram see p. 529.

Polygaleae (*BH.*) = Polygalaceae.

Polygalinae (*BH.*). The 3rd order of Polypetalae.

Polygonaceae (*EP.*, *BH.*). Dicots. (Archichl. Polygonales; Curvembryae *BH.*). 40 gen., 750 sp., chiefly N. temp.; a few trop., arctic, and southern. Most are herbs whose l. (exc. *Eriogoneae*) possess a peculiar sheathing stipule or *ochrea* (ocrea) clasping the stem above the leaf-base. This forms a char. feature of the fam. The infl. is primarily racemose, but the partial infls. usu. cymose. [See Eriogonum.] Fls. ☿, reg., cyclic or acyclic. The former have usu. the formula P 3+3, homochlamydeous; A 3+3, G (3); but many vary from this type. Oxyria is 2-merous; others, *e.g.* Eriogonum, Rheum, have branching of the outer sta. The acyclic fls. have P 5, arranged according to the 2/5 phyllotaxy (*e.g.* Polygonum), A 5—8, G (3). Ovary 1-loc. with 1 erect orthotr. ov. and 3 styles. Fls. pollinated by wind or by insects. Fr. almost always a triangular nut, with smooth exterior. The seed contains an excentric curved or straight embryo surrounded by mealy endosp., sometimes ruminate. The fruits are usually wind-distributed; the persistent P usu. forms a membranous wing. Others are provided with hooks.

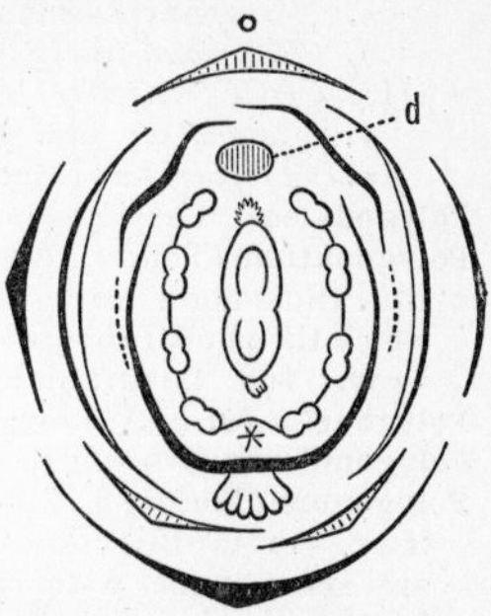

Floral diagram of *Polygala myrtifolia* (after Eichler); the gland *d* as in *P. Chamaebuxus*. Petals and bracts black; the missing petals represented by dotted lines, the missing sta. by *.

Classification and chief genera (after Dammer):

A. Flower cyclic, endosp. not ruminate.

I. *RUMICOIDEAE.*

1. *Eriogoneae* (no ochrea): Chorizanthe, Eriogonum.
2. *Rumiceae* (ochreate): Rumex, Rheum, Oxyria.

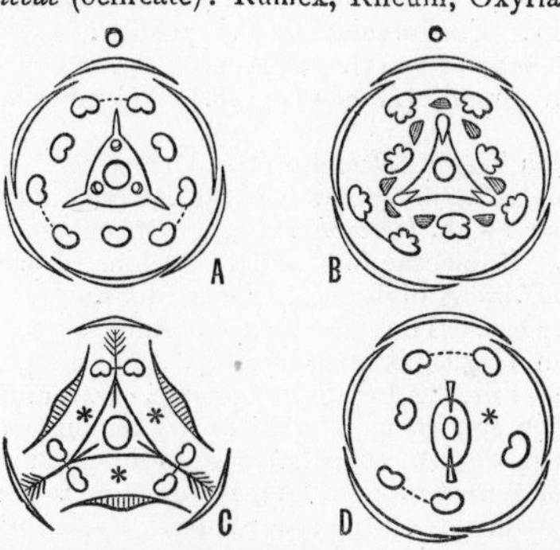

Floral diagrams (after Eichler). *A*, Rheum; *B*, *Polygonum tataricum*; *C*. Rumex; *D*. *Polygonum lapathifolium*. Bracts and bracteoles are omitted, and in *C* and *D* the axis also. Glands in *B* shaded. The asterisks represent missing sta

B. Acyclic (except a few Coccoloboideae).
II. *POLYGONOIDEAE* (endosp. not ruminate).
1. *Atraphaxideae* (shrubs): Calligonum.
2. *Polygoneae* (herbs): Polygonum, Fagopyrum.
III. *COCCOLOBOIDEAE* (ruminate).
1. *Coccolobeae* (usu. ☿): Muehlenbeckia, Coccoloba.
2. *Triplarideae* (usu. dioec.): Triplaris.

Polygonales. The 16th order of Archichlamydeae. *Cf.* p. xiv.

Polygonatum (Tourn.) Adans. Liliaceae (VII). 30 N. temp.; 3 in Brit. (Solomon's seal). There is a sympodial fleshy rhizome, upon which the annual shoots leave curious seal-like marks when they die away. Infl. unilat.; fl. homogamous, bee-pollinated.

Polygonella Michx. Polygonaceae (II. 2). 6 N. Am.

Polygoniflorae (Warming). The 5th order of Choripetalae.

Polygonum (Tourn.) L. Polygonaceae (II. 2). 275 cosmop., but esp. temp. (11 in Brit., knot-grass, bistort, &c.); herbaceous. Some are xero., some water plants (*e.g. P. amphibium* L., which may however be found almost as often on land, where its l. have not the stalks of the water form). The fls. are in spikes and panicles (the partial infl. is cymose). Fls. ☿, acyclic, usu. with a coloured 5-leaved P and about 8 sta. Honey is secreted at the base of the sta., and the fls. are visited by insects, but in varying degree (see the series of sp. described by Müller in *Fert. of Fls.* p. 509). Cleistog. fls. are found under the ochrea in *P. aviculare* L., &c. In *P. viviparum* L. (alpine Brit.) many of the fls. are replaced by bulbils in the lower part of the infl. (*cf.* Lilium, Allium). [*P. Fagopyrum* L. = Fagopyrum.]

Polygyne Phil. (*Plagiocheilus* p.p. *BH.*). Compositae (7). 1 Chili.

Polylepis Ruiz et Pav. Rosaceae (III. 5). 30 trop. S. Am.

Polylobium Eckl. et Zeyh. = Lotononis DC. p.p. (Legum.).

Polylophium Boiss. Umbelliferae (III. 7). 2 W. As.

Polymeria R. Br. Convolvulaceae (I). 7 Austr.

Polymnia L. Compositae (5). 15 Am.

Polymniastrum Small (*Polymnia* p.p.). Compositae (5). 1 E. U.S.

Polyochnella Van Tiegh. (*Ochna* p.p.). Ochnaceae. 12 trop. Afr.

Polyosma Blume. Saxifragaceae (V). 30 Khasias to trop. Austr.

Polyouratea Van Tiegh. (*Gomphia* p.p.). Ochnaceae. 4 Brazil.

Polyozus Lour. Rubiaceae (inc. sed.). 2 China, Cochinchina.

Polypetalae (*BH.*). A division of Dicotyledons.

Polyphragmon Desf. = Timonius Rumph. (Rubi.).

Polyplethia Van Tiegh. (*Balanophora* p.p.). Balanoph. 3 Indomal.

Polypodiaceae. Filicales Leptosporangiatae, *q.v.* for more detail. 130 gen. with 3000 sp., cosmop., rare in dry regions (see *Nat. Pfl.* for details of geogr. distr.). Mostly herbaceous perennials with a creeping rhizome or ± erect root-stock; many epiphytic. Leaves usu. large and pinnate, with sori on the lower sides. Each sorus consists usu. of a large number of stalked sporangia, each with a vertical incomplete annulus and dehiscing transversely. An indusium may or may not be present. *Cf.* Bower, *Ferns*, especially vol. iii.

Classification and chief genera (after Engler):

1. *Woodsieae* (sori term. or dorsal; indusium inf., extrorse or opening every way; spores bilateral); Woodsia, Cystopteris, Onoclea.
2. *Aspidieae* (sori usu. on backs of nerves; indusium sup. or o; spores bilateral; l. usu. unjointed): Dryopteris, Polystichum.
3. *Oleandreae* (sori as in 2; indusium kidney-shaped, oblique; spores kidney-shaped; l. divided): Oleandra.
4. *Davallieae* (sori on or near edge of a segment, with extrorse indusium): Nephrolepis, Lindsaya, Davallia.
5. *Asplenieae* (sori long or linear, unilat. along fertile nerves, with lat. indusium): Blechnum, Asplenium, Scolopendrium.
6. *Pterideae* (sori usu. long, term. or along fertile nerves; usu. without indusium, or edge of l. rolled back): Gymnogramma, Cheilanthes, Adiantum, Pteris, Pteridium.
7. *Vittarieae* (sori at edge or on nerves || midrib; l. unjointed): Vittaria.
8. *Polypodieae* (sori usu. roundish at end of a nerve; dead l. falling completely and leaving a scar): Drymoglossum, Polypodium, Cyclophorus, Drynaria.
9. *Acrosticheae* (lower side of l., in whole or part, covered with sporangia; no indusium): Elaphoglossum, Platycerium.

Polypodiopsis Carr. Coniferae (Taxaceae). 1 New Caledonia.

Polypodium L. (incl. *Grammitis*, *Pleopeltis*, *Selliguea*, &c.). Polypodiaceae. 600 cosmop. *P. vulgare* L. (polypody) in Brit. They have circular naked sori. Many trop. sp. are epiph., *e.g. P. Heracleum* Kze. The rhiz. creep over the supporting tree, and humus is collected in niches formed between it and the l. [*P. Dryopteris* L. (oak fern) = Dryopteris Linneana C. Chr.; *P. Phegopteris* L. (beech fern) = D. Phegopteris C. Chr.; *P. quercifolium* C. = Drynaria quercifolia J. Sm.]

Polypogon Desf. Gramineae (8). 10 warm temp. and trop.; 2 in Brit. (beard-grass).

Polypompholyx Lehm. Lentibulariaceae. 3 trop. Austr., S. Am.

Polyporandra Becc. Icacinaceae. 3 Malay Archipelago.

Polypremum L. Loganiaceae. 1 N. Am., W.I., Colombia.

Polypteris Nutt. (*Palafoxia EP.*). Compositae (6). 6 S.W. U.S., Mex.

Polyrrhiza Pfitz. Orchidaceae (II. 20). 4 W.I.

Polyschistis J. et C. Presl. Gramineae (11). 1 Phil. Is.

Polyscias Forst. Araliaceae (1). 80 palaeotrop.

Polysolenia Hook. f. Rubiaceae (I. 7). 1 Khasias.

Polyspatha Benth. Commelinaceae. 1 W. trop. Afr.

Polysphaeria Hook. f. Rubiaceae (II. 1). 7 E. trop. Afr.

Polystachya Hook. Orchidaceae (II. 5). 100 Afr., trop. As., Am.

Polystemma Decne. Asclepiadaceae (II. 4). 2 C. Am., Mexico.

Polystemonanthus Harms. Leguminosae (II. 3). 1 Liberia.

Polystichum Roth. Polypodiaceae. 112 cosmop. *P. aculeatum* (L.) Schott (prickly shield fern) Brit.

Polytaenia DC. Umbelliferae (III. 6). 1 N. Am.

Polytaxis Bunge (*Jurinea BH.*). Compositae (11). 1 Turkestan.

Polythecanthum Van Tiegh. (*Ochna* p.p.). Ochnaceae. 4 S.E. As.
Polythecium Van Tiegh. (*Ochna* p.p.). Ochnaceae. 50 palaeotrop.
Polytoca R. Br. Gramineae (1). 5 Indomal.
Polytrema C. B. Clarke. Acanthaceae (IV. B). 5 Malay Peninsula.
Polytrias Hack. Gramineae (2). 1 Java.
Polyura Hook. f. Rubiaceae (I. 2). 1 Assam.
Polyxena Kunth. Liliaceae (V). 10 S. Afr.
Polyzygus Dalzell. Umbelliferae (III. 5). 1 S. India.
Pomaceae (Warming) = Rosaceae (sub-fam. II).
Pomaderris Labill. Rhamnaceae. 20 Austr., N.Z.
Pomatosace Maxim. Primulaceae. 1 China.
Pomatostoma Stapf. Melastomaceae (I). 4 Borneo.
Pomatotheca F. Muell. (*Trianthema* p.p. *EP.*). Aizo. (II). 1 Austr.
Pomax Soland. ex Gaertn. Rubiaceae (II. 7). 1 E. Austr.
Pomazota Ridl. Rubiaceae (I. 2). 1 Malay Peninsula.
Pombea Mutis. Inc. sed. Nomen.
Pome, the fruit of Pyrus, &c.
Pomegranate, *Punica Granatum* L.
Pomelo, *Citrus decumana* Murr.
Pometia Forst. Sapindaceae (I). 5 Indomal.
Pomiform, apple-like.
Pommereschea Wittmack. Zingiberaceae (I). 2 Burma.
Pommereulla L. f. Gramineae (10). 1 India.
Pomona, an account of fruits.
Pomphidea Miers. Rutaceae (inc. sed.). (Apocyn. *BH.*) 1 Jamaica.
Pompion, pumpkin, *Cucurbita Pepo* L.
Pond-weed, *Potamogeton*; **Cape --**, *Aponogeton*.
Ponera Lindl. Orchidaceae (II. 6). 8 C. Am., Mexico.
Ponerorchis Reichb. f. (*Habenaria* p.p. *BH.*). Orchid. (II. 1). 1 Japan.
Pongamia Vent. (*Galedupa* Lam.). Leguminosae (III. 8). 1 Indomal.
Pontederia L. Pontederiaceae. 2 Am. Fls. trimorphic, heterostyled (*cf.* Lythrum). *P. crassipes* Mart. = Eichhornia crassipes.
Pontederiaceae (*EP.*, *BH.*). Monocots. (Farinosae; Coronarieae *BH.*). 6 gen. with 21 sp. trop. Water plants, floating or rooted, of sympodial structure, the successive axes ending in infls. (sympodial cymose pseudo-racemes). Often, *e.g.* in Eichhornia, the axillary shoot is adnate to the main shoot from which it springs. Sometimes extra branches are formed, and the axis of the infl. is often pushed to one side so that it appears to spring from a leaf-sheath. Fls. ·|·, P (3 + 3), persistent; A 3 + 3, epiphyllous, G̲ (3), 3-loc. with ∞ anatr. ovules, or 1-loc. with 1 ovule; style long, stigma entire or slightly lobed. Capsule or nut. Embryo central in the seed, scarcely, or not, shorter than the rich mealy endosp. *Chief genera:* Eichhornia, Pontederia.
Ponthieva R. Br. Orchidaceae (II. 2). 10 warm Am.
Pontya A. Chevalier. Moraceae (I). 1 Ivory Coast.
Pony (W.I.), *Tecoma serratifolia* G. Don.
Poonac, crushed seeds after oil-extraction, esp. *Cocos*.
Poor man's weather glass, *Anagallis arvensis* L.
Poortmannia Drake (*Trianaea* p.p. *EP.*). Solanaceae (3). 1 Ecuador.
Poplar, *Populus*.
Popowia Endl. Anonaceae (I). 25 E. Indomal.

Poppy, *Papaver*; **Californian -**, *Eschscholtzia*, *Platystemon*; **opium -**, *Papaver somniferum* L.; **Welsh -**, *Meconopsis cambrica* Vig.; **yellow horned -**, *Glaucium flavum* Crantz.
Populina Baill. Acanthaceae (IV. B). 1 Madag.
Populus L. Salicaceae. 20 N. temp. *P. alba* L. (white poplar) and *P. tremula* L. (aspen) in Brit. Like Salix, but fls. wind-pollinated, with no honey; usu. more sta. than Salix. The wood of *P. alba* is useful, and also that of *P. nigra* L. (black poplar) with its variety *pyramidalis* Spach (*P. fastigiata* Desf.), the Lombardy poplar, often cult., *P. canadensis* Michx. (cotton-wood tree, N. Am.) and others. *P. balsamifera* L. (balsam poplar) yields a resin (tacamahac, see Calophyllum).
Porana Burm. f. Convolvulaceae (I). 10 Indomal.
Poranthera Rudge. Euphorbiaceae (B. I). 5 Austr.
Poraqueiba Aubl. Icacinaceae. 3 N. Brazil, W.I.
Porcelia Ruiz et Pav. (*Uvaria* p.p. *EP.*). Anonaceae (I). 4 trop. Am.
Porcupine grass (Am.), *Stipa*; **- wood,** *Cocos nucifera* L.
Pores, dehiscence by, *cf.* Stamen.
Porlieria Ruiz et Pav. Zygophyllaceae. 3 Mexico, Andes. The leaflets of *P. hygrometrica* R. et P. spread out horiz. in the day time, but at night fold up in pairs. Timber useful.
Porochna Van Tiegh. (*Ochna* p.p.). Ochnaceae. 12 trop. Afr.
Porocystis Radlk. Sapindaceae (I). 1 Amazon valley, Guiana.
Porogamae, see Chalazogamae; **porogamic** (fert.), by micropyle.
Porophyllum Vaill. ex L. Compositae (6). 28 warm Am.
Porospermum F. Muell. Araliaceae (2). 1 N.E. Austr.
Porotheca K. Schum. = Chlaenandra Miq. (Menisp.). 1 New Guinea.
Porpax Lindl. (*Eria* p.p. *BH.*). Orchidaceae (II. 15). 6 Indomal.
Porphyranthus Engl. Burseraceae. 1 Cameroons.
Porphyrocodon Hook. f. Cruciferae (4). 1 Colombia.
Porphyrocoma Scheidw. (*Dianthera* p.p. *BH.*). Acanthaceae (IV. B). 2 trop. S. Am. Cult. orn. fl.
Porphyrodesme Schlechter (*Saccolabium* p.p.). Orchidaceae (II. 20). 1 New Guinea.
Porphyroglottis Ridl. Orchidaceae (II. *a*. II). 1 Borneo.
Porphyrospatha Engl. Araceae (VI). 2 C. Am.
Porphyrostemma Benth. ex Oliv. Compositae (4). 1 E. Centr. Afr.
Porrum (Tourn.) L. = Allium Tourn. p.p. (Lili.).
Portea C. Koch. Bromeliaceae (4). 5 Brazil. Cult. orn. infl.
Portenschlagia Vis. Umbelliferae (III. 5). 1 Dalmatia.
Porteria Hook. = Phyllactis Pers. (*BH.*) = Valeriana Tourn. p.p.
Portesia Cav. = Trichilia P. Br. (Meli.).
Portland arrowroot, *Arum maculatum* L.
Portlandia P. Br. Rubiaceae (I. I). 8 W.I., Mexico.
Portugal laurel, *Prunus lusitanica* L.
Portulaca L. Portulacaceae. 20 trop. and subtrop. (purslane). The fl. has a semi-inf. ovary and 4—∞ sta. It remains closed in bad weather. The sta. of *P. oleracea* L. are sensitive to contact and move toward the side touched.
Portulacaceae (*EP.*, *BH.*). Dicots. (Archichl. Centrospermae; Caryophyllinae *BH.*). 17 gen., 225 sp., cosmop., but esp. Am. Most are

annual herbs, often with fleshy l., and with stipules (sometimes repres. by axillary bundles of hairs). Fls. usu. in cymes (often dich. with tendency to cincinni), reg., ☿. K 2, the lower sepal (usu. ant.) overlapping the upper (the two are often regarded as bracteoles); C 5; A 5 + 5, or 5 opp. the petals, or some other number; G (2—8) usu. (3), sup. exc. in Portulaca, 1-loc. with several stigmas and 2—∞ campylotr. ov. on a central basal plac. The fls. secrete honey and are mostly insect-pollinated. Caps. with album. seeds; that of Claytonia and Montia is explosive; embryo more or less curved round the perisperm. *Chief genera:* Calandrinia, Claytonia, Montia, Portulaca, Lewisia.

Portulacaria Jacq. Portulacaceae. 2 S. Afr.

Portulaceae (*BH.*) = Portulacaceae.

Posadaea Cogn. Cucurbitaceae (2). 1 Colombia.

Posidonia Kon. Potamogetonaceae. 2 Austr., Medit. (used for packing glass).

Poskea Vatke. Boraginaceae (II). 1 Somaliland.

Posoqueria Aubl. Rubiaceae (I. 8). 5 S. Am., W.I.

Posterior, the side facing to the stem on which the flower is a branch (upper side in most floral diagrams).

Postia Boiss. et Blanche. Compositae (4). 4 Syria, Persia.

Posticous, on the posterior side.

Potalia Aubl. Loganiaceae. 1 trop. S. Am.

Potameia Thou. Lauraceae (II). 1 Madag.

Potamium (Cl.), a river formation.

Potamobryon Liebm. Podostemaceae. 3 Mexico.

Potamogeton (Tourn.) L. Potamogetonaceae. 90 cosmop. 11 or more (*cf.* Rubus) in Brit. (pond-weed). Water pl. with creeping sympodial rhiz. and erect leafy branches; all submerged or some floating. A series of types occurs, beginning with the floating sp. and ending with the narrow-leafed submerged ones. There can be no doubt of the origin of the P. from land pl., and Schenck looks upon *P. natans* L. as the sp. least modified to suit a water existence, *i.e.* the nearest to the ancestral type. The upper l. are ovate, leathery, and float; the lower submerged, sometimes linear. Then come such as *P. heterophyllus* Schreb. where the submerged l. are all narrow. Next *P. lucens* L., *P. crispus* L., &c. with all the l. lanceolate and submerged. Then in *P. obtusifolius* Mert. et Koch, *P. pusillus* L., &c., the leaves are narrow and of a long ribbon shape. *P. trichoides* Cham. et Schlecht. represents the most

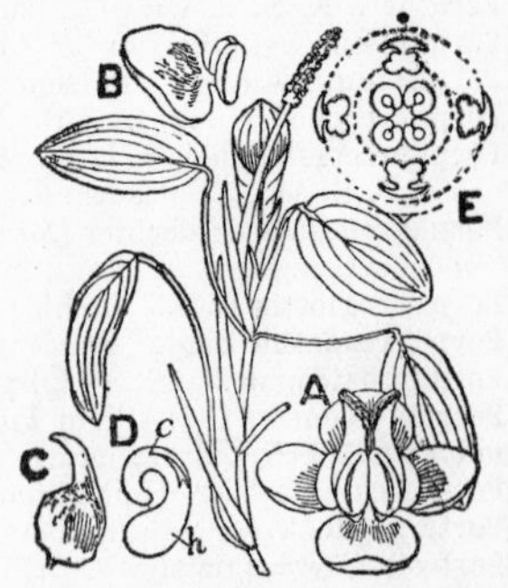

Flowering shoot of *Potamogeton natans*, reduced. A—E. *P. crispus*. A. Flower, enlarged. B. Single stamen, showing petaloid connective, enlarged. C. A fruit, enlarged. D. Embryo; *h*, hypocotyl; *c*, cotyledon, the letter points to the top of the sheath which encloses the plumule. E. Floral diagram. A, B, D, after Le Maout and Decaisne; E, after Eichler.

highly modified type (easily studied in a herbarium).

Hibernation in various ways; some green all winter; *P. natans*, &c. die down, leaving rhiz.; *P. pectinatus* L. forms tubers on special branches; *P. crispus* and others form winter buds with broad l. (not closely packed); *P. obtusifolius* ordinary winter buds. Fls. simple, in subaerial spikes. A 4, in two whorls, $\underline{G}$ 4. From connective of each sessile anther there grows out a cup-shaped expansion simulating a P-leaf. Fl. protog., wind-fert. The outer layer of pericarp contains air, so that achene floats and may be distr.

Potamogetonaceae (*EP.*; *Naiadeae* p.p. *BH.*). Monocots. (Helobieae; Apocarpae *BH.*; pp. iii, liv). 9/120, cosmop.; water pl., some marine. Usu. creeping stem or rhiz., mono- or sym-podial, attached to soil by adv. r., with erect branches upwards into water, usu. with ribbon l., submerged (exceptions in Potamogeton), usu. alt. in ½ phyllotaxy. Base sheathing; within sheath are the small scales (*squamulae intravaginales*) which occur in most Helobieae. Spike, cyme, or sol. fls. No true P, exc. Zannichellia ♀ and Althenia; Posidonia and Potamogeton show leaf-like outgrowths from sta. In some it is not easy to decide what is to be regarded as the fl. (*cf.* Zostera). Fl. ☿ or unisexual, reg., 1—4-merous; anthers sessile, sometimes connate; cpls. free, or 1 only, with 1 ov. in each, usu. pend. orthotr. Fr. 1-seeded; embryo usu. with well-developed hypocotyl; no endosp. Diagram, &c. on p. 534, and *cf.* genera.

Classification and Genera: [Monograph in *Pfl. R.*, 1907].

A. Fls. in spikes, often ☿:

1. *Zostereae* (axis of spike compressed, flat; marine): Zostera (cpl. rounded at base, fl. ☿), Phyllospadix (cpl. cordate at base; ♂ ♀).
2. *Posidonieae* (axis of spike terete; spike branched; marine): [Posidonia.
3. *Potamogetoneae* (axis at last; spike simple; fresh or brackish water): Potamogeton (spike cylindrical, A 4), Ruppia (spike 2-fld., A 2).

B. Fls. sol. or in cymes, ♂ ♀.

4. *Cymodoceae* (P none; pollen filiform; marine): Cymodocea (stigmas 2), Diplanthera (stigma 1).
5. *Zannichellieae* (P in ♀ fls.; pollen globose; fresh or brackish water): Zannichellia (♂ with no P; cpls. usu. 4), Althenia (♂ with cupuliform P; cpls. usu. 3).

Potamophila R. Br. Gramin. (6). 1 Austr.

Potaninia Maxim. Ros. (III. 2). 1 Mongolia. Epicalyx. K, C, A, 3, [G 1.

Potato, *Solanum tuberosum* L.; **sweet-,** *Ipomoea Batatas* Lam.

Potentilla L. (incl. *Comarum* L., *Tormentilla* L.). Ros. (III. 2). 300, nearly cosmop., chiefly N. temp. and arctic. 9 in Brit., incl. *P. Anserina* L. (silverweed), *P. reptans* L. (cinquefoil), *P. Tormentilla* Neck. (tormentil), *P. comarum* Nestl., &c. Herbs, usu. with creeping stems rooting at nodes (veg. repr.). Fl. with epicalyx of small green l., outside and alt. with the seps. (the stips. of seps. united in pairs; often one or more may be seen with two lobes, or fully divided). Fls. of class AB, homogamous, visited by flies; honey secreted by ring-shaped nectary within sta.

Poteranthera Bong. Melastom. (1). 4 Braz., Guiana. Fl. 5-merous.

Poteridium Spach, Rydberg (*Sanguisorba* p.p.). Ros. (III. 5). 1 N. Am.
Poterium L. (*BH.* incl. *Sanguisorba*, *q.v.* for Brit. sp.). Rosaceae (III. 5). 1 Italy, E. Medit.
Potherbs, *cf.* Edible Products.
Pothoidium Schott. Araceae (I). 2 Malaya.
Pothos L. Araceae (I). 60 Indomal., Madag. Monopodial (see fam.). Stem climbing, with adv. roots. The buds break through the axils, so that the branching seems infra-axillary. Fl. ☿. P 3+3.
Pothuava Gaudich. (*Aechmea* p.p. *BH.*). Bromeliaceae (4). 1 S. Am.
Pottingeria Prain. Saxifragaceae (V). 1 India.
Pottsia Hook. et Arn. Apocynaceae (II. 2). 3 India, China.
Pouchetia A. Rich. Rubiaceae (I. 8). 3 W. trop. Afr.
Poulsenia Eggers. Moraceae (II). 1 Ecuador.
Pounce, *Tetraclinis quadrivalvis* Mast.
Poupartia Comm. (*Spondias* p.p. *BH.*). Anacardiaceae (2). 4 Madag., Masc.
Pourouma Aubl. Moraceae (III). 20 trop. S. Am. Ed. fr.
Pourretia Ruiz et Pav. = Puya Molina (Bromel.).
Pourthiaea Decne. Rosaceae (II). 5 E. As.
Pouslowia Wight. Inc. sed. Nomen.
Pouteria Aubl. Sapotaceae (I). 30 trop. Am.
Pouzolzia Gaudich. Urticaceae (3). 40 palaeotrop. The root of *P. tuberosa* Wight is eaten in India.
Poverty grass (Am.), *Aristida dichotoma* Michx.
Pozoa Lag. (*Azorella* p.p. *BH.*). Umbelliferae (I. 2). 4 Austr., S. Am.
Pradosia Liais (*Lucuma* p.p. *BH.*). Sapotaceae (I). 1 Rio de Janeiro. Hard wood.
Praecox (Lat.), appearing early.
Praemorse, as if bitten off.
Praesepium Spreng. Rosaceae. Nomen.
Prageluria N.E. Br. = Pergularia (L.) N.E. Br.
Prairie, the grass country E. of the Rocky Mts.; **-clover** (Am.), *Petalostemon*; **-grass** (Am.), *Sporobolus asper* Kunth; **-turnip**, *Psoralea*.
Prainea King ex Hook. f. Moraceae (III). 3 Malaya.
Prangos Lindl. Umbelliferae (III. 4). 36 Medit., C. As.
Prantleia Mez (*Orthophytum* Beer). Bromeliaceae (4). 2 C. Brazil.
Praravinia Korth. Rubiaceae (I. 7). 1 Borneo.
Prasanthea Decne. = Paliavana Vand. (Gesner.).
Prasium L. Labiatae (III). 1 Medit.
Prasophyllum R. Br. Orchidaceae (II. 2). 32 Austr., N.Z.
Pratal, growing in meadows; **pratensis** (Lat.), of meadows.
Pratia Gaudich. Campanul. (III). 16 S. Am., Austr., N.Z., trop. As.
Prefoliation, vernation.
Premna L. Verbenaceae (4). 45 trop. and subtrop. |✻.
Prenanthella Rydberg (*Prenanthes* p.p.). Compositae (13). 1 N.W. Am.
Prenanthes Vaill. ex L. Compositae (13). 27 N. temp. and trop. Afr.
Preptanthe Reichb. f. (*Calanthe* p.p. *BH.*). Orchid. (II. 9). 2 trop. As.
Prepusa Mart. Gentianaceae (I). 3 Brazil.
Prescottia Lindl. Orchidaceae (II. 2). 22 trop. Am., W.I.

Preserving, *cf.* Collecting.
Preslia Opiz. Labiatae (VI). 1 W. Medit.
Prestoea Hook. f. Palmae (IV. 1). 2 Trinidad, Colombia.
Prestonia R. Br. Apocynaceae (II. 2). 30 trop. Am.
Pretrea J. Gay. Pedaliaceae. 1 S. and trop. Afr.
Pretreothamnus Engl. Pedaliaceae. 1 Somaliland.
Preussiella Gilg. Melastomaceae (I). 1 W. trop. Afr.
Prevostea Choisy (*Breweria* p.p. *BH.*). Convolv. (I). 18 trop. Afr., Am.
Prickly ash, *Zanthoxylum fraxineum* Willd.; **-heath,** *Pernettya*; **-lettuce,** *Lactuca*; **-pear,** *Opuntia*; **-pole** (W.I.), *Bactris*; **-poppy** (Am.), *Argemone*; **-shield-fern,** *Aspidium aculeatum* Sw.; **-withe** (W.I.), *Cereus triangularis* Mill.
Priestleya DC. Leguminosae (III. 3). 15 S. Afr.
Prim (Am.), privet, *Ligustrum vulgare* L.
Primine, outer coat of an ovule.
Primrose, *Primula vulgaris* Huds.; **Cape-,** *Streptocarpus*; **Chinese-,** *Primula sinensis* Sabine; **evening-,** *Oenothera*; **-willow** (W.I.), *Jussieua*.
Primula L. Primulaceae. 250 N. hemisph. chiefly in hilly districts. A few elsewhere, *e.g. P. farinosa* L., var. *magellanica* Hook., at the Str. of Magelhaen. The rhizome is a sympodium, each joint terminating in an infl. In some sp. this consists of successive whorls of fls. arranged up a long stalk, *e.g. japonica* A. Gray. A few of the more important sp. are: *P. sinensis* Sabine, the Chinese primrose, *P. elatior* Hill, the oxlip (Brit.); *P. vulgaris* Huds. (*P. acaulis* Hill), the primrose (Brit.), *P. veris* Lehm. (*P. officinalis* Jacq.), the cowslip (Brit.), *P. farinosa*, L. (Brit.), *P. japonica* A. Gray, *P. Auricula* L., the auricula with its many forms. A great many hybrids occur, and garden vars. In the double crowned cowslip the K has become petaloid, so that the fl. looks as if it had two Cs, one within the other.

The fls. are dimorphic, heterostyled. On one pl. are long-styled fls. with sta. halfway up the tube and the stigma at its mouth; on another plant are short-styled fls., with stigma halfway up and anthers at the mouth. The depth and narrowness of the tube suit the fl. to bees or butterflies, and these tend to carry pollen from long sta. to long style or from short to short. These 'legitimate' pollinations (see Lythrum) which are at the same time crossings, are the only ones which produce a full complement of fertile seed.

The fl. stalks in umbellate forms, *e.g.* cowslip, stand close and erect till the fls. open, then spread out, and close up again as the fr. ripens; thus the caps. is held erect and the seeds must be shaken out.
Primulaceae (*EP.*, *BH.*). Dicots. (Sympet. Primulales). 25 gen., 550 sp. cosmop., but esp. N. temp. 9 Brit. genera. Herbaceous pl., commonly perenn., with rhiz. or tubers; l. opp. or alt., exstip. Fls. often borne on scapes, which when > 1-flowered are term.; they are usually actinom., ☿, often heterostyled, and 5-merous, without bracteoles, the odd (4th) sepal post. K (5) persistent; C (5), reg. (exc. Coris), or 5, or 0 (Glaux); A 5, epipet. and opp. the pets.; occasionally 5 stds. alt. with the pets.; anthers intr. The presence of the stds. here

as in Myrsin. explains antepet. position of sta. as due to abortion of originally outer whorl. Formerly much discussion, esp. after Pfeffer's discovery of development of C from backs of sta. (Eichler's (*Blüthendiagramme*). $\underline{G}$ or ½-inf., syncp. with free-central plac., typically of 5 cpls., but this is not easily proved, as there are no partitions (*cf.* Caryoph.), and style and stigma are simple; ov. usu. ∞, spirally or in whorls on plac., ½-anatr. Caps. fr., 5-valved, usu. dehisc. by teeth at tip, one opp. each sep. Seeds few or many; embryo small, in fleshy or horny endosp. Fl. often heterostyled (*cf* Primula, also Hottonia, Glaux, Androsace). No econ. value; many cult. orn. fl.

Floral diagram of *Primula acaulis* (after Eichler).

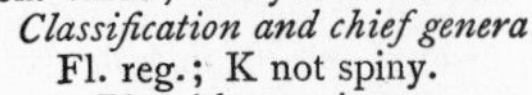

Classification and chief genera:

Fl. reg.; K not spiny.

Pl. without tubers.

1. *Androsaceae* ($\underline{G}$; C imbr.): Primula (C not reflexed, lobes entire or bifid, sta. on tube, ov. ∞), Dionysia (do.; ov. few), Androsace (do.; tube very short), Soldanella (do.; lobes fimbriate, caps. operculate), Hottonia (water pl.), Dodecatheon (C reflexed).

3. *Lysimachieae* ($\underline{G}$; C conv.): Lysimachia (caps. with valves; 5-merous), Trientalis (do.; 7-merous), Glaux (do.; apet.), Anagallis (caps. with lid).

4. *Samoleae* (G ½-inf.): Samolus only.

Pl. with tubers.

2. *Cyclamineae:* Cyclamen only.

Fl. irreg.; K spiny.

5. *Corideae:* Coris only.

Primulales (*EP.*, *BH.*). The 2nd (5th) order of Sympet. (Gamo.), pp.

Primulina Hance. Gesner. (I). 5 China. [xl, lii.

Prince's feather, *Amaranthus*; **-wood** (W.I.), *Hamelia*, *Cordia*, *Exostemma*.

Principes (*EP.*). The 5th order of Monocots.; p. iv.

Pringlea Anders. ex Hook. f. Crucif. (I). 1, *P. antiscorbutica* R. Br. (Kerguelen cabbage), on Kerguelen's I. Habit of cabbage, but fls. on lat. axes. "Winged insects cannot exist, because at every flight they run the risk of being drowned...the pl. has become modified for fert. by wind...exserted anthers...long filiform stigmatic papillae...still retains traces of...entomophilous ancestors...usu. devoid of pets., it occurs abundantly in shaded places with pets." (Muller). No septum in ovary.

Pringleochloa Scribner (*Opizia* p.p. *EP.*). Gramin. (II). 1 Mex.

Pringleophytum A. Gray (*Berginia* p.p. *EP.*). Acanth. (IV. B). 1 Calif.

Prinoides DC. = Ilex L. p.p. (Aquifol.).

Prinos Gronov. ex L. = Ilex Tourn. p.p. (Aquifol.).

Prinsepia Royle. Ros. (V). 1 Himal. Style lat. Oil from seeds.

Printzia Cass. Compositae (4). 5 S. Afr.
Prionachne Nees. Gramineae (9). 1 S. Afr.
Prionanthium Desv. (*Prionachne* p.p. *EP.*). Gram. (9). 3 Indomal., S. Afr.
Prionitis L. = Barleria L. p.p. (Acanth.).
Prionium E. Mey. Juncaceae. 1 S. Africa., *P. Palmita* E Mey. (*P. serratum* Buchen.), the palmiet, a shrubby aloe-like plant with a stem 1—2 metres high, covered with the fibrous remains of old l. It grows on the edges of streams, sometimes almost blocking them up. Veg. propagation takes place by formation of runners. Adv. roots form between the l. [Buchenau in *Bibl. Bot.*, No. 27.]
Prionophyllum C. Koch (*Dyckia* p.p. *BH.*). Bromel. (2). 2 S. Braz., Urug.
Prionosciadium S. Wats. Umbelliferae (III. 6). 10 Mexico, C. Am.
Prionotes R. Br. Epacridaceae (1). 1 Tasmania.
Prioria Griseb. Leguminosae (II. 2). 1 Panama, Jamaica.
Priotropis Wight et Arn. Leguminosae (III. 3). 2 E. Himal., Socotra.
Prismatocarpus L'Herit. Campanulaceae (1). 15 S. Afr.
Prismatomeris Thw. Rubiaceae (II. 9). 1 Ceylon, India.
Pritchardia Seem. et H. Wendl. (excl. *Washingtonia* H. Wendl.). Palmae (I. 2). 5 Fiji, Hawaiian Is.
Pritchardiopsis Becc. Palmae (I. 2). 1 New Caledonia.
Pritzelia Klotzsch = Begonia L. p.p. (Begon.).
Pritzelia F. Muell. Philydraceae. 1 New Guinea.
Priva Adans. Verbenaceae (1). 10 trop. and subtrop. The l. of *P. echinata* Juss. are used as tea; tubers of *P. laevis* Juss. ed.
Privet, *Ligustrum vulgare* L.
Probletostemon K. Schum. Rubiaceae (I. 8). 1 Sierra Leone.
Proboscella Van Tiegh. Ochnaceae. 2 trop. Afr.
Proboscidea Schmid. (*Martynia* p.p.). Martyniaceae. 6 warm Am.
Procerus (Lat.), lofty.
Process, a projecting appendage.
Prochnyanthes S. Wats. Amaryllidaceae (II). 1 Mexico.
Prockia P. Br. ex L. Flacourtiaceae (5). 4 trop. Am.
Prockiopsis Baill. Flacourtiaceae (2). 1 Madag.
Procris Comm. ex Juss. Urticaceae (2). 5 palaeotrop.
Procumbent, prostrate.
Proliferous, bearing offshoots.
Prolification, formation of buds in the axils of floral l.
Promenaea Lindl. (*Zygopetalum* p.p. *BH.*). Orchid. (II. β. 11). 5 Braz.
Promotion nut, *Anacardium occidentale* L.
Pronaya Huegel. Pittosporaceae. 1 W. Austr.
Pronuba (moth), *cf.* Yucca.
Propulsive mechanisms, *cf.* Dispersal of Seeds.
Proscephalium Korth. Rubiaceae (II. 5). 1 Java.
Proserpinaca L. Haloragidaceae. 4 N. Am. 3-merous. *Ann. Bot.* 18, 579.
Prosopanche de Bary. Hydnoraceae. 1 Argentina.

Prosopis L. Leguminosae (I. 4). 30 trop. and subtrop., some xero., without l., many thorny, the thorns being epidermal, or metamorphosed branches or stipules. *P. juliflora* DC. (trop. Am.) is the mezquit tree (fodder, &c.). *P. alba* Griseb. has sweet succulent pods (algaroba blanca), used as food.

Prosopostelma Baill. Asclepiadaceae (II. 1). 1 W. trop. Afr.

Prostanthera Labill. Labiatae (II). 40 Austr.

Prosthecidiscus J. Donnell Smith. Asclepiadaceae (II. 1). 1 Guatem.

Protamomum Ridl. Musaceae. 1 Malaya.

Protandry, *cf.* Dichogamy.

Protanthera Rafin. Liliaceae. Nomen. 2 N. Am.

Protarum Engl. Araceae (VII). 1 Seychelles.

Protea L. Proteaceae (I). 75 S. and trop. Afr. Fls. in showy heads, often with coloured bracts.

Proteaceae (*EP.*, *BH.*). Dicotyledons (Archichl. Proteales; Daphnales *BH.*). 50 gen., 960 sp. "which have a very char. distr.; there are in Austr. 591, trop. E. As. 25, New Caled. 27, N.Z. 2, Chili 7, trop. S. Am. 36, south-west Cape Col. 262, Madag. 2, Mts. of trop. Afr. 5" (Engler). The great majority live in regions where there is annually a long dry season. Correlated with this is the fact that they are mostly xero. Nearly all shrubs and trees with entire or much-divided exstip. l., which have commonly a thick cuticle and often a covering of hairs further checking transpiration. The fls. are borne in racemes, spikes, heads, &c., and are often very showy; many have their pollen freely exposed, though they are not wind-fert.—a peculiarity perhaps connected with their life in a dry climate (compare the Acacias of Australia).

The fls. are usu. ☿, often ·|·. P (4), corolline, valvate; the l. commonly bent or rolled back when open; sta. 4, inserted on the tepals, and usu. with only the anthers free; $\underline{G}$ 1, ovules many or few or one, pend. or not, the micropyle facing the base of the ovary. Style term., long, often bent inwards. Follicle, capsule, drupe or nut; seed exalbum. The ovary is sometimes borne on a gynophore and at its base are commonly nectarial outgrowths. The fls. are protandrous and adapted to insect-fert.

Classification and chief genera (see discussion in *Nat. Pfl.*):

I. *PERSOONIOIDEAE* (fls. single in axils of bracts; ovules single, few or 2; drupe or nut, one seeded): Persoonia, Protea, Leucadendron.

II. *GREVILLOIDEAE* (fls. in pairs; ovules several or 2; fr. usu. dehisc., many seeded): Grevillea, Hakea, Banksia.

Proteales. The 13th order of Archichlamydeae. *Cf.* p. xii.

Protection against grazing animals is obtained by stinging hairs (*Loasaceae*, *Urticaceae*, &c.), by prickles, &c., or by disagreeable taste; **- of buds**, see Bud; **- of honey**, *cf.* Flower-classes; **- of flowers**, see Flower-movements; **- of leaves**, see Movements; **- of young leaves**, *Amherstia*, *Brownea*, &c.

Proteids, complex organic bodies, containing C, H, O, and N.

Proteocarpus Börner = Carex L. p.p. (Cyper.).

Proteopsis Mart. et Zucc. Compositae (I). 2 campos of S. Braz.

Proterandry, -ogyny, protandry, &c. *Cf.* Dichogamy.

Prothallus, the sexual pl.; *Pteridophyta*, *Filicineae*, &c.
Protium Burm. f. Burseraceae. 60 trop. Some yield good balsam resins.
Proto- (Gr. pref.), first, earliest; **-corm**, *Lycopodiaceae*; **-gyny**, see Dichogamy; **-plasm**, the living substance of pl.
Protolirion Ridl. (*Petrosavia* p.p.). Liliaceae (I). 1 Mal. Penin.
Protomegabaria Hutchinson. Euphorbiaceae (A. I. 1). 2 trop. Afr.
Protorhus Engl. Anacardiaceae (3). 9 Madag., S. Afr.
Protoschwenkia Solereder. Solanaceae (5). 1 Bolivia.
Proustia Lag. Compositae (12). 10 Andes, temp. S. Am.
Proximal, nearest to axis.
Pruinose, with waxy powdery secretion on the surface.
Prumnopitys Phil. = Podocarpus L'Hérit. p.p. (Conif.).
Prune, *Prunus domestica* L.
Prunella L. (*Brunella* Tourn.). Labiatae (VI). *P. vulgaris* L. (self-heal) cosmop. (incl. Brit.), 5 Medit. Eur. The fr. K is closed and points up in dry air, but opens and stands horiz. in damp.
Prunus (Tourn.) L. (incl. *Amygdalus* Tourn., *Cerasus* Tourn.). Rosaceae (V). 85 N. temp.; a few trop. *P. insititia* L. (bullace), *P. spinosa* L. (sloe or blackthorn), *P. avium* L. (gean), *P. Padus* L. (bird-cherry), in Brit. The fl.-buds are laid down in August or September of the preceding year. There is 1 cpl., which gives rise to a drupe, while the hollow recept. usu. falls away. Many sp. are cult. for their fr., *e.g.* *P. Armeniaca* L. (apricot), *P. domestica* L. (plum, prune), *P. Amygdalus* Stokes (almond), *P. Persica* Stokes (peach, with its smooth-fruited variety the nectarine), *P. Cerasus* L. (cherry), &c. *P. Laurocerasus* L. is the cherry laurel; it has extra-floral nectaries on the backs of the l., showing as brownish patches against the midribs. The spines of some sp. are axillary, as in Crataegus.
Pruriens (Lat.), causing itching.
Przewalskia Maxim. Solanaceae (2). 2 C. As.
Psacalium Cass. = Senecio Tourn. p.p. (*BH*) = Cacalia L. p.p.
Psamma Beauv. = Ammophila Host. (Gram.).
Psammanthe Reichb. Caryophyllaceae (inc. sed.). Nomen.
Psammisia Klotzsch. Ericaceae (III. 2). 35 Andes, Guiana.
Psammogeton Edgew. Umbelliferae (III. 2). 4 W. As.
Psammogonum Nieuwland (*Polygonella* p.p.). Polygon. (II. 2). 2 N. Am.
Psammomoya Diels et Loesener. Celastraceae. 2 Austr.
Psammophilous, sand-loving.
Psammotropha Eckl. et Zeyh. Phytolaccaceae (Aizo. *BH.*). 5 S. Afr.
Psathura Comm. ex Juss. Rubiaceae (II. 5). 6 Madag., Mascarenes.
Psathyranthus Ule. Loranthaceae (I). 1 Upper Amazon.
Psathyrotes A. Gray. Compositae (8). 4 W. U.S., North Mexico.
Psedera Necker ex Greene (*Ampelopsis*, &c. p.p.). Vitaceae. 10 N. temp. and subtrop.
Psednotrichia Hiern. Compositae (3). 1 trop. Afr.
Pselium Lour. (*Pericampylus BH.*). Menispermaceae. 1 Cochinchina.
Psephellus Cass. = Centaurea L. p.p. (Comp.).
Pseud-, pseudo- (Gr. pref.), false; **-axis**, a sympodium; **-berry**, *Gaultheria*, *Urera*, *Viscum*; **-bulb**, *Orchidaceae*; **-carp**, the product of the

ovary, together with any other organ that developes into the fr., *Pyrus*, *Rosa*. &c.; **-catkin**, *Humulus*; **-head**, *Maclura*, *Moraceae*, *Urticaceae*; **-panicle**, *Humulus*; **-raceme**, *Hypericum*, *Maclura*, *Moraceae*; **-spike**, *Moraceae*, *Morus*; **-umbel**, *Hypericum*, *Moraceae*.

Pseudabutilon R. E. Fries (*Abutilon* p.p.). Malv. (2). 10 warm Am.

Pseudagrostistachys Pax et K. Hoffm. (*Agrostistachys* p.p.). Euphorbiaceae (A. II. 2). 1 W. Afr.

Pseudais Decne. Thymelaeaceae. 1 Moluccas.

Pseudalomia Zoll. et Morr. Compositae. Nomen.

Pseudanthistiria Hook. f. (*Andropogon* p.p. *EP.*). Gramin. (2). 4 Indomal.

Pseudanthus Sieb. ex Spreng. Euphorbiaceae (B. I). 7 Austr.

Pseudarthria Wight et Arn. Leguminosae (III. 7). 5 Afr., trop. As.

Pseuderanthemum Radlkf. Acanth. (IV. B). 60 trop. Cult. orn. fl.

Pseuderia Schlechter. Orchidaceae (II. 15). 7 Malay Archipelago.

Pseudibatia Malme. Asclepiadaceae (II. 4). 4 S. Am.

Pseudima Radlk. (*Sapindus* p.p. *BH.*). Sapindaceae (I). 1 N. trop. S. Am.

Pseudixus Hayata. Loranthaceae (II). 1 E. As., Austr.

Pseudobaeckea Niedenzu. Bruniaceae. 7 S. Afr.

Pseudobahia A. Gray, Rydberg (*Monolopia* p.p.). Comp. (6). 2 Calif.

Pseudobarleria T. Anders. (*Petalidium BH.*). Acanth. (IV. A). 15 Afr.

Pseudobastardia Hassler (*Sida* p.p.). Malvaceae (2). 2 Brazil.

Pseudoblepharis Baill. Acanthaceae (IV. B). 5 trop. Afr.

Pseudobotrys Moes. Icacinaceae. 1 New Guinea.

Pseudobravoa Rose (*Bravoa* p.p.). Amaryllidaceae (II). 1 Mexico.

Pseudobraya Korshinsky. Cruciferae (4). 1 C. As.

Pseudobromus K. Schum. (*Brachyelytrum* p.p.). Gramin. (8). 2 Afr.

Pseudocadia Harms (*Cadia* p.p.). Leguminosae (III. 1). 1 trop. Afr.

Pseudocalyx Radlk. Acanthaceae (III). 1 Madagascar.

Pseudocarapa Hemsl. Meliaceae (III). 1 Ceylon.

Pseudocarpidium Millsp. (*Vitex* p.p.). Verben. (4). 3 Cuba, Florida.

Pseudocaryophyllus Berg. = Myrtus Tourn. p.p. (Myrt.).

Pseudocedrela Harms (*Cedrela* p.p.). Meliaceae (II). 3 trop. Afr.

Pseudocentrum Lindl. Orchidaceae (II. 2). 8 trop. Am., W.I.

Pseudochrosia Blume. Apocynaceae (I. 3). 1 New Guinea.

Pseudocinchona A. Chevalier ex E. Perrot. Rubi. (I. 5). 1 trop. Afr.

Pseudoclinium O. Ktze. (*Leptoclinium* Gardn.). Comp. (2). 1 Goyaz.

Pseudoconnarus Radlk. (*Connarus* p.p.). Connaraceae. 1 Amazonas.

Pseudocroton Muell.-Arg. Euphorbiaceae (A. II. 2). 1 C. Am.

Pseudocydonia C. K. Schneider (*Chaenomeles* p.p.). Ros. (II). 1 China.

Pseudocymopterus Coulter et Rose (*Cymopterus* p.p.). Umbelliferae (III. 6). 5 S.W. U.S.

Pseudocynometra O. Ktze. = Maniltoa Scheff. (Legum.).

Pseudocytisus O. Ktze. = Vella DC. (Crucif.).

Pseudodracontium N.E. Br. Araceae (IV). 3 Cochinchina.

Pseudoernestia Krasser (*Ernestia* p.p.). Melastom. (I). 1 Venezuela.

Pseudoeugenia Scortech. (*Eugenia* p.p. *EP.*). Myrt. (I). 2 Mal. Penin.

Pseudogaltonia O. Ktze. (*Hyacinthus* p.p.). Liliaceae V). 2 trop. Afr.

Pseudogardneria Raciborski (*Gardneria* p.p.). Logan. 2 E. As.
Pseudohamelia Wernham. Rubiaceae (I. 7). 1 trop. Am.
Pseudohydrosme Engl. Araceae (IV). 2 W. trop. Afr.
Pseudolachnostylis Pax. Euphorbiaceae (A. I. 1). 3 trop. Afr.
Pseudolarix Gord. Coniferae (Pinaceae, 21; see C. for gen. char.). 1 China, *P. Kaempferi* Gord., the golden pine. Like Larix, but distinguished chiefly by the deciduous fruit-scales.
Pseudoliparis Finet (*Microstylis* p.p.). Orchid. (II. 4). 1 N. G.
Pseudolmedia Tréc. Moraceae (II). 5 trop. Am., W.I.
Pseudolopezia Rose (*Lopezia* p.p.). Onagraceae (2). 2 N. Am.
Pseudomachaerium Hassler. Leguminosae (III. 8). 1 Paraguay.
Pseudomacodes Rolfe. Orchidaceae (II. 2). 1 Solomon Is.
Pseudomarsdenia Baill. Asclepiadaceae (II. 3). 1 Mexico.
Pseudomorus Bur. Moraceae (I). 1 Norfolk I.
Pseudomussaenda Wernham. Rubiaceae (I. 7). 4 trop. Afr.
Pseudonephelium Radlk. (*Nephelium* p.p. *BH.*). Sapind. (1). 1 Borneo.
Pseudopanax C. Koch. Araliaceae (1). 6 temp. S. Am., N.Z.
Pseudopavonia Hassler. Malvaceae (3). 1 Paraguay.
Pseudopentatropis Costantin. Asclepiadaceae (II. 1). 1 Indochina.
Pseudophoenix H. Wendl. et Drude. Palmae (IV. 1). 1 Florida.
Pseudoprosopis Harms (*Prosopis* p.p.). Legumin. (I. 4). 2 trop. Afr.
Pseudopteris Baill. Sapindaceae (I). 1 Madag.
Pseudopteryxia Rydberg (*Cymopterus* p.p.). Umbell. (III. 5). 3 Rockies.
Pseudopyxis Miq. Rubiaceae (II. 6). 1 Japan.
Pseudoreoxis Rydberg (*Cymopterus* p.p.). Umbell. (III. 5). 2 Rockies.
Pseudorlaya Murb. (*Daucus* p.p.). Umbelliferae (III. 8). 1 W. Eur.
Pseudorobanche Rouy (*Alectra* p.p.). Scrophular. (III. 2). 1 S. Afr.
Pseudosarcolobus Costantin. Asclepiadaceae (II. 3). 1 Indochina.
Pseudosassafras Lecomte. Lauraceae (I). 1 China.
Pseudosciadium Baill. Araliaceae (3). 1 New Caled.
Pseudoseris Baill. (*Gerbera* p.p. *EP.*). Compositae (12). 2 Madag.
Pseudosmodingium Engl. Anacardiaceae (3). 3 Mexico.
Pseudosopubia Engl. (*Sopubia* p.p.). Scrophul. (III. 2). 5 trop. Afr.
Pseudospondias Engl. Anacardiaceae (2). 2 W. and C. trop. Afr.
Pseudostachyum Munro. Gramineae (13). 1 Himalaya.
Pseudostenosiphonium Lindau (*Strobilanthes* p.p.). Acanthaceae (IV. A). 5 Ceylon.
Pseudostonium O. Ktze. = Pseudostenosiphonium Lindau (Acan.).
Pseudostreblus Bur. in DC. Moraceae (I). 2 Indomal.
Pseudostriga Bonati. Scrophulariaceae (III. 2). 1 Cambodia.
Pseudotaenidia Mackenzie. Umbelliferae (III. 6). 1 N. Am.
Pseudotragia Pax. Euphorbiaceae (A. II. 2). 2 S.W. Afr.
Pseudotrophis Warburg. Moraceae (I). 2 New Guinea, Phil. Is.
Pseudotsuga Carr. (*Tsuga* Carr. p.p. *BH.*). Coniferae (Pinaceae, 15; see C. for gen. char.). 3 W. N. Am., E. As., incl. *P. Douglasii* Carr. (*P. mucronata* Sudw.), the Douglas fir of W. N. Am., useful for masts, &c.
Pseudoxalis Rose (*Oxalis* p.p.). Oxalidaceae. 1 Mexico.
Psiadia Jacq. Compositae (3). 35 Arabia, Afr., Madag.
Psidiastrum Bello. (*Eugenia* p.p. *EP.*). Myrtaceae (I). 1 Porto Rico.

Psidiopsis Berg. Myrtaceae (I). 1 Venezuela. Ed. fr.
Psidium L. Myrtaceae (I). 110 trop. Am., W.I. Many yield ed. fr., *e.g. P. Guajava* L., the guava.
Psila Phil. Compositae (4). 1 Chili.
Psilactis A. Gray. Compositae (3). 3 Mexico.
Psilanthele Lindau. Acanthaceae (IV. B). 3 trop. S. Am., Jamaica.
Psilanthus Hook. f. Rubiaceae (II. 4). 2 trop. W. Afr.
Psilium (Cl.), a prairie formation.
Psilobium Jack. Rubiaceae (I. 7). 2 Sumatra.
Psilocarphus Nutt. Compositae (4). 4 W. U.S., Chili.
Psilocarya Torr. (*Ryncospora BH.*). Cyperaceae (I). 6 Am., Austr.
Psilochilus Rodr. (*Cleistes* p.p. *EP.*). Orchid. (II. 2). 1 Brazil.
Psilonema C. A. Mey. = Alyssum L. (Crucif.).
Psilopeganum Hemsley. Rutaceae (I). 1 C. China.
Psilostachys Hochst. (*Psilotrichium EP.*). Amarant. (2). 4 trop. | *.
Psilostrophe DC. (*Riddellia* Nutt.). Compositae (6). 6 S.W. U.S.
Psilotaceae. Psilotales. Two gen. (Psilotum, Tmesipteris) with 4 sp. trop. and subtrop. The mature sporophyte has no roots, their functions being performed by the branched rhiz. The aerial branches bear only scale-l. in Psilotum. The sporangia are 2- or 3-loc., borne on small two-lobed sporophylls. "There has been much disagreement as to the morphological nature of the sporangiophores of the Psilotaceae. The two chief views are the following: (1) that the whole sporangiophore is a single foliar member; (2) that it is a reduced axis bearing a terminal synangium and two l. The recent very careful researches of Bower upon the origin of the sporangiophore and synangium confirm the former view" (Campbell; see also Bower in *Phil. Trans.* CLXXXV, 1894, p. 473).

"The fully-developed synangium (2-loc. in Tmesipteris, 3-loc. in Psilotum) has the outer walls of the loculi composed of a superficial layer of large cells, beneath which are several layers of smaller ones. The cells composing the septa are narrow tabular ones; occasionally the septum is partially absent....Bower regards the whole synangium as homologous with the single sporangium of Lycopodium" (Campbell). For prothallus see *Trans. R. S. Edinb.* 1918 (2 papers), *Phil. Trans.* B, 213, 1925.
Psilotales. The 5th class of Pteridophyta.
Psilotrichum Blume. Amarantaceae (2). 15 palaeotrop.
Psilotum Sw. Psilotaceae. 3 warm. They are probably ± saprophytic in their habit, and have neither roots nor green l., but only green stems. See fam. for details of sporangia, &c. Veg. repr. is common, small gemmae being formed upon the rhiz. At first no structural differentiation is visible in these, but apical cells are formed later.
Psiloxylon Thou. ex Tul. (*Fropiera BH.*). Flacourt. (inc. sed.). 1 Masc.
Psilurus Trin. Gramineae (12). 1 S. Eur. to Afghanistan.
Psittacanthus Mart. (*Loranthus* p.p. *BH.*). Loranthaceae (I). 50 trop. Am.
Psophocarpus Neck. Leguminosae (III. 10). 5 palaeotrop. *P. tetragonolobus* DC. and others cult. ed. pods.
Psoralea L. Leguminosae (III. 6). 100 trop. and subtrop. *P. esculenta* Pursh (N. Am. prairie turnip) has ed. tuberous root.

Psorospermum Spach. Guttiferae (II). 20 trop. Afr., Madag.
Psychine Desf. Cruciferae (2). 1 N. Afr.
Psychotria L. (excl. *Mapourea* Aubl.). Rubiaceae (II. 5). 500 warm. Some heterostyled. Many have infl.-axis brightly coloured. [For *P. Ipecacuanha* Stokes see Uragoga.]
Psychrobatia Greene (*Rubus* p.p.). Rosaceae (III. 2). 1 N.W. Am.
Psychrogeton Boiss. (*Aster* p.p. *BH.*). Compositae (3). 1 Afghanistan.
Psychrophyton Beauverd (*Raoulia* p.p.). Compositae (4). 9 N.Z.
Psyllium Tourn. ex Juss. = Plantago L. p.p. (Plantag.).
Psyllocarpus Mart. Rubiaceae (II. 10). 5 Brazil.
Psyllothamnus Oliv. Caryophyllaceae (I. 4). 1 Aden.
Ptaeroxylon Eckl. et Zeyh. Meliaceae (I) (Sapind. *BH.*). 1 S. Afr., *P. utile* E. et Z. (sneezewood, cape mahogany), timber.
Ptarmica (Tourn.) Neck. = Achillea L. p.p. (Comp.).
Ptelea L. Rutaceae (IV). 6 N. Am. *P. trifoliata* L. cult. orn. shrub (shrubby trefoil). Fls. monoec. Fr. winged (*cf.* Ulmus).
Pteleocarpa Oliv. Boragin. (II) (Olacin. *BH.*). 2 Malay Pen., Borneo.
Ptelidium Thou. Celastraceae. 1 Madag.
Pteleopsis Engl. Combretaceae. 4 E. trop. Afr.
Pteralyxia K. Schum. (*Vallesia* p.p.). Apocyn. (I. 3). 1 Hawaiian Is.
Pterandra A. Juss. Malpighiaceae (II). 1 Brazil.
Pteranthus Forsk. Caryophyllaceae (I. 7). 1 Medit.
Pterichis Lindl. Orchidaceae (II. 2). 6 trop. S. Am.
Pteridium Gled. 1 cosmop., *P. aquilinum* Kuhn, the bracken. It has a creeping rhiz., bearing 2 ranks of l. At the base of the l. is a nectary, which ants visit. The sori are confluent along the l. margin, which is curved over them, while there is also a true indusium on the inner side of the sori (the char. of distinction from Pteris, in which the bracken used to be placed). Adv. buds appear on the back of the l. stalk, near the base.
Pteridocalyx Wernham. Rubiaceae (I. 3). 2 Brit. Guiana.
Pteridophyllum Sieb. et Zucc. Papaveraceae (I). 1 Japan.
Pteridophyta. Vascular Cryptogams, one of the four chief divisions of the Vegetable Kingdom. They have a well marked alternation of generations, the gametophyte (oophyte or sexual generation) being insignificant in size compared to the sporophyte (asexual generation), but still capable of independent growth. The life history of a typical Pteridophyte may be shown diagrammatically as follows, taking the fern as an example:

Fern-plant → sporophylls → sporangia → spores
↑ ↓
fertilised ovum ← {spermatozoid ← antheridia; ovum ← archegonia} ← prothallus.

The 'plant' or asexual generation alternates with the prothallus or sexual generation. In many P. there are ♂ and ♀ prothalli. The prothallus corresponds to the 'plant' in a moss or liverwort, whilst the sporogonium of these latter = 'plant' in a fern or lycopod.

The plant itself takes various forms in the different groups. Except in tree ferns and in fossil forms it does not attain great size. There is an erect stem in many ferns, &c.; others have creeping stems (*e.g.* Lycopodium and Selaginella), rhiz. (many Ferns), or floating stems (Hydropterideae). The l. are simple, except in many ferns. There is no primary tap-root, but roots are formed as required from the stem or l. Internally there are well marked vascular bundles in both stem and leaf, and many anatomical features of flg. pl. may be found here also.

The sporangia arise upon the l., either on the ordinary foliage as in most ferns, or on specially differentiated l. as in Osmunda, Equisetum, Lycopodiales, Hydropteridineae, &c. They may be sol. or in groups (*sori*); in the latter case often protected by a special outgrowth of the l., the *indusium*. The spores are formed by a complicated process from a single cell or row or layer of cells—the *archesporium*—inside the sporangium: each has a thick waterproof outside wall. The spores may be of one kind only, in which case the plant is termed *homo-* or *iso-sporous*, or of two kinds (*heterosporous*), when the smaller spore is termed the *microspore*, the larger the *mega-* or *macro-spore*; the former gives rise to a ♂ prothallus, the latter to a ♀.

Falling upon the soil (or into the water, in the case of the Hydropteridineae) the spores germinate under suitable conditions, giving rise to the *sexual* plants or *prothalli*. The prothallus is a small body without distinction into stem and l.; it absorbs materials from the soil (usually by rhizoids) and, being green, assimilates in the ordinary way. It bears the sexual organs—*antheridia* (♂) and *archegonia* (♀). In the homosporous forms these are both found on the same prothallus, except in Equisetum, where, though the spores are absolutely similar so far as we can tell, there are separate ♂ and ♀ prothalli, as in the heterosporous forms. In the antheridia are developed the motile ♂ cells or *spermatozoids*. Fert. takes place by aid of water. The mucilage contained in the neck of the archegonium is attractive to the spermatozoids, which swim up the neck of the archegonium. One of them finally fuses with the ovum or ♀ cell at the base of the archegonium, and the fertilised ovum (*zygote*) then develops into a new 'plant' or asexual generation, being nourished by the prothallus until it can assimilate for itself.

Classification (after Engler):

I. *Filicales*. L. usu. more strongly developed than stem, often big and much branched, usu. circinate in vernation. Sporangia on normal or special l., on edge or lower side, usu. in sori. Spermatozoid polyciliate.

1. Filicales Leptosporangiatae.
2. Marattiales.
3. Ophioglossales.

[II. *Sphenophyllales*. Fossil plants only.]

III. *Equisetales*. Homosporous (some fossils heterosporous), with dioec. prothalli. Stem much branched with jointed internodes and small sheathing whorls of l. (not green). Sporangia on peltate sporangiophores, forming a term. spike. Spermatozoids polyciliate.

IV. *Lycopodiales*. Homosporous or heterosporous; in the latter case the ♀ prothallus remains enclosed in the spore till fert. Stem simple or branched; l. many, small, usu. alt., entire.

Sporangia singly on upper side of leaf-bases, or in their axils. Spermatozoids biciliate.

1. Lycopodiales eligulatae.
2. Lycopodiales ligulatae.

V. *Psilotales*. Sporophylls bipartite. Sporangia 2—3-loc. Spermatozoids biciliate.

VI. *Isoetales*. Stem short, growing in thickness, with numerous long l. with ligula over a basal groove, in which is a sporangium; megaspores on outer sporophylls, microspores on inner. Spermatozoids polyciliate.

[VII. *Cycadofilices*. Fossil plants only.]

Pterigeron A. Gray. Compositae (4). 7 Austr.

Pterigostachyum Nees ex Steud. (*Dimeria* R. Br.). Gram. (2). 12 S.E. As.

Pteris L. Polypodiaceae. 160 cosmop. [For *P. aquilina* L., the bracken, see Pteridium.] Apogamy occurs in *P. cretica* L. (see Filicales Leptosporangiatae).

Pterisanthes Blume. Vitaceae. 12 trop. As.

Pternandra Jack. Melastomaceae (II). 12 Malaya. Berry. Calyptra 0.

Pternopetalum Franch. Umbelliferae (III. 5). 1 Tibet.

Ptero- (Gr. pref.), wing.

Pterocactus K. Schum. Cactaceae (II). 4 Argentina.

Pterocarpus L. Leguminosae (III. 8). 24 trop. Fruit winged. Several, esp. *P. Marsupium* Roxb., furnish kino, an astringent resin. *P. santalinus* L. f. yields red sandal-wood.

Pterocarya Kunth. Juglandaceae. 4 N. temp. |✻.

Pterocaulon Ell. Compositae (4). 15 Argentina to Texas.

Pterocelastrus Meissn. Celastraceae. 7 Cape Colony.

Pteroceltis Maxim. Ulmaceae. 1 N. China.

Pterocephalus Vaill. ex Adans. (*Scabiosa* p.p. *BH.*). Dipsacaceae. 20 Medit., Indomal., trop. Afr.

Pterochrosia Baill. Apocynaceae (I. 3). 3 New Caled.

Pterocladon Hook. f. Melastomaceae (I). 1 Peru.

Pterococcus Pall. = Calligonum L. p.p. (Polygon.).

Pterocoelion Turcz. Tiliaceae (inc. sed.). 1 Java.

Pterocymbium R. Br. (*Sterculia* p.p. *BH.*). Stercul. 2 Burma, Malaya.

Pterodiscus Hook. Pedaliaceae. 10 S. and trop. Afr.

Pterodon Vog. Leguminosae (III. 8). 4 Brazil, Bolivia.

Pterogastra Naud. Melastomaceae (I). 3 N. trop. S. Am.

Pteroglossaspis Reichb. f. Orchidaceae (II. 10). 3 E. trop. Afr.

Pterogonium Fee. Polypodiaceae. 2 Guiana.

Pterogyne Tul. Leguminosae (II. 2). 1 Brazil.

Pterolepis Miq. Melastomaceae (I). 30 trop. Am.

Pterolobium R. Br. (*Cantuffa* *EP.*). Leguminosae (II. 7). 5 palaeo trop.

Pteronema Pierre. Simarubaceae. 1 Burma.

Pteroneurum DC. = Cardamine Tourn. p.p. (Crucif.).

Pteronia L. Compositae (3). 60 S. Afr.

Pteropetalum Pax (*Euadenia* p.p. *EP.*). Capparid. (II). 1 Togoland.

Pteropogon DC. = Helipterum DC. p.p. (Comp.).

Pteropyrum Jaub. et Spach. Polygonaceae (II. 1). 5 S.W. As.

Pterorhachis Harms. Meliaceae (III). 1 Cameroons.
Pteroscleria Nees. Cyperaceae (II). 3 trop. Am., W.I.
Pterosicyos T. S. Brandegee. Cucurbitaceae (4). 1 Mexico.
Pterospermum Schreb. Sterculiaceae. 20 trop. As.
Pterospora Nutt. Pyrolaceae. 1 N. Am.
Pterostegia Fisch. et Mey. Polygonaceae (I. 1). 1 California.
Pterostemma Kränzl. Orchidaceae (II. 19). 1 Colombia.
Pterostemon Schau. Saxifragaceae (IV). 1 Mexico.
Pterostigma Benth. = Adenosma R. Br. p.p. (Scroph.).
Pterostylis R. Br. Orchidaceae (II. 2). 45 Austr., N.Z., New Caled. The median sepal, with the petals, forms a hood over the rest of the fl. The flap of the labellum hangs out below and is irritable. If an insect land on it, it instantly moves up and imprisons the visitor against the column; the only mode of escape is by squeezing past the stigma and anther. After half-an-hour the lip goes down again and is ready for another capture (Darwin, *Orchids*, p. 86).
Pterostyrax Sieb. et Zucc. (*Halesia* p.p.). Styrac. 3 Japan, China.
Pterotaberna Stapf (*Tabernaemontana* p.p.). Apocyn. (I. 3). 1 W. Afr.
Pterotheca Cass. Compositae (13). 10 Medit., C. As.
Pterothrix DC. Compositae (4). 3 Cape Colony.
Pterotropia Hillebrand. Araliaceae (1). 3 Hawaiian Is.
Pterotum Lour. Inc. sed. 1 Cochinchina.
Pteroxygonum Dammer et Diels. Polygonaceae (II. 2). 1 China.
Pterygiella Oliv. Scrophulariaceae (III. 3). 2 China.
Pterygodium Sw. Orchidaceae (II. 1). 15 S. Afr.
Pterygopappus Hook. f. Compositae (4). 1 Tasmania.
Pterygopodium Harms. Leguminosae (III. 8). 1 Cameroons.
Pterygota Schott. et Endl. (*Sterculia* p.p. *BH.*). Stercul. 4 trop. |✻.
Pteryxia Nutt. (*Cymopterus* p.p.). Umbelliferae (III. 5). 7 N. Am.
Ptilimnium Rafin. (*Discopleura* p.p.). Umbell. (III. 5). 3 N. Am.
Ptilocalais A. Gray, Greene (*Microseris* p.p.). Comp. (13). 1 N. Am.
Ptilochaeta Turcz. Malpighiaceae (1). 3 Brazil, Argentina.
Ptilotrichum C. A. Mey. (*Alyssum* p.p. *BH.*). Cruciferae (4). 10 Medit.
Ptilotus R. Br. Amarantaceae (2). 60 Austr.
Ptychandra Scheff. Palmae (IV. 1). 2 Moluccas.
Ptychanthera Decne. Asclepiadaceae (II. 4). 1 S. Domingo.
Ptychococcus Becc. Palmae (IV. 1). 3 New Guinea, Moluccas.
Ptychogyne Pfitz. (*Panisea* p.p.). Orchid. (II. 3). 2 Mal. Pen., Java.
Ptychomeria Benth. = Gymnosiphon Blume (Burmann).
Ptychopetalum Benth. Olacaceae. 6 trop. Am., W. Afr.
Ptychopyxis Miq. Euphorbiaceae (inc. sed.). 1 Malaya.
Ptychoraphis Becc. Palmae (IV. 1). 3 Malaya.
Ptychosema Benth. Leguminosae (III. 6). 1 W. Austr.
Ptychosperma Labill. Palmae (IV. 1). 15 E. Indomal. Fls. in threes, 2 ♂ and 1 ♀. *P.* (*Seaforthia*) *elegans* Blume cult. orn.
Ptychotis Koch (*Carum* p.p. *BH.*). Umbelliferae (III. 5). 6 Eur., Afr.
Ptyssiglottis T. Anders. Acanthaceae (IV. B). 5 Indomal.
Puberulous, minutely pubescent.
Pubescent, covered with fine soft hairs, downy.
Puccinia, *cf. Malva*.

Puccoon (Am.), *Lithospermum*, *Sanguinaria*; **yellow -**, *Hydrastis*.
Pudding-pipe tree, *Cassia*.
Puelia Franch. Gramineae (13). 4 W. trop. Afr.
Pueraria DC. Leguminosae (III. 10). 15 trop. As. to Japan. Fibre.
Pugionium Gaertn. Cruciferae (4). 2 Mongolia.
Pugiopappus A. Gray (*Leptosyne BH.*, *Coreopsis* p.p. *EP.*). Compositae (5). 3 California.
Pulchellus (Lat.), beautiful.
Pulicaria Gaertn. Compositae (4). 30 Eur., As., Afr. *P. dysenterica* Gaertn. (*Inula dysenterica* L.) in Brit. (flea-bane).
Pullea Schlechter. Cunoniaceae. 2 New Guinea.
Pulmonaria (Tourn.) L. Boraginaceae (IV. 3). 10 Eur. *P. officinalis* L. (lung-wort, formerly officinal) and *P. angustifolia* L. in Brit. Both have dimorphic heterostyled fls. which change from red to blue as they grow older (see fam.).
Pulque, *Agave*.
Pulsatilla (Tourn.) L. = Anemone Tourn. p.p. (Ranunc.).
Pultenaea Sm. Leguminosae (III. 2). 80 Austr.
Pulvinaria Fourn. Asclepiadaceae (II. 1). 1 Brazil.
Pulvinate, cushion-shaped.
Pulvinus, a swollen joint, often concerned in movement, *Galeopsis*, *Marantaceae*, *Mimosa*, *Neptunia*.
Pumelo, *Citrus decumana* Murr.
Pumilus (Lat.), low, small.
Pumpkin, *Cucurbita Pepo* L.
Punctate, dotted.
Punctum vegetationis (Lat.), growing point.
Pungens (Lat.), sharp-pointed.
Punica (Tourn.) L. Punicaceae (only genus). 2, one in Socotra, the other, *P. Granatum* L., the pomegranate, from the Balkans to the Himalayas, and cult. The young twigs have four wings, composed simply of epidermis and cortical parenchyma; these are early thrown off. The fl. is ☿, reg., perig. K 5—8, valvate; C 5—8, imbr.; A ∞; G adnate to receptacle. The mature ovary has a peculiar structure, due to a development like that in Mesembryanthemum. Two whorls of cpls. with basal plac. are laid down, and then a peripheral growth tilts them up from ||•|| to =•= so that two layers of loculi are formed and the placentation appears to be parietal. Ovules ∞, anatr. The arrangement is also seen in the fr., commonly termed a berry, but not strictly so. The pericarp (axial in part) is leathery, and the fleshy inner part round the seeds is really the outer layers of the seed coats. No endosp.
Punicaceae (*EP.*; *Lythraceae* p.p. *BH.*). Dicots. (Archichl. Myrtiflorae). Only genus Punica (*q.v.*).
Puniceus (Lat.), bright carmine.
Pupalia Juss. Amarantaceae (2). 7 Afr., Madag., As.
Pupunha palm, *Bactris*.
Purdiaea Planch. (*Costaea EP.*). Cyrillaceae. 5 Cuba, Colombia.
Purdieanthus Gilg. Gentianaceae (I). 1 Colombia.
Purging buckthorn, *Rhamnus cathartica* L.; **-cassia**, *Cassia Fistula* L.; **-flax**, *Linum catharticum* L.

Purgosea Haw. = Crassula L. (Crassul.).
Purple heart (W.I.), *Copaifera*; **- lip** (W.I.), *Vanilla*; **- loosestrife**, *Lythrum Salicaria* L.; **- top** (Austr.), *Verbena*.
Purpurella Naud. (*Tibouchina BH.*). Melastomaceae (8). 12 trop. S. Am.
Purpureus (Lat.), purple.
Purpusia T. S. Brandegee. Rosaceae (III. 2). 1 N. Am.
Purshia DC. Rosaceae (III. 3). 1 Pac. U.S.
Purslane, *Portulaca*; **sea -**, *Arenaria peploides* L.
Pusaetha L. (*Entada* Adans.). Leguminosae (I. 5). 12 trop.
Puschkinia Adams. Liliaceae (V). 2 W. As. Cult. orn. fl.
Pusillus (Lat.), small, weak, slender.
Pustule, a pimple or blister.
Putamen, the stone of a drupe.
Putoria Pers. Rubiaceae (II. 7). 3 Medit.
Putranjiva Wall. Euphorbiaceae (A. I. 1). 4 Indomal.
Putterlickia Endl. Celastraceae. 2 Cape Colony.
Puya Molina. Bromeliaceae (2). 25 Andes. Some 3 m. high, thick stem.
Pycnandra Benth. Sapotaceae (I). 1 New Caled.
Pycnanthemum Michx. Labiatae (VI). 15 N. Am.
Pycnanthus Warb. (*Myristica* p.p.). Myristicaceae. 5 trop. Afr.
Pycnarrhena Miers. Menispermaceae. 20 E. Indomal.
Pycnobotrya Benth. Apocynaceae (II. 1). 1 Gaboon.
Pycnobregma Baill. Asclepiadaceae (II. 4). 1 Colombia.
Pycnocoma Benth. Euphorbiaceae (A. II. 2). 12 trop. Afr., Masc.
Pycnocomon Hoffmgg. et Link (*Scabiosa* p.p. *BH.*). Dipsac. 2 Medit.
Pycnocycla Lindl. Umbelliferae (III. 1). 7 Abyssinia to N.W. India.
Pycnoneurum Decne. Asclepiadaceae (II. 1). 2 Madag.
Pycnophyllum Remy. Caryophyllaceae (I. 3). 8 Andes.
Pycnorhachis Benth. Asclepiadaceae (II. 3). 1 Malay Peninsula.
Pycnosphaera Gilg (*Faroa* p.p.). Gentianaceae (I). 2 trop. Afr.
Pycnospora R. Br. ex Wight et Arn. Legumin. (III. 7). 1 trop. As., Austr.
Pycnostachys Hook. Labiatae (VII). 15 trop. and S. Afr., Madag.
Pycnostelma Bunge ex Decne. Asclepiadaceae (II. 1). 2 China.
Pycnostylis Pierre. Menispermaceae. 2 E. trop. Afr., Madag.
Pycnothymus Small (*Satureia* p.p.). Labiatae (VI). 1 N. Am.
Pycreus Beauv. (*Cyperus* p.p. *EP.*). Cyperaceae (I). 100 cosmop.
Pygeum Gaertn. Rosaceae (V). 20 palaeotrop.
Pygmaeopremna Merrill. Verbenaceae (4). 1 Luzon.
Pygmaeus (Lat.), dwarf.
Pynaertia De Wild. Meliaceae (III). 1 Congo.
Pyramia Cham. Melastomaceae (I). 3 S. Brazil.
Pyramidium Boiss. Cruciferae (4). 1 Afghanistan.
Pyramidocarpus Oliv. Flacourtiaceae (1). 1 W. trop. Afr.
Pyramidoptera Boiss. Umbelliferae (III. 5). 1 Afghanistan.
Pyramidostylium Mart. = Salacia L. (Hippocrat.).
Pyrecnia Nor. Inc. sed. Nomen.
Pyrenacantha Wight. Icacinaceae. 10 S. and trop. Afr., W. As.
Pyrenaria Blume. Theaceae. 11 Indomal.

Pyrene, a single stone of a drupe.

Pyrethrum Hall. = Chrysanthemum Tourn. (Comp.).

Pyriform, pear-shaped.

Pyrola (Tourn.) L. (incl. *Moneses* Salisb.). Pyrolaceae. 15 N. temp. (5 Brit., wintergreen). Evergreens with creeping stocks. *P.* (*Moneses*) *uniflora* L. has adv. buds on the roots, and a solitary term. fl. The fls. of *P. minor* L. are in racemes, pend., without discs. There is no honey; the stigma projects beyond the anthers, but pollen may at last fall upon it from them. *P. rotundifolia* L. is similar. The seeds of P. are very light and are distr. by wind.

Pyrolaceae (*EP.*; *Ericaceae* p.p., *Monotropeae BH.*). Dicots. (Sympet. Ericales). 10 gen., 30 sp., cold N. temp. and arctic. The two Brit. genera represent the two types of habit found in the order—evergreen plants with sympodial growth from rhiz. (Pyrola), and saprophytes (Monotropa). The infl. is term.; it may be a true raceme (Pyrola), or a cyme, leafless or with scaly bracts. Fl. ☿ actinom. K 4—5; C (4—5) or 4—5; A 8—10, obdiplost.; $\underline{G}$ (4—5). The petals and sta. are often at the edge of a nectariferous disc. Anthers intr., opening by apical pores or transv. valves; pollen simple or in tetrads. Cpls. opp. petals; ovary imperfectly 4—5-loc. Style simple; ovules minute, ∞, anatr., on thick fleshy plac. Capsule. Seeds ∞, small, in loose testa. Embryo of few cells, without differentiation of cotyledons. *Chief genera:* Pyrola, Chimaphila, Monotropa, Sarcodes. *BH.* unite Pyrola and the green-leaved forms to Ericaceae, making a fam. Monotropeae for the saprophytes.

Pyronia × Veitch. Rosaceae. Hybrid, Pyrus-Cydonia (pear and quince). See *Journ. of Hered.* 1916, p. 416.

Pyrostegia C. Presl (*Bignonia* p.p. *BH.*). Bignon. (1). 10 S. Am.

Pyrostria Comm. ex Juss. Rubiaceae (II. 1). 8 Mauritius, Rodrigues.

Pyrrhopappus DC. (*Sitilias* Rafin.). Compositae (13). 6 N. Am.

Pyrrocoma Hook. (*Aplopappus* Cass.). Compositae (3). 20 N. Am.

Pyrularia Michx. Santalaceae. 2 N. Am., Himalaya.

Pyrus (Tourn.) L. (*BH.* incl. *Cydonia*, *Mespilus*). Rosaceae (II). 65 N. temp.; 6 in Brit., incl. *P. Aucuparia* Ehrh., the rowan or mountain ash, *P. Malus* L. the apple, &c. The recept. is hollowed out and united to the syncarpous ovary. The fls. are protogynous, and are visited by bees and many other insects. Several var. of pear (*P. communis* L.) are self-sterile. After fert. the fr. becomes a large fleshy pseudocarp (*pome*), the flesh consisting of the enlarged recept., while the gynaeceum forms the core. Several are cultivated for their fruit, *e.g. P. Malus* L. (apple), *P. communis* L. (pear), *P. germanica* Hook. f. (medlar). *P. japonica* Thunb. is often grown upon walls.

Pyxidanthera Michx. Diapensiaceae. 1 E. U.S.

Pyxidanthus Naud. (*Blakea BH.*). Melastomaceae (I). 3 N. trop. S. Am.

Pyxis, capsule opening by a lid that splits off, *Anagallis*.

Quadrania Nor. Inc. sed. Nomen.

Quadrasia Elmer. Flacourtiaceae (4). 1 Phil. Is.

Quadri- (Lat. pref.), four.

Quaternate, arranged in fours.

Quake-grass, *Briza*.

Qualea Aubl. Vochysiaceae. 32 trop. Am. G; plac. not thickened.
Quamash, *Camassia*.
Quamoclidion Choisy (*Mirabilis* p.p.). Nyctaginaceae. 4 N. Am.
Quamoclit Tourn. ex Moench (*Ipomoea* p.p. *BH.*). Convolvulaceae (I). 12 trop. Am. Cult. orn. fl.
Quapoya Aubl. (*Clusia* p.p. *BH.*). Guttiferae (IV). 3 Guiana, Peru.
Quaqua N.E. Br. (*Caralluma EP.*). Asclepiadaceae (II. 3). 1 S. Afr.
Quaquaversal, bending every way.
Quararibea Aubl. Bombacaceae. 7 warm Am.
Quartinia Endl. (*Rotala* p.p. *EP.*). Lythraceae. 1 Abyssinia.
Quassia L. Simarubaceae. 2 N.E. Brazil, W. Afr., *Q. amara* L. (Am.) is the source of quassia wood.
Quassia bark, *Picraena*, *Quassia*; **-wood**, *Quassia*.
Quebec oak, *Quercus alba* L.
Quebrachia Griseb. (*Schinopsis EP.*). Anacardiaceae (3). 5 S. Am
Quebracho, *Schinopsis*, *Aspidosperma*.
Queen-of-the-meadow, *Ulmaria Spiraea-Ulmaria* Hill.
Queensland nut, *Macadamia ternifolia* F. Muell.
Quekettia Lindl. Orchidaceae (II. 19). 3 Brazil.
Quelchia N.E. Br. Compositae (12). 1 Roraima (Brit. Guiana).
Queltia Salisb. = Narcissus Tourn. p.p. (Amaryll.).
Quercitron bark, *Quercus tinctoria* Bartr.
Quercus (Tourn.) L. (*BH.* incl. *Pasania* Oerst.). Fagaceae. 300 N. temp., Indomal., Pacific coasts, &c. The oaks are evergreen or deciduous trees, in the latter case esp. with well-developed winter buds. The cupule contains 1 ♀ fl. only (see fam.), and forms the acorn-cup at the base of the nut in fr. The ♂ fls. are sol. in pend. catkins. Anemoph. Many are important economic plants. Among the most noteworthy are: *Q. Aegilops* L. (E. Eur., W. As.), whose cupules and unripe acorns, known as valonia, are used in tanning, *Q. alba* L. (N. Am.), the white or Quebec oak (timber), *Q. Cerris* L. (Eur., W. As.), the Turkey oak (timber), *Q. Ilex* L. (Medit.), the holly oak (timber, bark for tanning), *Q. Robur* L. (Eur., W. As.), the British oak (it has two forms, *sessiliflora* Salisb., and *pedunculata* Ehrh.), yielding timber and tan bark, *Q. Suber* L. (Medit.), the cork oak, whose bark, stripped off in thick layers and flattened, forms ordinary cork, *Q. tinctoria* Bartr. (N. Am.), whose bark (quercitron bark) forms a yellow dye, and many others.
Queria Loefl. Caryophyllaceae (I. 1). 1 Medit.
Quesnelia Gaudich. Bromeliaceae (4). 6 S. Am.
Queteletia Blume (*Physurus* p.p. *BH.*). Orchidaceae (II. 2). 1 Java.
Quickset thorn, *Crataegus Oxyacantha* L.
Quiina Aubl. Quiinaceae. 18 trop. S. Am.
Quiinaceae (*EP.*; Guttiferae p.p. *BH.*). Dicots. (Archichl. Parietales). 2 gen., 20 sp., trop. S. Am. Shrubs and trees with evergr. stip. l. and small fls. in racemes or panicles, reg., ☿ or ♂ ♀. K, C 4—5, A 15—30, G (2—3) or (7) each with 2 axile ovules, and separate styles. Berry valvate with felted seeds.
Quill-wort, *Isoetes*.
Quillaja Molina. Rosaceae (I. 2). 3 temp. S. Am. *Q. Saponaria* Molina is the soap-tree of Chili; the powdered bark lathers with water.

Quinaria Rafin. (*Vitis* p.p. *BH.*, *Parthenocissus EP.*). Vitaceae. 10 temp. As., Am.
Quinary, in fives.
Quince, *Cydonia vulgaris* Pers.; **Bengal -**, *Aegle Marmelos* Corr.
Quinchamalium Juss. Santalaceae. 20 Andes.
Quincuncial, see Aestivation.
Quinetia Cass. Compositae (4). 1 W. Austr.
Quinine, *Cinchona*, *Remijia*.
Quinoa, *Chenopodium Quinoa* Willd.
Quinque- (Lat. pref.), five.
Quintinia A. DC. Saxifragaceae (v). 5 Phil. Is. to N.Z.
Quisqualis L. Combretaceae. 4 trop. Afr., As. *Q. indica* L. is erect below, ± twining above, with alt. l. Fl. shoots with opp. l.
Quivisia Comm. ex Juss. Meliaceae (III). 1 Madag., Mascarenes.
Quivisiantha Baill. Meliaceae (III). 1 Madag.
Racaria Aubl. (*Talisia* p.p. *EP.*). Sapindaceae (I). 1 Guiana.
Raceme, an infl. with main stem that grows steadily onwards, bearing fls. on lat. branches in acropetal succession, *Cruciferae*, *Ribes*; **racemose**, of racemes or of raceme type.
Rachicallis DC. Rubiaceae (I. 3). 1 W.I.
Rachis, the stalk of a cpd. l.
Racletia Adans. Inc. sed. Nomen.
Radackia Cham. et Endl. Leguminosae (inc. sed.). 1 Radack I.
Radamaea Benth. Scrophulariaceae (III. 2). 2 Madag.
Raddia Spreng. = Salacia L. (Hippocrat.).
Radermachera Zoll. et Morr. Bignoniaceae (2). 8 Indomal.
Radial symmetry, where the organ, &c. is divisible into two complementary halves by any plane including the axis.
Radiate stigma, *Papaver*.
Radical (l.), apparently springing from the root, *Anemone*.
Radicans (Lat.), rooting.
Radicle, the rootlet starting from the embryo in the seed.
Radicula Dill. (*Nasturtium* p.p.). Cruciferae (2). 20 N. Am.
Radinocion Ridl. (*Angraecum* p.p. *EP.*). Orchid. (II. 20). 1 S. Thomas.
Radiola (Dill.) Roth. Linaceae. 1 Eur. (incl. Brit.), N. Afr., temp. As., *R. linoides* Roth (all-seed). Infl. a dichasial cyme.
Radish, *Raphanus sativus* L.; **horse -**, *Cochlearia Armoracia* L.; **Japanese -**, or Daikon, *Raphanus sativus* L. (?).
Radix Columba, *Jateorhiza*; **- Pareirae bravae**, *Chondodendron*.
Radlkofera Gilg. Sapindaceae (I). 1 Cameroons.
Radlkoferella Pierre (*Lucuma* p.p.). Sapotaceae (I). 5 W.I.
Raffenaldia Godr. (*Cossonia* p.p. *EP.*). Cruciferae (2). 1 Algeria.
Rafflesia R. Br. Rafflesiaceae. 6 Malaya; parasitic on Vitis roots. *R. Arnoldi* R. Br. has a colossal fl. 18 in. across and weighing 15 lbs. It smells like putrid meat, and is visited by carrion flies.
Rafflesiaceae (*EP.*; *Cytinaceae* p.p. *BH.*). Dicots. (Archichl. Aristolochiales). 7 gen., 22 sp., trop. Parasitic herbs, whose veg. organs are reduced to what is practically a *mycelium* like that of a true Fungus, viz. a network of fine cellular threads ramifying in the tissues of the host. The fls. appear above ground, developing as adv. shoots upon the mycelium. They are unisexual, sometimes of enormous

size, reg., haplochlam. P (4—5), A ∞ on a column, $\overline{G}$ (4—6—8), with parietal plac., or ∞ twisted loc. Berry. Endosp. *Chief genera:* Rafflesia, Brugmansia, Pilostyles, Cytinus.

Rafinesquia Nutt. Compositae (13). 2 W. U.S.

Rafnia Thunb. Leguminosae (III. 3). 22 S. Afr.

Ragala Pierre (*Ecclinusa* Mart.). Sapotaceae (I). 1 French Guiana.

Ragged robin, *Lychnis Flos-Cuculi* L.

Ragi (India), *Eleusine Coracana* Gaertn.

Ragweed (Am.), *Ambrosia*; **-wort**, *Senecio Jacobaea* L.

Raillardella Benth. Compositae (8). 5 Mts. of California.

Raillardia Gaudich. Compositae (5). 12 Hawaiian Is.

Raimannia Rose (*Oenothera* p.p.). Onagraceae (2). 12 N. Am.

Raimondia Safford. Anonaceae (4). 1 Colombia.

Rain tree, *Pithecolobium Saman* Benth., *Andira inermis* H. B. K.

Rainiera Greene (*Prenanthes* p.p.). Compositae (13). 1 N. Am.

Raisin, *Vitis vinifera* L., &c.

Rajania L. Dioscoreaceae. 20 W.I.

Ramatuela H. B. et K. Combretaceae. 2 trop. Am.

Rambong, *Ficus elastica* Roxb.

Rambutan, *Nephelium lappaceum* L.

Ramelia Baill. Euphorbiaceae (A. II. 2). 1 New Caledonia.

Ramenta, chaffy scales.

Rameya Baill. Menispermaceae. 2 Madag., Comoros.

Ramie, *Boehmeria nivea* Gaudich., var. *tenacissima*.

Ramirezella Rose (*Vigna* p.p.). Leguminosae (III. 10). 5 Mexico.

Ramisia Glaziou ex Baill. Nyctaginaceae. 1 Rio de Janeiro.

Ramona Greene (*Audibertia* Benth.). Labiatae (VI). 10 N. Am.

Ramondia Rich. Gesneriaceae (I). 4 Mts. of S. Eur. Fl. almost reg. with 5 sta. and rotate C.

Ramose, freely branching.

Ramosia Merrill. Gramineae (10). 1 Phil. Is.

Rampion, *Phyteuma*.

Ramsons, *Allium ursinum* L.

Ramsted (Am.), *Linaria vulgaris* Mill.

Ramtil (India), *Guizotia abyssinica* Cass.

Ranales. The 18th order (*EP.*) of Archichlamydeae. The first order (*BH.*) of Polypetalae. *Cf.* pp. xvi, l.

Ranalisma Stapf. Alismaceae. 1 Selangor.

Randia Houst. ex L. Rubiaceae (I. 8). 125 trop. The two l. at a node are often unequal and one frequently aborts early. Thorns often occur. In *R. dumetorum* Lam. the thorn arises in the axil above the bud, and is carried up by intercalary growth.

Randonia Coss. Resedaceae. 1 Algeria.

Ranevea L. H. Bailey (*Ravenea* H. Wendl.). Palmae (IV. 1). 1 Comoros.

Ranunculaceae (*EP.*, *BH.*). Dicots. (Archichl. Ranales). 40 gen., 700 sp., chiefly N. temp. and well repres. in Brit. Most are herbaceous perennials with rhiz., usually of condensed (root-stock) form, and always sympodial. Each year's shoot ends in an infl. and a bud is formed in the axil of one of the l. at the base, which forms the next year's growth. In most the primary root soon dies away, and adv.

roots are formed from the stem; often (*e.g.* Aconitum, Ranunculus sp.) these swell up into tubers holding reserve materials. L. exstip., usu. alt., with sheathing bases and often very much divided. The chief exceptions to the above general statements, and special cases of interest, are described under the genera, *e.g.* Helleborus, Eranthis, Clematis, Ranunculus.

The infl. is typically determinate; in Anemone sp., Eranthis, &c., a single term. fl. is produced. More often a cymose branching occurs, the buds in the axils of the l. below the term. fl. developing in descending order. In Nigella sp. and others, after the term. fl. is formed, the buds below develop in ascending order, so that a raceme with an

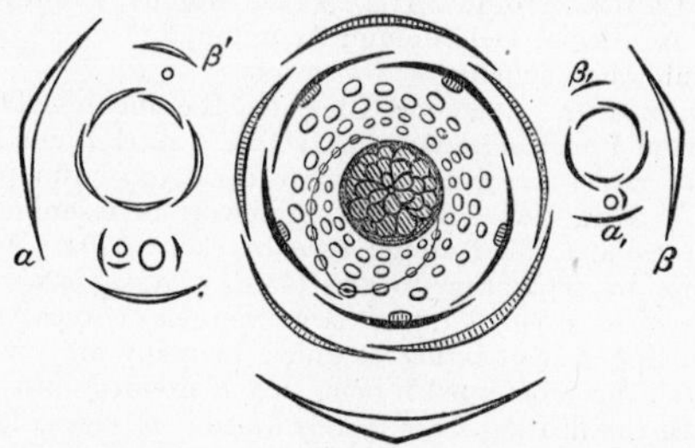

Ranunculus acris. Floral diagram of axillary dichasial cyme, with details of primary fl. Sta. according to the $\frac{8}{21}$ phyllotaxy. α β bracteoles of primary, α′ β′, α, β, of later, fls. After Eichler.

end fl. is formed; in Aconitum, &c. the same thing occurs, but the term. fl. rarely develops. In Nigella, Anemone, &c., there is an invol. of green leaves below the fl., usually alt. with the K.

Fl. itself typically spiral upon a ± elongated recept., but frequently the l. of the P in whorls; usu. reg. and ☿. The P usu. petaloid; rarely (*e.g.* Ranunculus) a true K and C. Frequently there occur nectaries of various patterns between the P proper and the sta.; these are usu. considered as modified petals, but it is as probable that they are derived directly from sta. An interesting series of transitions may be seen by comparing the following fls.: Caltha (honey secreted by cpls., 'calyx' present, nothing between it and sta.), Helleborus or Eranthis (honey secreted in little tubular 'petals'), Nigella (ditto, but 'petals' with a small leafy end), *Ranunculus auricomus* ('petals' distinct and coloured, with pocket-like nectary at base), *R. acris*, &c. (petals large, nectary at base). In Aconitum and Delphinium there is a ·|· fl. The sta. are usu. ∞ and spiral, the anthers extr.; the cpls. ∞, apocarpous, spiral, with either one basal or several ventral anatr. ovules. In Nigella the cpls. are united; there is only 1 in Actaea, which thus forms a link to Berberidaceae.

As a rule the fls. are protandrous, and the sta., as their anthers open, bend outwards from the centre. A series of fls. showing various grades of adaptation to insects may be found, *e.g.* Clematis (pollen fl.), Ranunculus (actinomorphic, honey scarcely concealed at all), Nigella (honey in little closed cavities), Aquilegia (honey in long spurs), Delphinium (ditto, but ⚲ also, and blue), &c.

Fr. a group of achenes or follicles (caps. in Nigella, berry in Actaea); seeds with minute embryo and oily endosp. The R. are mostly poisonous; a few, *e.g.* Aconitum, are or have been medicinal.

Classification and chief genera (after Prantl):

A. Ovules many: follicle, berry or capsule.

1. *Paeonieae* (no honey leaves; fls. usu. sol.; ovary wall fleshy; stigma broadened): Paeonia.
2. *Helleboreae* (usually honey-leaves; ovary wall rarely fleshy and then fls. in racemes; fls. sol. or in cymes or racemes): Caltha, Trollius, Helleborus, Nigella, Eranthis, Actaea, Aquilegia, Delphinium, Aconitum.

B. Ovule one; achene.

3. *Anemoneae*: Anemone, Clematis, Ranunculus, Thalictrum.

Ranunculastrum Fourr. = Ranunculus Tourn. p.p. (Ranunc.).

Ranunculus (Tourn.) L. Ranunculaceae (3). 300 cosmop., esp. N. temp.; 15 in Brit. *R. Ficaria* L. (pilewort or celandine) has tuberous roots, one formed at the base of each axillary bud; these may give rise by separation to new plants. *R. aquatilis* L. (water crowfoot) is often divided into a large number of so-called species; it has a floating stem bearing l. which in many are of two kinds (*heterophylly*), the submerged l. being much divided into linear segments, whilst the floating l. are merely lobed. *R. repens* L. (creeping buttercup or crowfoot) has creeping runners which root at the nodes and give rise to new pl. *R. acris* L. and *R. bulbosus* L. are other common buttercups; the latter has the base of the stem thickened for storage. Fls. in cymes, reg., with well-marked K and C (see fam. for diagram), protandrous and visited by a miscellaneous lot of insects (class AB). Honey is secreted in little pockets at the base of the petals.

Ranzania T. Ito (*Podophyllum* p.p.). Berberidaceae. 1 Japan.

Raoulia Hook. f. Compositae (4). 20 N.Z., Austr. Woolly herbs forming dense tufted whitish masses (vegetable sheep).

Rapa Tourn. ex L. = Brassica Tourn. (Crucif.).

Rapaceus (Lat.), turnip-shaped.

Rapanea Aubl. (*Myrsine* p.p. *BH.*). Myrsinaceae (11). 140 trop., subtrop.

Rapatea Aubl. Rapateaceae. 5 Guiana, N. Brazil.

Rapateaceae (*EP.*, *BH.*). Monocots. (Farinosae; Coronarieae *BH.*). 9 gen., 25 sp., S. Am. Herbs with 2-ranked narrow l.; infl. term. with 2 large spathes enclosing a head of spikelets, each of ∞ bracts and a term. ☿ reg. 3-merous heterochlam. fl. K (3), C (3), A 3+3, $\underline{G}$ (3), 3-loc. with ∞—1 ov. in each. Loculic. caps. Endosp. *Chief genus:* Rapatea.

Rape, **-oil**, *Brassica Napus* L.; **broom-**, *Orobanche*.

Raphanistrocarpus Baill. (*Momordica* p.p.). Cucurb. (3). 1 E. trop. Afr.

Raphanistrum Tourn. ex Adans. = Raphanus Tourn. p.p. (Crucif.).

Raphanocarpus Hook. f. Cucurbitaceae (3). 3 trop. Afr.

Raphanus (Tourn.) L. Cruciferae (2). 10 Medit., Eur., Java. *R.*

Raphanistrum L. in Brit.; pods jointed between seeds (lomentose). *R. sativus* L. (radish) with root-storage.
Raphe, the ridge where the stalk is attached to side of ovule.
Raphia Beauv. Palmae (III). 8 warm Afr., *R. vinifera* Beauv. (wine palm) also on the Amazon (see fam.). Spadix monoec.; the bracts have a curious sheathing form. Berry enclosed in large sheathing scales. In *R. Ruffia* Mart. roots develop between the dead leaf-bases; they curve upwards and are said to act as respiratory organs.
Raphiacme Harv. (*Raphionacme*). Asclepiadaceae (I). 15 S. Afr.
Raphides, needle-shaped crystals of Ca oxalate; *Arum*.
Raphidiocystis Hook. f. Cucurbitaceae (3). 3 trop. Afr., Madag.
Raphidophora Hassk. = Rhaphidophora Schott. (Arac.).
Raphiolepis Lindl. Rosaceae (II). 4 China, Japan.
Raphionacme Harv. (*Raphiacme*). Asclepiadaceae (I). 15 S. Afr.
Raphistemma Wall. Asclepiadaceae (II. 1). 2 Indomal.
Raphithamnus Miers. Verbenaceae (1). 1 Chili.
Rapinia Montr. Verbenaceae (4). 2 New Caled.
Rapistrum Tourn. ex Medic. Cruciferae (2). 10 Medit., mid-Eur.
Rapona Baill. (*Breweria* p.p.). Convolvulaceae (I). 1 Madag.
Raptostylus Post et O. Ktze. = Rhaptostylum Humb. et Bonpl.
Rapunculus Tourn. ex Mill. = Phyteuma L. (Campan.).
Rapuntium Tourn. ex Mill. = Lobelia L. (Campan.).
Raputia Aubl. Rutaceae (I). 5 trop. Am., W.I.
Rasamala, *Altingia excelsa* Nor.
Raspalia Brongn. (*Nebelia* Neck.). Bruniaceae. 6 S. Afr.
Raspberry, *Rubus Idaeus* L.; **blackcap -**, *Rubus occidentalis* L.
Rathbunia Britton et Rose (*Cereus* p.p.). Cactaceae (III. 1). 2 Mex.
Rati (India), *Abrus precatorius* L.
Ratibida Rafin. (*Lepachys BH.*, *Rudbeckia EP.*). Compositae (5). 2 N. Am.
Ratonia DC. (*Matayba EP.*). Sapindaceae (I). 36 warm Am.
Rattan canes, the stripped stems of climbing palms, esp. *Calamus*, *Daemonorops*, *Korthalsia*, *Plectocomia* (Ridley in *Str. Bull.* 1903).
Rattle box (Am.), **- wort** (W.I.). *Crotalaria*; **yellow -**, *Rhinanthus*.
Rattlesnake grass (Am.), *Glyceria canadensis* Trin.; **- plantain** (Am.), *Goodyera*; **- weed** (Am.), *Hieracium venosum* L.
Ratzeburgia Kunth. Gramineae (2). 1 Burma.
Rauia Nees et Mart. Rutaceae (I). 1 S.E. Brazil.
Rautanenia Buchenau. Alismaceae. 1 S.W. Afr.
Rauwenhoffia Scheff. Anonaceae (1). 2 Malaya.
Rauwolfia Plum. ex L. (incl. *Ophioxylon* L.). Apocynaceae (I. 3). 50 trop. L. often in whorls of 3 or 4.
Ravenala Adans. Musaceae. 2 Madag. and S. Am. They have a true sub-aerial stem, which bears large 2-ranked l. giving the pl. a peculiar fan-like appearance. *R. guyanensis* Steud. is the only Am. sp. of the suborder *Museae*. *R. madagascariensis* J. F. Gmel. is the traveller's tree, so-called because the water that accumulates in the leaf-bases has been used for drinking in cases of necessity. It may be found by piercing the base with a knife.
Ravenea H. Wendl. Palmae (IV. 1). 5 Comoros.
Ravenia Vell. Rutaceae (I). 5 Brazil, W.I.

Ravensara Sonnerat. Lauraceae (II). 4 Madag. *R. aromatica* J. F. Gmel. **is the** Madagascar clove (fr. a spice).

Ravnia Oerst. Rubiaceae (I. 5). 1 Costa Rica.

Rawsonia Harv. et Sond. Flacourtiaceae (I). 5 S. and trop. Afr.

Ray flowers, *Compositae*, *Umbelliferae*.

Razisea Oerst. **Acanthaceae** (IV. B). 1 Costa Rica.

Razor grass (W.I.), *Scleria pterota* Presl.

Re- (Lat. pref.), back or down; **-ceptacle**, see separate article; **-clinate**, bent downwards; **-current** (venation), veins returning towards mid-rib; **-curved**, bent back or down; **-duction**, see separate article; **-duplicate** (aestivation) see Aestivation (vernation), *Palmae*; **-flexed**, bent abruptly downwards or backwards; **-fracted**, bent sharply backward from the base; **-gression**, reversion; **-juvenescence**, renewal of growth from old or injured parts; **-production**, see separate article; **-supination**, *Lobelia*, *Lophanthus*, *Orchidaceae*; **-ticulate**, netted; **-tiform**, apparently netted; **-trorse**, directed back or downwards; **-tuse**, broadly notched (*Gd* in fig., Leaf); **-versed**, upside down, *Alstroemeria*, *Bomarea*, *Brachypodium*; **-version to type**, *Acacia*, *Bossiaea*, *Cactaceae*, *Russellia*; **-volute**, margins rolled outward.

Reaumuria L. Tamaricaceae. 15 E. Medit., C. As. Halophytes.

Reboudia Coss. et Dur. (*Erucaria BH.*). Cruciferae (2). 2 N. Afr., W. As.

Rebsamenia Conzatti. Malvaceae (2). 1 Mexico.

Rebutia K. Schum. (*Echinocactus* p.p. *EP.*). Cactaceae (III. 1). 5 S. Am.

Receptacle, the portion of stem upon which the fl. (or infl.) is actually borne. According to its form the ovary may be superior or inferior, the fl. hypo-, peri-, or epi-gynous (*q.v.* and see fig.).

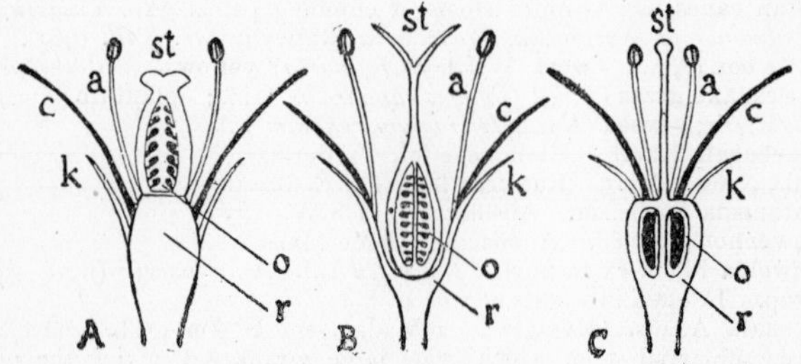

DIAGRAMMATIC LONGITUDINAL SECTIONS OF FLOWERS, to show types of receptacle, ovary, stigma &c. A, hypog. fl. with uniloc. ovary, parietal plac., and numerous ascending anatr. ovules with raphe downwards; stigma sessile, bilobed. B, perig. fl. with multi-loc. ovary, axile plac., and numerous horiz. anatr. ovules with raphe upwards; style with bifid stigma. C, epig. fl. with multi-loc. ovary, apical plac., and sol. pend. anatr. ovules with ventral raphe; style long with capitate stigma. *r*, recept.; *k*, calyx; *c*, corolla; *a*, stamens; *o*, ovary; *st*, stigma.

Fl., or P, K, C, A, may be *hypo-*, *peri-* or *epi-gynous*; the G *superior* or *inferior*. Perig. fls. may be shallowly or deeply perig.; in the latter case the *tube* is described as to length, texture, &c. There may be a *disc* in the fl. Sometimes outgrowths (*effigurations*) of the recept. are seen, *e.g.* in Passiflora, Capparidaceae, Orchidaceae, &c. Sometimes the recept. elongates between the whorls of floral members, *e.g.* in Lychnis between K and C, in Passiflora and in many Capparidaceae between C and A, in Capparis between A and G. If the elongated portion bears the sta. it is termed an *androphore*, if only the cpls., a *gynophore*. Other receptacular outgrowths are seen in epig. flowers, *e.g.* the wings on the inf. ovary of Begonia, the thorns (which sometimes bear fls.) on that of Tetragonia, the nectariferous disc of Umbelliferae, &c., and so on.

Rectipetality, tendency to grow in a straight line.

Red bay (Am.), *Persea carolinensis* Nees; **- bud** (Am.), *Cercis*; **- campion**, *Lychnis dioica* L.; **- cedar**, *Juniperus virginiana* L., (Austr.) *Cedrela*; **- head** (W.I.), *Asclepias curassavica* L.; **- hot poker**, *Kniphofia*; **- ink plant**, *Phytolacca decandra* L.; **- pepper**, *Capsicum annuum* L.; **- Peru bark**, *Cinchona succirubra* Pav.; **- root** (Am.), *Ceanothus*, *Lachnanthes*; **- sandalwood**, **- sanders**, *Pterocarpus santalinus* L. f.; **- sorrel**, *Hibiscus Sabdariffa* L.; **- spur-valerian**, *Centranthus*; **- top grass** (Am.), *Agrostis vulgaris* With.; **- water tree**, *Erythrophloeum*; **- wood**, *Sequoia sempervirens* Endl.; **- -, Indian**, *Chickrassia tabularis* A. Juss.; **- weed** (W.I.), *Phytolacca*.

Redfieldia Vasey. Gramineae (10). 1 Colorado.

Redowskia Cham. et Schlechtd. Cruciferae (4). 1 Kamtschatka.

Reduction, of complex infl., *Echinops*, *Euphorbia*, *Chorizanthe*, *Mirabilis*, *Xanthosia*; **- of l. surface**, *cf.* Xerophytes; **- of sporophylls** is common in fls. which very often have fewer in inner than outer whorls (*oligomery* in former, *pleiomery* in latter).

Reed, *Arundo*, *Phragmites*; **- bent grass** (Am.), *Calamagrostis*; **- grass**, *Phalaris*, **(W.I.)** *Arundo*; **- mace**, *Typha*; **paper -**, *Cyperus Papyrus* L.

Reedia F. Muell. Cyperaceae (II). 1 S.W. Austr.

Reesia Ewart. Amarantaceae (3). 1 N. Austr.

Reevesia Lindl. Sterculiaceae. 3 Himalaya to China.

Regelia Schau. Myrtaceae (II. 1). 3 W. Austr.

Regions, floral, see Floral Regions.

Rein-orchis (Am.), *Habenaria*.

Regma, fr. of Geraniaceae, a schizocarp breaking into cocci.

Regnellia Barb. Rodr. (*Bletia* p.p. *EP.*). Orchid. (II. 9). 1 Brazil.

Regnellidium Lindman. Marsiliaceae. 1 S. Brazil.

Regular (fl.), actinomorphic (*q.v.*) in symmetry.

Rehmannia Libosch. ex Fisch. et Mey. Scrophul. (III. 1). 4 Chi., Jap.

Reichardia Roth. (*Picridium BH.*). Compositae (13). 8 Medit.

Reicheella Pax. Caryophyllaceae (I. 3). 1 Chili.

Reichenbachanthus Barb. Rodr. Orchidaceae (II. 6). 1 Brazil.

Reichenbachia Spreng. Nyctaginaceae. 1 S. Brazil, Paraguay.

Reifferscheidia Presl (*Dillenia* p.p. *EP.*). Dillen. 1 S. Am.

Reimaria Fluegge. Gramineae (5). 4 warm Am.

Reimarochloa Hitchcock (*Reimaria* p.p.). Gramineae (5). 2 warm Am.

Reineckia Kunth. Liliaceae (VII). 1 China, Japan. Cult. orn. fl.
Reinhardtia Liebm. Palmae (IV. 1). 8 C. Am., Mexico.
Reinwardtia Dum. Linaceae. 2 N. India, China.
Reinwardtiodendron Koorders. Meliaceae (III). 1 Celebes.
Reissekia Endl. Rhamnaceae. 1 Brazil.
Relbunium Benth. et Hook. f. Rubiaceae (II. 11). 28 Mex. to Argent.
Relhania L'Hérit. Compositae (4). 18 S. Afr.
Remijia DC. Rubiaceae (I. 5). 15 S. Am. Bark a source of quinine.
Remirea Aubl. Cyperaceae (II). 1 trop.
Remusatia Schott. Araceae (VI). 2 Indomal. *R. vivipara* Schott has a tuberous stem which gives off upright shoots bearing scale-l.: in their axils are little tubers, each provided with a term. hook by which it may be carried away by an animal.
Remya Hillebr. Compositae (3). 2 Hawaiian Is.
Renanthera Lour. Orchidaceae (II. 20). 15 Malaya, Cochin China. Climbers. Cult. orn. fl.
Renantherella Ridl. (*Renanthera* p.p.). Orchid. (II. 20). 1 Malaya.
Renarda Regel. Umbelliferae (III. 4). 1 Turkestan.
Renealmia L. = Tillandsia L. (Bromel.).
Renealmia L. f. Zingiberaceae (I). 60 trop. Am., W.I., W. Afr.
Renewal shoots, *Sagittaria*.
Renggeria Meissn. Guttiferae (V). 2 trop. Brazil.
Rengifa Poepp. et Endl. (*Quapoya EP.*). Guttiferae (V). 3 trop. S. Am.
Reniform, kidney-shaped.
Rennellia Korth. (*Morinda* p.p. *EP.*). Rubiaceae (II. 9). 4 Malaya.
Repand, slightly sinuate.
Repens, reptans (Lat.), prostrate and rooting.
Replum, *Cruciferae*.
Reproduction is divided into *vegetative* (detachment of portions of the veg. organs, see Veg. Repr.) and *true*, by special cells, which may be asexual (*spores*), or sexual (*gametes*). The former germinate and give rise to *prothalli*; the latter unite in pairs, and give the asexual plant.
Reptonia A. DC. Sapotaceae (I) (Myrsin *BH.*). 2 C. As.
Rescue grass (Am.), *Bromus unioloides* H. B. et K.
Reseda Tourn. ex L. Resedaceae. 55 Medit., Eur.; 2 Brit. *R. odorata* L. (mignonette). Large post. disc; ovary and fr. open at apex. *R. lutea* L. (dyer's weld) yields a yellow dye.
Resedaceae (*EP.*, *BH.*). Dicots. (Archichl. Rhoeadales; Parietales *BH.*). 6 gen., 60 sp., chiefly Medit., also in Eur., As., S. Afr., Calif. Most are xero. herbs with alt. stip. l. and racemes of ·|· ☿ fls., with bracts but without bracteoles. The axis develops post. into a large disc, and upon this side the petals, &c. are usu. better developed than upon the ant. side of the fl. K 4—8; C 0—8; A 3—40; $\underline{G}$ (2—6) or 2—6, in the former case 1-loc. with parietal plac. Ovary open at the top; ovules 1—∞ per cpl., anatr. Fr. capsular; embryo curved; no endosp. *Chief genera:* Reseda, Oligomeris.
Reserves, *cf.* Edible Products, Vegetative Reproduction, &c.

Resins, products of secretion or disintegration, usu. formed in special cavities or passages; collected by tapping. Insoluble in water, soluble in alcohol, ether, or carbon disulphide; burn with a sooty flame. Roughly divisible into hard *resins* proper, *gum-resins* or mixtures of gum and resin, and *balsams*, fluid resins or resins dissolved in ethereal oils. **Resins** are derived from the distillation of the turpentines of Coniferae, &c., the hard *copals* or *animes* from Agathis, Hymenaea, Trachylobium, &c., the *dammars* from Canarium and other Burseraceae, Shorea and other Dipterocarpaceae, Dracaena, Guaiacum, Protium, Rhus, Xanthorrhea, &c. **Gum-resins** from Boswellia (frankincense), Calophyllum, Convolvulus, Dorema, Ferula, Garcinia (gamboge), &c. **Balsams** from Burseraceae (esp. Canarium), Commiphora, Coniferae (turpentines), Copaifera (balsam of Copaiba), Dipterocarpus, Liquidambar, Melanorrhoea, Myroxylon (balsam of Peru, Tolu), Opoponax, Pistacia (Chian turpentine, mastic), Populus, Styrax, Vateria, Vatica; **-passages**, channels in which resin flows. Barry, Drummond and Morrell, *Resins*, 1926.

Respiration, absorption of O and evolution of CO_2; *cf.* Aerenchyma.

Rest harrow, *Ononis.*

Restans (Lat.), persistent.

Restiaceae (*BH.*) = Restionaceae.

Restiaria Lour. Inc. sed. 1 China.

Restio L. Restionaceae. 110 S. Afr., Austr. Assimilation is performed by the green stems, the l. being reduced to sheaths.

Restionaceae (*EP.*, *BH.*). Monocots. (Farinosae; Glumaceae *BH.*). 19 gen., 250 sp., mostly in S. Afr. and Austr., a few in N.Z., Chili and Cochin China. Xero., usu. of tufted growth, with the general habit of Juncus; below ground is a rhiz. with scaly l., giving off erect cylindrical shoots bearing sheathing l. (rarely with ligules), which have a short blade, or sometimes none, in which case assim. is performed by the stem. Fls. dioec. (rarely monoec. or ☿), reg., in spikelets. P in two whorls, but single members often absent; A 3 or 2, opp. to the inner perianth-l.; $\underline{G}$ (3—1), 1—3-loc., with 1 pend. orthotr. ov. in each. Caps. or nut. Embryo lens-shaped, in mealy endosp. *Chief genus:* Restio.

Restrepia H. B. et K. Orchidaceae (II. 8). 15 trop. Am.

Retama Rafin. = Genista Tourn. p.p. (Legum.).

Retanilla Brongn. Rhamnaceae. 6 Chili, Peru.

Retinaculum, *Acanthaceae*, *Asclepiadaceae*, *Zostera.*

Retiniphyllum Humb. et Bonpl. Rubiaceae (I. 8). 10 trop. S. Am.

Retinispora Sieb. et Zucc. = Thuya L., &c. Seedlings of many sp. of the genera Chamaecyparis, Cupressus, Thuya, &c., exhibit, instead of the decussate appressed l. of the mature plant, spreading needle-l. (often in whorls of 4) like those of Abies, &c. (*cf.* Pinus, Acacia, &c.). If now these young seedlings be used as offsets, the new pl. thus formed retain throughout life this form of foliage; and pl. are thus obtained of totally different habit from that usual in these genera. To these 'seedling forms' the name R. was given. Many in gardens. The synonymy of some is: *R. decussata* hort. = Thuya orientalis; *R. filifera* Fowles = Cupressus obtusa; *R. juniperoides* Carr. = Thuya orientalis; *R. obtusa* Sieb. et Zucc. = Cupressus obtusa; *R. pisifera*

Sieb. et Zucc. = Cupressus pisifera; *R. recurvata* hort. and *R. rigida* Carr. = Thuya orientalis; *R. squarrosa* Sieb. et Zucc. and *R. stricta* hort. = Cupressus pisifera. For further synonymy see *Index Kewensis*.

Retinodendropsis Heim. Dipterocarpaceae. 1 Borneo.

Retting, rotting away the softer tissues, *cf. Linum*, *Cocos*.

Retzia Thunb. Loganiaceae (Solan. *BH.*). 1 S. Afr.

Reussia Endl. Pontederiaceae. 2 S. Am.

Reutera Boiss. = Pimpinella Riv. p.p. (Umbell.).

Reverchonia A. Gray. Euphorbiaceae (A. I. 1). 1 Texas.

Reya O. Ktze. (*Burchardia* R. Br.). Liliaceae (I). 2 Austr., Tasm.

Reyesia Clos (*Salpiglossis* p.p. *EP.*). Solanaceae (5). 1 Chili.

Reynaudia Kunth. Gramineae (6). 1 Cuba, S. Domingo.

Reynoldsia A. Gray (*Trevesia BH.*). Araliaceae (1). 4 Polynesia.

Reynosia Griseb. Rhamnaceae. 10 W.I., Florida. Endosp. ruminate.

Reynoutria Houtt. Inc. sed. 1 Japan.

Rhabdadenia Muell.-Arg. Apocynaceae (II. 1). 10 trop. Am., W.I.

Rhabdia Mart. Boraginaceae (II). 1 trop.

Rhabdodendron Gilg et Pilger. Rubiaceae (inc. sed.). 7 Amazon.

Rhabdophyllum Van Tiegh. (*Ouratea* Aubl.). Ochnac. 25 trop. Afr.

Rhabdosciadium Boiss. Umbelliferae (III. 2). 3 Persia.

Rhabdostigma Hook. f. Rubiaceae (II. 1). 1 E. Afr.

Rhabdothamnopsis Hemsl. Gesneriaceae (I). 1 China.

Rhabdothamnus A. Cunn. Gesneriaceae (I). 1 New Zealand.

Rhabdotheca Cass. = Launaea Cass. p.p. (Comp.).

Rhachicallis DC. Rubiaceae (I. 3). 1 W.I.

Rhachidospermum Vasey (*Jouvea* p.p. *EP.*). Gramineae (12). 1 Calif.

Rhachis, rachis; **rhaphe**, raphe.

Rhacodiscus Lindau. Acanthaceae (IV. B). 3 S. Am.

Rhacoma Adans. (*Leuzea BH.*, *Centaurea* p.p.). Comp. (11). 8 W.I., S. Am.

Rhacoma L. (*Myginda BH.*). Celastraceae. 15 W.I., trop. Am.

Rhadamanthus Salisb. Liliaceae (V). 2 S. Afr.

Rhagadiolus Tourn. ex Scop. (*BH.* incl. *Hedypnois* and *Garhadiolus*). Compositae (13). 1 Medit. Fr. linear, without pappus, completely enwrapped in an involucral bract.

Rhagodia R. Br. Chenopodiaceae (A). 12 Austr.

Rhamnaceae (*EP.*, *BH.*). Dicots. (Archichl. Rhamnales; Celastrales *BH.*). 40 gen., 500 sp., cosmop. Mostly trees or shrubs, often climbing (by aid of hooks in Ventilago, tendrils in Gouania, &c., twining stems in Berchemia): thorns occur in some, and especially in Colletia, &c. (*q.v.*). In these pl. too, serial buds occur in the l.-axils. L. simple, usu. with stip., never lobed or divided. Infl. cymose, usu. a corymb.

Fl. inconspic., ☿ or rarely unisexual, reg., sometimes apet. Recept. hollow, free from or united to the ovary. K 5—4, valvate; C 5—4, usu. small, often strongly concave, frequently clawed at base; A 5—4, alt. with sepals, usu. enclosed by the petals, at any rate at first. Disc usu. well developed, intra-staminal; G free or ± united to recept., 3—2- (rarely by abortion 1-) loc. (sometimes 4- or typically 1-loc); in each loc. 1 (rarely 2) basal ovule with downwardly-directed micropyle; style simple or divided. Fr. dry, splitting into dehisc. or indeh.

mericarps, or a drupe with 1 or several stones, or a nut. Endosp. little or none. Many of the dry fr. show special adaptations for wind-carriage, *e.g.* Paliurus, Ventilago. Closely related to Vitaceae, from which it is chiefly distinguished by the small petals, the recept., the endocarp and simple l.; it also approaches Celastraceae, the chief distinction being the antepetalous sta. Few are of economic value; see Zizyphus, Rhamnus, Hovenia. *Chief genera:* Ventilago, Paliurus, Zizyphus, Rhamnus, Hovenia, Ceanothus, Phylica, Colletia, Gouania.

Rhamnales. The 25th order of Archichlamydeae. *Cf.* p. xxx.

Rhamneae (*BH.*) = Rhamnaceae.

Rhamnella Miq. (*Microrhamnus BH.*). Rhamnaceae. 1 Japan, China.

Rhamnidium Reissek. Rhamnaceae. 5 trop. S. Am., W.I.

Rhamnoneuron Gilg. Thymelaeaceae. 1 Tonquin.

Rhamnus Tourn. ex L. Rhamnaceae. 100 cosmop., 2 in Brit., *R. cathartica* L. (common or purging buckthorn) and *R. Frangula* L. (alder buckthorn). Shrubs with alt. or opp. l. and small cymose clusters of fls. Two sections. To § 1, *Eurhamnus* (fls. usu. 4-merous, polyg. or dioec.), belong *R. Alaternus* L. (Medit.) and *R. cathartica* (Eur., As., Medit.), whose berries are purgative; the juice of the fr. is mixed with alum and evaporated, thus forming the paint known as sap-green; also *R. infectoria* L. (Mts. of S. Eur.) whose berries (graines d'Avignon or 'yellow berries') yield useful green and yellow dye-stuffs, and *R. chlorophora* Decne. from whose bark the Chinese prepare the dye known as 'Chinese green indigo' used in dyeing silk (*R. utilis* Decne. is also employed). To § 2, *Frangula* (fls. usu. 5-merous, ☿), belong *R. Frangula* (Eur., As., N. Afr.) whose bark is officinal (cathartic) and whose wood forms one of the best charcoals, *R. Purshiana* DC. in N. Am., whose bark (Cascara sagrada) is largely used as a cathartic, &c.

Rhamphicarpa Benth. Scrophulariaceae (III. 2). 8 palaeotrop.

Rhamphidia Lindl. = Hetaeria Blume (Orchid.).

Rhamphogyne Sp. Moore (*Abrotanella* p.p.). Compos. (3). 1 Rodrigues.

Rhanterium Desf. Compositae (4). 3 N.W. Afr. to Beluchistan.

Rhaphanistrocarpus Pax. Cucurbitaceae (3). 1 Mombasa.

Rhaphanocarpus Hook. f. Cucurbitaceae (3). 3 trop. E. Afr.

Rhaphanus L. (*Raphanus*). Cruciferae (2). 10 Medit., Eur., Java.

Rhaphidanthe Hiern. Ebenaceae. 2 trop. W. Afr.

Rhaphidiocystis Hook. f. Cucurbitaceae (3). 3 trop. Afr., Madag.

Rhaphidophora Hassk. Araceae (II). 60 Indomal. Sympodial climbing stems with clasping roots and pend. aerial roots. The pinnation of the l. arises like that in Monstera, *i.e.* by long holes arising between the ribs, and the margin finally breaking. Fls. ☿.

Rhaphidorhynchus Finet (*Angraecum* p.p.). Orchidaceae (II. 20). 22 trop. Afr., Madag., Masc.

Rhaphidospora Nees (*Justicia* p.p. *BH.*). Acanth. (IV. B). 6 palaeotrop.

Rhaphiolepis Lindl. Rosaceae (II). 4 subtrop. E. As.

Rhaphiophallus Schott (*Amorphophallus* p.p.). Araceae (IV). 1 S. Ind.

Rhaphiostylis Planch. (*Apodytes BH.*). Icacinaceae. 7 trop. W. Afr.

Rhaphis Lour. = Chrysopogon Trin. = Andropogon L. p.p. 18 warm.

Rhaphispermum Benth. Scrophulariaceae (III. 2). 1 Madag.

Rhaphitamnus Miers. Verbenaceae (I). I Chili.
Rhapidophyllum H. Wendl. et Drude. Palmae (I. 2). I S.E. U.S.
Rhapis L. f. Palmae (I. 2). 5 E. As. Cult. orn.
Rhaponticum (Vaill.) Hall. = Centaurea L. p.p. (Comp.).
Rhaptonema Miers. Menispermaceae. 4 Madag.
Rhaptopetalum Oliv. Scytopetalaceae (Olacin. *BH.*). 5 trop. Afr.
Rhatany root, *Krameria.*
Rhazya Decne. Apocynaceae (I. 3). 2 W. As.
Rhea, *Boehmeria nivea* Gaudich.
Rheedia L. Guttiferae (V). 17 trop. Am., Madag.
Rhektophyllum N.E. Br. Araceae (IV). I trop. W. Afr.
Rheotropism, sensitiveness to water stimulus.
Rhetinodendron Meissn. Compositae (8). I Juan Fernandez.
Rhetinosperma Radlk. Sapindaceae (I). I Queensland.
Rheum L. Polygonaceae (I. 2). 20 temp. and subtrop. As. Fls. like Rumex, but coloured and entomophilous, though they exhibit traces of anemophily in very large stigmas (*cf.* Poterium, &c.). *R. officinale* Baill. furnishes medicinal rhubarb; *R. Rhaponticum* L. is the rhubarb used as a vegetable.
Rhexia L. Melastomaceae (I). 7 E. U.S.
Rhigiocarya Miers. Menispermaceae. I trop. W. Afr.
Rhigiophyllum Hochst. Campanulaceae (I. I). I S. Afr.
Rhigospira Miers (*Tabernaemontana* L.). Apocynaceae (I. 3). 7 Brazil.
Rhigozum Burch. Bignoniaceae (2). 5 S. Afr.
Rhinacanthus Nees. Acanthaceae (IV. B). 6 palaeotrop.
Rhinanthus L. (incl. *Fistularia* L.). Scrophulariaceae (III. 3). 10 Eur., Medit., N. Am.; 2 in Brit. (yellow-rattle), common in damp pastures. Semi-parasites with loose pollen fls. (see fam.).
Rhinopteryx Niedenzu. Malpighiaceae (I). I Gambia.
Rhipidium, a monoch. cyme where each successive branch falls alt. on one side and the other of the relatively main axis, and all fls. are in one plane, *Iris, Juncus.*
Rhipogonum Forst. Liliaceae (XI). 5 E. Austr., N.Z.
Rhipsalis Gaertn. (incl. *Hariota, Pfeiffera*). Cactaceae (III. 3). 50 Brazil, Argentina. *R. Cassytha* L. is found in Ceylon and Madag., but quite possibly introduced (the only cactus out of Am.; see fam.). Epiph., rarely thorny, sometimes of Cereus-like structure, sometimes Phyllocactus-like, or with cylindrical stems (compare sp. of Euphorbia). Fr. fleshy.
Rhiz- rhizo- (Gr. pref.), root; **-carp,** pl. with sporangia on root-like processes, *Marsileaceae*; **-me,** see separate article; **-ophore,** *Selaginella.*
Rhizanthemum Van Tiegh. (*Loranthus* p.p.). Loranth. (I). 2 Malaya.
Rhizanthous, flowering from the root.
Rhizoboleae = Caryocaraceae.
Rhizocephalum Wedd. Campanulaceae (III). 4 Andes.
Rhizoma galangae, *Alpinia officinarum* Hance.
Rhizome, an underground creeping stem, usu. thickened, and mono- or sympodial, *Acorus, Alismaceae, Anemone, Asparagus, Balanophoraceae, Bambusa, Begonia, Bellis, Cyperaceae, Dioscorea, Equisetum, Eranthis, Gramineae, Iridaceae, Juncaceae, Lamium, Liliaceae, Musa, Ophioglossaceae, Petasites, Pteris, Ranunculaceae, Typha, Zingiber.*

Rhizophora L. Rhizophoraceae. 3, *R. Mangle* L. in Am., *R. mucronata* Lam. and another, Japan to S. Afr. These mangroves (*q.v.*) are moderate-sized trees with a great development of roots from the stem and branches. On the sub-aerial parts of the roots are large lenticels, probably serving in the same way as the aerenchyma of Bruguiera, &c. The seed germinates upon the tree, the hypocotyl projects at the micropyle and grows rapidly. The bark is used for tanning, yielding a substance known as cutch (*cf.* Acacia).

Rhizophoraceae (*EP.*, *BH.*). Dicots. (Archichl. Myrtiflorae; Myrtales *BH.*). 12 gen., 60 sp., trop., mostly Old World. See Mangroves. Trees usu. with opp. stip. l.; fls. sol. or in cymes, &c., ☿, hypo- to epi-gynous, reg. K usu. 4—8; C 4—8; A 8—∞, inserted on outer edge of perig. or epig. disc; G (2—5), 2—5-loc. with usu. 2 anatr. pend. ov. in each loc. Fr. a slightly soft berry. *Chief genera:* Rhizophora, Bruguiera, Weihea.

Rhodamnia Jack. Myrtaceae (I). 12 Malay Penins. to N.S. Wales.

Rhodanthe Lindl. = Helipterum DC. p.p. (Comp.).

Rhodax Spach = Helianthemum Tourn. (Cist.).

Rhodea Endl. = Rohdea Roth. (Lili.). 2 China, Japan.

Rhodes grass, *Chloris*.

Rhodiola L. = Sedum Tourn. p.p. (Crass.).

Rhodo- (Gr. pref.), rose red.

Rhodocalyx Muell.-Arg. Apocynaceae (II. 1). 1 campos of Minas Geraes. K coloured.

Rhodochiton Zucc. Scrophulariaceae (II. 3). 1 Mexico, *R. volubile* Zucc., a twiner with sensitive petioles (*cf.* Clematis). Cult. orn.

Rhodochlaena Thou. Chlaenaceae. 3 Madag.

Rhodoclada Baker = Asteropeia Thou. (Theaceae). 1 Madag.

Rhodocodon Baker. Liliaceae (V). 1 Madag.

Rhodocolea Baill. Bignoniaceae (4). 1 Madag.

Rhododendron L. (incl. *Azalea* L.). Ericaceae (I. 2). 250 N. temp., &c. "One sp. (*R. Lochae* F. Muell.) is found in trop. Austr., the greatest richness of sp. is in E. As., from S. China to the Himal. and Japan; a second and lesser abundance is found in temp. N. Am., and a few sp. in the arctic regions. 4 sp. in Mid. and S. Eur., 5 in Caucasus." (Drude.) Many sp. and hybrids cult. Shrubs and small trees with leathery l.; the l. of § *Azalea* last one year, those of the other subgenera usu. more. Large winter buds are formed covered with scale l.; the larger and stouter ones contain infls., the slender ones merely l. The branch bearing an infl. is continued by the formation of a bud in one of the upper axils. Some of the Indian sp. are epiph. The C is slightly ·|·, and the sta. and styles bend upwards to touch the under surface of a visiting insect. *R. ferrugineum* L. (alpine rose) is protandr. and visited by humble-bees.

Rhodogeron Griseb. Compositae (4). 1 Cuba.

Rhodohypoxis Nel. Amaryllidaceae (III). 2 S.E. Afr.

Rhodolaena Thou. Chlaenaceae. 3 Madag.

Rhodoleia Champ. ex Hook. Hamamelidaceae. 3 Hongkong to Java.

Rhodomyrtus Reichb. Myrt. (I). 6 trop. and E. As., Austr. Ed. fr.

Rhodopis Urb. (*Rudolphia* p.p.). Leguminosae (III. 10). 1 W.I.

Rhodora L. = Rhododendron L. p.p. (Eric.).

Rhodosciadium S. Wats. Umbelliferae (III. 6). 5 Mexico.

Rhodosepala Baker. Melastomaceae (I). 3 Madag.

Rhodospatha Poepp. et Endl. Araceae (II). 12 trop. Am.

Rhodosphaera Engl. Anacardiaceae (3). 1 E. Austr.

Rhodostachys Phil. Bromeliaceae (4). 7 S. Am. Cult. orn. infl.

Rhodothamnus Reichb. Ericaceae (I. 3). 1 E. Alps, E. Siberia.

Rhodotypos Sieb. et Zucc. Rosaceae (III. 1). 1 Japan, *R. kerrioides* S. et Z., a cult. orn. flg. shrub. It has opp. l., found in no other plant of the fam., except in seedlings of Prunus. There is an epicalyx (see Potentilla).

Rhoeadales. The 19th order of Archichlamydeae. *Cf.* p. xviii.

Rhoeadinae (Warming). The 9th order of Choripetalae.

Rhoeidium Greene (*Rhus* p.p.). Anacardiaceae (3). 7 Mexico, Texas.

Rhoeo Hance. Commelinaceae. 1 C. Am., Mex., W.I. Cult. orn. fl. and l.

Rhoicissus Planch. (*Vitis* p.p.). Vitaceae. 12 trop. and S. Afr.

Rhoium (Cl.), a creek formation.

Rhombochlamys Lindau. Acanthaceae (IV. B). 2 Colombia.

Rhomboidal, of rhomboid shape.

Rhombonema Schlechter. Asclepiadaceae (II. 1). 1 S. Afr.

Rhopalandria Stapf. Menispermaceae. 1 W. trop. Afr.

Rhopaloblaste Scheff. Palmae (IV. 1). 2 Moluccas, New Guinea.

Rhopalobrachium Schlechter et Krause. Rubiaceae (II. 1). 2 New Cal.

Rhopalocarpus Boj. Flacourtiaceae (inc. sed.). 3 Madag. *Cf.* Suppl.

Rhopalocnemis Jungh. Balanophoraceae. 2 E. Indomal.

Rhopalopilia Pierre. Opiliaceae. 3 W. trop. Afr.

Rhopalostylis H. Wendl. et Drude (*Kentia* p.p. *EP.*). Palmae (IV. 1). 2 Norfolk I., New Zealand.

Rhubarb, *Rheum officinale* Baill.; -(vegetable) *R. Rhaponticum* L.

Rhus (Tourn.) L. (incl. *Cotinus* Tourn. and *Toxicodendron* Tourn.). Anacardiaceae (3). 130 subtrop. and warm temp. *R. Coriaria* L. is the sumac (S. Eur.); its l., ground fine, are used for tanning and dyeing. *R. Toxicodendron* L. (N. Am., poison-ivy) climbs like ivy. Its juice produces ulcerations or erysipelas. *R. Cotinus* L. (Medit. to China) is the wig-tree, often cult. in shrubberies. Fls. polyg. The stalk of each drupe remains smooth, but the sterile parts of the panicle lengthen and become hairy. Then when ripe the stalks become detached at their joints, and the whole infl., with the fr. on it, falls to the ground and may be blown about. The wood yields the yellow dye 'young fustic.' *R. vernicifera* DC. is the lacquer-tree. Japan lacquer is obtained from notches in the stem. *R. succedanea* L. is the wax-tree of Japan; its crushed berries yield wax.

Rhynchanthera DC. Melastomaceae (I). 35 trop. Am.

Rhynchanthus Hook. f. Zingiberaceae (I). 2 Burma.

Rhynchelytrum Hochst. (*Tricholaena EP.*). Gramineae (5). 1 trop. Afr.

Rhynchocalyx Oliv. Lythraceae. 1 Natal.

Rhynchocarpa Schrad. = Kedrostis Medic. (Cucurb.).

Rhynchocorys Griseb. Scrophulariaceae (III. 3). 2 S. Eur. to Persia.

Rhynchodia Benth. Apocynaceae (II. 1). 2 E. Indomal.

Rhynchodium C. Presl = Psoralea L. (Legum.).

Rhynchoglossum Blume. Gesneriaceae (I). 2 Malay Archipelago.
Rhyncholacis Tul. Podostemaceae. 7 Guiana, Brazil.
Rhynchopera Börner = Carex L. p.p. (Cyper.).
Rhynchopyle Engl. Araceae (V). 4 Borneo.
Rhynchoryza Baill. (*Oryza* p.p. *EP.*). Gramineae (6). 1 Brazil.
Rhynchosia Lour. Leguminosae (III. 10). 120 trop. and subtrop.
Rhynchospermum Reinw. Compositae (3). 2 Himalaya to Japan.
Rhynchospora Vahl. Cyperaceae (II). 175 cosmop., esp. trop.
Rhynchosporous (fr.), ending in a beak.
Rhynchostigma Benth. (*Toxocarpus BH.*). Asclepiadaceae (II. 3). 3 trop. W. Afr.
Rhynchostylis Blume. Orchidaceae (II. 20). 2 Indomal. Cult. orn. fl.
Rhynchotechum Blume. Gesneriaceae (I). 9 Indomal.
Rhynchotheca Ruiz et Pav. Geraniaceae. 1 Peru to Colombia. C o.
Rhynchotropis Harms (*Indigofera* p.p.). Leguminosae (III. 6). 2 W. Afr.
Rhysopterus Coulter et Rose (*Cymopterus* p.p.). Umbelliferae (III. 5). 3 N. Am.
Rhysotoechia Radlk. Sapindaceae (I). 7 Austr., Malay Archip.
Rhyssocarpus Endl. (*Melanopsidium EP.*). Rubiaceae (I. 8). 1 trop. Am.
Rhyssolobium E. Mey. Asclepiadaceae (II. 3). 1 S. Afr.
Rhyssopteryx Blume. Malpighiaceae (I). 7 Malaya, N. Austr.
Rhyssostelma Decne. Asclepiadaceae (II. 1). 1 temp. S. Am.
Rhytachne Desv. Gramineae (2). 5 trop. Afr.
Rhyticarpus Sond. Umbelliferae (III. 5). 3 S. Afr.
Rhyticaryum Becc. Icacinaceae. 3 New Guinea.
Rhyticocos Becc. (*Cocos* p.p.). Palmae (IV. 2). 1 W.I.
Rhytidanthera Van Tiegh. Ochnaceae. 3 Colombia.
Rhytidophyllum Mart. Gesneriaceae (II). 12 W.I.
Rhytiglossa Nees = Dianthera Gronov. (*BH.*) = Justicia p.p.
Rhytispermum Link = Lithospermum L. (Borag.).
Rib grass, -wort plantain, *Plantago*.
Ribbon grass, *Phalaris arundinacea* L. var. *variegata*.
Ribeiria Arruda. Rosaceae (inc. sed.). Nomen.
Ribes L. Saxifragaceae (VI). 140 N. temp. and Andine; 4 in Brit. Shrubs, often with spines (emergences), and with racemes of fls. on 'short shoots.' $\overline{G}$ with two parietal plac. Fls. usu. homogamous, with self-pollination in default of insect-visits. *R. alpinum* L. is dioec. In *R. sanguineum* Pursh (cult. orn. shrub, flowering currant) the petals change from white to pink as the fls. grow older, and in *R. aureum* Pursh from yellow to carmine (see Fumaria, Boraginaceae). *R. rubrum* L. is the red, *R. nigrum* L. the black currant, *R. Grossularia* L. the gooseberry, all cult. for fr.
Rice, *Oryza sativa* L.; **Canada, Indian, Tuscarora-**, *Zizania aquatica* L.; **-paper**, *Tetrapanax papyrifera* C. Koch.
Richardia Houst. ex L. = Richardsonia Kunth.
Richardia Kunth = Zantedeschia Spreng. (Arac.).
Richardsonia Kunth. Rubiaceae (II. 10). 9 warm Am.
Richea R. Br. Epacridaceae (2). 8 Tasmania, Victoria.
Richella A. Gray. Anonaceae (2). 1 Fiji.

Richeria Vahl. Euphorbiaceae (A. I. 1). 3 Brazil, Peru.
Richthofenia Hosseus. Rafflesiaceae. 1 Siam.
Richweed (Am.), *Pilea.*
Ricinocarpos Desf. Euphorbiaceae (B. II). 13 Austr.
Ricinodendron Muell.-Arg. Euphorbiaceae (A. II. 5). 3 trop. W. Afr.
Ricinus (Tourn.) L. Euphorbiaceae (A. II. 2). 1 trop. Afr., *R. communis* L. (castor-oil), a shrub in trop., a herb in Eur. Monoec. The ♂ fl. has much-branched sta. The fr. explodes into the separate cpls., which at the same time open and drop the seeds. The seed is rich in oil, used medicinally and as a lubricant.
Ricotia L. Cruciferae (2). 5 E. Medit.
Riddellia Nutt. Compositae (6). 3 Mexico, Colorado, Utah.
Ridges on fruit, *Umbelliferae.*
Ridleya Pfitz. (*Sarcochilus* p.p. *BH.*). Orch. (II. 20). 1 Singapore.
Ridleyella Schlechter (*Bulbophyllum* p.p.). Orch. (II. 16). 1 N.G.
Ridolfia Moris. Umbelliferae (III. 5). 1 Medit.
Riedelia Oliv. Zingiberaceae (I). 50 Malay Arch. Lat. stds. unequal, [or 1.
Riedeliella Harms. Leguminosae (III. 1). 1 Brazil.
Riedlea Vent. = Melochia Dill. p.p. (Stercul.).
Riencourtia Cass. Compositae (5). 6 Guiana, Brazil.
Riesenbachia C. Presl. Onagraceae (2). 1 Mexico.
Rigens (Lat.), rigid.
Rigidella Lindl. Iridaceae (II). 3 Mexico, Guatemala.
Rigiolepis Hook. f. Ericaceae (III. 1). 1 Borneo.
Rigiopappus A. Gray. Compositae (6). 1 W. U.S.
Rigiostachys Planch. Simarubaceae. 2 Mexico.
Rindera Pall. Boraginaceae (IV. 1). 10 Medit., Eur., As., S. Afr.
Ringens (Lat.), gaping.
Ringworm shrub (W.I.), *Cassia alata* L.
Rinorea Aubl. (*Alsodeia BH.*). Violaceae. 80 warm. C sub-reg.
Riocreuxia Decne. Asclepiadaceae (II. 3). 5 S. and trop. Afr.
Riparius (Lat.), of river banks.
Ripple-grass (Am.), *Plantago.*
Riqueuria Ruiz et Pav. Rubiaceae (inc. sed.). 1 Peru.
Risleya King et Pantling. Orchidaceae (II. 6). 1 Himalaya.
Ritaia King et Pantling (*Ceratostylis* p.p.). Orchidaceae (II. *a*. III.). 1 Himalaya.
Ritchiea R. Br. Capparidaceae (II). 15 W. trop. Afr. A ∞.
Ritchieophyton Pax = Givotia Griff. (Euph.).
Rivalis (Lat.), growing by brooks.
Rivea Choisy. Convolvulaceae (I). 12 Indomal, S. Am.
Riverweed (Am.), *Podostemon.*
Rivina Plum. ex L. Phytolaccaceae. 3 trop. Am. P 4, A 4 or 8, $\underline{G}$ 1. Berry.
Rivularis (Lat.), growing beside rivulets.
Roast beef plant, *Iris foetidissima* L.
Robbia A. DC. (*Malouetia BH.*). Apocynaceae (II. 2). 7 Brazil, Guiana.
Robertiella Hanks (*Geranium* p.p.). Geran. 1 N. temp. (*G. Robertianum*).
Robertsonia Haw. = Saxifraga p.p. (Sax.).

Robin-run-in-the-hedge, *Nepeta Glechoma* Benth.

Robinia L. Leguminosae (III. 6). 6 N. Am. *R. Pseud-acacia* L. (false Acacia, locust) cult. in S. Brit. Stipules thorny. The leaflets move upwards in hot or dry air. The horiz. shoots branch in one plane, while the upright show radial symmetry. The base of the petiole forms a cap protecting a series of axillary buds.

Robinsonella Rose et Baker f. (*Sida* p.p.). Malvaceae (2). 6 Mexico, C. Am.

Robinsonia DC. Compositae (8). 8 Juan Fernandez.

Roborowskia Batalin. Papaveraceae (III). 1 C. As.

Rocambole (Am.), *Allium Scorodoprasum* L.

Rochea DC. Crassulaceae. 4 S. Afr. [*R. falcata* DC. = Crassula.]

Rochefortia Sw. Boraginaceae (II). 8 W.I., Colombia.

Rochelia Reichb. Boraginaceae (IV). 12 Medit. to Austr.

Rochonia DC. Compositae (3). 2 Madag.

Rock brake, curled, *Cryptogramma crispa* R. Br.; **- cress,** *Arabis*; **- pink,** *Dianthus*; **- rose,** *Helianthemum*, *Cistus*.

Rocket, *Hesperis*; **sea -,** *Cakile*; **yellow -,** *Barbarea*.

Rockia Heimerl (*Pisonia* p.p.). Nyctaginaceae. 1 Hawaiian Is.

Rod, golden, *Solidago*.

Rodetia Moq. (*Bosea* L.). Amarantaceae (2). 1 Himalaya.

Rodgersia A. Gray. Saxifragaceae (I). 2 China, Japan.

Rodigia Spreng. Compositae (13). 1 E. Medit.

Rodriguezia Ruiz et Pav. Orchidaceae (II. 19). 25 trop. Am. Between successive tubers there is often a long stretch of rhiz.

Rodschiedia Miq. (*Securidaca* L. p.p.). Legumin. (II. 2). 1 Guiana.

Roebelia Engel. (*Geonoma* p.p. *EP.*). Palmae (IV. 1). 1 Colombia.

Roella L. Campanulaceae (I). 12 S. Afr.

Roemeria Medic. Papaveraceae (II). 10 Medit. to Afghanistan.

Roeperia F. Muell. (*Gynandropsis* p.p. *BH.*). Capparid. (V). 1 N. Austr.

Roeperocharis Reichb. f. (*Habenaria* p.p. *BH.*). Orchidaceae (II. 1). 4 trop. E. Afr.

Roettlera Vahl = Didymocarpus Wall. p.p. (Gesn.) (100 palaeotrop.).

Rogeria J. Gay. Pedaliaceae. 4 trop. Afr.

Rogiera Planch. = Rondeletia L. (Rubi.).

Rogue, a sport or variation from type.

Rohdea Roth. Liliaceae (VII). 1 Japan, *R. japonica* Roth. It is said to be fert. by snails crawling over the fls.

Rohria Vahl = Berkheya Ehrh. p.p. (Comp.).

Rojasia Malme (*Gothofreda* p.p.). Asclepiadaceae (II. 1). 1 Brazil.

Rojasiophyton Hassler. Bignoniaceae (I). 1 Paraguay.

Rolandra Rottb. Compositae (I). 1 trop. Am.

Rolfea Zahlbruckner. Orchidaceae (II. 7). 1 Guiana.

Rollandia Gaudich. Campanulaceae (III). 6 Hawaiian Is.

Rollinia A. St Hil. Anonaceae (4). 22 trop. Am. Some have ed. fr.

Rolliniopsis Safford (*Rollinia* p.p.). Anonaceae (4). 4 Brazil.

Roman nettle, *Urtica*.

Romanzoffia Cham. Hydrophyllaceae. 4 N.W. N. Am., N.E. As.

Romneya Harv. Papaveraceae (II). 2 California.

Romulea Maratti. Iridaceae (I). 50 Eur., Medit. (1 Brit.). Cult.

Rondeletia L. Rubiaceae (I. 3). 100 warm Am., W.I.

Ronnbergia E. Morr. et André. Bromeliaceae (4). 2 Colombia.

Root, the organ for absorption from the soil (in most cases); **adventitious -**, see Adv. Root; **aerating -**, **aerial -**, see Aer. and Aer. Roots; **apogeotropic -**, *Bowenia*; **- as suckers**, see Parasites; **- as tendrils**, *Vanilla*; **- as thorns**, *Acanthorhiza*; **- as tubers**, *Bravoa*, *Dahlia*, *Dioscorea*, *Paeonia*, *Thladiantha*, *Uragoga*; **bitter -**, *Lewisia*; **buttress -**, *Palmae*, *Pandanaceae*; **- cap**, *Lemna*, *Pandanus*; **- climbers**, see Climbing Pl.; **fibrous -**, in tufts of uniform length, as in a grass; **- hairs**, the absorbing hairs near the tip of a root; **paint -**, *Lachnanthes*; **parasitic -**, see Parasites; **Pareira -**, **white**, *Abuta*; **- rubber**, *Carpodinus*, *Clitandra*; **-stock**, an erect, short rhiz., as in many ferns; **true -**, the result of the radicle of the embryo; **waterplant -**, see Water Pl.

Ropalocarpus Boj. Tiliaceae. 3 Madag.

Ropourea Aubl. Verbenaceae (inc. sed.). 1 Guiana.

Roridula L. Droseraceae. 2 S. Afr. Like Drosera, but with no movement of the leaf-tentacles. *Cf.* Suppl. (Byblidaceae).

Roripa Scop. (*Nasturtium* R. Br. p.p.). Cruciferae (2). 50 <u>✳</u>.

Rosa Tourn. ex L. Rosaceae (III. 6). 150 N. temp. and on trop. mts.; 6 in Brit., incl. *R. canina* L., the dog-rose. The thorns are epidermal appendages. The fl. of *R. canina* is a pollen fl. The fr. (hip) consists of a number of achenes enclosed in the fleshy recept. which closes over them after fert. *R. centifolia* L. is the form from which the cabbage rose is derived; and numerous forms of this and other sp. are cult. (see *Nat. Pfl.*). Otto of rose is distilled mainly from *R. damascena* Mill., cult. in the Balkans. [E. Willmot, *The genus Rosa*, London 1914; Baker, *Revised Classification of Roses* in Journ. Linn. Soc. 35, 1905, p. 70.]

Rosaceae (*EP.*; *BH.* incl. *Eucryphiaceae*). Dicots. (Archichl. Rosales). 100 gen., 2000 sp., cosmop. Trees, shrubs and herbs, usu. perenn.; l. alt. (exc. Rhodotypos), simple or cpd., usu. stip., the stipules often adnate to the petiole. Veg. repr. in various ways, but esp. by creeping stems—runners as in strawberry, or suckers as in raspberry. Fls. term., in racemose or cymose infls. of various types; great variety of forms. Receptacle generally ± hollowed, so that various degrees of perigyny occur. Frequently there is a central protuberance bearing the cpls., even in the forms with very much hollowed recept. In a few cases (subfams, II, IV) the cpls. are united to the recept. and fully inf. The recept. often forms a part of the fr. Fl. usu. ☿ and actinom. K 5, often with an epicalyx of outer and smaller l. (see Potentilla), usu. imbr.; C 5, usu. imbr.; A 2, 3 or 4 times as many as petals, or ∞, bent inwards in bud; G usu. apocarpous and sup., rarely syncarpous or inf.; cpls. as many or 2 or 3 times as many as

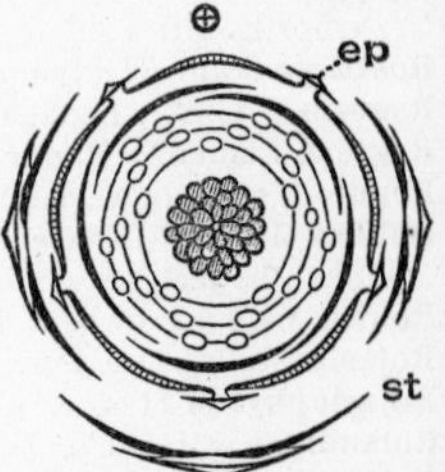

Floral Diagram of *Potentilla fruticosa* (after Eichler). ep. = epicalyx, st. = stipules of bracts and bracteoles.

petals, or ∞ or 1—4. Ovules anatr., usu. 2 in each cpl. Style often lat. or basal. Fr. various, dry or fleshy; often an aggregate of achenes (Potentilla) or drupes (Rubus), or a single drupe (Prunus), or pome (Pyrus), and so on (*cf.* genera, esp. those mentioned, and Fragaria, Geum, Rosa, Poterium). Seed usu. exalbum.

Fls. in general of simple type, with slightly concealed honey and ∞ sta., usu. protandrous. Poterium sp. are anemoph.

Few are of economic value (see Pyrus, Rubus, Fragaria, Prunus), but many are favourites as garden plants and shrubs.

Classification and chief genera (after Focke). Closely related to Saxifragaceae, some genera being almost arbitrarily placed in one or the other; also nearly allied to Calycanthaceae, Combretaceae, Myrtaceae (floral diagram of M. practically the same as that of § II), Thymelaeaceae, and Leguminosae (through § VI).

I. *SPIRAEOIDEAE* (cpls. 12—1, usu. 5—2, whorled, neither on special carpophore nor sunk in recept., with 2 or more ovules in each; fr. usu. dehisc.; sta. on broad base, tapering upwards; stipules often absent):
   1. *Spiraeeae* (follicle, seeds not winged): Spiraea.
   2. *Quillajeae* (follicle, seeds winged): Quillaja.
   3. *Holodisceae* (achene): Holodiscus (only genus).

II. *POMOIDEAE* (cpls. 5—2, united to inner wall of recept., usually syncarpous; axis fleshy in fruit, stipules):
   Pomarieae: Pyrus.

III. *ROSOIDEAE* (cpls. ∞ or rarely 1 on carpophore, sometimes enclosed in axis in fr.; fr. 1-seeded indeh.):
   1. *Kerrieae* (stips. distinct; axis not forming part of fr.; sta. tapering upwards from broad base; cpls. few, whorled; sta. ∞): Rhodotypos, Kerria.
   2. *Potentilleae* (as 5, but cpls. usu. ∞, in a head, or rarely few and then sta. also few):
      2 a. Rubinae (drupes, no epicalyx): Rubus.
      2 b. Potentillinae (achenes; seed pend.; usu. epicalyx): Fragaria, Potentilla.
      2 c. Dryadinae (as b, but seed erect): Geum, Dryas.
   3. *Cercocarpeae* (stipules slightly developed; torus tubular; cpl. 1; achene): Adenostoma, Purshia.
   4. *Ulmarieae* (torus flat or nearly so; sta. with narrow base): Ulmaria.
   5. *Sanguisorbeae* (torus cup-like enclosing cpls., hardening in fr.; cpls. 2 or more): Alchemilla, Agrimonia, Poterium.
   6. *Roseae* (torus cup-like or tubular, enclosing ∞ cpls., and fleshy in fr.): Rosa.

IV. *NEURADOIDEAE* (cpls. (5—10) united to torus, which is dry in fr.; herbs).
   Neuradeae: Neurada.

V. *PRUNOIDEAE* (cpl. 1, rarely 2—5, free of torus; drupe; trees with simple l.; style almost term.; ovules pend.; fls. reg.).
   Pruneae: Nuttallia, Prunus.

VI. *CHRYSOBALANOIDEAE* (as V, but style basal and ovules erect):

1 a. Chrysobalaninae (nearly reg.): Chrysobalanus.
1 b. Hirtellinae (zygomorphic): Hirtella.

Rosales. The 21st order (*EP.*) of Archichlamydeae. The 11th (*BH.*) of Polypetalae. *Cf.* pp. xx, li.

Rosanthus Small (*Gaudichaudia* p.p.). Malpigh. (I). 1 Mexico.

Roscheria H. Wendl. Palmae (IV. 1). 1 Seychelles.

Roscoea Sm. Zingiberaceae. 13 Himal. to China. *R. purpurea* Sm., often cult., has a ·|· fl. with two lips. Insects landing on the lower and probing are obstructed by two projecting spikes from the lower end of the anther; pressure on these brings the anther (with the stigma, which projects beyond it) down upon the insect's back. Protand. [Cf. Salvia.]

Rose, *Rosa*; **alpine -,** *Rhododendron ferrugineum* L., &c.; **Andes -,** *Befaria*; **-apple,** *Eugenia malaccensis* L.; **attar of -,** *Rosa damascena* Mill.; **-bay** (Am.), *Rhododendron*; **Christmas -,** *Helleborus*; **guelder -,** *Viburnum*; **Jamaica -** (W.I.), *Blakea trinervia* L.; **-mallow** (Am.), *Hibiscus*; **-mary,** *Rosmarinus officinalis* L.; **-of Jericho,** *Anastatica*; **-pink,** *Sabbatia*; **rock -,** *Helianthemum*; **-root,** *Sedum*; **-wood,** *Dalbergia*.

Roseanthus Cogn. Cucurbitaceae (3). 1 Mexico, Calif.

Roselle, rozelle, *Hibiscus Sabdariffa* L.

Rosenbachia Regel. Labiatae (I. 1), formerly Verben. 1 Turkestan.

Rosenbergia Oerst. = Cobaea Cav. p.p. (Polemon.). 2 trop. Am.

Rosenia Thunb. Comp. (4). 1 Cape Colony. Shrub. L. opp.

Rosiflorae (Warming). The 19th order of Choripetalae.

Rosilla Less. (*Dysodia* p.p. *EP.*). Compositae (6). 1 Mexico.

Rosin, *Pinus*; **-plant** (Am.), *Silphium*.

Rosmarinus (Tourn.) L. Labiatae (I. 2). 1 Medit., *R. officinalis* L. (rosemary), a xero. shrub with l. rolled back and stomata in hairy grooves on lower side (*cf.* Ericaceae, Empetrum). Oil of rosemary is employed in perfumery, &c.

Rostellaria Gaertn. f. Inc. sed. 1, habitat?

Rostellaria Nees (*Justicia* p.p.). Acanthaceae (IV. B). 10 As., Afr.

Rostellate, rostrate, beaked.

Rostellum, *Orchidaceae*.

Rostkovia Desv. Juncaceae. 1 S. Am., N.Z.

Rosulate, rosetted.

Rotaceus (Lat.), rotate, wheel-shaped, *Veronica*.

Rotala L. Lythraceae. 40 trop. and subtrop., in wet places.

Rotang, rattan.

Rotantha Baker (*Lawsonia* p.p. *EP.*). Lythraceae. 1 Madag.

Rothia Pers. Leguminosae (III. 3). 2 palaeotrop.

Rothrockia A. Gray. Asclepiadaceae (II. 4). 1 Arizona.

Rottboellia L. f. (*BH.* excl. *Ophiurus* Gaertn. f.). Gramineae (2). 35 trop. and subtrop.

Rottlera Roxb. = Mallotus Lour. (Euph.).

Rotund, orbicular-oblong.

Roubieva Moq. (*Chenopodium* p.p. *EP.*). Chenopodiaceae (A). 2 S. Am.

Roucheria Planch. Linaceae. 4 Guiana.

Roucou, annatto, *Bixa Orellana* L.

Rouge, *Carthamus tinctorius* L.
Rouhamon Aubl. = Strychnos L. (Logan.).
Roulinia Decne. Asclepiadaceae (II. 1). 15 Texas to Argentina.
Rouliniella Vail. (*Roulinia* p.p.). Asclepiadaceae (II. 1). 7 C. Am.
Roupala Aubl. Proteaceae (II). 40 trop. Am., Austr., New Caled.
Roupellia Wall. et Hook. (*Strophanthus* p.p. *EP.*). Apocynaceae (II. 1). 1 W. Afr.
Rourea Aubl. Connaraceae. 40 trop.
Roureopsis Planch. Connaraceae. 4 Malaya.
Roussea Smith. Saxifragaceae (V). 1 Mauritius.
Rousseauxia DC. Melastomaceae (I). 1 Madag.
Rousselia Gaudich. Urticaceae (4). 1 W.I.
Rouxia Husn. (*Agropyrum* p.p.). Gramineae (12). 1 Eur.
Rouya Coincy (*Thapsia* p.p.). Umbelliferae (III. 7). 1 Medit.
Rowan, *Pyrus Aucuparia* Ehrh.
Roxburghia Banks = Stemona Lour. (Stemon.).
Roxburghiaceae = Stemonaceae.
Royal fern, *Osmunda*; **- palm**, *Oreodoxa regia* H. B. et K.
Roydsia Roxb. Capparidaceae (III). 10 Indomal. Climbing shrubs.
Royena L. Ebenaceae. 15 Afr. *R. lucida* L. useful timber.
Roylea Wall. Labiatae (VI). 1 Himalaya.
Roystonea O. F. Cook. (*Oreodoxa* p.p.) Palmae (IV. 1). 3 N. Am., W.I.
Rozelle, roselle, *Hibiscus Sabdariffa* L.
Rubacer Rydberg (*Rubus* p.p.). Rosaceae (III. 2). 5 N. Am.
Rubber, the coagulated latex of caoutchouc-containing plants, esp. *Hevea*, *Manihot*, *Castilloa*, *Landolphia*, *Funtumia*, &c.; now very extensively cult. in the trop., esp. *Hevea brasiliensis* Muell.-Arg., *q.v.* See Euphorbiaceae, Apocynaceae, Moraceae, &c. and Willis, *Agriculture in the Tropics*, Lock, *Rubber and Rubber Planting*; **African -**, *Funtumia*, *Landolphia*, &c.; **Bolivian -**, *Sapium*; **Borneo -**, *Willughbeia*; **Ceara -**, *Manihot Glaziovii* Muell.-Arg., &c.; **Central American -**, *Castilloa*; **Columbian -**, *Sapium*; **Indian -**, *Ficus elastica* Roxb.; **Iré -**, *Funtumia*; **Lagos -**, *Funtumia*; **Madagascar -**, *Landolphia*, &c.; **Mangabeira -**, *Hancornia*; **Maniçoba -**, *Manihot*; **Mexican -**, *Castilloa*; **Para -**, *Hevea brasiliensis* Muell.-Arg. &c.; **Pernambuco -**, *Hancornia*; **silk -**, *Funtumia*; **virgen -**, *Sapium*; **West Indian -**, *Castilloa*; and see *Carpodinus*, *Clitandra*, *Eucommia*, *Parameria*, *Mascarenhasia*, *Urceola*.
Rubens (Lat.), blush-red.
Rubeola Tourn. ex Adans. = Crucianella L. (Rubi.).
Ruber (Lat.), red.
Rubia (Tourn.) L. Rubiaceae (II. 11). 15 Eur., As., Am. (1 in Brit.). *R. tinctorum* L. is the madder, formerly cult. for its dye (alizarin), which is now prepared artificially.
Rubiaceae (*EP.*, *BH.*). Dicots. (Sympet. Rubiales). 450 gen., 5500 sp., one of the largest fams. of pl. Most are trop., but a number (esp. *Galieae*) are temp., and Galium itself has a few arctic sp. Trees, shrubs and herbs with decussate stip. entire or rarely toothed l. The stips. exhibit great variety of form; they stand either between the petioles (*interpetiolar*) or between the petiole and the axis (*intrapetiolar*),

and are frequently united to one another and to the petioles, so that a sheath is formed round the stem. The two stips.—one from each l.—that stand side by side are usu. united, and in the *Galieae*, to which the Brit. sp. belong, are leaf-like, and often as large as the ordinary l.; a char. appearance is thus produced, the plants seeming to have whorls of l.; and it is only by noting the axillary buds that a clue is obtained to the real state of affairs. The number of organs—l. and stips.—in a whorl varies from 4 upwards, according to the amount of 'fusion' or 'branching' of the stips. The simplest case is a whorl of 6, each leaf having 2 separate stips.; if the stips. be united in pairs, a whorl of 4 results; if each stip. be branched into two, we get a whorl of 10, and, if the centre pair of half-stips. on either side be united, a whorl of 8.

Several are myrmecophilous (*cf.* Cecropia, Acacia), *e.g.* Myrmecodia, Cuviera, Duroia, Hydnophytum.

Infl. typically cymose. Sol. term. fls. rare; small dichasia more frequent; most common case a much branched cymose panicle.

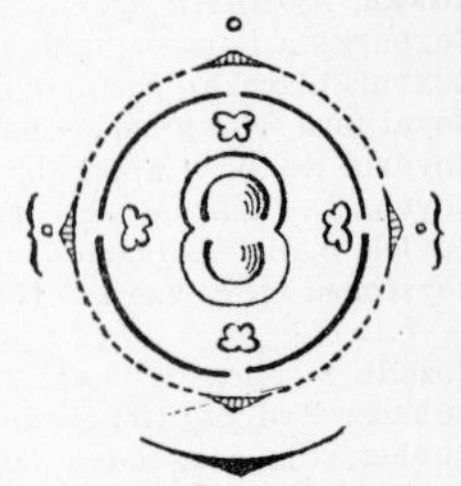

Floral diagram of Asperula, after Eichler.

Fl. usu. ☿, reg., epig., 4- or 5-merous. K 4—5, epig., often almost absent, usu. open in aestivation, sometimes with one sepal larger than the rest and brightly coloured (Mussaenda, &c.); C (4—5), valvate, conv., or imbr.; A 4—5, alt. with petals, epipet.; $\overline{G}$ (2) rarely (1—∞), 2-loc. with 1—∞ anatr. ov. in each loc.; ov. erect, pend., or horiz.; style simple; stigma capitate or lobed. Caps. (septi- or loculi-cidal), berry or schizocarp. Embryo small, in rich endosp.

Most have conspic. insect-pollinated fls. The Brit. sp. have small fls. with freely exposed or slightly concealed honey, chiefly visited by flies; many trop. sp. have bee- and Lepidoptera-fls. with long tubes. Honey usu. secreted by an epig. nectary round base of style. Heterostylism is common, and dioecism sometimes occurs.

Several are of economic importance, *e.g.* Cinchona, which yields quinine, while many of its allies have also valuable alkaloids, Coffea (coffee), Uragoga (ipecacuanha), Rubia, &c.

Classification and chief genera (after Schumann). The R. are closely allied to Caprifoliaceae (*q.v.*) and less nearly to Compositae, &c.

I. *CINCHONOIDEAE* (ovules ∞ in each loculus).

A. CINCHONINAE (fruit dry):

α. Fls. solitary or in decussate panicles.

a. Fl. regular; seed not winged; C valvate.

1. *Condamineeae*: Condaminea.

2. *Oldenlandieae*: Oldenlandia, Houstonia, Pentas.

b. As a, but C imbr. or conv.

3. *Rondeletieae*: Rondeletia.

c. As a, but C 2-lipped.

4. *Henriquezieae*: Henriquezia.

d. As b, but seed winged.

5. *Cinchoneae*: Cinchona, Bouvardia, Cosmibuena.
β. Fls. in heads.
6. *Naucleeae*: Uncaria, Nauclea.
B. GARDENINAE (fruit fleshy):
7. *Mussaendeae* (C valvate): Mussaenda.
8. *Gardenieae* (C imbr. or conv.): Randia, Gardenia, Posoqueria, Duroia.

II. *COFFEOIDEAE* (ovules 1 in each loculus).
A. GUETTARDINAE (ovule pendulous; micropyle facing upwards):
1. *Vanguerieae*: Plectronia, Cuviera.
2. *Guettardeae*: Guettarda.
3. *Chiococceae*: Chiococca.
B. PSYCHOTRIINAE (ovule ascending; micropyle facing downwards):
α. C convolute.
4. *Ixoreae*: Coffea, Ixora, Pavetta.
β. C valvate.
a. Ovules inserted at base of loculus.
5. *Psychotrieae*: Psychotria, Rudgea, Uragoga, Lasianthus, Myrmecodia.
6. *Paederieae*: Paederia.
7. *Anthospermeae*: Nertera, Coprosma, Mitchella.
8. *Coussareeae*: Faramea.
b. Ovules on septum.
9. *Morindeae* (stip. undivided, not leafy; trees and shrubs): Morinda.
10. *Spermacoceae* (stip. divided; shrubs and undershrubs): Borreria.
11. *Galieae* (stip. leafy; herbs): Sherardia, Crucianella, Asperula, Galium, Rubia.

Rubiales. The 8th order (*EP.*) of Sympetalae. The 1st (*BH.*) of Gamopetalae. The 8th (Warming) of Sympetalae.

Rubiginose, rust-coloured.

Rubus (Tourn.) L. Rosaceae (III. 2 a). 225 cosmop., esp. N. temp. (5 or 6 in Brit.). Fls. conspic.; honey secreted by a ring-shaped nectary upon the hollowed axis just within the insertion of the sta. Fls. homogamous, visited by many insects, including bees. Fr. an aggregate of drupes. *R. Chamaemorus* L., the cloudberry (arctic, Scotland), has creeping underground stems by means of which a large veg. repr. is carried on. Fls. sol., term. and unisexual, occasionally ☿. *R. Idaeus* L. (raspberry) multiplies largely by suckers—stems which grow out horiz. beneath the soil to some distance, then turn up and give rise to new pl. which flower in their second year. *R. fruticosus* L. (a general specific name for the ∞ var. of the common bramble or blackberry) is a hook-climber (the hooks being emergences) sprawling over the surrounding vegetation. Branches which reach the soil often take root there and grow up into new plants. *R. caesius* L. (dewberry) has fr. covered with bloom (wax) like grapes. *R. occidentalis* L. is the black-cap raspberry or trimbleberry of N. Am. *R. australis* Forst. f. has the blades of the leaves reduced to the minimum. Many sp. and vars. of blackberry, raspberry, &c. are cult. ed. fr. The loganberry, a form which appeared in 1881 in the grounds of Judge Logan at Santa Cruz, Calif., is usu. supposed to be a hybrid, but this is disputed. See *Journ. of Hered.* Nov. 1916, p. 504.

Ruckeria DC. Compositae (8). 3 S. Afr.

Rudbeckia L. (incl. *Lepachys* Rafin.). Compositae (5). 35 N. Am. Cult.

Ruderalis (Lat.), of waste places.

Rudgea Salisb. Rubiaceae (II. 5). 100 trop. Am., W.I. Some are heterostyled.

Rudimentary organs, organs repres. by functionless rudiments.

Rudolphia Willd. Leguminosae (III. 10). 3 W.I., C. Am.

Rue, *Ruta graveolens* L.; **goat's -**, *Galega*; **meadow -**, *Thalictrum*.

Ruellia Plum. ex L. Acanthaceae (IV A). 210 trop. and subtrop. The capsule explodes. The seeds possess surface hairs which, when wetted, swell and adhere to the soil. Cult. orn. fl.

Ruelliola Baill. Acanthaceae (IV. A). 1 Madag.

Ruelliopsis C. B. Clarke. Acanthaceae (IV. A). 2 S. trop. Afr.

Rufescens (Lat.), becoming reddish; **rufous**, reddish.

Rugose (dim. rugulose), wrinkled.

Ruizia Cav. Sterculiaceae. 3 Bourbon.

Rulac Adans. = Acer Tourn. (Acer.).

Rulingia R. Br. Sterculiaceae. 17 Austr., Madag.

Rumex L. Polygonaceae (I. 2). 100, esp. N. temp. (12 Brit., docks and sorrels). Fls. of the type usual in the fam., wind-fert., with large stigmas (see fam. for diagram, and *cf.* Rheum). Some have adv. shoots upon the roots, *e.g.* *R. acetosella* L. *R. Hydrolapathum* Huds. is said to produce aerating roots like a mangrove. The roots of *R. hymenosepalus* Torr. (N.W. Am.), the Canaigré, are used for tanning.

Rumfordia DC. Compositae (5). 3 Mexico.

Ruminate (endosp.), marbled, or marked by wavy transv. lines. *Anon.*

Rumphia L. (*Cordia* p.p. *EP.*). Boraginaceae (I), formerly Anacardiaceae. 1 Malaya.

Runcina Allem. Inc. sed. Nomen.

Runcinate (l.), like dandelion, *Taraxicum officinale* Weber.

Rungia Nees. Acanthaceae (IV. B). 24 trop. As. and Afr.

Runner, a creeping stem taking root at the nodes, *Ajuga*, *Fragaria*, *Hydrocharis*, *Isoloma*, *Limosella*, *Nephrolepis*, *Ranunculus*.

Rupestris, rupicolus (Lat.), growing on banks.

Rupicola Maiden et Betche. Epacridaceae (2). 1 Austr.

Ruppia L. Potamogetonaceae. 1 temp. and subtrop., *R. maritima* L., in salt or brackish water. A slender swimming pl., with the habit of a Potamogeton. The fls. are borne just at the surface of the water, where fert. occurs by floating pollen. Each spike of 2 fls. not enclosed in the spathe at the flowering time. The fl. has 2 sta. with small outgrowths from the connectives, and 4 cpls.

Ruprechtia C. A. Mey. Polygonaceae (III. 2). 25 warm S. Am.

Rupture-wort, *Herniaria*.

Ruralis (Lat.), of rustic places.

Rusa grass (and oil), geranium grass, *Cymbopogon Martini* Stapf.

Rusbya Britton (*Anthopterus EP.*). Ericaceae (III. 2). 2 Bolivia.
Rusbyanthus Gilg. Gentianaceae (I). 1 Bolivia.
Rusbyella Rolfe. Orchidaceae (II. 19). 1 Bolivia.
Ruscus (Tourn.) L. Liliaceae (VII). 3 Medit., Eur. *R. aculeatus* L., butcher's broom, in Brit., a small shrub. In the axils of scaly l. stand leaf-like phylloclades; half-way up each is another scaly l., in whose axil stands the fl. Berry. [Cf. Asparagus and Semele.]
Rush, *Juncus*; **beak-**, *Rhynchospora*; **bul-**, *Typha*; **Dutch-**, *Equisetum*; **flowering-**, *Butomus*; **-grass** (Am.), *Sporobolus*; **spike-**, *Eleocharis*; **wood-**, *Luzula*.
Ruspolia Lindau. Acanthaceae (IV. B). 2 Somaliland.
Russelia Jacq. Scrophulariaceae (II. 4). 8 trop. Am. *R. juncea* Zucc., often cult., is xero. with much reduced l. and pendulous green stems. Shoots sometimes appear under cult. with broad l. (perhaps a reversion to an ancestral type).
Russian thistle, *Salsola Kali*, L., var. *tragus* Moq.
Russowia C. Winkler. Compositae (11). 1 Turkestan.
Rust, *Berberis*, *Triticum*.
Rustia Klotzsch. Rubiaceae (I. 1). 6 trop. Am.
Ruta (Tourn.) L. Rutaceae (I). 50 Medit., As. *R. graveolens* L., rue, cult., is a strongly smelling shrub, owing to the presence in the l., &c., of an ethereal oil. The terminal fl. of the infl. is 5-merous, the lat. fls. 4-merous. The sta. lie in pairs in the boat-like petals; one by one they bend upwards over the stigma, dehisce and fall back; when all have done this, the stigma ripens, and finally the sta. again move up and effect self-fert. Chiefly visited by small flies. Rue is a narcotic and stimulant.
Rutabaga, *Brassica campestris* L.
Rutaceae (*EP.*, *BH.* add § II to *Meliaceae*). Dicots. (Archichl. Geraniales). 100 gen., with 800 sp. trop. and temp., esp. S. Afr. and Austr. Most are shrubs and trees, often xero., frequently of heath-like habit (*e.g.* Diosma). L. alt. or opp., exstip., usu. cpd., with

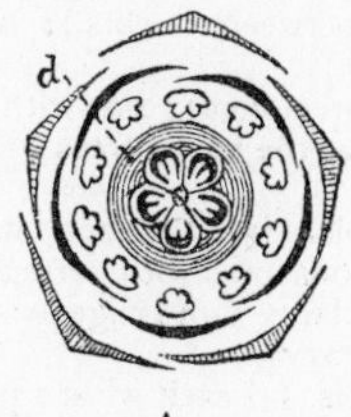

A

B

Floral diagrams of Rutaceae, after Eichler. A, *Ruta graveolens* (d=disc); B, *Citrus Aurantium*, single case showing variable numbers in stamen-bundles.

glandular dots, often aromatic. In many *Aurantieae* there are short shoots whose l. are reduced to thorns (*cf.* Cactaceae). Infl. of various forms, usu. cymose. Fl. ☿, rarely unisexual, reg. or ·|·, 5—4-merous (see Ruta), with a large disc below G. K or (K) 5 or 4, odd sepal post.; C 5 or 4 imbr.; A 10 or 8, obdiplost. or 5, 3, 2, or ∞, with intr. anthers; $\underline{G}$ (5 or 4), rarely (3—1) or (∞), often free at base and united above by the style (*cf.* Apocyn.), multiloc.; ov. 2—∞ or 1 in each loc., anatr. with ventral raphe and micropyle facing upwards. Fr. various; schizocarps, drupes, berries, &c. Seeds with or without endosp.

Several R. are or have been used in medicine, chiefly on account of the oils they contain, *e.g.* Ruta, Galipea, Toddalia, &c. Citrus yields important fruits (orange, &c.), and Chloroxylon a timber.

Classification and chief genera (after Engler): The groups of R. differ considerably among themselves, and several of them were formerly regarded as independent fams. The relationships to allied fams. are thus given by Engler:

Zygophyllaceae, Cneoraceae ← → Meliaceae, Burseraceae, Simarubaceae
↓
Rutaceae

I. *RUTOIDEAE.* Cpls. usu. 4—5, rarely 3—1, or > 5, often only united by the style, and ± divided when ripe; loculic. dehiscence usu. with separation of the endocarp; rarely 4—1 fleshy drupes.

1. *Zanthoxyleae* (woody plants, usu. with small greenish, reg., often unisexual fls.; cpl. rarely with > 2 ovules; embryo with flat cots. in endosp.): Zanthoxylum, Fagara, Choisya.

2. *Ruteae* (herbs or undershrubs, rarely shrubs, with moderate sized ☿ fls., sometimes slightly ·|·; cpls. usu. with > 2 ov.; endosp.): Ruta, Dictamnus.

3. *Boronieae* (undershrubs and shrubs, with reg. usu. ☿ fls.; endosp. fleshy, otherwise as 2): Boronia, Eriostemon, Correa.

4. *Diosmeae* (undershrubs and shrubs, rarely trees with simple l.; exalbum., embryo usu. straight with fleshy cots.): Calodendron, Adenandra, Diosma.

5. *Cusparieae* (shrubs and trees with reg. or ·|· fls.; endosp. little or 0; embryo curved, with radicle between the cots.): Almeidea, Galipea, Cusparia.

6. *Dictyolomeae* (fls. reg., haplostemonous; sta. with scales at base; cpls. with ∞ ovules, only united at the base; trees with double pinnate l.): Dictyoloma.

II. *FLINDERSIOIDEAE.* Cpls. (5—3), each with 2—8 2-ranked erect ovules; capsule loculic. or septic. with persistent endocarp; seed winged, exalbum.; woody plants with lysigenous glands.

Flindersieae: Flindersia, Chloroxylon.

III. *SPATHELIOIDEAE.* Cpls. (3) each with 2 pend. ov.; drupe winged; secretory cells and lysigenous oil-glands at margins of l.

Spathelieae: Spathelia.

IV. *TODDALIOIDEAE.* Cpls. (5—2) or 1, each with 2—1 ov.; drupe or dry winged fr.; endosp. or 0; l. and bark with lysigenous oil-glands.

Toddalieae: Ptelea, Toddalia, Skimmia.

V. *AURANTIOIDEAE.* Berry, often with periderm, and

with pulp derived from sappy emergences of cpl. wall. Seeds exalbum., often with 2 or more embryos. Lysigenous oil-glands.

Aurantieae: Glycosmis, Limonia, Atalantia, Feronia, Aegle, Citrus.

Ruthea Bolle (*Lichtensteinia BH.*). Umbelliferae (III. 5). 2 Canaries, St Helena.

Rutidea DC. Rubiaceae (II. 4). 15 trop. Afr., Madag.

Rutidosis DC. Compositae (4). 6 Austr.

Rutilans (Lat.), with glowing fls.

Rutilia Vell. Inc. sed. 1 Brazil.

Ruttya Harv. Acanthaceae (IV. B). 3 S. Afr.

Ruyschia Jacq. Marcgraviaceae. 3 trop. Am.

Ryania Vahl (*Patrisia* Rich.). Flacourtiaceae (7). 10 N. trop. S. Am.

Rydbergia Greene (*Actinella* p.p.). Compositae (6). 2 N. Am.

Rye, *Secale cereale* L.; **-grass,** *Lolium perenne* L.; **French --,** *Arrhenatherum.*

Rylstonea R. T. Baker. Myrtaceae (inc. sed.). 1 Austr.

Ryncospora Vahl. Cyperaceae (II). 175 temp. and trop.; 2 in Brit. in wet bogs (beak rush).

Ryparosa Bl. Flacourtiaceae (3). 10 Malaya. A (∞). Styles 0.

Ryssopterys Blume ex A. Juss. Malpighiaceae (1). 7 E. Indomal.

Ryssosciadium O. Ktze. = Rhysopterus Coulter et Rose (Umbell.).

Ryticaryum Becc. Icacinaceae. 4 New Guinea.

Rytidocarpus Coss. Cruciferae. 1 Morocco.

Rytidotus Hook. f. (*Bobea* p.p. *EP.*). Rubiaceae (II. 2). 1 Hawaiian Is.

Sabadilla Brandb. et Ratzebg. (*Schoenocaulon* A. Gray *BH.*). Liliaceae (1). 5 Georgia to Venezuela.

Sabal Adans. Palmae (I. 2). 10 warmer Am., W.I. *S. Palmetto* Lodd., &c. (palmetto or thatch palm), l. are used for thatching; the wood is also useful.

Sabaudia Buscalioni et Muschler. Labiatae (VII). 1 C. Afr.

Sabazia Cass. Compositae (5). 2 Mexico.

Sabbata Vell. Compositae (inc. sed.). 2 Brazil.

Sabbatia Adans. Gentianaceae (1). 12 N. Am. (rose pinks).

Sabia Colebr. Sabiaceae. 20 S. and E. As.

Sabiaceae (*EP.*, *BH.*). Dicots. (Archichl. Sapindales). 4 gen., 65 sp., trop. and E. As. Trees, shrubs or lianes with alt. exstip. imparipinnate or simple l. Infl. a panicle or cymose panicle, with bracts and bracteoles. Fls. usu. ☿. K (3—5), imbr. or free; C 4—5, sometimes united at base, imbr., the inner 2 much reduced; A 5, opp. petals, all or only 2 fertile, the rest being staminodial; G̲ (2) 2-loc.; in each loc. usu. 2 axile pend. or horiz. semi-anatr. ov. with micropyle upwards. Indeh. fr. with exalbum. seeds. *Chief genera:* Sabia, Meliosma.

Sabicea Aubl. Rubiaceae (I. 7). 30 trop. Am., Afr., Madag.

Sabina Hall = Juniperus Tourn. p.p. (Conif.). 5 N. temp.

Sabinea DC. Leguminosae (III. 6). 3 Panama, W.I.

Sabre bean, *Canavalia ensiformis* DC.

Sabulina Reichb. = Arenaria Rupp. (*BH.*). = Alsine Scop. p.p.

Sac, a pouch; **saccate,** with a pouch.

Saccardophytum Spegazzini. Solanaceae (inc. sed.). 1 Patagonia.

Saccellium Humb. et Bonpl. Boraginaceae (II). 1 Peru, Argentina.
Saccharodendron Nieuwland (*Acer* p.p.). Aceraceae. 5 N. Am.
Saccharum L. Gramineae (2). 12 trop., subtrop., incl. *S. officinarum* L. (sugar cane), a native(?) of trop. E. As., now cult. in most warm regions, esp. Java, Hawaii, U.S., &c. From the rhiz. there spring each year shoots which may reach 12—15 feet and a thickness of 2 inches; the outer tissues have much silica in their cell-walls. The infl. is a dense woolly spike, the first and second glumes of each spikelet being covered with long hairs. The cult. form has always been veg. propagated (pieces of the haulm, each bearing a bud, are planted), but recently a more vigorous race has been raised from seed. The sugar is contained in the soft central tissues of the stem; the canes are cut before flowering and crushed between rollers to extract the juice; afterwards it is boiled down under reduced pressure and laid out to crystallise.
Saccocalyx Coss. et Dur. (*Satureia* p.p. *BH.*). Labiat. (VI). 1 Alger.
Saccoglossum Schlechter. Orchidaceae (II. 16). 2 New Guinea.
Saccoglottis Endl. Humiriaceae. 10 trop. S. Am., Afr.
Saccolabium Blume. Orchidaceae (II. 20). 50 Indomal. Cult. orn. fl.
Saccolaria Kuhlmann. Lentibulariaceae. 1 Upper Amazon.
Saccolepis Nash (*Panicum* p.p.). Gramineae. 5 N. Am.
Saccoloma Kaulf. Dicksoniaceae. 8 trop. Am., E. As.
Saccopetalum Bennett. Anonaceae (2). 5 trop. As., Austr.
Saccostoma Wall. Labiatae (inc. sed.). 1 Indomal.
Sachsia Griseb. Compositae (4). 4 Cuba, Fla., Bahamas.
Sack tree (Ceylon), *Antiaris toxicaria* Leschen.
Sacleuxia Baill. Asclepiadaceae (II. 1). 1 Zanzibar.
Sacoglottis Mart. = Saccoglottis Endl. (Humir.).
Sacred bean or **lotus**, *Nelumbium speciosum* Willd.
Sacrosphendamus Nieuwland (*Acer* p.p.). Aceraceae. 1 N. Am.
Sadiria Mez (*Pimelandra* p.p.). Myrsinaceae (II). 4 Assam, Bhutan.
Sadleria Kaulf. Polypodiaceae. 4 Hawaiian Is.
Safflower, *Carthamus tinctorius* L.
Saffordia Maxon. Polypodiaceae. 1 Peru.
Saffordiella Merrill (*Leptospermum* p.p.). Myrt. (II. 1). 1 Phil. Is.
Saffranhout, *Elaeodendron croceum* DC.
Saffron, *Crocus sativus* L.; **meadow-**, *Colchicum autumnale* L.
Sage, *Salvia*, esp. *S. officinalis* L.; **-brush**, *Artemisia tridentata* Nutt., &c.; **-rose** (W.I.), *Turnera*; **wood-**, *Teucrium*.
Sageraea Dalzell (*Bocagea BH.*). Anonaceae (1). 6 Indomal.
Sageretia Brongn. Rhamnaceae. 12 warm E. As., N. Am.
Sagina L. Caryophyllaceae (I. 1). 20 N. temp.; 4 in Brit. (pearlwort). Small herbs with inconspic., sometimes apet. fls.
Sagittaria Rupp. ex L. Alismaceae. 33 Am., temp. |※, incl. *S. sagittifolia* L. (arrow-head) in Eur. (incl. Brit.), a water-plant with a short rhiz. bearing l. of various types, the number of each kind depending on the depth of the water, &c. The fully submerged l. are ribbon-shaped, the floating ones have an ovate blade, whilst those (usually the majority) that project above water are arrow-shaped (sagittate). In the axils are formed the 'renewal' shoots which last over the winter, short branches which burrow into the mud and swell up at the ends

each into a large bud whose central axis is swollen with reserve-materials; in spring this develops into a new plant. The diclinous racemose infl. projects above water; the ♀ fls. are lower down than the ♂. The ♂ contains ∞ sta., the ☿ ∞ cpls.

Sagittate (l.), with two lobes at base projecting towards stem.

Sagittipetalum Merrill. Rhizophoraceae. 2 Phil. Is.

Sago, *Metroxylon*, and *Arenga*, *Caryota*, *Cycas*, *Oreodoxa*, &c.

Sagotanthus Van Tiegh. (*Heisteria* p.p.). Olacaceae. 1 Guiana.

Sagotia Baill. Euphorbiaceae (A. II. 5). 1 N. Brazil, Guiana.

Sagraea DC. (*Clidemia* p.p. *EP.*). Melastomaceae (I). 20 trop. Am.

Saguerus Adans. = Arenga Labill. (Palm.).

Sagus Rumph ex Gaertn. = Metroxylon Rottb. (Palm.).

Sahagunia Liebm. (*Acanthinophyllum* Allem.). Moraceae (II). 3 trop. Am. *S. strepitans* Engl. (Braz.), good timber.

Sails, *cf.* Bamboos.

Sainfoin, *Onobrychis sativa* Lam.

St Dabeoc's heath, *Daboecia*; **- Ignatius' beans**, *Strychnos Ignatii* Berg.; **- John's bread**, *Ceratonia*; **- - wort**, *Hypericum*.

Saintpaulia H. Wendl. Gesneriaceae (I). 3 E. Afr., incl. *S. ionantha* H. Wendl. (Afr. violet). The fl. is like that of Exacum, with similar dimorphic symmetry. In some the style projects to the left over the C, in others to the right (cf. Exacum, Cassia).

Sakersia Hook. f. Melastomaceae (I). 2 Cameroons.

Sal, *Shorea robusta* Gaertn. f.

Salacia L. Hippocrateaceae. 100 trop., often lianes with dimorphic branches, one form suited for climbing.

Salacicratea Loes. Hippocrateaceae. 1 New Guinea.

Salacistis Reichb. f. (*Hetaeria BH.*). Orchidaceae (II. 2). 1 Java.

Salad oil, nominally olive oil, *Olea europea* L.

Salaxis Salisb. Ericaceae (IV. 2). 24 Cape Colony.

Salazaria Torr. Labiatae (IV). 1 S.W. U.S., Mexico.

Saldanhaea Bur. Bignoniaceae (I). 2 Brazil.

Saldania Sim. Leguminosae (III. 8). 1 S.E. Afr.

Saldinia A. Rich. Rubiaceae (II. 5). 2 Madag.

Salep, the dried tubers of some sp. of Orchis and (in India) Eulophia.

Salicaceae (*EP.*, *BH.*). Dicots. (Archichl. Salicales; anom. Incompletae *BH.*). 2 gen., 180 sp., N. temp., trop. and subtrop. Shrubs or trees with stip. l. and much veg. repr. by suckers. Fls. naked, in catkins or spikes, dioec. (many hybrids exist). The catkins arise in autumn and remain as buds through the winter, developing in early spring. The ♂ fl. consists of 2—30 sta. in the axil of a bract, the ♀ usu. of (2) cpls. transv. placed, syncarpous with parietal plac.; ovules ∞, anatr. Seeds exalbum. with basal tufts of hairs. *Genera:* Salix, Populus.

Salicales. The 3rd order of Archichlamydeae.

Salicaria Tourn. ex Mill. = Lythrum L. (Lythr.).

Saliciflorae (Warming). The 1st order of Choripetalae.

Salicornia (Tourn.) L. Chenopodiaceae (A). 10 on sea-coasts. *S. herbacea* L. (saltwort) cosmop., incl. Brit. Succulent herbs, with the habit of a cactus, leafless and with jointed nodes. Fls. in groups of 3 or more, one group sunk in the tissue on either side of each internode. P fleshy; sta. 1 or 2.

Salisburia Sm. = Ginkgo L. (Ginkg.).

Salix (Tourn.) L. Salicaceae. 160 cosmop. The sp. are difficult to separate and there are many hybrids (cf. Rubus, Rosa). 12 in Brit. (willow, sallow, &c.). Branching monopodial, but the term. bud usu. dies, and the next lat. bud continues the axis. Some have collateral buds in the axils. There is extensive veg. repr. by suckers. Some, *e.g.* *S. alba* L., are often pollarded, or cut off at a height of 8 feet or so; from the callus formed upon the wounds new shoots spring, and thus the 'crown' of shoots is produced. Among the Brit. sp. are *S. herbacea* L., the dwarf or arctic willow, a creeping alpine and arctic form, and *S. lanata* L., &c. alpine forms with very woolly l. The fls. contain honey, and as they appear in early spring, before the l., and when they have but few competitors, they receive a great many visits from insects, especially from bees. *S. viminalis* L. is the osier, whose twigs are used in making baskets, &c. *S. babylonica* L. is the weeping willow. *S. caprea* L. useful wood.

Sallal, *Gaultheria Shallon* Pursh.

Sallow, *Salix*.

Salmea DC. Compositae (5). 12 Mexico, W.I.

Salmeopsis Benth. Compositae (5). 1 S. Brazil, Paraguay.

Salmia Willd. = Carludovica Ruiz et Pav. (Cyclanth.).

Salomonia Heist. (*Polygonatum* p.p.). Liliaceae (VII). 2 N. Am.

Salomonia Lour. Polygalaceae. 8 E. As., Austr. Some are parasitic.

Salpichroa Miers. Solanaceae (2). 12 warm Am.

Salpiglossis Ruiz et Pav. Solanaceae (5). 8 S. Am. Cult. orn. fl.

Salpinga Mart. Melastomaceae (1). 3 S. Brazil. Cult. orn. fl.

Salpingacanthus Sp. Moore (*Ruellia* p.p. *EP.*). Acanth. (IV. A). 1 Brazil.

Salpingia Torr. et Gray (*Oenothera* p.p.). Onagr. (2). 4 Mexico, Texas.

Salpinxantha Hook. f. (*Geissomeria BH.*). Acanthaceae (IV. B). 1 Jamaica.

Salsify, *Tragopogon porrifolius* L.

Salsola L. Chenopodiaceae (B). 40 cosmop., maritime or on salt steppes. *S. Kali* L. (glass-wort) in Brit., a very fleshy plant with l. ending in spines. A var. *tragus* Moq. of this sp. (Russian thistle) has in recent years become a pest of agriculture in N. Am.

Salsuginosus (Lat.), growing where inundated by salt water.

Salt-bush, *Atriplex*, &c.; **-wort**, *Salsola*; **-steppe plants** (halophytes), *Chenopodiaceae*, *Frankeniaceae*, &c.

Saltia R. Br. Amarantaceae (2). 1 S. Arabia.

Salvador tea, *Gaultheria*.

Salvadora Garcin. ex L. Salvadoraceae. 2 W. As., Afr. *S. persica* L. is said to be the mustard of the Bible. Its l. taste like mustard.

Salvadoraceae (*EP.*, *BH.*). Dicots. (Archichl. Sapind.; Gentianales *BH.*). 3 gen., 8 sp., As., Afr. Shrubs and trees with opp. entire stip. l. and racemose infls. Fls. ☿ or unisexual, reg. K (2—4); C 4—5 or (4—5), usu. with teeth or glands on inner side; A 4—5, epipet. or not; $\underline{G}$ (2), 1—2-loc. with 1—2 erect anatr. ov. in each.

Fr. a 1-seeded berry or drupe. Seed exalbum. *Genera:* Azima, Dobera, Salvadora. The relationships are doubtful, for we do not know if the polypetaly of A. and D. is original or secondary.

Salver-shaped (C), ± flat, with long tubular portion, *Primula.*

Salvertia A. St Hil. Vochys. 1 campos of S. Brazil. Stigma lat.

Salvetia Pohl. Inc. sed. Nomen.

Salvia (Tourn.) L. Labiatae (VI). 550 trop. and temp. *S. Verbenaca* L. (sage) and *S. pratensis* L. (clary) in Brit. The sta. are reduced to 2 (the ant.), each of which has a sort of T-shape, the connective of the versatile anther being greatly elongated. The stalks of the sta. stand up together across the mouth of the fl., and a bee, in pushing down towards the honey, comes into contact with the inner end of the anther, and raising it causes the outer to descend upon its back and to rub it with pollen. In some forms of S. both ends of the lever bear fertile anthers; but in most the useless half-anther at the inner end is aborted, and the outer half of the connective is much longer than the inner (compare *S. officinalis* with *S. pratensis*). The fl. is protandrous, and in the later stage the style bends down and places the stigma in position to be touched first by an entering insect. Some have coloured bracts at the top of the infl., adding to its conspicuousness. *S. officinalis* L. (Medit.) is the garden sage.

Salviacanthus Lindau. Acanthaceae (IV. B). 1 Cameroons.

Salviastrum Scheele. Labiatae (VI). 3 Texas, New Mexico.

Salvinia (Mich.) Schreb. Salviniaceae. 10 trop. and warm temp., incl. *S. natans* (L.) All. The pl. floats freely on the water; at each node is a whorl of three l., and the whorls alt. with one another. There are two floating l. derived from the upper half of a segment of the apical cell (see fam.), and a submerged l. derived from the lower. There are no roots, their function being performed by the finely divided submerged l. (*cf.* Trapa, Ranunculus, Cabomba). The sporocarps are borne several together as outgrowths from the base of a submerged l. The microspores germinate inside the sporangium, the prothalli emerging through its wall as fine tubes, at the end of which the antheridia form.

Salviniaceae. Filicales Leptosporangiatae. Two genera, Salvinia (l. in whorls of 3) and Azolla (l. in two ranks), with 15 sp., trop. and temp. Water plants, with a stem floating upon the water, and growing by a two-sided apical cell (3-sided in the young embryo, as in other Filicales). A dorsiventral construction thus arises; segments are cut off right and left from the apical cell, and the first division of each of these segments divides it into a dorsal and a ventral half. In S. the dorsal halves give rise to the floating, the ventral to the submerged l.; in A. the former give rise to the l., the latter to the branches and roots. The sporangia are grouped into sori; the sorus is enclosed in a highly developed indusium, forming a sporocarp. Each contains only one kind of sporangium (micro- or mega-sporangia). The sporocarp is an outgrowth of a l.,—in S. of a submerged l., in A. of the ventral lobe of an ordinary l. The spore is covered with an *epispore*, consisting of hardened frothy mucilage. It sinks, when set free from the sporangium. On germ. the microspore forms a rudimentary ♂ prothallus consisting of one (? more) veg. cell and an antheridium. The megaspore forms a ♀ prothallus, which remains enclosed in the burst spore, and has two parts, an upper small-celled green part on which are borne the archegonia, and a lower colourless part (of one or more large cells), in which reserves are stored up for the use of the young plant which will be formed from a fert. ovum (*cf.* Selaginella and Phanerogams).

Salzmannia DC. Rubiaceae (II. 3). 1 E. Brazil.

Samadera Gaertn. Simarubaceae. 7 Madag., Indomal.

Saman, *Pithecolobium Saman* Benth.

Samara L. = Embelia Burm. p.p. (Myrsin.).

Samara, a winged 1-seeded indeh. achene or nut, *Acer*, *Banisteria*, *Fraxinus*, *Liriodendron*, *Ptelea*, *Pterocarpus*, *Ulmus*, *Ventilago*.

Sambucus (Tourn.) L. Caprifoliaceae. 20 N. temp., S. Am., As. to Austr. *S. nigra* L. (elder) and *S. Ebulus* L. in Brit. Differs from the rest of the fam. in having cpd. l. and extr. anthers; it also possesses well-marked stipules. Lenticels show clearly in the bark. *S. nigra* L. shows serial adv. buds. There has been some discussion about the proper position to be assigned to it; it has been put in Valerianaceae or in a new family, *Sambucaceae*, forming a link between Rubiales and Aggregatae. A wine is prepared from elder berries.

Sameraria Desv. (*Isatis BH.*). Cruciferae (2). 7 E. Medit.

Samoa millet, *Panicum*.

Samolus (Tourn.) L. Primulaceae. 10 cosmop., esp. ✳; *S. Valerandi* L. (brook-weed) in Brit. The whole pl. dies down in autumn, but young shoots form in summer and take root. The bracts of the fls. are 'adnate' to the axes, so as to look like sol. bracteoles (*cf.* Solanaceae).

Samphire, *Crithmum maritimum* L., (Am.) *Salicornia*.

Samuela Trelease. Liliaceae (VI). 2 Mexico, California.

Samyda L. Flacourtiaceae (7). 4 W.I., Mexico.

Samydaceae (*BH.*). A fam. in Passiflorales, comprising the gen. Samyda, Casearia, Banara, Abatia, Homalium, &c.; placed in Flacourtiaceae by Engler.

Sanchezia Ruiz et Pav. Acanthaceae (IV. A). 10 trop. S. Am.

San Domingo apricot, *Mammea americana* L.

Sand-binding plants, *Acacia*, *Ammophila*, *Carex*, *Distichlis*, *Elymus*, *Larrea*, *Lepidosperma*, *Stenotaphrum*, &c.; **-bur,** *Cenchrus tribuloides* L.; **-box tree,** *Hura*; **-dunes, flora of,** *cf.* Tansley, *Types of Brit. Veg.*; **-spurrey** (Am.), *Spergularia*; **-wort,** *Arenaria*.

Sandalwood, *Santalum album* L.; **red -,** *Pterocarpus santalinus* L.

Sandarach, *Tetraclinis quadrivalvis* Vent.

Sandbergia Greene (*Arabis* p.p.). Cruciferae (4). 1 N.W. N. Am.

Sanderella O. Ktze. = Parlatorea Barb. Rodr. (Orch.).

Sanders wood, Sandalwood.

Sandersonia Hook. Liliaceae (I). 1 Natal.

Sandoricum Cav. Meliaceae (III). 6 Mauritius, Indomal. Some have ed. fr.

Sanguinaria Dill. ex L. Papaveraceae (II). 1 Atl. N. Am., *S. canadensis* L., the blood-root. It has a thick rhiz. giving off annually one l. and a 1-flowered scape. The rhiz. is used in medicine.

Sanguineus (Lat.), blood-coloured.

Sanguisorba Rupp. ex L. (*Poterium BH.*). 30 N. temp. 2 Brit.,

S. minor Scop. and *S. officinalis* L., anemophilous, the former with long pend. sta.

Sanhilaria Baill. Bignoniaceae (I). 1 S. Brazil.

Sanicle, *Sanicula europea* L.

Sanicula (Tourn.) L. Umbelliferae (II. 1). 40 cosmop. exc. Austr. *S. europaea* L. (sanicle) in Brit. Fls. in cymose umbels, themselves arranged in dichasia. Fr. hooked, animal-distributed.

Sansevieria Thumb. Liliaceae (VIII). 60 trop. Afr., As. Xero. with fleshy l. *S. zeylanica* Willd. yields fibre (bow-string hemp).

Santalaceae (*EP.*; *BH.* incl. *Grubbiaceae*, *Myzodendraceae*). Dicots. (Archichl. Santalales; Achlamydosporeae *BH.*). 26 gen., 250 sp., of semi-parasitic shrubs, trees and herbs, resembling Loranthaceae in many ways, trop. and temp. Some are stem-parasites like mistletoe, others root-parasites like Rhinanthus (*e.g.* Thesium). L. opp. The total infl. may be a raceme, spike, head, &c., but often, instead of the single fl. in each axil, there is a little cyme of 3, as in Loranthaceae. Fls. ☿ or unisexual, with perig. or epig. disc and a simple P (sepaloid or petaloid); sta. =, and inserted on, the P-leaves. $\bar{G}$ 1-loc., with a central placenta bearing 1—3 ovules. Nut or drupe; seed 1, with no testa, and much endosp. *Chief genera:* Santalum, Thesium.

Santalales. The 14th order of Archichlamydeae. *Cf.* p. xii.

Santalina Baill. Rubiaceae (I. 8). 1 Madag.

Santalodes O. Ktze., **Santaloides** Schellenb. = Rourea Aubl. p.p.

Santalum L. Santalaceae. 10 Indomal. Parasitic trees. *S. album* L. (S. Ind., esp. Mysore) furnishes the true sandal-wood (yellow or white). Oil is distilled from it.

Santiria Blume. Burseraceae. 30 Malaya.

Santiridium Pierre = Pachylobus G. Don p.p. (Burser.).

Santiriopsis Engl. (*Santiria* p.p.). Burseraceae. 1 S. Thome.

Santolina Tourn. ex L. Compositae (7). 8 South Eur. *S. Chamaecyparissus* L. is officinal.

Sanvitalia Gualt. in Lam. Compositae (5). 8 warm Am. Cult. orn. fl.

Sap-green, *Rhamnus cathartica* L.; **-wood,** the young outer wood.

Sapidus (Lat.), with pleasant taste.

Sapindaceae (*EP.*; *BH.* incl. *Aceraceae*, *Hippocastanaceae*, *Melianthaceae*, *Staphyleaceae*). Dicots. (Archichl. Sapindales). 120 gen., 1000 sp., trop. and subtrop. 5 gen. (Serjania, Paullinia, &c.) with 300 sp. are lianes, the rest erect trees or shrubs. The lianes climb by tendrils, which are met. infl.-axes and are usu. branched or sometimes watch-spring-like; their stems often show peculiar internal anatomy. L. alt., stip. in the climbing sp., usu. cpd., pinnate; in the climbing sp. there is usu. a true term. leaflet, but not in the erect; in these one of the last pair of leaflets often becomes term., so that the l. is asymmetric. The tissues of the plants usually contain resinous or latex-like secretions in special cells. The infl. is cymose, usu. a cincinnus, with bracts and bracteoles.

Fl. unisexual (the sta. are apparently well developed in the ♀ so that it is easily mistaken for ☿, but the pollen is useless, and the anthers do not open), generally monoec., reg. or often obliquely ·|·, 5- or 4-merous. K usu. 5, rarely (5), imbr. or rarely valvate or open, sometimes apparently 4-merous by union of 2 sepals; C usu. 5, imbr., with well-marked disc between it and the sta.; A usu. 5 + 5 in one whorl, often with 2 absent, more rarely 5, 4, or ∞, inserted within or rarely upon the disc round the rudimentary ovary; G in ♀ fl. usu. (3), 3-loc. with term. style; ovules usu. 1 in each loc., ascending, with ventral raphe. Fr. a caps., nut, berry, drupe, schizocarp, or samara, usu. large, often red; seed often arillate, with no endosp.; embryo usu. curved.

Many S. are of economic value; several yield valuable timber; Nephelium, Litchi, and others furnish ed. fr.

Classification and chief genera (after Radlkofer):

I. *EUSAPINDACEAE* (ov. sol. in loc., erect or ascending, micropyle down): Serjania, Paullinia, Sapindus, Talisia, Schleichera, Litchi, Nephelium, Pappea, Cupania, Blighia.

II. *DYSSAPINDACEAE* (ov. usu. 2 or several in each loc., in the first case erect or pend., in the second horiz., rarely 1 pend. with micropyle up): Koelreuteria, Dodonaea.

Sapindales. The 24th order (*EP.*) of Archichlamydeae. The 10th (*BH.*) of Polypetalae. *Cf.* pp. xxvi, li.

Sapindus Tourn. ex L. Sapindaceae (I). 20 trop. and subtrop. exc. Afr. and Austr. The berries of *S. Saponaria* L. (Am.) contain saponin, form a lather with water, and may be used as soap.

Sapium P. Br. Euphorbiaceae (A. II. 7). 100 warm. Seeds of *S. sebiferum* Roxb. (tallow-tree, China) are coated with fat; they also yield an oil by pressure. Some yield rubber (Bolivian, Colombian).

Sapodilla plum, *Achras Sapota* L.

Saponaria L. Caryophyllaceae (II. 2). 20 N. temp., chiefly Medit. *S. officinalis* L. (soapwort) in Brit. Its leaves lather if rubbed with water. Fls. protandrous, butterfly-visited.

Saponin, *Chlorogalum*, *Gouania*, *Limonia*, *Sapindus*, *Saponaria*.

Sapota Plum. ex Mill. = Achras L. (Sapot.).

Sapotaceae (*EP.*, *BH.*). Dicots. (Sympet. Ebenales). 35 gen., 600 sp., trop., mostly trees with entire leathery l., sometimes stip. They are commonly hairy with 2-shanked hairs, and contain secretory passages in pith, cortex and l. Fls. sol. or in cymose bunches in the l. axils or on old stems, bracteolate, ☿, reg. or not. K 2 + 2, 3 + 3, 4 + 4, or 5; C usu. equal in number to sepals, and alt. with the K as a whole, as in Cruciferae, rarely in 2 whorls. In *Mimusopeae* the petals have dorsal appendages like themselves, giving the appearance of more than one whorl. Sta. in 2 or 3 whorls, but frequently the outer staminodial or absent; anthers commonly extr. G, syncarpous, multiloc.; cpls. = or twice the number of sta. in a whorl, or more; ovules at base of axile placenta, one in each loc., anatr. with micropyle facing down; style simple. Berry, the flesh sometimes sclerenchymatous near the surface. Seeds few or one, usually album.; endosp. oily; testa hard and rich in tannin.

Many S. furnish useful products, esp. gutta-percha and balata; see all genera below. A fam. of conspic. economic value.

Classification and chief genera (after Engler):

I. *Palaquieae* (petals without appendages): Bassia, Payena, Palaquium, Achras, Butyrospermum, Sideroxylon, Chrysophyllum.

II. *Mimusopeae* (petals with appendages—see above): Mimusops.

Sapote, *Lucuma mammosa* Gaertn. f.

Sappan wood, *Caesalpinia sappan* L.

Sapranthus Seem. (*Porcelia BH.*, *Uvaria* p.p. *EP.*). Anon. (1). 1 C. Am.

Sapria Griff. Rafflesiaceae. 1 Assam.

Saprophytes, plants which grow upon decaying organic matter and absorb the products of decay, *Burmanniaceae*, some *Gentianaceae* (*Bartonia*, *Obolaria*, &c.), *Monotropa*, some *Orchidaceae* (*Corallorhiza*, *Epipogon*, *Limodorum*, *Neottia*, &c.), *Triuridaceae*, the prothallus of *Ophioglossaceae*.

Saprosma Blume. Rubiaceae (II. 5). 20 Indomal.

Sapu (Ceylon), *Michelia Champaca* L.

Sapucaia nut, *Lecythis*.

Saraca L. Leguminosae (II. 3). 10 trop. As. Young shoots pend. (*cf.* Amherstia, Brownea). Fls. (scented at night) as temple offerings.

Saracha Ruiz et Pav. Solanaceae (2). 12 Bolivia to Mexico.

Saranthe Eichl. (*Myrosma BH.*). Marantaceae. 8 Brazil.

Sararanga Hemsl. Pandanaceae. 1 Solomon Is., New Guinea.

Sarcanthidion Baill. Icacinaceae. 1 New Caledonia.

Sarcanthus Lindl. Orchidaceae (II. 20). 30 Indomal., China. Cult.

Sarcaulis Radlk. Sapotaceae (1). 1 N. Brazil, Guiana.

Sarcinanthus Oerst. (*Carludovica* p.p. *BH.*). Cyclanth. 1 Costa Rica.

Sarcobatus Nees. Chenopodiaceae (B). 2 N. Am.

Sarcocalyx Walp. = Aspalathus L. (Legum.).

Sarcocapnos DC. Papaveraceae (III). 3 Medit.

Sarcocarp, the fleshy part of a drupe; **-testa,** of a seedcoat.

Sarcocaulon Sweet. Geraniaceae. 6 S. Afr. Xero.; fleshy stems. When the l. falls the base of the petiole hardens to a thorn.

Sarcocephalus Afzel. ex R. Br. Rubiaceae (I. 6). 10 palaeotrop.

Sarcochilus R. Br. Orchidaceae (II. 20). 40 Indomal. Polynesia.

Sarcochlaena Thou. Chlaenaceae. 4 Madag.

Sarcochlamys Gaudich. Urticaceae (3). 1 Indomal.

Sarcococca Lindl. Buxaceae. 5 Indomal.

Sarcocodon N. E. Br. (*Caralluma* p.p. *EP.*). Asclep. (II. 3). 4 S.W. As.

Sarcocolla L. Penaeaceae. 4 Cape Colony.

Sarcodes Torr. Pyrolaceae. 1 California.

Sarcodraba Gilg et Muschler (*Draba* p.p.). Crucif. (4). 1 Patag.

Sarcodum Lour. Leguminosae (III. 6). 1 Cochinchina.

Sarcoglottis Presl (*Spiranthes* p.p. *BH.*). Orchid. (II. 2). 10 trop., subtrop.

Sarcolaena Thou. Chlaenaceae. 4 Madag.

Sarcolobus R. Br. Asclepiadaceae (II. 3). 6 Malaya.

Sarcomelicope Engl. (*Evodia* p.p.). Rutaceae (I). 1 New Caled.

Sarcomphalus P. Br. Rhamnaceae. 5 W.I. *S. laurinus* Griseb. timber.

Sarcopetalum F. Muell. Menispermaceae. 1 E. Austr.

Sarcophrynium K. Schum. Marantaceae. 12 W. trop. Afr.

Sarcophyte Sparrm. Balanophoraceae. 1 Cape Colony.

Sarcopilea Urb. Urticaceae (2). 1 S. Domingo.
Sarcopodium Lindl. (*Bulbophyllum* p.p.). Orchid. (II. 16). 20 E. Indomal.
Sarcopteryx Radlk. Sapindaceae (I). 8 E. Indomal.
Sarcopyramis Wall. Melastomaceae (I). 3 India.
Sarcosperma Hook. f. Sapotaceae (I). 4 E. Indomal.
Sarcostemma R. Br. Asclepiadaceae (II. 1). 12 trop. and subtrop. |✻. Leafless xero. with slightly fleshy stems.
Sarcostigma Wight et Arn. Icacinaceae. 3 Indomal.
Sarcotheca Blume. Linaceae. 2 Borneo, Malay Peninsula.
Sarcotoechia Radlk. (*Cupania* p.p.; *Ratonia BH.*). Sapindaceae (I). 2 Austr.
Sarcozygium Bunge (*Zygophyllum* p.p. *EP.*). Zygophyll. 1 Mongolia.
Sarga Ewart. Gramineae (8). 1 N.W. Austr.
Sargentia S. Wats. Rutaceae (IV). 1 Mexico, Calif. Fr. ed.
Sargentodoxa Rehder et Wilson. Lardizabal. 1 China. *Cf.* Suppl.
Sarmentose, forming long runners.
Sarmienta Ruiz et Pav. Gesneriaceae (I). 1 Chili.
Sarothamnus Wimm. = Cytisus L. p.p. (Legum.).
Sarotheca Nees = Justicia L. (Acanth.).
Sarothra L. = Hypericum Tourn. (Guttif.).
Sarothrochilus Schlechter (*Trichoglottis* p.p.). Orchidaceae (II. 20). 1 Siam, Burma.
Sarracenia L. Sarraceniaceae. 7 Atl. N. Am. (side-saddle fl.), in sunny marshy places. Low herbs with rosettes of rad. l.; each l. is repres. by a long narrow pitcher with a flat green wing of tissue on the ventral side, serving chiefly for assim. The general structure of the pitcher is similar to that found in Nepenthes; it has a fixed lid projecting over the mouth, and the lip is usu. turned down inwards. The mouth bears numerous honey-glands; below these comes the 'slide-zone,' then the zone of hairs (*cf.* Nepenthes), and at the bottom is water in which the insects are drowned. The pitchers are often brightly coloured. In S. the entire l. is a pitcher, while in Nepenthes it is only part of the l., and in Cephalotus only certain l. Many cult. orn.; many hybrids.
Sarraceniaceae (*EP.*, *BH.*). Dicots. (Archichl. Sarraceniales; Parietales *BH.*). 3 gen., 9 sp., Am. Insectivorous pitcher-plants (see gen.) with rosettes of rad. l. and ☿ reg. fls. K 9—8—5, spiral, if > 5 the outer 3 small; C as many as inner sepals and alt. with them, or 0; A ∞; $\underline{G}$ (6—5—3) with ∞ anatr. ov. on inrolled cpl.-walls. Loculic. caps. with ∞ seeds; endosp. fleshy. *Genera:* Heliamphora (raceme; ovary 3-loc.), Sarracenia (fl. sol.; ovary 5-loc., the top of the pitcher simple), Darlingtonia (ditto, but the top of the pitcher fish-tail-shaped).
Sarraceniales. The 20th order of Dicots. Archichl. *Cf.* p. xx.
Sarsaparilla O. Ktze. Liliaceae (XI). 1 trop. Am.
Sarsaparilla, *Smilax*.
Sartwellia A. Gray. Compositae (6). 2 Texas, Mexico.
Saruma Oliv. Aristolochiaceae. 1 S.W. China.
Sasa Makino et Shibata (*Bambusa* p.p.). Gramin. (13). 8 Japan, As.
Sassafras L. Lauraceae. 1 Canada to Florida, *S. officinale* Nees et

Eberm. (*Laurus Sassafras* L.). The wood and bark yield oil of sassafras, used in medicine.

Sassafridium Meissn. Lauraceae (I). 3 trop. Am., W.I.

Satanocrater Schweinf. Acanthaceae (IV. A). 2 trop. Afr.

Satinwood, *Chloroxylon Swietenia* DC.

Sativus (Lat.), cultivated or planted.

Sattadia Fourn. Asclepiadaceae (II. 1). 1 C. Brazil.

Satureia L. (incl. *Calamintha* Lam.). Labiatae (VI). 130 warm regions. Fls. gynodioec. *S. hortensis* L. and *S. montana* L. (summer and winter savories) cult. condiments.

Saturna Nor. Euphorbiaceae (inc. sed.). Nomen.

Satyria Klotzsch. Ericaceae (III. 2). 4 trop. Am.

Satyrium L. Orchidaceae (II. 1). 70 S. Afr. to trop. As. Fl. not twisted, so that labellum uppermost; it is prolonged backwards into two spurs. The actual summit of the column is occupied by the stigma, the anther being bent round ⊥ to it.

Sau, *Albizzia stipulata* Boiv.

Sauerkraut, *Brassica oleraceae* L.

Saundersia Reichb. f. Orchidaceae (II. 19). 1 Brazil.

Saurauia Willd. Dilleniaceae. 250 trop. As., Am.

Sauroglossum Lindl. (*Spiranthes* p.p. *BH.*). Orchid. (II. 2). 3 trop. Am.

Sauromatum Schott. Araceae (VII). 4 palaeotrop. L. pedate (cymosely branched).

Sauropus Blume. Euphorbiaceae (A. I. 1). 30 Indomal.

Saururaceae (*EP.*; *Piperaceae* p.p. *BH.*). Dicots. (Archichl. Piperales). 3 gen., 4 sp., E. As. and N. Am. Herbs with ☿ fls., apparently primitively naked. A 6 or fewer; $\underline{G}$ 3—4 or (3—4), in the latter case with parietal plac.; ov. orthotr. Endo- and peri-sperm. *Chief genera:* Saururus, Houttuynia.

Saururus Plum. ex L. Saururaceae. 1 Japan to Phil. Is., 1 in E. U.S. Bog pl. with spikes of fls., br. usu. adnate to axis of its fl.

Saussurea DC. Compositae (II). 125 N. temp. *S. alpina* DC. alpine in Brit., with hairy l.; its fls. are blue, with sweet scent (the latter unusual in the order). Many have 3 cpls.

Sautiera Decne. Acanthaceae (IV. A). 1 Timor.

Sauvagesia L. Ochnaceae (Viol. *BH.*). 12 trop., esp. Brazil. 5 fertile sta., surrounded by ∞ stds. Cpls. 3. This gen. and a few others sometimes formed into a separate fam. or placed in Violaceae.

Sauvallea Wright. Commelinaceae. 1 Cuba.

Savannah, grass country broken by patches of forest or copse; **-flower** (W.I.), *Echites*; **-wattle** (W.I.), *Citharexylum*.

Savia Willd. Euphorbiaceae (A. I. 1). 20 W. Ind., trop. Am., Afr.

Savignya DC. Cruciferae (2). 2 Medit.

Savin, *Juniperus Sabina* L.

Savoury, *Satureia*.

Saw wort, *Serratula tinctoria* L.

Saxatilis (Lat.), growing on rocks.

Saxegothaea Lindl. Coniferae (Taxac. 3; see C. for gen. char.). 1 Andes of Patagonia. Fr. a many-seeded 'berry' like Juniperus.

Saxifraga Tourn. ex L. Saxifragaceae (I). 325 N. temp., Arctic,

Andes, chiefly alpine. 13 in Brit. (saxifrage). Most show xero. char., such as tufted growth, close packing of l. (esp. well shown in *S. oppositifolia* L.), succulence, hairiness, &c. Many are veg. repr. by offsets, or (*e.g. S. granulata* L.) by bulbils in the lower leaf-axils. Many exhibit chalk-glands at the tips or edges of the l. (*e.g. S. oppositifolia* at the tip); these are water-pores with nectary-like tissue beneath, secreting water containing chalk in solution. As the water evaporates, the chalk forms an incrustation. Fls. usu. in dich. cymes with cincinnus tendency. Every stage occurs from hypogyny to epigyny. Honey only partially concealed; fls. visited by miscellaneous insects. Most are protandrous. A few, *e.g. S. sarmentosa* Linn. f., have ⚲ fls.

Saxifragaceae (*EP.*; *BH.* incl. *Cephalotaceae*, *Cunoniaceae*). Dicots. (Archichl. Rosales). 90 gen., 750 sp. cosmop., chiefly temp. Most are perenn. herbs, a few shrubs or trees, with usu. alt., rarely stip. l. Many alpine and arctic forms of xero. habit. Infl. of various kinds, both racemose and cymose.

Fl. usu. ☿, reg., cyclic, 5-merous (exc. cpls.). Recept. flat or hollowed to various depths, so that sta. and P may be peri- or epigynous. K usu. 5; C 5, imbr. or valvate, sometimes (5) or 0; A usu. 5 + 5, obdiplost.; cpls. rarely free and as many as petals, usually fewer and joined below, often 2; plac. parietal or axile, with several rows of anatr. ov.; styles as many as cpls. Fls. mostly protandrous. Capsule or berry. Seed with rich endosp. round a small embryo.

Of little economic importance; Ribes yields valuable fr. Many favourites in horticulture, *e.g.* Saxifraga, Francoa, Philadelphus, Deutzia, Hydrangea, Escallonia.

Classification and chief genera:

I. *SAXIFRAGOIDEAE* (herbs of various habit; l. alt.; P 5- or rarely 4-merous; G usu. (2), hypo- or epi-gynous, 1- or 2-loc.): Saxifraga, Tellima, Chrysosplenium, Parnassia.

II. *FRANCOIDEAE* (perenn. herbs with rad. l. and spikes or racemes on naked scapes; fl. 4-merous; G 4-loc.): Francoa.

III. *HYDRANGEOIDEAE* (shrubs or trees; l. usu. opp., simple; P usu. 5-merous; sta. epig.; G 3—5-loc.): Philadelphus, Deutzia, Hydrangea.

IV. *PTEROSTEMONOIDEAE* (shrubs with alt. stip. simple l.; sta. 10; $\bar{G}$ 5-loc.; ov. 4—6, on axile plac.): Pterostemon.

V. *ESCALLONIOIDEAE* (shrubs or trees, rarely herbs; with simple alt. exstip. often leathery and gland-dotted l.; sta. = pets.; G superior to inferior; ov. ∞): Brexia, Escallonia.

VI. *RIBESIOIDEAE* (shrubs with alt. simple exstip. l. and racemes of fls.; $\bar{G}$ 1-loc. with 2 parietal plac.; berry): Ribes.

VII. *BAUEROIDEAE* (shrubs with opp. 3-foliate exstip. l. and simple axillary fls.; ovary semi-inf. with 2 parietal plac.; loculic. caps.): Bauera.

Saxifrage, *Saxifraga*; **burnet-**, *Pimpinella*; **golden-**, *Chrysosplenium*.

Saxifrageae (*BH.*) = Saxifragaceae.

Saxifragella Engl. Saxifragaceae (1). 1 Antarctic S. Am.

Saxifraginae (Warming). The 18th order of Choripetalae.

Saxifragopsis Small (*Saxifraga* p.p.). Saxifr. (1). 1 Calif.

Saxofridericia R. Schomb. Rapateaceae. 5 Guiana, N. Brazil.

Sayeria Kränzl. Orchidaceae (II. 15). 1 New Guinea.

Scabiosa (Tourn.) L. (*BH.* incl. *Knautia* L., *Pterocephalus* Vaill., *Succisa* Neck.). Dipsacaceae. 60 Eur., Medit.; 3 in Brit., incl. *S.* (*K.*) *arvensis* L. (scabious) and *S. Succisa* L. (devil's-bit scabious). The former has a large head of fls. (class B'); the C is drawn out upon the outer side (cf. Compositae), and this the more the further from the centre of the head. Honey is secreted by the upper surface of the ovary, and protected from rain by hairs. The sta. are ripe first, while the style with immature stigmas is quite enclosed in the C; later the sta. wither and the style occupies their place. The stigmas of the various fls. on the head ripen nearly together.

Scabious, *Scabiosa*; **sheep's bit-,** *Jasione montana* L.

Scabrous (dim. **scabrid, scaberulous**), scurfy.

Scaevola L. Goodeniaceae. 90 Austr., Polynes., trop. coasts. *S. Koenigii* Vahl furnishes a kind of rice paper; its pith is squeezed flat. It is a char. pl. of trop. beach jungle.

Scald, *Cuscuta.*

Scale leaves, the scaly l. on the outside of buds, rhizomes, &c., *Araceae, Casuarina.*

Scalesia Arn. Compositae (5). 15 Galapagos.

Scaligeria DC. (*Conopodium* p.p. *BH.*). Umbellif. (III. 4). 10 E. Medit.

Scalloped, crenate.

Scaly bulb, one with overlapping l., *Lilium.*

Scammony, *Convolvulus Scammonia* L.

Scandens (Lat.), climbing.

Scandivepres Loes. Celastraceae. 1 Mexico.

Scandix Tourn. ex L. Umbelliferae (III. 2). 12 Eur., Medit. *S. Pecten-Veneris* L. (Venus' comb) in Brit. The ripe mericarps separate with a jerk.

Scape, a stalk from the base of the pl. bearing only fls., *Amaryllidaceae, Taraxacum.*

Scapha Nor. = Saurauja Willd. (Dillen.).

Scaphispatha Brongn. Araceae (VII). 1 Bolivia.

Scaphochlamys Baker (*Kaempfera* p.p. *EP.*). Zingib. (I). 1 Malay Pen.

Scaphoid, boat-shaped, petals of *Loasa.*

Scaphopetalum Mast. Sterculiaceae. 5 trop. W. Afr.

Scaphosepalum Pfitz. Orchidaceae (II. 8). 10 N. trop. S. Am.

Scaphyglottis Poepp. et Endl. Orchidaceae (II. 6). 10 trop. Am.

Scapigerous, scape-bearing.

Scarious, thin, dry, not green, stiff.

Scarlet runner, *Phaseolus multiflorus* Willd.

Scelochilus Klotzsch. Orchidaceae (II. 19). 4 Andes.

Scented fls., cf. Perfumed; **-orchis,** *Gymnadenia conopsea* R. Br.

Scepa Lindl. = Aporosa Blume (Euph.).

Sceptrocnide Maxim. Urticaceae (I). 1 Japan.

Schachtia Karst. (*Duroia* p.p. *EP.*). Rubiaceae (I. 8). 1 Colombia.

Schaefferia Jacq. Celastraceae. 3 Texas to Colombia, W.I.

Schaetzellia Sch.-Bip. Compositae (2). 1 Mexico.

Schaffnera Benth. Gramineae (3). 1 Mexico.

Schaffnerella Nash (*Schaffnera* p.p.). Gramineae (3). 1 Mexico.
Schaueria Nees. Acanthaceae (IV. B). 8 trop. Am.
Schedonnardus Steud. Gramineae (11). 1 N. Am.
Schedonorus Beauv. = Bromus p.p. (Gram.).
Scheelea Karst. (*Attalea* p.p. *EP.*). Palmae (IV. 2). 5 trop. Am.
Schefferomitra Diels (*Mitrephora* p.p.). Anon. (2). 1 New Guinea.
Schefflera Forst. (incl. *Heptapleurum* Gaertn.). Araliaceae (1). 150 trop.
Schefflerodendron Harms. Leguminosae (III. 6). 2 trop. Afr.
Schelhammera R. Br. Liliaceae (1). 2 E. Austr.
Schenckia K. Schum. Rubiaceae (I. 3). 1 S. Brazil.
Scheuchleria Heynh. Compositae (inc. sed.). Nomen.
Scheuchzeria L. Scheuchzeriaceae. 1 N. temp. and arctic, incl. Brit.; *S. palustris* L., a marsh plant.
Scheuchzeriaceae (*EP.*; *Naiadeae* p.p. *BH.*) (*Juncaginaceae*). Monocots. (Helobieae). 5 gen., 20 sp. temp. Perenn. marsh herbs of grass-like habit; squamulae intravaginales (cf. Potamogetonaceae) in axils of sheathing l. Fls. ☿ or ♂ ♀ in racemes or spikes, reg., greenish, wind-fert., protog. P 3 + 3, homochlam., A 3 + 3, extr., $\underline{G}$ 3 + 3 sometimes united, but the outer whorl often abortive; stigmas sessile; 1 anatr. ov. in each cpl. Achene or schizocarp; exalbum.; embryo straight. *Chief genera:* Triglochin, Scheuchzeria, Lilaea.
Schickendantzia Pax. Amaryllidaceae (III). 2 Argentina.
Schickendantziella Spegazzini. Liliaceae (inc. sed.). 1 Argentina.
Schieckia Karst. (*Celastrus* p.p. *EP.*). Celastraceae. 1 trop. S. Am.
Schiedia Cham. et Schlecht. Caryophyllaceae (I. 1). 11 Hawaiian Is.
Schiedeophytum H. Wolff. Umbelliferae (III. 4). 1 Mexico.
Schiekia Meissn. Haemodoraceae. 1 warm S. Am.
Schilleria Kunth = Piper L. p.p. (Pip.).
Schima Reinw. ex Blume. Theaceae. 10 E. Indomal. *S. Wallichii* Choisy good timber.
Schimmelia Holmes (*Amyris* p.p.). Rutaceae (IV). 1 W.I.
Schimpera Hochst. Cruciferae (2). 2 E. Medit.
Schindleria H. Walter (*Villamilla* p.p.). Phytolacc. 5 Peru, Bolivia.
Schinnongia Schrank. Iridaceae (inc. sed.). 1 S. Afr.
Schinopsis Engl. (*Quebrachia BH.*). Anacardiaceae (3). 5 S. Am. The wood (quebracho) is hard and rich in tannin; used for tanning.
Schinus L. Anacardiaceae (3). 12 Mex. to Argent. *S. Molle* L. yields American mastic (resin); cult. for shade, &c. (pepper-tree).
Schinziella Gilg (*Canscora* p.p.). Gentianaceae (1). 2 trop. W. Afr.
Schismatoclaea Baker. Rubiaceae (I. 5). 4 Madag.
Schismatoglottis Zoll. et Mor. Araceae (V). 75 Malaya. At top of spadix, above the ♂ fls., are sterile fls. consisting of stds.
Schismus Beauv. Gramineae (10). 5 S. Afr., Medit.
Schistocarpaea F. Muell. Rhamnaceae. 1 Austr.
Schistocarpha Less. Compositae (8). 6 Mexico to Peru.
Schistocaryum Franch. Boraginaceae (IV. 2). 1 Yunnan.
Schistogyne Hook. et Arn. Asclepiadaceae (II. 1). 4 S. Am.
Schistonema Schlechter. Asclepiadaceae (II. 1). 1 Peru.
Schistostephium Less. Compositae (7). 6 S.E. Afr.
Schistostigma Lauterb. Euphorbiaceae (A. II. 5). 1 New Guinea.

Schivereckia Andrz. ex DC. (*Alyssum* p.p. *BH.*). Crucif. (4). 2 E. Medit.

Schizachne Hack. Gramineae (10). 1 Saghalien.

Schizachyrium Nees (*Andropogon* p.p.). Gramineae (2). 50 trop.

Schizaea Sm. Schizaeaceae. 25 trop. and subtrop. Sporangia in a double row on lower surface of each of the reduced fertile pinnae.

Schizaeaceae. Filicales Leptosporangiatae. 5 gen., 70 sp., chiefly trop. Am.; a few subtrop. or temp., mostly small ferns with but little stem. Lygodium is a curious leaf-climber. As in Osmunda, the sporangia are borne (exc. in Mohria) on special pinnae of the leaf, distinct from the ordinary veg. pinnae. The sporangia are sessile, usu. without indusium; at the apex is a cap-like annulus, and the sporangium dehisces longitudinally.

Chief genera: Schizaea, Aneimia, Lygodium, Mohria.

Schizandra Michx. Magnoliaceae. 7 trop. and warm temp. As., N. Am. Climbing shrubs with exstip. l. and spiral fls.

Schizanthus Ruiz et Pav. Solanaceae (5). 15 Chili. Fl. ·|·; stalk curved, and the two really upper petals form the lower lip which is 3—4-lobed, while the lat. petals are 4-lobed and the lowest petal forms the simple or slightly 2-lobed upper lip. Sta. 4, 2 fertile and 2 staminodial. Fl. like the papilionate Leguminosae (*cf.* Collinsia), and fert. in a similar way, usu. by an explosive movement (*cf.* Genista).

Schizeilema Domin (*Pozoa* Hook. f.). Umbel. (I. 2). 12 N.Z., Austr.

Schizo- (Gr. pref.), split-; **-carp**, a fr. that splits up, without opening of the cpls., into 1-seeded mericarps, *Euphorb.*, *Geran.*, *Malpigh.*, *Malv.*, *Sapind.*, *Tropaeol.*, *Umbellif.*; **-genous**, formed by splitting.

Schizobasis Baker. Liliaceae (III). 5 S. Afr.

Schizocalyx Wedd. Rubiaceae (I. 5). 1 Colombia.

Schizocapsa Hance. Taccaceae. 2 S.E. China, Siam.

Schizocarpum Schrad. Cucurbitaceae (3). 4 Mexico.

Schizocasia Schott. Araceae (VI). 4 Malaya.

Schizochilus Sond. Orchidaceae (II. 1). 10 Cape Colony.

Schizochlaena Thou. Chlaenaceae. 5 Madag.

Schizocodon Sieb. et Zucc. Diapensiaceae. 2 Japan.

Schizodium Lindl. (*Disa* p.p. *BH.*). Orchidaceae (II. 1). 10 S. Afr.

Schizoglossum E. Mey. Asclepiadaceae (II. 1). 50 trop. and S. Afr.

Schizolaena Thou. Chlaenaceae. 5 Madag.

Schizolepis Schrad. ex Nees = Scleria Berg. (Cyper.).

Schizolobium Vog. Leguminosae (II. 7). 1 S. Brazil.

Schizoloma Gaudich. Polypodiaceae. 15 trop. and subtrop.

Schizomeria D. Don. Cunoniaceae. 7 E. Austr., New Guin. Drupe.

Schizomeryta R. Viguier (*Meryta* p.p.). Aral. (I). 1 New Caled.

Schizonepeta Briq. (*Nepeta* p.p.). Labiatae (VI). 4 temp. As.

Schizonotus A. Gray. Asclepiadaceae (II. 1). 1 California.

Schizopepon Maxim. Cucurbitaceae (2). 2 China, Japan. Fls. ☿.

Schizopetalon Sims. Cruciferae (3). 5 Chili.

Schizophragma Sieb. et Zucc. Saxifragaceae (III). 4 Japan, China.

Schizopremna Baill. Verbenaceae (4). 1 Timor.

Schizoptera Turcz. Compositae (5). 2 Ecuador, Mexico.

Schizoscyphus (*Schizosiphon*) K. Schum. Legum. (II. 2). 1 N. Guin.

Schizostachyum Nees. Gramineae (13). 25 E. As.

Schizostephanus Hochst. (*Vincetoxicum* p.p. *BH.*). Asclepiadaceae (II. 1). 1 E. Afr.
Schizostigma Arn. Rubiaceae (I. 7). 1 Ceylon. Ovary 5—7-loc.
Schizostylis Backh. et Harv. Iridaceae (III). 2 S. Afr. *S. coccinea* Backh. et Harv. often cult. for its handsome fls.
Schizotrichia Benth. Compositae (6). 1 Peru.
Schizozygia Baill. Apocynaceae (I. 3). 1 Zanzibar.
Schkuhria Roth. Compositae (6). 11 W. Am.
Schlechtendalia Less. Compositae (12). 1 Brazil. A plant of very unusual habit (for this fam.), and with peculiar anatomy.
Schlechterella K. Schum. Asclepiadaceae (I). 1 E. Afr.
Schlechteria Bolus. Cruciferae (4). 1 W. Cape Colony.
Schlechterina Harms. Passifloraceae. 1 Mozambique.
Schlegelia Miq. Bignoniaceae (4). 3 W.I., Guiana.
Schleichera Willd. Sapindaceae (I). 1 trop. As., *S. trijuga* Willd. (Ceylon oak). Useful timber; aril of seed ed.; oil expressed from seed itself. Furnishes the best lac (Mirzapore lac).
Schleidenia Endl. = Heliotropium Tourn. (Borag.).
Schleinitzia Warb. (*Piptadenia* p.p. *EP.*). Legum. (I. 5). 1 N.G.
Schleropelta Buckley = Hilaria H. B. et K. p.p. (1 N. Am.).
Schlimmia Planch. et Linden. Orchidaceae (II. 13). 2 Colombia.
Schlumbergeria E. Morr. Bromeliaceae (1). 50 S. Am., W.I.
Schmalhausenia C. Winkler. Compositae (11). 1 C. As.
Schmalzia Desv. (*Rhus* p.p.). Anacardiaceae (3). 50 N. Am.
Schmidelia L. Sapindaceae (I). 55 S. Afr. and trop.
Schmidtia Steud. Gramineae (10). 2 Afr.
Schnella Raddi = Bauhinia L. p.p. (Legum.).
Schoberia C. A. Mey. = Suaeda Forst. p.p. (Chenop.).
Schoenefeldia Kunth. Gramineae (11). 4 trop. Afr. and As.
Schoenia Steetz. Compositae (4). 1 temp. Austr.
Schoenlandia Cornu. Pontederiaceae. 1 trop. Afr.
Schoenobiblus Mart. Thymelaeaceae. 3 trop. S. Am., W.I.
Schoenocaulon A. Gray. Liliaceae (I). 6 Am. Veratrin from seeds.
Schoenocephalium Seub. Rapateaceae. 2 N. Brazil.
Schoenocrambe Greene (*Sisymbrium* p.p.). Cruciferae (2). 3 N. Am.
Schoenodendron Engl. Cyperaceae (inc. sed.). 1 Cameroons. Tree.
Schoenolaena Bunge (*Xanthosia BH.*). Umbelliferae (I. 1). 2 W. Austr.
Schoenolirion Durand. Liliaceae (III). 4 N. Am.
Schoenorchis Reinw. Orchidaceae (II. 20). 5 Java, New Guin.
Schoenoxiphium Nees. Cyperaceae (III). 7 Afr.
Schoenus L. Cyperaceae (II). 70 Austr., N.Z., a few in Malaya, Am., Eur.; *S. nigricans* L. in Brit.
Schoepfia Schreb. Olacaceae. 15 trop.
Schoepfianthus Engl. ex De Wild. Olacaceae. 1 trop. Afr. Nomen.
Schollera Roth = Vaccinium L. p.p. (Eric.).
Scholtzia Schau. (*Baeckea* p.p. *EP.*). Myrtaceae (II. 1). 12 Austr.
Schombocattleya, **Schombolaelia**, **Schombolaeliocattleya**, **Schomburgkiocattleya** Hort. Orchidaceae. Hybrids of Schomburgkia.
Schomburgkia Lindl. Orchidaceae (II. 6). 12 trop. Am. Cult.
Schotia Jacq. (*Theodora* Medic.). Legum. (II. 3). 12 trop. and S. Afr.

Schoutenia Korth. Tiliaceae. 5 trop. E. As.
Schouwia DC. Cruciferae (2). 2 Arabia, N. Afr.
Schradera Vahl. Rubiaceae (I. 7). 5 W.I. to Amazon.
Schrankia Willd. Leguminosae (I. 3). 7 warm Am.
Schrebera Roxb. (*Nathusia* Hochst.). Oleaceae. 30 Afr., India.
Schrebera Thunb. (*Hartogia* L. f.). Celastraceae. 4 S. Afr., Madag.
Schrenkia Regel et Schmalh. Umbelliferae (III. 3). 5 N. As.
Schstschurowskia Schrenk. Umbelliferae (inc. sed.). 1 Kokania.
Schubea Pax. Euphorbiaceae (A. II. 2). 1 Cameroons.
Schubertia Mart. (*Araujia BH.*). Asclepiadaceae (II. 1). 6 S. Am.
Schultesia Mart. Gentianaceae (1). 18 trop. Am., Afr.
Schultzia Spreng. Umbelliferae (III. 5). 4 C. As., W. India.
Schumacheria Vahl. Dilleniaceae. 3 Ceylon.
Schumannia Kuntze (*Ferula* p.p.). Umbellif. (III. 6). 1 Turkestan.
Schumannianthus Gagnep. (*Phrynium* p.p.) Marantaceae. 1 S.E. As.
Schumanniophyton Harms (*Tetrastigma* p.p.). Rubi. (I. 8). 1 W. Afr.
Schuurmansia Blume. Ochnaceae (Viol. *BH.*). 12 Malay Archip.
Schuurmansiella H. Hallier (*Schuurmansia* p.p.). Ochn. 1 Borneo.
Schwabea Endl. Acanthaceae (IV. B). 5 Afr.
Schwackaea Cogn. Melastomaceae (I). 1 C. Am.
Schwalbea L. Scrophulariaceae (III. 3). 1 E. N. Am.
Schwannia Endl. Malpighiaceae (I). 6 warm S. Am. 6 fertile sta.
Schwartzkopffia Kränzl. Orchidaceae (II. 1). 1 W. trop. Afr.
Schweiggeria Spreng. Violaceae. 2 Brazil, Mexico.
Schweinfurthia A. Br. Scrophular. (II. 3). 3 E. Afr. to W. India.
Schweinitzia Ell. Pyrolaceae. 1 N. Am.
Schwendenera K. Schum. Rubiaceae (II. 10). 1 São Paulo.
Schwenkia L. Solanaceae (5). 20 trop. Am., Afr.
Schychowskya Endl. (*Fleurya* p.p.). Urtic. (1). 1 palaeotrop.
Sciadodendron Griseb. Araliaceae (2). 1 C. Am.
Sciadonardus Steud. Gramineae (nomen). 1 N. Am.
Sciadopanax Seem. (*Panax* p.p. *BH.*). Araliaceae (1). 1 Madag.
Sciadophyllum P. Br. (*Schefflera* p.p. *EP.*). Arali. (1). 25 trop. Am.
Sciadopitys Sieb. et Zucc. Coniferae (Pinaceae 22; see C. for gen. char.). 1 Japan, *S. verticillata* Sieb. et Zucc., the parasol-pine or umbrella-fir, planted round temples. Short shoots crowded together at ends of annual long shoots. Each like Pinus except that the two green needle-l. are 'fused' into a single needle grooved down the centre, so that at first glance they seem to be whorls of ordinary l. at the tip of each year's growth. The cones take two years to ripen. The wood is useful.
Sciadotenia Miers. Menispermaceae. 20 trop. S. Am.
Sciaphila Blume. Triuridaceae. 20 trop. Cf. *Flora*, 101, p. 395.
Scilla L. Liliaceae (V). 100 temp. |*. *S. festalis* Salisb. (*S. nutans* Sm.), wild hyacinth or English bluebell, in Brit. Bulbs with racemes.
Scillopsis Lem. = Lachenalia Jacq. p.p. (Lili.).
Scindapsus Schott. Araceae (II). 20 Indomal.
Scion, young shoot, twig used for grafting.
Sciophytium (Cl.), a shade formation.

Scirpodendron Zippel. Cyperaceae (II). 2 Indomal.

Scirpus (Tourn.) L. Cyperaceae (I). 200 cosmop. char. of wet moors, bogs and marshes; 15 in Brit. Stem usu. erect and angular, bearing 3 ranks of l. reduced to sheaths, and performing assim. Its base often gives rise to creeping rhiz. or to shoots ending in tubers like potatoes. The racemose many-flowered spikelets are aggregated into a terminal tuft. Fl. ☿, with 6 P-scales in two whorls; in many sp. protog.; in all wind-pollinated. *S. lacustris* L., sometimes termed bulrush, is used for matting, chair-seats, &c.

Scitamineae. The 10th order (*EP.*) of Monocots. A fam. (*BH.*) in Epigynae, incl. Musaceae, Marantaceae, Cannaceae, and Zingiberaceae of Engler. The 6th order (Warming) of Monocots.

Sclarea Tourn. ex Mill. = Salvia L. p.p. (Labi.).

Scler-, Sclero- (Gr. pref.), hard; **-caulous**, with dry hard stem; **-enchyma**, tissue with thick hard walls; **-phyllous**, with thick hard l.; **-sis**, hardening by lignification; **-testa**, woody layer of seed coat.

Sclerachne R. Br. Gramineae (1). 1 Java.

Scleranthaceae or Illecebraceae. See Caryophyllaceae.

Scleranthus L. Caryophyllaceae (I. 6). 10 Eur., As., Afr., Austr.; *S. annuus* L. (knawel), &c. in Brit. Fls. apet., self-fert.

Scleria Berg. Cyperaceae (II). 100 trop.

Sclerocalyx Nees (*Gymnacanthus EP.*). Acanthaceae (IV. A). 1 Mexico.

Sclerocarpus Jacq. Compositae (5). 7 Texas, C. Am., trop. Afr.

Sclerocarya Hochst. Anacardiaceae (2). 3 trop. Afr. Ed. fr.

Sclerocephalus Boiss. Caryophyll. (I. 4). 1 Medit., a char. plant.

Sclerochiton Harv. Acanthaceae (IV. B). 5 Afr.

Sclerochlaena Baill. Chlaenaceae. 1 Madag.

Sclerochloa Beauv. Gramineae (10). 1 Eur., As.

Sclerochorton Boiss. Umbelliferae (III. 5). 2 W. As.

Sclerodactylon Stapf. Gramineae (10). 1 Madag.

Sclerodictyon Pierre. Apocynaceae (I. 1). 1 Gaboon.

Sclerolaena R. Br. (*Bassia* p.p. *EP.*). Chenopodiaceae (A). 6 Austr.

Sclerolepis Cass. Compositae (2). 1 W. U.S.

Sclerolobium Vog. Leguminosae (II. 8). 15 Brazil, Guiana.

Scleromelum K. Schum. et Lauterb. Santalaceae. 1 New Guinea.

Scleromitrion Wight et Arn. = Hedyotis L. (*BH.*) = Oldenlandia L.

Scleronema Benth. (*Catostemma BH.*). Bombacaceae. 1 Brazil, Ecuador.

Scleroolaena Baill. (*Xylochlaena EP.*). Chlaenaceae. 1 Madag.

Sclerophylax Miers. Solanaceae (4). 4 Argentina.

Scleropoa Griseb. (*Festuca* p.p. *BH.*). Gramineae (10). 2 Medit.

Scleropogon Phil. Gramineae (10). 3 Chili, Mexico, Texas.

Scleropyrum Arn. Santalaceae. 2 Indomal.

Sclerosia Klotzsch. Ochnaceae (nomen). 1 Guiana.

Sclerosperma G. Mann et H. Wendl. Palmae (IV. 1). 1 W. trop. Afr.

Sclerostylis Blume = Atalantia Correa (Rut.).

Sclerotheca A. DC. Campanulaceae (III). 2 Society Is.

Sclerothrix C. Presl. Loasaceae. 1 trop. Am. 4-merous. Stds. 6—10.

Scobedia Labill. ex Steud. Labiatae (nomen). 1, habitat?

Scoke (Am.), *Phytolacca*.

Scoliopus Torr. Liliaceae (VII). 2 W. N. Am.
Scoliotheca Baill. Gesneriaceae (2). 1 Colombia.
Scolochloa Link (*Graphephorum BH.*). Gramineae (10). 2 N. temp.
Scolopendrium Adans. = Phyllitis Ludwig (Polypod.). *S. vulgare* Sm. (hart's tongue fern, Brit.) = P. Scolopendrium.
Scolopia Schreb. Flacourtiaceae (5). 30 warm |*; S. Afr. sp. timber.
Scolosanthes Vahl. Rubiaceae (II. 3). 6 W.I.
Scolymus Tourn. ex L. Compositae (13). 3 Medit.
Scoparia L. Scrophulariaceae (III. 1). 10 trop. Am.
Scopolia Jacq. Solanaceae (2). 4 Eur., As.
Scopularia Lindl. (*Holothrix BH.*). Orchidaceae (II. 1). 1 Cape Col.
Scopulophila M. E. Jones. Caryophyllaceae (I. b). 1 W. U. S.
Scorodendron Blume (*Lepisanthes* p.p. *EP.*). Sapindaceae (I). 1 Timor.
Scorodocarpus Becc. Olacaceae. 1 Borneo.
Scorodonia Adans. = Teucrium L. p.p. (Labi.).
Scorodophloeus Harms. Leguminosae (II. 2). 1 Cameroons.
Scorpaena Nor. Inc. sed. Nomen.
Scorpioid, infl. with fls. in 2 ranks, coiled like a scorpion's tail, *Boraginaceae*.
Scorpion grass, *Myosotis*.
Scorpiurus L. Legumin. (III. 7). 6 Medit. Pod twisted, indeh.
Scortechinia Hook. f. Euphorbiaceae (inc. sed.). 4 Malaya.
Scorzonella Nutt. (*Microseris* p.p.). Compositae (13). 3 Calif.
Scorzonera (Tourn.) L. Compositae (13). 100 Medit., C. Eur. and As. Roots of *S. hispanica* L., &c. are eaten as vegetables.
Scotch attorney (W.I.), *Clusia*; **-fir**, *Pinus sylvestris* L.; **-grass** (W.I.), *Panicum molle* Sw.; **-tish asphodel**, *Tofieldia*.
Scottellia Oliv. Flacourt. (1). 10 trop. Afr.
Scouring rush (Am.), *Equisetum*.
Scratch coco (W.I.), *Colocasia antiquorum* Schott.
Screw pine, *Pandanaceae*, *Pandanus*; **-tree** (W.I.), *Helicteres*.
Scribneria Hackel (*Lepturus* p.p.). Gramineae (12). 1 Calif., Oregon.
Scrobiculatus (Lat.), pitted.
Scrofella Maxim. Scrophulariaceae (II. 4). 1 China.
Scrophularia Tourn. ex L. Scrophulariaceae (II. 4). 120 N. temp.; 3 in Brit., incl. *S. aquatica* L. and *S. nodosa* L., the fig-worts. Perenn. herbs with opp. l., which on the lat. twigs are commonly anisophyllous. Fls. in tall infls. whose primary branching is racemose; the lat. shoots are dichasial. Sta. and style arranged along the lower lip of the C (upper usual in such fls.). The posterior sta., usu. absent in the fam., is repres. by a std. Fl. markedly protog., largely visited by wasps.
Scrophulariaceae (*EP.*, *BH.* unite II. 7 to *Globulariaceae* to form fam. *Selagineae*). Dicots. (Sympet. Tubiflorae; Personales *BH.*). 200 gen., 2600 sp., cosmop. Most are herbs and undershrubs, a few shrubs or trees (*e.g.* Paulownia), with alt., opp., or whorled exstip. l. Many exhibit interesting features in the veg. organs. Several are climbers (*e.g.* Maurandia, Rhodochiton, &c.). The Veronicas of N.Z. are xero. with resemblance in habit to certain Coniferae. A

number of sp. in III. 2 and 3 (below), *e.g.* Euphrasia, Bartsia, Pedicularis, grow in swampy grass-land and are parasitic by their roots upon the roots of the grasses. Suckers are formed at the points of contact, in spring; they absorb food till the summer, and later absorb organic compounds from the dead parts of the host, and function for storage of reserve-materials. The plants possess green l. of their own, and so are able to assimilate.

Infl. racemose or cymose, in the former case usu. a spike or raceme, axillary or term. (every variety in sp. of Veronica). Sol.

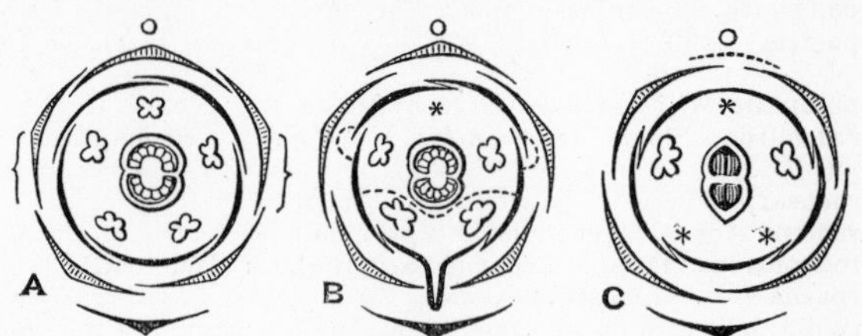

Floral diagrams of A, *Verbascum nigrum*, B, *Linaria vulgaris*, C, *Veronica Chamaedrys*; after Eichler.

axillary fls. in many, *e.g.* Linaria. Cymose infls. usu. dichasia, often united into complex corymbs, &c. Bracts and bracteoles usu. present. In Castilleja the upper l. and bracts brightly coloured.

Fl. ☿, ·|·, sometimes nearly reg. (Verbascum, &c.); considerable variety in structure, as illustrated by the floral diagrams given. The bulk of the fam. show the Linaria type. K (5), of various aestivations; C (5), median ·|·, often 2-lipped; A 4 (sometimes 2), didynamous, epipet., the post. sta. sometimes repres. by a std. (*e.g.* in Scrophularia and Pentstemon). Verbascum and its allies have an actinom. C and 5 sta.; Veronica (*q.v.*) shows 4 sepals (the post. one of the typical 5 absent), 4 petals (the post. pair of the 5 united), and 2 sta., the C. rotate. Other variations occur in the *Selagineae*, &c. Below the ovary is a honey-secreting disc. $\underline{G}$ (2), medianly placed (not obliquely as in Solanaceae), 2-loc., with axile plac.; ov. usu. ∞, less commonly few (*e.g.* Veronica, &c.), anatr.; style simple or bilobed. Fr. surrounded below by the persistent K, usu. a capsule (dehisc. in various ways) or a berry. Seeds usu. numerous, small, with endosp. Embryo straight or slightly curved.

Most have fls. ± adapted to insect-visits. Müller divides them into 4 types: (1) the Verbascum or Veronica type (see gen.) with open fl. and short tube (bees and flies), (2) the Scrophularia type (wasps), (3) the Digitalis and Linaria type with long wide tubes and the essential organs so placed as to touch the back of the insect (bees), and (4) the Euphrasia type or 'loose-pollen' fl., where the pollen is loose and powdery, and the anthers (protected by upper lip) have spines, &c., so that they may be shaken upon the entrance of the insect, which thus receives a shower of pollen. The fls. are seldom markedly dichogamous, but the stigma usu. projects beyond the sta.

so as to be first touched. Most are capable of self-fert. in default of visits. For further details see gen.

In Linaria, &c. (*q.v.*) there sometimes appears a terminal fl. to the raceme, and this exhibits *peloria*, having a symmetrical C with spurs to all the petals (*cf.* Ruta, or compare Aquilegia with Delphinium).

A number are or have been officinal, *e.g.* Digitalis; most are poisonous. Many favourite cult. orn. plants, *e.g.* Calceolaria, Mimulus, Pentstemon, Antirrhinum, Linaria, Veronica, Collinsia, &c.

Classification and chief genera (after von Wettstein):

A. Two post. C-teeth (or upper lip) cover lat. teeth in bud.

I. *PSEUDOSOLANEAE* (all l. usu. alt.; 5 sta. often present):

1. *Verbasceae* (C with very short tube or none, rotate or shortly campanulate): Verbascum, Celsia.
2. *Aptosimeae* (C with long tube): Aptosimum.

II. *ANTIRRHINOIDEAE* (lower l. at least opp.; the 5th sta. wanting or staminodial):

α. C 2-lipped; lower lip concave, bladder-like.

1. *Calceolarieae*: Calceolaria.

β. C almost actinom., or 2-lipped with flat or convex lips.

2. *Hemimerideae* (dehisc. caps.; C spurred or saccate at base, with no tube): Alonsoa.
3. *Antirrhineae* (as 2, but with tube): Linaria, Antirrhinum, Maurandia, Rhodochiton.
4. *Cheloneae* (dehisc. caps. or many-seeded berry; C not spurred or saccate; infl. cymose, cpd.): Russelia, Wightia, Collinsia, Scrophularia, Chelone, Pentstemon, Paulownia.
5. *Manuleae* (dehisc. caps.; C as in 4; infl. not cymose, usu. simple; anthers finally 1-loc.): Zaluzianskia, Lyperia.
6. *Gratioleae* (as 5, but anthers finally 2-loc.): Mimulus, Gratiola, Torenia.
7. *Selagineae* (drupe or indeh. few-seeded caps.): Hebenstretia, Selago.

B. Two post. teeth (or upper lip) of C covered in bud by one or both of the lat. teeth.

III. *RHINANTHOIDEAE*.

a. C-teeth all flat and divergent, or the 2 upper erect.

1. *Digitaleae* (anther-loc. finally united at tip; 2 upper C-lobes often erect; not paras.): Veronica, Digitalis.
2. *Gerardieae* (anther-loc. always separate, one often reduced; C-lobes all flat, divergent; often paras.): Gerardia.

b. 2 upper C-teeth form a helmet-like upper lip. Often paras.

3. *Rhinantheae*: Castilleja, Melampyrum, Tozzia, Euphrasia, Bartsia, Pedicularis, Rhinanthus.

Scrophularineae (*BH.*) = Scrophulariaceae.

Scrub, cf. *Acacia*; **-myrtle** (Austr.), *Backhousia*.

Scubalia Nor. Inc. sed. Nomen.

Scurrula L. = Loranthus L. (Lor.).

Scurvy grass, *Cochlearia officinalis* L.

Scutachne Hitchc. et Chase. Gramineae (5). 2 Cuba.

Scutate, scutiform, buckler-shaped.

Scutch grass (Am.), *Cynodon Dactylon* Pers.

Scutellaria Riv. ex L. Labiatae (IV). 200 cosmop. exc. S. Afr. 2 in Brit., *S. galericulata* L. and *S. minor* Huds. (skull-cap).
Scutellum, *Gramineae*.
Scutia Comm. ex Brongn. Rhamnaceae. 5 S. Afr., trop.
Scuticaria Lindl. Orchidaceae (II. 18). 2 trop. S. Am. Epiphytes, with no tubers, but long pendulous fleshy cylindrical stems. Cult. orn. fl.
Scutinanthe Thw. (*Canarium* p.p. *BH.*). Burseraceae. 1 Ceylon.
Scybalium Schott et Endl. Balanophoraceae. 4 trop. Am., W.I.
Scyphanthus D. Don (*Grammatocarpus BH.*). Loasaceae. 2 Chili.
Scypharia Miers (*Colletia BH.*). Rhamnaceae. 4 W. trop. Am.
Scyphellandra Thw. (*Alsodeia* p.p. *BH.*). Violaceae. 1 Ceylon.
Scyphiphora Gaertn. f. Rubiaceae (I. 8). 1 Indomal.
Scyphiphorous, cup-bearing.
Scyphocephalium Warb. Myristicaceae. 6 trop. W. Afr.
Scyphochlamys Balf. f. Rubiaceae (II. 1). 1 Rodrigues.
Scyphocoronis A. Gray. Compositae (4). 1 W. Austr.
Scyphogyne Brongn. Ericaceae (IV. 2). 10 S. Afr.
Scyphonychium Radlk. (*Cupania* p.p.). Sapind. (I). 1 N.E. Brazil.
Scyphopetalum Hiern (*Paranephelium* p.p. *EP.*). Sapind. (I). 1 Burma.
Scyphostachys Thw. Rubiaceae (I. 8). 2 Ceylon.
Scyphostegia Stapf. Monimiaceae (??). 1 Borneo.
Scyphostelma Baill. Asclepiadaceae (II. 1). 1 Colombia.
Scyphostrychnos Sp. Moore. Loganiaceae. 1 Nigeria.
Scyphosyce Baill. Moraceae (II). 2 trop. W. Afr.
Scytalia Gaertn. = Nephelium L. (Sapind.).
Scytanthus T. Anders. (*Thomandersia EP.*). Acanth. (IV. B). 1 W. Afr.
Scytanthus Liebm. (*Cytinus* p.p. *BH.*). Rafflesiaceae. 4 Mexico.
Scytopetalaceae (*EP.*). Dicots. (Archichl. Malvales). Only gen. Scytopetalum, *q.v.*
Scytopetalum Pierre. Scytopetalaceae. 10 trop. W. Afr. Trees or shrubs with alt. leathery l. and long-stalked fls. K dish-like, C 3—7, valvate, A ∞, G (4—6), each with 2—6 pend. ov. Fr. woody or drupaceous, 1-seeded.
Sea bean, *Entada scandens* Benth.; **- beet**, *Beta vulgaris* L.; **- blite**, *Suaeda maritima* Dum.; **- coast and salt-steppe pl.**, cf. Halophytes; **- buckthorn**, *Hippophaë rhamnoides* L.; **- grape**, *Coccoloba uvifera* L. &c.; **- heath**, *Frankenia*; **- holly**, *Eryngium*; **- Island cotton**, *Gossypium barbadense* L.; **- kale**, *Crambe maritima* L.; **- lavender**, *Statice*; **- milkwort**, *Glaux maritima* L.; **- pink**, *Armeria vulgaris* Willd.; **- purslane**, *Arenaria peploides* L.; **-side grape**, *Coccoloba*; **- rocket**, *Cakile maritima* Scop.
Seaforthia R. Br. = Ptychosperma Labill. (Palm.).
Sebaceus (Lat.), like lumps of tallow.
Sebaea Soland. ex R. Br. Gentianaceae (I). 100 warm |✻.
Sebastiania Spreng. Euphorbiaceae (A. II. 7). 80 trop., U.S.
Sebastiano-Schaueria Nees. Acanthaceae (IV. B). 1 Brazil.
Sebertia Pierre. Sapotaceae (II). 1 New Caledonia.
Sebestens, fr. of *Cordia Myxa* L.

Sebicea Pierre ex Diels=Tiliacora Colebr. (Menisp.).
Sebizia Mart. Vitaceae. Nomen.
Secale (Tourn.) L. Gramineae (12). 2 Medit., Eur., As. *S. cereale* L., the rye, is largely cult. in N. Eur. as a cereal, forming a staple food. There are no well-marked races. The hardy winter ryes are the best. Also used as fodder.
Secamone R. Br. Asclepiadaceae (II. 2). 60 palaeotrop.
Secamonopsis Jumelle. Asclepiadaceae (II. 2). 1 Madag.
Sechiopsis Naud. Cucurbitaceae (4). 1 Mexico.
Sechium P. Br. Cucurbitaceae (4). 1 trop. Am., *S. edule* Sw., cult. for its ed. fr. (chocho), containing one enormous seed.
Secondary shoots, adv. shoots when primaries occur, *Ailanthus*, *Anthurium*, *Podostemaceae*, *Testudinaria*, *Tristichaceae.*
Secondatia A. DC. Apocynaceae (II. 1). 5 trop. S. Am.
Secretania Muell.-Arg. (*Hyeronyma BH.*). Euph. (A. I. 1). 1 Gui.
-sect, divided to the base.
Secula Small. Leguminosae (III. 7). 1 W.I., Florida.
Secund, all directed to the one side.
Secundine, inner coat of ovule.
Securidaca L. Polygalaceae. 32 trop., exc. Austr. Climbers.
Securigera DC. (*Bonaveria* Scop.). Leguminosae (III. 5). 1 Medit.
Securinega Comm. ex Juss. Euphorb. (A. I. 1). 10 temp. and subtrop.
Sedastrum Rose. Crassulaceae. 7 Mexico.
Seddera Hochst (*Breweria* p.p.). Convolvulaceae (I). 18 palaeotrop.
Sedella Britton et Rose (*Sedum* p.p.). Crassulaceae. 2 Calif.
Sedge, *Carex*, *Cyperaceae*; **cotton-**, *Eriophorum*; **sword-**; *Lepidosperma.*
Sedum Tourn. ex L. Crassulaceae. 450 N. temp., 1 in Peru; 9 in Brit., incl. *S. Telephium* L. (orpine or livelong), *S. Rhodiola* DC. (rose-root), *S. anglicum* Huds. and *S. acre* L. (stonecrop or wall-pepper). Fleshy-leaved xero. Cult. orn. fl. and fol.
Seed, the product of the ovule after fert.; it contains the embryo, and if nothing else, is *exalbuminous*, but may contain reserve material outside the embryo (*albuminous*), which may be derived from the interior of the embryo-sac (*endosperm*), or from tissue outside this (*perisperm*). Usually mentioned after the fr. in descriptions. In form, &c. it may be large or small; spherical, ellipsoidal, &c.; anatr., amphitr., &c. like the original ovule. The testa may be smooth, or covered with small or large tubercles, papillae, granules, ribs, &c.; green, brown, or of other colours; thin or thick, woody (as in *Bertholletia*), with a fleshy outer layer (as in *Bixa*, *Cycas*, *Magnolia*, *Moraea*, &c.), hooked or winged (see below), or provided with hairs. It is usu. firm and tough, allowing very little evap. of water from the seed. Its outer cells sometimes have mucilaginous walls and swell when wetted, as in *Brassica*, *Collomia*, *Linum*, *Plantago*, &c.; sometimes there are scales or hairs upon it and these swell, as in many *Acanthaceae.* The testa is usu. marked with a scar, the *hilum*, where the stalk separated from the seed.

Many are covered by an extra coat (*aril*) that is developed like the original integuments, *i.e.* by a cup-like growth of tissue around the seed from the top of the stalk or rarely from the micropyle. Its development may be studied in fr. of *Euonymus*. Arillate seeds in *Celastraceae*, *Commelinaceae*, &c., *Dilleniaceae*, *Myristica*, *Nymphaeaceae*, *Passiflora*, *Sapindaceae*, *Taxus*, &c. In *Euphorbiaceae* the aril remains small and hard and is called a *caruncle*, but usu. it is fleshy.

The endosp. may be *starchy*, *farinaceous*, *floury*, or *mealy* (the cells containing starch and when powdered forming a floury dust) as in Triticum, *oily* as in Papaver, Ricinus, &c., *fleshy* as in Berberis, *horny* as in Coffea, *bony* as in Phoenix and Phytelephas, *ruminate* (marked by wavy transverse lines which give it a marbled look) as in Anonaceae, *mucilaginous*, &c.

The embryo (rarely embryos) may be straight, curved, twisted, &c. (and *cf.* Cruciferae). It may have one, two, or several cotyledons (important in classification), or rarely none, as in Cuscuta, &c.

Mention must be made of *adventitious* embryos of Alchornea, Funkia, Nothoscordum, &c., and of the peculiar cases of Ginkgo, and Gnetum, where the seed 'ripens' before fertilisation.

Seemannaralia R. Viguier. Araliaceae (1). 1 S. Afr.

Seemannia Regel. Gesneriaceae (II). 5 Peru, Bolivia.

Seetzenia R. Br. Zygophyllaceae. 1 Afr., As., in deserts.

Segetalis (Lat.), growing in grain fields.

Segments, the free portions of a concrescent K or C.

Segregate, kept separate.

Seguieria Loefl. Phytolaccaceae. 25 S. Am. L. leathery; stipules thorny. Powerful odour of garlic. Cpl. 1. Fr. a samara.

Seidelia Baill. Euphorbiaceae (A. II. 2). 2 S. Afr.

Seidlitzia Bunge et Boiss. Chenopodiaceae (B). 1 Armenia, Persia.

Selagineae (*BH.*). See Scrophulariaceae and Globulariaceae.

Selaginella Spring. The only genus of Selaginellaceae. 700 chiefly trop.; a few temp. *e.g. selaginoides* Link on boggy hill sides in Brit. Most live in damp places, esp. in forests, but a few xero. The embryo has a suspensor, and grows directly into the leafy plant which shows a habit very similar to Lycopodium—much-branched stem, often creeping, bearing roots on lower side and l. on upper, with term. cones of sporangia. L. spirally arranged as in most Lycopodiums (*e.g.* in *S. selaginoides*), or more commonly in 4 ranks, two outer ones of large, two inner ones of small l., thus giving the stem a dorsiventral structure. The roots in some, *e.g. S. Kraussiana* A. Br. and *S. Martensii* Spring, are borne on *rhizophores*, anomalous stem branches developed at the nodes and exhibiting a sort of intermediate structure between stem and root. The sporangia are placed at the bases of the l. in term. cones of radial symmetry. The mega-sporangia contain 4 large spores and can easily be distinguished by eye. On germ. a microspore produces a rudimentary ♂ prothallus bearing an antheridium. The megaspore forms a ♀ prothallus, which remains enclosed in the burst spore, and has an upper small-celled green portion and a lower large-celled storage portion as in Salviniaceae, &c.

S. lepidophylla Spring is a xero. which curls into a ball in the dry season, and may be rolled about by wind (*cf.* Anastatica).

Selaginellaceae. Lycopodiales. Only genus Selaginella (*q.v.*).

Selago L. Scrophulariaceae (II. 7). 140 S. and trop. Afr., Madag.

Selenia Nutt. Cruciferae (2). 2 S.W. U.S.

Selenicereus Britton et Rose (*Cereus* p.p.). Cactaceae (III. 1). 6 W.I., C. Am., Mexico.

Selenipedium Reichb. f. Orchidaceae (I. 2). 3 N. trop. S. Am. Ov. 3-loc.

Selenocera Zipp. ex Span. Rubiaceae (inc. sed.). 1 Timor.

Self coloured, of uniform tint; **-fertilisation**, from the pollen of the same fl., *Cephalanthera*, *Ophrys*, *Senecio*, many annuals, Cleistogamic fls., &c.; **-burying fl.**, *Trifolium*, *Trigonella*, **fr.**, *Arachis.*, *Voandzeia*, **seed**, *Erodium*; **-heal**, *Prunella*; **-sterility**, sterility to its own pollen, *Abutilon*, *Corydalis*.

Selinocarpus A. Gray. Nyctaginaceae. 4 S.W. U.S., Mexico.

Selinum L. Umbelliferae (III. 5). 16 ✻.

Selkirkia Hemsl. Boraginaceae (IV. 1). 1 Juan Fernandez.

Selleophytum Urb. Compositae (5). 1 Haiti.

Selliera Cav. Goodeniaceae. 2 Austr., N.Z., temp. S. Am. Fr. indeh.

Selliguea Bory = Polypodium L. (Polypod.).

Selloa H. B. et K. Compositae (5). 1 Mexico.

Sellocharis Taub. Leguminosae (III. 3). 1 S.E. Brazil.

Selwynia F. Muell. (*Cocculus* p.p. *EP.*). Menispermaceae. 1 Austr.

Selysia Cogn. Cucurbitaceae (2). 2 Brazil, Colombia.

Semaphore plant, *Desmodium gyrans* DC.

Semecarpus L. f. Anacardiaceae (4). 40 Indomal. The young fr. yields a black resin used as marking ink, &c.

Semeiandra Hook. et Arn. Onagraceae (2). 1 Mexico.

Semele Kunth. Liliaceae (VII). 1 Canaries, *S. androgyna* Kunth (*Ruscus androgynus* L.). A climbing shrub with leaf-like phylloclades in the axils of scale-l. Fls. in little cymes (cf. Asparagus) on edges of phylloclades. The new shoots rise from the soil, and grow long before the lat. branches, bearing the phylloclades, begin to unfold.

Semenovia Regel et Herder. Umbelliferae (inc. sed.). 1 C. As.

Semiaquilegia Makino (*Isopyrum* p.p.). Ranunc. (2). 1 Japan.

Semibegoniella C. DC. Begoniaceae. 2 Ecuador.

Seminiferous, seed-bearing.

Semiramisia Klotzsch (*Thibaudia* p.p. *EP.*). Eric. (III. 2). 2 S. Am.

Semonvillea J. Gay. Phytolaccaceae (Aizo. *BH.*). 2 S. and trop. Afr.

Sempervirens (Lat.), evergreen.

Sempervivum Rupp. ex L. Crassulaceae. 50 S. Eur., Himal., Abyss., &c. *S. tectorum* L. (houseleek, planted on cottages to keep slates in position) is a xero. with fleshy l. and veg. repr. by offsets.

Senaea Taub. Gentianaceae (1). 1 Minas Geraes.

Senapea Aubl. Inc. sed. 1 Guiana.

Senebiera DC. (*Coronopus* Rupp.). Cruciferae (2). 12 subtrop., Eur.; one nat. in Brit., *S. didyma* Pers.

Senecio (Tourn.) L. (incl. *Cineraria* L. p.p., *Kleinia* Haw., *Ligularia* Cass., &c.). Compositae (8). 2000 cosmop., 9 in Brit. (ragwort, groundsel, &c.). Shows § chars. well. The gen. includes pl. of most various habit. Some are climbers, *e.g. S. macroglossus* DC. (S. Afr.), which is remarkably like ivy. Many are xero. some with fleshy l., others with fleshy stems, others with hairy or inrolled l. (*cf.* Empetrum). The fls. of *S. vulgaris* L. (groundsel) are regularly self-fert. and are very inconspic.; there are no ray-florets. In *S.*

Jacobaea L. (rag-wort) there are ray-florets, and the conspic. fls. are largely visited by insects. The fleshy stems of *S.* (*K.*) *articulatus* Sch. Bip. (S. Afr.) separate at the joints and grow into new pl. *S. Johnstoni* Oliv. is a remarkable tree on Kilimandjaro.

Senefeldera Mart. Euphorbiaceae (A. II. 7). 4 Brazil.

Senega snake root, *Polygala Senega* L.

Senkenbergia Schau. (*Boerhaavia* p.p. *EP.*). Nyctagin. 3 N. Am.

Senna Tourn. ex Mill. = Cassia Tourn. p.p. (Legum.).

Senna, Alexandrian, Arabian, Italian, *Cassia*; **bladder-**, *Colutea.*

Sennenia Pau ex Sennen (*Trisetum* p.p.). Gramin. (9). 1 Eur.

Senra Cav. Malvaceae (4). 1 E. Afr., Arabia.

Sensitive fern (Am.), *Onoclea*; **-l. and petioles**, *cf.* Climbing Pl., Insectivorous Pl., Movements; **-plant**, *Mimosa pudica* L., *Neptunia*, &c.; **-sta.**, *Berberis*, *Centaurea* and many *Compositae*, *Portulaca*, *Sparmannia*; **-stigma**, *Martynia*, *Mimulus*, *Strobilanthes.*

Sepal, *cf.* Perianth; **-oid** (P), all of sepal-like l.

Sepalosiphon Schlechter. Orchidaceae (II. *a.* III). 1 New Guinea.

Septal, of hedgerows.

Septas L. = Crassula Dill. p.p. (Crass.).

Septate, divided by a partition wall or walls.

Septemfid, in seven divisions.

Septicidal, septifragal, *cf.* Fruit.

Septum, a partition, *e.g.* in a multiloc. ovary.

Sequoia Endl. (*Washingtonia* Winsl., *Wellingtonia* Lindl.). Coniferae (Pinaceae 26; see C. for gen. char.). 2 N.W. Am. *S. gigantea* Lindl. et Gord. is the mammoth tree of Calif., discovered in the Sierra Nevada in 1850. The tallest is 320 feet, the thickest 35 feet (Sargent; *cf.* Eucalyptus); the age of the largest is about 1500 years. In some museums are sections of a tree cut down in 1882 and showing 1335 annual rings. *S. sempervirens* Endl., the redwood, is even taller, though not so thick (340 and 28 feet), and is valued for its timber, &c.

Seradella, serratella, *Ornithopus sativus* Brot.

Seraphyta Fisch. et Mey. Orchidaceae (II. 6). 1 W.I.

Serapias L. Orchidaceae (II. 1). 5 Medit.

Serenoa Hook. f. Palmae (I. 2). 1 S.E. U.S.

Serial (branches, buds) one above another at same node, *cf.* Bud.

Serianthes Benth. Leguminosae (I. 1). 5 trop. As., Polynesia.

Sericeous, silky.

Sericocarpus Nees. Compositae (3). 5 U.S.

Sericocoma Fenzl. Amarantaceae (2). 15 S. and trop. Afr.

Sericocomopsis Schinz. Amarantaceae (2). 4 E. trop. Afr.

Sericodes A. Gray. Zygophyllaceae. 1 Mexico.

Sericographis Nees = Jacobinia Moric. (Acanth.)

Sericorema Lopriore (*Sericocoma* p.p.). Amarant. (2). 2 Afr.

Sericospora Nees. Acanthaceae (inc. sed.). 1 Antilles.

Sericostachys Gilg et Lopriore. Amarant. (2). 2 C. and W. Afr.

Sericostoma Stocks. Boraginaceae (IV. 4). 3 E. Afr. to N.W. India.

Sericotheca Rafin. (*Spiraea* p.p.). Rosaceae (I. 1). 14 N. and C. Am.

Seridia Juss. = Centaurea L. p.p. (Comp.).

Series, *cf.* Nomenclature.

Seringia J. Gay. Sterculiaceae. 1 E. Austr., New Guinea.
Serinia Rafin. (*Krigia BH.*). Compositae (13). 3 S. U.S.
Seriola L. = Hypochoeris L. p.p. (Comp.).
Seriphium L. = Stoebe L. (Comp.).
Seris Less. Compositae (12). 3 campos of S. and E. Brazil.
Serissa Comm. ex Juss. Rubiaceae (II. 7). 1 China, Japan, cult. medicinal.
Serjania Plum. ex Schum. Sapindaceae (I). 175 warm Am. Lianes with watch-spring tendrils and stip. l. Fr. a 3-winged schizocarp.
Serotinus (Lat.), late in the season.
Serpicula L. Haloragidaceae. 18 trop. and subtrop. Land or marsh pl.
Serrafalcus Parl. = Bromus L. p.p. (Gramin.).
Serrastylis Rolfe (*Macradenia* p.p. *EP.*). Orchid. (II. 18). 1 Colombia.
Serrate, margin with small teeth pointing forward; *cf.* Leaf, Fig. B.
Serratula Dill. ex L. Compositae (11). 40 Eur. to Japan. *S. tinctoria* L. (saw-wort) in Brit. is dioec.
Serresia Montr. Inc. sed. 1 New Caled.
Serruria Salisb. Proteaceae (I). 50 S. Afr.
Sersalisia R. Br. (*Lucuma* p.p.). Sapotaceae (I). 6 trop. Afr.
Sertifera Lindl. Orchidaceae (II. 7). 2 Ecuador, Peru.
Service berry, *Amelanchier.*
Sesame, *Sesamum indicum* L.; **-grass** (Am.), *Tripsacum.*
Sesamothamnus Welw. Pedaliaceae. 5 trop. Afr.
Sesamum L. Pedaliaceae. 15 trop. Afr., As. *S. indicum* L. largely cult. in India, &c. for the oil from seeds (gingili, sesame, &c.).
Sesban (W.I.), *Sesbania.*
Sesbania Scop. Leguminosae (III. 6). 24 trop. and subtrop. *S. aculeata* Poir. is a marsh plant, giving off floating roots from the base of the stem, covered with spongy aerenchyma (*cf.* Neptunia).
Seseli L. Umbelliferae (III. 5). 60 Eur., Afr., As., Austr.; 1 Brit.
Sesleria Scop. Gramineae (10). 10 Eur., W. As.; 1 Brit.
Sesqui- (Lat. pref.), one and a half; **-pedalis**, 1½ feet.
Sessea Ruiz et Pav. Solanaceae (4). 5 Andes.
Sessile, without stalk.
Sesuvium L. Aizoaceae (II). 5 trop. and subtrop. Halophytes.
Seta, a bristle.
Setaria Beauv. Gramineae (5). 100 trop. and warm temp. *S. italica* Beauv. (Italian millet) is cult. as a cereal in As.
Setariopsis Scribner ex Millsp. (*Setaria* p.p.). Gramineae (5). 2 Mexico.
Setchellanthus T. S. Brandegee. Capparidaceae (inc. sed.). 1 Mex.
Setcreasea K. Schum. et Sydow (*Treleasea* Rose). Commel. 8 N. Am.
Sethia H. B. et K. = Erythroxylum P. Br. p.p. (Erythr.).
Setilobus Baill. Bignoniaceae (I). 2 Brazil.
Setiscapella Barnhart (*Utricularia* p.p.). Lentib. 12 trop.
Setouratea Van Tiegh. (*Gomphia* p.p.). Ochnaceae. 8 Brazil.
Seville orange, *Citrus Aurantium* L., var. *Bigaradia* or *amara.*
Seven-year vine (W.I.), *Ipomoea tuberosa* L.
Sewerzowia Regel et Schmalh. (*Astragalus* p.p. *BH.*). Leguminosae (III. 6). 1 Turkestan.
Sex distribution; sta. and cpls. in one ☿ fl., *monoclinous*, in separate ♂ and ♀ fls., *diclinous*; ♂ and ♀ fls. on same pl., *monoecious*, on separate pl.,

dioecious. *Gynomonoecism* (☿ and ♀ on same pl., as in some Compositae, Labiatae, &c.), *gynodioecism* (☿ and ♀ on separate pl., as in Nepeta, Thymus, and other Labiatae, Plantago, many Caryophyllaceae, &c.), *andromonoecism* (☿ and ♂ on one pl., as in Veratrum), *androdioecism* (☿ and ♂ on separate pl., as in Dryas), *trioecism* (☿, ♂, ♀, each on its own pl., as in Silene sp.), *polygamy* (☿, ♂, ♀, in various combinations on one or more pl., as in Rhus, Fraxinus, &c.).

Seychellaria Hemsl. Triuridaceae. 1 Seychelles.

Seymeria Pursh (*Afzelia* Gmel.). Scrophulari. (III. 2). 9 N. Am.

Shadbush (Am.), *Amelanchier*.

Shaddock, *Citrus decumana* Murr.

Shade trees for crops, *Cedrela*, *Erythrina*, *Grevillea*, *Michelia*, *Pithecolobium*, *Poinciana*, *Schinus*, &c.

Shafera Greenman. Compositae (8). 1 Cuba.

Shaferocharis Urb. Rubiaceae (II. 3). 1 Cuba.

Shallon, *Gaultheria Shallon* Pursh.

Shallot, *Allium ascalonicum* L.

Sham honey, *Cleome*, *Lopezia*, *Parnassia*.

Shamrock, *Trifolium repens* L.

Shave grass (Am.), *Equisetum hyemale* L.

Shawia Forst. = Olearia Moench p.p. (Comp.).

She oak, *Casuarina*.

Shea butter, *Butyrospermum Parkii* Kotschy.

Sheareria Sp. Moore. Compositae (5). 1 China.

Sheep berry (Am.), *Viburnum Lentago* L.; **-bane** (W.I.), *Hydrocotyle*; **-sorrel**, *Rumex*; **vegetable -**, *Raoulia*.

Shellac, *Ficus*, and *cf.* Lac.

Shepherd's purse, *Capsella Bursa-pastoris* Medic.

Shepherdia Nutt. (*Lepargyrea EP.*). Elaeagnaceae. 3 N. Am. Recept. fleshy in fr. Fr. of *S. argentea* Nutt. (buffalo-berry) ed.

Sherardia Dill. ex L. Rubiaceae (II. 11). 1 Eur. (incl. Brit.), W. As., N. Afr., *S. arvensis* L., the field madder.

Sherbournea G. Don (*Amaralia EP.*). Rubiaceae (I. 8). 5 trop.

Sherwoodia House (*Shortia* Torr. et Gray). Diapensi. 4 Chi., Jap.

Shibataea Makino (*Bambusa* p.p.). Gramineae (13). 2 Japan.

Shield fern, *Dryopteris Filix-mas* (L.) Schott; **prickly --**, *Aspidium aculeatum* Sw.

Shin leaf (Am.), *Pyrola*.

Shingle wood (W.I.), *Nectandra*.

Shisham, *Dalbergia Sissoo* Roxb.

Shittim wood, *Dalbergia*.

Shoe flower, *Hibiscus Rosa-sinensis* L.; **-maker's bark** (W.I.), *Byrsonima*.

Shola, *Aeschynomene aspera* L.

Shoot, the part of the pl. that comes from the plumule; **adv.**, see Adv. Sh.; **long and short -**, or **- of limited and unlimited growth**, *Berberis*, *Cactaceae*, *Coniferae*, *Spergula*.

Shore weed, *Littorella lacustris* L.

Shorea Roxb. Dipterocarpaceae. 90 Ceylon to Phil. Is. *S. robusta* Gaertn. f. (sal) is a valuable timber tree, with wood like teak, and is largely grown in India. It forms gregarious forests.

Short shoots, see Shoots.
Shortia Torr. et Gray. Diapens. 1 N. Carolina, 1 E. As. (*cf.* Epigaea).
Showers of sulphur, *Pinus*.
Shrub, a woody pl. not > 30 ft. high, much branched to ground.
Shrubby trefoil, *Ptelea trifoliata* L.
Shuteria Wight et Arn. Leguminosae (III. 10). 5 trop. Afr., As.
Shuttleworthia Meissn. = Verbena L. (Verben.).
Sibangea Oliv. Euphorbiaceae (A. I. 1). 1 Gaboon.
Sibara Greene (*Cardamine* p.p.). Cruciferae (2). 6 Calif.
Sibbaldia L. (*Potentilla* p.p. *BH.*). Rosaceae (III. 2). 8 N. temp. |*.
Sibbaldiopsis Rydberg (*Potentilla* p.p.). Rosaceae (III. 2). 1 N. Am.
Siberian cedar, *Pinus Cembra* L.
Sibiraea Maxim. (*Spiraea* p.p. *BH.*). Rosaceae (I. 1). 1 Siberia.
Sibthorpia L. Scrophulariaceae (III. 1). 6 Eur., Medit., Nepal, Andes. *S. europaea* L. (Cornish money-wort) in S. England.
Sicana Naud. Cucurbitaceae (3). 1 trop. Am., W.I. Fr. ed.
Siccus (Lat.), dry, juiceless.
Sickingia Willd. Rubiaceae (I. 3). 14 trop. S. Am. Some medicinal.
Sicklepod (Am.), *Arabis canadensis* L.
Sicydium Schlechtd. Cucurbitaceae (2). 6 trop. Am.
Sicyomorpha Miers. Celastraceae. 2 Peru.
Sicyos L. Cucurbitaceae (4). 30 trop. Am., Polynes., Austr.
Sicyosperma A. Gray. Cucurbitaceae (4). 1 New Mexico, Texas.
Sida L. Malvaceae (2). 75 cosmop. Ov. 1 per loc., pend. Schizocarp.
Sidalcea A. Gray. Malvaceae (2). 12 N.W. Am.
Sidanoda Wooton et Standley (*Anoda* p.p.). Malv. (2). 1 New Mexico.
Sidastrum E. G. Baker (*Sida* p.p.). Malvaceae (2). 1 trop. Am.
Side oats, *Bouteloua*; **-saddle flower**, *Sarracenia*.
Sideranthus Nutt. (*Aplopappus* Cass.). Compositae (3). 12 N. Am.
Sideritis Tourn. ex L. Labiatae (VI). 45 N. temp. |*.
Siderocarpus Small (*Acacia* p.p.). Leguminosae (I. 2). 1 N. Am.
Sideroxylon (Dill.) L. Sapotaceae (I). 100 trop. Some ironwoods.
Siebera J. Gay. Compositae (11). 1 W. As.
Siegesbeckia L. Compositae (5). 4 trop. and warm. temp. Heads small, with invol. of 5 bracts, covered with very sticky glandular hairs, aiding in distr., the whole head breaking off.
Sieglingia Bernh. = Triodia R. Br. p.p. (Gramin.).
Sievekingia Reichb. f. Orchidaceae (II. 13). 4 trop. Am.
Sieversia Willd. (*Geum* p.p.). Rosaceae (III. 2). 10 N. Am.
Sigmatochilus Rolfe. Orchidaceae (II. 3). 1 Borneo.
Sigmatogyne Pfitzer (*Panisea* p.p.). Orchidaceae (II. 3). 2 Himalaya.
Sigmatosiphon Engl. Pedaliaceae. 1 S.W. Afr.
Sigmatostalix Reichb. f. Orchidaceae (II. 19). 25 trop. S. Am.
Sigmoid, S-shaped.
Silaus Bernh. Umbelliferae (III. 5). 8 N. temp. |* (1 Brit.).
Silene L. Caryophyllaceae (II. 1). 400 N. temp., esp. Medit. (7 in Brit.). Fls. of many (class F) adapted to butterflies, *e.g.* *S. acaulis* L. (moss-campion, a tufted alpine); others to moths, *e.g.* *S. inflata* Sm. (bladder campion), which emits scent at night.
Siler Crantz. Umbelliferae (III. 7). 1 Eur., Siberia.
Silicula, *Cruciferae*; **siliqua**, *Cruciferae*, *Capparidaceae*.

Siliquamomum Baill. Zingiberaceae (I). 1 Tonquin.
Silk cotton tree, *Eriodendron*; **-grass** (W.I.), *Nidularium*; **-weed,** *Asclepias*.
Silkworms, plants for, *Ailanthus*, *Lactuca*, *Maclura*, *Morus*.
Silky bent grass, *Apera*; **-oak** (Austr.), *Grevillea*.
Silphiosperma Steetz (*Brachycome* Cass.). Compositae (3). 1 Austr.
Silphium L. Compositae (5). 13 E. U.S. *S. laciniatum* L. is the 'compass-plant' of the prairies. In an exposed position its l. turn their edges to N. and S. and avoid the mid-day radiation. (*Cf.* Lactuca.) Cult. orn. fl.
Silvaea Phil. Portulacaceae. 4 Chili.
Silver bell tree (Am.), *Halesia*; **-berry** (Am.), *Elaeagnus argenteus* Pursh; **-fir,** *Abies*, *Picea*; **-tree,** *Leucadendron*; **-weed,** *Potentilla Anserina* L.
Silvia Allem. (*Neosilvia* Pax; *Endiandra BH.*, *Mezilaurus EP.*). Lauraceae (II). 2 Brazil. Wood useful.
Silvia Benth. Scrophulariaceae (III. 2). 2 Mexico.
Silvianthus Hook. f. Rubiaceae (I. 2). 1 E. Bengal.
Silvorchis J. J. Smith. Orchidaceae (II. 1). 1 Java.
Silybum Vaill. ex Adans. Compositae (11). 2 Medit. *S. Marianum* Gaertn. (milk-thistle, Brit.) is now widely distributed over the pampas, where it was introduced.
Simaba Aubl. Simarubaceae. 20 trop. S. Am.
Simaruba Aubl. Simarubaceae. 6 trop. Am., W.I.
Simarubaceae (*EP.*; *BH.* incl. *Brunelliaceae*, *Cneoraceae*, *Koeberliniaceae*). Dicots. (Archichl. Geraniales). 28 gen., 125 sp., trop. and subtrop. Shrubs and trees with alt. pinnate or simple l., never gland-dotted. Fls. small, reg., ☿, often ∞, in axillary compound panicles or cymose spikes. K and C 3—7-merous. K free or more often united; C imbr. or rarely valv.; disc between sta. and ovary ring- or cup-like, sometimes enlarged into a gynophore; A twice as many as petals, obdiplost., often with scales at the base; G (4—5) or less, often free below and united by the style or stigma; ovules usu. 1 in each loc. as in Rutaceae. Schizocarp or caps.; endosp. thin or none: embryo with thick cots. A few yield useful timber. Many have bitter bark, sometimes officinal. *Chief genera:* Simaruba, Ailanthus.
Simarubeae (*BH.*) = Simarubaceae.
Simarubopsis Engl. Simarubaceae. 1 Togoland.
Simbuleta Forsk. (*Anarrhinum* Desf.). Scrophulariaceae (II. 3). 12 Medit., W.As., Abyssinia.
Simethis Kunth. Liliaceae (III). 1 Brit., W. and S. Eur., N. Afr.
Simmondsia Nutt. Buxaceae. 1 California.
Simocheilus Klotzsch. Ericaceae (IV. 2). 40 S. Afr.
Simple fruit, one indivisible fr. from one fl.; -l., with 1 blade.
Simplicia T. Kirk. Gramineae (8). 1 New Zealand.
Simsia R. Br. Proteaceae (I). 5 W. Austr.
Sinapis L. (*Brassica* p.p. *BH.*). Cruciferae (2). 8 Medit., Eur. *S. arvensis* L. (charlock) is an abundant weed of cult.; our cornfields are yellow with it in summer. *S. alba* L. is the white mustard.
Sinapodendron Lowe (*Brassica* p.p. *BH.*). Crucif. (2). 5 Madeira, &c.
Sincoraea Ule. Bromeliaceae (4). 1 Bahia.

Sindechites Oliv. Apocynaceae (II. 1). 1 S.W. China.
Sindora Miq. Leguminosae (II. 2). 6 Malaya.
Sinensis (Lat.), Chinese.
Singana Aubl. Leguminosae (inc. sed.). 1 Guiana.
Sinistrorse, turned to the left.
Sinningia Nees. Gesneriaceae (II). 20 Brazil. *S. speciosa* Hiern, &c. cult. (generally known as Gloxinias). Tuberous plants. Usual propagation by planting l. on the soil; from the base of the petiole a new pl. arises by budding (*cf.* Begonia, Streptocarpus).
Sinofranchetia Hemsl. (*Parvatia* p.p.). Lardizabalaceae. 1 China.
Sinomenium Diels (*Cocculus* p.p.). Menispermaceae. 1 E. As.
Sinowilsonia Hemsl. Hamamelidaceae. 1 China.
Sinuate (l.), with teeth and notches rounded (Leaf, fig. D).
Sinus, bay, re-entrant angle.
Siolmatra Baill. Cucurbitaceae (I). 5 S. Am.
Sipanea Aubl. Rubiaceae (I. 3). 3 S. Am.
Siparuna Aubl. Monimiaceae. 120 trop. Am. W.I. Fr. fig-like.
Siphanthera Pohl. Melastomaceae (I). 12 Brazil, Guiana.
Siphoboea Baill. Gesneriaceae (I). 1 Phil. Is.
Siphocampylus Pohl. Campanulaceae (III). 110 trop. Am., W.I.
Siphocodon Turcz. Campanulaceae (I). 1 S. Afr.
Siphocolea Baill. Bignoniaceae (4). 3 Madag.
Siphonandrium K. Schum. Rubiaceae (I. 7). 1 New Guinea.
Siphonanthus L. = Clerodendron L. p.p. (Verben.).
Siphonella A. A. Heller (*Gilia* p.p.). Polemoniaceae. 1 W. N. Am.
Siphonella Small (*Fedia* p.p.). Valerianaceae. 2 N. Am.
Siphonia Rich. = Hevea Aubl. *S. elastica* Pers. = H. guianensis.
Siphonidium Armstr. Scrophulariaceae (III. 3). 1 New Zealand.
Siphonochilus Wood et Franks. Zingiberaceae (I). 1 Natal.
Siphonodon Griff. Celastraceae. 2 Malaya, Austr.
Siphonogamy, fertilisation by pollen tube.
Siphonoglossa Oerst. Acanthaceae (IV. B). 3 Am.
Siphonostegia Benth. Scrophulariaceae (III. 3). 3 As.
Siphonostelma Schlechter. Asclepiadaceae (II. 3). 1 S.W. Afr.
Siphonychia Torr. et A. Gray. Caryophyllaceae (I. 4). 2 Atl. N. Am.
Sipolisia Glaziou. Compositae (I). 1 Minas Geraes.
Siris, *Albizzia Lebbek* Benth.
Sirium L. = Santalum L. (Santal.).
Sisal hemp, *Agave sisalana* Perrine.
Sison L. Umbelliferae (III. 5). 2 Eur., incl. Brit., Medit.
Sissoo, *Dalbergia Sissoo* Roxb.
Sisymbrium (Tourn.) L. (*BH.* incl. *Alliaria*). Cruciferae (2). 80 N. temp. |✻; 3 Brit., incl. *S. officinale* Scop. (hedge-mustard).
Sisyndite E. Mey. Zygophyllaceae. 1 S. Afr.
Sisyranthus E. Mey. Asclepiadaceae (II. 3). 8 S. Afr.
Sisyrinchium L. Iridaceae (II). 75 Am. Cult. orn. fl.
Sisyrolepis Radlk. Sapindaceae (inc. sed.). 1 Siam.
Sitanion Rafin. (*Elymus* L. p.p.). Gramineae (12). 12 N. Am.
Sitilias Rafin. (*Pyrrhopappus* DC.). Compositae (13). 6 U.S., Mexico.
Sitka cypress, *Chamaecyparis nutkaensis* Lindl. et Gord.
Sium (Tourn.) L. Umbellif. (III. 5). 15 cosmop., exc. S. Am., Austr.

2 in Brit. (water-parsnip). *S. Sisarum* L. (skirret) cult. for tuberous roots.

Skimmia Thunb. Rutaceae (IV). 5 Himal. to Japan. *S. japonica* Thunb., often cult. for its handsome foliage and red berries.

Skirret, *Sium Sisarum* L.

Skolemora Arruda. Inc. sed. 1 Brazil.

Skull cap, *Scutellaria.*

Skunk cabbage, *Symplocarpus foetidus* Nutt.

Skytanthus Meyen. Apocynaceae (I. 3). 3 Brazil, Chili.

Slackia Griff. Gesneriaceae (I). 1 Burma.

Sladenia Kurz. Actinidiaceae (Ternstr. *BH.*). 1 Yunnan, Burma.

Sleep movements, *cf.* Movement.

Sloanea L. Elaeocarpaceae. 45 trop.

Sloe, *Prunus spinosa* L.

Sloetia Teijsm. et Binn. Moraceae (I). 2 Malaya.

Sloetiopsis Engl. Moraceae (I). 1 Usambara.

Small reed, *Calamagrostis.*

Smallia Nieuwland = Triorchos Small et Nash (Orchid.).

Smartweed (Am.), Polygonum.

Smeathmannia (Soland.) R. Br. (*Paropsia* p.p.). Flacourtiaceae (6) (Passiflor. *BH.*). 6 trop. Afr.

Smelophyllum Radlk. Sapindaceae (I). 1 S. Afr.

Smelowskia C. A. Mey. Cruciferae (4). 8 temp. As., Pac. N. Am.

Smilacina Desf. Liliaceae (VII). 20 Himalaya to C. Am.

Smilax (Tourn.) L. Liliaceae (XI). 300 trop. and subtrop. Most are climbing shrubs with net-veined l. At base of l. spring two tendrils, one on either side, usu. regarded as modified stip., though these organs scarcely occur in Monocots. Stems often furnished with recurved hooks which aid in climbing. Fls. dioec., in umbels. The dried roots of several S. Am. sp. form sarsaparilla.

Smirnowia Bunge. Leguminosae (III. 6). 1 Turkestan.

Smithia Ait. Leguminosae (III. 7). 35 trop. As., Afr.

Smithiantha O. Ktze. (*Naegelia* Regel). Gesneriaceae (II). 6 Mexico. Cult.

Smodingium E. Mey. Anacardiaceae (3). 1 S. Afr.

Smyrniopsis Boiss. (*Smyrnium* p.p. *BH.*). Umbellif. (III. 4). 3 E. Medit.

Smyrnium (Tourn.) L. Umbelliferae (III. 4). 7 Medit., Eur., Brit. *S. Olusatrum* L. (alexanders), formerly used like celery.

Smythea Seem. Rhamnaceae. 4 Malaya, Burma, Polynesia. Exalb.

Snail flower, *Arisaema.*

Snake gourd, *Trichosanthes anguina* L.; **-head** (Am.), *Chelone*; **-'s head**, *Fritillaria*; **-root**, *Cimicifuga*; **black--** (Am.), *Sanicula*; **button--** (Am.), *Liatris*; **Senega--**, *Polygala*; **-wood**, *Ophioxylon*, *Ophiocaryon.*

Snapdragon, *Antirrhinum majus* L., (W.I.) *Ruellia.*

Sneeze wood, *Pteroxylon*, (Am.) *Helenium*; **-wort**, *Achillea.*

Snow ball tree, *Viburnum Opulus* L.; **-berry**, *Symphoricarpus racemosus* Michx.; **-drop**, *Galanthus nivalis* L.; **-drop tree**, *Chionanthus*, *Halesia*; **-flake**, *Leucojum.*

Soap, *Chlorogalum*, *Liliaceae*, *Limonia*, *Sapindus*, *Saponaria*; **-berry**

tree (W.I.), *Sapindus*; **-tree**, *Quillaja*; **-wood** (W.I.), *Clethra*; **-wort**, *Saponaria*.
Soaresia Sch.-Bip. Compositae (1). 1 campos of S. Brazil.
Sobole, a shoot from the ground.
Sobolewskia Marsch.-Bieb. Cruciferae (2). 3 W. As.
Sobralia Ruiz et Pav. Orchidaceae (II. 7). 33 Peru to Mexico.
Social habit, forming homogeneous forests, pine, birch, beech.
Societies, Plant, see Plant societies.
Socotora Balf. f. (*Periploca* p.p. *EP.*). Asclepiadaceae (1). 1 Socotra.
Socotranthus O. Ktze. = Cochlanthus Balf. f. (Asclep.).
Socratea Karst. (*Iriartea* p.p. *EP.*). Palmae (IV. 1). 1 Brazil.
Sodiroa André. Bromeliaceae (1). 3 Colombia, Ecuador.
Soemmeringia Mart. Leguminosae (III. 7). 1 N.E. Brazil.
Soft grass, *Holcus*.
Sohnreyia Krause. Rutaceae (1). 1 Manáos.
Soja bean, *Glycine*.
Soja Moench = Glycine L. p.p. (Legum.).
Sola, *Aeschynomene aspera* L.
Solanaceae (*EP.*, *BH.* incl. *Nolanaceae*). Dicots. (Sympet. Tubiflorae; Polemoniales *BH.*). 72 gen., 1500 sp. trop. and temp.; chief centre C. and S. Am., where there are 36 local gen.; in Eur. and As. only § 2 is repres. Herbs, shrubs or small trees; l. in the non-flowering part usu. alt., but in the infl.-portion alt. or in pairs; the arrangement in pairs is due to the mode of branching and adnation as illustrated in the figure. In Datura the branching is dichasial, and the bracts are adnate to their axillary shoots up to the point at which the next

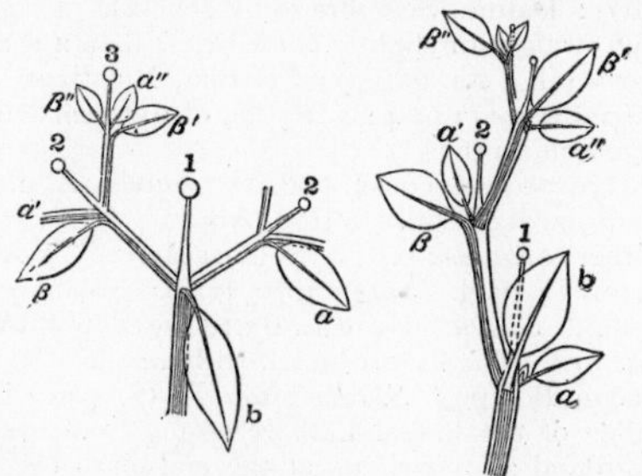

Branching in Solanaceae (after Eichler); *Datura Stramonium* (left) and *Atropa Belladonna* (right). 1, 2, 3, flrs. or infls. of successive orders; *b*, bract of 1, α β bracts of 2, and so on.

branches arise, so that α looks like the bracteole of 2, rather than its bract. In Atropa the branching is cincinnal, one of the two branches at a node remaining undeveloped, and the bract is again adnate to its axillary branch. Of the pair of l. thus found at any node, one is usu. smaller than the other. In Solanum, &c. further complications occur (see Eichler's *Blüthendiag.*).

Fls. sol. or in cymes, ☿, sometimes ·|·. K (5), persistent; C (5), of various forms, rarely 2-lipped, usually folded and conv.; A 5, alt.

with petals, epipet., or fewer in ·|· fls., often opening by pores; G (2), obliquely placed in the fl. (the post. cpl. to the right, the ant. to the left, when shown in a floral diagram), 2-loc., sometimes with secondary divisions (*e.g.* Datura), upon a hypog. disc; ov. 1—∞ in each loc., anatr. or slightly amphitr., on axile plac. (most often the plac. are swollen and the ov. numerous); style simple, with 2-lobed stigma. Berry or caps. Embryo curved or straight, in endosp. Fls. conspic., insect-visited; some, *e.g.* Nicotiana, suited to Lepidoptera. A few are economically important, *e.g.* Solanum (potato), Nicotiana (tobacco), Lycopersicum, Capsicum, &c.; Datura, Atropa, &c. are medicinal; several are favourites in horticulture.

Classification and chief genera (after von Wettstein): the S. are nearly related to Scrophulariaceae, the most general distinction being the oblique ovary: this however is by no means easily made out, and the zygomorphism of the fl. is most often used as a distinction. Certain genera of S. are nearly related to various Boraginaceae, Gesneriaceae, Nolanaceae, &c., and it is possible that the S. are not really a simple monophyletic family; they occupy a middle place between the Tubuliflorae with actinom. and those with zygom. fls.

A. Embryo clearly curved, through more than a semicircle. All 5 sta. fertile, equal or only slightly different in length.

1. *Nicandreae* (ovary 3—5-loc., the walls of the loc. dividing the placentae irregularly): Nicandra (only genus).
2. *Solaneae* (ovary 2-loc.): Lycium, Atropa, Hyoscyamus, Physalis, Capsicum, Solanum, Lycopersicum, Mandragora.
3. *Datureae* (ovary 4-loc., the walls dividing the placentae equally): Datura, Solandra (only genera).

B. Embryo straight or slightly curved (less than a semicircle).

4. *Cestreae* (all 5 sta. fertile); Cestrum, Nicotiana, Petunia.
5. *Salpiglossideae* (2 or 4 sta. fertile, of different lengths): Salpiglossis, Schizanthus.

Solandra L. = Hydrocotyle Tourn. (*BH.*) = Centella L. p.p. (Umb.).

Solandra Sw. Solanaceae (3). 6 trop. Am.

Solanopsis Börner (*Solanum* p.p.). Solanaceae (2). 2 Am.

Solanum (Tourn.) L. (incl. *Lycopersicum* Hill). Solanaceae (2). 1225 trop. and temp. *S. Dulcamara* L. (bittersweet, nightshade) and *S. nigrum* L. in Brit. The fls. are small, with a cone of anthers opening at the tip as in Borago. *S. tuberosum* L. (S. Am.) is the potato. From the axils of the lowest l. there spring branches which grow horiz. underground and swell up at the ends into tubers (potatoes). That these are stem structures is shown by their origin and by their possession of buds—the 'eyes.' Each eye is a small bud in the axil of an aborted l. (repres. by a semicircular rim). When the parent plant dies down in autumn the tubers become detached, and in the next season they form new plants by the development of the eyes, at the expense of the starch and other reserves stored in the tuber. By heaping earth against the stem, so as to cover more of the leaf-axils, more of the axillary shoots are made to become tuber-bearing; hence the value of ridging potatoes. *S. Lycopersicum* L. (Am.) is the tomato, cult. for ed. fr. *S. Melongena* L., the egg-fruit, is cult. in warm countries for ed. fr.

Solaria Phil. Liliaceae (IV). 1 Chili.
Soldanella L. Primulaceae. 6 Alps of Eur. The fls. expand at very low temperatures, often coming up through the snow; they have a mechanism like that of Erica.
Soldier plant (W.I.). *Calliandra.*
Solea Spreng. = Ionidium Vent. (*BH.*) = Hybanthus Jacq.
Solena Willd. = Posoqueria Aubl. (Rubi.).
Solenandra Hook. f. Rubiaceae (I. 5). 1 Cuba.
Solenanthus Ledeb. Boraginaceae (IV. 1). 15 Medit., C. As.
Solenidium Lindl. Orchidaceae (II. 19). 3 trop. Am. Column winged.
Solenixora Baill. Rubiaceae (II. 4). 1 Madag.
Solenocarpus Wight et Arn. Anacardiaceae (2). 1 India.
Solenocentrum Schlechter. Orchidaceae (II. 3). 1 Costa Rica.
Solenomelus Miers. Iridaceae (II). 2 Chili.
Solenophora Benth. Gesneriaceae (II). 3 Mexico, C. Am. $\overline{G}$
Solenoruellia Baill. Acanthaceae (IV. B). 1 Mexico.
Solenospermum Zoll. Celastraceae. 1 Java.
Solenostemma Hayne. Asclepiadaceae (II. 1). 1 Egypt, Arabia.
Solenostemon Thonn. (*Plectranthus* p.p. *BH.*). Labi. (VII). 8 W. Afr.
Solenosterigma Klotzsch ex K. Krause = Philodendron Schott.
Solenostigma Endl. = Celtis Tourn. p.p. (Ulm.).
Solenostyles Host. Acanthaceae (inc. sed.). 1, habitat?.
Solenotus Stev. = Astragalus Tourn. (Legum.).
Solfia Rechinger. Palmae (IV. 1). 1 Samoa.
Solidago (Vaill.) L. Compositae (3). 90 Am.; 1 in Eur. (incl. Brit.), *S. Virgaurea* L., the golden rod.
Soliera Clos (*Kurzamra EP.*). Labiatae (VI). 1 Chili.
Solitary (fl.), one per axil.
Soliva Ruiz et Pav. Compositae (7). 6 Am., Austr.
Sollya Lindl. Pittosporaceae. 2 W. Austr. Twiners.
Solmsia Baill. Gonystilaceae. 2 New Caledonia.
Solms-Laubachia Muschler. Cruciferae (4). 1 China.
Solomon's seal, *Polygonatum.*
Somalia Oliv. (*Barleria* p.p. *EP.*). Acanthaceae (IV. B). 1 trop. Afr.
Sommera Schlechtend. Rubiaceae (I. 7). 5 Amazon valley, Mexico.
Sommerfeltia Less. Compositae (3). 1 S. Andes. Char. pl.
Sommieria Becc. Palmae (IV. 1). 2 New Guinea.
Somphoxylon Eichl. Menispermaceae. 1 Guiana.
Sonchus (Tourn.) L. Compositae (13). 45 |✻, 3 Brit. (sow-thistle).
Sondaria Dennst. Rhamnaceae (inc. sed.). 1 Indomal.
Sonerila Roxb. (*Cassebeeria* Dennst.). Melastom. (1). 70 warm As.
Sonnea Greene. Boraginaceae (IV. 2). 6 Pac. N. Am.
Sonneratia L. f. (*Blatti* Adans.). Sonneratiaceae. 6 Indomal. Mangroves (*q.v.*), with the general habit of Rhizophoraceae. Aerial roots spring vertically out of the mud, arising as lat., negatively geotropic branches upon the ordinary roots; they are provided with aerenchyma, and appear to be respiratory organs.
Sonneratiaceae (*Blattiaceae*; *EP.*; *Lythraceae* p.p. *BH.*). Dicots. (Archichl. Myrtiflorae). 3 gen., 12 sp. trop. As. and Afr. Shrubs and trees with opp. entire exstip. l. and conspic. fls., heterochlam. or apet., ☿ or ♂ ♀, reg. K 4–8, C 4–8 or 0, A ∞, G (4–15), with one style and

multiloc. ov. with ∞ ovules. Caps. or berry; ∞ seeds, exalbum. *Chief gen.* Sonneratia, Duabanga.

Sonzaya Marchand (*Canarium* p.p. *EP.*). Burseraceae. 1 Austr.

Sophia L. 1735 (*Sisymbrium* p.p.). Cruciferae (2). 20 N. Am.

Sophia L. 1775 = Bombax L. p.p. (Bomb.).

Sophoclesia Klotzsch. Ericaceae (III. 2). 10 Andes, Guiana, W.I.

Sophora L. Leguminosae (III. 1). 25 trop. and warm temp. Winter-buds naked. The wood is very hard.

Sophrocattleya, Sophrolaelia, Sophrolaeliocattleya, Sophrocattlaelia × Hort. Orchidaceae. Hybrids of Sophronitis.

Sophronanthe Benth. = Gratiola Rupp. (Scroph.).

Sophronitis Lindl. Orchidaceae (II. 6). 4 S.E. Brazil. Cult. orn. fl.

Sopubia Buch.-Ham. Scrophulariaceae (III. 2). 20 palaeotrop.

Sorbaria A. Br. (*Spiraea* p.p. *BH.*). Rosaceae (I. 1). 5 N. As., N. Am.

Sorbaronia × C. K. Schneider. Rosaceae. Hybrid Sorbus-Aronia.

Sorbopyrus × C. K. Schneider. Rosaceae. Hybrid Sorbus-Pyrus.

Sorbus (Tourn.) L. = Pyrus Tourn. p.p. (Ros.).

Sordidus (Lat.), dirty white.

Sorghastrum Nash (*Andropogon* p.p.). Gramineae (2). 10 N. Am.

Sorgho, *Sorghum vulgare* Pers.

Sorghum L. (*Andropogon*, p.p.). Gramineae (2). 13 trop. and sub-trop. *S. vulgare* Pers. (millet or guinea corn), largely cult. in Medit. &c. as a cereal. From the haulm of the var. *saccharatum* Koern. sugar is sometimes prepared.

Soriferous, bearing sori.

Sorindeia Thou. Anacardiaceae (3). 20 trop. Afr., Madag.

Sorocea A. St Hil. Moraceae (II). 12 trop. Am.

Sorocephalus R. Br. Proteaceae (I). 10 S. Afr.

Sorosis, a fleshy multiple fruit, *Ananas*, &c.

Sorrel, *Rumex*; **wood -**, *Oxalis acetosella* L.

Sorus, a group of sporangia, *Cycadaceae*, *Filicales*, *Pteridophyta*.

Souari nut, *Caryocar*.

Souchong, *Thea*.

Soulamea Lam. Simarubaceae. 1 Moluccas to Fiji.

Soulangia Brongn. = Phylica L. (Rhamn.).

Souleyetia Gaudich. (*Pandanus* p.p. *EP.*). Pandanaceae. 1, habitat?.

Souliea Franch. Ranunculaceae (2). 1 China.

Sour grass, *Panicum conjugatum* Berg.; **- sop**, *Anona muricata* L.

Souroubea Aubl. (*Ruyschia BH.*). Marcgrav. 15 trop. Am., W.I. [G 5-loc.

Southern cold zone, see Zones of Veg.

Southernwood, *Artemisia Abrotanum* L.

Sow-bread, *Cyclamen*; **-thistle**, *Sonchus*.

Sowerbaea Smith. Liliaceae (III). 4 Austr.

Soy bean, *Glycine Soja* Sieb. et Zucc., *G. hispida* Maxim.

Soyauxia Oliv. Flacourtiaceae (6) (Passiflor. *BH.*). 5 W. trop. Afr.

Soyeria Monn. = Crepis Vaill. p.p. (Comp.).

Soymida A. Juss. Meliaceae (II). 1 Indomal. Astringent bark. Wood.

Spachea A. Juss. Malpighiaceae (II). 10 W.I., trop. S. Am.

Spadiceus (Lat.), chestnut-coloured, or bearing a spadix.

Spadiciflorae (Warming). The 3rd order of Monocots.

Spadix, a spike with fls. ± sunk in tissue, usu. enclosed in a *spathe* of 1 or > 1 large l., *Arac.*, *Cyclanthac.*, *Palmae*, *Zostera*.
Spananthe Jacq. Umbell. (I. 2). 1 trop. Am., W.I. Annual, to 2 m. [high.
Spanish bayonet, *Yucca*; **-berries**, *Rhamnus infectoria* L.; **-broom**, *Spartium junceum* L.; **-dagger**, *Yucca*; **-liquorice**, *Glycyrrhiza glabra* L.; **-needle**, *Bidens*; **-plum**, *Spondias*.
Spanoghea Blume (*Alectryon* p.p. *EP.*). Sapind. (I). 2 Malay Arch.
Sparattanthelium Mart. Hernand. (Combret. *BH.*). 6 trop. Am.
Sparattosperma Mart. ex DC. Bignon. (2). 4 Braz. K split one side.
Sparattosyce Bur. Mor. (II). 2 New Caled.
Sparaxis Ker-Gawl. Irid. (III). 4 Cape Col. Cult. orn. varieg. fl.
Sparganiaceae (*EP.*; *Typh.* p.p. *BH.*). Monocots. (Pandanales; pp. iii, liv). Only genus **Sparganium** (Tourn.) L. 18 N. temp., Austr., N.Z. 3 Brit. (burweed) in ponds. Creeping rhiz. and stem usu. projecting above water with l., and fls. in spherical heads, ♂ usu. higher up and more crowded than ♀. P 3—6, scaly, sepaloid; ♂ A 3—6, alt. with P when equal in number; ♀ $\underline{G}$ 1 or (2), with one ov. pend. near base of G, with micropyle up. Fr. drupaceous with album. seed. Fl. protog., anemoph.
Sparganophorus Vaill. ex Crantz. Comp. (1). 1 trop. Am., W.I., Afr.
Sparkleberry (Am.), *Vaccinium arboreum* Marsh.
Sparmannia L. f. Tili. 4 trop. and S. Afr. Fls. in cymose umbels (recognised by centrifugal order of opening). K 4, 2 sometimes petaloid. Sta. ∞ with ∞ stds., sensitive, moving outward when touched (*cf.* Helianthemum); no androphore.
Sparrow grass, *Asparagus*; **sparsus** (Lat.), scattered.
Spartina Schreb. Gramin. (11). 7 temp. (Brit.). Halophytes. *S. Townsendi* H. et J. Groves is spreading on the S. coast of England.
Spartium L. Legum. (III. 3). 1 Medit., *S. junceum* L. (Spanish broom), like broom in habit. Exstip. l. with one leaflet. Fls. explosive like Genista; they yield yellow dye, the pl. fibre.
Spartothamnella Briq. (*Spartothamnus* p.p.). Verben. (3). 1 Austr.
Spartothamnus A. Cunn. Verben. (3). 3 Austr.
Spatalla Salisb. Prot. (1). 25 S. Afr. Involv. 1—4-fld. Fl. slightly ·|·.
Spatallopsis Phillips (*Spatalla* p.p.). Prot. (1). 5 S. Afr.
Spathacanthus Baill. Acanth. (IV. B). 4 C. Am., Mex. (K) in pairs.
Spathantheum Schott. Arac. (VII). 2 Bolivia. G 6—8-loc.
Spathanthus Desv. Rapat. 2 Guiana. G 1-loc., 1-ovuled. L. 5' long. Spike one-sided.
Spathe, *cf.* Spadix.
Spathelia L. Rut. (III). 4 W.I.
Spathia Ewart in Ewart et Davies. Gramin. (2). 1 N. Austr.
Spathicarpa Hook. Arac. (VII). 6 Bolivia to Arg. Spadix adnate to spathe, monoec. Down centre 1—3 rows of ♂ fls. (stalked synandria); at sides ♀ fls. each of a bottle-shaped G with stds.
Spathidolepis Schlechter. Asclep. (II. 3). 1 New Guinea.
Spathiflorae. The 7th order of Monocots.; p. iv.
Spathiger Small (*Epidendrum* p.p.). Orchid. (II. 6). 10 warm Am., W.I.
Spathionema Taub. Legum. (III. 10). 1 trop. Afr.
Spathiphyllum Schott. Arac. (II). 30 trop. Am., Malay Arch., Phil. Is. Spathe partly adnate to spadix. Fl. ☿ with P. Cult. orn. pl.
Spathodea Beauv. Bignon. (2). 3 trop. Afr. Has large water-pores

on backs of leaflets near midrib. In *S. campanulata* the K is inflated and water secreted between it and the C.

Spathoglottis Blume. Orchidaceae (II. 9). 15 Indomal.

Spatholirion Ridl. Commelinaceae. 3 Malay Peninsula.

Spatholobus Hassk. Leguminosae (III. 10). 20 trop. As.

Spathulopetalum Chiov. Asclepiadaceae (II. 3). 1 Erythraea.

Spatterdock (Am.). *Nuphar*.

Spatularia Haw. (*Saxifraga* p.p. *EP.*). Saxifrag. (I). 8 N. Am., arctic.

Spatulate, spoon-shaped, l. of daisy.

Spear grass, *Stipa*, *Poa*, &c.; **-mint**, *Mentha*; **-wort** (Am.), *Ranunculus*.

Species, see Nomenclature.

Speciosus (Lat.), handsome.

Specklinia Lindl. = Pleurothallis R. Br. (Orchid.).

Spectabilis (Lat.), remarkable.

Spectans (Lat.), opposite.

Specularia Heist. Campanulaceae (I. 1). 10 N. temp., S. Am. *S. Speculum* A. DC., Venus' looking-glass, cult. orn. fl.

Speedwell, *Veronica*.

Speirantha Baker. Liliaceae (VII). 1 Shanghai.

Speirostyla Baker. Tiliaceae (Stercul. auct.). 1 Madag.

Spelt, *Triticum Spelta* L.

Spenceria Trimen. Rosaceae (III. 5). 1 W. China.

Spennera Mart. ex DC. = Aciotis D. Don (Melast.).

Speranskia Baill. Euphorbiaceae (A. II. 2). 3 China. Rhizome-herb.

Spergula L. Caryophyllaceae (I. 2). 3 temp. *S. arvensis* L., spurry, a general weed. The axillary shoots do not lengthen their internodes, so that the l. seem to be tufted. Fls. in cymes, gynomonoec. or gynodioec. Sometimes used as fodder.

Spergularia J. et C. Presl (*Buda* Adans., *Lepigonum* Wahlb., *Tissa* Adans.). Caryophyllaceae (I. 2). 20 cosmop., mostly halophytes.

Sperm- (Gr. pref.), seed or male; **-aphytes**, seed-plants; **-atozoid**, a swimming ♂ sexual cell.

Spermabolus Teijsm. et Binn. Magnoliaceae. 1 Moluccas.

Spermacoce Dill. ex L. (*BH.* incl. *Borreria*). Rubiaceae (II. 10). 2 warm Am.

Spermaphyta or Phanerogamae. One of the great divisions of the Vegetable Kingdom, comprising all those plants which produce seeds. Divided into Gymnospermae and Angiospermae.

Spermolepis Brongn. et Gris. Myrtaceae (II. 1). 2 New Caledonia.

Sphacele Benth. Labiatae (VI). 20 warm Am., Hawaiian Is.

Sphacophyllum Benth. Compositae (4). 5 Madag., Afr. trop.

Sphaeralcea A. St Hil. Malvaceae (2). 28 Cape Col., Am.

Sphaeranthus Vaill. ex L. Compositae (4). 20 palaeotrop.

Sphaerocardamum S. Schau. Cruciferae (4). 1 Mexico.

Sphaerocodon Benth. Asclepiadaceae (II. 3). 5 Afr.

Sphaerocoma T. Anders. Caryophyllaceae (I. 4). 2 Arabia, Persia.

Sphaerodendron Seem. (*Cussonia* p.p.). Araliaceae (I). 1 Angola.

Sphaerolobium Sm. Leguminosae (III. 2). 12 Austr.

Sphaeromeria Nutt. (*Chrysanthemum* p.p. *EP.*, *Tanacetum* p.p. *BH.*). Compositae (7). 4 N. Am.
Sphaeromorphaea DC. Compositae (7). 1 Indomal.
Sphaerophysa DC. (*Swainsona EP.*). Legum. (III. 6). 2 N. As., E. Medit.
Sphaerosepalum Baker. Cochlospermaceae. 2 Madag.
Sphaerosicyos Hook. f. Cucurbitaceae (3). 1 S. Afr., Masc. Is.
Sphaerostigma Fisch. et Mey. (*Oenothera BH.*, *Chamissonia* p.p. *EP.*). Onagraceae (2). 25 N. Am.
Sphaerostylis Baill. Euphorbiaceae (A. II. 2). 1 Madag.
Sphaerothalamus Hook. f. Anonaceae (1). 1 Borneo.
Sphaerothylax Bischoff ex Krauss. Podostemaceae. 1 Natal.
Sphagneticola O. Hoffm. Compositae (5). 1 Rio de Janeiro.
Sphallerocarpus Bess. (*Conopodium BH.*). Umbellif. (III. 2). 1 Eur.
Sphedamnocarpus Planch. ex Benth. et Hook. f. Malpighiaceae (I). 5 warm Afr., Madag.
Sphenandra Benth. Scrophulariaceae (II. 5). 2 S. Afr.
Sphenocentrum Pierre. Menispermaceae. 1 W. trop. Afr.
Sphenoclea Gaertn. Campanul. (I). 1 trop. Caps. circumscissile.
Sphenodesma Jack. Verbenaceae (6). 10 Indomal.
Sphenogyne R. Br. = Ursinia Gaertn. p.p. (Comp.).
Sphenopholis Scribner. Gramineae (9). 7 N. Am.
Sphenopus Trin. Gramineae (10). 1 Medit. Halophyte.
Sphenostemon Baill. Aquifoliaceae (?). 2 New Caledonia.
Sphenostigma Baker. Iridaceae (II). 5 trop. Am.
Sphenostylis E. Mey. (*Vigna BH.*). Leguminosae (III. 10). 5 Afr.
Sphenotoma Sweet (*Dracophyllum* p.p. *BH.*). Epacridaceae (2). 6 W. Austr.
Sphinctacanthus Benth. Acanthaceae (IV. B). 2 E. Bengal, Siam.
Sphinctanthus Benth. Rubiaceae (I. 8). 5 S. Am.
Sphinctospermum Rose (*Tephrosia* p.p.). Legum. (III. 6). 1 Mexico.
Sphondylium (Tourn.). Adans. = Heracleum L. (Umbell.).
Sphyranthera Hook. Euphorbiaceae (inc. sed.). 1 Andamans.
Sphyrospermum Poepp. et Endl. Ericaceae (III. 2). 5 trop. S. Am.
Spicate, in spikes, or spike-formed.
Spice, see Condiment; **-bush** (Am.), *Lindera*.
Spicule, a small spike.
Spider orchis, *Ophrys aranifera* Huds.; **-wort**, *Tradescantia*.
Spigelia L. Loganiaceae. 35 warm Am. Some, *e.g.* *S. Anthelmia* L. and *S. marilandica* L. (Indian pink, or pink-root), have apparent whorls of 4 l. close under the infl.; in reality the internode between two pairs is very short. Cyme like Boraginaceae. Capsule falls away leaving a sort of cupule. Style jointed.
Spignel, *Meum athamanticum* Jacq.
Spike, a raceme with fls. all sessile, *Piper*, *Plantago*; **-grass** (Am.), *Uniola*; **-let**, *Cyperaceae*, *Gramineae*; **-nard**, *Nardostachys*, (Am.) *Aralia racemosa* L.; **-rush**, *Eleocharis*.
Spilanthes Jacq. Compositae (5). 35 trop.
Spilocarpus Lem. Boraginaceae (inc. sed.). 1 Cuba.
Spinach, *Spinacia oleracea* L.; **New Zealand -**, *Tetragonia*.
Spinacia (Tourn.) L. Chenopodiaceae (A). 2 E. Medit. *S. oleracea*

L. is the spinach. Annual herbs with cymes of dioec. fls., anemoph. The bracteoles harden round the fr. as a membranous wing.

Spindle tree, *Euonymus*.

Spingula Nor. Inc. sed. Nomen.

Spinifex L. Gramineae (5). 4 Austr., Ceylon to Japan. Dioec. ♀ spikelets 1-flowered with long spiny bracts, massed together into a head. This breaks off when the fruits are ripe, and blows about (*cf.* Anastatica), finally sticking in the sand and breaking up.

Spinks, *Cardamine pratensis* L.

Spinose, spiny (l.), *Acantholimon*, *Acanthophyllum*, *Acanthus*, &c.

Spiracantha H. B. et K. Compositae (1). 1 C. Am., Colombia.

Spiradiclis Blume. Rubiaceae (I. 2). 3 Bengal to Java.

Spiraea L. (excl. *Ulmaria* Tourn.). Rosaceae (I. 1). 50 N. temp.

Spiraeanthemum A. Gray. Cunoniaceae. 6 Polynesia.

Spiraeanthus Maxim. Rosaceae (I. 1). 1 C. As.

Spiraeopsis Miq. Cunoniaceae. 5 Celebes.

Spiral (fl.), with l. spirally arranged, not in whorls.

Spiranthera A. St Hil. Rutaceae (1). 1 E. Brazil.

Spiranthes Rich. Orchidaceae (II. 2). 50 N. temp., S. Am.; 3 in Brit., incl. *S. autumnalis* Rich. (lady's tresses). *S. Romanzoffiana* Cham. et Schlecht., a native of N. Am. and Kamtschatka, occurs in meadows at Bantry Bay, Ireland, and has caused much discussion among geographical botanists (*cf.* Eriocaulon). Infl. twisted, so that the fls. form a spiral. For mechanism see Darwin, *Orchids*, p. 106.

Spire lily, *Galtonia*.

Spirea Pierre (*Aspilia* p.p. *EP.*). Compositae (5). 1 trop. Afr.

Spirella Costantin. Asclepiadaceae (II. 3). 1 Indochina.

Spirochloe Lunell (*Schedonnardus* Steud.). Gramineae (11). 1 N. Am.

Spirodela Schleiden (*Lemna* p.p. *BH.*). Lemnaceae. 2 cosmop. exc. Afr.

Spirolobium Baill. Apocynaceae (II. 1). 1 Cambodia.

Spirolobous, *Cruciferae*.

Spironema Lindl. Commelinaceae. 1 Mexico.

Spiropetalum Gilg. Connaraceae. 5 W. Afr.

Spirorhynchus Kar. et Kir. Cruciferae (2). 1 C. As.

Spirospermum Thou. Menispermaceae. 1 Madag.

Spirostachys S. Wats. Chenopodiaceae (A). 3 Am.

Spirostigma Nees. Acanthaceae (IV. A). 1 Brazil.

Spirotecoma Baill. Bignoniaceae (2). 1 Cuba.

Spirotheca Ulbrich. Bombacaceae. 2 Brazil.

Spirotropis Tul. Leguminosae (III. 1). 1 French Guiana.

Spitzelia Sch.-Bip. = Pieris L. p.p. (Comp.).

Spleenwort, *Asplenium*.

Splendens (Lat.), glittering.

Spodiopogon Trin. Gramineae (2). 8 As.

Spogel seed, *Plantago ovata* Forst.

Spondianthus Engl. (*Megabaria* p.p.). Euphorb. (A.I. 1). 2 W. trop. Afr.

Spondias L. Anacardiaceae (2). 6 trop. The 1—5-seeded drupe is ed. (hog-plum); endocarp fibrous outside.

Spondiopsis Engl. Anacardiaceae (2). 1 Kilimandjaro.

Spongopyrena Van Tiegh. (*Ochna* p.p.). Ochnaceae. 4 trop. Afr.

Spongostemma Van Tiegh. = Scabiosa Tourn. p.p. (Dips.).
Sponia Comm. ex Lam. = Trema Lour. (Ulm.).
Spontaneous movements, see Movements.
Spoonwood (Am.), *Kalmia latifolia* L.; **-wort**, *Cochlearia*.
Sporadic, scattered widely.
Sporangia, spore-receptacles, *Filicales*; **-iophore**, sp.-carrier.
Spore, an asexual repr. cell, *Filicales Pteridophyta*; **-ocarp**, *Filicales*, *Marsileaceae*, *Salviniaceae*; **-ophyll**, l. bearing - (incl. sta. and cpls.); **-ophyte**, the spore-bearing pl.
Sporobolus R. Br. Gramineae (8). 90 Am., warm |✻.
Sporoxeia W. W. Smith. Melastomaceae (I). 1 Burma.
Sport, a suddenly appearing marked deviation from existing type.
Spotted orchis, *Orchis maculata* L.
Spraguea Torr. Portulacaceae. 5 W. N. Am.
Sprekelia Heist. Amaryllidaceae (I). 1 Mexico, *S. formosissima* Herb., a greenhouse favourite (Jacobean lily).
Sprengelia Sm. Epacridaceae (2). 23 Austr., Tasmania.
Sprengeria Greene (*Lepidium* p.p.). Cruciferae (2). 3 S.W. U.S.
Spring beauty (Am.), *Claytonia*.
Spruce fir, Norway Spruce, *Picea excelsa* Link; **hemlock -**, *Tsuga canadensis* Carr.
Sprucea Benth. (*Sickingia* p.p. *EP.*). Rubiaceae (I. 3). 1 Brazil.
Spur, a drawn-out portion of base of sep. or pet. or (K) or (C), *Balsaminaceae*, *Centranthus*, *Orchidaceae*, *Valeriana*, *Viola*; or a short shoot in *Coniferae*; **- valerian**, *Centranthus*.
Spurge, *Euphorbia*; **- flax, - laurel**, *Daphne*.
Spurious dissepiment, false septum, *Cruciferae*, &c.
Spurry, *Spergula arvensis* L.
Spyridium Fenzl. Rhamnaceae. 30 temp. Austr.
Squamate, scaly.
Squamellaria Becc. Rubiaceae (II. 5). 2 Fiji.
Squamulae intravaginales, *Potamogetonaceae*.
Squarrosus (Lat.), roughly scurfy with spreading processes.
Squash, *Cucurbita Pepo* L., var.
Squaw root (Am.), *Conopholis*; **- weed** (Am.), *Senecio aureus* L.
Squill, *Urginea Scilla* Steinh.; **striped -**, *Puschkinia*.
Squinancy wort, *Asparula cynanchica* L.
Squirrel tail grass, *Hordeum jubatum* L.
Squirting cucumber, *Ecballium Elaterium* A. Rich.
Squitch grass, *Agropyron repens* Beauv.
Staavia Dahl. Bruniaceae. 7 S. Afr.
Staberoha Kunth. Restionaceae. 6 S. Afr.
Stachyacanthus Nees. Acanth. (inc. sed.). 1 Brazil. Fl. 4-merous.
Stachyanthemum Klotzsch in Schomb. = Cyrilla Garden. (Cyr.).
Stachyanthus Engl. Icacinaceae. 1 trop. Afr.
Stachyarrhena Hook. f. Rubiaceae (I. 8). 3 Amazon valley.
Stachycephalum Sch.-Bip. ex Benth. Compositae (5). 2 Andes.
Stachydesma Small (*Hedeoma* p.p.). Labiatae (VI). 2 N. Am.
Stachyothyrsus Harms. Leguminosae (II. 7). 2 trop. Afr.
Stachyphrynium K. Schum. Marantaceae. 10 Indomal.
Stachys (Tourn.) L. Labiatae (VI). 200 cosmop., exc. Austr.,

N.Z.; 5 in Brit., incl. *S. Betonica* Benth. (wound-wort), *S. palustris* L. (marsh betony). Tubers of *S. Sieboldi* Miq. (crosnes) ed.

Stachystemon Planch. Euphorbiaceae (B. 1). 3 W. Austr.

Stachytarpheta Vahl. Verbenaceae (1). 45 Am. L. of *S. dichotoma* Vahl (*S. jamaicensis* Gard.) sometimes used as tea.

Stachyuraceae (*EP.*; *Ternstroemiaceae* p.p. *BH.*). Dicots. (Archichl. Parietales). Only genus Stachyurus.

Stachyurus Sieb. et Zucc. Stachyuraceae. 4 Japan to Himal. Small shrubs. with alt. l. and ☿ or polyg. fls. in axillary racemes. K 4, C 4, A 4+4, G (4) with ∞ ov. Berry, ∞ seeds, aril, endosp.

Stackhousia Sm. Stackhousiaceae. 15 Austr., N.Z.

Stackhousiaceae. Dicots. (Archichl. Sapindales; Celastrales *BH.*). 2 gen., 18 sp., Austr., N.Z. Herbs ± xero. with racemose or cymose infls. of ☿ fls. K (5); C 5, perig.; disc present; A 5; $\underline{G}$ (2—5), 2—5-loc., with 1 erect anatr. ov. in each loc.; raphe ventral. Schizocarp. Seed with endosp. *Genera:* Stackhousia, Macgregoria. Closely allied to Celastraceae.

Stackhousieae (*BH.*) = Stackhousiaceae.

Stadmannia Lam. Sapindaceae (1). 1 Mauritius.

Staehelina L. Compositae (11). 6 Medit.

Staelia Cham. et Schlecht. Rubiaceae (II. 10). 10 S. Am.

Staff tree (Am.), *Celastrus*.

Stagger bush (Am.), *Andromeda Mariana* L.

Staghorn fern, *Platycerium*; **-moss**, *Lycopodium*.

Stahlia Bello. Leguminosae (II. 2). 1 Porto Rico. Good timber.

Stahlianthus O. Ktze. (*Kaempfera* p.p. *EP.*). Zingiber. (1). 1 Siam.

Stalagmitis Murr. = Garcinia L. p.p. (Guttif.).

Stamen, a microsporophyll in a fl., usu. a stalked organ, or *filament*, bearing an *anther*, the latter composed of 2 lobes or *thecae*, united by a prolongation of the filament, the *connective*, each lobe with two *pollen sacs*, opening by a definite line of dehiscence, or pore, to allow escape of pollen.

The *androeceum* or stamens may be *hypo-*, *peri-* or *epi-gynous*; *epi-phyllous-*, *-petalous*, or *-sepalous* (concrescent with P, C, or K); *diplostemonous* (in two whorls, the outer alt. with the C, and as numerous), *obdiplostemonous* (in two whorls, the outer opp. or *anteposed* to the pets., Caryophyllaceae), *haplo-* or *iso-stemonous* (in one whorl, alt. or anteposed to C, as in Primulaceae), or in 2 whorls (Rosaceae). The sta. may be few and *definite* (usu. under 20, often described as *mon-*, *di-androus*, &c., according to the number), or *indefinite* (over 20, Ranunculaceae, Rosaceae, &c.); they may be all free (*monandrous... polyandrous*), or concrescent in 1, 2, 3, many bundles (*mon-*, *di-*, *tri-poly-adelphous*) with free anthers, or including the anthers into one mass (*synandrium*, adj. *synandrous*) as in many Araceae, Cucurbitaceae, Cyclanthera, Phyllanthus sp.; they may be concrescent also with the gynaecium (*gynandrous*, Orchidaceae), or have the anthers only united (*syngenesious*, Compositae). There may be two sta. longer than the rest (*didynamous*, Labiatae), or 4 (*tetradynamous*, Cruciferae).

The anther may be *sessile* or on a *filament*; may be joined to the filament by its whole length (*adnate*, *dorsifixed*, A in fig.) or by its base (*innate*, *basifixed*), or balanced on it, forming a T (*versatile*, C);

may be *extrorse* or *introrse* (opening away from or towards, centre of fl.). Its dehiscence may also be *longitudinal* (A), or *transverse*, *valvular* (by lids, Berberidaceae, Lauraceae), or by *pores* (Ericaceae, Gentianaceae), &c., D. The thecae may be twisted as in Cochliostema, Columelliaceae, Cucurbitaceae. The pollen sacs may be numerous, as in Viscum, &c., *septate* or chambered (Mimoseae, some Onagraceae,

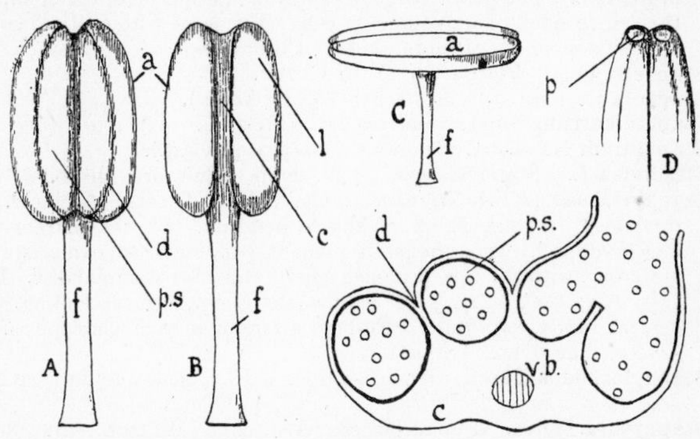

A, stamen with adnate anther from the front; *B*, the same from the back. *C*, stamen with versatile anther. *D*, tip of an anther with porous dehiscence. *E*, cross section of a ripe adnate anther to show pollen-sacs; the two sacs in the right-hand lobe have just opened. *a*, anther, *c*, connective, *d*, line of dehiscence, *f*, filament, *l*, anther-lobe, *p*, pore, *p.s.* pollen-sac, *v.b.* vascular bundle.

&c.). There may be *appendages* on the filaments (Amaryllidaceae, Hydrophyllaceae, Zygophyllum), or on the anthers (Ericaceae, Melastomaceae). The pollen may be *smooth*, or *warty*, *powdery* or *coherent*, *waxy*, &c.; it may be united into groups of 4 grains (*tetrads*, Ericaceae, &c.), or masses (*pollinia*, Asclepiadaceae, Orchidaceae).

Staminate fl., male.

Staminode, an aborted or vestigial stamen, *Acanthaceae*, *Araceae*, *Canna*, *Orchidaceae*, *Pentstemon*, *Scrophularia*; it may be small and papilla-like or petaloid (*Canna*, *Marantaceae*), or form a nectary, (*Loasaceae*).

Standard, *Leguminosae*.

Stanfieldia Small (*Aplopappus* p.p.). Compositae (3). 1 N. Am.

Stanfordia S. Wats. Cruciferae (4). 1 California.

Stangea Graebn. Valerianaceae. 5 Peru.

Stangeria T. Moore. Cycadaceae. 1 Natal, *S. paradoxa* T. Moore. See fam. for details.

Stanhopea Frost. Orchidaceae (II. 13). 25 trop. Am. Epiph. with large pendulous fls. Labellum very complex (*cf.* Coryanthes), forming with the column a sort of cage. Cult. orn. fl.

Stanhopeastrum Reichb. f. (*Stanhopea* p.p. *BH.*). Orchidaceae (II. 13). 1 Guatemala.

Stanleya Nutt. Cruciferae (1). 12 W. U.S. Sta. almost equal.
Stanleyella Rydberg (*Thelypodium* p.p.). Cruciferae (1). 1 N. Am.
Stapelia L. Asclepiadaceae (II. 3). 100 S. and trop. Afr., carrion-flowers. Like the Cacti and the fleshy Euphorbias they inhabit arid regions, and exhibit similar swollen stems, the l. reduced to thorns or scales, standing in 4 ranks corresponding to the usual l. arrangement in the fam. The green tissue occupies the periphery of the stem, and the centre is full of water storage cells. Fls. large with dull red colour and carrion smell, attracting flies. Corona double.
Stapfiella Gilg. Flacourt. (10). 1 C. Afr.
Stapfiola O. Ktze. = Demostachya Stapf. (Gram.).
Staphidiastrum Naud. = Sagraea DC. (Melast.).
Staphidium Naud. = Clidemia D. Don p.p. (Melast.).
Staphylea L. Staphyleaceae. 7 N. temp. Cult. orn. shrub.
Staphyleaceae (*EP.*; *Sapindaceae* p.p. *BH.*). Dicots. (Archichl. Sapindales). 6 gen., 20 sp., chiefly N. hemisph. Shrubs or trees with alt. or opp. l., usu. unequally pinnate, stip. Fls. in panicles, reg., 5-merous, with the axis forming a cupule and intra-staminal disc. K 5; C 5; A 5; $\underline{G}$ (3 or 2), 3-loc. with ∞ anatr. ov., usu. ascending, with ventral raphe. Capsule. Embryo straight, in rich endosp. *Chief genera:* Staphylea, Turpinia.
Staphylorhodos Turcz. Rosaceae (inc. sed.). Gen. dubium. 1 New Zeal.
Staphysora Pierre. Euphorbiaceae (A. I. 1). 3 W. trop. Afr.
Star anise, *Illicium*; **-apple**, *Chrysophyllum*; **-cucumber** (Am.), *Sicyos*; **-grass** (Am.), *Hypoxis*, *Aletris*; **-of Bethlehem**, *Ornithogalum*; **-of night** (W.I.), *Clusia rosea* Jacq.; **-thistle**, *Centaurea*; **-wort** (Am.), *Stellaria*, *Aster*; **water-wort**, *Callitriche*.
Starch, one of the chief carbohydrates of reserves; *cf.* Edible Products.
Starr grass, *Ammophila arundinacea* Host.
Stasium (Cl.), a stagnant pool formation.
Stathmostelma K. Schum. Asclepiadaceae (II. 1). 8 trop. Afr.
Statice Tourn. ex L. (excl. *Goniolimon* Boiss.). Plumbaginaceae. 130 cosmop., chiefly in steppes and salt marshes. *S. Limonium* L. (sea-lavender and 2 others, on the coast of Brit. Infl. cpd., mixed, the total infl. a spike, the partial a drepanium. Fls. many, *e.g. S. Limonium*, heterostyled like Primula.
Staudtia Warb. Myristicaceae. 2 W. Afr.
Stauntonia DC. Lardizabalaceae. 6 China, Japan.
Stauranthera Benth. Gesneriaceae (I). 4 Indomal.
Stauranthus Liebm. Rutaceae (IV). 1 S. Mexico.
Staurochilus Ridl. (*Trichoglottis* p.p.). Orchidaceae (II. 20). 1 Malay Peninsala.
Staurochlamys Baker. Compositae (5). 1 N. Brazil.
Staurogyne Wall. (*Ebermaiera BH.*). Acanth. (I). 45 trop. exc. Afr.
Staurophragma Fisch. et Mey. Scrophulariaceae (I. 1). 1 As. Min.
Stauropsis Reichb. f. Orchidaceae (II. 20). 5 S.E. As., Malaya.
Staurostigma Scheidw. (*Asterostigma EP.*). Araceae (VII). 5 Braz.
Stawellia F. Muell. Liliaceae (III). 1 S.W. Austr.
Stearine, *Cocos*.

Stearodendron Engl. (*Allanblackia* p.p. *EP.*). Gutt. (v). 1 E. Afr.
Stechmannia DC.=Jurinea Cass. p.p. (Comp.).
Steganthera Perk. Monimiaceae. 15 New Guinea, Celebes, &c.
Stegnosperma Benth. Phytolaccaceae. 1 California to W.I.
Stegolepis Klotzsch ex Koern. Rapateaceae. 1 Guiana.
Stegosia Lour. (*Rottboellia* p.p.). Gramineae (2). 1 N. Am.
Steinheilia Decne. Asclepiadaceae (II. 1). 1 Arabia.
Steinmannia Phil. f. Liliaceae (IV). 1 Chili.
Steirachne Ekman. Gramineae (10). 1 Ceara.
Steiractinia Blake. Compositae (5). 6 Ecuador, Colombia.
Steirodiscus Less. Compositae (8). 3 S. Afr.
Steironema Rafin. Primulaceae. 4 N. Am.
Steirosanchezia Lindau. Acanthaceae (IV. A). 1 Peru.
Stelechocarpus Hook. f. et Thoms. Anonaceae (1). 4 Malaya. Fr. ed.
Stelechospermum Blume. Guttiferae. Genus dubium. 1 Java.
Steleostemma Schlechter. Asclepiadaceae (II. 1). 1 Bolivia.
Stelestylis Drude. Cyclanthaceae. 1 E. Brazil.
Stelis Sw. Orchidaceae (II. 8). 160 trop. Am., W. I.
Stellaria L. (incl. *Malachium* Fries). Caryophyllaceae (I. 1). 100 sp. cosmop.; 7 in Brit. (chickweed, stitchwort). Of the Brit. sp., *S. media* Cyrill. has small homogamous fls. that fert. themselves in absence of insects; it flowers all the year, and in winter (? on account of weak light, cold, &c.) is often cleistogamic. The number of sta. is most often 3, but varies a good deal. The fls. of *S. graminea* L. are larger and protandr., but with autogamy, whilst in *S. Holostea* L. the fls. are still larger and very protandr. with little self-fert.
Stellariopsis Rydberg (*Potentilla* p.p.). Rosac. (III. 2). 1 N. Am.
Stellate, star-shaped.
Stellera J. G. Gmel. ex L. Thymelaeaceae. 8 temp. As.
Stellilabium Schlechter (*Telipogon* p.p.). Orch. (II. 18). 1 Peru.
Stellularia Benth. Scrophulariaceae (III. 2). 1 trop. W. Afr.
Stelmation Fourn. (*Metastelma* p.p. *EP.*). Asclep. (II. 1). 1 Brazil.
Stelmatocodon Schlechter. Asclepiadaceae (inc. sed.). 1 Bolivia.
Stelmatocrypton Baill. Asclepiadaceae (I). 1 Khasias, S. China.
Stelmatogonum Baill. Asclepiadaceae (II. 4). 1 Mexico.
Stem, the leaf-bearing part of the pl.; stem and leaf should always be described together for the sake of accuracy and conciseness. Stems may be *annual*, *biennial*, or *perennial*; *erect*, *climbing*, *twining*, *prostrate* or *procumbent*, *creeping*, *ascending* or *decumbent* (bending upwards from a prostrate base), *floating*, &c.; they may be *unbranched* (*simple*) or *branched* (describe mode of branching); if branched they may be *caespitose* (a tuft of shoots from the base, as in many grasses), *fastigiate* (many branches parallel to the stem, as in Lombardy poplar), or with *fascicles* (tufts) of lat. branches. The stem or branches may be a *corm*, *bulb*, *tuber*, *rhizome*, *runner*, *stolon*, *sucker*, *offset*, *phylloclade*, *tendril*, &c. Adnation may occur, or long and short shoots; the stem may be a *monopodium* or a *sympodium*; it may be 'condensed' bearing 'radical' leaves, and run out into a *scape* bearing only the fls., as in dandelion. It may be *herbaceous* (not woody above ground), *woody*, *succulent* or *fleshy*; *solid*, *hollow* (*fistular* if herbaceous); *straight*, *flexuose* (zigzag) &c.; *cylindrical*, *terete* (cylindrical

tapering), *angular*, *ribbed*, *winged*; *smooth*, *prickly*, *warty*, *hairy* (*cf.* Leaf, for degrees of hairiness). Polymorphism, if any, form and texture of bud scales and bud, growth in thickness, size and habit, bark (*smooth*, *warty*, *hairy*, &c.), colour, &c., must also be described. *Cf.* Climbers, Xero., &c.

Stemmadenia Benth. Apocynaceae (I. 3). 8 trop. Am., W.I.

Stemmatella Wedd. ex Sch.-Bip. Compositae (5). 2 Boliv., Colomb.

Stemodia L. Scrophulariaceae (II. 6). 30 trop.

Stemodiopsis Engl. Scrophulariaceae (II. 6). 4 trop. Afr.

Stemona Lour. Stemonaceae. 10 Indomal., China, Japan.

Stemonacanthus Nees = Ruellia Plum. p.p. (Acanth.).

Stemonaceae (*EP.*, *Roxburghiaceae BH.*). Monocots. (Liliiflorae; Coronarieae *BH.*). 3 gen., 12 sp., E. Ind., Am., Austr., &c. Perenn. herbs, often climbing, with axillary infls. of ☿ reg. fls. P 2 + 2 sepaloid, A 2 + 2, G̲ (2) 1-loc. with 1 anatr. ov. Caps. *Chief gen.* Stemona.

Stemonocoleus Harms. Leguminosae (II. 2). 1 Cameroons.

Stemonoporus Thw. (*Vateria* p.p. *BH.*). Dipterocarp. 15 Ceylon.

Stemonurus Blume (*Gomphandra* p.p. *BH.*). Icacinac. 12 Indomal.

Stemotria Wettst. et Harms. Scrophulariaceae (II. 2). 1 Peru.

Stenachaenium Benth. Compositae (4). 3 S. Brazil, Argentina.

Stenactis Cass. = Erigeron L. p.p. (Comp.).

Stenadenium Pax. Euphorbiaceae (A. II. 8). 1 E. Afr.

Stenandriopsis Sp. Moore. Acanthaceae (IV. B). 1 Madag.

Stenandrium Nees. Acanthaceae (IV. B). 20 warm Am.

Stenanthella Rydberg (*Stenanthium* p.p.). Liliaceae (1). 2 N. Am., E. As.

Stenanthemum Reiss (*Cryptandra* p.p. *EP.*). Rhamnaceae. 6 Austr.

Stenanthera Engl. et Diels. Anonaceae (4). 7 W. trop. Afr.

Stenanthium Kunth. Liliaceae (1). 5 N. Am.

Stenaria Rafin. = Houstonia L. p.p. (Rubi.).

Stenia Lindl. Orchidaceae (II. β. II.). 2 Guiana, Colombia.

Stenocalyx Berg. = Eugenia Mich. p.p. (Myrt.).

Stenocalyx Turcz. Malpighiaceae (inc. sed.). 1 Colombia.

Stenocarpha Blake. Compositae (5). 1 Mexico.

Stenocarpus R. Br. Proteaceae (II). 15 New Caled., E. Austr.

Stenocarpus (Lat.), narrow fruited.

Stenocereus Riccob. (*Cereus* p.p.). Cactaceae (III. 1). 1 Mexico.

Stenochilus R. Br. = Eremophila R. Br. (*BH.*) = Pholidia R. Br.

Stenochlaena J. Sm. Polypodiaceae. 12 trop.

Stenocline DC. Compositae (4). 11 Madag., Minas Geraes.

Stenocoryne Lindl. (*Bifrenaria* p.p.). Orchid. (II. 12). 10 S. Am.

Stenodiptera Koso-Poliansky. Umbelliferae (III. 6). 3 C. As.

Stenodon Naud. Melastomaceae (1). 2 S. Brazil.

Stenoglossum H. B. et K. Orchidaceae (II. 6). 1 Andes.

Stenoglottis Lindl. Orchidaceae (II. 1). 2 S. and trop. Afr.

Stenogyne Benth. Labiatae (III). 17 Hawaian Is.

Stenolirion Baker (*Crinum* p.p. *EP.*). Amaryllidaceae (1). 1 trop. Afr.

Stenolobium D. Don (*Tecoma* p.p. *BH.*). Bignoniaceae (2). 4 Am.

Stenomeria Turcz. Asclepiadaceae (II. 1). 2 Colombia.

Stenomeris Planch. Dioscoreaceae. 5 Phil. Is., Borneo.
Stenomesson Herb. Amaryllidaceae (I). 20 trop. Am.
Stenonema Hook. (*Dolichostylis BH.*). Cruciferae (4). 1 Colombia.
Stenonia Baill. Euphorbiaceae (A. I. 2). 1 Madag.
Stenoniella O. Ktze. = Stenonia Baill. (Euph.).
Stenopetalum R. Br. ex DC. Cruciferae (3). 8 S. and W. Austr.
Stenophragma Celak. Cruciferae (4). 10 N. temp.
Stenophyllus Rafin. (*Scirpus* p.p.). Cyperaceae (I). 2 N. Am.
Stenoptera C. Presl. Orchidaceae (II. 2). 4 trop. Am., W.I.
Stenorhynchus Rich. (*Spiranthes* p.p. *BH.*). Orchid. (II. 2). 20 trop. Am. Cult.
Stenosemia Presl. Polypodiaceae. 2 Malaya, Solomon Is.
Stenosiphon Spach. Onagraceae (2). 1 Texas.
Stenosiphonium Nees. Acanthaceae (IV. A). 5 Indomal.
Stenospermation Schott. Araceae (II). 21 trop. Am., sub-andine.
Stenostachys Turcz. (*Asperella* p.p. *EP.*). Gramineae (12). 1 N.Z.
Stenostelma Schlechter. Asclepiadaceae (II. 1). 1 Cape Colony.
Stenostephanus Nees. Acanthaceae (IV. B). 2 trop S. Am.
Stenostomum Gaertn. f. = Antirrhoea Comm. (Rubi.). 15 W.I.
Stenotaphrum Trin. Gramineae (5). 7 trop. and subtrop. *S. americanum* Schrank is useful for binding drift-sand (*cf.* Ammophila).
Stenothyrsus C. B. Clarke. Acanthaceae (IV. A). 1 Perak.
Stenotopsis Rydberg (*Aplopappus* p.p.). Compositae (3). 2 W. U.S.
Stenotus Nutt. (*Aplopappus* p.p.). Compositae (3). 6 N. Am.
Stenouratea Van Tiegh. Ochnaceae. 1 C. Am.
Stephanandra Sieb. et Zucc. Rosaceae (I. 1). 3 Japan, China.
Stephania Lour. Menispermaceae. 33 palaeotrop.
Stephanocoma Less. (*Berkheya* p.p. *EP.*). Compositae (10). 1 S. Afr.
Stephanodaphne Baill. Thymelaeaceae. 2 Madag., Comoros.
Stephanodoria Greene (*Xanthocephalum* p.p.). Compositae (3). 1 Mexico.
Stephanolepis Sp. Moore. Compositae (1). 1 trop. Afr.
Stephanomeria Nutt. Compositae (13). 15 W. N. Am.
Stephanopholis Blake (*Leptosyne* p.p.). Compositae (5). 1 Mexico.
Stephanophysum Pohl = Ruellia Plum. p.p. (Acanth.).
Stephanopodium Poepp. et Endl. Dichapetalaceae. 4 trop. S. Am.
Stephanorossia Chiov. Umbelliferae (III. 7). 2 E. trop. Afr.
Stephanostegia Baill. Apocynaceae (I. 3). 1 Madag.
Stephanostema K. Schum. Apocynaceae (inc. sed.). 1 Zanzibar.
Stephanotella Fourn. Asclepiadaceae (II. 3). 1 Brazil.
Stephanotis Thou. Asclepiadaceae (II. 3). 15 Madag., Malaya, Cuba. Cult. perf. fls.
Steppes, dry grassy plains, E. Eur., W. As.
Stera Ewart (*Pluchea* p.p.). Compositae (4). 3 W. Austr.
Sterculia L. Sterculiaceae. 100 trop. Fls. unisexual, apetalous.
Sterculiaceae (*EP.*, *BH.*). Dicots. (Archichl. Malvales). 48 gen., 660 sp., chiefly trop. Trees, shrubs, or herbs, with alt. stip. l.; some are lianes. Fls. in complex cymes, ☿, usu. reg., 5-merous. K (5), valvate, with no epicalyx; C often absent or small, conv.; A in 2 whorls, the outer staminodial or 0, the inner often branched, all ± united into a tube, anthers 2-loc.; $\underline{G}$ usu. (5), with 2—∞ anatr.

ovules in each, with the micropyle outwards; style simple, lobed. Fruit various, often a schizocarp. Endosperm. Cola and Theobroma (cacao) are economically important. *Chief genera:* Dombeya, Hermannia, Melochia, Buettneria, Theobroma, Helicteres, Sterculia, Cola.

Stereochlaena Hackel (*Chloridion* Stapf). Gramineae (5). 1 E. Afr.

Stereosandra Blume. Orchidaceae (II. 2). 1 Java.

Stereosanthus Franch. Compositae (8). 3 China.

Stereospermum Cham. Bignoniaceae (2). 12 trop. Afr., As.

Sterigma DC. Cruciferae (4). 6 C. As.

Steriphe Phil. (*Aplopappus* p.p.). Compositae (3). 1 Chili.

Steriphoma Spreng. Capparidaceae (II). 3 Trinidad to Peru.

Steris L. = Hydrolea L. (Hydrophyll.).

Sternbergia Waldst. et Kit. Amaryllidaceae (I). 5 E. Medit.

Sternotribe (fl.), dusting pollen on under side of visitor.

Sterrhium (Cl.), a moor formation.

Steudnera C. Koch. Araceae (VI). 8 Indomal.

Stevensia Poit. (*Rondeletia* p.p. *BH.*). Rubiaceae (I. 3). 1 Haiti.

Stevensonia J. Dunc. (*Phoenicophorium EP.*). Palm. (IV. 1). 1 Masc.

Stevia Cav. Compositae (2). 110 trop. and subtrop. Am.

Stewartia (*Stuartia*) L. Theaceae. 5 N. Am., Japan.

Stiburus Stapf. Gramineae (10). 2 S. Afr.

Stichoneuron Hook. f. Stemonaceae. 2 India, Malay Peninsula.

Stichorchis Thou. (*Liparis BH.*). Orchid. (II. 4). 40 As., Austr., Masc.

Stictocardia Hallier f. (*Ipomoea* p.p.). Convolv. (I). 3 Afr., Madag.

Stifftia Mikan (*Augusta* Leandr.). Compositae (12). 5 Brazil. Very large fls. (for Comp.). Shrubs. Cult. orn. fl. and fr.

Stigmamblys O. Ktze. = Amblyostigma Benth. (Asclep.).

Stigmanthus Lour. Rubiaceae (inc. sed.). 1 Cochinchina.

Stigmatococca Willd. (*Ardisia* p.p. *EP.*). Myrsinaceae. 1 Panama.

Stigmatodactylus Maxim. ex Makino. Orchid. (II. 2). 2 Java, Japan.

Stigmatophyllon (*Stigmaphyllon*) A. Juss. Malpigh. (I). 50 trop. Am., W.I.

Stigmatorhynchus Schlechter. Asclepiadaceae (II. 1). 3 Afr.

Stilbanthus Hook. f. Amarantaceae (2). 1 Himalaya.

Stilbe Berg. Verbenaceae (2). 5 S. Afr.

Stilbocarpa A. Gray. Araliaceae (2). 1 N.Z. islands.

Stillingia L. Euphorbiaceae (A. II. 7). 25 Am., Polynes., Mascarenes. [For *S. sebifera* Michx. see Sapium.]

Stilpnogyne DC. Compositae (8). 1 S. Afr.

Stilpnopappus Mart. ex DC. Compositae (1). 15 trop. S. Am.

Stilpnophyllum Hook. f. Rubiaceae (I. 5). 1 Peru.

Stilpnophytum Less. Compositae (7). 2 S. Afr. (karroo).

Stimpsonia Wright. Primulaceae. 1 Japan, China.

Stimulants, *cf.* Alcohol, Drinks.

Stinging hairs, *Girardinia*, *Laportea*, *Loasaceae*, *Malpighiaceae*, *Urtica*.

Stinkwood, *Gustavia*, *Ocotea*, &c.; **-wort** (Austr.), *Inula graveolens*.

Stipa L. Gramineae (8). 250 trop. and temp., usu. xero. *S. pennata* L. (feather grass, Steppes) and others have l. which roll inwards when the air is dry, covering the stomata and green tissue (which are on the upper side only) and exposing only the woody lower surface. The awn of the fr. is long, ending in a long feather, and hygroscopic, curling up when dry and uncurling when damp. The fr. is thin and sharply pointed, with backward-pointing hairs on the tip. As in Erodium, the awn when damped uncurls, and, if the point of the fr. be on the soil and the feather be entangled with other objects, drives the fr. into the soil. When the air dries the feather is drawn down, not the fr. up. *S. tenacissima* L. (N. Afr.) is the esparto grass, from which paper is extensively made.

Stipe, a stalk or leafstalk; **-itate**, on a special stalk.

Stipecoma Muell.-Arg. Apocynaceae (II. 1). 1 C. Brazil.

Stipel, a stipule of a leaflet.

Stiptanthus Briquet (*Anisochilus* p.p.). Labiatae (VII). 1 N. India.

Stipularia Beauv. Rubiaceae (I. 7). 3 trop. Afr.

Stipularia Delpino (*Thalictrum* p.p.). Ranunculaceae (3). 1 Himal.

Stipule, an outgrowth of the base of the l. (*q.v.*), usu. small, green, leafy; large, assimilating, in *Azara*, *Lathyrus Aphaca*, many *Rubiaceae* (esp. II. 11), *Viola*; scaly, aiding in bud protection (*q.v.*) in *Artocarpus*, *Magnolia*, &c.; repres. by hairs in *Anacampseros*, &c.; by tendrils in *Smilax*; by thorns in *Acacia*, *Machaerium*, *Paliurus*; **stipulate**, with stips.; **inter-** and **intra-petiolar**, *cf. Rubiaceae.*

Stipulicida (Rich.) Michx. Caryophyllaceae (I. 3). 1 S.E. N. Am.

Stirlingia Endl. (*Simsia* R. Br.). Proteaceae (I). 5 Austr.

Stironeurum Radlk. ex Willd. et Dur. Sapotaceae (I). 1 trop. Afr.

Stitchwort, *Stellaria.*

Stixis Lour. (*Roydsia* p.p. *BH.*). Capparidaceae (III). 6 S.E. As.

Stizolobium P. Br. = Mucuna Adans. p.p. (Legum.).

Stizophyllum Miers (*Bignonia* p.p. *BH.*). Bignoniaceae (I). 10 Braz

Stobaea Thunb. = Berkheya Ehrh. (Comp.).

Stock, *Matthiola incana* R. Br.; **Virginian-**, *Hesperis.*

Stocksia Benth. Sapindaceae (II). 1 Beluchistan.

Stoebe L. Compositae (4). 20 Bourbon, Madag., S. Afr.

Stokesia L'Hérit. Compositae (I). 1 S.E. U.S.

Stolidia Baill. Olacaceae. 1 Mauritius.

Stollaea Schlechter. Cunoniaceae. 1 New Guinea.

Stolon, a runner, *Pistia.*

Stolzia Schlechter. Orchidaceae (II. 9). 1 Nyassaland.

Stoma, a breathing pore.

Stomatostemma N. E. Br. (*Cryptolepis* p.p. *EP.*). Asclepiadaceae (I). 1 trop. Afr.

Stonecrop, *Sedum*; **-pine**, *Pinus Pinea* L.

Stool, a pl. from which offsets may be taken, or with several stems arising together.

Stopper (Am.), *Eugenia.*

Storage of reserves in pl. may take place in any part, most often below ground, often in the stem in trees or shrubs, and always in the seed; *cf.* Edible products.

Storax, *Liquidambar*, *Styrax.*

Storckiella Seem. Leguminosae (II. 5). 2 Fiji, New Caled.

Stork's bill, *Erodium.*

Stormia Sp. Moore (*Hexalobus* p.p.). Anonaceae (I). 1 S.W. Brazil.

Storthocalyx Radlk. Sapindaceae (I). 4 New Caled.
Stracheya Benth. Leguminosae (III. 7). I Tibet.
Stramineus (Lat.), straw-coloured.
Stramonium Tourn. ex Hall. = Datura L. p.p. (Solan.).
Stranvaesia Lindl. Rosaceae (II). 7 Himalaya, China.
Strapwort, *Corrigiola*.
Strasburg turpentine, *Abies pectinata* DC.
Strasburgeria Baill. Ochnaceae (Ternstr. *BH.*). I New Caled.
Stratiotes L. Hydrocharitaceae. I Eur. (incl. Brit.). *S. aloides* L. (water soldier). Short stem bearing roots and a number of aloe-like l. with toothed edges. In the summer it floats up to the surface and bears the (dioec.) fls. It sinks in autumn. It gives off numerous axillary shoots with big buds at the ends, and these grow into young plants, which become free and sink to the bottom, where they remain over winter.
Straussia A. Gray. Rubiaceae (II. 5). 5 Hawaiian Is.
Straussiella Hausskn. Cruciferae (4). I Persia.
Stravadium Juss. = Barringtonia Forst. p.p. (Lecyth.).
Strawberry, *Fragaria vesca* L.; **-tomato**, *Physalis*; **-tree**, *Arbutus*.
Streblacanthus O. Ktze. Acanthaceae (IV. B). 3 C. Am.
Streblorrhiza Endl. Leguminosae (III. 6). I Norfolk I.
Streblosa Korth. (*Psychotria* p.p.). Rubiaceae (II. 5). 4 Malaya.
Streblosiopsis Valet. Rubiaceae (inc. sed.). I Borneo.
Streblus Lour. Moraceae (I). I Indomal., used for paper in Siam.
Strelitzia (Banks) Ait. Musaceae. 5 S. Afr., cult. orn. fl. Fls. in cincinnus in axil of large spathe. Sepals free; the lat. petals united, irreg., enclosing the 5 sta.
Strempeliopsis Benth. Apocynaceae (I. 3). 2 Cuba, Jamaica.
Strephonema Hook. f. Combretaceae (Lythr. *BH.*). 4 W. trop. Afr.
Streptanthera Sweet. Iridaceae (III). 2 S. Afr.
Streptanthus Nutt. Cruciferae (I). 25 Pacif. N. Am.
Streptocalyx Beer. Bromeliaceae (4). 5 trop. Am.
Streptocarpus Lindl. Gesneriaceae (I). 30 Afr., Madag. (Cape primrose). In *S. polyanthus* Hook., &c., the embryo in the exalbum. seed has 2 cots. and a hypocotyl, but no plumule or radicle; the hypocotyl enters the soil, swells up at the end and develops absorbent hairs; presently however roots (adv.) form above the swelling, which dies off. One of the cots. continues to grow, while the other dies. Thus the young pl. consists of a large green cot. with few adv. roots. The cot. continues to grow, and reaches considerable size. Finally the infl. arises as a bud from the base of the petiole, and leafy shoots may also arise. (*Cf.* the artificial repr. of Sinningia.)
Streptocaulon Wight et Arn. Asclepiad. (I). 7 Indomal. G semi-inf.
Streptochaeta Schrad. Gramineae (6). 2 Brazil, Ecuador.
Streptogyne Beauv. Gramineae (10). 2 trop.
Streptolirion Edgew. Commelinaceae. 2 Himal., China.
Streptoloma Bunge. Cruciferae (4). I Turkestan.
Streptomanes K. Schum. Asclepiadaceae (I). I New Guinea.
Streptopetalum Hochst. Turneraceae. 2 trop. E. Afr.
Streptopus Michx. Liliaceae (VII). 5 N. temp.

Streptosolen Miers. Solanaceae (5). 1 trop. S. Am. Cult. orn. fl.
Streptothamnus F. Muell. Flacourtiaceae (5). 3 New S. Wales.
Streptotrachelus Greenm. Apocynaceae (II. 1). 1 Mexico.
Striate, with fine || lines.
Stricklandia Baker. Amaryllidaceae (I). 1 Ecuador.
Strictus (Lat.), very straight.
Striga Lour. Scrophulariaceae (III. 2). 22 palaeotrop., and S. Afr. Semiparasites like Rhinanthus.
Strigilia Cav. = Styrax L. (Styrac.).
Strigina Engl. Scrophulariaceae (III. 2). 1 C. Afr.
Strigose, with appressed stiff hairs or bristles.
Stringy bark, *Eucalyptus.*
Strobidia Miq. (*Alpinia* p.p.). Zingiberaceae (I). 1 Sumatra.
Strobila Nor. Inc. sed. Nomen.
Strobilacanthus Griseb. Acanthaceae (IV. B). 1 Panama.
Strobilanthes Blume (*Goldfussia* Nees). Acanthaceae (IV. A). 200 trop. As., Madag. Many occur gregariously in vast numbers, forming almost the sole undergrowth in forests. They fl. simultaneously and die down. Some, *e.g. S. anisophyllus* T. Anders., show marked anisophylly. The stigma is sensitive to contact (*cf.* Mimulus); when touched it moves downwards, and becomes pressed against the lower lip of the fl. Many cult. orn. fl.
Strobilanthopsis Sp. Moore. Acanthaceae (IV. A). 1 Rhodesia.
Strobile, strobilus, *Lycopodium.*
Strobilopanax R. Viguier (*Meryta* p.p.). Araliaceae (I). 2 New Caled.
Strobopetalum N. E. Br. Asclepiadaceae (II. 1). 2 Arabia.
Stroganowia Kar. et Kir. Cruciferae (2). 3 C. As.
Stromanthe Sond. Marantaceae. 8 trop. Am. Fls. antidromous.
Stromatopteris Mett. Gleicheniaceae. 1 New Caledonia.
Strombosia Blume. Olacaceae. 10 trop. Afr., Indomal.
Strombosiopsis Engl. Olacaceae. 1 Cameroons.
Strongylodon Vog. Leguminosae (III. 10). 8 Madag., Indomal.
Strong man's weed (W.I.), *Petiveria.*
Strongylomopsis Spegazz. Compositae (inc. sed.). 1 Fuegia.
Strophacanthus Lindau (*Dianthera* p.p.). Acanth. (IV. B). 2 Indomal.
Strophanthin, *Strophanthus.*
Strophanthus DC. Apocynaceae (II. 1). 28 Cape Col. to China. Free parts of petals long, threadlike; follicles divergent when ripe. The seeds of *S. hispidus* DC. (S. Afr.) furnish the drug strophanthin.
Strophioblachia Boerlage. Euphorbiaceae (A. II. 5). 2 Celebes.
Strophiole, caruncle.
Strophocactus Britton et Rose (*Cereus* p.p.). Cact. (III. 1). 1 Brazil.
Stropholirion Torr. Liliaceae (IV). 1 Calif.
Strumaria Jacq. Amaryllidaceae (I). 6 Cape Colony.
Strumpfia Jacq. Rubiaceae (II. 4). 1 W.I.
Struthanthus Mart. (*Loranthus* p.p. *BH.*). Loranth. (I). 45 trop. Am.
Struthiola L. Thymelaeaceae. 35 S. and trop. Afr.
Struthiopteris Weis. = Blechnum L. (Polypod.).
Strychnine, *Strychnos.*
Strychnopsis Baill. Menispermaceae. 1 Madag.

Strychnos L. Loganiaceae. 200 trop. Some, *e.g. S. Nux-vomica* L. (India, Ceylon), are erect trees, others are climbing shrubs, with curious hook-tendrils. The hook is a modified axillary shoot; the l. in whose axil it arises usu. becomes a scale l. If the hook catch upon a support it twines close round it and thickens and lignifies (*cf.* Clematis). Other sp. have axillary thorns. A few have a 1-loc. ovary with free-central placenta. Fr. a berry; the flesh is harmless, but the seeds are exceedingly poisonous, owing to the presence of strychnine in the seed-coats. From these seeds the alkaloid is chiefly obtained. *S. toxifera* Schomb. (S. Am.) yields the famous wourali or curare poison, with which the S. Am. Indians poison their arrows; it is obtained from the bark by scraping and maceration in water. The seeds of *S. potatorum* L. f. (clearing nut) are used to purify dirty water for drinking. They are rubbed on the inside of the vessel, and cause precipitation.

Stryphnodendron Mart. Leguminosae (I. 4). 10 trop. Am.

Stuartia (*Stewartia*) L. Theaceae. 5 N. Am., Japan.

Stuartina Sond. Compositae (4). 1 S. Austr.

Stubendorffia Schrenk. Cruciferae (2). 2 C. As.

Stuckenia Börner = Potamogeton p.p. (Potam.).

Stuckertia O. Ktze. = Choristigma F. Kurtz (Asclep.).

Stuckertiella Beauverd. Compositae (4). 2 Argentina.

Stuebelia Pax. Capparidaceae (II). 1 Colombia.

Stuhlmannia Taub. Leguminosae (II. 5). 1 trop. E. Afr.

Sturmia Rchb. (*Liparis BH.*). Orchidaceae (II. 3). 1 Eur., N. Am.

Styasasia Sp. Moore (*Isochoriste* p.p.). Acanthaceae (IV. B). 1 trop. Afr.

Stylarthropus Baill. (*Whitfieldia* Hook.). Acanth. (IV. A). 6 trop. Afr.

Style, *cf.* Ovary; **-opodium**, enlarged base of style.

Stylidiaceae (*Candolleaceae*) (*EP.*, *BH.*). Dicots. (Sympet. Companulatae; Campanales *BH.*). 6 gen., 100 sp., Austr., N.Z., S. Am., trop. As. Small herbs or undershrubs, ± xero., without latex. L. simple, exstip., almost grass-like, often in rad. rosettes with fls. on a scape; successive rosettes may be separated by a slightly leafy piece of stem. Rosettes sometimes almost bulbous, with aerial roots. Fls. in racemes or cymes, ☿ or unisex., usu. ·|·. K 5 or (5), odd sep. post.; C (5), the ant. pet. (*labellum*) often different from the rest; A 2 (post. lat.), rarely 3, united with style to form a gynostemium (*cf.* Orchidaceae, Asclepiadaceae), anthers extr.; $\overline{G}$ (2), usu. 2-loc., but sometimes the post. loc. aborted. Caps.; fleshy endosp. *Gen.* Levenhookia, Phyllachne, Stylidium.

Stylidieae (*BH.*) = Stylidiaceae.

Stylidium Lour. = Alangium Lam. (Alang.).

Stylidium Sw. (*Candollea* Labill.). Stylidiaceae. 85 Austr., N.Z., E. As. Some have irritable gynostemium. It bends over to one side, and may be released by a touch, when it springs over to the other. These periodic movements go on for some time (*cf.* nutation).

Stylisma Rafin. (*Breweria* p.p.). Convolv. (I). 8 Am., As., Austr.

Stylobasium Desf. Rosaceae (VI. a). 3 S.W. Austr.

Styloceras Juss. Buxaceae. 3 trop. Andes.

Stylochiton Lepr. Araceae (VII). 25 warm Africa. The monoec. infl. remains below the ground, only the tip protruding and opening.

Stylocline Nutt. Compositae (4). 3 W. U.S., Afghanistan.
Styloconus Baill. (*Blancoa* Lindl.). Amaryllid. (III). 1 S.W. Austr.
Stylocoryna Cav. = Randia Houst. (Rubi.).
Stylocoryne Wight et Arn. (*Tarenna BH.*). Rubi. (II. 4). 15 Indomal.
Stylogyne A. DC. (*Ardisia* p.p. *BH.*). Myrsin. 40 trop. Am., W.I.
Styloma O. F. Cook (*Pritchardia* p.p.). Palmae (I. 2). 16 Polynesia.
Stylophorum Nutt. Papaveraceae (II). 1 Atl. N. Am., 2 E. As.
Stylophyllum Britton et Rose (*Cotyledon* p.p.). Crass. 12 Calif.
Stylosanthes Sw. Leguminosae (III. 7). 25 trop. and subtrop.
Stylosiphonia T. S. Brandegee. Rubiaceae (I). 1 Mexico.
Stypandra R. Br. Liliaceae (III). 3 temp. Austr.
Styphelia Sm. (incl. *Cyathodes* Labill., *Leucopogon* R. Br.). Epacridaceae. 175 Austr., N.Z., New Caled., Sandwich Is., Malaya.
Styracaceae (*EP.*, *BH.* incl. *Symplocaceae*). Dicots. (Sympet. Ebenales). 6 gen., 125 sp., 3 centres of distribution—Brazil to Peru and Mexico, Virginia to Texas, Japan to Java. A single sp., *Styrax officinale*, is Mediterranean. Shrubs and trees with alt. simple l., usu. entire and often leathery. Infl. usu. racemose, with no bracteoles. Fl. ☿, reg. K (5—4); C (5—4), often nearly polypetalous; A twice as many as petals, in one whorl, united at base or into a tube, with narrow or linear, rarely round anthers; $\underline{G}$ (3—5), 3—5-loc. below, 1-loc. above, with 1 or few pend. anatr. ov. in each loc.; style simple, stigma capitate or lobed. Fr. drupaceous, with fleshy or dry dehisc. pericarp, and one or few seeds. Embryo straight, in endosp. *Chief genera:* Halesia, Styrax. For distinction between S. and Symplocaceae, see the latter. The absence of latex distinguishes S. from Sapotaceae, the ☿ fls. from Ebenaceae.
Styrax (Tourn.) L. Styracaceae. 100 with distr. of fam. *S. officinale* L. yields storax, a resin much used in ancient times. *S. Benzoin* Dryand. (Sumatra, &c.) yields the fragrant resin gum-benzoin, used medicinally and for incense.
Suaeda Forsk. Chenopodiaceae (B). 40 cosmop., on sea-coast, and in salt steppes. *S. maritima* Dum. (sea-blite) in Brit. Herbs with fleshy l. and dense cymes.
Suaveolens (Lat.), fragrant.
Sub- (Lat. pref.), under, below, nearly; **-genus, -family, -order,** &c., *cf.* Nomenclature; **-terranean fr.,** *Amphicarpaea, Arachis, Trifolium, Voandzeia*; **-tropical,** the warmest part of temp. zone.
Suberization, conversion into cork.
Subularia Ray ex L. Cruciferae (2). 1 Abyss., 1 Eur. (incl. Brit.), As., N. Am., *S. aquatica* L., the awl-wort, at the margin of lakes, usu. submerged, with long narrow l., nearly circular in section. The fls. may project and open, or remain submerged and fert. themselves in the bud. One of the few aquatic annuals.
Subulate, awl-shaped.
Succineus (Lat.), amber coloured.
Succisa Neck. (*Scabiosa* p.p. *BH.*). Dipsacaceae. 4 Medit., Eur.
Succisus (Lat.), abruptly broken off.
Succory, chicory, *Cichorium Intybus* L.
Succowia Medic. Cruciferae (2). 1 W. Medit., Teneriffe.
Succulence, *cf.* Xerophytes.

Suchtelenia Karel ex Meissn. Boraginaceae (IV. 1). 1 Caspian.
Sucker, a shoot arising below ground, a new shoot on an old stem, **-of parasites,** the modified root by which they absorb from hosts.
Suckleya A. Gray. Chenopodiaceae (A). 1 Rocky Mts.
Suffruticose herb, with base of stem woody, as in wallflower.
Sugar, one of the most important reserve carbohydrates, esp. obtained from *Saccharum officinarum* L. and *Beta vulgaris* L. var. *Rapa* Dumort, also from *Acer*, *Borassus*, *Caryota*, and many palms, *Sorghum*, &c. *Cf.* Willis, *Agriculture in the Tropics*; **-apple,** *Anona squamosa* L.; **-bean,** *Phaseolus lunatus* L.; **-beet,** *Beta vulgaris* L. var. *Rapa* Dumort; **-berry** (Am.), *Celtis*; **-cane,** *Saccharum officinarum* L.; **-maple,** *Acer saccharum* Marshall; **palm-,** *Arenga*, *Borassus*, *Caryota*, *Cocos*, &c.; **-pine,** *Pinus Lambertiana* Dougl.
Suksdorfia A. Gray. Saxifragaceae (I). 3 temp. Am.
Sulcate, furrowed.
Sullivantia Torr. et Gray. Saxifragaceae (I). 6 U.S.
Sulphur root, *Peucedanum officinale* L.
Sumac, *Rhus*; **West Indian-** (W.I.), *Brunellia*.
Sumatra camphor, *Dryobalanops aromatica* Gaertn. f.
Sumbavia Baill. Euphorbiaceae (A. II. 2). 2 E. Indomal.
Sumbaviopsis J. J. Smith. Euphorbiaceae (A. II. 2). 1 Malaya.
Summer grape, *Vitis aestivalis* Michx.; **-savoury,** *Satureia*.
Sumnera Nieuwland (*Thalictrum* p.p.). Ranunculaceae (3). 1 N. Am.
Sun dew, *Drosera*; **-drops** (Am.), *Oenothera fruticosa* L.; **-flower,** *Helianthus annuus* L.; **--, dwarf,** *Actinella*; **--, Mexican,** *Tithonia diversifolia* A. Gray.
Sunaptea Griff. = Vatica L. p.p. (Diptero.).
Sunipia Buch.-Ham. ex Sm. Orchidaceae (II. 16). 1 Himalaya, Burma.
Sunn hemp, *Crotalaria juncea* L.
Superior (ovary), above sta., &c. on recept. (*cf.* Ovary).
Super-, supra- (Lat. pref., over, above); **-posed,** vertically over; **-volute,** convolute.
Supinus (Lat.), lying face upwards.
Supple-jack (W.I.), *Paullinia*.
Suppression, complete absence of organ where one expects to find it.
Surculus (Lat.), a sucker.
Surette (W.I.), *Byrsonima*.
Suriana Plum. ex L. Simarubaceae. 1 trop. coasts.
Surinam poison (W.I.), *Tephrosia*.
Suringaria Pierre (*Barringtonia* p.p. *EP.*). Lecythid. 1 Cambodia.
Suspensor, *Selaginella*.
Susum Blume. Flagellariaceae. 2 Indomal.
Sutera Roth. (*Chaenostoma* p.p.). Scrophular. (II. 5). 115 Afr.
Suteria DC. = Psychotria L. (Rubi.).
Sutherlandia R. Br. Leguminosae (III. 6). 1 S. Afr.
Sutrina Lindl. Orchidaceae (II. 19). 1 Peru.
Suttonia Hook. f. Myrsinaceae (II). 15 New Zealand, Hawaiian Is.
Suture, line of junction.
Svida Opiz (*Cornus* p.p. *BH.*). Cornaceae. 8 N. Am.
Svitramia Cham. Melastomaceae (I). 1 S. Brazil.

Swainsona Salisb. Leguminosae (III. 6). 30 Austr., N.Z., N. As.
Swamp cypress, *Taxodium*.
Swartzia Schreb. (*Tounatea EP.*). Legum. (II. 9). 65 trop. Am., Afr.
Swede turnip, *Brassica campestris* L., var.
Sweertia L. = Swertia L. (Gentian.).
Sweet bark, Cascarilla bark; **-basil**, *Ocimum basilicum* L.; **-bay**, *Laurus nobilis* L.; **-briar**, *Rosa rubiginosa* L.; **-calabash**, *Passiflora maliformis* L.; **-cicely**, *Myrrhis odorata* Scop.; **-clover** (Am.), *Melilotus*; **-cumin**, *Pimpinella Anisum* L.; **-cup**, *Passiflora edulis* Sims.; **-fern**, *Myrica asplenifolia* L.; **-flag**, *Acorus Calamus* L.; **-gale**, *Myrica Gale* L.; **-gum**, *Liquidambar*; **-leaf** (Am.), *Symplocos*; **-lime**, *Citrus Medica* L. var. *Limetta*; **-maudlin**, *Achillea Ageratum* L.; **-pea**, *Lathyrus odoratus* L.; **-potato**, *Ipomoea Batatas* Lam.; **-sop**, *Anona squamosa* L.; **-sultan**, *Centaurea moschata* L., &c.; **-vernal grass**, *Anthoxanthum odoratum* L.; **-William**, *Dianthus barbatus* L.; **-wood** (W.I.), *Nectandra*, &c.
Sweetia Spreng. Leguminosae (III. 1). 10 S. Am.
Sweetiopsis Chodat et Hassl. (*Riedeliella EP.*). Leguminosae (III. 1). 1 Paraguay.
Swertia L. Gentianaceae (1). 90 cosmop., exc. Afr. *S. perennis* L. often cult. The corolla-segments bear each 2 nectaries on the upper side, consisting of little pits covered with hairs.
Swertopsis Makino. Gentianaceae (1). 1 Japan.
Swietenia Jacq. Meliaceae (II). 3 trop. Am., W.I., incl. *S. Mahogoni* Jacq., the mahogany, a valuable timber tree. *Cf. Tropenpflanzer*, XV. 479.
Swinburnia Ewart (*Tysonia* p.p.). Compositae (4). 1 Austr.
Swine cress (Am.), *Senebiera*.
Swintonia Griff. Anacardiaceae (1). 8 Malaya. Pets. form wings to fr.
Sword bean, *Canavalia ensiformis* DC.; **-sedge**, *Lepidosperma*.
Swynnertonia Sp. Moore. Asclepiadaceae (II. 3). 1 Rhodesia.
Syagrus Mart. = Cocos L. p.p. (Palm.).
Sycamore, *Acer pseudoplatanus* L.
Sychnosepalum Eichl. (*Sciadotaenia* Miers). Menispermaceae. 2 N. trop. S. Am.
Sycocarpus Britton. Meliaceae (III). 1 S. Am.
Sycomore fig, *Ficus Sycomorus* L.
Syconium, a fig fruit.
Sycopsis Oliv. Hamamelidaceae. 5 Khasias to China.
Sylitra E. Mey. Leguminosae (III. 6). 2 W. and S. Afr.
Sylvestris (Lat.), growing in woods.
Sym- (Gr. pref.), with, together, &c.; **-biosis**, *Cecropia*, Myrmecophily; **-metry**, *cf.* Actinomorphic, Zygomorphic, Asymmetrical, Enantiostyly, &c.; **-petalous**, with concrescent C; **-physis**, coalescence; **-podium**, a shoot in which the successive lat. branches in turn supersede the relatively main axis, which turns off to one side and looks like a branch, *Acorus*, *Aglaonema*, *Anthurium*, *Araceae*, *Eichhornia*, *Iridaceae*, *Liliaceae*, *Juncus*, *Narthecium*, *Orchidaceae*, *Peperomia*, *Ulmaceae*, *Vitis*, &c. And *cf.* Syn-.
Symbegonia Warb. Begoniaceae. 10 New Guinea.

Symbolanthus G. Don (*Lisianthus BH.*). Gentianaceae (I). 12 Andes.
Symbryon Griseb. Piperaceae. 1 Cuba.
Symmeria Benth. et Hook. f. Polygonaceae (III. 2). 2 trop. S. Am., W. Afr.
Sympegma Bunge. Chenopodiaceae (B). 1 C. As.
Sympetalae (*EP.*). The higher division of Dicotyledons.
Sympetalandra Stapf. Leguminosae (II. 1). 1 Malaya.
Sympetaleia A. Gray. Loasaceae. 2 Lower California.
Symphipappus Klatt (*Cadiscus EP.*). Compositae (6). 1 S. Afr.
Symphocoronis A. Gray = Scyphocoronis A. Gray (Comp.).
Symphonia L. f. Guttiferae (V). 6 Madag., trop. Am., Afr.
Symphorema Roxb. Verbenaceae (6). 3 Indomal.
Symphoria Pers. = Symphoricarpos Dill. (Caprif.).
Symphoricarpos Dill. ex Juss. Caprifoliaceae. 8 N. Am. *S. racemosus* Michx. (snowberry) cult. orn. shrub. The pend. fl. is fert. chiefly by wasps.
Symphyandra A. DC. Campanulaceae (I). 8 E. Medit. The pend. caps. opens at the base (*cf.* Campanula).
Symphyecarpon Pohl. Inc. sed. Nomen.
Symphyllia Baill. (*Adenochlaena BH.*). Euphorb. (A. II. 4). 2 India.
Symphyllocarpus Maxim. Compositae (4). 1 Manchuria.
Symphyllochlamys Gürke. Malvaceae (4). 1 E. trop. Afr.
Symphyllophyton Gilg. Gentianaceae (I). 1 Brazil.
Symphyoloma C. A. Mey. (*Heracleum* p.p. *BH.*). Umbellif. III. 6. 1 Caucasus.
Symphyonema R. Br. Proteaceae (I). 2 New S. Wales.
Symphyopappus Turcz. Compositae (2). 5 campos of S. Brazil.
Symphyostemon Miers. Iridaceae (II). 5 S. Am.
Symphytonema Schlechter. Asclepiadaceae (I). 1 Madag.
Symphytosiphon Harms. Meliaceae (III). 1 Madag.
Symphytum Tourn. ex L. Boraginaceae (IV. 3). 15 Medit., Eur. *S. officinale* L. (comfrey) and *S. tuberosum* L., with tubers like those of potato, in Brit. The pend. fl. is bee-visited; the entrance to the honey is narrowed by the C scales. Mech. of fl. as in Borago. Some cult. fodder, *e.g. S. asperrimum* Donn.
Sympieza Licht. ex Roem. et Sch. Ericaceae (IV. 2). 9 Cape Colony.
Symplectochilus Lindau (*Adhatoda* p.p.). Acanth. (IV. B). 2 Madag., Afr.
Sympleura Miers. Inc. sed. Nomen.
Symplocaceae (*EP.*; *Styracaceae* p.p. *BH.*). Dicots. (Sympet. Ebenales). Only genus Symplocos (*q.v.*). The chief distinction from Styracaceae is the inf. ov. of Symplocos and its complete division into loc.; the shape of the anthers is also different, and the sta. often more numerous.
Symplocarpus Salisb. Araceae (III). 1, *S. foetidus* Nutt., the skunk-cabbage, Japan, E. As., Atl. N. Am.
Symplocos Jacq. The only genus of Symplocaceae (*q.v.*). 290 trop. and subtrop. Shrubs and trees with alt. simple exstip. leathery l., and racemed bracteolate ☿ reg. fls. K (5), imbr.; C (5) or (5 + 5), imbr.; A 5 or 5 + 5 or 5 + 5 + 5 or more, epipet. or free of C; anthers round or ovate; G (2—5), inf. or semi-inf., with 2—4 anatr. pend. ov. on

an axile plac. in each loc. Style simple, stigma capitate or lobed. Fr. drupaceous, one seed in each loc. of the stone. Embryo straight or curved, in endosp.

Syn- (Gr. pref.; *cf.* sym-), with, together; **-andrium**, a concrescence of sta. including anthers, *Araceae*, *Ariopsis*, *Dieffenbachia*, *Cucurbitaceae*, *Cyclanthera*, *Phyllanthus*, *Pistia*; **-androdium**, a concrescence of stds., *Araceae*; **-androus**, with united sta.; **-angium**, a concrescence of sporangia, *Marattiaceae*, *Psilotaceae*; **-carpous**, with concrescent cpls.; **-genesious** (anthers), united, *Compositae*, *Goodeniaceae*; **-onym**, a name no longer used, but indicating the same pl. as the one in use, *e.g.* *Caprificus* Gasp. for Ficus Tourn. *Cf.* also Sym-.

Synadenium Boiss. in DC. Euphorbiaceae (A. II. 8). 12 Afr., Madag., Masc.

Synallodia Rafin. Gentianaceae (nomen). 1 Japan.

Synandra Nutt. Labiatae (VI). 1 U.S.

Synandrodaphne Gilg. Thymelaeaceae. 1 Cameroons.

Synandrodaphne Meissn. (*Nectandra* p.p. *EP.*). Lauraceae (I). 1 Colombia.

Synandrospadix Engl. Araceae (VII). 1 N. Argentina.

Synanthae. The 6th order of Monocots. *Cf.* p. iv.

Synantherias Schott (*Amorphophallus EP.*). Araceae (IV). 1 S. Ind., Ceyl.

Synaphea R. Br. Proteaceae (I). 8 W. Austr.

Synapsis Griseb. Scrophulariaceae (II. 4). 1 Cuba.

Synaptanthe Hook. f. Rubiaceae (I. 2). 1 subtrop. Austr.

Synaptolepis Oliv. Thymelaeaceae. 3 E. trop. Afr.

Syncarpia Tenore. Myrtaceae (II. 1). 2 E. Austr.

Syncephalantha Bartl. Compositae (6). 1 C. Am.

Syncephalum DC. Compositae (4). 1 Madag.

Synchodendron Boj. ex DC. Compositae (4). 1 Madag.

Synchoriste Baill. Acanthaceae (IV. B). 1 Madag.

Synclisia Benth. Menispermaceae. 1 trop. W. Afr.

Syncolostemon E. Mey. Labiatae (VII). 10 S. Afr.

Syndechites (*Sindechites*) Oliv. Apocynaceae (II. 1). 1 S.W. China.

Syndesmanthus Klotzsch (*Simocheilus* K.). Ericac. (IV. 2). 20 S. Afr.

Syndiclis Hook. f. Lauraceae (II). 1 Bhotan.

Syndyophyllum Laut. et K. Schum. Euphorbiaceae (A. II. 5). 2 New Guinea.

Synechanthus H. Wendl. Palmae (IV. 1). 3 trop. Am.

Synedrella Gaertn. Compositae (5). 2 trop. Am.

Synedrellopsis Hiern et O. Ktze. Compositae (5). 1 Argentina.

Synelcosciadium Boiss. (*Tordylium* p.p. *BH.*). Umbell. (III. 6). 1 Syria.

Synepilaena Baill. Gesneriaceae (II). 1 Colombia.

Syngonanthus Ruhl. Eriocaulonaceae. 80 S. Am., Afr.

Syngonium Schott. Araceae (VI). 15 W.I., trop. Am. Climbers with cymes of monoec. spadices. Synandrous.

Syngramma J. Sm. Polypodiaceae. 16 trop. As., Polynesia.

Synima Radlk. Sapindaceae (I). 1 Austr.

Synisoon Baill. Rubiaceae (I. 8). 1 Brit. Guiana.

Synnema Benth. (*Cardanthera EP.*). Acanthaceae (IV. A). 12 palaeotrop.
Synnotia Sweet. Iridaceae (III). 3 S. and trop. Afr.
Synoum A. Juss. Meliaceae (III). 2 Austr.
Synsepalum Baill. (*Sideroxylon* p.p.). Sapotaceae (I). 3 W. trop. Afr.
Synsiphon Regel (*Colchicum* p.p. *BH.*). Liliaceae (I). 1 C. As.
Syntherisma Walt. (*Panicum* p.p.). Gramineae (5). 15 N. Am.
Synthlipsis A. Gray. Cruciferae (3). 2 Mexico, Texas.
Synthyris Benth. in DC. Scrophulariaceae (III. 1). 8 Mts., W. N.Am.
Syntriandrum Engl. Menispermaceae. 3 W. trop. Afr.
Syntrichopappus A. Gray. Compositae (6). 2 W. U.S.
Syrenia Andrz. ex DC. (*Erysimum* p.p. *EP.*). Crucif. (4). 4 N. As., E. Eur.
Syrenopsis Jaub. et Spach (*Iberidella BH.*). Cruciferae (4). 1 E. Medit.
Syringa L. Oleaceae. 30 Eur., As. *S. vulgaris* L. is the lilac, cult. in Brit. Serial accessory buds in axils. Well-marked false dichotomy; the term. bud usu. fails to develop each spring and the two nearest lat. buds continue the growth. Winter buds scaly; the scales secrete a gummy substance as the bud elongates. Fls. in panicles, each branch with a term. fl. Seeds flat, slightly winged.
Syringa Tourn. ex Adans. = Philadelphus Riv. (Saxifr.).
Syringodea D. Don = Erica Tourn. p.p. (Eric.).
Syringodea Hook. f. Iridaceae (I). 10 S. Afr.
Syrrhonema Miers. Menispermaceae. 2 W. trop. Afr.
Syrtidium (Cl.), a dry sandbar formation.
Systematic Botany, the study of the relationships of plants.
Systemonodaphne Mez (*Goeppertia* p.p.). Lauraceae (II). 1 Guiana.
Syzygium Gaertn. (*Eugenia* p.p. *BH.*). Myrtaceae (I). 140 palaeotrop.
Szechenyia Kanitz (*Lloydia* p.p. *EP.*). Liliaceae (V). 1 China.
Szovitsia Fisch. et Mey. Umbelliferae (III. 5). 2 W. As.
Tabascina Baill. Acanthaceae (IV. B). 1 Mexico.
Tabashir, *cf.* Bamboos.
Tabebuia Gomez. Bignoniaceae (2). 20 trop. Am., W.I.
Taberna Miers (*Tabernaemontana* p.p.). Apocyn. (I. 3). 7 W.I., S. Am.
Tabernaemontana Plum. ex L. Apocynaceae (I. 3). 50 trop. Am.
Tabernanthe Baill. Apocynaceae (I. 3). 6 W. trop. Afr.
Tabescent, wasting, shrivelling.
Tabraca Nor. Anonaceae. Nomen.
Tabular, flattened horizontally.
Tacamahac, *Calophyllum*, *Populus*.
Tacazzea Decne. Asclepiadaceae (I). 10 trop. Afr.
Tacca Forst. Taccaceae. 15 trop. Creeping tuberous rhiz. bearing large branched l. on long stalks, and cymose umbels of fls. on scapes. P 3+3, reg.; A 3+3; $\overline{G}$ (3), 1-loc. with parietal plac. and ∞ anatr. ov. Style short, with 3 branches petaloid above, each 2-lobed with the stigmas on under sides. Berry. East Indian arrowroot is made from the rhiz. of *T. pinnatifida* Forst. and other sp.
Taccaceae (*EP.*, *BH.*). Monocots. (Liliiflorae; Epigynae *BH.*). 2

gen., Tacca (*q.v.*) and Schizocapsa (fr. a caps.). A difficult fam. to place.

Taccada pith, *Scaevola.*

Taccarum Brongn. Araceae (VII). 4 Brazil.

Tachia Aubl. Gentianaceae (I). 4 Guiana, Brazil.

Tachiadenus Griseb. Gentianaceae (I). 7 Madag.

Tachibota Aubl. Inc. sed. 1 Guiana.

Tachigalia Aubl. Leguminosae (II. 3). 6 trop. Am.

Tacoanthus Baill. (*Otacanthus* p.p.). Acanthaceae (IV. A). 1 Bolivia.

Tacsonia Juss. (*Passiflora* p.p. *EP.*). Passifloraceae. 50 trop. Am.

Taenidia Drude (*Pimpinella* p.p.). Umbelliferae (III. 5). 1 U.S.

Taeniochlaena Hook. f. Connaraceae. 4 Malay Peninsula, Burma.

Taeniophyllum Blume. Orchidaceae (II. 20). 40 Indomal.

Taeniopleurum Coulter et Rose. Umbelliferae (III. 5). 1 Oregon.

Taenitis Willd. Polypodiaceae. 2 trop. As., Fiji.

Tafalla D. Don. Compositae (4). 5 N. Andes.

Tagasaste, *Cytisus proliferus* L. f.

Tagetes L. Compositae (6). 20 warm Am. Cult. orn. fl.

Tainia Blume. Orchidaceae (II. 9). 12 E. As. Cult. orn. fl.

Tainionema Schlechter (*Secamone* p.p.). Asclep. (II. 1). 1 S. Domingo.

Tainiopsis Schlechter. Orchidaceae (II. 9). 1 Khasias.

Taiwania Hayata. Coniferae (Pinnaceae 24; see C. for gen. char.). 1 Formosa.

Taiwanites Hayata = Taiwania Hayata (Con.).

Talauma Juss. Magnoliaceae. 15 trop. E. As. and Am. Like Magnolia, but fr. indeh. or breaking off from a persistent base.

Talbotia Sp. Moore. Acanthaceae (IV. B). 1 Nigeria.

Talbotiella E. G. Baker. Leguminosae (II. 2). 1 Nigeria.

Talguenea Miers. Rhamnaceae. 2 Chili.

Taligalea Aubl. (*Amasonia BH.*). Verbenaceae (1). 6 trop. Am.

Talinaria T. S. Brandegee. Portulacaceae. 1 Mexico.

Talinella Baill. Portulacaceae. 1 Madag.

Talinopsis A. Gray. Portulacaceae. 1 New Mexico.

Talinum Adans. Portulacaceae. 15 Afr., Am., India.

Talipot palm, *Corypha umbraculifera* L.

Talisia Aubl. Sapindaceae (I). 33 S. Am.

Talisiopsis Radlk. Sapindaceae (II). 1 trop. Afr.

Tallicona, *Carapa guianensis* Aubl.

Tallow tree, *Pentadesma, Sapium.*

Tamacoari, *Caraipa.*

Tamarack, *Larix americana* Michx.

Tamaricaceae (*EP.*, *BH.* incl. *Fouquieriaceae*). Dicots. (Archichl. Parietales; Caryophyllinae *BH.*). 5 gen., 100 sp., temp. and subtrop. Desert, shore, and steppe pl. Shrubs or herbs with alt. exstip. l., often heath-like. Fls. sol. or in racemose infls., ebracteolate, ☿, reg., hypog. K (4—5); C 4—5; A 4—5, 8—10 or ∞, on a disc; $\underline{G}$ (4—5 or 2), 1-loc. Styles usu. free. Ovules ∞ or few, on basal-parietal plac., ascending, anatr. Caps. Seeds hairy. Embryo straight; endosp. or not. *Chief genera:* Reaumuria, Tamarix, Myricaria.

Tamarind, *Tamarindus indica* L.; **- plum, velvet -**, *Dialium*.

Tamarindus Tourn. ex L. Leguminosae (II. 3). 1 trop. Afr. (?), *T. indica* L., the tamarind, largely cult. in the trop. for its ed. fruit (the part eaten is the pulp round the seeds; it is also officinal). The 2 ant. pets. are reduced to bristles, and the 3 fertile sta. united below to a tube. The wood is useful.

Tamariscineae (*BH.*) = Tamaricaceae.

Tamarisk, *Tamarix gallica* L.

Tamarix L. Tamaricaceae. 65 Eur., As., Medit. *T. gallica* L. (tamarisk) in S.E. England. *T. mannifera* Ehrenb. (Egypt to Afghanistan) produces, owing to the punctures of the insect *Coccus manniparus*, the manna of the Bedouins, a white substance which falls from the twigs.

Tamatavia Hook. f. (*Chapeliera* p.p. *EP.*). Rubiaceae (I. 8). 1 Madag.

Tambourissa Sonner. Monimiaceae. 25 Madag., Mascarenes.

Tammsia Karst. Rubiaceae (I. 7). 1 Venezuela.

Tamonea Aubl. (*Miconia* Ruiz et Pav.). Melast. (I). 550 trop. Am., W.I.

Tamonea Aubl. Verbenaceae (1). 4 trop. Am., W.I.

Tampico fibre, *Agave*.

Tampoa Aubl. Inc. sed. 1 Guiana.

Tamus L. Dioscoreaceae. 2 Eur., Medit. *T. communis* L. (black bryony) in Brit. Climbing plants, hibernating by tubers formed by a lat. outgrowth of the first two internodes of the stem.

Tan (tannin), a bitter substance contained in bark, &c., used for tanning leather, &c., *Acacia* (cutch), *Betula*, *Butea*, *Byrsonima*, *Castanea* (chestnut), *Caesalpinia* (dividivi), *Eucalyptus*, *Gordonia*, *Larix*, *Phyllocladus*, *Pterocarpus*, *Quercus* (oak), *Rhizophora*, *Rhus*, *Rumex* (canaigre), *Schinopsis* (quebracho), *Terminalia*, *Tsuga*, &c. *Cf.* Dekker, *Die Gerbstoffe*, Berlin, 1913; Wiesner, *Rohstoffe*.

Tanacetum Tourn. ex L. (*Chrysanthemum* p.p. *EP.*). Compositae (7). 30 $\underline{*}$. *T. vulgare* L. (tansy) cult. as a popular remedy.

Tanaecium Sw. Bignoniaceae (1). 4 W.I. to N. Brazil.

Tanakea Franch. et Sav. Saxifragaceae (I). 1 Japan.

Tanghinia Thou. (*Cerbera BH.*). Apocynaceae (I. 3). 1 Madag.

Tania, *Xanthosoma* spp.

Tannodia Baill. Euphorbiaceae (A. II. 2). 2 Comoros, E. Afr.

Tansy, *Tanacetum vulgare* L.

Tanulepis Balf. f. Asclepiadaceae (1). 1 Rodrigues.

Taonabo Aubl. (*Ternstroemia* Mutis). Theaceae. 30 S. Am., As.

Tap root, a main root much longer than the branches.

Tapa cloth, *Broussonetia papyrifera* Vent.

Tapanhuacanga Vell. Rubiaceae (nomen). 1 Brazil.

Tape grass (Am.), *Vallisneria*.

Tapeinanthus Herb. Amaryllidaceae (1). 1 W. Medit.

Tapeinia Juss. Iridaceae (II). 1 Chili, Patagonia.

Tapeinidium (Presl) C. Chr. Polypodiaceae. 4 trop. As., Polynes.

Tapeinochilus Miq. Zingiberaceae (II). 20 E. Indomal.

Tapeinoglossum Schlechter. Orchidaceae (II. 16). 2 New Guinea.

Tapeinosperma Hook. f. Myrsinaceae (II). 26 Fiji, New Caled., Austr.

Tapeinostelma Schlechter. Asclepiadaceae (II. 3). 1 S. Afr. Xero.
Tapeinostemon Benth. Gentianaceae (I). 3 N. Brazil, Guiana.
Taphrium (Cl.), a ditch formation.
Taphrospermum C. A. Mey. (*Cochlearia* p.p. *BH.*). Crucif. (2). 2 C. As.
Tapina Mart. = Sinningia Nees p.p. (Gesn.).
Tapioca, *Manihot utilissima* Pohl, &c.
Tapirira Aubl. Anacardiaceae (2). 6 trop. S. Am.
Tapirocarpus Sagot. Burseraceae. 1 Guiana.
Tapiscia Oliv. Staphyleaceae. 1 China.
Tapura Aubl. Dichapetalaceae. 5 trop. Am., Afr.
Tar, *Coniferae*, *Pinus*. [*Cf.* Suppl.
Taraktogenos Hassk. (*Hydnocarpus* p.p.). Flacourt. (3). 4 Malaya.
Tarasa Phil. Malvaceae (2). 1 Chili.
Taravalia Greene (*Ptelea* p.p.). Rutaceae (IV). 3 Lower Calif.
Taraxacum L. Compositae (13). 25 temp. *T. officinale* Weber (dandelion), almost cosmop. The thick primary root is perenn. and crowned by a very short sympodial stem; each year a new bud is formed on the leafy axis, to come into active growth in the following year. The roots as they grow to maturity contract and thus drag the stem downwards so that it never rises much above the soil. If the root be cut through, a callus forms over the wound, and from this adv. shoots develop. The fl. mech., &c. are of the usu. type of the fam., and show the final autogamy very clearly.
Taraxia Nutt., Raimann (*Oenothera* p.p. *BH.*). Onagr. (2). 6 W. U.S.
Tarchonanthus L. Compositae (4). 3 S. Afr., Abyss. The wood of *T. camphoratus* L. is used for musical instruments.
Tardavel Adans. = Spermacoce Dill. (*BH.*) = Borreria G. F. W. Mey.
Tare, *Vicia*.
Tarenna Gaertn. Rubiaceae (I. 8). 40 trop. As., Afr.
Taro, *Colocasia antiquorum* Schott.
Tarrietia Blume. Sterculiaceae. 7 E. As., Austr. Good timber.
Tarsina Nor. Inc. sed. Nomen.
Tartarian lamb, *Cibotium Barometz* Link.
Tashiroa Matsumura. Melastomaceae (I). 2 Loo Choo Is.
Tasmanian myrtle, *Nothofagus Cunninghamii* Oerst.
Tassadia Decne. in DC. Asclepiadaceae (II. 1). 15 S. Am.
Tatea F. Muell. Verbenaceae (1). 1 Austr.
Taubertia K. Schum. Menispermaceae. 1 Brazil.
Tauscheria Fisch. Cruciferae (2). 2 C. As.
Tauschia Schlechtd. Umbelliferae (III. 4). 6 Mexico.
Tavaresia Welw. (*Decabelone* p.p. *EP.*). Asclepiad. (II. 3). 2 trop. Afr.
Taverniera DC. Leguminosae (III. 7). 7 N. Afr., W. As.
Taxaceae. A fam. of Coniferae (*q.v.*).
Taxanthema Neck. = Statice L. (Plumb.).
Taxodium Rich. (excl. *Glyptostrobus* Endl.). Coniferae (Pinaceae 28; see C. for gen. char.). 2 N. Am. (swamp-cypresses), *T. distichum* Rich. and *T. mexicanum* Carr. In the former, esp. in swampy ground, curious 'knees' are formed, hollow spherical branches projecting upwards from the roots, and supposed to be aerating organs (*cf.* Sonneratia).

Taxonomy, classification of plants by their affinities.

Taxotrophis Blume. Moraceae (I). 6 Indomal.

Taxus (Tourn.) L. Coniferae (Taxaceae, 9; see C. for gen. char.). 8 N. temp., incl. *T. baccata* L., the yew. No short shoots, but the l. of the spreading branches arrange themselves ± closely in two rows with their upper surfaces nearly in one plane, giving a dorsi-ventral structure to the shoot. Fls. dioec., sol. in the axils of the l. of the preceding year. The ♂ has a few scale-l. below and about 8 or 10 sta., each of which is shield-shaped with a number of pollen-sacs on the axial side of the shield arranged round its stalk like the sporangia in Equisetum. The ♀ has a rather complex structure. The primary axis bears scale-l. only. In the axil of one of the uppermost of these arises a shoot, continuing the line of the first axis and bearing 3 pairs of scales and a term. ovule. This is orthotr. with one integument, and develops into a seed surrounded by a cup-shaped red and fleshy aril.

The wood of the yew is valuable; in the middle ages it was the chief material used in making bows. The l. are very poisonous, but the aril is harmless. Birds swallow it, and thus dist. the seeds.

Tayotum Blanco. Inc. sed. 1 Phil. Is.

Tchihatchewia Boiss. Cruciferae (4). 1 Armenia.

Tea, *Thea*, *Catha*, *Ledum*, *Neea*, *Priva*, *Stachytarpheta*; **Algerian -**, *Paronychia*; **Australian -tree**, *Melaleuca*; **Labrador -**, *Ledum*; **Mexican -**, *Chenopodium*; **Oswego -**, *Monarda*; **Paraguay -**, *Ilex paraguensis* A. St Hil.; **-plant**, *Lycium*; **Salvador -**, *Gaultheria*; **West Indian -**, *Capraria*.

Teak, *Tectona grandis* L. f.; **bastard -**, *Butea frondosa* Roxb.

Tear thumb (Am.), *Polygonum*.

Teasel, *Dipsacus Fullonum* L.

Teclea Delile (*Toddalia BH.*). Rutaceae (IV). 10 trop. Afr.

Tecoma Juss. (*BH.* incl. *Tecomaria* Spach, *Campsis* Lour., *Campsidium* Seem., *Pandorea* Endl., and other gen.). Bignoniaceae (2). 90 trop. and warm Am. *T. radicans* Juss. climbs like ivy.

Tecomanthe Baill. Bignoniaceae (2). 1 New Guinea.

Tecomaria Spach (*Tecoma* p.p. *BH.*). Bignoniaceae (2). 5 S. Am., S. Afr.

Tecomella Seem. (*Tecoma* p.p. *BH.*). Bignoniaceae (2). 1 Arabia, S.W. As.

Tecophilea Bert. ex Colla. Amaryllidaceae (III). 2 Chili.

Tecticornia Hook. f. Chenopodiaceae (A). 1 Austr.

Tectona L. f. Verbenaceae (4). 3 Indomal. *T. grandis* L. f. is the teak, cult. in Java, India, &c., for its timber, which is very hard and durable; enormous quantities are used for ship-building, &c. There are two areas of teak, in the W. peninsula and Burma; it grows in deciduous forest, but not gregariously. The wood sinks in water unless thoroughly dried; this is effected in India by the process of 'girdling,' which consists in removing a ring of bark and sap-wood from the tree near the base. It soon dies, and is left standing for two years.

Teedia Rudolphi. Scrophulariaceae (II. 4). 2 S. Afr.

Teesdalia R. Br. Cruciferae (2). 2 Eur., Medit.; 1 Brit. Fls. in a corymb, which draws out into a raceme as flowering proceeds.
Teeth, small marginal lobes.
Teff grass, *Eragrostis abyssinica* Schrad.
Tegmen, inner coat of testa.
Teijsmannia Reichb. f. et Zoll. Palmae (I. 2). 1 Sumatra.
Teijsmanniodendron Koorders. Verbenaceae (4). 1, habitat?
Teinosolen Hook. f. Rubiaceae (I. 2). 4 Andes.
Teinostachyum Munro. Gramineae (13). 5 Indomal.
Telanthera R. Br. (*Alternanthera EP.*). Amarant. (3). 50 warm Am., Afr.
Telectadium Baill. Asclepiadaceae (1). 2 Tonquin.
Telegraph plant, *Desmodium gyrans* DC.
Telekia Baumg. (*Buphthalmum* p.p.). Compositae (4). 2 E. and C. Eur.
Teleology, doctrine of final causes.
Telephium S. F. Gray = Sedum L. p.p. (Crass.).
Telephium Tourn. ex L. Caryophyllaceae (I. 2) (Aiz. *BH.*). 3 Medit.
Telesilla Klotzsch. Asclepiadaceae (nomen). 1 Guiana.
Telesonix Rafin. (*Saxifraga* p.p.). Saxifragaceae (1). 1 N. Am.
Telfairia Hook. Cucurbitaceae (2). 2 trop. Afr., Masc. *T. pedata* Hook. is cult. for its seeds, which are ed. and also yield oil.
Telina E. Mey. = Lotononis Eckl. et Zeyh. p.p. (Legum.).
Telinaria Presl = Cytisus L. p.p. (Legum.).
Teline Medic. = Cytisus L. (Legum.).
Teliostachya Nees = Lepidagathis Willd. (Acanth.).
Telipogon H. B. et K. Orchidaceae (II. 19). 80 trop. S. Am.
Tellima R. Br. Saxifragaceae (1). 1 N.W. Am.
Telmatium (Cl.), a wet meadow formation.
Telmatophila Mart. ex Baker. Compositae (1). 1 Piauhy.
Telminostelma Fourn. Asclepiadaceae (II. 1). 1 C. Brazil.
Telopea R. Br. Proteaceae (II). 3 E. Austr., Tasmania.
Telophyllum Van Tiegh. (*Myzodendron* p.p.). Myzodendr. 1 Fuegia.
Telosma Coville (*Cynanchum* p.p.). Asclepiadaceae (II. 1). 1 Guam.
Telotia Pierre. Menispermaceae. 1 Further India.
Teloxys Moq. (*Chenopodium* p.p. *EP.*). Chenopodiaceae (A). 3 As., Am.
Temnadenia Miers. Apocynaceae (inc. sed.). 22 S. Am.
Temnolepis Baker. Compositae (5). 1 Madag.
Temnopteryx Hook. f. Rubiaceae (I. 7). 1 trop. W. Afr.
Temple tree, *Plumeria acutifolia* Poir.
Templetonia R. Br. Leguminosae (III. 3). 7 Austr. Like Bossiaea.
Tenagocharis Hochst. (*Butomopsis BH.*). Butomaceae. 1 palaeotrop.
Tenaris E. Mey. Asclepiadaceae (II. 3). 5 Afr.
Tendril, a stem or leaf modified into a thread-like organ which clasps round any slender object with which it comes into contact; *cf.* Climbing Plants.
Tenellus (Lat.), very tender or dainty.
Tengah bark, *Ceriops*.
Tentacles, *cf.* Insectivorous Plants.
Tenuifolius (Lat.), thin-leaved.

Teonongia Stapf. Moraceae (I). 1 Tonquin.
Teosinte, *Euchlaena mexicana* Schrad.
Tepals, the l. of a homogeneous P.
Tepary, *Phaseolus acutifolius* A. Gray, var. *latifolius* Freeman.
Tephea Delile. Apocynaceae (inc. sed.). 1 trop. Afr.
Tephroseris Reichb. = Senecio Tourn. p.p. (Comp.).
Tephrosia Pers. Leguminosae (III. 6). 140 trop. and subtrop.
Tepualia Griseb. Myrtaceae (II. 1). 1 Chili. Hard wood.
Teramnus Sw. Leguminosae (III. 10). 6 trop.
Terana La Llave. Compositae (inc. sed.). 1 Mexico.
Terauchia Nakai. Liliaceae (III). 1 Corea.
Teratology, the study of monstrosities.
Terebinthus (Tourn.) P. Br. (*Pistacia* p.p. *BH.*; *Bursera*, &c. p.p.). Anacardiaceae (3). 60 N. Am.
Terete, cylindrical tapering.
Terminalia L. Combretaceae. 120 trop. The fr. of many are winged (see fam.). Those of *T. Chebula* Retz. and others (myrobalans) are used in dyeing and tanning, and also in medicine. The seed of *T. Catappa* L. is ed. (country almond). *T. glabra* Wight et Arn. has aerating roots. The bark is burnt for lime. Good timber: tan from bark.
Terminthodia Ridley. Rutaceae (I). 3 Malay Peninsula.
Ternary, trimerous.
Ternate, with three leaflets arising from same point.
Terniola Tul. = Lawia Tul. (Trist.).
Ternstroemia Mutis ex L. f. (*Taonabo* Aubl.). Theaceae. 85 S. Am., As. Afr.
Ternstroemiaceae. A fam. in Bentham and Hooker's 5th cohort (Guttiferales) divided into several fams. by Engler. The bulk of the genera are placed in *Theaceae*, the rest in *Caryocaraceae*, *Marcgraviaceae*, *Stachyuraceae*, *Dilleniaceae*, *Guttiferae*, &c.
Ternstroemiopsis Urb. (*Eurya* p.p.). Theaceae. 1 Hawaiian Is.
Terrellia Lunell (*Elymus* p.p.). Gramineae (12). 6 N. Am.
Tersonia Moq. Phytolaccaceae. 2 W. Austr.
Tertrea DC. (*Machaonia* p.p. *EP.*). Rubiaceae (II. 2). 1 Martinique.
Tessarandra Miers (*Linociera BH.*). Oleaceae. 1 Brazil.
Tessaria Ruiz et Pav. Compositae (4). 4 Argentina to Calif.
Tessellate, chequer-worked.
Tessenia Bubani (*Erigeron* p.p.). Compositae (3). 20 N. Am.
Tesmannia Harms. Leguminosae (II. 2). 10 W. Afr.
Testa, the seed coat, *cf.* Seed.
Testaceus (Lat.), brick-red.
Testudinaria Salisb. Dioscoreaceae. 3 S. Afr. incl. *T. Elephantipes* Salisb. (Hottentot bread). General habit of a Dioscorea, but an enormous tuber, the swollen first internode of the stem, projecting out of the soil, with a thick outer coating of cork. From it yearly, during the wet season, springs by adv. budding the year's shoot, a long thin climbing stem with large l. and small fls. This dies down in the dry season, and the corky covering protects the mass of the plant from drought.
Tetaris (Lindl. in) Chesn. Boraginaceae (inc. sed.). 2 Mesopotamia.

Tetilla DC. Saxifragaceae (II). 1 Chili.

Tetra- (Gr. pref.), four; **-cyclic,** in four whorls; **-delphous,** in four bundles; **-dynamous,** with four long and two short, sta. of *Cruciferae*; **-merous,** with parts in fours; **-morphic,** in four forms; **-ndrous,** with four sta.; **-pterous,** four-winged.

Tetracanthus A. Rich. Compositae (5). 1 Cuba.

Tetracarpaea Hook. f. Saxifragaceae (V). 1 Tasmania.

Tetracarpidium Pax. Euphorbiaceae (A. II. 2). 1 Cameroons.

Tetracentron Oliv. Trochodendraceae. 1 China.

Tetracera L. Dilleniaceae. 25 trop., esp. Am. Aril branched.

Tetrachaete Chiovenda. Gramineae (3). 1 Erythraea.

Tetrachne Nees. Gramineae (11). 1 Cape Colony.

Tetrachondra Petrie. Tetrachondr. 2 New Zealand, Patag.

Tetraclea A. Gray. Labiatae (I). 1 S. U.S., Mexico.

Tetraclinis Mast. Coniferae (Pinaceae 31; see C. for gen. char.). 1 N.W. Afr., *T. articulata* Mast., the source of Arar wood and sandarach resin or pounce. See *Ann. Bot.* XXVII. 577.

Tetraclis Hiern. Ebenaceae. 1 Madag.

Tetracme Bunge. Cruciferae (4). 5 E. Medit.

Tetracmidion Korshinsky. Cruciferae (4). 1 W. As.

Tetracoccus Engelm. ex Parry. Euphorbiaceae (A. I. 1). 1 Lower Calif.

Tetracronia Pierre. Rutaceae (V). 1 Cochinchina.

Tetractomia Hook. f. Rutaceae (I). 6 Malaya.

Tetractys Spreng. Ranunculaceae (genus dubium). 1 S. Afr.

Tetracustelma Baill. (*Lachnostoma* p.p.). Asclepiad. (II. 4). 2 Mexico.

Tetrad, a group of 4, usu. pollen grains, *Ericaceae*.

Tetradenia Benth. Labiatae (VI). 3 Madag.

Tetradenia Nees (*Litsea* Lam. *BH.*). Lauraceae (I). 30 trop. As., Austr.

Tetradia Bennett. Sterculiaceae. 1 Java.

Tetradiclis Stev. ex Bieb. Zygophyllaceae (Rut. *BH.*). 1 W. As., Egypt.

Tetradymia DC. Compositae (8). 5 N.W. Am.

Tetraena Maxim. Zygophyllaceae. 1 Mongolia.

Tetragamestus Reichb. f. (*Ponera BH.*). Orchidaceae (II. 6). 2 trop. Am.

Tetragastris Gaertn. (*Hedwigia BH.*). Burseraceae. 3 W.I., C. Am.

Tetraglochidion K. Schum. Euphorbiaceae (A. I. 1). 1 New Guinea.

Tetraglochin (Kunze in) Poepp. (*Margyricarpus BH.*). Ros. (III. 5). 1 Chili.

Tetragonia L. Aizoaceae (II). 25 Cape Col., Austr., N.Z., &c. Sometimes 2 fls. stand one above the other in the same axil. From the fr. thorny projections grow out which may bear fls. (an argument for the axial nature of the inf. ovary). *T. expansa* Murr. is often used as a vegetable (New Zealand spinach).

Tetragonolobus Scop. (*Lotus* p.p. *BH.*). Leguminosae (III. 5). 7 Eur., Medit.

Tetragonotheca L. Compositae (5). 3 U.S., Mexico.

Tetragyne Miq. Euphorbiaceae (inc. sed.). 1 Sumatra.

Tetralix Griseb. Flacourtiaceae (inc. sed.). 1 Cuba.

Tetralopha Hook. f. Rubiaceae (II. 9). 5 Borneo, Phil. Is. Style 0.

Tetrameles R. Br. Datiscaceae. 1 Indomal.
Tetrameris Naud. = Comolia DC. (Melast.).
Tetramerista Miq. Theaceae (Ochnaceae *BH.*). 2 Malaya.
Tetramerium Gaertn. f. = Faramea Aubl. p.p. (Rubi.).
Tetramerium Nees. Acanthaceae (IV. B). 7 C. Am.
Tetramicra Lindl. Orchidaceae (II. 6). 7 W.I., trop. S. Am.
Tetramolopium Nees. Compositae (3). 7 Hawaiian Is.
Tetranema Benth. Scrophulariaceae (II. 4). 1 Mexico. Cult. orn. fl.
Tetraneuris Greene (*Actinella* p.p.). Compositae (6). 30 N. Am.
Tetranthera Jacq. = Litsea Lam. (Laur.).
Tetranthus Sw. Compositae (5). 4 S. Domingo, Cuba.
Tetrapanax C. Koch (*Fatsia BH.*). Araliaceae (1). 1 Formosa, *T. papyrifer* C. Koch, the rice-paper tree. Pith split into thin sheets and pressed.
Tetrapathaea Reichb. (*Passiflora* p.p. *BH.*). Passiflor. 1 N. Zealand.
Tetraperone Urb. (*Pinillonia* p.p.). Compositae (5). 1 Cuba.
Tetrapetalum Miq. Anonaceae (1). 1 Borneo.
Tetraphyllaster Gilg. Melastomaceae (1). 1 W. trop. Afr.
Tetraphyllum Griff. Gesneriaceae (1). 1 N.E. Bengal, Siam.
Tetraphysa Schlechter. Asclepiadaceae (II. 1). 1 Colombia.
Tetraplacus Radlk. (*Otacanthus EP.*). Scrophular. (II. 6). 1 Brazil.
Tetraplandra Baill. (*Algernonia BH.*). Euphorb. (A. II. 7). 5 Brazil.
Tetraplasandra A. Gray. Araliaceae (1). 8 E. Malaya, Hawaiian Is.
Tetrapleura Benth. Leguminosae (I. 4). 3 trop. W. Afr.
Tetrapogon Desf. Gramineae (11). 5 Medit.
Tetrapteris Cav. Malpighiaceae (1). 70 trop. Am., W.I. Lianes.
Tetrapterygium Fisch. et Mey. (*Sameraria* p.p. *EP.*). Cruc. (2). 2 W. As.
Tetrardisia Mez. Myrsinaceae (II). 1 Java.
Tetraria Beauv. (*Elynanthus* Nees). Cyperaceae (II). 30 ✻.
Tetrariopsis C. B. Clarke. Cyperaceae (II). 1 Austr.
Tetrarrhena R. Br. Gramineae (7). 4 Austr.
Tetrasiphon Urb. Celastraceae. 1 W.I.
Tetraspidium Baker. Scrophulariaceae (III. 2). 1 Madag.
Tetrastemma Diels ex H. Winkler. Anonaceae (1). 1 Cameroons.
Tetrastigma Planch. (*Vitis* p.p.). Vitaceae. 40 warm As., Austr.
Tetrastigma K. Schum. (*Schumanniophytum* Harms). Rubiaceae (I. 8). 1 Cameroons.
Tetrastylidium Engl. Olacaceae. 2 S. Brazil.
Tetrastylis Barb. Rodr. (*Passiflora* p.p.). Passifl. 1 Rio de Jan.
Tetrasynandra Perkins (*Kibara* p.p.). Monimiaceae. 3 Austr.
Tetrataxis Hook. f. Lythraceae. 1 Mauritius.
Tetrathalamus Lauterb. Guttiferae (V). 1 New Guinea.
Tetratheca Sm. Tremandraceae. 20 S. and W. Austr.
Tetrathylacium Poepp. et Endl. Flacourtiaceae (7). 1 trop. S. Am.
Tetrathyrium Benth. (*Loropetalum BH.*). Hamamelidaceae. 1 Hongkong.
Tetraulacium Turcz. Scrophulariaceae (II. 6). 1 Brazil.
Tetrazygia Rich. Melastomaceae (1). 15 W.I.
Tetreilema Turcz. Verbenaceae (?). 2 Chili, Bolivia.

Tetroncium Willd. Scheuchzeriaceae (Naiad. *BH.*). 1 Str. of Magellan.
Tetrorchidium Poepp. et Endl. Euphorbiaceae (A. II. 6). 4 trop. Am.
Tetrorum Rose (*Sedum* p.p.). Crassulaceae. 1 S.E. U.S.
Tetrouratea Van Tiegh (*Gomphia* p.p.). Ochnaceae. 1 Brazil.
Teucridium Hook. f. Verbenaceae (4). 1 New Zealand.
Teucrium (Tourn.) L. Labiatae (1). 100 cosmop.; 4 in Brit. (wood sage or germander), incl. *T. scorodonia* L. Fl. with small upper lip, protandr. with movement of style and sta.
Texiera Jaub. et Spach. Cruciferae (2). 1 Syria.
Teysmannia (*Teijsmannia*) Reichb. f. et Zoll. Palmae (I. 2). 1 Sum.
Thacombauia Seem. Euphorbiaceae (inc. sed.) (Humir. *BH.*). 1 Fiji.
Thalamus, the receptacle, *q.v.*
Thalassia Banks. Hydrocharidaceae. 1 Ind. and Pac., 1 Atl. Ocean.
Thalassium (Cl.), a sea formation.
Thalia L. Marantaceae. 7 Am., Afr. The std. β (see fam.) present.
Thalictrum Tourn. ex L. Ranunculaceae (3). 10 N. temp. (*T. flavum* L., meadow-rue, and 2 others in Brit.). Fls. small; P sepaloid or slightly coloured and soon falling. Some are visited by pollen-seeking insects, but *T. minus* L. and others are wind-fert. and protog., retaining traces of entomophilous ancestry in a slight cohesiveness of the pollen and the fact that the anthers dehisce successively.
Thalloid, of thallus form; **thallus**, *Podostemaceae*, *Tristichaceae*.
Thaminophyllum Harv. Compositae (7). 2 Cape Colony.
Thamnea Soland. ex R. Br. Bruniaceae. 4 S. Afr.
Thamnochortus Berg. Restionaceae. 25 S. Afr.
Thamnoseris Phil. f. Compositae (inc. sed.). 1 Chili.
Thamnosma Torr. et Frem. Rutaceae (1). 4 S.W. U.S., Socotra, S. Afr.
Thapsia L. Umbelliferae (III. 7). 6 Medit.
Thapsus Rafin. = Verbascum Tourn. (Scroph.).
Thaspium Nutt. Umbelliferae (III. 5). 3 N. Am.
Thatch-palm, *Sabal*, *Thrinax*, &c.
Thaumatocaryum Baill. (*Antiphytum* *EP.*). Boragin. (IV. 4). 1 Brazil.
Thaumatococcus Benth. Marantaceae. 1 W. trop. Afr.
Thaumatophyllum Schott. Araceae (?). 1 Amazonas.
Thayeria Copeland. Polypodiaceae. 1 Phil. Is.
Thea L. (*Camellia* p.p. *BH.*). Theaceae. 16 India to Japan. The chief is *T. sinensis* L., the tea plant, largely cult. in China, India, Ceylon, Japan, &c. *T. assamica* J. W. Mast. (perhaps only a var.) is also cult. It has larger l. When growing wild it forms a small tree, but in cult. is kept pruned into a small bush. The young shoots (bud and 2 or more l.) are nipped off, withered, rolled (to express a little juice), then fermented (except for green tea), dried, and sorted into grades (pekoe, souchong, congou, &c.). *Cf.* Watt, *Commercial Prod. of India.* [*Synonymy: T. Bohea* L. and *T. viridis* L. = T. sinensis; *T. Camellia* Hoffmgg. = Camellia japonica.]
Theaceae (*EP.*; *Ternstroemiaceae* p.p. *BH.*). Dicots. (Archichl. Parietales). 24 gen., 375 sp., trop. and subtrop. Trees or shrubs with simple alt. leathery l. Fls. usu. sol., ☿, often partly spiral. K 5,

6 or 7, reg. imbr. persistent; C 5 (4—9, ∞), imbr.; A ∞, rarely 5—10—15, free or in bundles or united into a tube; G 2—3—5—10-loc. with 2—4—∞ anatr. ov. in each, styles as many, free or united. Caps. or dry drupe, usu. with persistent columella; embryo usu. curved, with little or no endosp. Thea is of economic importance; Camellia cult. orn. fl. *Chief genera:* Thea, Camellia, Gordonia, Ternstroemia, [Eurya.

Theca, a sporangium, an anther-loc.

Thecacoris A. Juss. Euphorb. (A. I. 1). 10 trop. Afr., Madag.

Thecanisia Rafin. = Spiraea L. p.p. (Ros.).

Thecocarpus Boiss. Umbell. (III. 1). 1 Persia. Mericarps not separating.

Thecophyllum E. André (*Guzmania* p.p.). Bromel. (1). 40 trop. Am.

Thecostele Reichb. f. Orchid. (II. β. 11). 4 Burma, Malaya. Infl. basal.

Theetsee, *Melanorrhoea usitata* Wall. (Malaya).

Theileamia Baill. (*Phaylopsis* p.p. *EP.*). Acanth. (IV. A). 1 Madag.

Thelasis Blume. Orchid. (II. 16). 15 Indomal., China. 3 outer anthers sometimes developed.

Thelepogon Roth. ex Roem. et Schult. Gramin. (2). 1 Abyss. to India.

Thelesperma Less. Comp. (5). 8 Am. Inner br. connate. Pappus like [Bidens.

Thellungia Stapf. Gramin. (8). 1 Austr. (?).

Thelygonaceae = Cynocrambaceae.

Thelygonum L. (*Cynocrambe* Tourn. *q.v.*). Cynocramb. 2 Canaries to C. As., incl. *T. Cynocrambe* L. (*C. prostrata* Gaertn.).

Thelymitra Forst. Orchid. (II. 2). 25 Malaya, Austr., N.Z. Fl. almost reg. Column with 2 petaloid wings round fertile sta. Some fert. themselves in bud, the fl. afterwards expanding.

Thelypodiopsis Rydberg (*Thelypodium* p.p.). Crucif. (1). 4 Rockies.

Thelypodium Endl. Crucif. (1). 40 U.S., Mex.

Thelyra DC. = Parinarium Aubl. (Ros.).

Thelysia Salisb. = Iris p.p. (Irid.).

Themeda Forsk. (*Anthistiria*, *q.v.*). Gramin. (12). 12 warm |*.

Themistoclesia Klotzsch (*Anthopterus EP.*). Eric. (III. 2). 5 N. Andes.

Thenardia H.B. et K. Apocyn. (II. 2). 1 Mex. (A).

Theobroma L. Stercul. 20 trop. Am., incl. *T. Cacao* L., *T. pentagona* Bernoulli, and others, producing cacao, cocoa, or chocolate. Young l. red, pend. Fls. on old wood. Pets. cap-like at base. Stds. almost petal-like. Fr. large, tough, indeh., berry-like, with nearly exalb. seeds, which yield cocoa after roasting, &c. Cocoa-butter by pressing seeds. C. J. J. van Hall, *Cocoa*, 1914.

Theodora Medic. (*Schotia* Jacq.). Legum. (II. 3). 12 trop. and S. Afr.

Theodorea Barb. Rodr. (*Gomesa EP.*). Orchid. (II. 19). 1 Brazil.

Theophrasta L. Theophrast. 2 W.I. Thorny scales on upper part of stem. Serial buds in axils, fls. in axils of scales on these.

Theophrastaceae (*EP.*; *Myrsin.* p.p. *BH.*). Dicots. (Sympet. Primulales; pp. xli, lii). 4/60 trop. Am., Sandw. Is. ♄ with alt. exstip. l., often crowded at end of stem. Fl. ☿ or ♂ ♀, reg. K 5, C (5), A 5 opp. pets. with 5 stds., extr.; G 1-loc. with ∞ ov. on free-central or rarely basal plac., and simple style. Drupe with ∞—2 seeds; endosp. *Genera:* Theophrasta, Deherainia, Clavija (stds. fleshy), Jacquinia.

Theriophonum Blume. Arac. (VII). 5 S. Ind., Ceylon.

Thermium (Cl.), a hot-spring formation. [E. U.S. Rhiz. herbs.

Thermopsis R. Br. (*Thermia* Nutt.). Legum. (III. 2). 18 Himal. to

Thermotropism, curvature dependent upon temperature.
Therophon (*Therofon*) Rydberg (*Boykinia* p.p.). Saxifr. (1). 4 N. Am.
Theropogon Maxim. Liliaceae (VII). 1 Himalaya.
Therorhodion Small (*Rhododendron* p.p.). Eric. (I. 2). 2 N.W. Am., N.E. As.
Thesidium Sonder. Santalaceae. 6 S. Afr.
Thesium L. Santalaceae. 235 temp. and trop. *T. humifusum* DC. in Brit. (bastard toad-flax). Herbaceous root-parasites with green l. (see Scrophulariaceae). Fls. ☿, in racemes. Bract adnate to peduncle, and with the 2 bracteoles forms a sort of involucre. P (3—5), tubular. G inf. *Cf. Kew Bull.* 1915.
Thespesia Soland. Malvaceae (4). 5 warm |✻. *T. populnea* Corr. [a common strand plant.
Thespesocarpus Pierre (*Diospyros* p.p. *EP.*). Ebenaceae. 1 trop. Afr.
Thespidium F. Muell. Compositae (4). 1 trop. Austr.
Thespis DC. Compositae (3). 1 Nepal to Burma.
Thevenotia DC. Compositae (11). 2 W. As.
Thevetia L. Apocynaceae (I. 3). 8 trop. Am. W.I. L. alt.
Thevetia Vell. Rutaceae (inc. sed.). 1 Brazil.
Thevetiana O. Ktze. = Thevetia Vell. (Rut.).
Thibaudia Ruiz et Pav. (incl. *Ceratostema* Juss.). Ericaceae (III. 2). 50 trop. Am., often cult. orn. fl.
Thieleodoxa Cham. (*Alibertia* p.p. *BH.*). Rubi. (I. 8). 1 C. Braz. Fr. ed.
Thiersia Baill. Rubiaceae (II. 5). 1 Guiana.
Thigmotropism, curvature induced by rough surface.
Thiloa Eichl. (*Combretum* p.p. *BH.*). Combretaceae. 5 Brazil.
Thimble berry (Am.), *Rubus occidentalis* L.
Thinium (Cl.), a dune formation.
Thinobia Phil. (*Nardophyllum* p.p. *EP.*). Compositae (2). 1 Chili.
Thinouia Planch. et Triana. Sapindaceae (1). 10 warm S. Am.
Thiseltonia Hemsl. Compositae (4). 1 W. Austr.
Thismia Griff. Burmanniaceae. 14 Indomal., trop. Afr., S. Am. Saprophytes. See Groom in *Ann. of Bot.*, June 1895.
Thistle, *Carduus*, *Cnicus*, *Onopordon*, &c.; **blessed -**, *Cnicus*; **carline -**, *Carlina*; **cotton -**, *Onopordon*; **globe -**, *Echinops*: **milk -**, *Silybum*; **Russian -**, *Salsola*; **Scottish -**, *Onopordon Acanthium* L.: **sow -**, *Sonchus*; **star -**, *Centaurea*; **yellow -** (W.I.), *Argemone*.
Thladiantha Bunge. Cucurbitaceae (1). 8 E. As. to Java. Climbing herbs with root-tubers.
Thlaspi (Tourn.) L. Cruciferae (2). 60 N. temp.; 3 Brit. (penny-cress).
Thollonia Baill. (*Icacina* p.p. *EP.*). Icacinaceae. 1 French Congo.
Thomandersia Baill. (*Scytanthus BH.*). Acanthaceae (IV. B). 3 W. Afr.
Thomasia J. Gay. Sterculiaceae. 25 Austr.
Thomassetia Hemsl. (*Brexia* p.p. *EP.*). Saxifragaceae (V). 1 Seychelles.
Thompsonella Britton et Rose (*Echeveria* p.p.). Crass. 2 Mexico.
Thomsonia Wall. Araceae (IV). 1 Himalaya, Assam.
Thonnera De Wild. Anonaceae (1). 1 Congo.

Thonningia Vahl. Balanophoraceae. 5 trop. Afr.

Thoracosperma Klotzsch (*Simochilus* K.). Ericaceae (IV. 2). 5 S. Afr.

Thoracostachyum Kurz (*Mapania* p.p. *EP.*). Cyperaceae (II). 2 Malaya.

Thorea Rouy (*Avena* p.p.). Gramineae (9). 1 France.

Thoreldora Pierre. Rutaceae (V). 1 Cochinchina.

Thorelia Hance. Inc. sed. 1 Cochinchina.

Thorn, a stiff pointed outgrowth, which may be of various origin, *e.g.* epidermal, *Prosopis*, *Rosa*, epidermal with lower tissue (emergence), *Ribes*, branches, *Carissa*, *Colletia*, *Crataegus*, *Gleditschia*, *Gymnosporia*, *Haematoxylon*, *Hydrolea*, *Plectronia*, flower-stalk, *Mesembryanthemum*, leaf, *Azima*, *Cactaceae*, *Chuquiraga*, *Citrus*, *Limonia*, leaflet, *Cycadaceae*, midrib, *Astragalus*, *Fouquieria*, ovary, *Tetragonia*, petiole, *Astragalus*, root, *Acanthorhiza*, *Iriartea*, stipules, *Acacia*, *Machaerium*, *Paliurus*, *Polygala*, *Seguieria*, *Zizyphus*; **thorn**, *Crataegus*; **- apple**, *Datura*; **black -**, *Prunus spinosa* L.; **Kaffir -**, *Lycium*; **kangaroo -**, *Acacia*.

Thorncroftia N. E. Br. Labiatae (VII). 1 Transvaal.

Thoroughwort (Am.), *Eupatorium*.

Thoro-wax, throw-wax, *Bupleurum rotundifolium* L.

Thorvaldsenia Liebm. Orchidaceae (inc. sed.). 1 Mexico.

Thottea Roxb. Aristolochiaceae. 6 Malaya.

Thouinia Poit. Sapindaceae (I). 15 W. I., Mexico. Lianes.

Thouinidium Radlk. (*Thouinia* p.p. *BH.*). Sapindaceae (I). 4 W.I., C. Am.

Thozetia F. Muell. Asclepiadaceae (II. 3). 1 Austr.

Thraulococcus Radlk. (*Sapindus* p.p. *BH.*). Sapindaceae (I). 2 India.

Threlkeldia R. Br. Chenopodiaceae (A). 3 Austr.

Thrift, *Armeria vulgaris* Willd.

Thrinax L. f. ex Sw. Palmae (I. 2). 15 W.I. (thatch-palm). The l. are used for roofing, and the plants also yield useful fibre.

Thrincia Roth. = Leontodon L. p.p. (Comp.).

Thrincoma O. F. Cook. Palmae (I. 2). 1 Porto Rico.

Thringis O. F. Cook. Palmae (I. 2). 2 Porto Rico.

Thrixspermum Lour. (*Sarcochilus* R. Br.). Orchidaceae (II. 20). 15 Malaya.

Thrum-eyed (*Primula*), short-styled.

Thryallis L. = Galphimia Cav. (Malpigh.).

Thryallis Mart. Malpigh. (II). 3 warm S. Am. K umbrella-like after fert.

Thryocephalon Forst. = Kyllinga Rottb. (Cyper.).

Thryothamnus Phil. Verbenaceae (I). 1 Chili.

Thryptomene Endl. Myrtaceae (II. 2). 22 Austr., esp. W.

Thuarea Pers. Gramineae (5). 1 Indomal., on the coast.

Thuja (*Thuya*) L. Coniferae (Pinaceae 38; see C. for gen. char.). 6 China, Japan, N. Am., *T. occidentalis* L. is the American, *T. orientalis* L. the Chinese, Arbor-vitae. The l. are small and closely appressed to the stems, which show dorsi-ventral symmetry. Cones of 3 or 4 pairs of scales, the uppermost sterile and often united to form the *columella*, the lowest also often sterile.

[*Synonymy: T. dolabrata* Thunb. = Thujopsis dolabrata; *T. chilensis* Don = Libocedrus chilensis; *T. Doniana* Hook. = L. Doniana;

T. tetragona Hook. = L. tetragona; *T. gigantea* Carr. = Libocedrus decurrens.]

Thujopsis Sieb. et Zucc. Coniferae (Pinaceae 36; see C. for gen. char.). 1 Japan, *T. dolabrata* Sieb. et Zucc.

Thunbergia Retz. (*BH.* incl. *Meyenia* Nees). Acanthaceae (III). 150 palaeotrop. Many cult. orn. fl. Many twiners. The bracteoles enclose the K and tube of the fl. and are often united post. K truncate, or many-toothed.

Thunbergianthus Engl. Scrophulariaceae (III. 2). 1 St Thomas.

Thunia Reichb. f. (*Phaius* p.p. *BH.*). Orchid. (II. 9). 4 E. Indomal.

Thuranthos C. H. Wright. Liliaceae (V). 1 S. Afr.

Thuraria Molina. Inc. sed. 1 Chili.

Thurberia Benth. Gramineae (8). 2 Texas, Ärkansas.

Thurnia Hook. f. Thurniaceae. 2 Guiana. Herbs with narrow l., and heads of fls. on 3-angled stalks with several long bracts. Fls. ☿, reg., 3-merous; homochlam. A 6, $\underline{G}$ (3), 3-loc. with 1—∞ ov. in each. Caps. 3-seeded. Endosp.

Thurniaceae (*EP.*; *Juncaceae* p.p. *BH.*). Monocots. (Farinosae). Only genus Thurnia, *q.v.*

Thurovia Rose. Compositae (6). 1 Texas.

Thurya Boiss. et Bal. Caryophyllaceae (I. 1). 1 Asia Minor.

Thuspeinanta Durand (*Tapeinanthus* Boiss.). Labi. (VI). 2 W. As.

Thuya L. = Thuja L. (Conif.).

Thyella Rafin. (*Jacquemontia* p.p.). Convolv. (I). 12 trop. Am.

Thylacanthus Tul. Leguminosae (II. 8). 1 Ämazon valley.

Thylachium Lour. Capparidaceae (II). 12 E. trop. Afr., Madag., Masc.

Thylacospermum Fenzl. Caryophyllaceae (I. 1). 1 C. As.

Thymbra L. Labiatae (VI). 1 S.E. Eur., W. As.

Thyme, *Thymus*; **thymol**, *Carum copticum* Benth. et Hook. f.

Thymelaea Tourn. ex Scop. Thymelaeaceae. 20 Medit., temp. As.

Thymelaeaceae (*EP.*, *BH.*). Dicots. (Archichl. Myrtiflorae; Daphnales *BH.*). 38 gen., 550 sp., temp. and trop., esp. in Afr. Most are shrubs with entire alt. exstip. l., racemose infls. Fl. usu. ☿, reg., 4—5-merous. Recept. much hollowed, usu. forming a deep tube of leafy consistence ('calyx-tube'); outgrowths of the axis are sometimes found at the base of the tube round the ovary. K petaloid, like the tube, usu. imbr.; C conspic. or small or o; A as many or twice or half as many as sepals, inserted on edge of tube; $\underline{G}$ 1- or rarely 2-loc., each loc. with 1 pend. anatr. ov. with ventral raphe; style simple. Achene, berry, or drupe, often enclosed in the persistent recept.: a few have caps. Embryo straight; endosp. little or none.

Chief genera: Gnidia, Thymelaea, Daphne, Pimelea. The family is a very natural one, but with no very close affinities.

Thymelaeales. Formerly the 21st order of Archichlamydeae.

Thymelaeinae (Warming). The 17th order of Choripetalae.

Thymophylla Lag. (*Dysodia* p.p. *EP.*). Compositae (6). 18 Mex., Texas.

Thymopsis Benth. Compositae (6). 1 Cuba.

Thymus Tourn. ex L. Labiatae (VI). 33 N. |✻. *T. Serpyllum* L.

(thyme) in Brit. Fls. gynodioec. with marked protandry. *T. vulgaris* L. (garden thyme) used in flavouring.

Thyrocarpus Hance. Boraginaceae (IV. 1). 3 China.

Thyroid, shield-like.

Thyroma Miers (*Aspidosperma* Mart. et Zucc. p.p.). Apocynaceae (I. 3). 9 Brazil, W.I.

Thyrsacanthus Nees (*Odontonema EP.*). Acanth. (IV. B). 25 trop. Am.

Thyrsanthus Benth. = Forsteronia G. F. W. Mey. (Apocyn.).

Thyrsodium Salzm. ex Benth. Anacard. (3). 4 trop. S. Am., W. Afr.

Thyrsopteris Kunze. Polypodiaceae. 1 Juan Fernandez.

Thyrsostachys Gamble (*Rottboellia* p.p.). Gram. (2). 2 Khasias.

Thyrsus, an ovate panicle.

Thysanocarex Börner = Carex Dill. p.p. (Cyper.).

Thysanocarpus Hook. Cruciferae (4). 6 Calif.

Thysanolaena Nees. Gramineae (4). 1 trop. As. (tiger grass).

Thysanospermum Champ. ex Benth. Rubiaceae (I. 5). 1 Hongkong.

Thysanotus R. Br. Liliaceae (III). 22 Austr., S.E. As.

Thysanurus O. Hoffm. Compositae (1). 1 Angola.

Thysanus Lour. Inc. sed. 1 China.

Thysselinum Adans. = Peucedanum Tourn. (*BH.*) = Selinum L.

Tiarella L. Saxifragaceae (1). 4 China, N. Am.

Tibouchina Aubl. Melastomaceae (1). 200 trop. Am.

Tickseed (Am.), *Coreopsis*; **-trefoil** (Am.), *Desmodium*.

Ticorea Aubl. Rutaceae (1). 3 Guiana.

Tiedemannia DC. (*Peucedanum* p.p. *BH.*). Umbell. (III. 6). 4 N. Am.

Tieghemella Pierre. Sapotaceae (inc. sed.). 2 W. trop. Afr.

Tieghemopanax Viguier (*Polyscias EP.*). Aral. (1). 26 Austr., N. Cal.

Tigellum, plumule.

Tiger flower, *Tigridia pavonia* Ker-Gawl.

Tigridia Juss. Iridaceae (II). 7 Mexico, C. Am. *T. Pavonia* Ker-Gawl. (tiger flower), cult. orn. fl. The fls. only last 8—12 hours.

Tiles, *cf.* Bamboos.

Tilia (Tourn.) L. Tiliaceae. 18 N. temp. *T. platyphyllos* Scop. and other limes in Brit. Note leaf-mosaic (see fam.). The l. are usu. covered with honey-dew (see Acer). Fls. in little cymes, arising from axils of l. of current year; the axillary growing point elongates transversely, giving rise to two buds, one of which forms the infl., the other the bud for the next year's growth. The further development of the infl. is complex, but throughout there occurs 'adnation' of bracts to the axes arising in their axils, particularly noticeable in the first l. of the infl.-axis, which forms a wing, covering the fls. Honey is secreted at the base of the sepals. Fls. protandrous, dependent upon insects for fert.; largely visited by bees &c., and a valuable source of honey. Fr. a nut. Endosp. very oily. The wood of lime and of *T. americana* L. (bass-wood) is useful. The inner fibre of the bark (bass) is very useful for tying.

Tiliaceae (*EP.*; *BH.* incl. *Elaeocarpaceae*). Dicots. (Archichl. Malvales). 35 gen., 380 sp., trop. and temp., chiefly S.E. As. and Brazil. Trees or shrubs, rarely herbs, with alt. stip. l., often showing well-marked

2-ranked arrangement. In the trees the shoots spread out horiz. and the insertions of the l. are upon the upper half, so that the divergence is not ½. The end bud of the branch does not develop in the next year. Frequently the l. is asymmetrical, with the smaller side towards the branch. In the herbs the l. are in two ranks diverging at a right angle; torsion of the l. occurs later on and produces a dorsiventrality. The infl. is always, at least after the first branching, cymose, and often very complex, *e.g.* in Tilia and Triumfetta (*q.v.*).

Fl. usu. ☿, reg., 5—4-merous. K 5 or (5), valvate: C 5, rarely 0, often glandular at base; A usu. ∞, free or united in groups, inserted at base of petals or on androphore, with dithecous anthers; G 2—∞-loc., with 1—∞ ov. in each; ov. usu. ascending, ± anatr.; style simple, with capitate or lobed stigma. The T. yield useful timber, jute (Corchorus) and other fibre. The most constant distinction from Malvaceae is in the dithecous anthers, from Theaceae in the valvate calyx, &c. *Chief genera:* Corchorus, Sparmannia, Tilia, Grewia, Triumfetta.

Tiliacora Colebr. Menispermaceae. 15 Indomal.

Tillaea Mich. ex L. Crassulaceae. 20 cosmop. (1 Brit.).

Tillaeastrum Britton (*Tillaea* p.p.). Crassulaceae. 2 N. Am.

Tillandsia L. Bromeliaceae (1). 400 warm Am. Some resemble the rest of the fam.—epiphytes with pitchers—while others, and especially *T. usneoides* L. (long moss, Spanish moss, old man's beard, vegetable horsehair), show a different habit, hanging in long grey festoons from the branches of trees, looking rather like a lichen (esp. Usnea). At the base, each of the pendent stems is wound round its support, and as the apex grows on downwards the older parts die away, leaving the axile strand of sclerenchyma (the 'horsehair'). The whole pl. is thickly covered with the usual scaly hairs for absorbing the water trickling over it. It has no storage reservoir for water at all. The fls. appear but rarely. The pl. is largely distributed from tree to tree by the wind. Birds also use it for nesting and thus carry it about. [See Schimper, *Die epiph. Vegetat. Amerikas*, p. 67, Plate II.] It is used like horsehair. Some cult. orn. infl.

Tiller, a sucker from base of stem.

Tilmia O. F. Cook (*Martinezia* p.p.). Palmae (IV. 2). 2 trop. S. Am.

Timber, any woody growth of sufficient thickness to be workable into useful objects. The wood of a stem (Dicot.) grows in thickness, adding one layer each year (in temp. zones), recognizable in cross section as a *ring of growth*, or *annual ring*. In the trop., the rings are not usu. so clear, and more than one may form in a year. In longitudinal section (esp. radial), the medullary rays of the wood show as the *silver grain*. As a rule the sap runs up in the outer part of the wood (*sap-wood* or *alburnum*), while the inner part becomes more dry and hard (*heart-wood* or *duramen*). The pores in the wood seen in cross section are the large vessels in which the sap runs, and the greater the proportion of them (*e.g.* in climbing plants) the more *coarse-grained* is the wood.

Physical characters, such as hardness, weight per unit bulk, density or compactness of grain, breaking strain, fuel value, and the like, are also of great importance.

By far the most important source of timber is the *Coniferae* (*q.v.*), which give the deals, firs, pines, larches, hemlocks, spruces, cypresses, &c. Among the ∞ other important genera are *Acacia* (blackwood), *Acer* (maple), *Adenanthera*, *Afzelia*, *Ailanthus*, *Albizzia* (siris), *Andira*, *Arctostaphylos* (manzanita), *Artocarpus* (jak), *Baphia* (camwood), *Barringtonia*, *Bassia*, *Berrya* (Trincomali wood), *Betula* (birch), *Bombax*, *Brosimum*, *Brya* (cocus, Jamaica ebony), *Bucklandia*, *Buxus* (box), *Cabralea*, *Caesalpinia* (Brazil-wood, sappan), *Calophyllum*, *Caraipa*, *Carya* (hickory), *Caryocar*, *Castanea* (chestnut), *Casuarina* (ironwood, beefwood), *Catalpa*, *Cecropia*, *Cedrela* (cedar, toon), *Celtis*, *Cercis*, *Chickrassia* (Indian red wood), *Chloroxylon* (satinwood), *Copaifera*, *Cornus*, *Corylus*, *Crataegus* (hawthorn), *Cupania*, *Curtisia* (assegai wood), *Dalbergia* (rosewood, &c.), *Dimorphandra* (mora), *Diospyros* (ebony, &c.), *Dipterocarpaceae*, *Duguetia* (lancewood), *Ebenaceae*, *Eperua* (wallaba), *Erica* (bruyere, briar), *Erythrina* (kaffirboom), *Eucalyptus* (gum, karri, jarrah, &c.), *Euonymus* (spindlewood), *Fagara* (W.I. satin), *Fagus* (beech), *Feronia*, *Ficus*, *Flindersia*, *Fraxinus* (ash), *Garcinia*, *Gleditschia*, *Gmelina*, *Grevillea* (silky oak), *Guaiacum* (lignum vitae), *Haematoxylon* (logwood), *Heritiera*, *Herminiera*, *Hymenaea*, *Ilex* (holly), *Jacaranda*, *Juglans* (walnut), *Khaya* (Afr. mahogany), *Lagerstroemia*, *Laurelia*, *Laurus*, *Leguminosae*, *Liquidambar* (satin walnut), *Liriodendron* (white wood), *Lophira* (Afr. oak), *Maba*, *Machaerium*, *Maclura* (bowwood), *Melaleuca*, *Melanoxylon*, *Melia*, *Mesua*, *Metrosideros* (rata), *Michelia*, *Mimusops*, *Murraya*, *Myoporum*, *Nectandra* (greenheart), *Nyssa*, *Ochroma* (corkwood), *Ocotea* (stinkwood), *Olea* (olive, N.Z. maire), *Oldfieldia* (Afr. oak), *Ostrya* (leverwood), *Palmae* (several, such as *Borassus*, *Cocos*, &c. give useful small timber), *Pappea*, *Pericopsis*, *Peumus*, *Pittosporum*, *Planera*, *Platanus* (plane), *Populus* (poplar), *Pterocarpus* (padouk, red sanders), *Quassia*, *Quercus* (oak), *Robinia* (locust), *Royena* (zwartbast), *Salix* (willow), *Santalum* (sandalwood), *Schleichera* (Ceylon oak), *Shorea* (sal), *Sophora*, *Stenocarpus* (beefwood), *Swartzia* (beefwood), *Swietenia* (mahogany), *Tectona* (teak), *Terminalia*, *Tilia* (lime, basswood), *Tristania* (brushbox), *Ulmus* (elm), *Vatica*, *Xylia*, *Zelkova*, *Zizyphus* (cogwood), and many more. It should be noted that the common name of a timber is no proof of its botanical origin. New timbers brought upon the market must be given familiar names, and Swietenia as a source of mahogany, for example, has been almost superseded by Khaya. For details see Stone's *Timbers of Commerce*, and Gamble's *Indian timbers*, and manuals of forestry.

Timeroyea Montr. (*Pisonia* p.p. *EP.*). Nyctaginaceae. 1 New Caled.

Timonius Rumph. Rubiaceae (II. 2). 30 Indomal.

Timothy grass, *Phleum pratense* L.

Tina Roem. et Schult. (*Ratonia BH.*). Sapindaceae (I). 8 Madag.

Tinantia Scheidw. Commelinaceae. 3 trop. Am., W.I.

Tinctorius (Lat.), used for dyeing.

Tinguarra Parl. Umbelliferae (III. 2). 3 Medit.

Tiniaria Reichb. (*Polygonum* p.p.). Polygonaceae (III. 2). 3 N. Am.

Tinnea Kotschy et Peyr. Labiatae (I). 10 trop. Afr.

Tinnia Nor. Inc. sed. Nomen.

Tinomiscium Miers. Menispermaceae. 7 trop. As.

Tinopsis Radlk. (*Gelonium* p.p.). Sapindaceae (I). 1 Madag.
Tinospora Miers. Menispermaceae. 25 palaeotrop.
Tiphium (Cl.), a pool formation.
Tipuana Benth. Leguminosae (III. 8). 3 S. Am.
Tipularia Nutt. Orchidaceae (II. 5). 2 N. Am., Himal. to Japan.
Tiquiliopsis A. A. Heller (*Coldenia* p.p.). Borag. (II). 1 Rockies.
Tirania Pierre. Capparidaceae (inc. sed.). 1 Cochinchina.
Tirium (Cl.), a bad-land formation.
Tisonia Baill. Flacourtiaceae (4). 7 Madag.
Tissa Adans. (*Spergularia BH.*). Caryophyll. (I. 2). 20 cosmop.
Titanotrichum Solereder (*Rehmannia* p.p.). Scroph. (III. 1). 1 Formosa.
Tithonia Desf. ex Juss. Compositae (5). 10 C. Am., Cuba. *T. diversifolia* A. Gray (Mexican sunflower) now a common weed in trop. As.
Tithymalopsis Klotzsch et Garke (*Euphorbia* p.p.). Euphorbiaceae (A. II. 8). 15 N. Am.
Tithymalus Tourn. ex Hall. (*Euphorbia* p.p.). Euph. (A. II. 8). 15 N. Am.
Tittmannia Brong. Bruniaceae. 3 S. Afr.
Tittmannia Reichb. = Vandellia L. (*BH.*) = Lindernia All.
Tium Medic. (*Astragalus* p.p.). Leguminosae (III. 6). 10 N. Am.
Tmesipteris Bernh. Psilotaceae. 1 Austr., N.Z., Polynes., *T. tannensis* Bernh. It grows as an epiphyte (? parasite) on the trunks of tree ferns. The rhizome bears large lanceolate green l.
Toad flax, *Linaria*; **bastard --,** *Thesium*.
Tobacco, *Nicotiana*.
Tococa Aubl. Melastomaceae (I). 40 trop. S. Am.
Tocoyena Aubl. Rubiaceae (I. 8). 8 S. Am., Cuba.
Todaroa Parl. Umbelliferae (III. 5). 2 Teneriffe.
Toddalia Juss. Rutaceae (IV). 1 trop. As., Afr., Madag.
Toddaliopsis Engl. Rutaceae (IV). 1 Zanzibar.
Toddy, *Borassus*, *Caryota*, *Cocos*, &c.; **- palm,** *Caryota urens* L.
Todea Willd. Osmundaceae. 1 S. Afr., Austr., *T. africana* Willd. (*T. barbara* Moore); apogamous (see Filicales).
Toechima Radlk. Sapindaceae (I). 6 Austr., New Guinea.
Tofieldia Huds. Liliaceae (I). 15 N. temp., Andes. *T. palustris* Huds. (Scottish asphodel) in Brit. 3-lobed invol. (*calyculus*) beneath the K.
Tolbonia O. Ktze. Compositae (3). 1 Annam.
Tolmiea Torr. et Gray. Saxifragaceae (I). 1 Pac. N. Am., *T. Menziesii* Torr. et Gray. Adv. buds on upper part of petiole. Axial cup split down ant. side. Pets. thread-like; only 3 post. sta. occur.
Tolpis Adans. Compositae (13). 15 Azores, Canaries, Medit.
Tolu, balsam of, *Myroxylon toluiferum* H. B. et K.
Toluifera L. (*Myroxylon* Forst., *q.v.*). Legum. (III. 1). 8 trop. S. Am.
Tomato, *Solanum Lycopersicum* L.; **gooseberry -, strawberry -,** *Physalis*; **tree -,** *Cyphomandra*.
Tomentose, with cottony felt of hairs.
Tomex Thunb. = Litsea Lam. (Laur.).
Tonalanthus T. S. Brandegee. Compositae (5). 1 Mexico.

Tondin G. W. Schilling. Inc. sed. 1 Guiana.
Tonduzia Pittier (*Rauwolfia* p.p.). Apocynaceae (I. 3). 2 C. Am.
Tonella Nutt. ex A. Gray. Scrophulariaceae (II. 4). 2 W. U.S.
Tonestus A. Nelson (*Aplopappus* p.p.). Compositae (3). 3 N. Am.
Tonina Aubl. Eriocaulonaceae. 1 trop. S. Am., W.I.
Tonka or **Tonquin bean,** *Dipteryx odorata* Willd.
Tontelea Aubl. = Salacia L. (Hippocrat.).
Tooart, towart (Austr.), *Eucalyptus gomphocephala* DC.
Toon, *Cedrela Toona* Roxb.
Toona M. Roem. (*Cedrela* p.p. *BH.*). Meliaceae (I). 8 As., Austr.
Toothache grass (Am.), *Ctenium*; **-tree,** *Zanthoxylum*; **-weed,** *Spilanthes*; **-wort** (Am.), *Dentaria*.
Toothwort, *Lathraea squamaria* L.
Topee tampo, *Calathea Allouia* Lindl.
Topiary, formal ornamental gardening.
Topobea Aubl. Melastomaceae (I). 20 warm Am. Ed. fr.
Topographical agents in distr., mountains, rivers, seas, soil, &c.
Tordylium Tourn. ex L. Umbelliferae (III. 6). 16 Eur. (1 Brit.), N. Afr., As.
Torenia L. Scrophulariaceae (II. 6). 22 trop.
Torgesia Bornmüller. Gramineae (8). 1 Palestine.
Toricellia DC. Cornaceae. 3 Himalaya, China.
Torilis Adans. (*Caucalis BH.*). Umbellif. (III. 2). 23 Medit., N. As., Afr.
Tormentil, *Potentilla Tormentilla* Neck.
Tormentilla (Tourn.) L. = Potentilla L. (Ros.).
Tornabenea Parl. ex Webb. Umbelliferae (III. 7). 3 Cape Verde Is.
Tornelia Gutierrez = Monstera Adans. (Arac.).
Torralbasia Krug. et Urb. (*Euonymus* p.p.). Celastraceae. 2 W.I.
Torresia Allem. (*Amburana* Schwacke et Taub.). Legum. (III. 1). 1 Braz.
Torreya Arn. Coniferae (Taxaceae 8; see C. for gen. char.). 4 N. Am., China, Japan. Like Taxus. The timber is useful.
Torricellia DC. Cornaceae. 3 Himalaya, China.
Torrubia Vell. (*Pisonia* Plum.). Nyctaginaceae. 9 Am., W.I.
Torulinium Desv. (*Mariscus BH.*, *Cyperus* p.p. *EP.*). Cyperaceae (I). 6 W.I., Colombia to Chili.
Torulose, cylindrical with slight contractions.
Torus, floral receptacle, *q.v.*
Total parasites, those that take all food from the host.
Touch me not, *Impatiens*.
Touchardia Gaudich. Urticaceae (3). 1 Hawaiian Is.
Touchiroa Aubl. (*Crudia* Schreb.). Legum. (II. 3). 2 Borneo, Burma.
Toulicia Aubl. Sapindaceae (I). 10 trop. S. Am.
Touloucouna, *Caraipa*.
Tounatea Aubl. (*Swartzia* Schreb.). Leguminosae (II. 9). 60 trop. Am., Afr.
Tournefortia L. Boraginaceae (III). 120 trop. and subtrop. Trees and shrubs.
Tournefortiopsis Rusby. Rubiaceae (II. 2). 1 Bolivia.
Tournesol, *Chrozophora tinctoria* A. Juss.

Tourneuxia Coss. Compositae (13). 1 Algeria.
Tournonia Moq. Basellaceae. 1 Colombia.
Touroulia Aubl. Quiinaceae. 3 Guiana, Brazil.
Tourrettia Fougeroux. Bignoniaceae (5). 1 Peru to Mexico.
Tous les mois, *Canna edulis* Ker-Gawl.
Touteria Eaton et Wright (*Mentzelia* p.p.). Loasaceae. 17 N. Am.
Tovaria Neck. = Smilacina Desf. (Lili.). 20 Himal. to N. Am.
Tovaria Ruiz et Pav. Tovariaceae. 2 W.I., S. Am. Herbs with term. racemes. Fl. ☿, reg. K, C, A, 8, G̲ (6—8) with plac. reaching to centre, and ∞ ovules. Berry. Endosp.
Tovariaceae (*EP.*, *Capparidaceae* p.p. *BH.*). Dicots. (Archichl. Rhoeadales). Only genus Tovaria, *q.v.*
Tovomita Aubl. Guttiferae (v). 30 trop. Am.
Tovomitopsis Planch. et Triana (*Chrysochlamys BH.*). Guttiferae (v). 10 trop. Am.
Tow, *Linum usitatissimum* L.
Towel gourd, *Luffa*.
Townsendia Hook. Compositae (3). 18 Rocky Mts.
Townsonia Cheeseman. Orchidaceae (II. 2). 1 New Zealand.
Toxanthera Hook. f. Cucurbitaceae (2). 2 S. and trop. Afr.
Toxanthes Turcz. Compositae (4). 2 S. and W. Austr.
Toxicodendron (Tourn.) L. (*Rhus* p.p.). Anacard. (3). 35 N. Am.
Toxicodendrum Thunb. Euphorbiaceae (A I. 1). 1 Cape Colony.
Toxicophlaea Harv. = Acokanthera G. Don (Apocyn.).
Toxicoscordion Rydberg (*Zygadenus* p.p.). Liliaceae (I). 10 N. Am.
Toxocarpus Wight et Arn. (*Secamone EP.*). Asclepiadaceae (II. 1). 22 palaeotrop.
Tozzettia Savi = Alopecurus L. (Gram.).
Tozzia L. Scrophulariaceae (III. 3). 1 Alps, 1 Carpathians. Semiparasites, with loose-pollen fls. (see fam.).
Trabeculae, *Isoetes*.
Tracaulon Rafin. (*Polygonum* p.p.). Polygon. (II. 2). 20 Am., As., Austr.
Tracheliopsis Buser (*Campanula* p.p.). Campan. (I. 1). 3 Medit.
Trachelium Tourn. ex L. Campanul. (I). 7 Medit. Cult. orn. fl.
Trachelospermum Lem. Apocynaceae (II. 1). 8 India to Japan.
Trachyandra Kunth = Anthericum L. p.p. (Lili.).
Trachycarpus H. Wendl. Palmae (I. 2). 5 E. As.
Trachydium Lindl. Umbelliferae (III. 4). 12 E. Afr. to China.
Trachylobium Hayne. Leguminosae (II. 3). 3 trop. As., E. Afr. These yield copal, which is dug up from the soil near the roots or in a half-fossilised condition from places where trees once existed.
Trachymene DC. = Platysace Bunge (Umbell.).
Trachymene Rudge. Umbelliferae (I. 1). 14 Austr. to Borneo.
Trachynotia Michx. = Spartina Schreb. (Gram.).
Trachyphrynium Benth. Marantaceae. 6 trop. Afr.
Trachypogon Nees. Gramineae (2). 2 Am., S. Afr., Madag.
Trachypteris Andrée. Polypodiaceae. 1 trop. Am.
Trachys Pers. Gramineae (3). 1 coast of India.
Trachyspermum Link (*Carum* p.p. *BH.*). Umbellif. (III. 6). 12 Afr., S. As.

Trachystemon D. Don. Boraginaceae (IV. 3). 2 Medit.

Trachystigma C. B. Clarke (*Didymocarpus* p.p. *EP.*). Gesneriaceae (I). 1 trop. Afr.

Tracyanthus Small (*Zygadenus* p.p.). Liliaceae (1). 1 N. Am.

Tradescantella Small (*Tradescantia* p.p.). Commelin. 2 N. Am.

Tradescantia Rupp. ex L. Commelinaceae. 35 trop. and N. Am. *T. virginiana* L. (spider-wort), &c. Cult. orn. fl. 6 perfect sta. covered with hairs. Protandr. Infl. a cincinnus.

Tragacanth, *Astragalus*, esp. *gummifer* Labill.

Tragacantha Tourn. ex L. = Astragalus Tourn. (Legum.).

Traganthes Wallr. (*Eupatorium* p.p.). Compositae (2). 5 N. Am.

Traganum Delile. Chenopodiaceae (B). 2 Medit.

Tragia Plum. ex L. Euphorbiaceae (A. II. 2). 135 trop., subtrop.

Tragium Spreng. = Pimpinella Riv. p.p. (Umbell.).

Tragoceros H. B. et K. Compositae (5). 4 Mexico. The C of ♀ fl. becomes rigid after fert., and forms a double hook upon the fr.

Tragopogon (Tourn.) L. Compositae (13). 35 N. temp. |✻ (*T. pratensis* L., goat's beard, in Brit.). The fl.-heads of the Brit. sp. close at midday, whence its name of 'John-go-to-bed-at-noon.' *T. porrifolius* L. (salsify) sometimes grown as a vegetable.

Tragopyrum Bieb. = Atraphaxis L. (Polygon.).

Tragoselinum Tourn. ex Hall. = Pimpinella Riv. p.p. (Umb.).

Tragus Hall. Gramineae (3). 2 trop. and subtrop.

Trailing arbutus, *Epigaea repens* L.; **- azalea,** *Loiseleuria*.

Trailliaedoxa W. W. Smith et Forrest. Rubi. (inc. sed.). 1 W. China.

Tralliana Lour. Inc. sed. 1 Cochinchina.

Translator, *Asclepiadaceae*.

Transpiration, evaporation of water from plant.

Trap flowers, fls. which entrap visitors, allowing them to escape by another road, or at another time, past the essential organs, *Aristolochia*, *Arum*, *Asarum*, *Ceropegia*, *Coryanthes*, *Cypripedium*, *Magnolia*.

Trapa L. Onagraceae (1), sometimes in a special fam. Hydrocaryaceae. 3 |✻ (horn-nut), incl. *T. natans* L. Water pl. with floating l. and submerged adv. roots which contain chlorophyll and assimilate. Fl. ☿, 4-merous, perig., with a disc. above the sta. G 2-loc., with one anatr. pend. ov. in each; raphe ventral. Seed large, exalbum., in a horned nut; used as food in China, &c.

Trapella Oliv. Pedaliaceae. 2 China, Japan.

Trapeziform, of unsymmetrical 4-sided shape.

Trasus S. F. Gray = Carex Dill. p.p. (Cyper.).

Trattinickia Willd. Burseraceae. 2 trop. S. Am.

Traunia K. Schum. Asclepiadaceae (II. 3). 1 Kilimandjaro.

Trautvetteria Fisch. et Mey. Ranunculaceae (3). 6 Japan, N. Am.

Traveller's joy, *Clematis*; **- tree,** *Ravenala*.

Treacle mustard, *Erysimum*.

Tread softly (Am.), *Jatropha*.

Trechonaetes Miers. Solanaceae (2). 3 Chili.

Treculia Decne. ex Tréc. Moraceae (II). 6 W. trop. Afr. The seeds of *T. africana* Decne. (okwa) are ground into meal.

Tree, a woody plant usu. with only one stem at base and > 20 feet high;

- **fern,** *Alsophila, Brainea, Cyathea, Dicksonia, Hemitelia,* &c.; **- of heaven,** *Ailanthus*; **- tomato,** *Cyphomandra*.

Trefoil, *Trifolium*; **bird's foot-,** *Lotus*; **shrubby-,** *Ptelea*.

Treichelia Vatke. Campanulaceae (I). I S. Afr.

Treleasea Rose (*Setcreasea EP.*). Commelinaceae. 5 N. Am.

Trema Lour. Ulmaceae. 30 trop.

Tremacanthus Sp. Moore. Acanthaceae (IV. A). I Matto Grosso.

Tremandra R. Br. Tremandraceae. 2 W. Austr.

Tremandraceae (*EP., BH.*). Dicots. (Archichl. Geraniales; Polygalinae *BH.*). 2 gen., 26 sp. Austr. Herbs with whorled, alt. or opp., exstip. l. Fls. dichlam., reg. K 4—5, rarely (4—5), valvate; C 4—5, valvate; A 8, 10, or rarely 6; $\underline{G}$ (2), medianly placed; style and stigma simple; ovules I or 2 in each loc., anatr. Caps., loculic. or also septic. Album. seed, with or without aril. *Genera:* Tetratheca, Tremandra.

Tremandreae (*BH.*) = Tremandraceae.

Tremanthera F. Muell. Theaceae. I New Guinea.

Trematolobelia Zahlbr. ex Rock (*Lobelia* p.p.). Campanulaceae (III). I Hawaiian Is.

Trematosperma Urb. Icacinaceae. I Somaliland.

Trembleya DC. Melastomaceae (I). 14 S. Brazil.

Trentepohlia Roth. = Heliophila Burm. f. (Crucif.).

Trepocarpus Nutt. ex DC. Umbelliferae (III. 5). I S. U.S.

Tresanthera Karst. (*Rustia BH.*). Rubiaceae (I. I). 2 Venezuela, W.I.

Tretocarya Maxim. Boraginaceae (IV. 2). 2 China, Himalaya.

Treubella Pierre (*Palaquium* p.p.). Sapotaceae (I). I Sumatra.

Treubia Pierre (*Lophopyxis EP.*). Icacinaceae. I Ceram.

Treutlera Hook. f. Asclepiadaceae (II. 3). I Sikkim.

Trevesia Vis. Araliaceae (I). 4 Indomal.

Trevirana Willd. = Achimenes P. Br. p.p. (Gesn.).

Trevoa Miers. Rhamnaceae. 3 Andes.

Trevoria F. C. Lehmann. Orchidaceae (II. 13). 2 Ecuador, Colombia.

Trewia L. Euphorbiaceae (A. II. 2). I Indomal.

Tri- (Gr. and Lat. pref.), three; **-adelphous, -androus, -carpellary, -chotomous** (branching into 3), **-cyclic** (with 3 whorls), **-farious** (facing 3 ways), **-fid, -foliate,** (with 3 leaflets), **-gonous** (3-angled), **-lobous, -locular, -merous** (parts in 3s), **-morphism** (with 3 forms, *Lythrum*, &c.), **-oecism** (☿, ♂, ♀, each on its own pl., *Silene* sp.), **-pterous** (3-winged), **-quetrous** (3-edged, with hollow faces), **-stichous** (in 3 ranks), **-ternate** (thrice ternate), &c., &c.

Triactina Hook. f. et Thoms. Crassulaceae. I Sikkim.

Triaenophora Solereder (*Rehmannia* p.p.). Scroph. (III. I). I China.

Triainolepis Hook. f. Rubiaceae (II. 5). 2 E. Afr., Madag.

Trianaea Planch. et Linden (*Dyssochroma* p.p. *BH.*). Solanaceae (3). I Colombia.

Trianea Karst. = Limnobium Rich. (*BH.*) = Hydromystria G. F. W. Mey.

Trianoptiles Fenzl (*Ecklonea BH.*). Cyperaceae (II). I S. Afr.

Trianosperma Mart. = Cayaponia Silva Manso p.p. (Cucurb.).

Trianthema L. Aizoaceae (II). 13 trop.

Trianthera Wettst. (*Calceolaria* p.p.). Scrophul. (II. I). I Peru.

Trias Lindl. Orchidaceae (II. 16). 3 Indomal.

Triaspis Burchell. Malpighiaceae (I). 12 trop. and S. Afr.
Tribeles Phil. Saxifragaceae (V). 1 temp. S. Am.
Triblemma R. Br. ex DC. = Bertolonia Raddi (Melast.).
Tribonanthes Endl. Amaryllidaceae (III). (Haemodor. *BH.*) 5 S.W. Austr.
Tribrachya Korth. (*Morinda* p.p. *EP.*). Rubiaceae (II. 9.) 1 Sumatra.
Tribroma O. F. Cook (*Theobroma* p.p.). Sterculiaceae. 1 Colombia.
Tribulus Tourn. ex L. Zygophyllaceae. 12 Afr., As., Am., Medit. (caltrops). The mericarps have sharp rigid spines which may stick into the foot of an animal. Each contains 3—5 seeds, and is divided by cross walls which develop after fert.
Tricalistra Ridley. Amaryllidaceae (II). 1 Malay Peninsula.
Tricalysia A Rich. Rubiaceae (I. 8). 50 trop. Afr., As.
Tricardia Torr. Hydrophyllaceae. 1 W. U.S.
Tricera Schreb. = Buxus L. p.p. (Bux.). 24 W.I.
Triceros Lour. Anacardiaceae (inc. sed.). 1 Cochinchina.
Trich- (Gr. pref.), hair; **-ome**, a hair structure.
Trichacanthus Zoll. et Mor. Acanthaceae (IV. B). 1 Java.
Trichadenia Thw. Flacourtiaceae (3). 1 Ceylon.
Trichaetolepis Rydberg (*Adenophyllum* p.p.). Comp. (6). 1 Mex., S.W. U.S.
Trichantha Hook. Gesneriaceae (I). 2 Colombia.
Trichanthemis Regel et Schmalh. Compositae (7). 1 Turkestan.
Trichanthera H. B. et K. Acanthaceae (IV. A). 1 trop. Am.
Trichelostylis Lestib. = Fimbristylis Vahl p.p. (Cyper.).
Trichera Schrad. = Scabiosa Tourn. (*BH.*) = Knautia L. p.p.
Trichilia P. Br. Meliaceae. 175 trop.
Trichinium R. Br. (*Ptilotus* p.p. *EP.*). Amarantaceae (2). 55 Austr.
Trichlora Baker. Liliaceae (IV). 1 Peru.
Trichloris Fourn. ex Benth. Gramineae (11). 2 Mexico.
Trichobasis Turcz. Myrtaceae (inc. sed.). 1 Austr.
Trichocalyx Balf. f. Acanthaceae (IV. B). 2 Socotra.
Trichocarya Miq. (*Angelesia BH.*). Rosaceae (VI. b). 2 Sumatra.
Trichocaulon N. E. Br. Asclepiadaceae (II. 3). 12 S. Afr.
Trichocentrum Poepp. et Endl. Orchidaceae (II. 19). 16 trop. Am. Cult.
Trichocephalus Brongn. = Phylica L. (Rhamn.).
Trichocereus Riccob. (*Cereus* p.p.). Cactaceae (III. 1). 20 temp. S. Am.
Trichoceros H. B. et K. Orchidaceae (II. 19). 8 Peru, Colombia.
Trichochiton Komarov. Cruciferae (4). 1 Turkestan.
Trichochloa Beauv. = Muehlenbergia Schreb. p.p. (Gram.).
Trichocladus Pers. Hamamelidaceae. 6 S. and trop. Afr.
Trichocline Cass. Compositae (12). 30 S. Am., S.W. Austr.
Trichocoronis A. Gray. Compositae (2). 3 Texas, Mexico.
Trichodesma R. Br. Boraginaceae (IV. 1). 20 palaeotrop.
Trichodiclida Cerv. (*Blepharidachne EP.*). Gramineae (10). 2 Mexico.
Trichodium Michx. = Agrostis L. (Gramin.).
Trichodypsis Baill. Palmae (IV. 1). 2 Madag.
Trichoglottis Blume. Orchidaceae (II. 20). 15 Malay Archipelago.
Trichogonia Gardn. Compositae (2). 12 trop. S. Am.
Trichogyne Less. = Ifloga Cass. (Comp.).

Tricholaena Schrad. Gramineae (5). 10 Afr., Madag., Medit. *T. rosea* Nees is cult. for dry bouquets.
Tricholepis DC. Compositae (11). 12 Indomal.
Tricholobus Blume. Connaraceae. 3 Malaya, Austr.
Trichomanes L. Hymenophyllaceae. 240 cosmop.; *T. radicans* Sw., the bristle fern, in Ireland.
Trichonema Ker-Gawl. = Romulea Maratti (Irid.).
Trichoon Roth. (*Phragmites* p.p.). Gramineae (10). 1 trop. As., Austr.
Trichopilia Lindl. Orchidaceae (II. 19). 20 trop. Am. Cult. orn. fl.
Trichopteryx Nees. Gramineae (9). 40 trop. and S. Afr., Madag., Braz.
Trichoptilium A. Gray. Compositae (6). 1 W. U.S.
Trichopus Gaertn. Dioscoreaceae. 1 Indomal.
Trichosacme Zucc. Asclepiadaceae (II. 4). 1 Mexico.
Trichosandra Decne. Asclepiadaceae (II. 3). 1 Mauritius.
Trichosanthes L. Cucurbitaceae (3). 42 E. Indomal.
Trichoscypha Hook. f. Anacardiaceae (3). 25 trop. Afr.
Trichosma Lindl. Orchidaceae (II. *a*. II). 1 Himal. Axis lengthened at top carrying lat. sepals forward, forming a chin. Cult.
Trichospermum Blume (*Diclidocarpus EP.*). Tiliaceae. 3 Malaya, Fiji.
Trichospira H. B. et K. Compositae (5). 1 trop. Am.
Trichosporum D. Don (*Aeschynanthus BH.*). Gesner. (I). 70 Indomal, China.
Trichostachys Hook. f. Rubiaceae (II. 5). 6 W. trop. Afr.
Trichostelma Baill. Asclepiadaceae (II. 4). 1 Mexico.
Trichostema Gronov. ex L. Labiatae (I). 8 N. Am.
Trichostephanus Gilg. Flacourtiaceae (6). 1 Cameroons.
Trichostigma A. Rich. Phytolaccaceae. 4 trop. Am.
Trichotheca Ndz. = Byrsonima Rich. p.p. (Malpigh.). 50 Malaya.
Trichotosia Blume (*Eria* p.p.). Orchidaceae (II. 15). 60 Indomal.
Trichouratea Van Tiegh. (*Gomphia* p.p.). Ochnaceae. 25 Brazil, W.I.
Trichovaselia Van Tiegh. Ochnaceae. 1 Venezuela.
Trichymenia Rydberg (*Hymenopappus* p.p.). Compositae (6). 1 S.W. U. S.
Triclisia Benth. Menispermaceae. 12 trop. Afr., Madag.
Tricomaria Gill. ex Hook. f. Malpighiaceae (I). 1 Argentina.
Tricomariopsis Dubard. Malpighiaceae (I). 1 Madag.
Tricoryne R. Br. Liliaceae (III). 6 Austr.
Tricostularia Nees. Cyperaceae (II). 7 Indomal.
Tricuspidaria Ruiz et Pav. (*Crinodendron EP.*). Elaeocarp. 2 Peru, Chili.
Tricuspis Beauv. = Triodia R. Br. p.p. (Gram.).
Tricycla Cav. (*Bougainvillaea* p.p. *EP.*). Nyctaginaceae. 1 Argentina.
Tricyrtis Wall. Liliaceae (I). 5 Himal., E. Asia. Cult. orn. fl.
Tridactyle Schlechter (*Angraecum* p.p.). Orchid. (II. 20). 3 Nyassaland.
Tridalia Nor. Inc. sed. Nomen.
Tridax L. Compositae (5). 18 trop. Am.

Tridens Roem. et Schult. (*Triodia* p.p.). Gramineae (10). 7 N. Am.
Tridesmis Lour. (*Croton* p.p. *EP.*). Euphorbiaceae (A. II. 1). 1 China.
Tridesmostemon Engl. Sapotaceae (1). 1 Cameroons.
Tridianisia Baill. Icacinaceae. 1 Madag.
Tridimeris Baill. Anonaceae (1). 1 Mexico.
Tridophyllum Neck. (*Potentilla* p.p.). Rosaceae (III. 2). 9 Am.
Trientalis Rupp. ex L. Primulaceae. 3 N. temp. *T. europaea* L. (chickweed winter-green) in Brit. Rhiz. with erect stem bearing about 4—7 l. in a tuft and a few 7-merous fls.
Trifax Nor. Inc. sed. Nomen.
Trifolium (Tourn.) L. Leguminosae (III. 4). 290 temp. and subtrop.; 20 in Brit. (clover, trefoil, shamrock). The fl. has the simplest mechanism in the fam., the sta. and style emerging as the keel is depressed by an insect resting on the wings, and returning when it is released. The fls. of white clover are an important source of honey; those of red clover are too long-tubed for hive-bees and are visited by humble-bees. *T. subterraneum* L. has two kinds of infl., one normal, the other becoming subterranean. Only 3 or 4 of its fls. develop, the rest forming grapnels (each sepal forming a reflexed hook); the stalk of the infl. bends downwards and gradually forces the fls. under the earth, where the fr. ripen (*cf.* Arachis). *T. badium* Schreb. has a wing upon the fr. formed by the persistent C., *T. fragiferum* L. a bladdery 'wing' formed by the K. The clovers are important pasture and hay plants; among the chief are *T. repens* L. (white or Dutch clover), *T. pratense* L. (red clover), *T. hybridum* L. (alsike), &c.
Triglochin Riv. ex L. Scheuchzeriaceae. 12 cosmop.; 2 in Brit. (arrow-grass), in fresh water- or salt-marshes (*T. palustre* L. and *T. maritimum* L.). Tufted herbs with leafless flg. scapes ending in spikes or racemes. L. linear, fleshy in the maritime sp. P 3+3, A 3+3, G (3+3), or sometimes 3 with 3 abortive cpls. between the fertile. By a process of secondary growth the inner whorl of P comes to stand higher on the axis than the outer sta. Fl. protog., wind-pollinated. The pollen collects in the hollowed bases of the P-leaves. The ripe cpls. surround a central beak (*cf.* Geranium), and are prolonged outwards at the base into long sharp spines, by whose means, breaking away from the beak, they may be animal-distr.
Trigonachras Radlk. (*Sapindus* p.p. *BH.*). Sapindaceae (1). 4 Malaya.
Trigonella L. Leguminosae (III. 4). 70 Medit., Eur. (1 Brit.), As., S. Afr., Austr. *T. Foenum-graecum* L. (fenugreek) is sometimes cult. as curry stuff and for veterinary medicine. The fls. of *T. Aschersoniana* Urban bury themselves like those of Arachis.
Trigonia Aubl. Trigoniaceae. 26 trop. Am.
Trigoniaceae (*EP.*; *Vochysiaceae* p.p. *BH.*). Dicots. (Archichl. Geraniales). Trigonia. Woody pl., often climbing, with alt. or opp. l., stip. or not, and ☿ obliquely ·|· fls. K (5), C 5, A 5, 6, or 10—12, ± united below, $\underline{G}$ (3) each with ∞—2 ov. Caps. Endosp. *Genera:* Trigonia (l. opp.), Ligletia (l. alt.).
Trigoniastrum Miq. Polygalaceae. 2 Malaya.
Trigonidium Lindl. Orchidaceae (II. 18). 10 trop. Am. Pollinia 4.
Trigonocapnos Schlechter. Papaveraceae (III). 1 S. Afr.

Trigonocaryum Trautv. Boraginaceae (IV. 3). 1 Caucasus.
Trigonochlamys Hook. f. (*Santiria* p.p. *EP.*). Burseraceae. 1 Mal. Pen.
Trigonopleura Hook. f. Euphorbiaceae (A. II. 5). 1 Malay Peninsula.
Trigonosciadium Boiss. (*Heracleum* p.p. *BH.*). Umbell. (III. 6). 2 W. As.
Trigonospermum Less. Compositae (5). 3 S. Mexico.
Trigonostemon Blume. Euphorbiaceae (A. II. 5). 30 Indomal., C. As.
Trigonotis Stev. Boraginaceae (IV. 4). 16 mid and S.E. As.
Triguera Cav. Solanaceae (2). 1 S. Spain, Algeria.
Trigyneia Schlecht. Anonaceae (1). 11 trop. Am., W. I.
Trilepisium Thou. Inc. sed. 1 Madag.
Trilisa Cass. Compositae (2). 2 Atl. U.S.
Trilix L. = Prockia P. Br. (Flacourt.).
Trillium L. Liliaceae (VII). 30 E. As., N. Am. *Cf.* Paris. Cult.
Trilocularia Schlechter. Balanopsidaceae. 1 New Caled.
Trimenia Seem. Monimiaceae. 4 Fiji.
Trimeria Harv. Flacourtiaceae (9). 4 S. and trop. Afr.
Trimeza Salisb. Iridaceae (II). 6 W.I., S. Am.
Trimorpha Cass. (*Erigeron* p.p.). Compositae (3). 15 Eur., As., Afr.
Trimorphopetalum Baker. Geraniaceae. 1 Madag.
Trincomalee wood, *Berrya Ammonilla* Roxb.
Trineuron Hook. f. = Abrotanella Cass. (Comp.).
Trinia Hoffm. Umbelliferae (III. 5). 12 Eur., N. As., Medit. (1 Brit.).
Triniella Calest. (*Trinia* p.p.). Umbelliferae (III. 5). 3 S.E. Eur.
Triniochloa Hitchcock. Gramineae (9). 3 Mexico to Ecuador.
Triodia R. Br. Gramineae (10). 20 temp., and Am. trop. 1 Brit.
Triodon DC. (*Diodia* p.p. *EP.*). Rubiaceae (II. 10). 5 trop. Am.
Triolena Naud. Melastomaceae (I). 5 W. trop. Am.
Triomma Hook. f. Burseraceae. 1 Malay Penins., Sumatra.
Triopteris L. Malpighiaceae. 3 trop. Am., W.I.
Triorchos Small (*Cyrtopodium* p.p.). Orchidaceae (II. 10). 1 N. Am.
Triosteum L. Caprifoliaceae. 8 Himal., E. As., N. Am.
Tripetaleia Sieb. et Zucc. (*Elliottia BH.*). Eric. (I. 1). 2 Japan.
Tripetalum K. Schum. Guttiferae (V). 1 New Guinea.
Triphasia Lour. Rutaceae (V). 1 India.
Triphlebia Baker. Polypodiaceae. 3 Malaya, Phil. Is.
Triphora Nutt. (*Pogonia BH.*). Orchidaceae (II. 2). 8 N. and trop. Am.
Triplachne Link. Gramineae (8). 1 Sicily.
Triplaris Loefl. Polygonaceae (III. 2). 10 trop. S. Am. All are said to harbour ants in their hollow stems (*cf.* Cecropia). Fl. cyclic (see fam.), dioecious. The 3 outer P-leaves grow into long wings which project beyond the fr. and may aid in distribution.
Triplasandra Seem. (*Tetraplasandra* p.p. *EP.*). Aral. (1). 4 Hawaii.
Triplasis Beauv. (*Triodia* p.p. *EP.*). Gramineae (10). 3 N. Am.
Tripleurospermum Sch.-Bip. = Matricaria Tourn. (Comp.).
Triplocephalum O. Hoffm. Compositae (4). 1 E. trop. Afr.
Triplochiton K. Schum. Sterculiaceae. 4 trop. Afr.
Triplostegia Wall. ex DC. Valerianaceae (Dips. *BH.*). 4 Himal. China

Triplotaxis Hutchinson. Compositae (I). 2 trop. Afr.
Tripodandra Baill. (*Rhaptonema* p.p.). Menispermaceae. 1 Madag.
Tripogon Roth. Gramineae (11). 10 trop. As., Afr.
Tripolium Nees = Aster Tourn. p.p. (Comp.).
Tripsacum L. Gramineae (I). 7 warm Am. *T. dactyloides* L. is a fodder; it is like Euchlaena, but with ♂ and ♀ fls. in same infl.
Tripteris Less. Compositae (9). 35 S. Afr. to Arabia. Fr. 3-winged.
Tripterocalyx Hook. (*Abronia* p.p.). Nyctaginaceae. 5 N. Am.
Tripterodendron Radlk. Sapindaceae (I). 1 Brazil.
Tripterygium Hook. f. Celastraceae. 2 E. As.
Triptilion Ruiz et Pav. Compositae (12). 16 Chili.
Triptolemea Mart. = Dalbergia L. p.p. (Legum.).
Triraphis R. Br. Gramineae (10). 10 Austr., Afr.
Triscenia Griseb. Gramineae (4). 1 Cuba.
Trisciadia Hook. f. (*Coelospermum* p.p. *EP.*). Rubi. (II. 9). 1 Penang.
Triscyphus Taub. ex Warm. Burmanniaceae. 1 Rio de Janeiro.
Trisema Hook. f. (*Hibbertia* p.p. *EP.*). Dilleniaceae. 4 New Caled.
Trisepalum C. B. Clarke. Gesneriaceae (I). 3 Burma.
Trisetaria Forsk. Gramineae (8). 2 Egypt, Abyssinia.
Trisetum Pers. Gramineae (9). 55 temp. *T. flavescens* Beauv. in Brit., a good forage grass.
Trismeria Fée. Polypodiaceae. 2 trop. Am., Paraguay.
Tristachya Nees. Gramineae (9). 10 trop., exc. Austr.
Tristagma Poepp. et Endl. Liliaceae (IV). 5 Chili, Patagonia.
Tristania R. Br. Myrtaceae (II. 1). 22 Malaya to New Caled. (brush box).
Tristellateia Thou. Malpighiaceae (I). 15 palaeotrop., esp. Madag.
Tristemma Juss. Melastomaceae (I). 12 trop. Afr., Madag., Masc.
Tristicha Thou. Tristichaceae. 4 trop.
Tristichaceae (*cf.* Willis in *Linn. Soc. Journ.* XLIII. p. 49) (*Podostemaceae* p.p.). 3 gen., 6 sp. trop. Herbs of rapid water in hill streams (*cf.* Podostemaceae) with creeping thread-like roots giving off (exc. Lawia, where the primary axis is flattened into a thallus and gives off) large numbers of secondary shoots with minute delicate simple exstip. l. P 3—5 or (3—5), reg., sepaloid, A 3, 5, ∞, or 1, $\underline{G}$ (2—3) 2—3-loc. with ∞ anatr. ov. Caps. *Genera:* Tristicha, Lawia, Weddellina.
Tristichocalyx Miers (*Legnephora* p.p.). Menispermaceae. 1 Austr.
Tristira Radlk. Sapindaceae (I). 4 Malaya. Fr. 3-winged.
Tristiropsis Radlk. Sapindaceae (I). 4 Mariannes, Solomons, N.G.
Tristis (Lat.), dull coloured.
Trisyngyne Baill. Euphorbiaceae (A. II. 7). 2 New Caled.
Tritaxis Baill. Euphorbiaceae (A. II. 3). 4 Indomal.
Triteleia Dougl. (*Brodiaea* p.p.). Liliaceae (IV). 20 W. Am.
Trithrinax Mart. Palmae (I. 2). 3 S. Am. Fls. ☿.
Trithuria Hook. f. (*Juncella EP.*). Centrolepidaceae. 2 Austr., N. Z.
Triticum L. Gramineae (12). 15 Medit., Eur., W. As. Spikelets 2—5-flowered, in a dense spike. 3 sp. of wheat, with numerous subspecies, are cult. but the parent forms cannot be traced, and there is dispute as to the specific rank of these forms. *T. monococcum* L. is the one-grained wheat or small spelt (the grains of spelt do not fall out of the glumes when threshed), *T. polonicum* L. the Polish wheat,

and *T. sativum* Lam. the wheat proper, with 3 races, the ordinary spelt, the earliest cultivated (*T. spelta* L.), the 2-grained wheat (*T. dicoccum* Schr.), and *T. sativum tenax*, of which there are 4 sub-races, (1) the hard or flint wheat (*T. durum* Desf.) used for macaroni, &c., (2) the turgid or rivet wheat (*T. turgidum* L.), (3) the dwarf wheat (*T. compactum* Host.), and (4) the common wheat (*T. vulgare* Vill.) in ∞ vars. All are sometimes considered as forms of *T. vulgare*. *Cf.* Percival, *Agric. Botany*; Körnicke and Werner, *Handb. d. Getreidebaues*, Bonn, 1885, Percival, *The Wheat Plant*, 1921.

Tritoma Ker-Gawl. = Kniphofia Moench (Lili.).

Tritomopterys Niedenzu (*Gaudichaudia* p.p.). Malpighiaceae (1). 8 Mexico, C. Am.

Tritonia Ker-Gawl. Iridaceae (III). 50 S. and trop. Afr. Cult. orn.

Triumfetta Plum. ex L. Tiliaceae. 75 trop. Herbs or shrubs, often with extrafloral nectaries at base of l. On each internode of infl. are usu. at least three 3-flowered dichasial cymes. The first and oldest is opp. to the l.; the rest stand alt. right and left between the first and the l. Fruit with hooked spines (animal distr.).

Triuridaceae (*EP.*, *BH.*). Monocots. (Triuridales; Apocarpae *BH.*). 2 gen., 40 sp., trop. As., Afr., Am. Little saprophytes with scale l. and small fls. on long stalks, ☿ or ♂ ♀. P 3—8, corolline, valvate, A in ♂ 3, 4 or 6, G in ♀ ∞, each with 1 basal ov. and 1 style. Thick pericarp; much endosp. *Genera:* Sciaphila, Triuris.

Triuridales. The 3rd order of Monocots. **Triuris**, *cf.* Suppl.

Trivalvaria Miq. (*Polyalthia BH.*). Anonaceae (2). 4 Malaya.

Trivial (name), specific.

Trixago Hall = Stachys Tourn. (Lab.).

Trixago Stev. = Bartsia L. p.p. (*BH.*) = Bellardia All.

Trixis P. Br. Compositae (12). 35 warm Am.

Trizeuxis Lindl. Orchidaceae (II. 19). 1 Colombia.

Trochetia DC. Sterculiaceae. 8 St Helena, Mauritius, Madag.

Trochiscanthes Koch. Umbelliferae (III. 5). 1 S. Eur.

Trochlear, pulley-shaped.

Trochocarpa R. Br. Epacridaceae (3). 6 Austr.

Trochocodon Candargy. Campanulaceae (I. 1). 1 Greece.

Trochodendraceae (*EP.*; *Magnoliaceae* p.p. *BH.*). Dicots. (Archichl. Ranales). 3 gen., 6 sp., E. As. Trees or shrubs with alt. exstip. l., and fls. sol. or in racemes, ☿ or monoecious, naked. A ∞, $\underline{G}$ 5—∞. Caps. or achenes. *Chief genus:* Trochodendron.

Trochodendron Sieb. et Zucc. Trochodendraceae. 1 Japan.

Trochomeria Hook. f. Cucurbitaceae (3). 20 Afr., Madag. Dioec.

Trochomeriopsis Cogn. Cucurbitaceae (2). 1 Madag.

Trollius L. Ranunculaceae (2). 12 N. temp. and Arctic. (*T. europaeus* L., globe-flower, in Brit.) The 'sepals' completely cover in the fl. Fl. homogamous, and regularly fert. itself.

Troostwykia Miq. Connaraceae. 1 Sumatra.

Tropaeolaceae (*EP.*; *Geraniaceae* p.p. *BH.*). Dicots. (Archichl. Geraniales). Only genus Tropaeolum (*q.v.*).

Tropaeolum L. Tropaeolaceae. 50 S. Am., Mexico (Nasturtium or Indian cress of gardens). Most are herbs climbing by sensitive petioles (*cf.* Clematis), with cpd. or peltate l.; some have tubers at base of stem. Fl. ·|· with post. spur formed by axis under post. sepal. K 5, imbr.; C 5; A 4+4; G (3), 3-loc. with 1 ovule in each, anatr., pend. with micropyle facing upwards and outwards; style simple. Schizocarp, with no beak. Seed exalbum.

Trophis P. Br. Moraceae (1). 6 trop. Am., W.I.

Trophisomia Roj. Moraceae (1). 1 Argentina.

Tropical regions, *cf.* Floral; **-zone**, *cf.* Zones of Veg.

Tropidia Lindl. Orchidaceae (II. 2). 12 Indomal., Polynesia.

Tropidocarpum Hook. Cruciferae (3). 2 Calif.

Tropidopetalum Turcz. Inc. sed. 1 Java.

Tropophytes, pl. xero. at one period of the year, hygrophytic at another, *e.g.* bulbs, many tubers, *Anastatica* and other annuals, *Bowiea*, *Testudinaria*, &c., and trees that drop the l. *e.g.* *Bombacaceae*; see Caatinga.

Troximon Nutt. Compositae (13). 25 W. Am.

True fruit, product of ovary only; **-reproduction**, by special cells.

Trujanoa La Llave. Euphorbiaceae (inc. sed.). 1 Mexico.

Trumpet flower, *Bignonia*, *Datura*, &c.; **-reed** (W. I.), *Arundo*; **-tree**, *Cecropia*; **-weed** (Am.), *Eupatorium purpureum* L.

Trumpets (Am.), *Sarracenia flava* L.

Truncate, with broad straight end, as if bitten off.

Trybliocalyx Lindau. Acanthaceae (IV. B). 1 Guatemala.

Trymalium Fenzl. Rhamnaceae. 5 W. Austr.

Trymatococcus Poepp. et Endl. Moraceae (1). 5 trop. S. Am., Afr.

Tryphostemma Harv. Passifloraceae. 30 Afr.

Tschudya DC. = Oxymeris DC. (*BH.*) = Leandra Raddi (Melast.).

Tsimatimia Jumelle et Perrier (*Rheedia* p.p.). Guttiferae (V). 1 Madag.

Tsuga Carr. Coniferae (Pinaceae 14; see C. for gen. char.). 9 As., N. Am.: evergreen trees with habit of Picea. *T. canadensis* Carr. is the hemlock spruce, found in a large part of N. Am. and valued for its wood, bark (used in tanning), pitch (canada pitch), &c. For *T. Douglasii* Carr. (Douglas fir) see Pseudotsuga.

Tsusiophyllum Maxim. Ericaceae (I. 2). 1 Japan.

Tube, the concrescent part of K or C.

Tuber, a swollen stem or root in which reserves are stored, *Arum*, *Basellaceae*, *Begonia*, *Bravoa*, *Corydalis*, *Dahlia*, *Dioscorea*, *Helianthus*, *Ipomoea*, *Monotropa*, *Orchidaceae*, *Orchis*, *Oxalis*, *Paeonia*, *Scirpus*, *Sinningia*, *Tamus*, *Thladiantha*, *Ullucus*.

Tuberaria Spach (*Helianthemum* p.p. *BH.*). Cistaceae. 12 Medit., Eur.

Tubercle, Leguminosae; **-culate**, with knobby projections.

Tuberose, *Polianthes tuberosa* L.

Tuberostyles Steetz. Compositae (2). 1 Colombia.

Tubiflora Gmel. (*Elytraria* Vahl). Acanthaceae (1). 5 trop., subtrop.

Tubiflorae. The 6th order (*EP.*) of Sympetalae; the 4th (Warming).

Tubocapsicum Makino (*Capsicum* p.p.). Solanaceae (2). 1 Japan.

Tubutubua Post et O. Ktze. = Tapeinochilus Miq. (Zingib.).

Tuerckheimia Dammer. Palmae (nomen). 1 Guatemala.

Tuerckheimocharis Urb. Scrophulariaceae (II. 5). 1 S. Domingo.

Tula Adans. Rubiaceae (inc. sed.). 1 Peru.

Tulasnea Naud. Melastomaceae (1). 2 Brazil.

Tulbaghia Heist. = Agapanthus L'Herit. (Lili.).
Tulbaghia L. Liliaceae (IV). 12 trop. and S. Afr.
Tulip, *Tulipa*; **Cape -,** *Haemanthus*; **- tree,** *Liriodendron*, (Ceylon) *Thespesia*, (W.I.) *Paritium*.
Tulipa L. Liliaceae (V). 50 N. temp. |✱ (tulip), esp. on the steppes of C. As. The seeds are flat, and the capsule, even when the fl. is pend., stands erect (censer-mechanism). Many cult. orn. fl.
Tulipastrum Spach (*Magnolia* p.p.). Magnoliaceae. 2 N. Am.
Tumamoca Rose. Cucurbitaceae (2). 1 Arizona.
Tumboa Welw. = Welwitschia Hook. f. (Gnet.).
Tumescent, somewhat tumid; **tumid**, swollen.
Tumionella Greene (*Aplopappus* p.p.). Compositae (3). 1 S.W. U.S.
Tunaria O. Ktze. Solanaceae (4). 1 Bolivia.
Tundras, frigid deserts, char. by scanty covering of the ground, and xero. char. of veg. Mosses and lichens predominate.
Tunica Hall. Caryophyllaceae (II. 2). 20 Medit.
Tunicated bulb, with l. completely enwrapping, as in onion.
Tupa G. Don = Lobelia Plum. p.p. (Campan.).
Tupeia Blume = Henslowia Blume (Santal.).
Tupeia Cham. et Schlecht. Loranthaceae (I). 1 New Zealand.
Tupelo, *Nyssa*.
Tupidanthus Hook. f. et Thoms. Araliaceae (I). 1 Khasias to Burma.
Tupistra Ker-Gawl. Liliaceae (VII). 5 E. Indomal., China. Cult. orn.
Turbinate, cone-shaped.
Turetta Vell. Inc. sed. 1 Brazil.
Turf, an association in which Gramineae dominate.
Turgenia Hoffm. = Caucalis L. p.p. (Umbell.).
Turgeniopsis Boiss. (*Caucalis* p.p. *BH.*). Umbell. (III. 2). 1 W. As.
Turgidity, tension from content of water.
Turion, a scaly sucker or shoot from the ground.
Turkey-berry (W.I.), *Solanum*; **- oak,** *Quercus Cerris* L.; **- red,** *Peganum Harmala* L.
Turmeric, *Curcuma longa* L.
Turnera Plum. ex L. Turneraceae. 70 trop. and subtrop. Am.
Turneraceae (*EP.*, *BH.*). Dicots. (Archichl. Parietales; Passiflorales *BH.*). 6 gen., 105 sp., chiefly trop. Am. and Afr. Trees, shrubs and herbs, with alt. usu. exstip. l., whose teeth are sometimes glandular. Fls. usu. sol. in the leaf-axils, ☿, reg., perig. K 5, imbr., usu. with a hemispherical swelling on inner side; C 5; A 5; $\underline{G}$ (3), 1-loc. with parietal plac.; styles 3; ov. 3—∞, anatr. Fr. a caps., loculic. Seed with funicular aril, and copious endosp. Nearly all have dimorphic heterostyled fls. (*cf.* Primula). Many have extrafloral nectaries. Self-fert. occurs in absence of insect visits, by the C withering and pressing anthers and stigmas together. *Chief genus:* Turnera.
Turnip, *Brassica campestris* L.; **Indian -,** *Arisaema*; **prairie -,** *Psoralea*.
Turnsole, *Chrozophora tinctoria* A. Juss.
Turpentine, the balsams or fluid resins of the *Coniferae*, *Burseraceae*, &c.; when distilled oil of turpentine passes over, and resin is left,

Coniferae, *Abies*, *Picea*, *Pinus*; **Chian -**, *Pistacia*; **oil of -**, *Pinus*; **Strasburg -**, *Abies*; **- tree**, *Bursera*; **Venice -**, *Larix*.

Turpinia Vent. Staphyleaceae. 10 trop. As., Am.

Turraea L. Meliaceae (III). 50 palaeotrop.

Turraeanthus Baill. Meliaceae (III). 4 W. trop. Afr.

Turrigera Decne. Asclepiadaceae (II. 1). 2 temp. S. Am.

Turritis Tourn. ex L. (*Arabis* p.p. *BH.*). Cruciferae (4). 5 N. temp., Austr.

Turtle grass (W.I.), *Thalassia*; **- head** (Am.), *Chelone*.

Tuscarora rice, *Zizania aquatica* L.

Tussacia Reichb. Gesneriaceae (I). 5 trop. Am., W.I.

Tussacia Willd. Inc. sed. 1 S. Am.

Tussilago (Tourn.) L. Compositae (8). 1 Eur. (incl. Brit.), N. Afr., As., *T. Farfara* L., colt's foot. The fls. appear in spring before the l.; the pl. multiplies and hibernates by underground offshoots. The fl.-head is monoec.; in the centre are about 40 ♂ fls., surrounded by about 300 ♀. The ♂ retain the style, as usual, to act as pollen-presenter, but it has no stigmas. Honey is secreted in the ♂ fls., but not in the ♀. The ♀ fls. being the outer ones are ripe before the ♂, and self-fert. is almost impossible.

Tutcheria Dunn. Theaceae. 2 China.

Tutsan, *Hypericum*.

Tutuca Molina. Ericaceae (inc. sed.). 2 Chili.

Tway-blade, *Listera*.

Tweedia Hook. et Arn. = Oxypetalum R. Br. (Asclep.).

Twig-rush (Am.), *Cladium*.

Twin flower (Am.), *Linnaea*; **- leaf**, *Jeffersonia*.

Twining plants, *cf.* Climbing Plants.

Twisted stalk (Am.), *Streptopus*; **-ing of fl. stalk**, *Downingia*, *Fumaria*, *Impatiens*, *Lobelia*, *Melianthaceae*, *Orchidaceae*; **of leaf**, *Alstroemeria*, *Bomarea*; **of stem**, *Pandanus*; **of anther theca**, *Cochliostema*, *Columelliaceae*, *Cucurbitaceae*.

Twitch grass, *Agropyron repens* Beauv.

Tydaea Decne. = Isoloma Decne. (*BH.*) = Kohleria Regel p.p.

Tyle berry (W.I.), *Jatropha multifida* L.

Tylecarpus Eng. Icacinaceae. 1 New Guinea.

Tylodontia Griseb. (*Astephanus* p.p.). Asclepiadaceae (II. 1). 1 Cuba.

Tyloglossa Hochst. = Justicia Houst. p.p. (Acanth.).

Tylophora R. Br. Asclepiadaceae (II. 3). 50 palaeotrop.

Tylophoropsis N. E. Br. (*Tylophora* p.p.). Asclepiad. (II. 1). 2 E. Afr.

Tylostemon Engl. Lauraceae (II. 1). 30 trop. Afr.

Tynanthus Miers. Bignoniaceae (I). 10 trop. S. Am.

Type, the ideal repres. of a group; **- specimen**, that from which the original description of a sp. was drawn up.

Typha L. Typhaceae. 12 temp. and trop., in marshes; 2 in Brit. (reed-mace, cat's-tail, bulrush). The lower part of the stem is a thick rhiz.; the upper projects high out of the water (l. 2-ranked) and bears the infl., a dense spike, divided into two parts, the upper ♂ (usu. yellow), the lower ♀ (brown). Fls. naked: ♂ fl. of 2—5 sta., the connective projecting beyond the anthers; pollen in tetrads; fl. enclosed in a number of hairs: ♀ similarly enclosed, of 1 cpl. with 1 pend. ov., micropyle towards the base or ventral side of the ovary. Fl. anemoph. Achenes covered by the long downy hairs mentioned, which aid in distr. Seed album.; embryo straight.

Typhaceae (*EP.*; *BH.* incl. *Sparganiaceae*). Monocots. (Pandanales; Nudiflorae *BH.*). Only genus Typha (*q.v.*).

Typhonium Schott. Araceae (VII). 25 Indomal.

Typhonodorum Schott. Araceae (V). 1 Madag., E. Afr.

Tyrimnus Cass. Compositae (11). 1 W. As., S. Eur.

Tysonia Bolus. Boraginaceae (IV. 1). 1 S.E. Afr.

Tysonia F. Muell. (*Neotysonia* Dalla Torre et Harms). Comp. (4). 1 Austr.

Tzellemtinia Chiov. Rhamnaceae. 1 E. trop. Afr.

Uapaca Baill. Euphorbiaceae (A. I. 1). 30 trop. Afr., Madag.

Ubochea Baill. Verbenaceae (1). 1 Cape Verde Is.

Ucria Targ. Inc. sed. Nomen lapsum. *Cf.* Index Kewensis.

Ucriana Spreng. (*Augusta* Pohl). Rubiaceae (I. 3). 1 E. Brazil.

Udora Nutt.=Elodea Michx. (Hydrochar.).

Uebelinia Hochst. Caryophyllaceae (II. 1). 2 E. Afr.

Uechtritzia Freyn. Compositae (12). 1 Armenia.

Ugni Turcz. (*Myrtus* p.p. *BH.*). Myrtaceae (I). 11 Andes, Mexico. Ed. fr.

Ule, *Castilloa.*

Uleanthus Harms. Leguminosae (III. 1). 1 Amazon valley.

Ulearum Engl. Araceae (VII). 1 Upper Amazon valley.

Uleophytum Hieron. Compositae (2). 1 Peru. Climber.

Ulex L. Leguminosae (III. 3). 20 W. Eur., N. Afr.; 3 in Brit., *U. europaeus* L., *U. nanus* Forst. and *U. Gallii* Planch., the gorse, furze, or whin, covering large areas, esp. on heaths. The l. are reduced in size, and many branches reduced to green spines (xerophytism). The fls. explode like Genista, and the fr. explodes by the twisting up of its valves in dry air. The seeds in germination show interesting transition-stages from the usual compound l. seen in the order to the needle-l. of the mature pl. (*cf.* Acacia).

Uliginosus (Lat.), growing in swamps.

Ullucus Caldas. Basellaceae. 1 Andes, *U. tuberosus* Caldas. Lat. branches of the rhiz. swell into tubers like potatoes, and are used as food.

Ulmaceae (*EP.*; *Urticaceae* p.p. *BH.*). Dicots. (Archichl. Urticales). 13 gen., 130 sp., trop. and temp. Trees with sympodial stems, bearing 2-ranked simple often asymmetrical l. with stips. Fls. usu. in cymose clusters, generally unisexual. P 4—5, free or united, sepaloid, theoretically belonging to two whorls; A 4—5, opp. the perianth-l., in two whorls; $\underline{G}$ rudimentary in ♂ fl., in the ♀ of (2) cpls., sometimes 2-loc. but usu. 1-loc., the second loc. aborting; ov. 1 per loc., anatr. or amphitr., pend., style linear or bifid. Nut, samara or drupe. Seed usu. with no endosp. The wood of many is useful. *Chief genera:* Ulmus, Celtis.

Ulmaria (Tourn.) Hill (*Spiraea* p.p. *BH.*). Rosaceae (III. 4). 10 N. temp. *U. palustris* Moench (*Spiraea Ulmaria*, meadow-sweet) and *U. Filipendula* Hill (*S. Filipendula*, dropwort) in Brit.

Ulmus (Tourn.) L. Ulmaceae. 18 N. temp. and Mts. of trop. Asia.

U. montana With. (wych elm) and *U. campestris* L. (elm) in Brit. Growth sympodial, the term. bud being suppressed. L. asymmetrical, one side larger than the other (*cf.* Begonia). The fls. are ☿ and come out before the l. as little reddish tufts, each a short axis with a number of l., beginning 2-ranked at the base and going over to 5-ranked above. There are no fls. in the axils of the lowest 10 or 12; in the axils of the upper l. are fls. arranged in small dich. cymes (*cf.* Betulaceae), which are reduced, in *U. campestris* and others, to the one central fl. Each fl. has P 4—8 and as many sta. with 1-loc. ovary. [See Chalazogamae.] Fr. a samara. The elm supplies a valuable timber.

Umbel, an infl. in which the stalks of the fls. all spring from the top of the main stalk.

Umbellales (*BH.*). The 15th order of Polypetalae.

Umbelliferae (*EP.*, *BH.*). Dicots. (Archichl. Umbelliflorae). 200 gen., 2700 sp., cosmop., chiefly N. temp. Many in Brit. Most can be recognized by habit; herbs with stout stems, hollow internodes, and alt. exstip. sheathing l. with their blades much divided pinnately. A few, *e.g.* Hydrocotyle and Bupleurum, have entire l. Infl. usu. a cpd. umbel. At the top of the stalk of each partial umbel, an invol. of bracts is often found (the bracts of the outer fls.), and a similar larger invol. often occurs at the top of the main stalk bearing the cpd. umbel; the latter is sometimes termed the involucre in contradistinction to the *involucels* of the partial umbels. A term. fl. often occurs, *e.g.* in Daucus. In a number of genera (*e.g.* Astrantia, Hydrocotyle) simple umbels occur, cymose in type (as the non-centripetal order of opening of fls. shows) and often arranged in cymose groupings, *e.g.* in Sanicula. Eryngium has a cymose head. Some sp. of Xanthosia and Azorella have such cymose infls. reduced to single fls., and these infls. have commonly invols. of bracts.

Fl. usu. ☿ and reg. (see below), epig. K 5, usu. very small, the odd sepal post.; C 5 (rarely 0), usu. white or yellow; A 5, intr.; $\overline{G}$ (2), antero-post., 2-loc.; in each loc. one pend. ovule, anatr., with ventral raphe. On top of the ovary is an epig. disc, prolonged into two short styles.

The massing of the fls. into dense infls. makes them conspic. (*cf.* Compositae), and this is aided by the zygomorphism of the C often seen; the outer petals of the outer fls. are drawn out (*cf.* Cruciferae) so as to form a sort of ray. Honey is secreted by the disc; it is accessible to all insects (fam. in class **A**). The chief visitors are flies; fls. very protandrous, the ♂ stage being most commonly over before the ♀ begins.

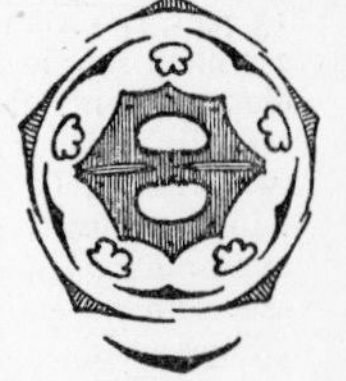

Floral diagram.

The ovary ripens into a very char. fruit, a dry schizocarp, which splits down the septum between cpls. into 2 mericarps, each containing one seed. The two are generally held together at first by a thin stalk (*carpophore*) running up between them. The structure of the pericarp is of great importance in determining the gen. It is nearly always necessary to have ripe fr. in order to identify one of the U. The shape is often important; the outer surface of each mericarp has generally 5 projecting *primary ridges*, two of which (the *lateral ridges*) are at the edges where the splitting takes place. Between these are sometimes *secondary ridges*, 4 to each mericarp. In the furrows are often found oil-cavities (seen as small openings in cross-section) known as *vittae*. The seed is often united to the pericarp; it is album. with small embryo in oily endosp., which is usu. cartilaginous in texture. The shape of the endosp. as seen in cross-section is of importance; it may be crescentic, or ventrally grooved, or concave on ventral side. The fr. often shows adaptations for distr.; in many (*e.g.* Heracleum and allies) the mericarp is thin and flat, suited to wind-carriage; in others (*e.g.* Daucus) it has hooks. See also Scandix.

Many U. are economically useful, but as a rule they are poisonous. See Daucus (carrot), Pastinaca (parsnip), Apium (celery), Crithmum (samphire), Foeniculum (fennel), Archangelica, Carum, Ferula, Pimpinella, Coriandrum, Petroselinum, &c.

Classification and chief genera (after Engler):

I. *HYDROCOTYLOIDEAE* (fr. with no free carpophore, and woody endocarp: vittae none or in main ribs).

1. *Hydrocotyleae* (fr. with narrow surface of union, lat. flattened): Hydrocotyle, Azorella.
2. *Mulineae* (fr. with flattened or rounded back; ✳): Bowlesia.

II. *SANICULOIDEAE* (endocarp soft, exocarp rarely smooth; style long with capitate stigmas, surrounded by ring-like disc; vittae various).

1. *Saniculeae* (ov. 2-loc.; fr. 2-seeded, with broad surface of union; vittae): Eryngium, Astrantia, Sanicula.
2. *Lagoecieae* (ov. 1-loc.; fr. 1-seeded; vittae indistinct); *Lagoecia.*

III. *APIOIDEAE* (endocarp soft, sometimes hardened by sub-epidermal fibre layers; style on apex of disc; vittae).

A. Primary ridges projecting, the lat. sometimes wing-like; no secondary ridges.

a. Secondary umbels each with 1 or few ♀ fls. surrounded by ♂.

1. *Echinophoreae* (fr. enclosed by hardened stalks of ♂ fls.): Echinophora.

b. Fls. all ☿, or irreg. polygamous.

α. Seed at surface of union deeply forked or hollow.

2. *Scandicineae* (parenchyma around carpophore with crystal layer): Chaerophyllum, Anthriscus, Torilis.
3. *Coriandreae* (without crystal layer; fr. ovate-spherical, nut-like, rarely long, with woody sub-epidermal layer): Coriandrum.
4. *Smyrnieae* (narrow surface of union, mericarps rounded outwards): Smyrnium, Conium.

β. Seeds flattened at surface of union.

5. *Ammineae* (primary ridges all alike; seed semicircular in section): Bupleurum, Apium, Petroselinum, Carum, Pimpinella, Seseli, Foeniculum, Oenanthe, Ligusticum.

6. *Peucedaneae* (lat. ribs much broader, forming wings; seed narrow in section): Angelica, Ferula, Peucedanum, Pastinaca.

B. Lat. ridges equal or larger than primary; vittae in furrows or under secondary ridges.

7. *Laserpitieae* (secondary ridges very marked, often extended into broad undivided or wavy wings): Laserpitium, Thapsia.

8. *Dauceae* (ribs with spines): Daucus.

Umbelliflorae. The 30th order (*EP.*) of Archichlamydeae; the 23rd (Warming) of Choripetalae.

Umbellularia Nutt. Lauraceae (I). 1 Calif., *U. californica* Nutt., the California olive, with useful timber.

Umbilicate, peltate, or depressed in centre.

Umbilicus DC. (*Cotyledon* p.p.). Crassulaceae. 10 Medit.

Umbonate, with central boss.

Umbraculiferous, like an expanded umbrella.

Umbrella fir, *Sciadopitys*; **-grass** (Am.), *Fuirena*; **-leaf** (Am.), *Diphylleia*; **-tree,** *Acacia*, *Magnolia.*

Umbrinus (Lat.), umber-coloured.

Umbrosus (Lat.), of shady places.

Umtiza Sim. Leguminosae (II. 3). 1 S. Afr.

Unamia Greene (*Aster* p.p.). Compositae (3). 4 mid atl. U.S.

Uncaria Schreb. (*Ourouparia* Aubl.). Rubiaceae (I. 6). 35 trop. They climb by hooks, which are metam. infl.-axes, and sensitive to continued contact; after clasping they enlarge and become woody. *U. Gambier* Roxb. (gambir; Straits Sett.) is a valuable source of tan.

Uncarina Stapf (*Harpagophytum* p.p.). Pedaliaceae. 5 Madag.

Uncariopsis Karst. (*Schradera* p.p. *EP.*). Rubi. (I. 6). 1 Columbia.

Uncasia Greene (*Eupatorium* p.p.). Compositae (2). 30 N. Am.

Uncate, uncinate, hooked.

Uncifera Lindl. Orchidaceae (II. 20). 2 Khasias.

Uncinia Pers. Cyperaceae (III). 30 ✳, Mexico, W.I. The axis of origin of the fl. projects beyond the utricle in the form of a long hook, serving as a means of dispersal for the fr.

Undershrub, a low-growing woody plant, *e.g. Calluna.*

Undulate, wavy.

Ungeria Schott et Endl. Sterculiaceae. 1 E. Austr., Norfolk I.

Ungernia Bunge. Amaryllidaceae (I). 1 Persia.

Ungnadia Endl. Sapindaceae (II). 1 Texas, Mexico (Mex. buckeye).

Unguiculate, ungulate, clawed.

Uni- (Lat. pref.), one; **-corn plant** (Am.), *Martynia*; **-foliolate,** with one leaflet, *Berberis*, *Citrus*; **-lateral, -locular,** &c.; **-parous,** monochasial; **-sexual** (fl.), with sta. *or* cpls.

Unifolium Hall (*Maianthemum* Weber). Liliaceae (VII). 10 N. Am.

Uniola L. Gramineae (10). 8 Am. Useful pasture. Cult. orn.

Unisexuales (*BH.*). The 7th series of Incompletae.

Unona L. f. Anonaceae (I). 50 trop. As., Afr., some climbing by recurved hooks which are infl.-axes. Fr. an aggregate of stalked berries, constricted between the seeds like a lomentum.

Unonopsis R. E. Fries (*Trigyneia* p.p.). Anon. (I). 10 Mex., trop. Am.

Upas tree, *Antiaris toxicaria* Lesch.
Urachne Trin. = Oryzopsis Michx. (Gram.).
Uragoga L. (*Psychotria* p.p. *BH.*, *Cephaelis* Sw.). Rubiaceae (II. 5). 130 trop. *U.* (*C.*) *Ipecacuanha* Baill. (*P. Ipecacuanha* Stokes) is the ipecacuanha (Brazil), a herb with decumbent stem, and roots thickened somewhat like rows of beads. Root used in medicine.
Uralepsis Nutt. = Triodia R. Br. p.p. (Gram.).
Urandra Thw. (*Lasianthus* p.p.). Icacinaceae. 10 Indomal.
Uraria Desv. Leguminosae (III. 7). 12 palaeotrop.
Urbania Phil. Verbenaceae (1). 2 Chili.
Urbanodendron Mez (*Aydendron* p.p.). Lauraceae (II). 1 E. Brazil.
Urbanodoxa Muschler (*Cremolobus* p.p.). Cruciferae (1). 1 Peru.
Urbanosciadium H. Wolff. Umbelliferae (III. 4). 1 Peru.
Urbinella Greenman. Compositae (6). 1 Mexico.
Urbinia Rose (*Echeveria* p.p.). Crassulaceae. 5 Mexico.
Urceocharis × Mast. Hybrid Urceolina – Eucharis (*Gard. Chr.* 1892).
Urceola Roxb. Apocynaceae (II. 1). 8 E. Indomal.
Urceolate, urn-shaped.
Urceolina Reichb. Amaryllidaceae (1). 3 Andes.
Urechites Muell.-Arg. Apocynaceae (II. 1). 5 W.I., Florida.
Urelytrum Hack. Gramineae (2). 3 trop. and S. Afr.
Urena Dill. ex L. Malvaceae (3). 3 trop. and subtrop. Schizocarp, the individual cpls. provided with hooks. Useful fibre.
Urens (Lat.), stinging.
Urera Gaudich. Urticaceae (1). 22 trop. Stinging hairs powerful. Achene enclosed in persistent fleshy P. (pseudo-berry).
Urginea Steinh. Liliaceae (V). 40 Medit., Afr., India. *U. Scilla* Steinh. (*U. maritima* Baker, squill), large bulbs used in medicine.
Urmenetia Phil. (*Onoseris* p.p. *EP.*). Compositae (12). 1 Chili.
Urnularia Stapf (*Willughbeia*, &c. p.p.). Apocyn. (I. 1). 5 Malaya.
Urobotrya Stapf. Opiliaceae. 4 trop. Afr.
Urochlaena Nees. Gramineae (10). 2 S. Afr.
Urodesmium Naud. (*Pachyloma* DC.). Melastomaceae (1). 2 Brazil.
Uropappus Nutt. = Microseris D. Don, p.p. (Comp.).
Uropetalon Ker-Gawl. = Dipcadi Medic. p.p. (Lili.).
Urophyllum Wall. Rubiaceae (I. 7). 40 trop. Afr. to Japan.
Uroskinnera Lindl. Scrophulariaceae (II. 4). 2 C. Am., Mexico.
Urospatha Schott. Araceae (IV). 15 trop. Am. Rhiz. spongy.
Urospermum Scop. Compositae (13). 2 Medit.
Urostephanus Robinson et Greenman. Asclepiadaceae (II. 4). 1 Mexico.
Urostigma Gasp. = Ficus Tourn. p.p. (Mor.).
Urotheca Gilg. Melastomaceae (1). 1 E. trop. Afr.
Ursinea Gaertn. Compositae (10). 60 S. Afr., Abyssinia.
Urtica (Tourn.) L. Urticaceae (1). 30 temp. (nettles). Herbs with opp. l. and stips. (sometimes united in pairs between the petioles, as in Rubiaceae), usu. covered with stinging hairs. The various types of infl. are well shown in the 3 Brit. sp. In general the infl. is a dich. cyme with tendency to cincinnus by preference of the β-bracteole. In *U. pilulifera* L. (Roman nettle) the ♂ and ♀ infls. spring side by side from each node, the ♂ catkin-like, the ♀ a pseudo-head. In *U. urens*

L. (small nettle) a panicle is formed containing both ♂ and ♀ fls. In *U. dioica* L. (large or common nettle) there is a panicle, but each sex is confined to its own plant. P 4; A 4, opp. to P leaves. The sta. are bent down inwards in the bud, and when ripe spring violently upwards and bend out of the fl., the anther turning inside out, so that the loose powdery pollen is ejected as a little cloud, and may be borne by wind to the stigma. The ♀ fl. has a 1-loc., 1-ovuled ovary with a large brush-like stigma. Achene enclosed in the persistent P. Young tops eaten like spinach. Useful fibre from stems.

Urticaceae (*EP.*; *BH.* incl. *Moraceae*, *Ulmaceae*, *Cynocrambaceae*). Dicots. (Archichl. Urticales). 41 gen., 480 sp., trop. and temp. Most are herbs or undershrubs, with no latex, and with alt. or opp. stip. l. Infl. cymose often 'condensed' into pseudo-heads, &c. Fls. usu. unisexual and reg. P 4—5, free or united, sepaloid; sta. as many, bent down inwards in bud and exploding when ripe; $\underline{G}$ 1-loc. with 1 erect basal orthotr. ov. and 1 style. Achene. Seed usu. with rich oily endosp.; embryo straight. Boehmeria, Urtica, Maoutia and others are used as sources of fibre.

Classification and chief genera (after Engler):

A. With stinging hairs. P (4—5) in ♀. L. alt. or opp.

1. *Urereae:* Urtica, Urera, Laportea.

B. No stinging hairs.

2. *Procrideae* (P of ♀ 3-merous, stigma paint-brush-like): Pilea, Pellionia, Elatostema.
3. *Boehmerieae* (♂ usu. with 4—5 sta. No invol.): Boehmeria, Maoutia.
4. *Parietarieae* (P present; bracts often united in invol.): Parietaria.
5. *Forskohleeae* (♂ fl. reduced to 1 sta.).

Ulmaceae are distinguished by infl., aestivation of sta., and ovule, and Moraceae by presence of latex, and also usu. by ovule, embryo, &c.

Urticales. The 12th order of Archichlamydeae. *Cf.* p. xii.

Urticastrum Fabricius = Laportea Gaudich. (Urtic.).

Urticiflorae (Warming). The 4th order of Choripetalae.

Urucury nut, *Maximiliana.*

Urvillea H. B. et K. Sapind. (1). 10 warm Am. Lianes like Serjania.

Usteria Willd. Loganiaceae. 1 trop. W. Afr.

Ustilago antherarum, *Lychnis.*

Utleria Bedd. Asclepiadaceae (1). 1 S. India.

Utricle, *Cyperaceae.*

Utricularia L. Lentibulariaceae. 210 trop. and temp., the latter all aquatic. Some Brazilian sp. are confined to the pitchers of the Bromeliaceae. 3 in Brit.; *U. vulgaris* L., the bladder-wort, common. The morphology is interesting, for the usual distinctions drawn between root, stem and l. cannot be applied here. The common bladderwort is a submerged water pl. with finely-divided l.; it never has roots, even in the embryo. The fls. project above water on short shoots, and there are also short shoots with small l., which arise from the main axis and grow upwards to the surface. Upon the ordinary submerged l. are borne the bladders, curious hollow structures with trap-door entrances. Small Crustacea and other animals push their way into the bladders and are not able to escape, for the doors only open from outside. The plant takes up the products of the decay of the organisms thus captured; it is very doubtful whether any special ferment is secreted. Other sp. are land pl. with peculiar runners, which develop in the moss or other substratum, on which they grow, and there bear the bladders. Others again, *e.g. U. montana* Poir., are epiph. with water storage in tuberous branches. The l. of all these forms are simple. Goebel (*Pflanzenbiol. Sch.*) has investigated the development of U. and finds that all these parts—l., bladders, runners, water-shoots, erect shoots, &c.—are practically equivalent to one another, and that the same rudiment at the growing point may give rise to any one of them, or that they may themselves change from one to another type. Similarly on germ. a lot of spirally-arranged primary l. are produced, and then one or two water-shoots appear lat. on the growing point, bearing no direct relation to the l. in position, but apparently homologous with them. "Like Genlisea, U. possessed originally a leaf-rosette, ending with an infl., and consisting partly of bladders. Then were added the swimming water-shoots or (in land forms) runners, which though externally unlike leaves (since they develop indefinitely and produce leaves and infls.) yet are originally homologous with them." For further details see Goebel, *loc. cit.* Hibernation in Brit. sp., &c. by winter buds full of reserves, which drop off and sink.

Uvaria L. Anonaceae (1). 100 warm |✻. Mostly lianes with recurved hooks (infl.-axes). The connective of the anther is usu. leafy.

Uvariastrum Engl. Anonaceae (1). 2 W. trop. Afr.

Uvariopsis Engl. ex Engl. et Diels. Anonaceae (1). 1 Cameroons.

Uvarius (Lat.), like a bunch of grapes.

Uva-Ursi Tourn. ex Moench = Arctostaphylos Adans. p.p. (Eric.).

Uvifera L., O. Ktze. = Coccoloba L. (Polygon.).

Uvularia L. Liliaceae (1). 4 E. N. Am. Cult. orn. fl.

Vaccaria Medic. (*Saponaria* p.p. *BH.*). Caryophyll. (II. 2). 3 Eur., W. As.

Vacciniaceae (*BH.*) = Ericaceae (§ III. *Vaccinioideae*).

Vacciniopsis Rusby. Ericaceae (III. 2). 1 Bolivia.

Vaccinium L. (incl. *Oxycoccus* Tourn.). Ericaceae (III. 1). 150 ✻, Andes, Madag. 4 in Brit. *V. Myrtillus* L. the whortle-, bil- or blae-berry, common in hilly districts. *V. uliginosum* L. at high levels. Both have deciduous l. and blue berries. *V. Vitis-Idaea* L., the cow- or whimberry (often called cranberry by error), also a mountain sp., evergr. *V. Oxycoccus* L., the cranberry, in mountain bogs, a trailing evergr. with l. edges rolled back. The fls. resemble Erica, both in structure and mech., but ov. inf.; largely visited by bumble-bees. The fleshy fr. is ed. (used for jams, &c.) and is much distr. by birds. That of the N. Am. sp. *V. pennsylvanicum* Lam. is called blue huckle-berry.

Vagaria Herb. Amaryllidaceae (1). 1 Syria.

Vaginate, sheathed.

Vagnera Adans. (*Smilacina* p.p.). Liliaceae (VII). 10 N. Am.

Vahadenia Stapf (*Landolphia* p.p.). Apocynaceae (I. 1). 1 Congo.

Vahea Lam. (*Landolphia* p.p.). Apocynaceae (I. 1). 2 trop. Afr., Madag.
Vahlia Thunb. Saxifragaceae (I). 4 warm Afr., As. Fls. in pairs (cymes); G̅.
Vahy, *Landolphia madagascariensis* Benth. et Hook. f.
Vailia Rusby. Asclepiadaceae (II. 1). 1 Bolivia.
Vaillantia Tourn. ex L. Rubiaceae (II. 11). 2 Medit.
Valcarcelia Lag. Leguminosae. Nomen.
Valdivia Remy. Saxifragaceae (V). 1 Chili.
Valentiana Rafin. Inc. sed. 1 Abyssinia.
Valentina Speg. Boraginaceae (III). 1 Patagonia.
Valentiniella Speg. (*Valentina* p.p.). Boraginaceae. 1 Patagonia.
Valenzuelia Bert. Sapindaceae (I). 2 Chili, Argentina.
Valerian, *Valeriana*; **red spur -,** *Centranthus*.
Valeriana Tourn. ex L. Valerianaceae. 200 Eur., As., Afr., Am. *V. officinalis* L. and *V. dioica* L. in Brit. (valerian). Fls. protandr. The K forms a pappus upon the fr.
Valerianaceae (*EP.*, *BH.*). Dicots. (Sympet. Rubiales; Asterales *BH.*). 8 gen., 350 sp., Eur., As., Afr., Am. Herbs with exstip. l. and dich. branching. Fls. in cymose panicles, &c., ☿ or unisexual, asymmetric, usu. 5-merous. K sup., little developed at time of flowering, afterwards often forming a pappus as in Compositae; C usu. (5), often spurred at base; A 1—4, epipet., alt. with petals; anthers intr.; G̅ (3); only 1 loc. is fertile, and contains 1 pend. anatr. ov. Achene. Seed exalbum. *Chief genera:* Valerianella, Valeriana, Centranthus.
Valerianella Tourn. ex Hall. (*BH.* incl. *Plectritis* DC.). Valerianaceae. 50 N. temp.; 4 Brit. (corn-salad or lamb's lettuce). Seed-dispersal mech. various. In *V. Auricula* DC. the sterile loc. of the fr., in *V. vesicaria* Moench the K, is inflated, in *V. discoidea* Loisel. it forms a parachute, whilst in others it is provided with hooks.
Valerianopsis C. A. Muell. (*Valeriana* p.p. *EP.*). Valer. 7 Brazil.
Valetonia Durand ex Engl. Icacinaceae. 1 Brazil.
Validallium Small (*Allium* p.p.). Liliaceae (IV). 1 N. Am.
Vallaris Burm. f. Apocynaceae (II. 2). 6 Indomal.
Vallea Mutis ex L. f. Elaeocarpaceae. 3 Colombia, Peru.
Vallecula (Lat.), grooves in fruit.
Vallesia Ruiz et Pav. Apocynaceae (I. 3). 2 Florida to Argentina.
Vallisneria Mich. ex L. Hydrocharitaceae. 3 trop. and subtrop. *V. spiralis* L. (Eur.) a dioec. submerged water-pl. with ribbon l. ♂ fls. in dense spikes enclosed in spathes; when ready to open the fls. break off and float up to the surface, where they open. ♀ fl. sol. on very long stalk, which brings it to the surface; it has green P, inf. ov. and 3 large stigmas. Pollination occurs on the surface (*cf.* Elodea); and after it the stalk curls up into a close spiral, dragging the young fr. to the bottom to ripen. Veg. repr. by runners, rooting at the ends.
Vallota Herb. Amaryllidaceae (I). 1 Cape Colony. Cult. orn. fl.
Valonia, *Quercus Aegilops* L.
Valvate (aestivation), l. touching, not overlapping.
Valves, the portions into which a fruit splits.
Valvular dehiscence (anther), *Berberis*, *Lauraceae*.
Vanclevea Greene (*Grindelia* p.p.). Compositae (3). 1 Utah.

Vancouveria C. Morr. et Dcne. (*Epimedium* p.p. *EP.*). Berberidaceae. 2 N.W. Am.
Vanda Jones. Orchidaceae (II. 20). 25 Indomal. Epiph. with fleshy l., sometimes cylindrical. Cult. orn. fl.
Vandellia L. (*Lindernia* All.). Scrophul. (II. 6). 30 trop., subtrop.
Vandopsis Pfitz. (*Vanda* p.p.). Orchidaceae (II. 20). 8 E. Indomal.
Vangueria Juss. Rubiaceae (II. 1). 40 trop. Afr., As., Madag.
Vanhouttea Lem. (*Houttea* Decne.). Gesneriaceae (II). 4 Brazil.
Vanilla Plum. ex L. Orchidaceae (II. 2). 30 trop. Climbers with fleshy l. and thin velamen (see fam.). *V. planifolia* Andr. (Mex.) is cult.; its pods form the spice vanilla.
Vanilla, *Vanilla planifolia* Andr.; **- grass** (Am.), *Hierochloe*.
Vanillosma Spach = Piptocarpha R. Br. p.p. (Comp.).
Vanillosmopsis Sch.-Bip. Compositae (I). 7 Brazil.
Vaniotia Léveillé. Scrophulariaceae (III. 1). 1 China.
Vanoverberghia Merrill. Zingiberaceae (I). 2 Luzon.
Vantanea Aubl. Humiriaceae. 5 Brazil, Guiana.
Varangevillea Baill. Verbenaceae (5). 1 Madag.
Vargasia Ernst (*Caracasia* Szysz.). Marcgraviaceae. 2 Venezuela.
Variation expresses the fact that no two beings are exactly alike, and that there may exist constant slight differences between two forms, expressed in the idea of *varieties*, *e.g.* a pink and a white variety of the same rose. *Cf.* Nomenclature.
Varilla A. Gray. Compositae (5). 2 Texas, Mexico.
Varnish, a solution of resin in oil of turpentine, alcohol, or other solvent; *cf.* resins; **Chinese - tree**, *Aleurites Fordii* Hemsl.
Varronia P. Br. (*Cordia* p.p.). Boraginaceae (I). 4 W.I.
Varthemia DC. (*Iphiona BH.*). Compositae (4). 4 Egypt to N.W. India.
Vasconcellea A. St Hil. = Carica L. p.p. (Caric.).
Vasconcellosia Caruel (*Carica* p.p. *EP.*). Caricaceae. 1 Brazil.
Vaselia Van Tiegh. (*Elvasia* p.p.). Ochnaceae. 1 Brazil.
Vaseyanthus Cogn. Cucurbitaceae (4). 2 Calif.
Vasivaea Baill. Tiliaceae. 1 Amazon valley.
Vassobia Rusby. Solanaceae (2). 1 Bolivia.
Vateria L. Dipterocarpaceae. 3 Seychelles, S. India. *V. indica* L. yields a gum-resin (Indian copal, white dammar).
Vatica L. Dipterocarpaceae. 45 Indomal. Several yield resins and useful timbers.
Vaupelia Brand (*Trichodesma* p.p.). Boragin. (IV. 1). 6 trop. Afr.
Vauquelinia Correa ex Humb. et Bonpl. Rosaceae (I. 2). 4 Mex., Ariz.
Vausagesia Baill. Ochnaceae. 2 S. trop. Afr.
Vavaea Benth. Meliaceae (III). 5 Polynesia.
Vazea Fr. Allem. ex Mart. Olacaceae (nomen). 1 Brazil.
Veatchia A. Gray. Anacardiaceae (3). 1 California.
Vegaea Urb. Myrsinaceae (II). 1 S. Domingo.
Vegetable (for eating), *cf.* Edible Products; **- horsehair**, *Tillandsia*; **- ivory**, *Palmae*, *Phytelephas*; **- marrow**, *Cucurbita Pepo* L., var.; **- oyster**, *Tragopogon porrifolius* L.; **- sheep**, *Raoulia*.
Vegetation, see Forms of -, Zones of -.

Vegetative reproduction, by the detachment of portions of the veg. system, which may grow into new plants; a branch may be detached without modification (water pl., rhizomes, &c.), or may be specialised, with supplies of reserves; special cases are bulbs, bulbils, corms, tubers, buds, &c.; *Agave* (bulbils), *Agropyron* (rhizomes), *Ajuga* (runners), *Allium*, *Asplenium*, *Begonia* (adv. buds, tubers), *Bellis* (rhizomes), *Bertolonia*, *Bryophyllum* (adv. buds), *Cactaceae* (mammillae), *Carda mine*, *Carex* (off-shoots), *Chlorophytum* (special shoots), *Crassula* (pl. in place of fl.), *Crassulaceae*, *Cystopteris*, *Epilobium*, *Fadyenia*, *Fragaria* (runners), *Gagea*, *Gesneriaceae* (suckers), *Globba*, *Hymenophyllaceae* (gemmae), *Lilium*, *Limnobium*, *Limosella* (runners), *Lycopodium* (bulbils), *Mammillaria* (mammillae), *Mercurialis* (rhizomes), *Nasturtium*, *Nephrolepis*, *Ophioglossum* (adv. buds), *Opuntia* (branches), *Oxalis*, *Polygonum*, *Potentilla*, *Prionium*, *Psilotum* (gemmae), *Ranunculus*, *Remusatia* (hooked bulbils), *Rosaceae*, *Rubus*, *Saccharum*, *Salicaceae* (suckers), *Sempervivum* (offsets), *Senecio* (stem joints), *Sinningia*, *Tussilago*, *Vallisneria*, *Zingiber*.

Veins (of l.), the stiff vascular bundles running throughout.

Veitchia H. Wendl. Palmae (IV. 1). 4 Fiji, New Hebrides.

Velaea DC. (*Arracacia BH.*). Umbelliferae (III. 4). 20 N. Am.

Velamen, *Araceae*, *Orchidaceae*.

Velezia L. Caryophyllaceae (II. 2). 4 Medit. to Afghanistan.

Vella L. Cruciferae (2). 3 W. Medit. Thorns = stems.

Velleia Sm. Goodeniaceae. 18 Austr. Ovary ± sup.

Vellozia Vand. Velloziaceae. 70 trop. Am., esp. campos.

Velloziaceae (*EP.*; *Amaryllidaceae* p.p. *BH.*). Monocotyledons (Liliiflorae). 2 gen., 170 sp., Brazil, Afr., Madag. Xero., chiefly of rocky places or dry campos. Perenn. with dichot. branched stems and l. in rosettes (*cf.* Aloe). Upper parts of stems clothed with fibrous sheaths of old l., lower parts with adv. roots. The stem is thin, but its coating of roots may be inches deep. Water poured over the roots disappears as if into a sponge, and the pl. is thus able to supply itself from dew, &c. during the dry season. The l. also are xero. Fls. sol., term., reg. P 3+3, corolline; A 3+3, or ∞, in bundles. $\overline{G}$ 3-loc., with placenta in the form of lamellae, ± peltately widened or thickened at the outer side. Ovules ∞. Caps. Endosp. *Genera:* Vellozia, Barbacenia. Chief differences from Amaryllid. in A and plac.

Velloziella Baill. (*Digitalis* p.p.). Scrophul. (III. 1). 1 Brazil.

Velophylla Benj. Clarke. Podostemaceae. 1 Brazil.

Veltheimia Gleditsch. Liliaceae (V). 3 S. Afr. Cult. orn. fl.

Velutinus (Lat.), velvety.

Velvet bean, *Mucuna*; **-bur** (W.I.), *Priva*; **-grass** (Am.), *Holcus lanatus* L.; **-leaf** (W.I.), *Cissampelos Pareira* L.; **-seed** (W.I.), *Guettarda*; **-tamarind**, *Dialium*.

Velvitsia Hiern. Scrophulariaceae (III. 2). 1 Angola.

Venation, arrangemeut of the veins in a l.

Venegasia DC. Compositae (6). 1 California.

Venenatus (Lat.), poisonous.

Venice turpentine, *Larix europea* DC.

Venidium Less. (*Arctotis* p.p. *EP.*). Compositae (10). 18 S. Afr.

Venose, with veins.

Ventenata Koel. Gramineae (9). 3 Eur., As. Minor.

Ventilago Gaertn. Rhamnaceae. 10 palaeotrop. Some climb by hooks. Fr. with wing on upper end, formed from style after fert.

Ventral (surface), upper, towards axis, but not consistently used.

Ventricose (C), with basal part swollen out all round.

Venulose, thickly veined.

Venus' comb, *Scandix*; **- flytrap**, *Dionaea*; **- looking glass**, *Specularia*.

Veprecella Naud. Melastomaceae (I). 20 Madag.

Vepris Comm. ex A. Juss. (*Toddalia BH.*). Rutaceae (IV). 6 palaeotrop.

Veratrilla Franch. Gentianaceae (I). 1 China.

Veratrin, *Schoenocaulon*, *Veratrum*.

Veratrum (Tourn.) L. Liliaceae (1). 50 N. temp. Rhiz. with leafy stem and racemes, lower fls. ☿, but upper usu. ♂ by abortion (*andromonoecism*). Sometimes pl. occur with ♂ fls. only. Protandr. Seeds with membranous border. Veratrin is obtained from the rhiz.; that of *V. album* L. is known as white hellebore root.

Verbascum Tourn. ex L. Scrophulariaceae (I. 1). 210 N. temp. |✻; 6 Brit. (mullein). Large perenn. herbs with stout tap-roots, wrinkled like Taraxacum. Infl. primarily racemose, but lat. fls. often replaced by condensed dichasia (*cf.* Labiatae). For structure and diagram see fam. Fls. visited for pollen by bees and drone-flies. Those of several formerly officinal (flores Verbasci).

Verbena Linn. Verbenaceae (I). 100 trop. and temp. *V. officinalis* L., the vervain (Brit.), was formerly in great repute as a remedy in eye-diseases, its bright-eyed C, like that of Euphrasia, being supposed, under the old doctrine of signatures, to indicate its virtues in that direction. Several cult. orn. perf. fl.

Verbena oil, *Lippia*, *Cymbopogon*.

Verbenaceae (*EP.*; *BH.* incl. *Phrymaceae*). Dicots. (Sympet. Tubiflorae; Lamiales *BH.*). About 70 gen., 750 sp., almost all trop. and subtrop. Herbs, shrubs or trees; many lianes, *e.g.* sp. of Lantana, Clerodendron, Vitex; xero. also, often armed with thorns, frequent. L. usu. opp., rarely whorled or alt., entire or divided, exstip. Infl. racemose or cymose, in the former case most often a spike or head, often with an invol. of coloured bracts. The cymes usu. dich. with a cincinnus tendency (*cf.* Caryophyllaceae); sometimes they also form heads.

Fl. usu. ☿, ·|·, usu. 5-merous. K (5) [or (4—8)], hypog.; C (5), usu. with narrow tube, rarely campanulate, often 2-lipped; A 4, didynamous, rarely 5 or 2, or of equal length, alt. with C-lobes, with intr. anthers; $\underline{G}$ usu. (2), rarely (4) or (5), usu. 4-lobed, originally 2- (or more) loc., but very early divided into 4 (or more) loc. by the formation of a 'false' septum in each loc. (*cf.* Labiatae); plac. axile, with 2 ov. per cpl. (*i.e.* 1 in each loc. after septation); ovules ana- to ortho-tr., basal, lat. or pend., but always with the micropyle directed downwards. Style term., rarely ± sunk between lobes of ovary (contrast Labiatae); stigma usu. lobed. Fr. generally a drupe, more rarely a caps. or schizocarp. Seed usu. exalbum.

Several are useful as sources of timber, *e.g.* Tectona. See also Lippia, Priva, Clerodendron, &c., for other economic uses.

Classification and chief genera (after Briquet):

A. Infl. spicate or racemose. Ovule usu. basal, erect, anatr.

1. *Verbeneae* (no endosperm): Verbena, Lantana, Lippia, Priva, Petraea, Citharexylum.
2. *Stilbeae* (endosperm): Stilbe.

B. Infl. of cymose type. Cymes often united into panicles, corymbs, &c.; if axillary, often reduced to 1 fl.

a. Ovule lat. (sometimes very high up) semi-anatr. Ovary fully or imperfectly 4—10-loc.

3. *Chloantheae* (fr. usu. drupaceous, never caps.; endosperm): Chloanthes.
4. *Viticeae* (as 3, but no endosperm): Callicarpa, Tectona, Vitex, Clerodendron.
5. *Caryopterideae* (fr. caps.-like, 4-valved; the valves fall taking the stones with them or loosen them from the placental axis): Caryopteris.

b. Ovule apical, pend., orthotr.

6. *Symphoremeae* (ov. 2-loc. to centre; fr. dry, 1-seeded): Symphorema.
7. *Avicennieae* (ov. imperfectly 4-loc.; fr. caps., 2-valved, 1-seeded; mangroves): Avicennia (only gen.).

Verbesina L. Compositae (5). 80 warm Am.

Verdickia De Wild. Liliaceae (III). 1 Congo.

Vereia Andr. = Kalanchoe Adans. (Crass.).

Verhuellia Miq. Piperaceae. 2 W.I.

Verinea Merino. Gramineae (8). 1 Spain.

Verlotia Fourn. (*Marsdenia EP.*). Asclepiadaceae (II. 3). 5 Brazil.

Vermiform, worm-shaped.

Vernal grass, sweet, *Anthoxanthum odoratum* L.

Vernalis (Lat.), of Spring.

Vernation (arrangement of l. in bud), *cf.* Leaf.

Vernonia Schreb. Compositae (1). 650 Am., Afr., As., very common in grassy places. Style typical of § 1 (*cf.* classification of C.).

Veronica (Tourn.) L. Scrophulariaceae (III. 1). 250 extra-trop., many alpine; 17 in Brit. (speedwell). The Brit. sp. are herbaceous (often woody below); fls. in term. or lat. racemes. The post. sepal of the 5 typical of this fam. is absent, and the two post. petals are united into one large one, so that the P is 4-merous (see fam. for diagram). The 2 sta. and style project horiz. from the rotate C. A small percentage of fls. exhibit a different number of parts (*e.g.* 5 petals). The fert. of the fl. in *V. Chamaedrys* L., the commonest Brit. sp., is performed chiefly by drone-flies. The style projects over the lower petal, while the two sta. project lat. Honey is secreted at the base of the ovary and concealed by the hairs at the mouth of the short tube. Insects alighting on the lower petal touch the style and grasp the bases of the sta., thus causing the anthers to move inwards and dust them with pollen. The peduncles stand close up against the main stem of the raceme whilst the fls. are in bud, diverge as the fls. open, and again close up as they wither. Caps. with a few flattened seeds suited to wind-distr. In *V. arvensis* L. and other sp. that live in damp places, the capsule merely cracks as it dries and only opens so far as to allow the seeds to escape when thoroughly wetted; the seeds then become slimy (*cf.* Linum).

Many exotic sp. are shrubby, with handsome spikes of fls.; often cult. In N.Z. the genus is char. alpine; 81 sp. occur, of which 77 are endemic. Some are small trees; most are shrubby. Many, *e.g.* *V. cupressoides* Hook. f., are xero. with reduced l. appressed to stem, so that the twigs resemble those of Cupressus and other Coniferae.

Veronicastrum Heist. ex Fabr. = Veronica Tourn. (Scroph.).

Verreauxia Benth. Goodeniaceae. 3 W. Austr. Nut.

Verrucose, warty.

Verrucularia A. Juss. Malpighiaceae (II). 1 Bahia.

Versatile (anther), balanced on filament, forming a T.

Verschaffeltia H. Wendl. Palmae (IV. 1). 1 Seychelles.

Versicolor (Lat.), changing colour.

Versteggia Valeton. Rubiaceae (II. 4). 1 New Guinea.

Verticil, a whorl; **-aster**, false-, *Labiatae*; **-late**, in whorls.

Verticillatae. The 1st order of Dicots. Archichl.

Verticordia DC. Myrtaceae (II. 2). 40 Austr., esp. W.

Vervain, *Verbena officinalis* L.

Vesicaria Tourn. ex Adans. Cruciferae (4). 2 Eur.

Vesicular, as if of small bladders.

Vesselowskya Pampanini (*Geissois* p.p.). Cunoniaceae. 1 Austr.

Vestia Willd. Solanaceae (4). 1 Chili.

Vestigial organs, functionless rudiments.

Vetch, *Vicia*; **kidney-**, *Anthyllis*; **milk-**, *Astragalus*.

Vetiver, khus-khus, *Vetiveria zizanioides* Stapf.

Vetiveria Thou. (*Andropogon* p.p.). Gramineae (2). 8 palaeotrop., incl. *V. zizanioides* Stapf, the khus-khus (*A. squarrosus* L. f., *A. muricatus* Retz), whose roots are woven into fragrant mats, baskets, fans, &c., which give off scent when sprinkled with water.

Vexillaria Hoffmgg. = Centrosema DC. (Legum.).

Vexillum, *Leguminosae*.

Viable, capable of germination.

Viborgia Thunb. (*Cytisus* p.p.). Leguminosae (III. 3). 7 S. Afr.

Viburnum L. Caprifoliaceae. 110 temp. and subtrop., esp. As., N. Am. Winter buds of some naked, *i.e.* with no scale-l. The outer fls. of the cymose corymb are neuter in some, *e.g.* *V. opulus* L. (guelder-rose), having a large C, but at cost of essential organs. In the cult. guelder-rose all the fls. are neuter.

Vicarya Stocks. Inc. sed. Nomen.

Vicatia DC. Umbelliferae (III. 4). 3 Himalaya.

Vicia Tourn. ex L. Leguminosae (III. 9). 150 N. temp., and S. Am.; 10 in Brit. (vetch, tare). Most are climbers with leaf-tendrils. Fl. mech. typical of many L. Pollen early shed by anthers into apex of keel; upon style, below stigma, is a brush of hairs which carries out the pollen when keel is depressed (see fam.). *V. sativa* L. and many other vetches are valuable fodder pl.; *V. Faba* L. is the broad bean, with its many vars.

Vicoa Cass. (*Inula* p.p. *EP.*). Compositae (4). 6 trop. As., Afr.

Victoria Lindl. Nymphaeaceae (III). 3 trop. Am. *V. regia* Lindl. is the giant water-lily of the Amazon; it has the habit of Nymphaea, but is of enormous size. The floating l. may be 2 m. across; the edge is turned up to a height of several cm., and on the lower side the ribs project and are armed with spines. Fl. like Nymphaea but fully epig. Fr. also similar; the seeds contain both endo- and peri-sperm. They are roasted and eaten in Brazil. The plant is now cult.; it was discovered in 1801, but not brought into general notice till 1837.

Vieraea Sch.-Bip. Compositae (4). 1 Canaries.

Vieusseuxia D. Delaroche = Moraea Mill. p.p. (Irid.).

Vigna Savi. Leguminosae (III. 10). 50 trop. *V. sinensis* Endl. is the cherry-bean or cow-pea (trop. As.); pods eaten like French beans. *V. Catjang* Endl. (blackeye pea) is also cult.

Vignea Beauv. = Carex Dill. (Cyper.).

Vigneopsis De Wild. Leguminosae (III. 10). 1 Congo.

Vignidula Börner = Carex Dill. p.p. (Cyper.).

Viguiera H. B. et K. Compositae (5). 80 warm Am., W.I.

Vilfa Beauv. = Sporobolus R. Br. (Gram.).

Villadia Rose (*Cotyledon*, &c. p.p.). Crassulaceae. 12 Mexico.

Villamilla Ruiz et Pav. (*Rivina* p.p. *EP.*). Phytolacc. 4 trop. Am.

Villanova Lag. Compositae (6). 8 Arizona to Chili.

Villaresia Ruiz et Pav. Icacinaceae. 10 Brazil, Chili. *V. Congonha* (DC.) Miers is used like maté (Ilex).

Villaria Rolfe. Rubiaceae (I. 8). 1 Phil. Is.

Villarsia Vent. Gentianaceae (II). 1 Cape Col., 9 Austr. The water plant often known under this name is a Limnanthemum.

Villebrunia Gaudich. Urticaceae (3). 8 Ceylon to Japan. *V. integrifolia* Gaudich. yields a good fibre.

Villose, villous, with long weak hairs.

Villouratea Van Tiegh. Ochnaceae. 1 Brazil.

Vilmorinia DC. Leguminosae (III. 6). 1 S. Domingo.

Vilshenica Thou. Inc. sed. Nomen.

Vimen P. Br. Inc. sed. Nomen.

Viminaria Sm. Leguminosae (III. 2). 1 Austr.

Vimineous, with long flexible twigs.

Vinca L. (*BH.* incl. *Lochnera* Rchb.). Apocynaceae (I. 3). 5 Eur., W. As. *V. minor* L. and *V. major* L., the periwinkles, nat. in England. The anthers stand above the stigmatic disc, but the stigma itself is on the under surface, so that self-fert. is not caused as the insect's tongue enters the fl.

Vincetoxicopsis Costantin. Asclepiadaceae (II. 3). 1 Indochina.

Vincetoxicum Rupp. (*Cynanchum* p.p. *EP.*). Asclepiadaceae (II. 1). 40 warm.

Vine, *Vitis*; (in U.S.) any climbing or running stem.

Vinegar, *Borassus*, *Cocos*, *Vitis*, &c.

Viola Tourn. ex Linn. Violaceae. 400 cosmop., chiefly N. temp. Several in Brit. *V. odorata* L. and *V. canina* L. are the sweet and dog violets, *V. tricolor* L. the pansy or heart's-ease, and others are also well known. Many sp. and vars. cult. Herbs with large stips., on which glands sometimes occur. Fls. usu. one in each axil; sometimes (*e.g.* *V. tricolor*) a veg. shoot arises above the fl. in the same axil. The intr. anthers form a close ring round the ovary, below the style, which ends in a variously shaped head on whose ant. surface is the stigma, often a hollow pocket. The lower pet. forms a landing-place and is often prolonged backwards into a spur, in which collects honey, secreted by processes projecting into it from the lower sta. Honey guides show as streaks upon the C leading to nectaries. These fls. are as a rule incapable of self-fert. In *V. tricolor* the pollen is shed on to the ant. pet., and the lower edge of the stigma is guarded by a flap which the insect, when withdrawing, closes; and thus the fl.'s own pollen does not reach the stigma. The small-flowered sub-species *V. arvensis* Murr. has not this flap and fertilises itself. In *V. odorata* the stigma is merely the bent-over end of the style, and is first touched as the insect enters. The size, colour, &c. of the flower of this sp. and of *V. canina* render them suited to bees.

In many, *e.g. V. canina, V. odorata, V. sylvestris*, Lam., the fls. are rarely visited, and little seed is set. They usu. flower early in the season; later on appears a second form of fl. on the same pl. These are the *cleistogamic* fls., which never open, but set seed by self-fert. In *V. canina* this fl. looks like a bud; the seps. remain shut, there are 5 minute pets., 2 ant. sta. with anthers containing a little pollen (only enough for fert.—there is no waste as in open fls.) and 3 other abortive sta.; pistil much as usual. The anthers are closely appressed to the stigma; the pollen-grains germinate within them, and the tubes burrow through the anther-walls into the stigma. *V. odorata* has similar fls., but with all 5 sta. fertile. The production of these fls. ensures the setting of seed.

Fr. a 3-valved capsule; seeds very hard and slippery. One plac. with its seeds remains attached to each valve; as this dries it bends upwards into a U-shape, squeezing the seeds against one another and shooting them out (cf. Claytonia, Buxus).

Violaceae (*EP.*, *BH.* incl. *Sauvagesieae* of Ochnaceae). Dicots. (Archichl. Parietales). 15 gen., 800 sp., cosmop. Annual or perennial herbs, or shrubs. L. alt., stip., usu. undivided. Fls. 1 or 2 in each axil, in usu. racemose infls., bracteolate, ☿, usu. ·|·. K 5, persistent; C 5, hypog., usu. ·|·, the ant. petal often spurred to hold the honey, with descending aestivation; A 5, alt. with petals, hypog., forming a ring round the ovary; filament very short, anther intr., connective usu. with membranous prolongation; $\underline{G}$ (3), 1-loc. with 1—∞ anatr. ov. on each of the parietal plac. Style simple. Fr. a 3-valved loculic. caps. Endosp. *Chief genera:* Alsodeia, Viola.

Violarieae (*BH.*), Violaceae and *Sauvagesieae* of Ochnaceae.

Violet, *Viola*; **African -**, *Saintpaulia*; **dame's -**, *Hesperis*; **essence of -**, *Iris florentina* L.; **water -**, *Hottonia*.

Viorna Reichb. (*Clematis* p.p.). Ranunculaceae (3). 15 N. Am.

Viper's bugloss, *Echium vulgare* L.

Virchowia Schenk (*Ilysanthes* p.p. *EP.*). Scrophular. (II. 6). 1 Cuba.

Virea Adans. = Leontodon L. p.p. (Comp.).

Virecta Afzel ex Sm. Rubiaceae (I. 2). 10 trop. Afr.

Virens (Lat.), green.

Virgatus (Lat.), twiggy.

Virgilia Lam. Leguminosae (III. 1). 1 Cape Colony. Useful wood.

Virginian cowslip (Am.), *Mertensia virginica* DC.; **- creeper**, *Parthe-*

nocissus; **-snakeroot** (Am.), *Aristolochia Serpentaria* L.; **-stock**, *Malcomia maritima* Ait.

Virgin's bower (Am.), *Clematis.*

Virgularia Ruiz et Pav. = Gerardia L. (Scroph.).

Viridescens (Lat.), greenish; **viridis** (Lat.), green.

Virola Aubl. (*Myristica* p.p. *BH.*). Myristicaceae. 27 trop. Am.

Viscago Hall. = Silene L. (Caryoph.).

Viscainoa Greene. Zygophyllaceae. 1 Lower California.

Viscaria Riv. ex Rupp. (*Lychnis* p.p. *BH.*). Caryophyllaceae (II. 1). 5 N. temp. *V. viscosa* Aschers. (catchfly) Brit.

Viscid, viscosus (Lat.), sticky.

Viscin, *Loranthaceae, Viscum.*

Viscum Tourn. ex L. Loranthaceae (II). 20 |✻. *V. album* L. in Brit. (mistletoe) is a semiparasitic shrubby evergr., growing on apple, hawthorn, oak, &c., and drawing nourishment from its host by suckers. It is repeatedly branched in a dich. manner, the central stalk usu. ending in an infl. Each branch bears two green leathery l., and repres. a year's growth. The unisexual dioec. fls. are in groups of three. No calyculus. Sta. completely fused to the P-leaf. Pollen-sacs very numerous. Ovary as usual. The fls. secrete honey and are visited by flies. Pseudo-berry. The layer of viscin prevents the bird that eats the berry from swallowing the seed, which it scrapes off its bill on to a branch, where it adheres and germinates.

Visenia Houtt. = Melochia Dill. p.p. (Sterc.).

Visiania DC. = Ligustrum Tourn. (Olea.).

Vismia Vand. Guttiferae (II). 27 trop. Am.

Visnea L. f. Theaceae. 1 Canaries.

Vitaceae (*EP.*; *Ampelidaceae BH.*). Dicots. (Archichl. Rhamnales; Celastrales *BH.*). 11 gen., 450 sp., mostly trop. and subtrop. Climbing or rarely erect shrubs, with alt. stip. l. Infl. cymose, usu. complex; bracteoles present. Fl. reg., ☿ or not. K (4—5), small and cup-like, very slightly lobed; C 4—5, valvate, often united at the tips and falling off as a hood upon the opening of the bud; A 4—5, opp. to the petals, at the base of a hypog. disc, with intr. anthers; $\underline{G}$ usu. (2), rarely 3—6, multi-loc. with usually 2 collat. anatr. ov., erect with ventral raphe. Berry. Endosp.; embryo straight. Vitis is economically important. *Chief genera:* Vitis, Leea.

Vitaeda Börner = Ampelopsis p.p. (Vit.).

Vitellaria Gaertn. f. (*Lucuma BH.*). Sapotaceae (I). 15 trop. Am. *V. mammosa* Radlkf. (marmalade tree) ed. fr.

Vitex Tourn. ex L. Verbenaceae (4). 75 trop. and temp.

Viticella Dill., Small (*Clematis* p.p. *BH.*). Ranuncul. (3). 1 Eur.

Vitiphoenix Becc. (*Hydriastele* p.p. *EP.*). Palmae (IV. 1). 1 Fiji.

Vitis (Tourn.) L. (*BH.* incl. *Ampelopsis* Michx., *Cissus* L., *Quinaria* Rafin.). Vitaceae. 40 $\underline{✻}$. The vines are climbing pl., with tendrils which repres. modified infls.; the stem is usu. regarded as a sympodium, each axis in turn ending in a tendril, but there has been much argument upon the subject. The tendril may attach itself by the ordinary coiling method, or may be negatively heliotropic and thus force its way into the crevices of the support: in these crevices the tips of the tendrils form large balls of tissue, the outer parts of which become mucilaginous and cement the tendril to its support. *V. vinifera* L. (Orient, N.W. India) is the cult. grape, cult. in most warm countries. About 3000 million gallons of wine are made every year. When dried the fruits form raisins; the sultana raisin is a seedless var. The currants of commerce are the fruit of the Corinthian variety (currant is a corruption of Corinth). *V. aestivalis* Michx. (summer-grape) and *V. Labrusca* L. (fox-grape) are N. Am. sp. which have been largely introduced into Eur., as they resist the attacks of the dreaded insect, Phylloxera, better than the Eur. sp. For Virginian creepers *cf.* Parthenocissus.

Vitis-Idaea Tourn. ex Moench = Vaccinium L. p.p. (Eric.).

Vittadinia A. Rich. Compositae (3). 8 New Guinea, Austr., New Caled., N.Z., S. Am. (Australian daisy).

Vittae, *cf. Umbelliferae.*

Vittaria Sm. Polypodiaceae. 50 trop. and subtrop.

Vittate, striped lengthwise.

Viviania Cav. Geraniaceae. 30 S. Am.

Vivipary, germination in the fr., *cf.* Mangroves; also applied to many cases of veg. repr. (*q.v.*), esp. by bulbils.

Voacanga Thou. Apocynaceae (I. 3). 20 Malaya, Madag., Afr.

Voandzeia Thou. Leguminosae (III. 10). 1 trop. Afr., Madag., *V. subterranea* Thou.; it buries its young fr. like Arachis. The seed is ed. and the pl. is largely cult. (Bambarra groundnut).

Vochisia Juss. (*Vochysia* Poir.). Vochysiaceae. 54 trop. Am.

Vochysiaceae (*EP.*, *BH.* incl. *Trigoniaceae*). Dicots. (Archichl. Geraniales; Polygalineae *BH.*). 5 gen., 80 sp., trop. Am. Trees and shrubs, rarely herbs, with opp. or whorled simple l., with or without stips. Fls. ☿, typically 5-merous, obliquely ·|·; K united at base, deciduous, one sepal often spurred; C usu. 3—1, perig. or epig.; 1 fertile sta. and stds.; cpls. (3) each with ∞—2 ov. with 2 integuments. Fr. indeh. or a loculic. caps.; no endosp. *Chief genus* Vochisia.

Vogelia Lam. Plumbaginaceae. 3 S. Afr. to India.

Voharanga Costantin et Bois. Asclepiadaceae (II. 1). 1 Madag.

Vohemaria Buchenau. Asclepiadaceae (II. 1). 1 Madag.

Volatile oils, *cf.* Oils.

Volkameria L. = Clerodendron L. p.p. (Verben.).

Volkensia O. Hoffm. Compositae (1). 1 E. trop. Afr.

Volkensiella H. Wolff. Umbelliferae (III. 5). 1 E. C. Afr.

Volkensiophyton Lindau. Acanthaceae (IV. A). 1 E. trop. Afr.

Volkensteinia Van Tiegh. (*Gomphia* p.p.). Ochnaceae. 2 Brazil.

Volubilis (Lat.), twining.

Volutarella Cass. (*Centaurea* p.p. *EP.*). Compositae (11). 5 Medit. to India.

Vonitra Becc. (*Dypsis* p.p.). Palmae (IV. 1). 2 Madag.

Vonroemeria J. J. Smith. Orchidaceae (II. 15). 1 New Guinea.

Vossia Wall. et Griff. Gramineae (2). 1 trop. As., Afr. A swimming grass, which with *Saccharum spontaneum* L. makes the great grass bars of the Nile.

Vossianthus O. Ktze. = Sparmannia L. (Tili.).

Votomita Aubl. Inc. sed. 1 Guiana.

Vouacapoua Aubl. (*Andira* Lam. *q.v.*). Legum. (III. 8). 25 trop. Am., Afr.

Vouapa Aubl. (*Macrolobium* Schreb.). Legum. (II. 3). 20 trop. Am., Afr.

Voyara Aubl. Inc. sed. 1 Guiana.

Vouarana Aubl. (*Cupania* p.p. *BH.*). Sapindaceae (I). 1 Guiana, Braz.

Voyria Aubl. (*BH.* incl. *Leiphaimos* Cham. et Schlecht. *Voyriella* Miq.). Gentianaceae (I). 3 Guiana.

Voyriella Miq. Gentianaceae (I). 1 Guiana, N. Brazil.

Vriesia Lindl. (*Tillandsia* p.p. *BH.*). Bromeliaceae (I). 60 trop. Am. Cult.

Vrydagzynea Blume. Orchidaceae (II. 2). 12 Malaya, Polynesia.

Vulcanisation of rubber, its combination with sulphur, &c.

Vulgaris (Lat.), common.

Vulneraria Tourn. ex Hall. = Anthyllis Riv. p.p. (Legum.).

Vulpia C. C. Gmel. = Festuca Tourn. p.p. (Gram.). 25 temp.

Vuylstekeara × Hort. Orchidaceae. Hybrid of Cochlioda, Miltonia and Odontoglossum.

W (fl. class), fls. fertilised by wind, cf. Pollination; *Artemisia*, *Betulaceae*, *Calluna*, *Carex*, *Casuarina*, *Coniferae*, *Corylus*, *Cycadaceae*, *Cyperaceae*, *Elaeagnaceae*, *Empetrum*, *Fraxinus*, *Gramineae*, *Humulus*, *Juglandaceae*, *Juncaceae*, *Mercurialis*, *Platanus*, *Potamogeton*, *Quercus*, *Rumex*, *Sparganium*, *Spinacia*, *Thalictrum*, *Triglochin*, *Typhaceae*, *Ulmaceae*, *Urticaceae*, *Zea*.

Waahoo (Am.), *Euonymus atropurpureus* Jacq.

Wachendorfia Burm. Haemodoraceae. 7 Cape Colony. Transv. zygomorphism in fl. but not obvious on account of twisting of stalk.

Wagatea Dalz. Leguminosae (II. 7). 1 S.W. India.

Wageneria Klotzsch = Begonia Tourn. p.p. (Begon.).

Wahlenbergia Schrad. (*BH.* incl. *Hedraeanthus* Griseb.). Campanulaceae (I. 1). 120 chiefly S. temp. *W. hederacea* Rchb. (*Campanula hederacea* L.), the ivy-leaved bell-flower, in Brit. Fl. like Campanula. Capsule loculic. (the chief difference between these two gen.).

Wailesia Lindl. (*Dipodium BH.*). Orchidaceae (II. 17). 2 Malaya.

Waitzia Wendl. Compositae (4). 6 S. and W. temp. Austr.

Wake robin, *Arum maculatum* L., (Am.) *Trillium*.

Walafrida (*Selago* p.p. *BH.*). Scrophular. (II. 7). 35 S. and trop. Afr.

Waldheimia Kar. et Kir. (*Allardia BH.*). Compositae (7). 8 Himal.

Waldsteinia Willd. Rosaceae (III. 2). 4 N. temp.

Walking-fern, *Asplenium rhizophyllum* Kunze; **-sticks**, *cf. Bamboos*, *Arundo*, *Rattans*, *Zanthoxylum*, &c.

Wall flower, *Cheiranthus Cheiri* L.; **-pepper**, *Sedum*; **-spleenwort** *Asplenium Ruta-muraria* L.

Wallaba, *Eperua falcata* Aubl.

Wallacea Spruce. Ochnaceae. 1 Amazon valley.

Wallaceodendron Koorders. Leguminosae (I. 1). 1 Celebes.

Wallenia Sw. Myrsinaceae (II). 15 W.I.

Walleria J. Kirk. Amaryllidaceae (III). 4 trop. Afr., Madag.

Wallichia Roxb. Palmae (IV. 1). 3 Himal. to Malaya.

Walnut, *Juglans regia* L.; **country -**, *Aleurites*; **East Indian -**, *Albizzia Lebbek* Benth.; **Otaheite -** (W.I.), *Aleurites*; **satin -**, *Liquidambar styraciflua* L.
Walpersia Harv. et Sond. Leguminosae (III. 3). 1 S. Afr.
Walsura Roxb. Meliaceae (III). 15 Indomal.
Waltheria L. Bombacaceae (Sterculiaceae *BH.*). 30 trop. Am.
Waluewa Regel (*Oncidium* p.p. *EP.*). Orchidaceae (II. 19). 1 Brazil.
Wampi, *Clausena Wampi* Oliv.
Wangenheimia Moench. Gramineae (10). 1 Spain, N. Afr.
Wangerinia Franz (*Calandrinia* p.p.). Portulacaceae. 1 Chili.
Wara, *Calotropis gigantea* Ait.
Warburgia Engl. Winteranaceae. 1 E. Afr.
Wardenia King. Araliaceae (1). 1 Malay Peninsula.
Warea Nutt. Cruciferae (1). 2 Florida.
Warionia Benth. et Coss. Compositae (12). 1 N.W. Sahara.
Warmingia Reichb. f. Orchidaceae (II. 19). 2 Brazil.
Warneckea Gilg. Melastomaceae (III). 1 E. trop. Afr.
Warpuria Stapf. Acanthaceae (IV. A). 1 Madag.
Warrea Lindl. Orchidaceae (II. 10). 2 Peru, Colombia.
Warreella Schlechter. Orchidaceae (II. 14). 2 Guiana, Colombia.
Warszewiczella Reichb. f. (*Zygopetalum* p.p. *BH.*). Orchidaceae (II. β. 11). 10 Peru, Colombia, C. Am., W.I. Cult. orn. fl.
Warscewiczia Klotzsch. Rubiaceae (I. 3). 4 trop. Am., W.I.
Wart cress (Am.), *Senebiera*; **- herb** (W.I.), *Rhynchosia*.
Wasabia Matsumura (*Eutrema* p.p.). Cruciferae (2). 2 Japan.
Washingtonia Rafin. (*Osmorhiza* Rafin.). Umbelliferae (III. 2). 12 N. Am.
Washingtonia H. Wendl. (*Pritchardia* p.p. *EP.*). Palmae (I. 2). 2 S. Calif., Arizona.
Washingtonia Winsl. = Sequoia Endl. (Conif.).
Wasp flowers, *Cotoneaster*, *Epipactis*, *Ficus*, *Hedera*, *Scrophularia*, *Symphoricarpus*.
Water arum (Am.), *Calla*; **- avens**, *Geum*; **- carriage** of seeds, *cf.* Dispersal; **- chestnut**, *Trapa*; **- chinquepin** (Am.), *Nelumbium*; **- coconut**, *Nipa*; **- cress**, *Nasturtium officinale* R. Br.; **- crowfoot**, *Ranunculus*; **- daffodil**, *Sternbergia*; **- dropwort**, *Oenanthe*; **- grass**, *Panicum molle* Sw.; **- hemlock**, *Cicuta*; **- hyacinth**, *Eichhornia crassipes* Solms; **- hyssop** (W.I.), *Herpestis*; **-leaf**, *Hydrophyllum*; **- lemon**, *Passiflora laurifolia* L.; **- lettuce**, *Pistia*; **- lily**, *Nymphaea*, *Nuphar*, *Victoria*; **- melon**, *Citrullus vulgaris* Schrad.; **- milfoil**, *Myriophyllum*; **- nymph** (Am.), *Nymphaea*; **- parsnip**, *Sium*; **- pennywort** (Am.), *Hydrocotyle*; **- pepper**, *Elatine*; **- pimpernel** (Am.), *Samolus*; **- plantain**, *Alisma Plantago* L.; **- plants**, see separate article below; **- pores**, *Conocephalus*, *Saxifraga*, *Spathodea*; **- rice**, *Zizania*; **- soldier**, *Stratiotes*; **- starwort**, *Callitriche*; **- storage**, *cf.* Xerophytes; **- thyme**, *Elodea*; **- vine** (W.I.), *Doliocarpus*, &c.; **- violet**, *Hottonia*; **- weed**, *Elodea*; **- willow** (Am.), *Dianthera*; **- wort** (Am.), *Elatine*.
Water plants (*hydrophytes*), a well-marked form of veg., contrasting with meso- and xero-phytes. All in this book are derived from land pl.; many are very old, widely dispersed. They show rapid

growth, frequent branching, much veg. repr. They have no rigid anatomy, and are marked by absence of cuticle, stomata, &c., and by presence of enormous intercellular spaces. The l. shows 4 types, (1) the floating l. of *Hydrocharis*, *Nymphaeaceae*, *Ranunculus*, *Trapa*, &c., a round l. with cuticle and stomata above; (2) the awl-shaped type of submerged l. of *Isoetes*, *Lobelia*, *Subularia*, &c., plants which can often survive upon land; (3) the ribbon type of most Monocots., *e.g.* *Vallisneria*, *Potamogeton*, *Ruppia*, *Zostera*; (4) the much divided type with linear segments, *Bidens*, *Ceratophyllum*, *Myriophyllum*, *Podostemaceae*, *Ranunculus*, *Trapa*, &c. Heterophylly is common, *cf.* *Cabomba*, *Callitriche*, *Potamogeton*, *Ranunculus*, *Sagittaria*, *Salvinia*, *Trapa*, &c.

Many hibernate by buds formed at the ends of branches, full of reserves, *e.g.* *Hydrocharis*, *Myriophyllum*, *Potamogeton* sp., *Utricularia*, by tubers, *Potamogeton*, sp., *Sagittaria*, by rhizomes, *Potamogeton*, sp., *Nymphaeaceae*. *Cf.* *Lemnaceae*.

Most are perennials; annuals in *Marsilea*, *Naias*, *Subularia*. Fls. usu. wind- or insect-pollinated, but *Ruppia*, *Zostera*, &c. are fert. under water. The seeds usu. sink, and often show interesting features in germination. A few *amphibious* pl. exist, which can also live on land, *e.g.* *Littorella*, *Polygonum*. In the trop. occur the interesting fams. *Hydrostachyaceae*, *Podostemaceae*, and *Tristichaceae* (*q.v.*), in swift water.

Cf. also *Aldrovanda*, *Alismaceae*, *Aponogeton*, *Araceae*, *Azolla*, *Butomaceae*, *Eichhornia*, *Elatinaceae*, *Elodea*, *Hippuris*, *Hydrocleys*, *Jussieua*, *Lemna*, *Limnanthemum*, *Limnobium*, *Nelumbium*, *Nipa*, *Nuphar*, *Nymphaea*, *Peplis*, *Pistia*, *Pontederiaceae*, *Potamogetonaceae*, *Rumex*, *Samolus*, *Sesbania*, *Stratiotes*, *Victoria*, *Zannichellia*, &c., and see Schenk, *Die Wassergewächse*, and Schimper's and Warming's *Plant Geography*, Arber's *Water Plants*, &c.

Watsonamra O. Ktze., Standley (*Pentagonia* Benth.). Rubiaceae (I. 7). 9 Mexico, C. Am.

Watsonia Mill. Iridaceae (III). 35 S. Afr. Cult. orn. fl.

Wattle, *Acacia*.

Wax, *Ceroxylon*, *Copernicia*, *Myrica*, *Palmae*, *Rhus*; **-flower**, *Angraecum*, *Hoya*; **-gourd**, *Benincasa*; **Japan -**, *Rhus vernicifera* DC.; **-myrtle**, *Myrica*; **-palm**, *Copernicia cerifera* Mart.; **-tree**, *Rhus*; **waxy leaf**, *Agave*, *Crambe*, *Dischidia*, *Elymus*, &c.

Wayfaring tree, *Viburnum*.

Weather plant, *Abrus precatorius* L.; **-thistle**, *Carlina*.

Webbia DC. = Vernonia Schreb. p.p. (Comp.).

Webera Schreb. (*Tarenna* Gaertn.). Rubi. (I. 8). 30 trop. As., Afr.

Weberbauera Gilg et Muschler (*Braya* p.p.). Crucif. (4). 1 Peru, Arg.

Weberbauerella Ulbrich. Leguminosae (III. 7). 1 Peru.

Weberocereus Britton et Rose (*Cereus* p.p.). Cact. (III. 1). 3 C. Am., W.I.

Websteria S. H. Wright (*Dulichium* Pers.). Cyperaceae (I). 1 Florida.

Weddellina Tul. Tristichaceae. 1 Guiana, N. Brazil., *W. squamulosa* Tul. Roots ± flattened, with haptera, shoots borne at their edges. Two kinds, veg. to 2½ feet long and much branched, and short unbranched flowering ones. Between the branches of the long shoots are branches of limited growth, as in Tristicha.

Wedding flower, *Francoa.*
Wedelia Jacq. Compositae (5). 65 trop. and warm temp.
Wedeliella Cockerell (*Allionia* p.p.). Nyctaginaceae. 3 N. Am.
Weeds, *cf. Ageratum, Cactaceae, Capsella, Cynara, Eichhornia, Elodea, Galinsoga, Gomphocarpus, Lactuca, Salsola, Tithonia, Xanthium,* &c.
Weeping willow, *Salix babylonica* L.
Wehlia F. Muell. Myrtaceae (II. 2). 5 W. Austr.
Weigelia Pers., **Weigela** Thunb. = Diervilla Tourn.
Weigeltia A. DC. (*Cybianthus BH.*). Myrsinaceae (II). 21 W.I., trop. S. Am.
Weigeltia Reichb. Leguminosae. Nomen.
Weights, *Abrus precatorius* L., *Ceratonia Siliqua* L.
Weihea Spreng. Rhizophoraceae. 18 Ceylon, Madag., trop. Afr. Fls. fully hypog. Sometimes placed near to Elaeocarpus.
Weinmannia L. Cunoniaceae. 80 ⁂ exc. S. Afr.
Weld, *Reseda lutea* L.
Weldenia Schult. Commelinaceae. 1 Mexico.
Welfia H. Wendl. Palmae (IV. 1). 2 C. Am.
Wellingtonia Lindl. = Sequoia Endl. (Conif.).
Wellstedia Balf. f. Boraginaceae (V). 1 Socotra.
Welsh poppy, *Meconopsis cambrica* Vig.
Welwitschia Hook. f. (*Tumboa* Welw.). Gnetaceae. 1 sp., *W. mirabilis* Hook. f. (*T. Bainesii* Welw.), a remarkable plant discovered by Baines in Damaraland in W. trop. Afr., and shortly afterwards by Welwitsch in Mossamedes, and described by Hooker in *Trans. Linn. Soc.* 1883 (*q.v.*). Specimens in most museums. The plant has a peculiar habit, and grows for at least a century, and probably much longer. Its native climate is a markedly desert one, with a mere trifle of rainfall, the bulk of the moisture being derived from sea fogs, which cause a heavy deposit of dew. Seeds are produced in large quantities, and being enclosed in the winged P are blown about, and germinate in the occasional wet years. The stem is stout, with a two-lobed form and almost circular in section. It narrows downwards into a stout tap-root. At the edges of the two lobes are two grooves, from each of which springs a l. These l. are the first pair after the cots. and are the only l. the plant ever has; they go on growing at the base throughout its life, wearing away at the tips and often becoming torn down to the base. The stem continues to grow in thickness, and exhibits concentric grooves upon the top surface. In the outer (younger) of these grooves the fls. appear, in cpd. dichasia of small (♂) or larger (♀) spikes; they are covered by bracts which become bright red after fert. The fls. are dioec., and are produced annually. Pollination by insects. In the ♂, there is a P of 2 + 2 l., the outer whorl transv. to the bract; sta. 6, united below, with 3-loc. anthers; gynaeceum rudimentary, but with the integument of the ovule looking like a style and stigma. In the ♀, the perianth-l. are fused into a tube, and are equivalent to the two outer l. of the ♂; there is no trace of sta. Ovule 1, erect, with the integument drawn out beyond it. Seed with endosp. and perisperm, enclosed in the P which becomes winged. [See Gymnospermae, and Pearson in *Phil. Trans.* 198, 1906.]

Welwitschiella O. Hoffm. Compositae (6). 1 Angola.
Welwitschiina Engl. (*Triclisia* p.p.). Menisperm. 1 Angola.
Wendlandia Bartl. Rubiaceae (I. 3). 20 Indomal., China. L. sometimes whorled.
Wendlandiella Dammer. Palmae (IV. 1). 1 Brazil.
Wendtia Meyen. Geraniaceae. 3 Chili.
Wenzelia Merrill. Rutaceae (V). 1 Phil. Is.
Werneria H. B. et K. Compositae (8). 32 Andes, Himal., Abyss.
West Indian arrowroot, *Maranta arundinacea* L.; **-bark,** (W.I.), *Exostemma*; **-birch,** *Bursera gummifera* L.; **-boxwood,** *Casearia praecox* Griseb.; **-cedar,** *Cedrela*; **-ebony,** *Brya Elenus* DC.; **-locust tree,** *Hymenaea.*
Westia Vahl. Leguminosae (inc. sed.). 2 Guinea.
Westringia Sm. Labiatae (II). 12 Austr.
Wetria Baill. (*Alchornea BH.*). Euphorbiaceae (A. II. 2). 2 Mal. Arch.
Wetriaria O. Ktze. (*Pycnocoma* Benth.). Euph. (A. II. 2). 8 Afr., Masc.
Wettinia Poepp. ex Endl. Palmae (IV. 1). 3 trop. Am.
Wettsteinia Petrok. Compositae (11). 1 Turkestan.
Weymouth pine, *Pinus Strobus* L.
Wheat, *Triticum*; **cow -,** *Melampyrum*; **-grass,** *Agropyron.*
Wheelerella G. B. Grant. Boraginaceae (IV. 2). 2 W. N. Am.
Whim berry, *Vaccinium Vitis-Idaea* L.
Whin, *Ulex*; **petty -,** *Genista.*
Whipplea Torr. Saxifragaceae (III). 2 U.S.
White bryony, *Bryonia dioica* Jacq.; **-bent grass,** *Agrostis alba* L.; **-cedar,** *Chamaecyparis, Chickrassia, Libocedrus,* &c.; **-dammar,** *Vateria*; **-grass** (Am.), *Leersia*; **-head** (W.I.), *Parthenium*; **-hellebore,** *Marrubium*; **-horse** (W.I.), *Portlandia*; **-ipecacuanha,** *Ionidium Ipecacuanha* Vent.; **-mustard,** *Sinapis alba* L.; **-oak,** *Quercus alba* L.; **-Pareira root,** *Abuta*; **-pitch,** a form of common resin; **-rot,** *Hydrocotyle*; **-water-lily,** *Nymphaea alba* L.; **-weed,** *Ageratum,* (Am.) *Chrysanthemum Leucanthemum* L.; **-wood,** *Oreodaphne, Tecoma,* &c.
Whiteheadia Harv. Liliaceae (V). 1 S. Afr.
Whitfieldia Hook. Acanthaceae (IV. A). 6 trop. Afr.
Whitfordia Elmer. Leguminosae (III. 8 or 6). 1 Phil. Is.
Whitlavia Harv. = Phacelia Juss. p.p. (Hydrophyll.).
Whitlow grass, *Draba*; **-wort** (Am.), *Paronychia.*
Whitneya A. Gray. Compositae (6). 1 California.
Whorl (l., &c.), several at a node; **false -,** *Labiatae.*
Whortle berry, *Vaccinium Myrtillus* L.
Wiasemskya Klotzsch. Rubiaceae. Nomen.
Wiborgia Roth. = Galinsoga Ruiz et Pav. (Comp.).
Wiborgia Thunb. Leguminosae (III. 3). 10 S. Afr.
Widdringtonia Endl. (*Callitris* p.p.). Coniferae (Pinaceae 34; see C. for gen. char.). 5 trop. and S. Afr. Cf. Masters, Notes on W., in *Linn. Soc. Journ.* 37, p. 267.
Widgrenia Malme. Asclepiadaceae (II. 1). 1 Minas Geraes.
Wiedemannia Fisch. et Mey. Labiatae (VI). 2 Armenia.

Wielandia Baill. Euphorbiaceae (A. I. 1). 1 Seychelles.
Wiesneria (*Wisneria*) M. Mich. Alismaceae. 3 palaeotrop.
Wig tree, *Rhus Cotinus* L.
Wigandia H. B. et K. Hydrophyllaceae. 6 Mts. of trop. Am.
Wightia Wall. Scrophulariaceae (II. 4). 2 Himalaya, Borneo.
Wikstroemia Endl. Thymelaeaceae. 20 Indomal., China. Some are parthenogenetic.
Wilbrandia Presl. Boraginaceae (inc. sed.). 1 Martinique.
Wilbrandia Silva Manso. Cucurbitaceae (2). 7 Brazil.
Wilcoxia Britton et Rose (*Cereus* p.p.). Cact. (III. 1). 2 S.W. U.S., Mex., Arg.
Wild allspice (Am.), *Lindera*; **-bean** (Am.), *Apios*; **-chamomile** (Am.), *Matricaria*; **-ginger** (Am.), *Asarum*; **-hyacinth**, *Scilla*.
Wilde preume (S. Afr.), *Pappea*.
Wilga (Austr.), *Geijera parviflora* Lindl.
Wilkesia A. Gray. Compositae (5). 2 Hawaiian Is. Small trees.
Wilkiea F. Muell. (*Kibara* p.p. *BH*.). Monimiaceae. 5 E. Austr.
Willardia Rose. Leguminosae (III. 6). 1 Mexico. Timber.
Willdenowia Thunb. Restionaceae. 15 S. Afr. The stems of some are used in making brooms.
Willemetia Neck. (*Chondrilla BH.*). Compositae (13). 2 Medit.
Williamsia Merrill. Rubiaceae (I. 7). 5 Phil. Is.
Willisia Wmg. Podostemaceae. 1 S. India. There is a small thallus, with closely crowded erect shoots with 4 closely packed ranks of scaly l., and ribbon-like l. at the tips. Each shoot bears one fl. (cf. Willis in *Ann. Perad.* I, p. 369, 1902).
Willkommia Hackel. Gramineae (11). 4 S.W. and trop. Afr.
Willow, *Salix*; **-herb**, *Epilobium*.
Willugbaeya Neck. (*Mikania* p.p.). Compositae (2). 10 Am.
Willughbeia Roxb. Apocynaceae (I. 1). 10 Indomal. Some, *e.g.* *W. edulis* Roxb. (Assam—Borneo), and *W. firma* Bl. (Java, &c.), contain rubber in their latex, and are used as sources of rubber.
Wilsonia R. Br. Convolvulaceae (1). 4 Austr.
Wimmeria Schlechtd. Celastraceae. 6 Mexico, C. Am.
Winchia A. DC. Apocynaceae (I. 1). 1 Martaban.
Wind fertilisation, see Pollination; **-flower**, *Anemone*; **seed-distr. by -**, see Dispersal of seeds.
Windsor bean, *Vicia Faba* L.
Wine palm, *Borassus*, *Caryota*, *Phoenix*, *Raphia*, &c.
Wings on fruit, *cf.* Dispersal; **on ovary**, *Leguminosae*, *Begonia*, &c.; **on stem**, *Baccharis*.
Winklera Regel. Cruciferae (4). 1 Turkestan.
Winklerella Engl. Podostemaceae. 1 trop. Afr.
Winter aconite, *Eranthis hyemalis* Salisb.; **-berry** (Am., W.I.), *Ilex*; **-buds**, see Buds; **-cherry**, *Physalis*; **-cress**, *Barbarea*; **-green**, *Gaultheria*, *Pyrola*; **--, chickweed**, *Trientalis*; **-heliotrope**, *Petasites*.
Winter's bark, *Drimys Winteri* Forst.
Winterana L. (*Canella* P. Br.). Winteranaceae. 2 W.I., trop. Am. *W. Canella* L. yields the medicinal Canella bark.
Winteranaceae (*Canellaceae*; *EP.*, *BH.*). Dicots. (Archichl. Parie-

tales). 4 gen., 7 sp., with marked discontinuity in distr. (S. Am., E. Afr., Madag.). Trees with alt., leathery, entire, exstip., gland-dotted l. Fls. sol. or in racemes or cymes, ☿, reg. K 4—5, imbr.; C 4—5 free or united, or o; A (∞) completely united into a tube with extr. anthers; G (2—5), 1-loc., with 2—∞ semi-anatr. ov. on each parietal plac. Berry. Embryo straight or slightly curved in rich endosp. *Genera:* Cinnamodendron, Cinnamosma, Warburgia, Winterana.

Wire grass, *Eleusine*, *Paspalum*, *Poa*, &c.

Wislizenia Engelm. Capparidaceae (v). 2 S.W. U.S.

Wisneria (*Wiesneria*) M. Micheli. Alismaceae. 3 palaeotrop.

Wissadula Medic. Malvaceae (2). 25 trop.

Wistaria Nutt. (*Bradburya* Rafin. in part, *Kraunhia* Rafin.). Leguminosae (III. 6). 5 China, Japan, E. N. Am. *W. Chinensis* DC. (China) is a climbing shrub often cult. orn. sweet-scented fls. The floral mech. like Trifolium. The pods explode violently.

Witch-hazel, *Hamamelis*; **-es' broom**, *Betula*.

Withania Pauq. Solanaceae (2). 5 palaeotrop. and subtrop. *W. coagulans* Dun. is used in India in preparing cheese.

Witheringia L'Hérit. = Bassovia Aubl. (Solan.).

Witsenia Thunb. Iridaceae (II). 1 Cape Colony. Cult. orn. fl.

Wittia K. Schum. Cactaceae (III. 1). 3 Brazil.

Wittmackia Mez (*Aechmea* p.p.). Bromel. (4). 2 W.I., E. trop. S. Am.

Wittrockia Lindau. Bromeliaceae. 1 Brazil.

Wittsteinia F. Muell. Ericaceae (II. 2). 1 S.E. Austr. Ov. inf. Berry.

Woad, *Isatis tinctoria* L.; **- waxen** (Am.), *Genista*.

Woehleria Griseb. Amarantaceae (3). 1 Cuba.

Wolf's bane, *Aconitum*; **- milk**, *Euphorbia*.

Wolffia Horkel ex Schleid. Lemnaceae. 12 trop. and temp. *W. arrhiza* Wimm. in Brit. (the smallest of flowering plants).

Wolffiella Hegelm. (*Wolffia* p.p.). Lemnaceae. 5 Am.

Wolfia Dennst. Zingiberaceae (inc. sed.). 1 Indomal.

Wollastonia DC. ex Decne. = Wedelia Jacq. p.p. (Comp.).

Wood *cf.* Timber; **- anemone**, *Anemone nemorosa* L.; **- apple**, *Feronia*; **Arar -**, *Widdringtonia quadrivalvis* Mast.; **assegai -**, *Curtisia*; **- avens**, *Geum*; **bass -**, *Tilia americana* L.; **beef -**, *Casuarina*, *Stenocarpus*, *Swartzia*; **-betony**, *Stachys*; **-bine**, *Lonicera Periclymenum* L.; **bow -**, *Maclura*; **black -**, *Acacia*, *Dalbergia*; **Brazil -**, *Caesalpinia*; **cam -**, *Baphia*; **Campeachy -**, *Haematoxylon*; **Canary white -**, *Liriodendron*; **Chittagong -**, *Chickrassia*; **East Indian rose -**, *Dalbergia*; **Indian red -**, *Chickrassia*: **iron -**, *Mesua*, &c., &c.; **- fern** (Am.), *Aspidium*; **lance -**, *Duguetia*; **lever -**, *Ostrya*; **log -**, *Haematoxylon*; **- nettle** (Am.), *Laportea*; **- oil**, *Aleurites*, *Dipterocarpus*, &c.; **peach -**, *Caesalpinia*; **porcupine -**, *Cocos*; **- ruff**, *Asperula odorata* L.; **- rush**, *Luzula*; **- sage**, *Teucrium*; **sandal -**, **Sanders -**, *Santalum*, *Pterocarpus*; **sappan -**, *Caesalpinia*; **- sorrel**, *Oxalis*; **spindle -**, *Euonymus*; **Trincomali -**, *Berrya*; **yellow -**, *Cladrastis*. And *cf.* Timber.

Woodburnia Prain. Araliaceae (1). 1 Burma.

Wooden pear, *Xylomelum.*
Woodfordia Salisb. Lythraceae. 2, 1 Abyss., and 1 (*W. floribunda* Salisb.) Madag., Ind., Ceyl., China, Timor.
Woodia Schlechter. Asclepiadaceae (II. 1). 4 S. Afr.
Woodrowia Stapf. Gramineae (8). 1 India.
Woodsia R. Br. Polypodiaceae. 25 alpine and arctic. *W. ilvensis* Br. and *W. hyperborea* Br. rare alpine ferns in Brit.
Woodwardia Sm. Polypodiaceae. 7 *.
Woollsia F. Muell. (*Lysinema* p.p.). Epacridaceae (2). 1 E. Austr.
Wootonia Greene. Compositae (5). 1 New Mexico.
Worcesterianthus Merrill. Olacaceae. 1 Phil. Is.
Worm grass (Am., W.I.), *Spigelia Anthelmia* L.; **- seed,** *Chenopodium*; **- wood,** *Artemisia.*
Wormia Rottb. (*Dillenia* p.p. *EP.*). Dilleniaceae. 35 trop. As., Afr. The bud is protected by a sheathing petiole.
Wormskioldia Thonn. Turneraceae. 8 trop. Afr.
Wound wort, *Stachys Betonica* Benth.
Wourali, *Strychnos toxifera* Schomb.
Wrack grass, *Zostera.*
Wrightia R. Br. Apocynaceae (II. 2). 14 palaeotrop.
Wrixonia F. Muell. Labiatae (II). 1 W. Austr.
Wulfenia Jacq. Scrophulariaceae (III. 1). 3 E. Medit., Himal.
Wulffia Neck. Compositae (5). 2 W.I., S. Am.
Wulfhorstia C. DC. Meliaceae (II). 1 trop. Afr.
Wullschlaegelia Reichb. f. Orchidaceae (II. 2). 2 W.I., Brazil.
Wunderlichia Riedel. Compositae (12). 3 Brazil.
Wunschmannia Urb. (*Bignonia* p.p.). Bignoniaceae (1). 1 Haiti.
Wurmbea Thunb. Liliaceae (I). 7 S. and S. trop. Afr., W. Austr.
Wych elm, *Ulmus montana* With.
Wyethia Nutt. Compositae (5). 12 W. N. Am.
Wyomingia A. Nelson. Compositae (3). 5 Wyoming.
Xanth-, xantho- (Gr. pref.), yellow.
Xantheranthemum Lindau (*Chamaeranthemum BH.*). Acanthaceae (IV B). 1 Peru. Cult. orn. fl.
Xanthisma DC. Compositae (3). 1 Texas. Cult. orn. fl.
Xanthium (Tourn.) L. Compositae (5). 4 Medit. They have been so widely distr. by man (unintentionally) that it is hard to discover their native place. Fls. in unisexual heads, single or in axillary cymes, the ♂ at the ends of the branches. The ♀ head has 2 fls., enclosed in a prickly gamophyllous invol., only the styles projecting from it through openings in the two horns of the invol. The frs. are enclosed in the hard woody invol., which is covered with hooks and well suited to animal-distr. One sp. has gradually spread in this way from the East of Europe. "In 1828 it was brought into Wallachia by the Cossack horses, whose manes and tails were covered with the burrs. It travelled in Hungarian wool, and in cattle from the same region, to Regensburg, and on to Hamburg, appearing here and there on the way." Strenuous laws for its extirpation have been enforced in South Africa, where at one time it had become so common as seriously to impair the value of the wool.
Xanthocephalum Willd. Compositae (3). 12 warm Am.

Xanthoceras Bunge. Sapindaceae (II). 2 N. China. Ed. seed.
Xanthocercis Baill. Leguminosae (III. 8). 1 Madag.
Xanthochymus Roxb. = Garcinia L. p.p. (Guttif.).
Xanthopappus C. Winkler. Compositae (11). 1 N. China.
Xanthophyllum Roxb. Polygalaceae. 45 Indomal. G 1-loc. with parietal plac. Nut one-seeded.
Xanthophytum Reinw. Rubiaceae (I. 2). 3 Java to Fiji.
Xanthorrhiza Marshall (*Zanthorhiza*). Ranuncul. (2). 1 Atl. N. Am.
Xanthorrhoea Sm. Liliaceae (III). 11 Austr. The best known is *X. hastilis* R. Br., the grass-tree, or black-boy, a char. plant of the Austr. veg. It has the habit of an Aloe or Dasylirion, with a long bulrush-like spike of fls. (really cymose as may be seen from the many bracts on the individual fl.-stalks). P sepaloid (X. is placed in Juncaceae by Benth.-Hooker). From the bases of the old leaves trickles a resin, used in making varnish, sealing-wax, &c.
Xanthosia Rudge. Umbelliferae (I. 1). 15 Austr. The umbels in some are reduced to single fls.
Xanthosoma Schott. Araceae (VI). 40 trop. Am., W.I. Large herbs (fig. in Kerner's *Nat. Hist.*). *X. appendiculatum* Schott has a pocket at the back of the leaf due to a tangential division of the embryonic leaf. Fls. monoec., naked; synandria. Rhiz. of some ed. like Colocasia. Cult. (yautia).
Xanthostemon F. Muell. Myrtaceae (II. 1). 18 New Caled., E. Austr.
Xanthoxalis Small (*Oxalis* p.p.). Oxalidaceae. 15 N. Am.
Xanthoxylum J. F. Gmel. (*Zanthoxylum* L. *q.v.*). Rutaceae (I). 9 temp. E. As., N. Am.
Xatardia Meissn. Umbelliferae (III. 5). 1 Pyrenees.
Xenia, direct influence of foreign pollen on the mother pl.
Xenochloa Lichtenstein. Gramineae (inc. sed.). 1 S. Afr.
Xenodendron K. Schum. et Lauterb. Sonneratiaceae. 1 New Guinea.
Xenogamy, pollination from another plant.
Xenophya Schott. Araceae (VII). 1 New Guinea.
Xeraea L. = Gomphrena L. (Amarant.).
Xeranthemum Tourn. ex Linn. Compositae (11). 6 Medit., Orient.
Xero- (Gr. pref.), dry; **-chastic**, opening by drying; **-hylium** (Cl.), a dry forest formation; **-phile**, **-phytic**, adj. forms of **-phytes**, pl. living where the water supply is limited (i.e. esp. in the subtropics, or as halophytes or epiphytes), and with various arrangements reducing transpiration. Nearly all have thick cuticle, thick or leathery l., reduced number of stomata, smaller intercellular spaces. Some have (1) stomata sunk in pits, often covered with hair, *Aloe*, *Nerium*, *Pinus*, or in grooves, *Cactaceae*, *Capparidaceae*, *Cassiope*, *Casuarina*, *Cheilanthes*, *Empetrum*, *Equisetum*, *Phylica*, *Rosmarinus*, *Spartium*, *Vaccinium*; (2) l. rolling up with stomata on hollow side in dry air, *Ammophila*, *Stipa*, and other grasses; (3) surface covering of hair, *Helichrysum*, *Leontopodium*, *Stachys*, or wax, *Agave*, *Aloe*, many *Crassulaceae* and *Liliaceae*, or of silica, *Crassula*; (4) thick sap, *Aloe*; (5) overlapping of l., *Aloe*, *Apicra*, *Calluna*, *Crassulaceae*, *Gasteria*; (6) tufted growth, *Azorella*, *Draba*, *Raoulia*, and many alpines, *e.g.* *Androsace*, *Gnaphalium*; (7) reduction of transpiring surface in various ways, *Aspalathus*, *Baccharis*, *Casuarina*, *Coni-*

ferae, *Cupressus*, *Cytisus*, *Empetraceae*, *Epacridaceae*, *Ericaceae*, *Genista*, *Grevillea*, *Hakea*, *Juncus*, *Pinus*, *Restio*, *Rhamnaceae*, *Rubus*, *Russellia*, *Rutaceae* (*Diosma*), *Spartium*, *Ulex*, *Veronica*; (8) phylloclades, *Bossiaea*, *Carmichaelia*, *Colletia*, *Hibbertia*, *Muehlenbeckia*, *Phyllanthus*, *Ruscus*, *Semele*, phyllodes, *Acacia*, *Oxalis*, twisted l., *Eucalyptus*, isobilateral l., *Iris*, *Narthecium*, *Phormium*; (9) sleep-movement of l., *Leguminosae*; (10) storage of water in aqueous tissue, *Aeschynanthus*, *Peperomia*, or in whole or large part of the (succulent) plant, *Agave*, *Aizoaceae*, *Aloe*, *Anacampseros*, *Asclepiadaceae*, *Cactaceae*, *Ceropegia*, *Crassulaceae*, *Cynanchum*, *Drymoglossum*, *Echidnopsis*, *Euphorbia*, *Fourcroya*, *Gasteria*, *Haworthia*, *Huernia*, *Mesembryanthemum*, *Salicornia*, *Sansevieria*, *Sarcocaulon*, *Sarcostemma*, *Sempervivum*, *Senecio*, *Stapelia*, and the peculiar cases of *Bombacaceae* and *Bromeliaceae*. Bud-protection is common; the fls. are usu. produced in the dry season, and the seeds often protected against drought. *Cf.* also *Acantholimon*, *Acanthophyllum*, *Acanthosicyos*, *Acanthus*, *Adenium*, *Adenostoma*, *Alhagi*, *Amaryllidaceae*, *Argyrolobium*, *Artemisia*, *Astragalus*, *Banksia*, *Beschorneria*, *Boucerosia*, *Calibanus*, *Chenopodiaceae*, *Cochlospermum*, *Convolvulaceae*, *Dasylirion*, *Espeletia*, *Ephedra*, *Geissoloma*, *Helipterum*, *Jatropha*, *Koeberlinia*, *Labiatae*, *Larrea*, *Lewisia*, *Lycopodium*, *Nolina*, *Opuntia*, *Othonna*, *Penaeaceae*, *Polygonum*, *Prosopis*, *Proteaceae*, *Resedaceae*, *Saxifraga*, *Sedum*, *Selaginella*, *Stackhousiaceae*, *Stylidiaceae*, *Tamariscaceae*, *Testudinaria*, *Velloziaceae*, *Verbenaceae*, *Welwitschia*, *Zygophyllaceae*. Cf. also Epiphytes, Halophytes, Tropophytes, and see Schimper's *Geography of Plants*; Warming, *Ecological Plant Geography*, &c.

Xerochlamys Baker. Chlaenaceae. 1 S. Madag.

Xerochloa R. Br. Gramineae (5). 3 Austr.

Xerocladia Harv. Leguminosae (I. 4). 1 temp. S. Afr.

Xerococcus Oerst. Rubiaceae (I. 7). 1 Costa Rica.

Xeronema Brongn. et Gris. Liliaceae (III). 2 New Caled., N. Zeal.

Xerophyllum Rich. in Michx. Liliaceae (I). 3 N. Am.

Xerophyta Juss. = Vellozia Vand. (*BH.*) = Barbacenia Vand. p.p.

Xeroplana Briq. Verbenaceae (2). 1 S. Afr.

Xerorchis Schlechter. Orchidaceae (II. 7). 1 Manaos.

Xerospermum Blume. Sapindaceae (I). 8 S.E. As., Malay Archip.

Xerotes R. Br. (*Lomandra EP.*). Juncaceae. 32 Austr.

Xerotia Oliv. Caryophyllaceae (I. 3). 1 Arabia.

Ximenesia Cav. = Verbesina L. p.p. (Comp.).

Ximenia Plum. ex L. Olacaceae. 5 trop. *X. americana* L. good wood.

Xiphagrostis Coville (*Saccharum* p.p.). Gramineae (2). 1 Malaya, &c.

Xiphidium Loefl. Haemodoraceae. 2 trop. Am., W.I.

Xiphion Tourn. ex Mill. = Iris Tourn. (Irid.).

Xolisma Rafin. (*Andromeda* p.p.). Ericaceae (II. 1). 4 N. Am.

Xylanche G. Beck. Orobanchaceae. 1 Himalaya.

Xylem, the wood of the vascular bundles, of stem or root.

Xylia Benth. Leguminosae (I. 5). 3 trop. As., Afr. Good timber.

Xylinabaria Pierre. Apocynaceae (II. 1). 2 Indochina.

Xylobium Lindl. Orchidaceae (II. 12). 24 trop. Am. Cult. orn. fl.

Xylocalyx Balf. f. Scrophulariaceae (III. 2). 1 Socotra.

Xylocarpus Koen. (*Carapa BH.*). Meliaceae (III). 2 palaeotrop. coasts.

Xylochlaena Baill. Chlaenaceae. 1 N. Madag.

Xylolobus O. Ktze. = Xylia Benth. (Legum.).

Xylomelum Sm. Proteaceae (II). 4 Austr. The fruits are known as wooden pears, being of the size of a large pear, and looking ed. at first glance. Inside is a thick wall of woody tissue enveloping the winged seeds. It splits along the post. side.

Xylonagra Donn. Sm. et Rose (*Hauya* p.p.). Onagr. (2). 1 Lower Calif.

Xylophacos Rydberg (*Astragalus* p.p.). Legum. (III. 6). 10 N. Am.

Xylophragma Sprague (*Tecoma* p.p.). Bignoniaceae (2). Braz., Peru.

Xylophylla L. = Phyllanthus L. p.p. (the sp. with phylloclades).

Xylopia L. Anonaceae (4). 60 trop. Fr. used as peppers.

Xylopleurum Spach (*Oenothera* p.p. *BH.*). Onagr. (2). 10 trop. Am. Cult.

Xylorhiza Nutt. (*Aster* p.p.). Compositae (3). 5 N. Am.

Xylosma Forst. f. (*Myroxylon* Forst.). Flacourtiaceae (4). 60 warm.

Xylosteon Tourn. ex Adans. (*Lonicera* p.p.). Caprifoliaceae. 3 N. Am.

Xylotheca Hochst. (*Oncoba* p.p.). Flacourtiaceae (2). 10 trop. Afr.

Xymalos Baill. (*Xylosma* p.p.). Flacourtiaceae (inc. sed.). 1 Natal.

Xyridaceae. Monocot. (Farinosae; Coronarieae *BH.*). 2 gen. (Xyris, Abolboda), 70 sp. trop. and subtrop., mostly Am. Mostly marsh plants, herbaceous, tufted, with radical sheathing l. and spikes or heads of ☿ fls. P heterochlam. K 3, the lat. sepals small, the ant. large, enclosing the corolla; C (3); A 3, epipet., the outer whorl absent or repres. by stds.; $\underline{G}$ (3), 1-loc. or imperfectly 3-loc., with parietal or free basal plac. and ∞ orthotr. ov. Caps. Embryo small, in mealy endosp. [See review in *Bot. Gaz.* 1895, p. 313.]

Xyrideae (*BH.*) = Xyridaceae.

Xyris Gronov. ex L. Xyridaceae. 180 trop. and subtrop.

Xysmalobium R. Br. Asclepiadaceae (II. 1). 20 S. and trop. Afr.

Xystris Schreb. Inc. sed. Nomen.

Xystrolobus Gagnep. Hydrocharidaceae. 1 Yunnan.

Yacca tree (W.I.), *Podocarpus*.

Yam, *Dioscorea*; **-bean,** *Pachyrhizus, Dolichos*.

Yard grass (Am.), *Eleusine*.

Yarrow, *Achillea Millefolium* L.

Yate, *Eucalyptus cornuta* Labill.

Yaupon (Am.), *Ilex Cassine* L.; **-grass** (Am.), *Eleusine*.

Yautia, *Xanthosoma*.

Yaw-weed (W.I.), *Morinda umbellata* L.

Yellow archangel, *Lamium*; **-bark,** *Cinchona*; **-berries,** *Rhamnus infectoria* L.; **-bird's nest,** *Monotropa*; **-bugle,** *Ajuga*; **-cedar,** *Chamaecyparis*; **-cress,** *Barbarea*; **-deal,** *Pinus sylvestris* L.; **-flag,** *Iris Pseudacorus* L.; **-horned poppy,** *Glaucium*; **-loosestrife,** *Lysimachia vulgaris* L.; **-pimpernel,** *Lysimachia nemorum* L.; **-pine,** *Pinus echinata* Mill.; **-puccoon,** *Hydrastis*; **-rattle,** *Rhinanthus*; **-rocket,** *Barbarea*; **-seal,** *Hydrastis*; **-toadflax,** *Linaria*; **-water lily,** *Nuphar luteum* Sibth. et Sm.; **-wood,** *Cladrastis*; **-wort,** *Chlora*.

Yerba buena, *Micromeria*; **-mate**, *Ilex paraguensis* A. St Hil.
Yew, *Taxus baccata* L.
Ylang-ylang, *Cananga odorata* Hook. f.
Yoania Maxim. Orchidaceae (II. 2). 1 Japan.
Yorkshire fog, *Holcus*.
Young fustic, *Rhus Cotinus* L.
Youngia Cass. = Crepis Vaill. p.p. (Comp.).
Ypsilandra Franch. Liliaceae (1). 1 Tibet.
Yuca, cassava, *Manihot utilissima* Pohl, &c.
Yucca Dill. ex L. Liliaceae (VI). 30 S. U.S., C. Am., W.I. Many cult. orn. (Adam's needle). Stem short, growing in thickness, and branching occasionally (*cf.* Dracaena); at the end is a rosette of fleshy and pointed l. Fls. large, white, in panicle. Remarkable mode of pollination (for details and figures see Riley in *3rd Ann. Rep. Missouri Bot. Gdn.* 1892). This is one of the few cases of mutual dependence and adaptation of a single fl. and a single insect—Pronuba, a moth. The fl. emits its perfume esp. at night, and is then visited by the moths. The female has a long ovipositor with which she can penetrate the tissue of the ovary of the fl., and possesses peculiar prehensile, spinous, maxillary tentacles confined to the genus. She begins soon after dark, collecting a load of pollen, and shaping it into a pellet about thrice as large as her head. She then flies to another fl. and deposits a few eggs in the ovary, piercing its wall with her ovipositor. Having done this she climbs to the top and presses the ball of pollen into the stigma. The ovules are thus fertilised, and are so numerous that there are plenty for the larvae to feed upon and also to repr. the plant.

The leaves of *Y. filamentosa* L. and other sp. furnish an excellent fibre (*cf.* Agave).

Zaa Baill. (*Tabebuia* p.p.). Bignoniaceae (4). 1 Madag.
Zacintha (Tourn.) L., Gaertn. Compositae (13). 1 Medit.
Zaczatea Baill. (*Raphiacme EP.*). Asclepiadaceae (1). 1 Angola.
Zahlbrucknera Reichb. Saxifragaceae (1). 1 E. Eur.
Zalacca Rumph. Palmae (III). 10 Indomal. Fr. ed.
Zalaccella Becc. (*Calamus* p.p.). Palmae (III. 2). 1 Cochinchina.
Zaluzania Pers. Compositae (5). 10 C. Am.
Zaluzianskya F. W. Schmidt. Scrophulariaceae (II. 5). 20 S. Afr.
Zamia L. Cycadaceae (see fam. for gen. char.). 30 trop Am.
Zamioculcas Schott. Araceae (1). 1 E. trop. Afr. L. pinnate.
Zanha Hiern. Burseraceae. 1 Angola.
Zannichellia Mich. ex L. Potamogetonaceae. 1 cosmop., *Z. palustris* L., in fresh or brackish water. Fls. monoec.; ♀ term.; from the axil of its lower bracteole springs the ♂. From the axil of the upper a new branch may arise, bearing ♀ and ♂ fls. again. The ♂ fl. consists of 1 or 2 sta., the ♀ of usu. 4 cpls., surrounded by a small cup-like P. Pollination under water as in Zostera, but the pollen is spherical.
Zanonia Linn. Cucurbitaceae (1). 3 Indomal., *Z. indica* L., *Z. macrocarpa* Blume. The latter has enormous flat winged seeds, remarkably like those of many Bignoniaceae.
Zantedeschia Spreng. (*Richardia* Kunth, *q.v.*). Araceae (V). 10 Afr.

Zanthorhiza L'Hérit. Ranuncul. (2). 1 Atl. N. Am. Fls. 5-merous.

Zanthoxylum L. (*BH.* incl. *Fagara* L.). Rutaceae (I). 20 temp. E. As., N. Am. Several cult. orn. shrubs. *Z. piperitum* DC., the Japan pepper, yields fr. used as a condiment. The bark of *Z. fraxineum* Willd. (prickly ash or toothache-tree) is used in Am. as a remedy for toothache. Some yield good timber.

Zapania Lam. = Lippia Houst. p.p. (Verben.).

Zataria Boiss. Labiatae (VI). 1 Persia, Afghanistan.

Zauschneria Presl. Onagraceae (2). 3 Calif., Mexico. Cult. orn. fl.

Zea L. Gramineae (I). 1 sp., *Zea Mays* L., the maize or Indian corn, apparently originally Mexican, now cult. in most trop. and subtrop. regions. A tall annual grass, with term. ♂ infl. and ♀ infls. in the axils of the foliage-l. ♂ spikelets in pairs, 2-flowered. The ♀ infl. forms a 'cob' with long filamentous stigmas hanging out at the end (fls. pollinated by wind). The cob is enveloped when young by large spathe-l., and consists of combined spikes; each two rows of fls. visible on its surface correspond to one spike of fls. The cult. forms are 8-, 10-, 12-, or 24-rowed. *Cf.* Euchlaena, in which the spikes are distinct and form a tuft. Each spike consists of one-flowered spikelets. Fr. the familiar maize-seed, in which the structure of a grass-fruit can easily be made out; the embryo occupies the white portion near the pointed end.

A most important cereal; it is termed corn in the U.S., like wheat in England, oats in Scotland. The grain is made into flour (Indian meal) or cooked without grinding; green corn (unripe cobs) forms a favourite vegetable, the l. are useful as fodder, the dry cobs as firing; the spathes are used in paper-making, and so on. [See Harshberger's monograph (botanical and economic) in *Contrib. Bot. Lab. Univ. Pennsylv.* I. 1893.]

Zebrina Schnitzl. Commelinaceae. 2 Mexico, Texas. Cult. orn. fol.

Zedoary, *Curcuma Zedoaria* Rosc.

Zehneria Endl. = Melothria L. p.p. (Cucurb.).

Zeia Lunell (*Agropyron* p.p.). Gramineae (12). 15 N. Am.

Zelkova Spach. Ulmaceae. 4 N. temp. |✻. Timber valuable.

Zenkerella Taub. Leguminosae (II. 2). 1 Cameroons.

Zenkeria Trin. Gramineae (9). 2 India, Ceylon.

Zenkerina Engl. Acanthaceae (I). 1 Cameroons.

Zenkerophytum Engl. ex Diels. (*Syrrheonema* p.p.). Menispermaceae. 1 W. Afr.

Zenobia D. Don (*Andromeda* p.p. *EP.*). Ericaceae (II. 1). 2 N. Am.

Zeocriton Beauv. = Hordeum Tourn. p.p. (Gram.).

Zephyra D. Don. Amaryllidaceae (III) (Haemodor. *BH.*). 1 Chili.

Zephyranthes Herb. Amaryllidaceae (I). 60 warm Am. Cult. orn. fl.

Zerdana Boiss. Cruciferae (4). 2 Mts. of Persia.

Zerumbet Garsault (*Kaempfera* p.p.). Zingiberaceae (I). 1 trop. As.

Zeugites P. Br. Gramineae (10). 6 trop. Am.

Zeuxine Lindl. Orchidaceae (II. 2). 20 trop. Afr., Indomal.

Zexmenia La Llave. Compositae (5). 40 trop. and subtrop. Am.

Zeyheria Mart. Bignoniaceae (2). 2 Brazil.

Zezegany (W. I.), *Sesamum indicum* L.

Zichya Hueg. = Kennedya Vent. p.p. (Legum.).
Zieria Sm. Rutaceae (1). 10 E. Austr.
Zieridium Baill. Rutaceae (1). 1 New Caled.
Zilla Forsk. Cruciferae (2). 2 N. Afr.
Zimapania Engl. et Pax. Euphorbiaceae (A. II. 3). 1 Mexico.
Zimmermannia Pax. Euphorbiaceae (A. I. 1). 1 E. Afr.
Zingiber Adans. Zingiber. 80 As. Labellum large; opp. to it are the style and the petaloid fertile sta. The stigma has many rays. *Z. officinale* Rosc. is the ginger; it is always repr. by veg. methods, and is quite sterile (*cf.* Musa). Largely cult.; the rhiz. are dug up and killed in boiling water. According to whether the rind is or is not scraped off, the product is known as 'scraped' or 'coated' ginger.
Zingiberaceae (*EP.*; *Scitamineae* p.p. *BH.*). Monocots. (Scitamineae). 45 gen., 800 sp., trop., chiefly Indomal. Perenn. herbs usu. with sympodial fleshy rhiz., often with tuberous roots. Aerial stem, if any, short; sometimes an apparent stem is formed as in Musa by the rolled up leaf-sheaths. L. 2-ranked, with short stalks and sheathing bases. At the top of the sheath is a char. ligule (*cf.* Gramineae). Fls. in racemes, heads, or cymes. Their morphology much discussed (see Eichler's *Blüthendiag.* or *Nat. Pfl.*). Bracteole often sheathing (as in fig.). K (3), the odd one ant., C 3, usu. different in colour and texture from the outer P-leaves. Of the possible 6 members of the A (two whorls), the post. one of the inner whorl is present as a fertile epipet. sta., and the other two of this whorl are united to form the petaloid *labellum* (not equivalent to that of Orchids), which may be 2- or 3-lobed; the ant. sta. of the outer whorl is always absent; the other two may be absent (as in Renealmia) or may be present as large leafy stds. right and left of the fertile sta. (*cf.* with Cannaceae and Marantaceae). $\bar{G}$ (3), 3-loc., with ∞ anatr. or semi-anatr. ov. Fr. usu. a loculic. caps. Seeds with perisperm. The fam. contains several economic plants; see Curcuma, Costus, Alpinia, Zingiber, Amomum, Elettaria.

Floral diagram of Renealmina, modified from Eichler, showing bract, sheathing bracteole, calyx, corolla, labellum (LAB), &c.

Classification and chief genera:

I. *ZINGIBEROIDEAE* (l. 2-ranked; lat. stds. different or wanting; pl. aromatic): Hedychium, Kaempfera, Curcuma, Globba, Zingiber, Amomum, Renealmia, Alpinia.

II. *COSTOIDEAE* (l. alt.; lat. stds. usu. wanting; sub-aerial parts not aromatic): Costus, Tapeinochilus.

Zinnia L. Compositae (5). 12 N. Am., cult. orn. fl. L. opp. or whorled. Fr. winged.
Zinowiewia Turcz. Celastraceae. 1 Mexico.
Zippelia Blume. Piperaceae. 1 Java.
Zizania Gronov. ex Linn. Gramineae (6). 1 Am., N.E. As., *Z. aquatica* L. (*Hydropyrum esculentum* Link), Canada rice, is used as a cereal by the N. Am. Indians.

Zizaniopsis Doell. et Aschers. Gramineae (6). 3 Brazil, U.S.
Zizia Koch (*Carum* p.p. *BH.*). Umbelliferae (III. 5). 2 N. Am.
Ziziphora L. Labiatae (VI). 12 Medit., C. As.
Ziziphus Tourn. ex L. Rhamnaceae. 40 Indomal., trop. Am., Afr., Austr., Medit. Stips. often repres. by thorns; one is sometimes recurved whilst the other is straight (*cf.* Paliurus); occasionally only one is developed. *Z. chloroxylon* Oliv. (cogwood; Jamaica) hard tough wood. Fr. of many ed.; those of *Z. Lotus* Lam. (Medit.) are said to be the Lotus fruits of antiquity; those of *Z. vulgaris* Lam. (E. Medit.) are known as French jujubes; those of *Z. Joazeiro* Mart. are used in Brazil as fodder. *Z. Spina-Christi* Willd. is said to have furnished the crown of thorns (*cf.* Paliurus).
Zoegea L. Compositae (11). 5 W. As.
Zoelleria Warb. Boraginaceae (IV). 1 New Guinea.
Zoidiogamy, fertilisation by spermatozoids.
Zoisia (*Zoysia*) Willd. Gramineae (3). 3 Masc. Is. to New Zealand.
Zollernia Maximil. et Nees. Leguminosae (II. 9). 5 Brazil.
Zollikoferia DC. = Launaea Cass. p.p. (Comp.).
Zollingeria Kurz. Sapindaceae (I). 2 Burma, Indochina.
Zombiana Baill. Myoporaceae. 1 trop. Afr.
Zomicarpa Schott. Araceae (VII). 3 S. Brazil.
Zomicarpella N.E. Br. Araceae (VII). 1 Colombia.
Zonanthemis Greene (*Hemizonia* p.p.). Compositae (5). 2 Calif.
Zonanthus Griseb. Gentianaceae (I). 1 Cuba.
Zones of vegetation, the six zones into which the earth can be divided, occupied by similar types of vegetation with the same periods of growth and the same general adaptation to environment. The divisions are climatic-ecological, and the systematic relationships of the plants are neglected (*cf.* Floral Regions).

I. *The northern Glacial Zone* (the arctic region, and all beyond the tree limit, whether towards the poles, or at high levels—the alpine zone). Period of growth usu. short, temperature low, soil liable to be hot in the day, cold at night. Vegetation mainly xerophytic; veg. repr. well marked.

II. *The northern Zone of cold winters* (from the N. limit of trees to the region where evergr. begin to predominate and the land is parched in summer). Period of growth 4—7 months; summers not usu. parching. Mesophytism predominant; vast areas covered by forests; heaths and other formations of drier areas common.

III. *The northern Zone of hot summers* (the subtrop. regions). No real winter, but perhaps an interruption of vegetation in Jan. Xerophytism well marked, though some regions are wet. Forest, copse (*e.g.* maqui, chaparral), steppe, and prairie all common.

IV. *The tropical Zone* (wherever in the trop. the rainfall is enough to prevent the formation of desert). No real interruption of vegetation. Forest (mesophytic) very common, also parkland or savannah.

V. *The southern Zone of hot summers*: much like III.

VI. *The southern cold Zone*: much like I.

See Schimper, *Plant Geography*; Warming, *Ecological Pl. Geog.*, &c.
Zoophily, pollination by animals.
Zornia J. F. Gmel. Leguminosae (III. 7). 12 trop., esp. Am.

Zosima Hoffm. (*Zozimia EP.*). Umbelliferae (III. 6). 6 W. As.

Zostera Linn. Potamogetonaceae. 6 temp., subarct., subtrop., in salt water on gently sloping shores. *Z. marina* L. and *Z. nana* Roth. in Brit. (eel-grass or grass-wrack). The lower part of the stem creeps, rooting as it advances, and has monopodial branching; the branches grow upwards and exhibit sympodial branching, complicated by union of axillary shoot to main shoot for some distance

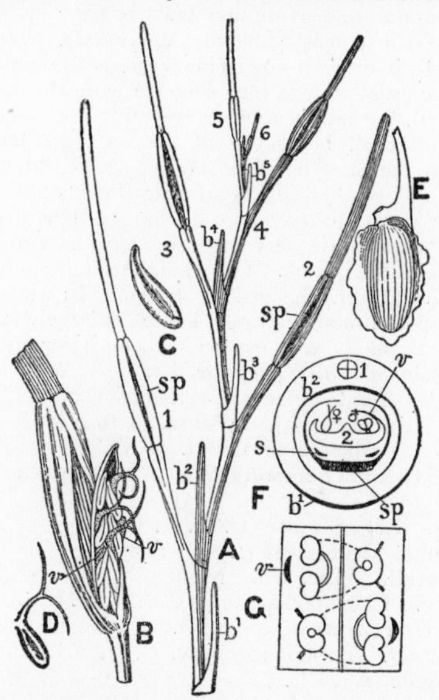

A. Diagram of branching in floral shoot. 1—6, successive shoots, every other one being shaded; b^1, b^2...fore-leaves on these shoots; *sp*, spathes (not indicated in the upper shoots). B. Spathe of *Z. nana* with flattened spadix taken out; *v*, the retinaculum; ×2. C and D. Half-anther and pistil of same, more enlarged. E. Fruit of *Z. marina*, the thin pericarp turned back to show the seed, ×2½. F. Diagram of a main axis, 1, with its fore-leaf (b^1) and the axillary shoot 2, with its fore-leaf (b^2); *sp*, spathe borne on 2, surrounding the spadix; *s*, intravaginal scales; *v*, bracteole. G. Diagram of part of spadix with two flowers; *v*, bracteole.

A, F, G, after Eichler; B, C, D, from *English Botany*; E, after Le Maout and Decaisne.

above its point of origin. This is most easily seen in the infl. region; the branching is that of a rhipidium, but shoot 2, which springs from the axil of a l. on shoot 1, is adnate to 1 up to the point at which the first l. is borne on 2; this l. occupies the angle between the two shoots where they separate. Shoot 1 (and 2, 3, &c. successively) is pushed aside and bears an infl. (Eichler's *Blüthendiag.* or *Nat. Pfl.* for details and figs.) L. long, linear, sheathing at base.

Infl. a flattened spadix, enclosed at flowering time in a spathe (the sheath of the uppermost l.). This is open down one side, and on the corresponding side of the spadix the fls. are borne, the essential organs forming two vertical rows, each composed of a cpl. and a sta. alt. On the outer side of the spadix next the sta. is often a small l. (*retinaculum* of systematic works). The midrib of the cpl. faces outwards. Each cpl. contains one ovule and has two flat stigmas. The sta. consists of two half anthers, joined by a small connective. It is difficult to decide what is the actual 'flower' in this plant; the usual view is that each sta. with the cpl. on the same level forms a fl., the retinaculum representing the bract.

	cpl. sta.	ret.
ret.	sta. cpl.	
	cpl. sta.	ret.

Fert. peculiar, Z. being one of the water pl. most completely modified from the ancestral land-pl. type. Fl. submerged like the rest of the pl. The pollen grains are long threads of the *same* specific gravity as salt water, so that when discharged they float freely at any depth. The stigmas are very large, and thus have a good chance of catching some of the grains. The whole mech. is similar in principle to that of a wind-fert. pl. Fr. an achene. In winter it hibernates without any special modification. The pl. is largely used for packing glass, stuffing cushions, &c., esp. in Venice. [For further details see fam., and Schenk's *Wassergewächse.*]

Zosterella Small. Pontederiaceae. 1 Pennsylvania.

Zoysia Willd. Gramineae (3). 3 Masc. Is. to New Zealand.

Zozimia Hoffm. Umbelliferae (III. 6). 6 W. As.

Zschokkea Muell.-Arg. (*Lacmellia BH.*). Apocynaceae (I. 1). 8 trop. S. Am.

Zuccagnia Cav. Leguminosae (II. 7). 1 Chili.

Zuccarinia Blume. Rubiaceae (I. 8). 1 Java.

Zuccarinia Maerklin. Inc. sed. Nomen.

Zuckia Standley. Chenopodiaceae (A). 1 S.W. U.S.

Zuelania A. Rich. (*Casearia* p.p. *BH.*). Flacourtiaceae (7). 2 W.I.

Zwackhia Sendtner. Boraginaceae (IV. 5). 1 S.E. Eur.

Zwartbast, *Royena lucida* L.

Zwingera Schreb. = Simaba Aubl. (Simarub.).

Zycona O. Ktze. = Allendea La Llave (Comp.).

Zygadenus Michx. Liliaceae (1). 12 N. Am., Siberia.

Zygalchemilla Rydberg (*Alchemilla* p.p.). Rosaceae (III. 5). 1 trop. Am.

Zyganthera N. E. Br. (*Pseudohydrosme* p.p.). Araceae (IV). 1 Gaboon.

Zygella Sp. Moore. Iridaceae (II). 1 Matto Grosso.

Zygia Walp. = Albizzia Durazz. p.p. (Legum.).

Zygo- (Gr. pref.), yoke-; **-morphism**, symmetry about one plane through axis only, *cf.* floral diagrams of *Labiatae*, *Papaveraceae*, *Scrophulariaceae*; usu. antero-post., it is *diagonal* in *Solanaceae*, *transverse* in *Anigozanthos*, *Haemodoraceae*, some *Papaveraceae*, *right* and *left-handed* in *Cassia*, *Exacum*, *Saintpaulia*; **-te**, the cell produced by the union of the sexual gametes.

Zygobatemannia × Rolfe, **Zygocolax** × Rolfe, **Zygonisia** × Rolfe, **Zygomena** × Hort. Orchidaceae. Hybrids of Zygopetalum with Batemannia, Colax, Aganisia, and Zygosepalum (Menadenium).

Zygodia Benth. Apocynaceae (II. 1). 4 trop. Afr.
Zygogynum Baill. Magnoliaceae. 3 New Caled.
Zygomenes Salisb. = Cyanotis D. Don (Commel.).
Zygonerion Baill. (*Strophanthus* p.p.). Apocyn. (II. 1). 1 Angola.
Zygoon Hiern. Rubiaceae (I. 8). 1 Zambesi.
Zygopetalum Hook. (incl. *Pescatorea* Rchb. f.). Orchidaceae (II. 14). 20 trop. Am. The base of the column forms a chin. Cult. orn. fl.
Zygophyllaceae (*EP.*, *BH.*). Dicots. (Archichl. Geraniales). 22 gen., 160 sp., xero- or halo-phytes, trop. and subtrop. Most are woody perennials; l. opp., stip., usu. hairy, fleshy or leathery. Fls. in cymes, reg., ☿. K 5; C 5; A 5 + 5, obdiplost. and with ligular appendages; $\underline{G}$ (5), 5-loc. with 1 or more pend. ov. in each loc. Fr. usu. a caps. Seeds with or without endosp. Guaiacum, Peganum, &c. furnish useful products. *Chief genera:* Zygophyllum, Guaiacum, Porlieria, Larrea, Peganum, Tribulus. Closely related to Rutaceae.
Zygophyllidium Small (*Euphorbia* p.p.). Euph. (A. II. 8). 1 N. Am.
Zygophyllum L. Zygophyllaceae. 60 |✻, deserts and steppes. L. and twigs fleshy.
Zygoruellia Baill. Acanthaceae (IV. A). 1 Madag.
Zygosepalum Reichb. f. (*Zygopetalum BH.*). Orchid. (II. 14). 2 trop. S. Am.
Zygostates Lindl. Orchidaceae (II. 19). 4 Brazil.
Zygostelma Benth. Asclepiadaceae (I). 1 Siam.
Zygostelma Fourn. Asclepiadaceae (II. 1). 1 Brazil.
Zygostigma Griseb. Gentianaceae (I). 2 Brazil, Argentina.

Suggestions for additions to and corrections of the preceding pages can be noted on this slip, which can be detached when desired, signed, and sent to Dr J. C. Willis, c/o University Press, Cambridge

SUPPLEMENT.

TEXT CORRECTIONS, AND NEW GENERA.

This supplement will be brought up to date at intervals.

Aa Reichb. f. = Altensteinia H.B. et K. (Orchid.). 12 Andes.
Abalon Adans. = Helonias L. (Lili.). 10 N. Am.
Abama Adans. (*Narthecium* p.p.). Lili. (1). 6 N. temp.
Abaphus Rafin. = Gethyllis L. (Amaryll.). 1 S. Afr.
Abbottia Rafin. = Triglochin L. (Scheuchzer.). 3 N. temp.
Abelicea Reichb. = Zelkova Spach (Ulm.). 10 N. temp.
Abromeitia Mez. Myrsin. (inc. sed.). 1 New Guinea.
Acaciella Britton et Rose (*Acacia* p.p.). Legum. (I. 2). 50 S.W. U.S. to C. Am., Jamaica.
Acaciopsis Britton et Rose (*Acacia* p.p.). Legum. (I. 2). 15 Mexico, Texas.
Acalyphopsis Pax et K. Hoffm. Euphorb. (A. II. 2). 1 Celebes.
Acanthambrosia Rydberg (*Franseria* p.p.). Comp. (5). 1 Lower Calif.
Acanthea Pharm. ex Wehmer. Acanth. Nomen.
Acanthinophyllum Allem. = Sahagunia Liebm. (Mor.). 1 Brazil.
Acanthophora Merrill. Aral. (2). 1 Phil. Is.
Acanthopteron Britton (*Mimosa* p.p.). Legum. (I. 5). 1 Mexico.
Acanthorhipsalis Britton et Rose (*Rhipsalis* p.p.). Cact. (III. 3). 3 Andes.
Acanthosabal Prosch. Palm. (I. 2). 1 Rio Grande do Sul (Brazil).
Acaroid, the resin of *Xanthorrhoea* (Austr.).
Acaulon N. E. Brown (*Mesembryanthemum* p.p.). Aizo. (II). 1 S. Afr.
Aceraceae. *Cf. Pfl. R.* 1902.
Aceratorchis Schlechter. Orchid. (II. 1). 2 China.
Achariaceae, line 2, after fl. *add* with no deep recept. as in Passifl.
Achasma Griff. = Amomum L. p.p. (Zingiber.). 20 E. Indomal.
Achneria Munro. Now = Afrachneria Sprague.
Achradelphia O. F. Cook (*Achras* p.p.). Sapot. (I). 1 S. Am.
Acmispon Rafin. (*Hosackia* p.p.). Legum. (III. 5). 6 N. Am.
Acmopyle. *Add Cf. Phil. Trans.* 210, p. 253.
Acostaea Schlechter. Orchid. (II. 8). 2 Costa Rica.
Acrilia Griseb. = Trichilia L. (Meli.).
Acroceras Stapf. Gramin. (5). 10 trop.
Acrodon N. E. Brown (*Mesembryanthemum* p.p.). Aizo. (II). 2 S. Afr.
Acronema Edgew. Umbell. (III. 5). 8 Himal., China.
Acrostichum. *Add Cf.* Bower in *Ann. Bot.* 31, 1917, p. 1.
Acrostigma O. F. Cook et Doyle. Palm. (IV. 1). 1 Colombia.
Acrosynanthus Urb. Rubi. (I. 3). 1 Cuba.
Actephilopsis Ridley. Euphorb. (A. I. 1). 1 Malay Penins.
Actinidiaceae (Dillen. p.p.). Dicots. (Archichl. Parietales; p. xxxi). 4/300 E. As. Climbing shrubs with alt. simple exstip. l. and small hypog. fls. usu. in axillary cymose clusters, ☿ or ♂ ♀. K 5, C 5, A 10

or more, anthers inflexed in bud; G (5) or more, multi-loc. with ∞ axile anatr. ov. Berry or caps. Endosperm. *Gen.:* Saurauia, Actinidia, Clematoclethra, Sladenia.

Actinophloeus. *Add* Solomons, Bismarcks.

Actinophora Wall. Tili. Nomen. 1 Java.

Acuan Medic. (*Desmanthus* p.p.). Legum. (I. 3). 30 warm Am., W.I.

Adamaram Adans. = Terminalia L. (Combret.).

Adarianta Knocke (*Pimpinella* p.p.). Umbell. (III. 5). 1 Balearics.

Adelocaryum Brand (*Cynoglossum* p.p.). Borag. (IV. 1). 7 E. Afr. to E. As.

Adenodaphne Sp. Moore. Laur. (II). 1 New Caled.

Adenogyne Klotzsch = Sebastiana Spreng. (Euphorb.).

Adenola Rafin. Onagr. (I). 1 Peru.

Adenorachis Nieuwland (*Aronia* p.p.). Ros. (II). 4 N. Am.

Adenorima Rafin. (*Euphorbia* p.p.). Euphorb. (A. II. 8). 15 W.I., Mex.

Adenosciadium Wolff. Umbell. (III. 5). 1 S.E. Arabia.

Adenostephanus Klotzsch. = Euplassa Salisb. (Prot.).

Adenothola Lemaire (*Manettia* p.p.). Rubi. (I. 5). 1 Brazil.

Adinandrella Exsel. Theac. 1 Portuguese Congo.

Adiscanthus Ducke. Rut. (I. 5). 1 Amazon valley.

Adoxa. *Add* P homochlam. *Cf.* Sprague in *Linn. Journ.* 47, 471.

Aedula Nor. Inc. sed. Nomen.

Aeginetiaceae = Orobanchaceae p.p. *Cf.* Livera in *Ann. R. B. G. Peraden.* X, 1927, p. 145. Includes Christisonia, Cliffordia, Legocia, Campbellia, Hyobanche.

Aegochloa Benth. = Navarretia Ruiz et Pav. (Polemon.).

Aembilla Adans. = Scolopia Schreb. (Flacourt.).

Aeschrion Vell. = Picraena Lindl. (Simarub.). 2 W.I.

Aextoxicaceae. A fam. near Sapind., composed only of Aextoxicon. G 1-loc. Seed 1.

Afgekia Craib. Legum. (III. 6). 1 Siam.

Afrachneria Sprague (*Achneria* Munro). Gram. (9). 7 S. Afr.

Afraegle Engl. Rut. (V). 3 W. Afr.

Aframmi Norman (*Carum* p.p.). Umbell. (III. 5). 1 Angola.

Afrobrunnichia Hutch. et Dalziel. Polygon. (III. 1). 2 W. trop. Afr.

Afrolicania Mildbraed. Ros. (VI. 1a). 1 Liberia, Cameroons.

Afrotrewia Pax et K. Hoffm. Euphorb. (A. II. 2). 1 Cameroons.

Afrotrichloris Chiov. Gramin. (II). 1 E. Afr.

Afrovivella Berger. Crassul. 1 Buahit Mt.

Afzelia Gmel. Scrophular. (III. 1). 10 S.U.S., Mexico.

Agalinis Rafin. (*Gerardia* p.p.). Scroph. (III. 2). 20 S.U.S., W.I.

Agaloma Rafin., Nieuwland (*Euphorbia* p.p.). Euph. (A. II. 8). 15 N. Am.

Agdestis. *Read* Mex. to Brazil, W.I.

Aglaomorpha Schott. Polypod. (8). 8 E. Indomal.

Agrestis Bubani (*Agrostis* p.p.). Gramin. (8). 2 N. Am.

Agrimonoides Miller = Agrimonia L. (Ros.).

Ahouai Miller = Thevetia L. (Apocyn.).

Aigiros Rafin. = Populus Tourn. p.p. (Salic.).

Aiolon Lunell (*Anemone* p.p.). Ranunc. (3). 1 N. Am.

Aistopetalum Schlechter. Cunon. 2 New Guinea.

Ajugoides Makino (*Stachys* p.p.). Labiat. (VI). 1 Japan.
Aklema Rafin. (*Euphorbia* p.p.). Euphorb. (A. II. 8). 2 trop. Am.
Alangium. *Add* 30 trop. Afr. to Japan and Fiji.
Alatus (Lat.), winged.
Albolboa Hieron. = Abolboda Humb. et Bonpl. (Xyrid.).
Alcantarea (Morren) Harms (*Vriesia* p.p.). Bromel. (III). 7 W.I., trop. S. Am.
Alcimandra Dandy (*Michelia* p.p.). Magnol. 1 S.E. As.
Alcineanthus Merrill. Euphorb. (A. II. 6). 2 Phil. Is.
Alcmene Urb. Anon. (inc. sed.). 1 Tobago.
Aleisanthia Ridl. (*Xanthophytum* p.p.). Rubi. (I. 2). 1 Kelantan.
Alepyrum Hieron. *Add* Centrolepid.
Aleurites. *Add A. Fordii* Hemsl. in *Hook. Ic.*, tt. 2801–2, *cordata* Steud. &c. (China, Japan), give tung or China wood oil; *A. triloba* Forst. (Indomal.) candlenut oil, and *A. moluccana* Willd. (Indomal.) &c. give lumbang oil. All drying oils.
Alexa Wight. Apocyn. (I. 3). 1 Para.
Alfaroa Standley. Jugland. 1 Costa Rica.
Alistilus N. E. Brown. Legum. (III. 10). 1 Bechuanaland.
Alkekengi Miller = Physalis L. (Solan.).
Alleizettella Pitard. Rubi. (I. 8). 1 Annam.
Alleizettia Dubard et Dop. Rubi. (I. 7). 1 Madag.
Allioniaceae = Nyctaginaceae.
Aloinopsis Schwantes. Aizo. (II). 8 S. Afr.
Alpaminia O. E. Schulz (*Eudema* p.p.). Crucif. (2). 1 Peru.
Alsinaceae = Caryophyllaceae, § 1.
Alsine L. = Stellaria L. (Caryophyll.).
Alsinella Hill = Sagina L. (Carophyll.).
Alternifolius (Lat.), with alt. l.
Amaranthoides Miller = Gomphrena L. (Amarant.).
Amarcrinum × Hort. Amaryllis × Crinum hybrid. 1 Hort.
Amblynotus I. M. Johnston (*Eritrichium* p.p.). Borag. (IV. 2). 1 Siberia.
Amblyopetalum Malme (*Oxypetalum* p.p.). Asclep. (II. 1). 1 S. Brazil.
Amelanchus Franz Müller ex V. Ros. (*Amelanchier* p.p.). Ros. (II). 3 N. temp.
Amelasorbus × Rehder. Amelanchier × Sorbus hybrid. 1 U.S.
Amentotaxus Pilger (*Cephalotaxus* p.p.). Conif. (Tax.). 1 China.
Amerimnon P. Br. (*Dalbergia* p.p.). Legum. (III. 8). 20 S.E. As.
Amesia A. Nelson et Macbride (*Epipactis* p.p.). Orchid. (II. 2). *Cf. Bot. Gaz.* 56, 1913, p. 472.
Amides, crystallisable bodies, containing C, H, O, and N; asparagin &c.
Ammandra O. F. Cook. Palm. (V). 1 Colombia.
Ammanthus Boiss. et Heldr. (*Chrysanthemum* p.p.). Comp. (7). 3 Medit.
Ammiaceae = Umbelliferae.
Ammocodon Standley (*Echinocarpus* p.p.). Tili. 1 S.W. U.S.
Ammoides Adans. Umbell. (III. 5). 2 Medit.
Ammopursus Small (*Laciniaria* p.p.). Comp. (2). 1 Florida.
Amoebophyllum N. E. Brown. Aizo. (II). 1 Namaqualand.

Amomis Berg. = Pimenta Lindl. (Myrt.).
Amparoa Schlechter (*Odontoglossum* p.p.). Orchid. (II. 19). 2 Costa Rica, Mexico.
Ampelothamnus Small (*Pieris* p.p.). Eric. (II. 1). 1 N. Am.
Amphitoma Gleason. Melastom. (I). 1 Colombia.
Amygdalaceae = Rosaceae, §§ V, VI.
Ana- (Gr. pref.), up.
Anabaenella Pax et K. Hoffm. (*Plukenetia* p.p.). Euphorb. (A. II. 2). 1 E. Brazil.
Anacheilium Hoffmgg. (*Epidendrum* p.p.). Orchid. (II. 6). 1 Fla., W.I., C. Am.
Anadelphia Stapf. Gramin. (2). 1 trop. Afr.
Anadenanthera Speg. (*Piptadenia* p.p.). Legum. (I. 5). 2 Brazil.
Anamtia Koidz. Myrsin. (II. 2). 1 Japan.
Anapodophyllum Miller = Podophyllum L. (Berberid.).
Anastrophea Wedd. Podost. 1 Abyss.
Ancistrocactus Britton et Rose (*Echinocactus* p.p.). Cact. (III. 1). 3 Texas, Mex.
Ancoumea Pierre. Burser. 1 Gaboon. 5-merous. Disc extrastaminal.
Ancylostemon Craib. Gesner. (I). 2 Yunnan.
Anda Juss. = Joannesia Vell. (Euphorb.).
Andesia Haumann (*Oxychloe* p.p.). Junc. 1 S. Andes.
Andromycia. For VI *read* VII.
Andropterum Stapf. Gramin. (2). 1 trop. Afr.
Androsiphon Schlechter. Lili. (V). 1 Cape Col.
Androstylanthus Ducke. Mor. (II). 1 Amazon valley.
Anelsonia Macbride et Payson (*Draba* p.p.). Crucif. (4). 1 N.W. U.S.
Anemonanthera DC. (*Anemone* p.p.). Ranunc. (3). 2 N. temp.
Angoseseli Chiov. Umbell. (III. 5). 1 Angola.
Angostylidium (Muell.-Arg.) Pax et K. Hoffm. (*Plukenetia* p.p.). Euphorb. (A. II. 2). 1 W. trop. Afr.
Anidrum Necker = Bifora Hoffm. (Umbell.).
Anisophyllaceae, a family for Anisophyllea, *q.v.*
Anisostichus Bureau (*Bignonia* p.p.). Bignon. (I). 1 N. Am.
Annesijoa Pax et K. Hoffm. Euphorb. (A. II. 3). 1 New Guinea.
Anneslia Salisb. (*Calliandra* p.p.). Legum. (I. 1). 100 warm.
Anoectocalyx Triana. Melast. (I). 2 Venez. 6-merous. K-teeth unequal.
Anomacanthus Good (*Gillettiella* de Wild et Dur.). Acanth. (II). 1 Angola. Drupaceous.
Anoniodes Schlechter. Tili. 10 New Guinea.
Anonocarpus Ducke. Mor. (II). 1 Amazon valley.
Anota Schlechter (*Saccolabium* p.p.). Orchid. (II. 20). 3 Malaya.
Anotea Kunth (*Malvaviscus* p.p.). Malv. (3). 2 Mexico.
Anthaenatiopsis Mez (*Panicum* p.p.). Gramin. (5). 2 Brazil, Paraguay.
Anthalogea Rafin. (*Polygala* p.p.). Polygal. 1 N. Am.
Antheliacanthus Ridl. Acanth. (IV. B). 1 Siam.
Anthelis Rafin. = Cistus p.p. (*BH.*) = Fumana Spach (Cist.).
Antheroporum Gagnep. Legum. (III. 8). 2 Siam, Cochinchina.
Anthobryum Phil. Franken. 3 Chile, Bolivia.

Anthocoma K. Koch (*Rhododendron* p.p.). Eric. (I. 2). 1 N. As., Himalaya.
Anthocortus Nees in Lindl. Restion. 1 S.W. Cape Col.
Anthurium. *Add* W.I.
Antidesma. For 90 *read* 150.
Antunesia O. Hoffm. = Newtonia O. Hoffm. (Comp.).
Anurosperma Hallier (*Nepenthes* p.p.). Nepenth. 1 Seychelles.
Aparisthmium Endl. (*Alchornea* p.p.). Euphorb. (A. II. 2). 1 warm S. Am.
Apassalus Kobuski (*Dyschoriste* p.p.). Acanth. (IV. A). 3 S.E. U.S., W.I.
Apatesia N. E. Brown. Aizo. (? hybrid). 2 S. Afr.
Aphaca Miller = Lathyrus L. (Legum.).
Aphanocyclic, with whorls not obvious, *e.g.* Nymphaeaceae.
Aphanostemma Schlechter. Asclep. Nomen. 1 China.
Aphelandrella Mildbraed. Acanth. (IV. B). 1 E. Peru.
Aphyllon Torr. et Gray. Orobanch. 2 U.S.
Apinella Neck. = Trinia Hoffm. (Umbell.).
Apinus Neck. (*Pinus* p.p.). Conif. (Pin.). 2 N. Am.
Apodandra Pax et K. Hoffm. (*Plukenetia* p.p.). Euphorb. (A. II. 2). 2 Peru, Bolivia.
Apoia Merrill (*Discocalyx* p.p.). Myrsin. (II). 1 Phil. Is.
Apoplanesia Presl. (*Microlobium* p.p.). Legum. (inc. sed.). 1 Mex., C. Am.
Apotaenium K.-Pol. (*Chaerophyllum* p.p.). Umbell. (III. 2). 1 Himal.
Appunettia Good. Rubi. (II. 9). 1 Angola.
Aptenia N. E. Brown (*Mesembryanthemum* p.p.). Aizo. (II). 1 S. Afr.
Apteranthera C. H. Wright. Amarant. (2). 1 Aldabra.
Apurimacia Harms. Legum. (III. 6). 4 N. Andes.
Arabidella O. E. Schulz (*Erysimum* p.p.). Crucif. (2). 1 Austr.
Arachnis Blume (*Arachnanthe* p.p.). Orchid. (II. 20). 4 Malaya.
Arceuthos Antoine et Kotschy. Conif. (Pin.). 1 Greece, As. Minor.
Arcoa Urb. Euphorb. (A. II. 3). 1 Haiti.
Arcyosperma O. E. Schulz (*Sisymbrium* p.p.). Crucif. (2). 1 Himal.
Arecastrum Becc. (*Cocos* p.p.). Palm. (IV. 2). 1 Brazil.
Arequipa Britton et Rose (*Echinocactus* p.p.). Cact. (III. 1). 2 Peru, Chile.
Argeta N. E. Brown. Aizo. (II). 1 S. Afr.
Argostemmella Ridley Rubi. (I. 2). 2 Borneo.
Argyroderma N. E. Brown. Aizo. (II). 6 S. Afr.
Ariadne Urb. Rubi. (II. 4). 1 Cuba.
Aridaria N. E. Brown (*Mesembryanthemum* p.p.). Aizo. (II). 7 S. Afr.
Arisacontis. For inc. sed. *read* IV.
Arisanorchis Hayata. Orchid. (II. 2). 1 Formosa.
Aristoclesia Coville (*Platonia* p.p.). Guttif. (V). 1 Guiana, trop. Afr.
Aristopetalum Schlechter. Cunon. 2 New Guinea.
Armodorum Breda (*Aerides* p.p.). Orchid. (II. 20). 3 E. As.
Armola Montandon (*Atriplex* p.p.). Chenopod. (A). 3 temp.
Arnoldoschultzia Mildbraed. Sapot. 1 Cameroons. Nomen.
Aromadendrum Blume (*Talauma* p.p.). Magnol. 1 Malay Penins., Java.

Arrojadoa Britton et Rose. Cact. (III. 1). 2 E. Brazil.
Arrojadoa Mattf. Comp. (2). 1 Bahia.
Arsenococcus Small (*Andromeda* p.p.). Eric. (II. 1). 2 N. Am.
Artemisiastrum Rydberg (*Artemisia* p.p.). Comp. (7). 1 Calif.
Aspalathoides K. Koch (*Anthyllis* p.p.). Legum. (III. 5). 4 Medit., Eur.
Asparagus fern, *Asparagus plumosus* Baker.
Aspazoma N. E. Brown (*Mesembryanthemum* p.p.). Aizo. (II). 1 S. Afr.
Aspidophyllum Ulbr. Ranunc. (3). 1 Peru.
Aspris Adans. (*Aira* p.p.). Gramin. (9). 7 Eur.
Assonia Cav. (*Dombeya* p.p.). Stercul. 3 Masc. Is.
Asteranthemum Kunth = Smilacina Desf. (Lili.).
Asterigeron Rydberg (*Aster* p.p.). Comp. (3). 1 W. U.S.
Asterolepidion Ducke. Icacin. 1 Amazon valley.
Asteropyrum J. R. Drumm. et J. Hutch (*Isopyrum* p.p.). Ranunc. (2). 2 China.
Astilboides Engl. Saxifrag. (I). 1 N. China.
Astridia Dinter et Schwantes (*Mesembryanthemum* p.p.). Aizo. (II). 1 S. Afr.
Astrophytum Lemaire (*Echinocactus* p.p.). Cact. (III. 1). 4 Mexico.
Asyneuma Griseb. et Schenck (*Phyteuma* p.p.). Campan. (I. 1). 4 Medit.
Atamosco Adans. (*Zephyranthes* p.p.). Amaryll. (I. 1). 35 Am.
Atenia Hook. et Arn. (*Carum* p.p.). Umbell. (III. 5). 3 N. Am.
Athernotus Dulac (*Calamagrostis* p.p.). Gramin. (8). 4 N. temp.
Athroandra (Hook. f.) Pax et K. Hoffm. (*Claoxylon* p.p.). Euphorb. (A. II. 2). 20 W. trop. Afr.
Aucuparia Riv. ex Rupp. (*Sorbus* p.p.). Ros. (II). 2 W. U.S.
Auerodendron Urb. Rhamn. 4 Cuba, Bahamas.
Augouardia Pellegr. Legum. (II. 2). 1 French Congo.
Auliza Salisb. (*Epidendrum* p.p.). Orchid. (II. 6). 80 warm Am., W.I.
Aulonemia Goudot. Gramin. (13). 1 Colombia, Venezuela.
Aulosolena K.-Pol. (*Sanicula* p.p.). Umbell. (II. 1). 4 W. Am.
Aureolaria Rafin. (*Gerardia* p.p.). Scroph. (III. 2). 10 E. U.S.
Austrocactus Britton et Rose (*Cereus* p.p.). Cact. (III. 1). 1 Patagonia.
Austromuellera C. T. White. Proteac. (inc. sed.). 1 Queensland.
Austrotaxus Compton. Conif. (Tax.). 1 New Caled. *Linn. Journ.* 45.
Autranella A. Chevalier (*Mimusops* p.p.). Sapot. (II). 1 trop. Afr.
Aveledoa Pittier. Olac. 1 Venez.
Avesicaria Barnh. (*Utricularia* p.p.). Lentibul. 5 Brazil.
Avetra H. Perrier. Dioscor. 1 E. Madag.
Aylostera Speg. (*Echinocactus* p.p.). Cact. (III. 1). 1 Uruguay.
Azadirachta. *Add* Meliac. and W.I.
Azolla. After *A. nilotica add* Decne.
Azorellopsis H. Wolff. Umbell. (I. 2). 1 Bolivia.
Baccaurea. For trop. Afr. &c. *read* Indomal.
Bahamia Britton et Rose (*Acacia* p.p.). Legum. (I. 2). 1 Bahamas.
Balanophoraceae. For G̅ *read* G̲.
Balantium. For Cyath. *read* Dickson.
Bambekea Cogn. (*Cucumeropsis* p.p.). Cucurb. (3). 1 Cameroons, Congo.
Bambos Retz (*Guadua* p.p.). Gramin. (13). 1 Mexico.

Baobab Adans. = Adansonia L. (Bombac.).
Baphia. *Cf. Linn. Journ.* 45, p. 221.
Barbeyaceae (Ulmaceae p.p.). Dicots (Archichl. Urticales). 1/1 N.E. Afr., Arabia (Barbeya). Trees with opp. simple exstip. l. and dioec. reg. apet. fls. A 6—9, G 1-loc. with one pend. anatr. ov. Dry indeh. fr.; no endosp.
Barbosella Schlechter (*Restrepia* p.p.). Orchid. (II. 8). 15 C. and S. Am.
Barneoudia Gay. Ranunc. (3). 4 Chile, Arg.
Barnhartia Gleason. Styrac. 1 Brit. Guiana.
Barombia Schlechter (*Angraecum* p.p.). Orchid. (II. 20). 1 Cameroons.
Bartschella Britton et Rose (*Mammillaria* p.p.). Cact. (III. 2). 1 Lower California.
Barylucuma Ducke. Sapot. (I). 1 Para.
Basiphyllaea Schlechter (*Bletia* p.p.). Orchid. (II. 6). 1 Cuba.
Bathiea Schlechter (*Aeranthes* p.p.). Orchid. (II. 20). 1 Madag.
Batidophaca Rydberg (*Astragalus* p.p.). Legum. (III. 6). 25 S. U.S., Mex.
Bauerella Schindler. Legum. (III. 7). 1 Austr.
Baumiella Wolff. Umbell. (III. 5). 1 trop. Afr.
Beccariophoenix Jumelle et Perrier. Palm. (IV. 1). 1 Madag.
Beckeria, *read* Becheria.
Beclardia A. Rich. (*Epidendrum* p.p.). Orchid. (II. 6). 2 Madag., Masc.
Beesia Balf. f. et W. W. Smith. Ranunc. (1). 1 Burma, Yunnan.
Behen Moench. (*Silene* p.p.). Caryophyll. (II. 1). 1 Rhine valley.
Belandra Blake. Apocyn. (II. 1). 1 Brit. Honduras.
Belharnosia Adans. = Sanguinaria L. (Papav.). 1 Atl. N. Am.
Beloglottis Schlechter (*Spiranthes* p.p.). Orchid. (II. 20). 2 trop. Am.
Bemarivea Choux (*Cupania* p.p.). Sapind. (I). 1 Madag.
Bembicidium Rydberg. Legum. (III. 6). 1 Cuba.
Benedictella Maire. Legum. (III. 5). 1 Morocco.
Bentinckiopsis Becc. (*Cyphokentia* p.p.). Palm. (IV. 1). 3 Carolines, Bonins.
Bequaertiodendron de Wild. Sapot. (I). 1 Belgian Congo.
Berchemiella Nakai. Rhamn. 2 China, Japan.
Bergeranthus Schwantes (*Mesembryanthemum* p.p.). Aizo. (II). 5 S. Afr.
Bermudiana Adans. (*Sisyrinchium* p.p.). Irid. (II). 10 Am.
Berteroella O. E. Schulz (*Sisymbrium* p.p.). Crucif. (2). 1 E. As., Jap.
Berula Koch. Umbell. (III. 5). 2, one N. temp., one trop. and S. Afr.
Betchea Schlechter. Cunon. 5 New Guinea, N.E. Austr.
Bifolium Petiver = Listera p.p. (Orchid.).
Bigaradia oil, the oil of Seville bitter orange peel.
Bijlia N. E. Brown (*Hereroa* p.p.). Aizo. (II). 1 S. Afr.
Bikukulla Adans. = Dicentra Bernh. (Papav.).
Bilegnum Brand (*Rindera* p.p.). Borag. (IV. 1). 1 Persia.
Binghamia Britton et Rose (*Cephalocereus* p.p.). Cact. (III. 1). 2 Peru.
Bird of Paradise flower (Am.), *Strelitzia.*
Bizonula Pellegr. Sapind. (I). 1 French Congo.

Blandibractea Wernh. Rubi. (I. 3). 1 Brazil.
Blepharidium Standley. Rubi. (I. 5). 1 Guatemala.
Boesenbergia O. Ktze. = Gastrochilus Wall. p.p. (Zingiber.).
Boholia Merrill. Rubi. (II. 1). 1 Phil. Is.
Boivinella A. Camus. Gramin. (5). 1 Madag., Comoros.
Bolusanthemum Schwantes (*Mesembryanthemum* p.p.). Aizo. (II). 1 S. Afr.
Bolusiella Schlechter (*Listrostachys* p.p.). Orchid. (II. 20). 5 W. and S.E. Afr.
Bombacopsis Pittier (*Pachira* p.p.). Bombac. 2 Panama, Costa Rica.
Bommeria Fournier (*Gymnopteris* p.p.). Polypod. 4 Am.
Boninofatsia Nakai (*Fatsia* p.p.). Aral. (I). 2 Bonin.
Bonnayodes Blatter et Hallb. Scroph. (II. 6). 1 Bombay.
Borderea. *Omit* Chile.
Borodinia Busch. Crucif. (4). 1 E. Siberia.
Botryomeryta R. Viguier. Aral. (I). 1 New Caledonia.
Botryopsis Miers = Chondodendron Ruiz et Pav. (Menisp.). 2 Peru, Bolivia.
Botrys Reichb. (*Chenopodium* p.p.). Chenopod. (A). 10 N. temp.
Bottegoa Chiov. Sapind. (I). 1 Somaliland.
Bovonia Chiov. Labi. (VII.). 1 Belgian Congo.
Brabyla L. = Brabejum L. (Prot.).
Brachionostylum Mattf. Comp. (8). 1 New Guinea.
Brachyachne Stapf. Gramin. (II). 2 trop. Afr., Austr.
Brachycereus Britton et Rose. Cact. (III. 1). 1 Galapagos.
Brachycyrtis Koidzumi (*Tricyrtis* p.p.). Lili. (I). 1 Japan.
Brachymeris DC. = Marasmodes DC. (Comp.).
Brachyramphus DC. = Lactuca Tourn. (Comp.).
Brachystele Schlechter (*Spiranthes* p.p.). Orchid. (II. 2). 15 warm S. Am., Trinidad.
Bracteanthus Ducke. Monim. 1 Para.
Bragantia. After Lam. *omit* p.p.
Bramia Lam. (*Bacopa* p.p.). Scroph. (II. 6). 20 warm.
Brassicaceae = Cruciferae.
Brassicella Fourreau (*Brassica* p.p.). Crucif. (2). 6 Eur., Medit.
Braunsia Schwantes. Aizo. (II). 3 S. Afr.
Brenesia Schlechter. Orchid. (II. 8). 1 Costa Rica.
Breyniopsis Beille. Euphorb. (A. I. 1). 1 Cochinchina.
Briar root. *Add E. arborea* L.
Briggsia Craib. Gesner. (I). 2 Yunnan, Burma.
Brittonrosea Speg. = Echinofossulocactus Lawrence (Cact.).
Bromelica Farwell (*Melica* p.p.). Gramin. (10). 5 U.S.
Bromuniola Stapf et C. E. Hubbard. Gramin. (10). 1 Angola.
Brongniartikentia Becc. (*Cyphokentia* p.p.). Palm. (IV. 1). 1 New Caledonia.
Brossaea L. = Gaultheria L. (Eric.).
Brousemichia Bal. Gramin. (8). 1 Tonquin.
Brownanthus Schwantes = Trichocyclus N. E. Brown (Ficoid.).
Browningia Britton et Rose (*Cereus* p.p.). Cact. (III. 1). 1 Peru, Chile.
Buchanania Pierre = Buchanania Spreng. (Anacard.).
Buchtienia Schlechter. Orchid. (II. 2). 1 Bolivia.

Burkillia Ridley. Legum. (III. 6). 1 Malay Penins.
Buxus. *Cf.* Boxwoods of Commerce. *Bull. Torr. Bot. Cl.*, 1921, p. 297.
Byblidaceae. A small family (Byblis, Roridula) placed near Pittosporaceae. Herbs or undershrubs with crowded exstip. linear glandular-hairy l. and ⊕ ☿ fls. K, C, A 5 hypog., anthers by pores, $\underline{G}$ (2—3), 2—3-loc. with 1—2 pend. or ∞ axile ov., and capitate stigma. Caps. loculicidal. Endosperm.
Caconapea Cham. (*Herpestis* p.p.). Scroph. (II. 6). 5 trop. Am.
Cactaceae. *Cf.* Britton and Rose, *The C.*
Cactus L. (*Melocactus* Link et Otto, Britton et Rose). Cact. (III. 1). 20 trop. Am., W. I.
Caelebogyne J. Sm. (*Alchornea* p.p.). Euphorb. (A. II. 2). 2 E. Austr.
Cajalbania Urb. Legum. (III. 6). 1 Cuba.
Cake, the residue after crushing seed for oil; *e.g.* coconut cake (copra), cottonseed cake, linseed cake, &c.
Calamophyllum Schwantes (*Mesembryanthemum* p.p.). Aizo. (II). 3 S. Afr.
Calatola Standley. Icacin. 2 Mexico.
Calceolus Adans. = Cypripedium L. p.p. (Orchid.).
Calderonia Standley. Rubi. (I. 1). 1 Salvador.
Calhounia A. Nels. (*Lagascea* p.p.). Comp. (5). 15 Am.
Callista Lour. (*Dendrobium* p.p.). Orchid. (II. 15). 2 Indochina.
Callistigma Dinter et Schwantes. Aizo. (II). 1 S. Afr.
Callistylon Pittier (*Coursetia* p.p.). Legum. (III. 6). 1 Venez.
Callitropsis Compton. Conif. (Pin.). 1 New Caled. *Linn. Journ.* 45, 432.
Callopsis. For Araceae (I), *read* (VII).
Callus (grass), the swollen base of inf. palea, adnate to axis.
Calocarpum Pierre (*Lucuma* p.p.). Sapot. (I). 3 trop. Am.
Caloglossum Schlechter (*Cymbidium* p.p.). Orchid. (II. 17). 4 Madag.
Calophanoides Ridley (*Justicia* p.p.). Acanth. (IV. B). 1 Indomal., China.
Calopsis, *read* Restion. 10 S. Afr.
Calorophus, *read* Restion. 3 Austr., Tasm., N.Z.
Calospatha Becc. (*Daemonorops* p.p.). Palm. (III. 2). 1 Malay Penins.
Calpidisca Barnh. (*Utricularia* p.p.). Lentibul. 60 trop., S. Afr.
Calpidosicyos Harms. Cucurb. (3). 1 E. trop. Afr.
Calyptosepalum S. Moore. Santal. 1 Sumatra.
Calyptracordia Britton. Boragin. (I). 1 W.I.
Camchaya Gagnep. Comp. (1). 1 Cambodia.
Camelliaceae = Theaceae.
Cammarum Hill = Eranthis Salisb. (Ranunc.).
Campestigma Pierre. Asclep. (II. 3). 1 Indochina.
Campos (Brazil), open grass country with patches of timber.
Camptophytum Pierre ex A. Chevalier. Rubi. (inc. sed.). 1 Congo.
Campulosus Desv. (*Ctenium* p.p.). Gramin. (11). 2 Am.
Campylopus Spach (*Hypericum* p.p.). Guttif. (II). 3 N. temp.
Campylotheca Cass. (*Bidens* &c. p.p.). Comp. (5). 6 Sandw. Is.
Campylotropis Bunge (*Lespedeza* p.p.). Legum. (III. 7). 20 warm As.
Cantleya Ridl. Icacin. 1 Johore.
Cape cowslip (Am.), *Lachenalia.*
Capellia Blume = Warmia Rottb. (Dillen.).

Capethia Britton. Ranunc. (3). 2 W.S. Am.
Capillipedium Stapf. Gramin. (2). 6 warm |✻.
Capitanopsis S. Moore. Labiat. (VII). 1 Madag.
Capnorchis Borck., Ludw. = Dicentra Bernh. (Papav.).
Carara Medic. (*Coconopus* p.p.). Crucif. (2). 6 cosmop.
Cardenasia Rusby (*Bauhinia* p.p.). Legum. (II. 4). 1 Upper Amaz.
Cardiocrinum Endl., Lindl. (*Lilium* p.p.). Lili. (V). 3 E. As.
Cardionema DC. = Pentacaena Bartl. (Caryoph.). 5 Pac. Am.
Carlephyton Jumelle. Arac. (VII). 1 Madag.
Carpanthea N. E. Brown. Aizo. (II). 1 S. Afr.
Carpentia Ewart. Convolv. (I). 1 N. Austr.
Carpobrotus N. E. Brown (*Mesembryanthemum* p.p.). Aizo. (II). 20 S. Afr., N.Z., Austr., W. Am.
Carruanthus Schwantes. Aizo. (II). 1 S. Afr.
Carumbium Reinw. = Homalanthus Juss. (Euphorb.).
Cashalia Standley. Legum. (II. 9). 1 Salvador.
Casparea H.B.K. = Bauhinia L. p.p. (Legum.).
Cassythaceae. A family containing Cassytha only.
Catadysia O. E. Schulz. Crucif. (2). 1 Peru.
Catalepis Stapf et Stent. Gramin. (11 or 3). 1 Transvaal.
Catatia Humbert. Comp. (4). 2 Madag.
Catharanthus G. Don (*Lochnera* Reichb.). Apocyn. (I. 3). 3 trop.
Catocoma Benth. = Bredemeyera Willd. (Polygal.).
Catostigma O. F. Cook et Doyle. Palm. (IV. 1). 1 Colombia.
Caucaliopsis Wolff. Umbell. (III. 2). 1 Nyasaland.
Caudoleucaena Britton et Rose (*Leucaena* p.p.). Legum. (I. 3). 1 S. U.S.
Caudoxalis Small. (*Oxalis* p.p.). Oxalid. 1 S. Afr.
Cavaleriella Léveillé. Caprifol. 2 China.
Cavaraea Speg. Legum. 1 Arg.
Cavea W. W. Smith et Small. Comp. (4). 1 Sikkim.
Cayratia Juss. Vit. 10 E. Indomal.
Cebatha Forsk. = Cocculus DC. (Menisp.).
Cedrelinga Ducke. Legum. 5 trop. Am.
Celastraceae. *Add* L. stip., opp. or alt.
Celeri Adans. (*Apium* p.p.). Umbell. (III. 5). 1 N. temp.
Cenesmon Gagnep. Euphorb. (A. II. 2). 6 Indoch., Yunnan.
Centinodium Montandon (*Polygonum* p.p.). Polygon. (II. 2). 1 N. temp. (*P. aviculare* L.).
Centrogonium Schlechter (*Pelexia* p.p.). Orchid. (II. 2). 7 trop. Am., W.I.
Centrosolenia Benth. = Episcia Mart. p.p.
Centrostachys Wall. (*Achyranthes* p.p.). Amarant. (2). 12 warm.
Cephalangraecum Schlechter (*Angraecum* p.p.). Orchid. (II. 20). 5 W. trop. Afr.
Cephalomammillaria Frič. (*Mammillaria* p.p.). Cact. (III. 2). 2 Texas.
Cephalophyllum Haw. = Mesembryanthemum Dill. p.p. (Aizo.).
Cephalophyllum N. E. Brown (*Mesembryanthemum* p.p.). Aizo. (II). 30 S. Afr.
Cephaloschefflera Merrill (*Schefflera* p.p.). Aral. (I). 10 Phil. Is.
Cerastium. For N. temp. *read* almost cosmop.
Ceratophytum Pittier. Bignon. (I). 2 Venez.

Cercidiphyllaceae (*EP.*; *Magnol.* p.p. *BH.*). Dicots. (Archichl. Ranales, p. xvii). Only genus **Cercidiphyllum** Sieb. et Zucc. (2 Japan), with opp. l. and united stips. Fl. sol. dioec., naked. A ∞ united at base, G 2—5 stalked, with ∞ ov. Follicle. Endosp.
Cerochlamys N. E. Brown. Aizo. (11). 1 S. Afr.
Chaetobromus Nees. Gramin. (9). 3 S. Afr.
Changium H. Wolff. Umbell. (III. 4). 1 China.
Charlock, *Sinapis alba* L.
Chasmatophyllum Dinter et Schwantes (*Mesembryanthemum* p.p.). Aizo. (11). 3 S. Afr.
Chasmopodium Stapf. Gramin. (2). 2 trop. Afr.
Chaunanthus O. E. Schulz (*Thelypodium* p.p.). Crucif. (1). 1 Mexico.
Cheesemania O. E. Schulz (*Cardamine* p.p.). Crucif. (2). 5 N.Z., Tasm.
Cheiranthesimum × Bois. Cheiranthus-Erysimum hybrid. 1 Hort.
Cheiridopsis N. E. Brown (*Mesembryanthemum* p.p.). Aizo. (11). 25 S. Afr.
Cheirinia Link (*Erysimum* p.p.). Crucif. (4). 20 N. temp.
Chelonanthera Blume (*Pholidota* p.p.). Orchid. (II. 16). 2 Malay Arch.
Chelyocarpus Dammer. Palm. (I. 2). 1 Amazonas.
Chersodoma Phil. Comp. (8). 1 Chile.
Chesneya Lindl. = Calophaca Fisch. p.p. (Legum.).
Chiapasia Britton et Rose (*Epiphyllum* p.p.). Cact. (III. 1). 1 Mexico.
Chiastophyllum (Ledeb.) Stapf. Crassul. 1 Caucasus.
Chikusichloa Koidz. Gramin. (5). 1 Japan.
Chilocardamum O. E. Schulz (*Sisymbrium* p.p.). Crucif. (2). 1 Patagonia.
Chimaeras. *Cf.* Cytisus; Weiss in *Biol. Reviews*, v, Cambridge.
Chionocharis I. M. Johnston. Boragin. (IV. 2). 1 Himalaya.
Chiovendaea Speg. Legum. 1 Arg.
Chloachne Stapf. Gramin. (5). 25 Afr. Hooker, *Ic.* 3072.
Chloranthaceae. Before G *add* G̅ or.
Chlorocaulon Klotzsch = Chiropetalum A. Juss. (Euphorb.).
Chloroleucon Britton et Rose. Legum. (III. 8). 1 Honduras.
Chloropatane Engl. *Read* = Claoxylon A. Juss. (Euphorb.).
Chodaphyton Minod (*Stemodia* p.p.). Scroph. (II. 6). 1 Paraguay.
Choenomeles Lindl. = Cydonia Tourn. p.p. (Ros.).
Chomutowia B. Fedtsch. Plumbag. 1 Turkestan.
Chondropetalum Rottb. Restion. 18 S. Afr.
Chonocentrum Pierre. Euphorb. (A. I. 1). 1 Amazonas.
Chonopetalum Radlk. Sapind. (1). 1 Spanish Guinea.
Chorilepidella Van Tiegh. (*Loranthus* p.p.). Loranth. (1). 1 Phil. Is.
Chorisandra R. Br. *Cf.* Chorizandra.
Chorisiva Rydberg (*Iva* p.p.). Comp. (5). 1 Nevada.
Chorispermum Br. in Aitk. = Chorispora R. Br. (Crucif.).
Choristemon Williamson. Epacrid. (3). 1 Victoria.
Christophoriana Moench (*Actaea* p.p.). Ranunc. (2). 2 N. temp.
Chromolucuma Ducke. Sapot. (1). 1 Para.
Chronanthos K. Koch = Genista L. p.p. (Legum.).
Chrozophora. *Add* India and Cameroons.
Chrysophäe K.-Pol. (*Chaerophyllum* p.p.). Umbell. (III. 5). 2 E. Medit.

Chytraculia P. Br. = Calyptranthes Sw. (Myrt.).
Cibotium. For Cyath. *read* Dickson. Bower, *Ferns*, i, 263.
Cicerbita Wallr. (*Lactuca* p.p.). Comp. (13). 60 N. temp., and trop. Mts.
Ciceronia Urb. Comp. (2). 1 Cuba.
Cionandra Griseb. = Cayaponia Silva Manso p.p. (Cucurb.).
Citrus. *Cf.* Coit, *Citrus Fruits*.
Cladobium Schlechter (*Spiranthes* p.p.). Orchid. (II. 2). 5 Brazil.
Clarorivinia Pax et K. Hoffm. (*Mallotus* p.p.). Euphorb. (A. II. 1). 1 New Guinea.
Clavipodium Desv. ex Grüning = Beyeria Miq. (Euphorb.).
Cleistocactus Lemaire (*Cereus* p.p.). Cact. (III. 1). 3 temp. S. Am.
Clematopsis Bojer ex Hutch. (*Clematis* p.p.). Ranunc. (3). 10 Madag., trop. Afr.
Clemensiella (*Clemensia*) Schlechter. Asclep. (II. 3). 1 Phil. Is.
Cleretum N. E. Brown (*Mesembryanthemum* p.p.). Aizo. (II). 8 S. Afr.
Clethra. *Add* l. exstip.; C imbr.; anthers by pores; ov. ∞ in each loc.; style crenate, or with 3 short stigmas.
Cliffordia Livera (*Christisonia* p.p.). Orobanch. 5 Ceylon, India.
Clinosperma Becc. (*Cyphokentia* p.p.). Palm. (IV. 1). 1 New Caledonia.
Clitandropsis S. Moore. Apocyn. (I. 1). 1 New Guinea.
Clomenocoma Cass. (*Dysodia* p.p.). Comp. (6). 10 S. U.S., Mex., C. Am.
Clonostylis S. Moore. Euphorb. (A. II. 2). 1 Sumatra.
Coccineorchis Schlechter (*Spiranthes* p.p.). Orchid. (II. 2). 1 Peru.
Coccomelia Ridl. (*Parinarium* p.p.). Ros. (VI b). 1 Malay Penins.
Cochemiea (Brandegee) Walton (*Mammillaria* p.p.). Cact. (III. 2). 5 Lower Calif.
Codazzia Karst. et Triana, 1854. Bignon.
Codonechites Markgraf. Apocyn. (II. 1). 1 Acre.
Codonoboea Ridl. Gesner. (I). 3 Pahang.
Coelestina Cass. (*Ageratum* p.p.). Comp. (2). 1 Mexico, New Mex.
Coelophragmus O. E. Schulz (*Sisymbrium* p.p.). Crucif. (2). 2 Mexico.
Coelopyrena Val. Rubi. (II. 5). 1 New Guinea, Amboina.
Coilocarpus Domin (*Anisacantha* p.p.). Chenopod. (A). 1 Queensland.
Cojoba Britton et Rose (*Mimosa* p.p.). Legum. (I. 5). 20 C. Am., Mex., W.I.
Colensoa Hook. f. (*Pratia* p.p.). Campanul. (III). 1 New Zealand.
Coleophora Miers = Daphnopsis Mart. (Thymel.).
Collandra Lemaire = Columnea L. p.p. (Gesner.).
Collania Herb. = Bomarea l. p.p. (Amaryll.). 10 trop. Am.
Colobanthera Humbert. Comp. (3). 1 Madag.
Colobogyne Gagnep. Comp. (5). 1 Annam.
Colubrina Montandon (*Polygonum* p.p.). Polygon. (II. 2). 2 N. temp. and arctic.
Commelinantia Tharp (*Tradescantia* p.p.). Commelin. 2 C. Am.
Commelinidium Stapf. Gramin. (5). 3 W. Afr.
Comptonella Baker f. Rut. (I. 1). 1 New Caled.
Conceveibastrum Pax et K. Hoffm. (*Alchornea* p.p.). Euphorb. (A. II. 2). 1 Amazonas.

Congdonia Jepson (*Sedum* p.p.). Crassul. 1 Calif.
Congonha, *Ilex paraguensis* St Hil.
Conophyllum Schwantes. Aizo. (II). 8 S. Afr.
Conophytum N. E. Brown (*Mesembryanthemum* p.p.). Aizo. (II). 100 S. Afr.
Consolida S. F. Gray (*Delphinium* p.p.). Ranunc. (2). 10 E. Medit.
Copedesma Gleason. Melastom. (I). 1 Brit. Guiana.
Copiapoa Britton et Rose (*Echinocactus* p.p.). Cact. (III. 1). 6 Chile.
Cordemoya Baill. (*Mallotus* p.p.). Euphorb. (A. II. 2). 1 Masc.
Cordiera A. Rich. = Alibertia A. Rich. (Rubi.).
Cordiglottis J. J. Smith. Orchid. (II. 20). 1 Sumatra.
Cordula Rafin. (*Cypripedium* p.p.). Orchid. (I. 2). 50 trop. As.
Cordylophorum Rydberg (*Epilobium* p.p.). Onagr. (2). 1 W. U.S.
Coreosma Spach (*Ribes* p.p.). Saxifrag. (VI). 2 N. Am.
Coriandropsis Wolff (*Coriandrum* p.p.). Umbell. (III. 3). 1 Kurdistan.
Corpuscularia Schwantes (*Mesembryanthemum* p.p.). Aizo. (II). 8 S. Afr.
Corryocactus Britton et Rose (*Cereus* p.p.). Cact. (III. 1). 3 Peru, Bolivia.
Corynophyllus Schott = Amorphophallus Blume p.p. (Arac.).
Coryphantha (Engelm.) Lemaire (*Mammillaria* p.p.). Cact. (III. 2). 40 Mex., U.S., Canada.
Cosmiza Rafin. (*Utricularia* p.p.). Lentibul. 2 Austr.
Costaricaea Schlechter. Orchid. (II. 6). 1 Costa Rica.
Costaricia H. Christ. Polypod. (inc. sed.). 1 Costa Rica.
Cotylonia Norman. Umbell. (I. 1). 1 W. China.
Coutaportla Urb. (*Portlandia* p.p.). Rubi. (I. 1). 1 Mexico.
Coutiria Vell., 1799. Apocyn. 1 Bahia.
Craigia W. W. Smith et W. E. Evans. Stercul. 1 Yunnan.
Crambella Maire (*Crambe* p.p.). Crucif. (2). 1 Morocco.
Craspedolobium Harms. Legum. (III. 6). 1 Yunnan.
Crassina Scepin = Zinnia L. (Comp.).
Craterianthus Valeton ex K. Heyne. Rubi. (I. 7). 1 Sumatra, Borneo.
Cremnobates Ridl. Rhizophor. 1 New Guinea.
Crindonna × Hort. Crinum-Belladonna hybrid. 1 Hort.
Crinonia Blume (*Pholidota* p.p.). Orchid. (II. 16). 3 Malay Penins., Java, Sumatra.
Critonia P. Br. = Eupatorium Tourn. p.p. (Comp.).
Crocanthemum Spach = Halimium Willk. (Cist.).
Crocanthus L. Bolus. Aizo. (II). 3 S. Afr.
Crossangis Schlechter (*Listrostachys* p.p.). Orchid. (II. 20). 1 Cameroons.
Crosslandia W. V. Fitzger. Cyper. (I). 1 W. Austr.
Crozophyla Rafin. = Codiaeum Juss. (Euphorb.).
Crucifera E. H. L. Krause = Cardamine L. p.p. (Crucif.).
Cryophytum N. E. Brown (*Mesembryanthemum* p.p.). Aizo. (II). 45 S. Afr.
Cryptanthus Osbeck. Inc. sed. Nomen.
Crypteroniaceae. A family near Lythr. comprising only Crypteronia.
Cryptophila H Wolff. Pyrol. 1 Alabama.
Cryptorhiza Urb. Myrt. (I). 1 Haiti.

Ctenardisia Ducke. Myrsin. (II). 1 Para.
Ctenocladus Engl. Mor. (I). 1 Cameroons.
Ctenolepis Hook. f. = Blastania Kotschy et Peyr. (Cucurb.).
Ctenomeria Harv. (*Tragia* p.p.). Euphorb. (A. II. 2). 2 S. Afr.
Cubincola Urb. Euphorb. (A. I. 1). 1 Cuba.
Curcas Adans. (*Jatropha* p.p.). Euphorb. (A. II. 3). 10 trop.
Curtisina Ridl. Sapind. (I). 1 Penang.
Cuscatlania Standley. Nyctagin. 1 Salvador.
Cuscutaceae = Convolvulaceae, § II.
Cyanococcus Rydberg (*Vaccinium* p.p.). Eric. (III. 1). 2 N. Am.
Cyanthillium Blume (*Vernonia* p.p.). *Cf.* Gleason in *Bull. Torr. Bot. Club*, 40, 1913, 306.
Cyatheaceae. *Cf.* Bower, *Ferns*, ii, 293.
Cyathomone S. F. Blake (*Narvalina* p.p.). Comp. (5). 1 Ecuador.
Cyclacanthus S. Moore. Acanth. (IV. B). 1 Indochina.
Cyclandra Ltbch. Guttiferae (inc. sed.). 2 New Guinea.
Cyclobalanopsis Oerst. = Quercus Tourn. p.p. (Fagac.).
Cycnopodium Naud. = Graffenrieda DC. (Melastom.).
Cylindrophyllum Schwantes. Aizo. (II). 3 S. Afr.
Cylindrosperma Ducke (*Aspidosperma* p.p.). Apocyn. (I. 3). 1 Amazon valley.
Cymatocarpus O. E. Schulz (*Sisymbrium* p.p.). Crucif. (2). 1 C. As.
Cymbidiella Rolfe (*Cymbidium* p.p.). Orchid. (II. 1). 3 Madag.
Cynoctonum J. F. Gmel. (*Mitreola* L.). Logan. 4 warm.
Cynopuma Lunell (*Apocynum* p.p.). Apocyn. (II. 1). 3 N. Am.
Cynosorchis Thou. = Cynorchis Thou. (Orchid.).
Cynoxylum Rafin. = Cornus L. (Corn.).
Cynthia D. Don (*Krigia* p.p.). Comp. (13). 5 W. N. Am.
Cyphorima Rafin. (*Lithospermum* p.p.). Boragin. (IV. 4). 2 N. Am.
Cyrillopsis Kuhlm. Cyrill. 1 Para.
Cyrtidium Schlechter (*Chrysocychnis* p.p.). Orchid. (II. 13). 2 Colombia.
Cyrtococcus Stapf. Gramin. (5). 7 palaeotrop.
Cystium Stev. (*Astragalus* p.p.). Legum. (III. 6). 10 N. temp.
Cytisanthus Lang = Genista L. p.p. (Legum.).
Cytisophyllum Lang (*Cytisus* p.p.). Legum. (III. 3). 1 S. Eur.
Dalbergiella E. G. Baker. Legum. (III. 8). 2 S. trop. Afr.
Dalzielia Turrill. Asclep. (II. 3). 1 W. trop. Afr.
Danthoniopsis Stapf. Gramin. (4). 1 Angola.
Dapedostachys Börner. Cyper. Nomen.
Daphniphyllaceae. A family near to Euphorb., comprising only the genus Daphniphyllum Blume (*cf.* below).
Daphniphyllum. *Read* 25 Indomal., China.
Dasillipe Dubard. Sapot. (I). 1 Annam.
Dasydesmus Craib. Gesner. (I). 1 China.
Dasypetalum Pierre ex A. Chevalier. Flacourt. (I). 1 Congo.
Dasystoma Rafin. (*Gerardia* p.p.). Scroph. (III. 2). 1 New Mexico.
Dasytropis Urb. Acanth. (IV. B). 1 Cuba.
Daturicarpa Stapf. Apocyn. (II. 1). 3 Belgian Congo.
Daubentonia DC. (*Sesbania* p.p.). Legum. (III. 6). 5 Am.

Daubentoniopsis Rydberg (*Aeschynomene* p.p.). Legum. (III. 7). 1 Mexico.
Davidia. For Cornaceae *read* Nyssaceae.
Deamia Britton et Rose (*Cereus* p.p.). Cact. (III. 1). 1 Mex., C. Am., Colombia.
Decastylocarpus Humbert. Comp. (1). 1 Madag.
Decazyx Pittier et Blake. Rut. (1). 1 Honduras.
Decemium Rafin. (*Hydrophyllum* p.p.). Hydrophyll. 1 Atl. N. Am.
Decorsella A. Chevalier. Urtic. Nomen.
Deeringothamnus Small. Anon. (2). 1 Florida.
Deiregyne Schlechter (*Spiranthes* p.p.). Orchid. (II. 2). 8 Mex., C. Am.
Delphiniastrum Nieuwland = Delphinium Tourn. p.p. (Ranunc.).
Delpya Pierre ex Radlk. (*Paranephelium* p.p.). Sapind. (1). 1 Siam.
Dendrium Desv. = Leiophyllum Hedw. f. (Eric.).
Dendrobryon Klotzsch et Pax. Euphorb. (A. II. 7). Nomen.
Dendrocereus Britton et Rose (*Cereus* p.p.). Cact. (III. 1). 1 Cuba.
Dendrodaphne Beurl. Inc. sed. 1 Panama.
Dendropemon Blume (*Loranthus* p.p.). Loranth. (1). 15 W.I.
Dendrophyllanthus S. Moore. Euphorb. (A. I. 1). 1 New Caled.
Denea O. F. Cook. Palm. (IV). 1 Lord Howe I.
Denmoza Britton et Rose (*Echinocactus* p.p.). Cact. (III. 1). 1 Arg.
Dentoceras Small. Polygon. (II. 2). 1 Florida.
Depanthus S. Moore. Gesner. (1). 1 New Caled.
Deparia Hook. et Grev. Filices Leptosp. (inc. sed.). 3 Hawaii, Peru, New Caled.
Derenbergia Schwantes (*Mesembryanthemum* p.p.). Aizo. (II). 15 S. Afr.
Derenbergiella Schwantes. Aizo. (II). 1 S. Afr.
Descantaria (Schlechtend.) Bruckner. Commelin. 20 trop. Am.
Desmazeria Dumort (*Brizopyrum* Link). Gramin. (10). 4 Medit., S. Afr.
Desmophyllum Webb. et Berth. = Ruta L. (Rut.).
Desmopsis Safford (*Unona* p.p.). Anon. (1). 5 C. Am.
Desmos Safford (*Unona* p.p.). Anon. (1). 30 |✻.
Desmothamnus Small (*Andromeda* p.p.). Eric. (II. 1). 2 N. Am.
Deuteromallotus Pax et K. Hoffm. (*Mallotus* p.p.). Euphorb. (A. II. 2). 1 Madag.
Deutzianthus Gagnep. Euphorb. (A. II. 2). 1 Tonquin.
Diacrodon Sprague. Rubi. (II. 10). 1 Ceara.
Dialypetalanthus Kuhlm. Rubi. (I. 5). 1 Para.
Diaphractanthus Humbert. Comp. (1). 1 Madag.
Dichanthium Willemet. Gramin. (2). 8 warm |✻.
Dichoglottis Fisch. et Mey., 1836. Caryoph. (II. 2). 1 Caspian.
Dichondraceae. A family containing Dichondra only.
Dichylium Britton (*Poinsettia* p.p.). Euphorb. (A. II. 8). 1 C. Am., W.I.
Dicksoniaceae. Filices Leptosp. *Cf.* Bower, *Ferns*, ii, 260.
Diclidantheraceae. A family near Styrac., comprising Diclidanthera.
Diclinanona Diels. Anon. (4). 1 E. Peru.
Dicrocaulon N. E. Brown (*Mesembryanthemum* p.p.). Aizo. (II). 6 S. Afr.

Diectonis Kunth. Gramin. (2). 1 trop. Annual.
Dielsiocharis O. E. Schulz (*Alyssopsis* p.p.). Crucif. (4). 1 Persia.
Diheteropogon Stapf (*Andropogon* p.p.). Gramin. (2). 1 N. Nigeria.
Dilleniaceae. *Cf.* Actinidiaceae.
Dimerandra Schlechter (*Epidendrum* p.p.). Orchid. (II. 6). 4 trop. Am.
Dimerocarpus Gagnep. Mor. (I). 1 Tonquin.
Dimorphorchis Rolfe. Orchid. (II. 20). 1 Borneo.
Dinizia Ducke. Legum. (I. 4). 1 Amazon valley.
Dinteranthus Schwantes. Aizo. (II). 4 S. Afr.
Diodella Small. Rubi. (II. 10). 1 Florida, W.I.
Dioticarpus Dunn. Dipterocp. 1 S. India.
Diplacorchis Schlechter (*Brachycorythis* p.p.). Orchid. (II. 1). 5 S. trop. and S. Afr.
Diplocarex Hayata. Cyper. (III). 1 Formosa.
Diplofatsia Nakai (*Fatsia* p.p.). Aral. (I). 1 Formosa.
Diplosoma Schwantes. Aizo. (II). 1 S. Afr.
Dipsacaceae. Triplostegia is now placed in Valerianaceae.
Dipteridaceae. A family comprising only Dipteris. *Cf.* Bower, *Ferns*, ii, 311.
Dipterostele Schlechter. Orchid. (II. 18). 5 trop. Am.
Discalyxia Markgraf. Apocyn. (I. 3). 3 New Guinea.
Discocactus Pfeiffer. Cact. (III. 1). 7 Brazil, Paraguay.
Discoclaoxylon (Muell.-Arg.) Pax et K. Hoffm. (*Claoxylon* p.p.). Euphorb. (A. II. 2). 5 W. trop. Afr.
Discocleidion (Muell.-Arg.) Pax et K. Hoffm. (*Cleidion* p.p.). Euphorb. (A. II. 2). 2 Central China.
Discyphus Schlechter (*Spiranthes* p.p.). Orchid. (II. 2). 1 Venez., Trinidad.
Disiphon Schlechter. Eric. (II. 2). 1 N.E. New Guinea.
Disocactus Lindl. (*Cereus* p.p.). Cact. (III. 1). 2 C. Am.
Distictis Mart. ex Meissn. (*Macrodiscus* Bureau). Bignon. (1). 1 Cuba.
Distomocarpus O. E. Schulz. Crucif. (2). 1 Morocco.
Distreptus Cass. = Elephantopus L. (Comp.).
Dodecas L. f. = Crenea Aubl. (Lythr.).
Doerpfeldia Urb. Rhamn. 1 Cuba.
Dolichostegia Schlechter. Asclep. (II. 3). 1 Phil. Is.
Dolichostemon Bonati. Scroph. (II. 6). 1 Annam.
Dolichothele Britton et Rose (*Mammillaria* p.p.). Cact. (III. 2). 3 Texas, Mexico.
Dolichovigna Hayata. Legum. (III. 10). 1 Formosa.
Dominia Fedde (*Maidenia* Domin). Umbell. (II. 1). 1 New S. Wales.
Dorotheanthus Schwantes. Aizo. (II). 2 S. Afr.
Douepia Camb. Crucif. (4). 1 N.W. India.
Drabastrum O. E. Schulz (*Sisymbrium* p.p.). Crucif. (2). 1 S.E. Austr.
Drabella Nábělek. Crucif. (4). 1 Turkestan.
Dracophilus Dinter et Schwantes (*Mesembryanthemum* p.p.). Aizo. (II). 2 S. Afr.
Drosace A. Nelson (*Androsace* p.p.). Primul. (I). 1 Rocky Mts.
Drosanthemum Schwantes (*Mesembryanthemum* p.p.). Aizo. (II). 30 S. Afr.
Dryadodaphne S. Moore. Laur. (I). 1 New Guinea.

Dubardella H. J. Lam. Sapot. (I). I Borneo.
Duckeodendron Kuhlm. Solan. (2). I Para.
Dugaldia Cass. (*Helenium* p.p.). Comp. (6). 3 W. N. Am.
Dugagelia Gaudich. Inc. sed. Nomen.
Dupatya Vell. = Paepalanthus Mart. (Eriocaul.).
Duperrea Pierre ex Pitard in Lecomte. Rubi. (II. 4). 2 India, China, S E. As.
Durra, *Sorghum Durra* Stapf.
Dybowskia Stapf. Gramin. (2). I Congo.
Dyscritothamnus B. L. Robinson. Comp. (2). I Mexico.
Dysosma R. E. Woodson (*Podophyllum* p.p.). Berberid. I China.
Ebenaceae. *Add* l. exstip.; A free or united, isomerous or in two whorls.
Ebenopsis Britton et Rose (*Acacia* p.p.). Legum. (I. 2). 3 Tex., Mex.
Eberlanzia Schwantes (*Mesembryanthemum* p.p.). Aizo. (II). 7 S. Afr.
Ebracteola Dinter et Schwantes. Aizo. (II). 2 S. Afr.
Eccremis Willd. Lili. (III). I Peru, Colombia. (A) thick.
Eccremocactus Britton et Rose. Cact. (III. I). I Costa Rica.
Echinofossulocactus Lawrence in Loudon (*Echinocactus* p.p.). Cact. (III. I). 25 Mexico.
Echinoglochin A. Brand (*Allocarya* p.p.). Borag. (IV. 2). 8 Pac. N. Am.
Echinomastus Britton et Rose (*Echinocactus* p.p.). Cact. (III. I). 6 Mexico, S. U.S.
Echinosophora Nakai (*Sophora* p.p.). Legum. (III. I). I Korea.
Echinus L. Bolus (*Mesembryanthemum* p.p.). Aizo. (II). I S. Afr.
Ecliptostelma T. S. Brandegee. Asclep. (II. I). I Mexico.
Eddo, *Colocasia antiquorum* Schott, var. *esculenta* Schott.
Ehretiaceae = Boraginaceae, §§ I, II.
Eisocreocriton Quisumb. et Merrill. Melastom. (I). I Phil. Is.
Ekmania Gleason (*Vernonia* p.p.). Comp. (I). I Cuba.
Ekmanianthe Urb. (*Tecoma* p.p.). Bignon. (2). 2 Cuba.
Ekmaniocharis Urb. Melastom. (I). I San Domingo.
Elaeophora Ducke. Euphorb. (A. II. 2). I Para.
Elateriospermum Blume. Euphorb. (A. II. 3). I E. Indomal. C o.
Elcomarhiza Barb. Rodr. Asclep. (II. 3). I Amazonas.
Eleutherandra van Slooten. Flacourt. (3). I Sumatra, Borneo.
Eleutherostigma Pax et K. Hoffm. Euphorb. (A. II. 2). I Colombia.
Eleutherostylis Burret. Tili. I New Guinea.
Elisia Milano. Solan. Gen. fabulosum.
Elleimatenia K.-Pol. (*Myrrhis* p.p.). Umbell. (III. 2). I Chile.
Elmerrillia Dandy (*Talauma* p.p.). Magnol. 5 S.E. As., Malaya, Phil. Is.
Elymandra Stapf. Gramin. (2). I Upper Guinea.
Elyonurus Humb. et Bonpl. Gramin. (2). 15 warm.
Emiliella S. Moore. Comp. (8). I Angola.
Enchosanthera King et Stapf ex Guillaumin (*Anplectrum* p.p.). Melastom. (I). I Malay Penins.
Endresiella Schlechter. Orchid. (II. 13). I Costa Rica.
Enemion Rafin. Ranunc. (2). 5 E. As., N. Am.
Enneatypus Herzog. Polygon. (III. I). I Bolivia.
Enochoria Baker f. Aral. (I). I New Caled.

Entadopsis Britton (*Mimosa* p.p.). Legum. (I. 5). 2 W. I., C. and S. Am.
Eosanthe Urb. Rubi. (II. 4). 1 Cuba.
Ephippiocarpa Markgraf (*Callichilia* p.p.). Apocyn. (I. 3). 1 Gazaland.
Epibaterium Forst. (*Cocculus* p.p.). Menisperm. 1 E. U.S.
Epilyna Schlechter. Orchid. (II. 7). 1 Costa Rica.
Epithecia Knowles et Westc. = Dichaea Lindl. (Orchid.).
Epithelantha Weber (*Mammillaria* p.p.). Cact. (III. 2). 1 Tex., Mex.
Erdisia Britton et Rose. Cact. (III. 1). 4 Peru, Chile.
Eremodraba O. E. Schulz (*Sisymbrium* p.p.). Crucif. (2). 1 N. Chile.
Eremohylema A. Nelson (*Polypappus* p.p.). Comp. (4). 1 New Mexico.
Eremonanus I. M. Johnston (*Polypappus* p.p.). Comp. (4). 1 Calif.
Eremopogon Stapf. Gramin. (2). 4 warm |*.
Erepsia N. E. Brown (*Mesembryanthemum* p.p.). Aizo. (II). 25 S. Afr.
Ericopsis C. A. Gardn. Eric. (II. 2). 1 W. Austr.
Eriocycla Lindl. Umbell. (III. 5). 6 alpine, Persia to China.
Eriolopha Ridl. (*Alpinia* p.p.). Zingiber. (I). 18 New Guinea.
Eriothymus J. A. Schmidt = Keithia Benth. (BH.) = Hedeoma Pers.
Ernestella Germain (*Rosa* p.p.). Ros. (III. 6). 1 S.E. China.
Erxlebenia Opiz (*Pyrola* p.p.). Pyrol. 1 N. temp.
Erythrorhipsalis Berger (*Rhipsalis* p.p.). Cact. (III. 3). 1 S. Brazil.
Escobaria Britton et Rose (*Mammillaria* p.p.). Cact. (III. 2). 10 Mex., Texas.
Espostoa Britton et Rose. Cact. (III. 1). 1 Ecuador.
Euanthe Schlechter (*Vanda* p.p.). Orchid. (II. 20). 1 Phil. Is.
Eubotrys Nutt. (*Leucothoe* p.p.). Eric. (II. 1). 2 N. Am.
Eucalyptus. *Cf.* Maiden's recent monograph.
Euchorium Ekman et Radlk. Sapind. (II). 1 Cuba.
Eucommia. *Cf. Kew Bull.* 1921, p. 177.
Eulaliopsis Honda (*Spodiopogon* p.p.). Gramin. (2). 1 India, China, Phil. Is., Formosa.
Euleria Urb. Anacard. (2). 1 Cuba.
Euploca Nutt. (*Heliotropium* p.p.). Boragin. (III). 3 N. Am.
Eurychaenia Griseb. = Miconia Ruiz et Pav. (Melastom.).
Eurychona Schlechter (*Angraecum* p.p.). Orchid. (II 20). 2 trop. Afr.
Eurycorymbus Hand.-Mazz. Sapind. (II). 1 China.
Eurystigma L. Bolus. Aizo. (II). 1 Cape Colony.
Eustachys Desv. (*Chloris* p.p.). Gramin. (II). 6 trop. Am., W.I.
Euthamnus Schlechter. Gesner. (I). 1 New Guinea.
Evodiopanax Nakai (*Panax* p.p.). Aral. (2). 2 China, Japan.
Exandra Standley. Rubi. (I. 1). 1 Mexico, Salvador.
Excavatia Markgraf (*Ochrosia* p.p.). Apocyn. (I. 3). 3 New Guinea, Bismarck and Marianne Is.
Exotheca Anderss. Gramin. (2). 1 Abyssinia, E. Afr.
Facheiroa Britton et Rose. Cact. (III. 1). 1 Brazil.
Fadyenia Endl. = Garrya Dougl. (Garry.).
Farreria I. B. Balf. et W. W. Sm. Thymel. Nomen.
Faucaria Schwantes. Aizo. (II). 5 S. Afr.
Feddea Urb. Comp. (12). 1 Cuba.

Fenerivea Diels. Anon. (1). 1 Madag.
Fenixia Merrill. Comp. (5). 1 Phil. Is.
Feracacia Britton et Rose (*Acacia* p.p.). Legum. (I. 2). 2 Cuba.
Ferocactus Britton et Rose (*Echinocactus* p.p.). Cact. (III. 1). 30 S.W. U.S., Mexico.
Fezia Pittier. Crucif. (2). 1 Morocco.
Finetia Schlechter. Orchid. (II. 20). 1 China.
Fishlockia Britton et Rose (*Acacia* p.p.). Legum. (I. 2). 1 Mexico.
Fissipetalum Merrill. Olac. 1 Borneo.
Fittingia Mez. Myrsin. (II). 2 New Guinea.
Flagellate, with whip-like runners.
Flexanthera Rusby. Rubi. (I. 1). 1 Colombia.
Floccose, bearing tufts of hairs.
Fluminea Fries. Gramin. (10). 2 N. temp.
Fodder. *Cf. Kew Bull.* 1919, p. 1.
Foleyola Maire. Crucif. (4 ?). 1 Sahara.
Forasaccus Bubani = Bromus p.p. (Gramin.).
Forbesina Ridley. Orchid. (II. 3). 1 Sumatra.
Formania W W. Smith et Small. Comp. (7?). 1 Yunnan.
Fourneaua Pierre ex Prain in Dyer (*Grossera* p.p.). Euphorb. (A. II. 2). 1 W. trop. Afr.
Fractiunguis Schlechter (*Hexisea* p.p.). Orchid. (II. 6). 3 trop. Am.
Fragariopsis St Hil. (*Plukenetia* p.p.). Euphorb. (A. II. 2). 1 S. Brazil.
Frailea Britton et Rose (*Echinocactus* p.p.). Cact. (III. 1). 10 subtrop. S. Am.
Franklinia Bartr. ex Marshall. Theac. 1 Georgia (U.S.).
Fransiella Guillaumin. Rubi. (I. 8). 1 New Caled.
Fremontodendron Coville. Stercul. 1 Calif. (slippery elm).
Fremya Brongn. et Gris. = Xanthostemon F. Muell. (Myrt.)
Freyliniopsis Engl. Scroph. (II. 4). 1 Damaraland.
Friar's balsam, a tincture largely composed of gum benzoin.
Froelichiella R. E. Fries (*Gomphrena* p.p.). Amarant. (3). 1 Goyaz.
Fumariaceae. *Cf.* Hutchinson in *Kew Bull.* 1921, p. 97.
Funkiella Schlechter (*Spiranthes* p.p.). Orchid. (II. 2). 1 Mexico.
Gaedawakka L. = Chaetocarpus Thw. (Euphorb.).
Galeottiella Schlechter (*Spiranthes* p.p.). Orchid. (II. 2). 1 Mexico.
Galliaria Bubani (*Amaranthus* p.p.). Amarant. (2). 5 N. Am.
Gallienia Dubard et Dop. Rubi. (I. 8) 1 Madag.
Gamosepalum Schlechter (*Spiranthes* p.p.). Orchid. (II. 2). 1 Mexico.
Gampsoceras Stev. Ranunc. (3). 1 As. Minor.
Gardenia J. Colden ex Garden, 1756 = Hypericum p.p. (Guttif.).
Garigue, dry waste almost bare ground, with xerophytic scrub. *Cf.* Ecological books.
Gastrorchis Schlechter (*Phajus* p.p.). Orchid. (II. 9). 4 Madag.
Gatnaia Gagnep. Euphorb. (A. I. 2). 1 Indochina.
Gaudinopsis Eig (*Ventenata* p.p.). Gramin. (9). 1 As. Minor.
Geanthus Reinw. (*Amomum* p.p.). Zingiber. (1) 45 Malaya, Polynesia.
Genistella Moench 1794 = Genista p.p. (Legum.).
Gennaria Parlat. (*Platanthera* p.p.). Orchid. (II. 1). 1 W. Medit.
Genosiris Labill. = Patersonia R. Br. (Irid.).

Gentianusa Pohl (*Gentiana* p.p.). Gentian. (1). 15 N. temp.
Geocaulon M. L. Fernald (*Comandra* p.p.). Santal. 1 Canada, N.E. U.S.
Geogenanthus Ule (*Chamaeanthus* Ule). Commelin. 2 trop. S. Am.
Geunsia Blume (*Tamonea* Aubl.). Verben. (1). 4 trop. Am., W.I.
Gibbsia Rendle in Gibbs. Urtic. (3). 2 Dutch New Guinea.
Gilgiochloa Pilger. Gramin. (4). 1 Tanganyika.
Giliastrum Rydberg (*Gilia* p.p.). Polemon. 1 W. U.S.
Gilletiodendron Vermoesen (*Cynometra* p.p.). Legum. (II. 2). 3 Belgian Congo.
Gitara Pax et K. Hoffm. (*Tragia* p.p.). Euphorb. (A. II. 2) 1 Venez.
Glandulifera Frič. (*Mammillaria* p.p.). Cact. (III. 2). 2 Mexico.
Gleicheniaceae. *Cf.* Bower, *Ferns*, ii, 193.
Glume, Cyperaceae, Gramineae.
Glycoxylon Ducke (*Chrysophyllum* p.p.). Sapot. (1). 4 Amazon valley.
Glycydendron Ducke. Euphorb. (A. II. 2). 1 Amazon valley.
Glyphostylus Gagnep. Euphorb. (A. II. 7). 1 Laos.
Goadbyella Rogers. Orchid. (II. 2). 1 W. Austr.
Godefroya Gagnep. (*Cleistanthus* p.p.). Euphorb. (A. I. 2). 1 Cambodia.
Goerziella Urb. (*Amaranthus* p.p.). Amarant. (2). 1 Cuba.
Gonioanthela Malme (*Metastelma* p.p.). Asclep. (II. 1). 1 S. Brazil.
Goniostoma Elmer. Magnol. 1 Phil. Is.
Gossweilerodendron Harms (*Pterygopodium* p.p.). Legum. (III. 8). 1 Congo.
Gossypiospermum Urb. (*Casearia* p.p.). Flacourt. (7). 1 Cuba.
Gossypium. After forms (line 3) *read* arise mainly from a few spp. including..., and after *G. barbadense add G. hirsutum*, L. (Am.).
Gouinia Fourn. Gramin. (11). 4 warm Am.
Govantesia Llanos = Champereia Griff. (Santal.).
Gramen E. H. L. Krause (*Festuca* p.p.). Gramin. (10). 1 N. temp. (*F. rubra* L.).
Graminastrum E. H. L. Krause. Gramin. (8). 1 Peru.
Gramineae. *Cf.* Hooker, *Ic. Pl.* 3068–3100.
Grammosperma O. E. Schulz. Crucif. (3). 1 Patagonia.
Grangeopsis Humbert. Comp. (3). 1 Madag.
Greenovia Webb. et Berth. Crassul. 4 Canaries.
Gregoria Duby = Dionysia Fenzl p.p. (Primul.).
Greyiaceae Hutch. (*Melianth.* p.p.). *Cf.* Hutchinson, *Families of Flowering Plants*, p. 202.
Guapeba Gomes (*Pouteria* p.p.). Sapot. (1). 5 trop. Am.
Guerreroia Merrill. Comp. (5). 1 Phil. Is.
Guidonia DC. = Casearia Jacq. p.p. (Flacourt.).
Gulubiopsis Becc. Palm. (IV. 1). 1 Pelew Is.
Guttiferales. The 5th order of Polypetalae (*BH.*); p. l.
Gutzlaffia Hance (*Strobilanthes* p.p.). Acanth. (IV. A). 3 S.E. As.
Gyaladenia Schlechter (*Platanthera* p.p.). Orchid. (II. 1). 3 S. and S. trop. Afr.
Gymnocalycium Pfeiff. (*Echinocactus* p.p.). Cact. (III. 1). 25 S. Am.
Gymnophragma Lindau. Acanth. (IV. B). 1 N.E. New Guinea.
Gymnopoma N. E. Brown. Aizo. (II). 1 Cape Col.
Gymnostichum Schreb. = Asperella Humb. p.p. (Gramin.).

Gymplatanthera × G. Camus. Orchid. Gymnadenia × Platanthera hybrid.
Gynocardia. Chaulmoogra oil appears only to come from Taraktogenos, q.v.
Gynophoraria Rydberg. Legum. (III. 6). 1 Yukon Territory.
Haagea Frič. Cact. 1, habitat?
Habroneuron Standley. Rubi. (I. 7). 1 Mexico.
Hackelia I. M. Johnston (*Eritrichium* p.p.). Boragin. (IV. 2). 4 C. and E. As.
Haematostemon (Muell.-Arg.) Pax et K. Hoffm. (*Astrococcus* p.p.). Euphorb. (A. II. 2). 1 Amazonas.
Haemodoraceae. In genera, for Haemanthus *read* Haemodorum.
Haitia Urb. Lythr. 1 Haiti.
Haitimimosa Britton (*Mimosa* p.p.). Legum. (I. 5). 1 Haiti.
Halacsyella Jancken. Campanul. (I. 1). 1 Greece.
Halimiocistus × Jancken. Cist. Halimium × Cistus hybrid.
Halliophytum I. M. Johnston. Euphorb. (A. I. 1). 3 Mexico, Calif.
Hamatocactus Britton et Rose (*Echinocactus* p.p.). Cact. (III. 1). 1 Texas, Mex.
Handelia Heimerl (*Achillea* p.p.). Comp. (7). 1 C. As.
Hanguana Blume (*Astelia* R. Br.). Flagellar. 1 Malaya, Phil. Is.
Hanslia Schindl. (*Hedysarum* p.p.). Legum. (III. 7). 1 E. Indomal.
Hapalorchis Schlechter (*Spiranthes* p.p.). Orchid. (II. 2). 4 trop. S. Am.
Haplophyllum Reichb. (*Ruta* p.p.). Rut. (I. 2). 4 Medit.
Haplormosia Harms (*Ormosia* p.p.). Legum. (III. 1). 2 Liberia, Cameroons.
Hariota DC. (*Rhipsalis* p.p.). Cact. (III. 3). 2 Brazil.
Harmsiodoxa O. E. Schulz (*Blennodia* p.p.). Crucif. (2). 3 Austr.
Harnackia Urb. Comp. (6). 1 Cuba.
Harpagocarpus Hutch. et Dandy. Polygon. (II. 2). 1 Uganda.
Harrysmithia H. Wolff. Umbell. (III. 5). 1 Central China.
Hatiora Britton et Rose (*Rhipsalis* p.p.). Cact. (III. 3). 3 Rio de Janeiro.
Hayacka Pohl. Inc. sed. Nomen.
Hebe Comm. ex Juss. = Veronica L. p.p. (the $\overline{*}$ spp.).
Hecastophyllum H.B. et K. = Dalbergia L. (Legum.).
Hecatostemon Blake. Flacourt (7). 1 Venez.
Hedinia Ostenf. (*Hutchinsia* p.p.). Crucif. (4). 1 Himalaya.
Hediosma L. = Nepeta Riv. (Labi.).
Hedyachras Radlk. Sapind. (1). 1 Luzon.
Hegnera Schindl. (*Uraria* p.p.). Legum. (III. 7). 1 S.E. As.
Helicteropsis Hochr. Malv. (4). 1 Madag.
Hellenocarum Wolff. Umbell. (III. 5). 2 mid-Medit.
Helorchis Schlechter (*Peristylus* p.p.). Orchid. (II. 1). 1 Madag.
Hemianthus Nutt. (*Micranthemum* p.p.). Scroph. (II. 6). 6 N. Am., Cuba.
Hemibaccharis S. F. Blake (*Baccharis* p.p.). Comp. (3). 15 C. Am.
Hemigymnia Stapf. Gramin. (5). 4 palaeotrop.
Hemiscolopia van Slooten (*Scolopia* p.p.). Flacourt. (5). 1 Java, Sumatra.

Hemisphaerocarya A. Brand (*Oreocarya* p.p.). Boragin. (IV. 2). 8 S. U.S., Mexico.

Hemsleya. *Read* 8 China, Phil. Is.

Henryettana A. Brand. Boragin. (IV. 4). 1 Yunnan.

Hereroa Dinter et Schwantes. Aizo. (II). 5 S. Afr.

Herodotia Urb. et Ekman. Comp. (8). 1 Haiti.

Herrea Schwantes. Aizo. (II). 1 S. Afr.

Herreanthus Schwantes. Aizo. (II). 1 S. Afr.

Hesperhodos Cockerell (*Rosa* p.p.). Ros (III. 6). 3 S.W. N. Am.

Hesperogeton K.-Pol. (*Sanicula* p.p.). Umbell. (II. 1). 1 N.W. Am.

Hesperonix Rydberg (*Astragalus* p.p.). Legum. (III. 6). 5 W. U.S.

Hesperopeuce Lemmon (*Tsuga* p.p.). Conif. (Pin.). 1 W. N. Am.

Hesperothamnus T. S. Brandegee (*Lonchocarpus* p.p.). Legum. (III. 8). 1 Lower Calif.

Heterocarpha Stapf et C. E. Hubbard. Gramin. (10). 1 Tanganyika.

Heterochiton Graebn. et Mattfeld (*Herniaria* p.p.). Caryoph. (I. 4). 10 Medit.

Heteromera Montrouz (*Leptostylis* Benth.). Sapot. (1). 2 New Caled.

Heteromeris Spach = Halimium Willk. p.p. (Cist.).

Heteropleura Sch.-Bip. = Hieracium L. p.p. (Comp.).

Heteroporidium Van Tiegh. = Ochna L. p.p. (Ochn.). 2 trop. Afr.

Heteropyxidaceae. A fam. near Elaeagn., containing the anomalous genus **Heteropyxis.** *Cf.* Hutchinson, *Families of Flowering Plants*, p. 245.

Heterosteca Desv. = Bouteloua Lag. (Gramin.).

Hexapora Hook. f. = Microspora Hook. f. (Laur.).

Hickelia A. Camus. Gramin. (13). 1 Madag.

Hickenia Britton et Rose (*Echinocactus* p.p.). Cact. (III. 1). 1 Arg.

Hickenia Lillo (*Oxypetalum* p.p.). Asclep. (II. 1). 1 Arg.

Hierochloe R. Br. *Cf.* Mez in *Fedde*, *Rep.* xvii, 1921, p. 291.

Hieronymusia Engl. Saxifrag. (1). 1 S. Andes.

Himantandra F. von Muell. The only gen. of **Himantandraceae** (Dicots. Archichl. Ranales). 2 Moluccas, New Guinea, E. Austr. ♄ with shield hairs and alt. exstip. l. Fls. with br., operculum, spiral, achlam., ☿. A ∞ perig.; outer and inner stds.; cpls. united at base. *Cf.* Diels in *Engl. Jb.* 55, p. 126.

Hippia. *Read* Hippion.

Hirschfeldia Moench (*Erucastrum* p.p.). Crucif. (2). 2 Medit., Socotra.

Hitcheniopsis (Baker) Valeton (*Curcuma* p.p.). Zingiber. (1). 10 S.E. As.

Hochberga Pohl. Inc. sed. Nomen.

Hoita Rydberg (*Psoralea* p.p.). Legum. (III. 6). 12 W. Am.

Holcolemma Stapf et C. E. Hubbard. Gramin. (5). 2 E. Afr., S. India, Ceylon.

Hollermayera O. E. Schulz. Crucif. (4). 1 Chile.

Holodiscus. *Omit* N. before Am.

Holopeira Miers = Cocculus DC. (Menisp.).

Holopyxidium Ducke (*Lecythis* p.p.). Lecythid. 2 Amazon valley.

Holtzea Schindl. Legum. (III. 7). 1 N. Austr.

Homaliopsis S. Moore. Flacourt. (9). 1 Madag.

Homalocenchrus Mieg. = Oryza L. p.p. (Gramin.).

Homalocephala Britton et Rose (*Echinocactus* p.p.). Cact. (III. 1). 1 Texas, Mexico.
Hordelymus Jessen (*Elymus* p.p.). Gramin. (12). 1 Eur., W. As.
Hordeum. *Cf.* Regel, *Bull. Appl. Bot.* 1915. Bews, *Grasses of the World.*
Hormopetalum Lauterb. Rut. (V). 3 New Guinea.
Hormuzakia Gusul. Boragin. (IV. 3). 1 E. Medit.
Hoseanthus Merrill (*Hosea* p.p.). Verben. (4). 1 Sarawak.
Hottea Urb. Myrt. (I. 1). 3 San Domingo.
Hoyella Ridley. Asclep. (II. 3). 1 Sumatra.
Huberodaphne Ducke. Laur. (II). 1 Amazon valley.
Huebneria Schlechter (*Orleanisia* p.p.). Orchid. (II. 6). 1 Amazonas.
Hugueninia Reichb. (*Descurainia* p.p.). Crucif. (4). 2 W. Eur.
Hulemacanthus S. Moore. Acanth. (IV. B). 1 New Guinea.
Humblotiodendron Engl. Rut. (IV). 1 Comoros.
Humboldtiella Harms (*Robinia* p.p.). Legum. (III. 6). 1 trop. S. Am., Trinidad.
Humirianthera Huber. Icacin. 1 Para.
Hunsteinia Lauterb. Rut. (I. 1). 1 New Guinea.
Hyalosema Rolfe (*Bulbophyllum* p.p.). Orchid. (II. 16). 15 Malay Arch.
Hybochilus Schlechter. Orchid. (II. 19). 1 Costa Rica.
Hybosema Harms (*Robinia* p.p.). Legum. (III. 6). 1 Mex., C. Am.
Hydrangeaceae = Saxifragaceae, § III.
Hydrobryopsis Engl. Podostem. 1 S. Kanara (India).
Hydrocharis. *Cf.* Arber, *Water Plants.*
Hydrotrida Willd. = Herpestis Gaertn. f. (Scroph.). 2 S.E. U.S.
Hymendocarpum Pierre ex Pitard. Rubi. (II. 5). 1 Cambodia.
Hymenocyclus Dinter et Schwantes. Aizo. (II). 4 S. Afr.
Hymenophyllaceae. *Cf.* Bower, *Ferns*, ii, p. 234.
Hypagophytum Berger. Crassul. 1 Abyssinia.
Hyparrhenia. *Read* Gramin. (2). 60 warm.
Hypobrichia Torr. et Gray = Peplis L. (Lythr.).
Hypogynium Nees in Stapf. Gramin. (2). 5 trop. Am., W. and S. Afr.
Hypolepis. For Polypod. *read* Dickson.
Hystrix Moench. Gramin. (12). 2 U.S., Himal., N.Z.
Iboza N. E. Brown (*Moschosma* p.p.). Labi. (VII). 12 S. and trop. Afr.
Ichthyomethia P. Br. Legum. (III. 9). 1 warm Am., W.I.
Icicaster Ridley (*Santiria* p.p.). Burser. 1 S. Malay Penins.
Idenburgia L. S. Gibbs. Monim. 2 N.W. Dutch New Guinea.
Ilocania Merrill. Cucurb. (3). 1 Phil. Is.
Imerinaea Schlechter. Orchid. (II. 5). 1 Madag.
Imitaria N. E. Brown. Aizo. (II). 1 S. Afr.
Indocalamus Nakai (*Arundinaria* p.p.). Gramin. (13). 7 Indomal., China, Formosa.
Indorouchera Hallier (*Rouchera* p.p.). Lin. 3 S.E. As., Malaya.
Inhambanella Engl. (*Mimusops* p.p.). Sapot. (2). 2 trop. and S. Afr.
Inophloeum Pittier. Mor. (II). 1 Panama.
Iodocephalus Gagnep. Comp. (I). 2 Indochina.
Isatis. *Cf.* Harris, *A primitive Dye Stuff*; Hurry, *The Woad Plant.*

Ischnocarpus O. E. Schulz (*Sisymbrium* p.p.). Crucif. (2). 1 New Zealand.

Ismelia Cass. = Chrysanthemum Tourn. p.p. (Comp.). 2 Canaries.

Isodichyophorus Briquet ex A. Chev. Labi. (I). 1 Senegambia.

Isometrum Craib. Gesner. (I). 1 China.

Ixtlania M. E. Jones. Acanth. (I). 1 Mexico.

Jacqueshuberia Ducke. Legum. (II. 7). 1 Amazon valley.

Jambolifera L. = Acronychia Forst. (Rut.).

Jardinea Steud. Gramin. (2). 3 trop. Afr.

Jasminocereus Britton et Rose (*Cereus* p.p.). Cact. (III. 1). 1 Galapagos.

Jenmaniella Engl. Podostem. 4 Brit. Guiana.

Johnstonella A. Brand. Boragin. (IV. 2). 2 S. Calif.

Jubaeopsis Becc. Palm. 1 Pondoland.

Jubistylis Rusby. Malpigh. (I). 1 Upper Amazon.

Jumelleanthus Hochr. Malv. (4). 1 Madag.

Juppia Merrill. Menisperm. 1 Borneo.

Jupunba Britton et Rose (*Acacia* p.p.). Legum. (I. 2). 15 W.I. to Para.

Juttadinteria Schwantes (*Mesembryanthemum* p.p.). Aizo. (II). 5 S. Afr.

Kalbreyeriella Lindau. Acanth. (IV. B). 1 Colombia.

Killipia Gleason. Melastom. (I). 1 Colombia.

Kingdonwardia Marquand. Gentian. (I). 1 S.E. Tibet.

Kingiella Rolfe. Orchid. (II. 20). 5 Indomal.

Klaineastrum Pierre ex A. Chevalier. Melastom. (III). 1 Gaboon.

Klingia Schönland. Amaryll. (I. 2). 1 Namaland.

Kmeria Dandy (*Magnolia* p.p.). Magnol. 1 Cambodia.

Koordersiochloa Merrill. Gramin. (9). 1 Java.

Krebsia Harv. = Gomphocarpus R. Br. (Asclep.).

Kremeria Coss. et Dur. Crucif. (2). 1 Algeria.

Krokia Urb. Myrt. (I). 3 Cuba.

Kuekenthalia Börner. Cyper. Nomen.

Kunstlerodendron Ridley. Euphorb. (A. II. 2). 2 Malay Penins.

Lacunaria Ducke. Quiin. 6 Brazil, Guiana.

Lagenocarpus Klotzsch = Salaxis Salisb. p.p. (Eric.).

Lagoseris M. Bieb. 1810 = Pterotheca Cass. (Comp.).

Lagothamnus Nutt. = Tetradymia DC. p.p. (Comp.).

Laguna Cav., 1786. Malv.

Lamechites Markgraf. Apocyn. (II. 2). 1 New Guinea.

Lamellate, composed of thin plates.

Lamiofrutex Lauterb. Rut. (V). 1 New Guinea.

Lampetia Rafin. = Mollugo L. (Aizo.).

Lamprophragma O. E. Schulz (*Thelypodium* p.p.). Crucif. (I). 1 Mex., S. U.S.

Lankesterella Ames. Orchid. (II. 2). 1 Costa Rica.

Lapidaria Dinter et Schwantes = Dinteranthus Schwantes p.p. (Aizo.).

Laretia, Laricopsis. Place below Lardizabalaceae.

Lasiarrhenum I. M. Johnston (*Onosma* p.p.). Boragin. (IV. 4). 1 S. Mexico.

Lasiochlamys Pax et K. Hoffm. (*Cyclostemon* p.p.). Euphorb. (A. I. 1). 1 New Caled.

Lasiorrhachis Stapf. Gramin. (2). 1 C. Madag.

Lasiurus Boiss. Gramin. (2). 2 trop. Afr., India.
Lathraea. *L. Clandestina* is also parasitic on beech, poplar, &c.
Laxoplumeria Markgraf. Apocyn. (I. 3). 1 E. Peru.
Leaoa Schlechter et C. Porto (*Hexadesmia* p.p.). Orchid. (II. 6). 1 Rio de Janeiro.
Lecointea Ducke. Legum. (II. 9). 1 Amazon valley.
Lecomtella A. Camus. Gramin. (5). 1 Madag.
Ledocarpon Desf. = Balbisia Cav. (Geran.).
Ledonia Spach = Cistus Tourn. p.p. (Cist.).
Legocia Livera (*Campbellia* p.p.). Orobanch. 1 India, Ceylon.
Legousia Durand = Specularia Heist. (Campanul.).
Leipoldtia L. Bolus (*Mesembryanthemum* p.p.). Aizo. (II). 1 S. Afr.
Leitneria. *L. floridana* Chapm. (corkwood), the only sp., in S. U.S.
Lemphoria O. E. Schulz (*Sisymbrium* p.p.). Crucif. (2). 1 Austr.
Lemuranthe Schlechter (*Habenaria* p.p.). Orchid. (II. 1). 2 Madag.
Lemurella Schlechter (*Angraecum* p.p.). Orchid. (II. 20). 1 W. Madag.
Lendneria Minod (*Stemodia* p.p.). Scroph. (II. 6). 1 trop. Am., W.I.
Leocereus Britton et Rose. Cact. (III. 1). 3 E. Brazil.
Leonardia Urb. Euphorb. (A. II. 5). 1 Haiti.
Lepeostegeres Blume (*Loranthus* p.p.). Loranth. (I). 2 Malay Penins., Borneo.
Lepia Hill, 1759 = Zinnia L. (Comp.).
Lepiaglaia Pierre. Meli. (III). 4 Cochinchina.
Lepidella. For Lepidaria *read* Loranthus.
Lepidocordia Ducke. Boragin. (III). 1 Para.
Lepidopharynx Rusby. Amaryllid. (I. 2). 1 Bolivia.
Lepismium Pfeiffer (*Rhipsalis* p.p.). Cact. (III. 3). 1 S.E. Brazil.
Leplaea Vermoesen. Meli. (III). 1 Belgian Congo.
Leptocentrum Schlechter (*Angraecum* p.p.). Orchid. (II. 20). 3 trop. Afr., Comoros.
Leptoceras Lindl. = Caladenia R. Br. (Orchid.).
Leptocereus. *Read* 8 W.I.
Leptocoryphium Nees. Gramin. (5). 2 warm Am., W.I.
Leptofeddia Diels. Solan. (5). 1 Peru.
Leptonychiopsis Ridley. Stercul. 1 Johore.
Leptosaccharum A. Camus. Gramin. (5). 1 Brazil, Paraguay.
Leptosiphon Benth. = Gilia Ruiz et Pav. p.p. (Polemon.). 10 Pac. N. Am.
Leptospermopsis S. Moore. Myrt. (II. 1). 1 S.W. Austr.
Letestua Lecomte. Sapot. (2). 2 French Congo.
Leucadenia × Schlechter. Orchid. Gymnadenia × Leucorchis hybrid. 2 Switzerland.
Leucas. Delete comma *after* trop.
Leuciva Rydberg (*Iva* p.p.). Comp. (5). 1 S. U.S.
Leucocalantha Barb. Rodr. Bignon. (I). 1 Amazonas.
Leucocorema Ridley. Icacin. 1 New Guinea.
Leucocraspedum Rydberg (*Frasera* p.p.). Gentian. (I). 5 W. N. Am.
Leucophäe Webb. et Berth. = Sideritis L. p.p. (Labi.). 17 Canaries.
Leucopremna Standley (*Jacaratia* p.p.). Caric. 1 Mexico, C. Am.
Leucotella × Schlechter. Orchid. Nigritella × Leucorchis hybrid.
Leycephyllum Piper. Legum. (III. 10). 1 Costa Rica.
Liabellum Rydberg (*Liabum* p.p.). Comp. (8). 3 Mexico.

Libanotis Crantz 1767. Umbellif. *Cf. Index Kewensis*, 7th Suppl.
Libyella Pampan. (*Poa* p.p.). Gramin. (10). 1 Cyrenaica.
Licaria Aubl. Inc. sed. 1 Guiana.
Lilaeopsis Greene (*Crantzia* Nutt.). Umbell. (III. 5). 30 Am., Austr., Tasm., N.Z. *Cf.* Hill in *Linn. Journ.* 47, p. 525.
Limnobotrya Rydberg (*Ribes* p.p.). Saxifrag. (VI). 3 N. Am.
Limnodea L. H. Dewey. Gramin. (8). 1 Florida to Texas.
Lindelofia. *Read* 15 N. Afr., As.
Linoma O. F. Cook. Palm. (IV. 1). 1 Peru (?).
Liriothamnus Schlechter (*Anthericum* p.p.). Lili. (III). 1 Namaqualand.
Lissocarpaceae. A fam. composed of Lissocarpa only.
Literature. *Add Index Londinensis* (figures of plants).
Lithachne Beauv. Gramin. (5). 2 C. Am., W.I.
Lithophila Sw. (*Achyranthes* p.p.). Amarant. (2). 4 W.I., Galapagos.
Lithops N. E. Brown (*Mesembryanthemum* p.p.). Aizo. (II). 10 S. Afr.
Litocarpus L. Bolus (*Mesembryanthemum* p.p.). Aizo. (II). 1 S. Afr.
Litosiphon Pierre ex A. Chevalier (*Lovoa* p.p.). Meli. (II). 1 Congo.
Litrisa Small. Comp. (2). 1 Florida.
Lobelia Adans. = Scaevola L. (Gooden.).
Lobivia Britton et Rose (*Echinocactus* p.p.). Cact. (III. 1). 25 S. Andes.
Locandia Adans. = Samadera Gaertn. (Simarub.).
Locoweed, spp. of Aragallus and Astragalus, frequent in the grass country of mid-west U.S. and Canada.
Lomagramma J. Sm. Polypod. (9). 3 Malay Archip., Polynesia.
Lommelia Jumelle et Perrier. Palm. (IV. 1). 1 Madag.
Lonchophaca Rydberg (*Phaca* p.p.). Legum. (III. 6). 2 S.W. U.S.
Lophoptilon Gagnep. Comp. Nomen.
Lophosoria Presl (*Alsophila* p.p.). 1 warm Am., W.I.
Loranthaceae. *Add* with endosperm or not.
Loroma O. F. Cook. Palm. (IV. 1). 2 N. Austr.
Lortetia Seringe, 1849 = Passiflora L. p.p.
Lothiania Kränzlin (*Masdevallia* p.p.). Orchid. (II. 8). 2 Colombia.
Loxsoma. With Loxsomopsis this makes the fam. Loxsomaceae. *Cf.* Bower, *Ferns*, ii, 252.
Loxsomopsis Christ. Loxsom. 3 trop. Am.
Lucaya Britton et Rose (*Acacia* p.p.). Legum. (I. 2). 1 Cuba, Bahamas.
Lueheopsis Burret. Tili. 5 N. Brazil, Guiana.
Luetzelburgia Harms. Legum. (III. 1). 2 Brazil.
Lugoa DC. = Gonospermum Less. (Comp.). 1 Canaries.
Lutzia Gandoger (*Alyssum* p.p.). Crucif. (4). 3 Crete.
Lycianthes Hassl. (*Solanum* &c. p.p.). Solan. (2). 400 trop. and temp. *Cf.* Rusby in *Bull. Torr. Bot. Cl.* 53, 1926, 210; &c.
Lycocarpus O. E. Schulz (*Sisymbrium* p.p.). Crucif. (2). 1 Spain.
Lyroglossa Schlechter (*Spiranthes* p.p.). Orchid. (II. 2). 2 Brazil, Trinidad.
Lysimachusa Pohl = Lysimachia L. (Primul.).
Lysiopetalum F. von Muell. Stercul. 2 W. Austr. K free.
Macary butter, *read* bitter.
Macbrideina Standley. Rubi. (I. 5). 1 Peru.
Machaerocereus Britton et Rose (*Cereus* p.p.). Cact. (III. 1). 2 Lower Calif.

Machairophyllum Schwantes. Aizo. (II). 2 S. Afr.
Macrobiota Komarov. Conif. (inc. sed.). 1 E. Siberia.
Macrocatalpa Britton (*Catalpa* p.p.). Bignon. (2). 3 W.I.
Macroditassa Malme. Asclep. (II. 1). 1 S. Brazil.
Macroglossum Copeland. Maratt. 2 Borneo.
Macropharynx Rusby. Apocyn. (II. 1). 1 Bolivia.
Macropodiella Engl. Podostem. 1 Cameroons.
Macroptilium Urb. (*Phaseolus* p.p.). Legum. (III. 10). 2 trop. Am., W.I.
Madhuca J. F. Gmel. (*Bassia* Koen.). Sapot. (1). 60 Indomal.
Magnoliaceae. *Cf.* Winteraceae, below.
Mahawoa Schlechter. Asclep. (II. 1). 1 Minahassa.
Maidenia Domin (*Hydrocotyle* p.p.). Umbell. (II. 1). 2 Austr.
Maierocactus Rost. (*Astrophytum* p.p.). Cact. (III. 1). 1 Mexico.
Maihueniopsis Speg. Cact. (II). 1 Arg.
Malachium Fries = Stellaria L. p.p. (Caryoph.).
Malvalthaea × Iljin. Malv. Malva-Althaea hybrid. 1 Caucasus.
Mamillopsis F. A. C. Weber (*Mammillaria* p.p.). Cact. (III. 2). 2 Mexico.
Manekia Trelease. Piper. 1 Hispaniola.
Manganaroa Speg. (*Acacia* p.p.). Legum. (I. 2). 12 warm Am.
Manilkara Adans. = Mimusops L. (Sapot.).
Manuleopsis Thellung. Scroph. (II. 5). 1 Hereroland.
Mappianthus Hand.-Mazz. Icacin. 1 Yunnan.
Marattiaceae. *Cf.* Bower, *Ferns*, ii, 95.
Maresia Pomel (*Malcomia* p.p.). Crucif. (4). 5 Medit.
Mareyopsis Pax et K. Hoffm. (*Mareya* p.p.). Euphorb. (A. II. 2). 1 Cameroons.
Margaritaria L. F. Euphorb. (A. I. 1). 4 warm Am., W.I.
Margaritolobium Harms (*Gliricidia* p.p.). Legum. (III. 6). 1 Venez.
Margyracaena × Bitter. Ros. Acaena-Margyricarpus hybrid. 1 Chile.
Marilaunidium O. Ktze. (*Nama* p.p.). Hydrophyll. 20 Am.
Mariposa lily (Am.), *Calochortus*.
Mariscus Zinn. = Cladium Schrad. (Cyper.).
Marlothistella Schwantes. Aizo. (II). 1 S. Afr.
Marsileaceae. *Cf.* Bower, *Ferns*, ii, 176.
Massartina Maire. Boragin. (IV. 4). 1 Sahara.
Mastersiella Gilg-Benedict. Restion. 10 S.W. Cape Col.
Mastigostyla I. M. Johnston. Irid. (II). 1 Peru.
Matoniaceae. *Cf.* Bower, *Ferns*, ii, 220.
Matucana Britton et Rose (*Echinocactus* p.p.). Cact. (III. 1). 1 Peru.
Mecardonia Ruiz et Pav. Scroph. (III. 1). 4 warm Am.
Mecca balsam. *Cf.* Balm of Gilead.
Mediocactus Britton et Rose. Cact. (III. 1). 2 Brazil, Arg., Peru.
Medusagynaceae. A fam. near to Ochn. and Marcgrav., containing only Medusagyne.
Meeboldia H. Wolff. Umbell. (III. 4). 1 Himalaya.
Megaliabum Rydberg (*Vernonia* p.p.). Comp. (8). 2 Mexico.
Megalopanax Ekman. Aral. (2). 1 Cuba.
Megaloprotachne C. E. Hubbard. Gramin. (5). 1 Bechuanaland.
Meialisia Rafin. = Adriana Gaudich. p.p. (Euphorb.).

Meiandra Markgraf. Melastom. (I). 2 E. Peru.
Meiomeria Standley. Chenopod. (A). I Mexico.
Melanidion E. L. Greene. Crucif. I Canada.
Melanocarpum Hook. f. = Pleuropetalum Hook. f. (Amarant.).
Melanolepis Reichb. f. et Zoll. (*Mallotus* p.p.). Euphorb. (A. II. 2). I Malay Arch., Polynes.
Meliandra Ducke. Melastom. (III). I Para.
Melliodendron Hand.-Mazz. Styrac. I China.
Meloneura Rafin. (*Utricularia* p.p.). Lentibular. 6 | ✻.
Mendelism. *Cf.* Punnett, *Mendelism.*
Menendezia Britton (*Tetrazygia* p.p.). Melastom. (I). 3 Porto Rico.
Menestoria DC. Rubi. (inc. sed.). Genus delendum.
Meniscoid, watch-glass-shaped.
Menodoropsis Small (*Menodora* p.p.). Oleac. I S.W. U.S.
Mentocalyx N. E. Brown. Aizo. (II). I S. Afr.
Meopsis K.-Pol. (*Daucus* p.p.). Umbell. (III. 8). 2 W. Medit.
Meretricia Neraud. Rubi. Nomen.
Meringogyne H. Wolff. Umbell. (III. 5). I Mossamedes.
Merkusia de Vriese = Scaevola L. p.p. (Gooden.).
Merwia B. Fedtsch. Umbell. (III. 6). I Transcaspia.
Mesadenus Schlechter (*Spiranthes* p.p.). Orchid. (II. 2). 5 trop. Am., W.I.
Mesaulosperma van Slooten (*Poliothyrsis* p.p.). Flacourt. (4). 2 Malay Archip.
Mesosetum Steud. = Panicum L. (Gramin.).
Metachlamydeae = Sympetalae.
Metaxya Presl. Protocyath I S. Am. *Cf.* Bower, *Ferns*, ii, 288.
Meteoromyrtus Gamble. Myrt. (I). I Wynaad.
Metrodorea. For Rio de Janeiro *read* E. Brazil.
Mexianthus B. L. Robinson. Comp. (2). I Mexico.
Meyerophytum Schwantes. Aizo. (II). I S. Afr.
Meziothamnus Harms. Bromel. (II). I N. Arg., Bolivia.
Micraeschynanthus Ridley. Gesner. (I). I Malay Penins.
Microbiota Komarov. Conif. (Pin.). I Siberia.
Microcardamum O. E. Schulz (*Draba* p.p.). Crucif. (4). I temp. S. Am.
Microcaryum I. M. Johnston (*Eritrichium* p.p.). Boragin. (IV. 2). 4 W. Himal., Turkestan.
Microclisia Benth. = Pleogyne Miers (Menisp.).
Micromystria O. E. Schulz (*Blennodia* p.p.). Crucif. (2). 2 Austr.
Micropterum Schwantes. Aizo. (II). I S. Afr.
Microsemma. For Flacourt. *read* Thymel.
Microsisymbrium O. E. Schulz (*Sisymbrium* p.p.). Crucif. (2). 4 C. As. to N.W. Am.
Microtheca Schlechter. Orchid. (II. I). I Madag.
Miersiophyton Engl. = Rhigiocarya Miers (Menisp.).
Mila Britton et Rose. Cact. (III. I). I Peru.
Millspaughia. *Read* = Gymnopodium Rolfe (Polygon.). 3 C. Am.
Miltitzia A. DC. (*Emmenanthe* p.p.). Hydrophyll. 6 Pac. N. Am.
Mimosopsis Britton et Rose (*Mimosa* p.p.). Legum. (I. 5). 25 S. U.S. to C. Am.
Miscanthidium Stapf. Gramin. (2). 4 trop. and S. Afr.

Mischopleura Wernh. ex Ridley. Eric. (I. 2). 2 New Guinea.
Mitrastemonaceae. *Cf. Bot. Mag., Tokyo,* 1911, p. 253.
Mitrella Miq. (*Melodorum* p.p.). Anon. (4). 3 Malay Archip.
Mitrophyllum Schwantes. Aizo. (II). 8 S. Afr.
Mizonia A. Chevalier. Amaryllid. Nomen. 1 Sudan.
Mnemion Spach = Viola L. (Viol.).
Mnesithea Kunth. (*Ophiurus* p.p.). Gramin. (2). 8 Indomal.
Mocinna. *Cf.* Johnston in *Contr. Gray Hbm.* 70 and 78, 1924.
Mohria Britton = Halesia L. (Styrac.).
Mohrodendron Britton. Styrac. 4 S. U.S.
Molineria Colla. Amaryllid. (III). 7 Indomal.
Moliniopsis Hayata (*Molinia* p.p.). Gramin. (10). 1 Japan.
Moluchia Medic. = Melochia L. (Stercul.).
Mommsenia Urb. et Ekman. Melastom. (I). 1 Haiti.
Monandriella Engl. Podostem. 1 Cameroons.
Monandrodendron Mansfeld. Flacourt. (4). 1 Colombia.
Monanthemum Griseb. = Piptocarpha R. Br. (Comp.).
Mondia Skeels (*Chlorocodon* p.p.). Asclep. (I). 1 S. Afr.
Mondo Adans. (*Ophiopogon* Ker Gawl.). Lili. (VIII). 15 Japan to Himal.
Moniera Juss. = Herpestis Gaertn. (Scroph.).
Monilaria Schwantes (*Mesembryanthemum* p.p.). Aizo. (II). 5 S. Afr.
Monium Stapf. Gramin. (2). 1 French Guinea.
Monocardia Pennell. Scroph. (II. 6). 4 Colombia, Panama.
Monocephalium S. Moore. Icacin. 1 Cameroons.
Monocymbium Stapf. Gramin. (2). 1 trop. and S. Afr.
Monopholis S. F. Blake (*Chaenocephalus* p.p.). Comp. (5). 4 Ecuador, Peru.
Monoplegma Piper (*Canavalia* p.p.). Legum. (III. 10). 1 Costa Rica.
Monoptera Sch.-Bip. = Chrysanthemum L. p.p. (Comp.). 1 Canaries.
Monotheca (*Reptonia*) A. DC., Theophrast. 2 Arabia to Afghanistan.
Monothrix Torr. = Laphamia A. Gray (Comp.).
Monotrema Koernicke. Rapat. 2 Venezuela.
Montagueia Baker f. Anacard. (3). 1 New Caled.
Montbretiopsis L. Bolus. Irid. (III). 1 S. Afr.
Montiastrum Rydberg (*Montia* p.p.). Portulac. 1 W. N. Am.
Monotrema Koernicke (*Stegolepis* Klotzsch). Rapat. 2 Venez.
Monvillea Britton et Rose (*Cereus* p.p.). Cact. (III. 1). 7 S. Am.
Mosdenia Stent (*Perotis* p.p.). Gramin. (3). 1 Transvaal.
Mostacillastrum O. E. Schulz (*Sisymbrium* p.p.). Crucif. (2). 3 Arg.
Mouretia Pitard in Lecomte. Rubi. (I. 3). 1 Tonquin.
Mozartia Urb. (*Myrcia* p.p.). Myrt. (I). 1 Cuba.
Mozinna Ortega = Jatropha L. p.p. (Euphorb.).
Mucizonia (DC) Berger. Crassul. 1 Iberia, N. Afr., Canaries.
Muiria N. E. Brown. Aizo. (II). 1 S. Afr.
Mulfordia Rusby. Zingiber. (II). 1 Bolivia.
Murdannia Royle (*Aneilema* p.p.). Commelin. 50 S.E. As., Austr., trop. Afr., S. Am.
Murtughas O. Ktze. = Lagerstroemia L. (Lythr.).
Musa. *Add* The sp. cult. in the Canaries is *M. Cavendishii* Lambert ex Paxt. (China).

Musilia Velen. (*Astericus* p.p.). Comp. (4). 1 Arabia.
Mycaranthes Blume = Eria Lindl. p.p. (Orchid.).
Myconella Sprague. Comp. (7). 1 Medit. *Kew Bull.*, 1928, p. 269.
Myosurandra. *Add* (*Myrothamnus* p.p.).
Myrmecodendron Britton et Rose (*Acacia* p.p.). Legum. (I. 2). 12 Mex., C. Am.
Myrmeconauclea Merrill (*Nauclea* p.p.). Rubi. (I. 6). 1 Malaya.
Myrobalanifera Houttuyn 1774. Combret. 1 E. Indies.
Myrtekmania Urb. (*Eugenia* p.p.). Myrt. (I). 1 Cuba.
Mytilaria Lecomte. Hamamelid. 1 Laos.
Namibia Dinter et Schwantes. Aizo. (II). 5 S. Afr.
Nanodes Lindl. = Epidendrum p.p. (Orchid.).
Napeodendron Ridley. Sapind. (I). 1 Selangor.
Nasturtiopsis Boiss. (*Sisymbrium* p.p.). Crucif. (2). 1 N. Afr., Arabia.
Naucleopsis Miq. (*Perebea* p.p.). Mor. (II). 3 trop. Am.
Navaea Webb et Berth. = Lavatera L. p.p. (Malv.). 1 Canaries.
Navarretia. *N. cotulifolia* Hook. et Arn. is 4-merous; *N. filicaulis* Greene is both loculicid. and septicid.; some dehisce irreg.
Nazia Adans. (*Cenchrus* p.p.). Gramin. (5). 2 trop. and temp.
Necramium Britton. Melastom. (inc. sed.). 1 Trinidad.
Nelia Schwantes. Aizo. (II). 1 S. Afr.
Nelumbium. Line 3, *read*: The latter is sometimes supposed to be the sacred lotus. *Omit* sentence beginning: Sculptures of it. And *cf.* Nymphaea.
Nematostemma Choux. Asclepiad. (II. 1). 1 Madag.
Nemcia Domin (*Oxylobium* p.p.). Legum. (III. 2). 12 W. Austr.
Nemorosa Nieuwland (*Anemone* p.p.). Ranunc. (3). 2 N. temp.
Neoabbottia Britton et Rose. Cact. (III. 1). 1 Hispaniola.
Neobakeria Schlechter (*Polyxena* p.p.). Lili. (V). 7 S. Afr.
Neobartlettia Schlechter. Orchid. (II. 2). 2 Guiana, N. Brazil.
Neobesseya Britton et Rose (*Mammillaria* p.p.). Cact. (III. 2). 4 Midwest U.S.
Neobracea (*Bracea*) Britton. Apocyn. (I. 3). 1 Bahamas.
Neogardneria Schlechter (*Zygopetalum* p.p.). Orchid. (II. 14). 1 Guiana.
Neohouzeaua (Camus) Gamble (*Teinostachyum* p.p.). Gramin. 3 S.E. As.
Neohusnotia A. Camus. Gramin. (5). 1 Indochina.
Neolloydia Britton et Rose. Cact. (III. 2). 7 subtrop. N. Am.
Neomammillaria Britton et Rose (*Mammillaria* Haw.). Cact. (III. 2). 150 Mexico to Nevada and Venezuela, W.I.
Neomarica Sprague (*Marica* Ker). Irid. (II). 15 trop. Am.
Neomartinella Pilger. Crucif. (inc. sed.). 1 China.
Neomillspaughia S. F. Blake. Polygon. (III. 1). 2 C. Am.
Neomimosa Britton et Rose (*Mimosa* p.p.). Legum. (I. 5). 7 Mexico, C. Am.
Neomphalea Pax et K. Hoffm. (*Omphalea* p.p.). Euphorb. (A. II. 7). 1 New Guinea.
Neopalissya Pax (*Alchornea* p.p.). Euphorb. (A. II. 2). 1 Madag.
Neopeltandra Gamble (*Phyllanthns* p.p.). Euphorb. (A. I. 1). 2 Indomal.
Neoporteria Britton et Rose (*Echinocactus* p.p.). Cact. (III. 1). 7 Chile.

Neoraimondia Britton et Rose. Cact. (III. 1). 1 W. Peru.
Neoregnellia Urb. Stercul. 1 Cuba.
Neoschroetera (*Schroeterella*) Briquet. Zygophyll. 4 warm Am.
Neosepicaea Diels. Bignon. (2). 1 New Guinea.
Neotessmannia Burret. Tili. 1 Peru.
Neothymopsis Britton et Millspaugh. Comp. (6). 2 Cuba, Bahamas.
Neotrewia Pax et K. Hoffm. (*Mallotus* p.p.). Euphorb. (A. II. 2). 1 Phil. Is.
Neotrigonostemon Pax et K. Hoffm. Euphorb. (A. II. 5). 1 Burma.
Neottianthe Schlechter (*Gymnadenia* p.p.). Orchid. (II. 1). 8 N. temp. |✻.
Neoturczaninowia K.-Pol. Umbell. (III. 6). No spp. descr.
Neoveitchia Becc. (*Veitchia* p.p.). Palm. (IV. 1). 1 Fiji Is.
Neowawraea Rock. Euphorb. (A. I. 1). 1 Hawaiian Is.
Neowollastonia Wernh. in Ridl. Apocyn. (I. 3). 1 New Guinea.
Neowormia Hutchinson et Summerhayes (*Wormia* p.p.). Dillen. 1 Seychelles.
Neozenkerina Mildbr. Scroph. (II. 6). 1 Cameroons.
Nephrodesmus Schindler (*Arthroclianthus* p.p.). Legum. (III. 7). 3 New Caledonia.
Nephroica Miers = Cocculus DC. p.p. (Menisp.).
Nephromeria Schindler (*Desmodium* p.p.). Legum. (III. 7). 8 trop. S. Am.
Nephrostylus Gagnep. Euphorb. (A. II. 4). 1 Annam.
Nernstia Urb. (*Portlandia* p.p.). Rubi. (I. 1). 1 Mexico.
Nesocaryum I. M. Johnston. Boragin. (IV. 2). 1 Chile.
Neuontobotrys O. E. Schulz (*Sisymbrium* p.p.). Crucif. (2). 1 Chile, Arg.
Neurelmis Rafin. = Jalambica Rafin. (Comp.).
Neurolakis Mattf. Comp. (1). 1 Cameroons.
Neurolepis Meissn. 1843; Pilger. Gramin. (13). 10 trop. S. Am.
Neurotecoma K. Schum. (*Tecoma* p.p.). Bignon. (2). 1 Cuba.
Nidema Britton et Millsp. (*Epidendrum* p.p.). Orchid. (II. 6). 2 W.I., trop. S. Am.
Nigrorchis Godfery. Orchid. Nigritella × Orchis hybrid.
Nimiria Prain ex Craib. Legum. (I. 2). 1 Siam.
Nobeliodendron O. C. Schmidt. Laur. (II). 1 Cuba.
Nopalxochia Britton et Rose. Cact. (III. 1). 1 Mexico.
Norta Adans. (*Sisymbrium* p.p.). Crucif. (2). 10 |✻.
Nothopegiopsis Lauterb. Anacard. (4). 1 New Guinea.
Notiosciadium Speg. Umbell. (III. 5). 1 Arg.
Notodontia Pierre ex Pitard. Rubi. (I. 2). 2 Indochina.
Notoxylinon Lewton (*Fugosia* p.p.). Malv. (4). 8 Austr.
Nouhouysia Lauterb. Guttif. (IV). 1 New Guinea.
Nowacka Pohl. Inc. sed. Nomen.
Nowodworskya Pohl. Inc. sed. Nomen.
Nyachia Small. Caryophyll. (I. 4). 1 Florida.
Nyctaginaceae. *Add* seed with perisperm.
Nyctelea Scop. (*Ellisia* p.p.). Hydrophyll. 3 N. Am.
Nyssopsis. For (Corn.) *read* (Nyss.).
Obregonia Frič. (*Echinocactus* p.p.). Cact. (III. 1). 1 Mexico.

Octamyrtus Diels. Myrt. (I). 3 New Guinea.
Ochrocodon Rydberg (*Fritillaria* p.p.). Lili. (v). I W. N. Am.
Octoknema Pierre. *Read* The only gen. of **Octoknemataceae** (*Olac.* p.p.) (Dicots. Archichl. Santalales, p. xv). 4 trop. Afr. ♄ with alt. l. and stellate hairs. Fls. ☿. P 2+3, A 2+3 anteposed, $\overline{G}$ I-loc. with thread-like plac. pressed against the wall, and 3 pend. ov. Drupe I-seeded.
Ocyroe Phil. (*Nardophyllum* p.p.). Comp. (3). I Chile.
Oddoniodendron de Wild. Legum. (II. 3). I Belgian Congo.
Odontotrichum Zucc., emend. Rydberg (*Cacalia* p.p.). Comp. (8). 35 Mexico, S.W. U.S.
Odostima Rafin. = Moneses Salisb. (Pyrol.).
Odyssea Stapf (*Diplachne* p.p.). Gramin. (10). 2 Red Sea, S.W. Afr.
Oedibasis K.-Pol. (*Carum* p.p.). Umbell. (III. 5). 2 C. As.
Ogiera Cass. = Eleutheranthera Poit. (Comp.).
Olgaea Iljin (*Carduus* p.p.). Comp. (11). 12 C. As.
Oligoceras Gagnep. Euphorb. (A. II. 3). I Indochina.
Olmedioperebea Ducke. Mor. (II). I Amazon valley.
Olymposciadium Wolff. Umbell. (III. 5). I Mt. Olympus.
Omiltemia Standley. Rubi. (I. 3). I Mexico.
Oncostylis Nees = Fimbristylis Vahl (*IK*) = Psilocarya Torr.
Ophellantha Standley. Euphorb. (A. II. 2). I Salvador.
Ophiobostryx Skeels (*Bowiea* Harv., q.v.). Lili. (III). I S. Afr.
Ophioglossaceae. *Cf.* Bower, *Ferns*, ii. 42.
Ophthalmophyllum Dinter et Schwantes. Aizo. (II). 2 S. Afr.
Orchyllium Barnh. (*Utricularia* p.p.). Lentibul. 12 trop. Am.
Oregandra Standley. Rubi. (II. 4 or 5). I Panama.
Oreochorte K.-Pol. (*Anthriscus* p.p.). Umbell. (III. 2). I China.
Oreogenia I. M. Johnston (*Eritrichium* p.p.). Boragin. (IV. 2). 7 C. As.
Oreonana Jepson (*Deweya* p.p.). Umbell. (III. 4). 2 Calif.
Oreophyton O. E, Schulz (*Arabis* p.p.). Crucif. (2). I Abyss.
Oreorhamnus Ridley. Rhamn. I Perak.
Oreosparte Schlechter. Asclepiad. (II. 3). I Minahassa.
Ormosiopsis Ducke (*Clathrotropis* p.p.). Legum. (III. I). I Para.
Orophoma Spruce (*Mauritia* p.p.). Palm. (III). 2 Amazon valley, Venez.
Orostachys Fisch. (*Umbilicus* p.p.). Crassul. 10 temp. As.
Oroya Britton et Rose (*Echinocactus* p.p.). Cact. (III. I). I Peru.
Orthachne Nees. Gramin. (8). I Chile.
Orthopterum L. Bolus. Aizo. (II). I S. Afr.
Orthosphenia Standley. Celastr. I Mexico.
Oscularia Schwantes (*Mesembryanthemum* p.p.). Aizo. (II). 4 S. Afr.
Osiodendron Pohl. Inc. sed. Nomen.
Osmhydrophora Barb. Rodr. Bignon. (I). I Amazonas.
Osmoglossum Schlechter (*Odontoglossum* p.p.). Orchid. (II. 19). 5 C. Am.
Osmundaceae. *Cf.* Bower, *Ferns*, ii, 126.
Ossea Lonic. ex Nieuwl. = Cornus L. p.p. (Corn.).
Otocarpus Durieu (*Rapistrum* p.p.). Crucif. (2). I Algeria.
Otocephalus Chiov. Rubi. (II. 7). I Angola.

Otostylis Schlechter (*Zygopetalum* p.p.). Orchid. (II. 14). 3 trop. S. Am., Trinidad.
Ottoschmidtia Urb. Rubi. (II. 2). 1 Cuba.
Oudneya R. Br. Crucif. (2). 1 N. Afr.
Ourisianthus Bonati. Scroph. (III. 1). 1 Indochina.
Owataria Matsumura. Guttif. (V). 1 Formosa, Liukiu Is.
Oxycarpha Blake. Comp. (5). 1 Venezuela.
Oxychlamys Schlechter. Gesner. (I). 1 New Guinea.
Ozoroa Delile = Heeria Meissn. (Anacard.).
Pachycornus Coville; Standley (*Schinus* p.p.). Anacard. (3). 1 Lower Calif.
Pachylarnax Dandy. Magnol. 1 S.E. As.
Pachymitus O. E. Schulz (*Blennodia* p.p.). Crucif. (2). 2 Austr.
Pachystegia Cheeseman (*Olearia* p.p.). Comp. (3). 1 N.Z.
Pachystelma T. S. Brandegee. Asclepiad. (II. 1). 1 Mexico.
Pachystylidium Pax et K. Hoffm. (*Tragia* p.p.). Euphorb. (A. II. 2). 1 Java, Phil. Is.
Paedicalyx Pierre ex Pitard. Rubi. (I. 2). 1 Laos.
Pagella Schönland. Crassul. 1 Cape Col.
Painteria Britton et Rose (*Pithecolobium* p.p.). Legum. (I. 1). 4 Mexico.
Palandra O. F. Cook. Palm. (V). 1 Ecuador.
Pallasia Scop. = Crypsis Ait. (Gramin.).
Palmervandenbroeckia L. S. Gibbs. Aral. (I). 1 Dutch New Guinea.
Palmoglossum Klotzsch ex Rchb. f. = Pleurothallis R. Br. p.p. (Orchid.).
Pameroon bark (W.I.), *Trichilia moschata* Sw.
Panetos Rafin. = Houstonia L. p.p. (Rubi.).
Pantadenia Gagnep. Euphorb. (A. II. 3). 1 Cochinchina.
Pantorrhynchus Murb. = Trachystoma O. E. Schulz (Crucif.).
Panulia Baill. = Ligusticum L. p.p. (Umbell.).
Paolia Chiov. Rubi. (I. 8). 1 Somaliland.
Pappobolus Blake. Comp. (5). 1 Bolivia.
Papuaea Schlechter. Orchid. (II. 2). 1 New Guinea.
Papuechites Markgraf (*Strophanthus* p.p.). Apocyn. (II. 1). 1 New Guinea.
Papuzilla Ridley. Crucif. (2). 1 New Guinea.
Para grass, *Panicum barbinode* Trin. (Brazil).
Parabenzoin Nakai (*Benzoin* p.p.). Laur. (II). 2 Japan.
Parachimarrhis Ducke. Rubi. (I. 1). 1 Amazon valley.
Paracryphia Baker f. Eucryph. 1 New Caledonia.
Paractaenium Beauv. Gramin. (5). 1 Austr.
Paradina Pierre ex Pitard. Rubi. (I. 6). 2 Indochina.
Parahancornia Ducke (*Hancornia* p.p.). Apocyn. (I. 1). 1 Amazon valley.
Paramachaerium Ducke (*Machaerium* p.p.). Legum. (III. 8). 1 northern S. Am.
Parantennaria Beauverd (*Antennaria* p.p.). Comp. (4). 1 Austr.
Parapactis W. Zimm. (*Epipactis* p.p.). Orchid. (II. 2). 1 C. Eur.
Paraphyadanthe Mildbraed. Flacourt. (I). 3 Cameroons.
Paraquilegia J. R. Drumm. et J. Hutch. Ranunc. (2). 4 south C. As.
Pararistolochia Hutchinson et Dalziel (*Aristolochia* p.p.). Aristoloch. 12 W. trop. Afr.

Paraselinum Wolff. Umbell. (III. 5). 1 Peru.
Parasenecio W. W. Smith et Small. Comp. (8). 1 Szechuan.
Parasitipomoea Hayata. Convolv. (1). 1 Formosa.
Parastyrax W. W. Smith. Styrac. 1 Burma.
Parasyringa W. W. Smith (*Syringa* p.p.). Oleac. 1 Yunnan.
Pariti Adans. (*Hibiscus* p.p.). Malv. (4). 20 trop.
Parodiodoxa O. E. Schulz (*Thlaspi* p.p.). Crucif. (2). 1 N. Arg.
Paropyrum Ulbr. (*Isopyrum* p.p.). Ranunc. (2). 1 west C. As.
Paroxygraphis W. W. Smith. Ranunc. (3). 1 Sikkim.
Parsonsia P. Br. = Cuphea Adans. (Lythr.). 4 trop. Am., W.I.
Paspalidium Stapf. Gramin. (5). 12 warm.
Paspalum. After temp. *for* Am. where *read* In Am. they.
Passaveria Mart. et Eichl. = Ecclinusa Mart. (Sapot.).
Pedinogyne A. Brand (*Eritrichium* p.p.). Boragin. (IV. 2). 1 Sikkim, Tibet.
Pedinopetalum Urb. et H. Wolff. Umbell. (III. 5). 1 San Domingo.
Pediocactus Britton et Rose (*Echinocactus* p.p.). Cact. (III. 1). 1 W. U.S.
Pediomelum Rydberg (*Psoralea* p.p.). Legum. (III. 6). 25 N. Am.
Peekeliopanax Harms. Aral. (1). 1 New Guinea.
Peersia L. Bolus (*Mesembryanthemum* p.p.). Aizo. (II). 1 S. Afr.
Pegaeophyton Hayek et Hand.-Mazz. (*Braya* p.p.). Crucif. (4). 1 China.
Pelagatia O. E. Schulz. Crucif. (2). 1 Peru.
Pelagodoxa Becc. Palm. (I. 2). 1 Marquesas.
Pelidnia Barnh. (*Utricularia* p.p.). Lentibul. 18 palaeotrop.
Pelonastes Hook. f. = Myriophyllum L. (Halorag.).
Peltaea Standley (*Pavonia* p.p.). Malv. (3). 4 trop. Am., W.I.
Peltobractea Rusby. Malv. (3). 1 Bolivia.
Peltophoropsis Chiov. Legum. (III. 8). 1 E. Afr.
Peltophorus Desv. Gramin. (2). 5 India, trop. Afr.
Penaeaceae. For Thymelaeales *read* Myrtiflorae.
Penelopeia Urb. (*Coccinea* p.p.). Cucurb. (4). 1 Haiti.
Peniculifera Ridley. Stercul. 1 Penang.
Peniophyllum Pennell (*Oenothera* p.p.). Onagr. (2). 1 S. U.S.
Penstemon (Mitch.) Smidel. Scroph. (II. 4). 7 W. U.S.
Pentabrachium Muell.-Arg. Euphorb. (A. I. 1). 1 W. trop. Afr.
Pentacrypta Lehm. Umbell. (III. 4). 1 Mexico.
Pentamera Blume. Asclepiad. (1). 1 Sumatra. No corona.
Pentastira Ridley. Icacin. 2 New Guinea.
Penthorum. For Crassul. *read* Saxifrag.
Pentstemonopsis Rydberg (*Pentstemon* p.p.). Scroph. (II. 4). 1 Idaho, Montana.
Perakanthus Robyns ex Ridley (*Canthium* p.p.). Rubi. (II. 1). 2 Perak.
Perantha Craib. Gesner. (1). 3 Yunnan.
Peratanthe Urb. Rubi. (II. 7). 2 Cuba, Haiti.
Periglossum Decne. = Cordylogyne E. Mey. (Asclepiad.).
Perilimnastes Ridley (*Anerincleistus* p.p.). Melastom. (1). 1 Pahang.
Peripetasma Ridley. Menisperm. 1 Selangor.
Perrierbambus A. Camus. Gramin. (13). 2 Madag.

Perrieriella Schlechter. Orchid. (II. 20). 1 Madag.
Perulifera A. Camus. Gramin. (4). 1 Madag.
Pescatobollea × Rolfe. Orchid. Hybrid, Pescatorea × Bollea.
Petalocaryum Pierre ex A. Chevalier. Olac. 1 Gaboon.
Petalocentrum Schlechter (*Sigmatostalix* p.p.). Orchid. (II. 19). 10 trop. S. Am.
Petalochilus R. S. Rogers. Orchid. (II. 2). 2 New Zealand.
Petalonema Schlechter. Asclepiad. (II. 1). 1 Luzon.
Petchia Livera. Apocyn. (I. 3). 1 Ceylon.
Petermannia. After Dioscor. *add* (?).
Petesia (P. Br.) L. Rubi. (II. 4). 3 Mexico, Porto Rico.
Phacelurus Griseb. Gramin. (2). 3 warm E. Afr., As.
Phaenopus DC. = Lactuca Tourn. (Comp.).
Phaeonychium O. E. Schulz. Crucif. (4). 1 W. Tibet.
Phanerocalyx S. Moore. Olac. 2 Cameroons, Nigeria.
Phanerotaenia St John (*Polytaenia* p.p.). Umbell. (III. 6). 1 Texas, Okl.
Phellosperma Britton et Rose (*Mammillaria* p.p.). Cact. (III. 2). 1 W. U.S.
Phenianthus Rafin. (*Lonicera* p.p.). Caprifol. 2 N. Am.
Phidiasia Urb. Acanth. (IV. B). 1 Cuba.
Philageria ×. Lili. Hybrid, Philesia × Lapageria.
Phlebiophragmus O. E. Schulz (*Thelypodium* p.p.). Crucif. (1). 1 Peru.
Phoenicimon Ridley. Sapind. (1). 1 Malay Penins.
Pholiurus Trin. Gramin. (12). 4 | *.
Phormangis Schlechter (*Angraecum* p.p.). Orchid. (II. 20). 1 W. Afr.
Phryne Bubani (*Stenophragma* p.p.). Crucif. (4). 4 Mts. of S. Eur., Caucasus.
Phyllapophysis Mansfeld. Melastom. (1). 1 New Guinea.
Phyllitis. *Add Cf.* Scolopendrium.
Phyllocara Gusul. Boragin. (IV. 3). 1 E. Medit.
Phyllocharis Diels. Campanul. (III). 2 New Guinea. Infl. epiphyllous.
Phyllocoryne Hook. f. = Scybalium Schott et Endl. (Balanophor.).
Phyllorchis Thou. 1808. Orchid. (II. 16). 1 Madag., Masc.
Phyllothamnus × C. K. Schneider. Eric. Hybrid, Rhodothamnus × Phyllodoce.
Phymosia Desv. (*Abutilon* p.p.). Malv. (1). 40 Am., W.I., S. Afr.
Physoceras Schlechter. Orchid. (II. 1). 5 Madag.
Physospermopsis H. Wolff (*Arracacia* p.p.). Umbell. (III. 4). 1 Yunnan.
Phytolaccaceae. *Add* L. entire, alt.
Picea A. Dietr. 1824 = Picea Link (Conif.).
Picroxylon Warb. Simarub. 1 Siam.
Pierreodendron A. Chevalier. Simarub. 1 Gaboon.
Pilgerochloa Eig. (*Ventenata* p.p.). Gramin. (9). 1 As. Minor.
Pinus. *Cf.* Sargent, *Man. of the Timbers of N. Am.*
Piquetia Hallier (*Thea* p.p.). Theac. 1 Indochina.
Pirazzia Chiov. (*Matthiola* p.p.). Crucif. (4). 1 Abyss., Eritrea.
Pirottantha Speg. Legum. 1 Arg.
Pisophaca Rydberg (*Phaca* p.p.). Legum. (III. 6). 20 N. Am.
Pithecodendron Speg. Legum. (I. 1). 1 Arg., Paraguay.
Pitygentias Gilg (*Gentiana* p.p.). Gentian. (1). 2 Peru.

Pityranthes Viv. Umbell. (III. 5). 10 Afr., Syria.
Pityrocarpa Britton et Rose (*Piptadenia* p.p.). Legum. (I. 5). 1 Mexico.
Placospermum C. T. White et Francis. Prot. (II). 1 Queensland. *Proc. R. S. Qsld.* 35, 1923, 79.
Plaesianthera Livera (*Cardanthera* p.p.). Acanth. (IV. A). 1 Ceylon.
Plagiogyria Kunze. *Read* Plagiogyr. 12 Indomal., C. Am.
Plagiogyriaceae. *Cf.* Bower, *Ferns*, ii, 275.
Plagiopetalum Rehder. Melastom. (I). 1 China.
Plagiorhegma Maxim. (*Jeffersonia* p.p.). Berberid. 1 N.E. As.
Plagiorrhiza Hallier (*Kayea* p.p.). Guttif. (IV). 1 Burma, Malaya.
Plastolaena Pierre ex A. Chevalier (*Schumanniophyton* Harms). Rubi. (I. 8). 1 Congo.
Platanus. *Cf.* Henry, *Proc. R. Irish Acad.* xxxv. 1919.
Platonia Kunth = Planotia Munro (Gramin.).
Platycraspedum O. E. Schulz. Crucif. (2). 1 E. Tibet.
Platyzoma R. Br. Gleichen. 1 N.E. Austr.
Plectranthrastrum T. C. E. Fries. Labi. (VII). 1 Tanganyika.
Pleiacanthus Rydberg (*Lygodesmia* p.p.). Comp. (13). 1 W. U.S.
Pleianthemum K. Schum. ex A. Chevalier. Tili. 1 Ivory Coast.
Pleioblastus Nakai (*Arundinaria* p.p.). Gramin. (13). 7 Japan, China.
Pleiochasia Barnh. (*Utricularia* p.p.). Lentibul. 20 Austr., N.Z.
Pleiospermum Swingle (*Limonia* p.p.). Rut. (V). 2 Indomal.
Pleodiporochna. *Add* Ochn.
Pleomele. *Cf. Kew Bull.* 1914.
Pleuraphis Torr. (*Hilaria* p.p.). Gramin. (3). 3 W. U.S.
Pleurochaenia Griseb. = Miconia Ruiz et Pav. (Melastom.).
Pleurodiscus Pierre ex A. Chevalier. Sapind. (I). 2 W. Afr.
Pleuropogon. After N. Temp. *add* N. Am.
Pleuropteropyrum Gross (*Polygonum* p.p.). Polygon. (II. 2). 3 N. Am., N. As.
Ploiarium Korthals. Theac. 3 E. Indomal.
Pneumaria Hill = Mertensia Roth. (Boragin.).
Pocillaria Ridley. Icacin. 1 New Guinea.
Podandrogyne Ducke. Capparid. (V). 1 E. Peru.
Podangis Schlechter (*Angraecum* p.p.). Orchid. (II. 20). 1 W. Afr.
Pohliella Engl. Podostem. 1 Cameroons.
Poikilogyne E. G. Baker in L. S. Gibbs. Melastom. (II). 8 Dutch New Guinea.
Poilania Gagnep. Comp. (3). 1 Annam.
Poilaniella Gagnep. Euphorb. (A. II. 5). 1 Annam.
Polliniopsis Hayata. Gramin. (2). 1 Formosa.
Polybaea Klotzsch in Endl. = Bernardia Adans. p.p. (Euphorb.).
Polycodium Rafin. (*Vaccinium* p.p.). Eric. (III. 1). 4 N. Am.
Polycycliska Ridley. Rubi. (I. 7). 1 Sumatra.
Polyodon H. B. et K. (*Bouteloua* p.p.). Gramin. (11). 1 S.W. U.S.
Polyotus Nutt. = Gomphocarpus R. Br. (Asclepiad.).
Polypappus Nutt. = Tessaria Ruiz et Pav. (Comp.).
Polypleurella Engl. (*Polypleurum* Wmg.). Podostem. 1 Siam.
Polypleurum Taylor. Podostem. 2 Indomal.
Polypsecadium O. E. Schulz (*Thelypodium* p.p.). Crucif. (1). 1 Bolivia.
Pomatocalpa Breda (*Cleisostoma* p.p.). Orchid. (II. 20). 12 Indomal.

Ponapea Becc. Palm. (IV. 1). 1 Carolines.
Porfiria Bödeker. Cact. (III. 2). 1 Mexico.
Porodittia G. Don (*Trianthera* p.p.). Scroph. (II. 1). 1 Peru.
Pothomorpha Miq. = Heckeria Kunth (Piper.).
Pragmatropa Pierre (*Euonymus* p.p.). Celastr. 1 Himalaya.
Pragmotessara Pierre (*Euonymus* p.p.). Celastr. 6 N. temp. |*.
Preauxia Sch.-Bip. = Chrysanthemum Tourn. p.p. (Comp.). 4 Canaries.
Priamosia Urb. Flacourt. (4). 1 San Domingo.
Princea Dubard et Dop. Rubi. (I. 7). 1 Madag.
Procopiana Gusul. Boragin. (IV. 3). 1 S.E. Eur.
Prosanerpis S. F. Blake. Melastom. (I). 1 Honduras.
Prosaptia Presl (*Davallia* p.p.). Filices (inc. sed.). *Cf.* Bower, *Ferns*, iii, 254.
Prosartema Gagnep. Euphorb. (A. II. 5). 1 Indochina.
Protocyatheaceae. *Cf.* Bower, *Ferns*, ii, 282.
Protomarattia Hayata. Maratt. 1 Tonquin.
Psammochloa Hitchcock. Gramin. (8). 1 Mongolia.
Psammophora Dinter et Schwantes. Aizo. (II). 2 S. Afr.
Psathyrotopsis Rydberg. Comp. (8). 1 Mexico.
Pseudacoridium Ames (*Dendrochilum* p.p.). Orchid. (II. 16). 1 Phil. Is.
Pseudactis S Moore. Comp. (8). 1 Belgian Congo.
Pseudaegiphila Rusby. Verben. (4). 1 Upper Amazon.
Pseudalbizzia Britton et Rose (*Acacia* p.p.). Legum. (I. 2). 1 W.I.
Pseudammi Wolff. Umbellif. (III. 5). 1 Siberia.
Pseudananas Hassler (*Ananas* p.p.). Bromel. (IV). 1 Paraguay, N. Arg.
Pseudannona Safford (*Anona* p.p.). Anon. (4). 2 Madag., Masc.
Pseudarabidella O. E. Schulz (*Sisymbrium* p.p.). Crucif. (2). 1 S. Austr.
Pseudechinolaena Stapf. Gramin. (2). 1 trop.
Pseudellipanthus Schellenb. Connar. 2 Borneo.
Pseuderucaria O. E. Schulz (*Moricandia* p.p.). Crucif. (4). 3 Morocco.
Pseudobartlettia Rydberg (*Psathyrodes* p.p.). Comp. (8). 1 S. W. U.S., Mexico.
Pseudobromus K. Schum. Gramin. (8). 3 S. and E. Afr., Madag.
Pseudocarum Norman. Umbell. (III. 5). 1 Uganda.
Pseudochaetochloa Hitchcock. Gramin. (5). 1 W. Austr.
Pseudochimarrhis Ducke (*Chimarrhis* p.p.). Rubi. (I. 1). 2 Amazon valley.
Pseudoclappia Rydberg. Comp. (6). 1 New Mexico.
Pseudocoix A. Camus. Gramin. (13). 1 Madag.
Pseudocopaiva Britton et Wilson (*Copaifera* p.p.). Legum. (II. 2). 1 Cuba.
Pseudocrupina Velen. Comp. (4). 1 Arabia.
Pseudocryptocarya Teschn. (*Cryptocarya* p.p.). Laur. (II). 1 New Guinea.
Pseudoctomeria Kränzl. Orchid. (II. 8). 1 Costa Rica.
Pseudoentada Britton et Rose (*Inga* p.p.). Legum. (I. 1). 1 C. Am.
Pseudoglochidion Gamble. Euphorb. (A. I. 1). 1 Anamalais.
Pseudogomphrena R. E. Fries. Amarant. (3). 1 Minas Geraes.
Pseudogoodyera Schlechter (*Goodyera* p.p.). Orchid. (II. 2). 1 Cuba

Pseudolobelia A. Chevalier. Scroph. Nomen.
Pseudophacelurus A. Camus (*Rottboellia* p.p.). Gramin. (2). 2 India, China, Japan.
Pseudopogonatherum A. Camus. Gramin. (2). 4 trop. As.
Pseudorhipsalis Britton et Rose (*Rhipsalis* p.p.). Cact. (III. 3). 2 Costa Rica, Jamaica.
Pseudosasa Makino (*Bambusa* p.p.). Gramin. (13). 5 Japan.
Pseudoscolopia Gilg. Flacourt. (5). 1 S. Afr.
Pseudosedum (Boiss.) Berger. Crassul. 2 C. As.
Pseudoselinum Norman (*Selinum* p.p.). Umbell. (III. 5). 1 Angola.
Pseudosicydium Harms. Cucurb. (2). 1 E. Peru.
Pseudosmilax Hayata. Lili. (XI). 2 Formosa.
Pseudosorghum A. Camus. Gramin. (2). 2 trop. As.
Pseudospigelia Klett (*Spigelia* p.p.). Logan. 1 trop. S. Am.
Pseudostelis Schlechter (*Stelis* p.p.). Orchid. (II. 8). 3 Brazil.
Pseudovossia A. Camus. Gramin. (2). 1 Indochina.
Pseudoweinmannia Engl. Cunon. 2 Queensland.
Pseudowillughbeia Marcgraf. Apocyn. (I. 1). 1 N.E. New Guinea.
Pseuduvaria Miq. = Orophea Blume p.p. (Anon.). *Phil. Journ. Sci.* 1915, p. 255.
Psiadiella Humbert. Comp. (3). 1 Madag.
Psilathera Link. Gramin. (10). 1 Alps.
Psilotum. *Cf.* Lawson, and Darnell-Smith, in *Trans. R. Soc. Edinb.* lii, 1918.
Psoralidium Rydberg (*Psoralea* p.p.). Legum. (III. 6). 15 W. N. Am.
Psorobates Rydberg (*Dalea* p.p.). Legum. (III. 6). 2 Calif., Mexico.
Psorodendron Rydberg (*Dalea* p.p.). Legum. (III. 6). 12 S.W. U.S., Mexico.
Psorothamnus Rydberg (*Dalea* p.p.). Legum. (III. 6). 8 S.W. U.S., Mexico.
Psychanthus Ridley (*Alpinia* p.p.). Zingiber. (I). 6 New Guinea.
Pteridium. *Add* Polypod.
Pterochlaena Chiov. Gramin. (5). 1 Katanga.
Pterocissus Urb. et Ekm. Vitac. 1 Haiti.
Pterococcus Hassk. (*Plukenetia* p.p.). Euphorb. (A. II. 2). 3 palaeotrop.
Pteroglossa Schlechter (*Stenorrhynchus* p.p.). Orchid. (II. 2). 2 temp. S. Am.
Pteroloma Hochst. et Steud. = Dipterygium Desv. (Capparid.).
Pteromimosa Britton (*Mimosa* p.p.). Legum. (I. 5). 2 C. Am., Bahamas.
Pteropepon Cogn. (*Sicydium* p.p.). Cucurb. (2). 2 Rio de Janeiro.
Pterophacos Rydberg (*Astragalus* p.p.). Legum. (III. 6). 1 Utah.
Pterospartum K. Koch = Genista L. p.p. (Legum.).
Pterygiosperma O. E. Schulz. Crucif. (2). 1 Patagonia.
Pterygoloma Hanst. = Alloplectus Mart. (Gesner.).
Ptiloria Rafin. (*Stephanomeria* p.p.). Comp. (13). 1 W. N. Am.
Ptychocarpus Kuhlm. Flacourt. (inc. sed.). 1 Para.
Pubilaria Rafin. = Simethis Kunth. (Lili.).
Puccinellia Parl. (*Glyceria* p.p.). Gramin. (10). 30 N. temp.
Punjuba Britton et Rose (*Pithecolobium* p.p.). Legum. (I. 1). 1 Costa Rica.
Pycnophyllopsis Skottsb. Caryoph. (I. 3). 1 Patagonia.

Pycnoplinthus O. E. Schulz (*Braya* p.p.). Crucif. (2). 1 Tibet.
Pycnothryx M. E. Jones = Drudeophytum Coulter et Rose (Umbell.).
Pyrogennema Lunell (*Epilobium* p.p.). Onagr. (2). 1 N. temp.
Pyronia ×. Ros. Hybrid Pyrus-Cydonia.
Pyrrheima Hassk. Commelin. 1 trop. S. Am.
Pyrsonota Ridley. Cunon. 1 New Guinea.
Pythagorea Rafin. = Lythrum L. p.p. (Lythr.).
Quiabentia Britton et Rose (*Pereskia* p.p.). Cact. (1). 1 S. Brazil.
Quinquelobus Benj. Inc. sed. Farrago Scrophulacearum.
Raddia Bertol. Gramin. (5). 5 warm Am., W.I.
Raillardiopsis Rydberg (*Raillardella* p.p.). Comp. (8). 2 Calif.
Raimondianthus Harms. Legum. (III. 7). 1 Peru.
Ramischia Opiz (*Pyrola* p.p.). Pyrol. 1 N. temp.
Ramonia Schlechter. Orchid. (II. 6). 1 Costa Rica.
Ramorinoa Speg. Legum. (III. 8). 1 Arg.
Raphanopsis Welw. = Oxygonum Burch. (Polygon.).
Raphiostyles Benth. et Hook. f. Icacin. 4 trop. W. Afr.
Rapistrella × Pomel. Crucif. Rapistrum × Cordylocarpus hybrid. 1 Alg.
Rapistrum Crantz 1769 = Raphanus, &c. p.p.
Raritebe Wernh. Rubi. (I. 8). 1 Colombia.
Razumovia Spreng. = Centranthera R. Br. (Scroph.).
Rendlia Chiov. Gramin. (11). 2 Katanga.
Rensonia S. F. Blake. Comp. (1). 1 Salvador.
Resinocaulon Lunell (*Silphium* p.p.). Comp. (5). 1 E. U.S.
Restinga (Brazil), the vegetation of a sandy coast.
Resupination (fl.), Campanul., Melianth., Orchid.
Reticulate, netted; **retiform**, apparently netted; **retuse**, broadly notched.
Rhampholepis Stapf (*Panicum* p.p.). Gramin. (5). 30 trop.
Rhaptocalymma Börner. Cyper. Nomen.
Rhinephyllum N. E. Brown. Aizo. (II). 2 S. Afr.
Rhipidoglossum Schlechter (*Aeranthes* p.p.). Orchid. (II. 20). 5 trop. and S. Afr.
Rhipsalidopsis Britton et Rose (*Rhipsalis* p.p.). Cact. (III. 3). 1 Panama.
Rhizophoraceae. *Add* G to $\overline{G}$.
Rhodax Spach = Helianthemum Adans. p.p. (Cist.).
Rhodazalea Hort. Eric. Rhododendron × Azalea hybrid. 1 Hort.
Rhodochlamys Schau. = Salvia Tourn. (Labi.).
Rhombophyllum Schwantes (*Mesembryanthemum* p.p.). Aizo. (II). 1 S. Afr.
Rhopalocarpaceae. A fam. containing only Rhopalocarpus.
Rhopalocyclus Schwantes. Aizo. (II). 3 S. Afr.
Rhopalopodium Ulbr. (*Ranunculus* p.p.). Ranunc. (3). 7 N. Andes.
Rhynchocarpa Blake (*Cyphosperma* p.p.). Palm. (IV. 1). 1 New Caledonia.
Rhyncholaelia Schlechter (*Brassavola* p.p.). Orchid. (II. 6). 2 Mexico, C. Am.
Rhynchophreatia Schlechter (*Thelasis* p.p.). Orchid. (II. 16). 1 Pelew Is.
Rhysolepis Blake (*Viguiera* p.p.). Comp. (5). 2 Mexico.
Rhytidomene Rydberg (*Psoralea* p.p.). Legum. (III. 6). 15 N. Am.

Richeriella Pax et K. Hoffm. Euphorb. (A. I. 1). 1 Phil. Is.
Ricinella Muell.-Arg. = Adelia L. p.p. (Euphorb.).
Ridan Adans. = Actinomeris Nutt. (Comp.).
Rinoreocarpus Ducke. Viol. 1 Amazon valley.
Riseleya Hemsl. Euphorb. (A. I. 1). 1 Seychelles.
Robeschia Hochst. (*Sisymbrium* p.p.). Crucif. (2). 1 W. As.
Robinsoniodendron Merrill (*Maoutia* p.p.). Urtic. (3). 1 Amboina.
Robiquetia Gaudich. = Saccolabium Blume p.p. (Orchid.).
Rodrigueziopsis Schlechter (*Rodriguezia* p.p.). Orchid. (II. 19). 2 S. Brazil.
Roezliella Schlechter (*Sigmatostalix* p.p.). Orchid. (II. 19). 5 Colombia.
Rolfeëlla Schlechter (*Holothrix* p.p.). Orchid. (II. 1). 1 Madag.
Rompelia K.-Pol. (*Angelica* p.p.). Umbell. (III. 6). 3 N. temp.
Ronabea Aubl. = Psychotria L. (Rubi.).
Roodia N. E. Brown (*Mesembryanthemum* p.p.). Aizo. (II). 1 S. Afr.
Rorella Hall (*Drosera* p.p.). Droser. 1 W. U.S.
Roridulaceae = Byblidaceae, q.v.
Roseia Frič. Cact. 1 Mexico.
Roseocactus A. Berger. Cact. (III. 2). 3 Texas, Mexico.
Rose of Sharon (Am.), *Hibiscus syriacus* L.
Rossittia Ewart. Rut. (I). 1 N. Austr.
Rosularia (DC.) Stapf (*Umbilicus* p.p.). Crassul. 20 temp. As.
Roussea L. = Russelia Jacq. (Scroph.).
Roystonea. *Read* 3 trop. Am. Includes *Oreodoxa regia*, q.v.
Rudicularia Moç. et Sesse ex Ramirez = Semiandra Hook et Arn. (Onagr.).
Runyonia Rose. Amaryllid. (II). 1 Texas, Mexico.
Rupicapnos Pomel (*Fumaria* p.p.). Papav. (III). 25 N. Afr., Spain.
Ruschia Schwantes. Aizo. (II). 18 S. Afr.
Rutosma A. Gray (*Thamnosma* p.p.). Rut. (I. 2). 2 N. Am.
Ryncholeucaena Britton et Rose (*Leucaena* p.p.). Legum. (I. 3). 1 Texas, Mexico.
Sacchrosphendamus Nieuwland (*Acer* p.p.). Acer. 1 N. Am. (sugar maple).
Saccolena Gleason. Melastom. (I). 1 Colombia.
Saccoloma. For Polypod. *read* Dickson.
Sadymia Griseb. = Samyda L. (Flacourt.).
Salacighia Loos. Hippocrat. 1 Cameroons. Nomen.
Salaciopsis Baker f. Celastr. 1 New Caled.
Saloa Stuntz (*Blumenbachia* p.p.). Loas. 1 Arg.
Salpianthus Humb. et Bonpl. Nyctagin. 4 Mexico, C. Am.
Salvetia Pohl. Inc. sed. Nomen.
Salviniaceae. *Cf.* Bower, *Ferns*, iii, 260.
Samanea Merrill (*Pithecolobium* p.p.). Legum. (I. 1). 1 S. Am.
Sambo (W.I), *Cleome*.
Samolus. *Cf.* Arber, *Water Plants*.
Samuelssonia Urb. et Ekman. Acanth. (IV. B). 1 Haiti.
Sanguisorba. *Add* Ros. (III. 5).
Sanidophyllum Small. Guttif. (II). 1 Florida.
Santalaceae. For l. opp. *read* opp. or alt.
Sapphoa Urb. Acanth. (IV. B). 1 Cuba.
Sarcoclinium Wight = Agrostistachys Dalz. (Euphorb.).

Sarcophagophilus Dinter. Asclep. (II. 3). 1 Great Namaqualand.
Sarcorhynchus Schlechter (*Mystacidium* p.p.). Orchid. (II. 20). 2 Cameroons.
Sarcostoma Blume = Dendrobium L. p.p. (Orchid.).
Sarcotheca Blume. Oxalid. 15 Malaya.
Sargentodoxaceae Hutchinson = Lardizabalaceae p.p., distinguished by spirally arranged carpels.
Saribus Blume = Livistona R. Br. (Palm.).
Saugetia Hitchcock et Chase. Gramin. (11). 1 Cuba.
Saurauiaceae = Actinidiaceae.
Sauvalella Rydberg (*Corynella* p.p.). Legum. (III. 6). 1 Cuba.
Savastana Schrank = Hierochloe S. G. Gmel. (Gramin.).
Saviniona Webb et Berth. (*Lavatera* p.p.). Malv. (2). 10 N. temp.
Saxicolella Engl. Podostem. 1 Cameroons.
Saxifraga. *Cf. Pfl. R.*, 1916.
Scambopus O. E. Schulz (*Blennodia* p.p.). Crucif. (2). 2 E. and S. Austr.
Scandicium Thell. (*Scandix* p.p.). Umbell. (III. 2). 1 Medit.
Scaphiophora Schlechter (*Thismia* p.p.). Burmann. 1 New Guinea.
Scaphium Endl. (*Sterculia* p.p.). Stercul. 4 Malay Penins., Borneo.
Scaphocalyx Ridley. Flacourt. (3). 2 Malay Penins.
Scariola F. W. Schmidt = Lactuca L. (Comp.).
Schefferopsis Ridley. Aral. (1). 1 Perak. G 8-loc.
Schiedeella Schlechter (*Spiranthes* p.p.). Orchid. (II. 2). 8 Mexico, C. Am.
Schimperella Wolff. Umbell. (III. 5). 1 Abyss.
Schismocarpus Blake. Loas. 1 Mexico.
Schistophragma Benth. (*Conobea* p.p.). Scroph. (II. 6). 5 Am.
Schizaeaceae. *Cf.* Bower, *Ferns*, ii, 153.
Schizandraceae (*Magnoliaceae* p.p.). 2/20 (Schizandra, Kadsura), distr. as Magnol., but not S. Am. Climbing shrubs with exstip. l. and unisex. axillary spiral fls. A ∞ ± completely united into a globose mass. Berry. Endosp.
Schizobasopsis Macbride. Lili. (III). 1 S. Afr. (*Bowiea volubilis* Harv.).
Schizogyna Cass. = Inula L. (Comp.).
Schlagintweitiella Ulbr. Ranunc. (3). 1 Tibet, W. China.
Schlechteranthus Schwantes. Aizo. (II). 1 Namaqualand.
Schlechterosciadium Wolff. Umbell. (III. 6). 1 Cape Col.
Schlumbergera Lemaire (*Epiphyllum* p.p.). Cact. (III. 1). 2 Brazil.
Schmidtottia Urb. (*Portlandia* p.p.). Rubi. (I. 1). 10 Cuba.
Schnabelia Hand.-Mazz. Verben. (5). 1 China.
Schoenoplectus Palla, Rchb. (*Scirpus* p.p.). Cyper. (1). 4 ✱.
Schonlandia L. Bolus (*Mesembryanthemum* p.p.). Aizo. (II). 1 S. Afr.
Schrameckia Danguy. Monim. 1 Madag.
Schrankiastrum Hassl. Legum. (I. 3). 1 Paraguay.
Schroeterella Briquet (*Larrea* p.p.). Zygophyll. 4 warm Am.
Schwantesia L. Bolus (*Mesembryanthemum* p.p.). Aizo. (II). 10 S. Afr.
Schwantesia Dinter. Aizo. (II). 1 S. Afr.
Sclerocactus Britton et Rose (*Echinocactus* p.p.). Cact. (III. 1). 2 S.W. U.S.
Sclerodictyon Pierre = Dictyophleba Pierre (Apocyn.).

Sclerostachya A. Camus (*Saccharum* p.p.). Gramin. (2). 2 S.E. As.
Scoliaxon Payson (*Cochlearia* p.p.). Crucif. (2). 1 Mexico.
Scrobicularia Mansfeld. Melastom. (inc. sed.). 1 New Guinea.
Scyphostegiaceae (*Monimiaceae* p.p.). *Cf.* Hutchinson, *The fams. of Flowering Plants*, p. 229.
Scytodephyllum Pohl. Inc. sed. Nomen.
Sebesten Adans. (*Cordia* p.p.). Boragin. (1). 12 warm Am.
Segra seed (W.I.), *Fevillea cordifolia* L.
Segurola Larrañaga. Legum. Nomen.
Sehima Forsk. Gramin. (2). 6 warm |*.
Selaginaceae. *Cf.* Scroph. II. 7, and Globular.
Selerothamnus Harms. Legum. (III. 10). 3 Mexico.
Semiarundinaria Makino. Gramin. (13). 3 As.
Sempervivella Stapf. Crassul. 4 W. Himalaya. *Bot. Mag.* t. 8985.
Senegalia Rafin. (*Mimosa* p.p.). Legum. (I. 5). 70 warm Am., W.I.
Sepalosaccus Schlechter. Orchid. (II. 18). 1 Costa Rica.
Sepikea Schlechter. Gesner. (1). 1 New Guinea.
Septotheca Ulbr. Bombac. 1 Peru.
Serapicamptis Godfery. Orchid. Hybrid Serapias × Anacamptis. 1 Italy.
Sericolea Schlechter. Elaeocarp. 5 Mts. of New Guinea.
Serpentaria, *Asarum canadense* L.
Sesban Adans. (*Aeschynomene* p.p.). Legum. (III. 7). 15 warm.
Sesseopsis Hassl. (*Sessea* p.p.). Solan. (4). 1 Paraguay.
Setosa Ewart = Chamaeraphis R. Br. (Gramin.). 1 N. Austr.
Shantzia Lewton (*Thespesia* p.p.). Malv. (4). 1 Rhodesia.
Shortiopsis Hayata (*Shortia* p.p.). Diapens. 2 Formosa.
Sicrea H. Hallier (*Schoutenia* p.p.). Tili. 1 Siam.
Siemensia Urb. (*Portlandia* p.p.). Rubi. (I. 1). 1 Cuba.
Simonenium Diels (*Cocculus* p.p.). Menisperm. 1 E. As.
Simsia A. Gray (*Encelia* p.p.). Comp. (5). 25 N. Am., Jamaica.
Sinclairiopsis Rydberg (*Liabum* p.p.). Comp. (8). 1 Mexico.
Sinobambusa Makino (*Arundinaria* p.p.). Gramin. (13). 2 As.
Sinocrassula Berger. Crassul. 3 Himalaya, W. China.
Sinodielsia Wolff. Umbell. (III. 5). 1 Yunnan.
Sinolimprichtia H. Wolff. Umbell. (III. 4). 1 E. Tibet.
Siphokentia Burret. Palm. (IV. 1). 1 Moluccas.
Siphonanthera Pohl. Inc. sed. Nomen.
Siphonella Nutt. ex A. Gray = Gilia Ruiz et Pav. p.p. (Polemon.).
Skoliostigma Lauterb. Anacard. (2). 1 New Guinea.
Smilax (of florists), *Asparagus asparagoides* Wight.
Smithiella Dunn. Urtic. (2). 1 E. Himalaya.
Snowdenia C. E. Hubbard. Gramin. (5). 1 Uganda.
Sobennikoffia Schlechter. Orchid. (II. 20). 2 Madag.
Sodiroella Schlechter. Orchid. (II. 18). 1 Ecuador.
Solanaceae. Line 1 *omit* Nolan.
Solanocharis Bitter (*Poecilochroma* p.p.). Solan. (2). 1 Bolivia.
Solenangis Schlechter (*Angraecum* p.p.). Orchid. (II. 20). 2 W. Afr.
Solenochasma Fenzl in J. F. Jacquin. Acanth. (IV. B). 1 trop. Am.
Solisia Britton et Rose (*Pelecyphora* p.p.). Cact. (III. 2). 1 Mexico.
Solonia Urb. Myrsin. (II. 2). 1 Cuba.
Sonderina Wolff. Umbell. (III. 5). 4 S. Afr.

Sophiopsis O. E. Schulz (*Hutchinsia* p.p.). Crucif. (2). 3 Mts. of C. As.
Sophronitella Schlechter (*Sophronitis* p.p.). Orchid. (II. 6). 1 Brazil.
Sopropis Britton et Rose (*Prosopis* p.p.). Legum. (I. 4). 1 Lower Calif.
Soria Adans. = Euclidium R. Br. (Crucif.).
Spaniopappus B. L. Robinson. Comp. (2). 15 warm Am.
Speea Loes. Lili. (IV). 2 Chile.
Spermolepis Nutt. Umbell. (III. 5). 4 N. Am., Hawaiian Is.
Sphaerocaryum Nees = Isachne R. Br. (Gramin.).
Sphaerocoryne Scheff. ex Ridley. Anon. (1). 3 Malay Penins., Siam.
Spheneria Kuhlm. (*Paspalum* p.p.). Gramin. (5). 1 Guiana, Brazil.
Sphenomeris Maxon. Polypod. (4). 3 trop.
Spider lily (Am.), *Hymenocallis*.
Spirillus J. Gay = Potamogeton L. (Pot.).
Spiroceratium Wolff (*Pimpinella* p.p.). Umbell. (III. 5). 1 Balearics.
Spirostachys Sond. (*Excoecaria* p.p.). Euphorb. (A. II. 7). 4 E. and S. Afr.
Stachyopsis Popov. et Wedemsky. Labi. (VI). 2 Turkestan.
Stapeliopsis Pillans. Asclepiad. (II. 3). 1 S. Afr.
Stapfiella Gilg. Flacourt. (7). 1 C. Afr.
Stave-wood (W.I.), *Simaruba amara* Aubl.
Stefanoffia Wolff. Umbell. (III. 5). 1 mid-Medit.
Steinbachiella Harms. Legum. (III. 8). 1 Bolivia.
Steinhauera Presl 1838 = Sequoia Endl. p.p. (Conif.).
Stelephuros Adans. (*Phleum* p.p.). Gramin. (8). 1 N. temp. (*P. pratense* L.).
Stemodiacra Browne (*Stemodia* p.p.). Scroph. (II. 6). 1 trop. S. Am., W.I.
Stenanona Standley. Anon. (4). 1 Panama.
Stenodraba O. E. Schulz (*Sisymbrium* p.p.). Crucif. (2). 6 S. Andes.
Stenodrepanum Harms. Legum. (II. 7). 1 Arg.
Stenolobium Benth. = Calopogonium Desv. (Legum.).
Stereocarpus Hallier (*Thea* p.p.). Theac. 1 Laos.
Sterigmapetalum Kuhlm. Rhizophor. 1 Para.
Sterropetalum N. E. Brown. Aizo. (II). 1 Little Namaqualand.
Stetsonia Britton et Rose (*Cereus* p.p.). Cact. (III. 1). 1 Arg.
Steveniella Schlechter (*Platanthera* p.p.). Orchid. (II. 1). 1 W. As.
Stigmatocarpum L. Bolus (*Mesembryanthemum* p.p.). Aizo. (II). 2 S. Afr.
Stoeberia Dinter et Schwantes. Aizo. (II). 3 S. Afr.
Stomatium Schwantes. Aizo. (II). 6 S. Afr.
Stomoisia Rafin. (*Utricularia* p.p.). Lentibul. 50 temp. and trop.
Strainer-vine (W.I.), *Luffa*.
Strasburgeriaceae. A fam. near Ochn. containing only Strasburgeria.
Streptachne R. Br. Gramin. (8). 1 Austr.
Streptanthella Rydberg (*Streptanthus* p.p.). Crucif. (1). 1 W. U.S.
Streptolophus Hughes. Gramin. (5). 1 Angola.
Strobus Opiz (*Pinus* p.p.). Conif. (Pin.). 1 W. N. Am.
Strombocactus Britton et Rose (*Mammillaria* p.p.). Cact. (III. 2). 1 Mexico.
Strychnodaphne Nees = Ocotea Aubl. p.p. (Laur.).
Stylagrostis Mez = Deyeuxia Clar. p.p. (Gramin.).

Stylolepis Lehm. Comp. (4). 1 Austr.
Stylotrichium Mattf. Comp. (2). 2 Bahia.
Styphonia Nutt. = Rhus L. p.p. (Anacard.).
Styrax. *Read* was supposed to yield storax (*cf.* Liquidambar).
Sulitia Merrill. Rubi. (I. 5). 1 Phil. Is.
Suregada (Roxb.) Jones ex Willd. = Gelonium Roxb. (Euphorb.).
Svenhedinia Urb. (*Talauma* p.p.). Magnol. 1 Cuba.
Sweet bay (Am.), *Magnolia virginiana* L.
Symphoricarpos Boehm. 1760. Caprifol. 1 Hort.
Symphyglossum Schlechter (*Cochlioda* p.p.). Orchid. (II. 19). 2 trop. S. Am.
Symphyobasis Krause (*Velleia* p.p.). Gooden. 1 W. Austr.
Symphysia Presl = Hornemannia Vahl (Eric.).
Synaptera Griff. (*Vatica* p.p.). Dipterocp. 12 Indomal.
Syncretocarpus Blake. Comp. (5). 2 Peru. Xero.
Syndesmon Hoffmgg. Ranunc. (3). 1 E. N. Am.
Syntrinema H. Pfeiff. Cyper. (II). 1 Bahia, Goyaz.
Syringidium Lindau. Acanth. (IV. B). 1 Colombia.
Syrmatium Vog. (*Lotus* p.p.). Legum. (III. 5). 6 Mexico, Pac. N. Am.
Systeloglossum Schlechter. Orchid. (II. 19). 1 Costa Rica.
Syzygiopsis Ducke. Sapot. (I). 1 Para.
Tacinga Britton et Rose. Cact. (II). 1 Bahia.
Tahitia Burret. Tili. 1 Tahiti.
Tainiopsis Hayata (*Tainia* p.p.). Orchid. (II. 9). 1 Formosa.
Tamala Rafin. (*Persea* p.p.). Laur. (I). 3 N. Am., W.I.
Tanarius Rumph. = Macaranga Thou. (Euphorb.).
Taraktogenos, *cf.* Gynocardia in Suppl.
Tauroceras Britton et Rose (*Acacia* p.p.). Legum. (I. 2). 2 Mexico, Costa Rica.
Taya (W.I.), *Xanthosoma peregrinum* Griseb.
Tecoma. Line 3 after temp. *add* Am.
Tectaria Cav. (*Polypodium* p.p.). Polypod. (8). 40 warm.
Telemachia Urb. Hippocrat. 1 Trinidad.
Temnocalyx Robyns ex Ridley. Rubi. Nomen.
Tenorea Spreng. = Bupleurum L. (Umbell.).
Terminaliopsis Danguy (*Terminalia* p.p.). Combret. 1 Madag.
Teruncius Lunell (*Thlaspi* p.p.). Crucif. (2). 1 N. palaeotemp.
Tessmanniacanthus Mildbraed. Acanth. (IV. B). 1 E. Peru.
Tessmannianthus Markgraf. Melastom. (I). 1 E. Peru.
Tessmanniophoenix Burret. Palm. (I. 2). 1 E. Peru.
Testulea Pellegr. Ochn. 1 French Congo.
Tetracarpum Moench (*Schkuhria* Roth.). Comp. (6). 12 W Am.
Tetrachondraceae. A fam. near Boragin., containing only Tetrachondra.
Tetraeugenia Merrill. Myrt. (I). 1 Sarawak.
Tetraplasia Rehder. Rubi. (II. 1). 1 Liu-chiu Is.
Tetrapodenia Gleason. Malpigh. (II). 1 Brit. Guiana.
Tetrasida Ulbr. Malv. (2). 1 Peru.
Tetraspis Chiov. Malpigh. (I). 1 Somaliland.
Tetratome Poepp. et Endl. = Mollinedia Ruiz et Pav. (Monim.). 7 trop. Am.

Thamnocalamus Munro (*Arundinaria* p.p.). Gramin. (13). 5 E. As.

Thellungiella O. E. Schulz (*Sisymbrium* p.p.). Crucif. (2). 2 C. and E. As., N.W. N. Am.

Thelocactus Britton et Rose (*Echinocactus* p.p.). Cact. (III. 1). 12 Mexico.

Thelypetalum Gagnep. Euphorb. (A. II. 5). 1 Cochinchina.

Thinogeton Benth. (*Cacabus* p.p.). Solan. (2). 2 Galapagos.

Thorelia Gagnep. Comp. (1). 1 Indochina.

Thorella Briquet (*Sison* p.p.). Umbell. (III. 5). 1 Eur.

Thornbera Rydberg (*Dalea* p.p.). Legum. (III. 6). 5 S.W. U.S.

Thrasya H. B. et K. (*Panicum* p.p.). Gramin. (5). 5 trop. S. Am.

Thunbergiella Wolff (*Oenanthe* p.p.). Umbell. (III. 5). 1 S. Afr.

Thylacitis Renealm. = Gentiana Tourn. (Gent.).

Thylacophora Ridley. Zingiber. (1). 1 New Guinea.

Tibouchinopsis Markgraf. Melastom. (1). 1 Bahia.

Tidestromia Standley (*Cladothrix* Nutt). Amarant. (3). 3 W. U.S., Mexico.

Tiliaceae. *Add* fr. usu. caps. or schizocp.; endosp.

Timouria Rostev. in B. Fedtsch. Gramin. (8). 1 C. As.

Tintinabulum Rydberg (*Gilia* p.p.). Polemon. 1 Arizona.

Tirpitzia H. Hallier. Lin. 1 S.W. China.

Titanopsis Schwantes. Aizo. (II). 3 S. Afr.

Tmesipteris. For prothallus, &c., *cf.* Sykes in *Ann. Bot.* 22, p. 63, and *Phil. Trans.* B, 213, 1925, p. 143; and Lawson in *Trans. R. S. Edinb.* 51, 1917, p. 785.

Tobagoa Urb. Rubi. (II. 10). 1 Tobago.

Tobinia Desv. = Fagara L. p.p. (Rut.).

Tomostina Rafin. = Draba L. p.p. (Crucif.).

Tongoloa H. Wolff (*Pimpinella* p.p.). Umbell. (III. 5). 3 E. Tibet.

Torchwood (W.I.), *Amyris balsamifera* L., *Casearia icosandra* Planch. et Triandr.

Torrenticola Domin. Podostem. 1 Queensland.

Torresia Ruiz et Pav. (*Hierochloe* R. Br.). Gramin. (7). 12 temp.

Tortuella Urb. Rubi. (II. 10). 1 San Domingo.

Torularia O. E. Schulz (*Sisymbrium* p.p.). Crucif. (2). 12 C. As., Medit.

Toumeya Britton et Rose (*Mammillaria* p.p.). Cact. (III. 2). 1 New Mexico.

Toxylon Rafin. = Maclura Nutt. (Mor.).

Trachelanthus Kunze = Solenanthus Ledeb. p.p. (Boragin.).

Trachelosiphon Schlechter (*Spiranthes* p.p.). Orchid. (II. 2). 3 Brazil, W.I.

Trachomitum Woodson (*Apocynum* p.p.). Apocyn. (II. 1). 2 N. temp. | ✻.

Trachysciadium Eckl. et Zeyh. Umbell. (III. 5). 1 Cape Col.

Trachyspermum. For Afr. *read* Indomal., Cameroons.

Trachystoma O. E. Schulz (*Brassica* p.p.). Crucif. (2). 1 Morocco.

Tragiella Pax et K. Hoffm. Euphorb. (A. II. 2). 3 E. and S. Afr.

Tragiopsis Pomel. Umbell. (III. 5). 3 Medit., S. Afr.

Tramoia Schwacke et Taub. ex Glaziou. Urtic. Nomen.

Traunsteinera Reichb. (*Orchis* p.p.). Orchid. (II. 1). 2 Eur., Medit.

Tremacron Craib. Gesner. (1). 2 Yunnan.

Tremanthus Pers. = Styrax L. (Styrac.). 4 Peru.
Triacis Griseb. = Turnera L. (Turn.).
Triaena H. B. et K. Gramin. (11). 1 Mexico.
Triandrophora Schwarz. Capparid. (v). 1 Port Darwin.
Tribolacis Griseb. = Turnera L. (Turn.).
Tribroma. For Colombia *read* 1 trop. Am.
Tribulocarpus S. Moore (*Tetragonia* p.p.). Aizo. (II). 1 S.W. Afr.
Trichlisperma Rafin. (*Polygala* p.p.). Polygal. 1 N. Am.
Trichocoryne S. F. Blake. Comp. (6). 1 Mexico.
Trichodiadema Schwantes. Aizo. (II). 8 S. Afr.
Trichoneura Anderss. (*Diplachne* p.p.). Gramin. (10). 6 warm Am., Afr.
Trichosanchezia Mildbraed. Acanth. (IV. A). 1 E. Peru.
Trifidacanthus Merrill. Legum. (III. 7). 1 Phil. Is.
Trikalis Rafin. = Suaeda Forsk. (Chenop.).
Trillesianthus Pierre ex A. Chevalier. Tili. 1 Congo.
Trilopus Mitch = Hamamelis L. (Hamam.).
Trimeniaceae. *Cf.* E. G. Baker in *Linn. Journ.* 45, p. 384.
Triodanis Rafin. (*Campanula* p.p.). Campanul. (I. 1). 3 N. Am.
Trionum Medic. (*Hibiscus* p.p.). Malv. (4). 1 palaeotrop.
Triorchis Millan, Nieuwland (*Ophrys* p.p.). Orchid. (II. 1). 10 N. Am.
Tripentas Casp. (*Hypericum* p.p.). Guttif. (II). 1 Eur.
Triphysaria Fisch. et Mey. (*Orthocarpus* p.p.). Scroph. (III. 3). 2 W. N. Am.
Tristemonanthus Loes. Hippocrat. 1 Cameroons.
Tritoniopsis L. Bolus. Irid. (III). 1 S. Afr.
Triuris Miers. Triurid. 2 Brazil.
Triurocodon Schlechter (*Thismia* p.p.). Burmann. 1 Rio de Janeiro.
Tropalanthe S. Moore. Sapot. (1). 2 New Caledonia.
Truellum Houttuyn 1777. Polygon. 1 Japan.
Trychinolepis B. L. Robinson. Comp. (2). 1 Peru.
Tryothamnus Phil. Verben. (1). 1 Chile.
Tsoongia Merrill. Verben. (4). 1 China.
Tuberolabium Yamamoto. Orchid. (II. 20). 1 Formosa.
Tumion Rafin. (*Torreya* Arn.). Conif. (Tax. 5). 4 N. Am., China, Japan.
Tung oil, *Aleurites Fordii* Hemsl., *A. cordata* Steud., &c.
Turbine Rafin. (*Ipomoea* p.p.). Convolv. (I). 20 trop.
Turczaninoviella K.-Pol. Umbell. (I. 1). No spp. described.
Turricula Macbride (*Nama* p.p.). Hydrophyll. 1 Calif.
Ulbrichia Urb. Malv. (4). 1 San Domingo.
Uldinia J. M. Black. Umbell. (I. 1). 1 S. Austr.
Umbellulanthus S. Moore. Erythroxyl. 1 Mayumbe.
Unanuea Ruiz et Pav. (*Stemodia* p.p.). Scroph. (II. 6). 2 Colombia, Ecuador.
Uranthera Pax et K. Hoffm. Euphorb. (A. II. 5). 1 Siam.
Uranthoecium Stapf. Gramin. (5). 1 New S. Wales.
Urariopsis Schindl. Legum. (III. 7). 1 S.E. As.
Urceola Vand. Inc. sed. 1 Brazil.
Urocarpidium Ulbr. Malv. (2). 1 Peru.
Urochloa Beauv. Gramin. (5). 18 trop., chiefly |*.
Urophysa Ulbr. Ranunc. (2). 2 China.
Uruparia O. Ktze = Ourouparia Aubl. (Rubi.).

Usoricum Lunell (*Onagra* p.p.). Onagr. (2). 1 N. Am.
Utahia Britton et Rose (*Echinocactus* p.p.). Cact. (III. 1). 1 Utah.
Utsetela Pellegr. Mor. (II). 1 Gaboon.
Uvariella Ridley (*Ellipeia* p.p.). Anon. (1). 4 trop. As.
Vachellia Wight et Arn. (*Acacia* p.p.). Legum. (I. 2). 1 trop.
Valeria Minod (*Stemodia* p.p.). Scroph. (II. 6). 1 Rio de Janeiro.
Valerianoides (Boerh.) Medic. (*Valeriana* p.p.). Valerian. 40 warm Am.
Valota Adans. (*Andropogon* p.p.). Gramin. (2). 4 warm Am.
Valvaria Seringe (*Clematis* p.p.). Ranunc. (3). 4 temp.
Vananthes Haw. (*Grammanthes* DC.). Crassul. 1 Cape Col.
Vangueriopsis Robyns. Rubi. Nomen.
Vanzijlia L. Bolus (*Mesembryanthemum* p.p.). Aizo. (II). 1 Namaqualand.
Vasquezia Phil. = Villanova Lag. (Comp.).
Vaughania S. Moore. Legum. (III. 6). 1 Madag.
Vaupellia Griseb. = Gesneria L. p.p. (Gesner.).
Veconcibea Pax et K. Hoffm. (*Conceveiba* p.p.). Euphorb. (A. II. 2). 2 trop. Am.
Vedela Adans. Inc. sed. Nomen.
Verena Minod (*Stemodia* p.p.). Scroph. (II. 6). 1 Paraguay.
Veronicella (Heister) Fabr. = Veronica L. (Scroph.).
Versteggia. *Read* Versteegia.
Vesicarpa Rydberg (*Artemisia* p.p.). Comp. (7). 1 W. U.S.
Vexillifera Ducke. Legum. (II. 9). 1 Amazon valley.
Viguierella A. Camus et Stapf. Gramin. (10). 1 Madag.
Vincentella Pierre = Sideroxylon L. p.p. (Sapot.).
Vincentia Gaudich. (*Cladium* p.p.). Cyper. (II). 10 Masc. to Polynes.
Vitaliana Sesl. 1758. Primul. 1 Pyrenees.
Vitellariopsis Baill. = Mimusops L. p.p. (Sapot.).
Viticella Mitch. 1769 = Nemophila Nutt. (Hydrophyll.).
Viticipremna Lam. (*Premna* p.p.). Verben. (4). 3 New Guinea, Bismarcks, Phil. Is.
Vogelia Medic. = Neslia Desv. (Crucif.).
Volkensinia Schinz (*Kentrosphaera* p.p.). Amarant. (2). 1 trop. Afr.
Volvulus Medic. = Calystegia R. Br. (Convolv.).
Wahlbergella Fries (*Lychnis* p.p.). Caryophyll. (II. 1). 10 N. temp.
Walleniella P. Wils. Myrsin. (II). 1 Cuba.
Wardaster Small. Comp. (3). 1 W. China.
Warneria L. = Gardenia Ellis (Rubi.).
Wasatchia M. E. Jones = Festuca L. p.p. (Gramin.).
Weingaertneria Bernh. = Corynephorus Beauv. (Gramin.).
Wercklea Fittier et Standley. Malv. (4). 1 Costa Rica.
Werckleocereus Britton et Rose (*Cereus* p.p.). Cact. (III. 1). 2 C. Am.
Werdermannia O. E. Schulz. Crucif. (2). 1 Chile.
Wernhamia S. Moore. Rubi. (I. 5?). 1 Bolivia.
Wettinella O. F. Cook et Doyle (*Wettinia* p.p.). Palm. (IV. 1). 2 Andes.
Whitfordiodendron Elmer (*Adinobotrys* Dunn). Legum. (III. 6). 6 Indomal., China.
Whytockia W. W. Smith. Gesner. (1). 1 W. China.
Wide, *cf. Age and Area.*
Wilckia Scop. = Malcomia R. Br. (Crucif.).

Wilhelminia Hochr. Malv. (4). 1 New Guinea.
Wilmattia Britton et Rose. Cact. (III. 1). 1 Guatemala, Honduras.
Windsorina Gleason. Rapat. 1 Brit. Guiana.
Wineberry, *Rubus phoenicolasius* Maxim. (Japan).
Winteraceae (*Magnol.* p.p.). *Cf.* Hutchinson in *Kew Bull.* 1921, 185.
Wolfia Spreng. Inc. sed. 1 Brazil.
Woodiella Merrill. Anon. (2). 1 Borneo.
Xanthomyrtus Diels (*Myrtus* p.p.). Myrt. (I). 15 New Guinea, New Caled.
Xanthophytopsis Pitard. Rubi. (I. 2). 1 Tonquin.
Xantonnea Pierre ex Pitard. Rubi. (I. 8). 3 Indochina.
Xantonneopsis Pitard. Rubi. (I. 8). 1 Indochina.
Xerocarpa Lam. Verben. (4). 1 New Guinea.
Xerodraba Skottsb. (*Eudema* p.p.). Crucif. (2). 6 S. Patagonia.
Xylochlamys Domin. Loranth. (1). 1 Queensland.
Xymalos Baill. Monim. 3 trop. and S. Afr.
Xyochlaena Stapf in Prain = Tricholena Schrad (Gramin.).
Yabea K.-Pol. (*Caucalis* p.p.). Umbell. (III. 2). 1 Calif.
Yarina O. F. Cook. Palm. (V). 1 Peru.
Yolanda Hoehne. Orchid. 1 São Paulo.
Yvesia A. Camus. Gramin. (5). 1 Madag.
Zehntnerella Britton et Rose (*Cereus* p.p.). Cact. (III. 1). 1 Bahia.
Zephyranthella Pax (*Hippeastrum* p.p.). Amaryllid. (I. 2). 1 Arg.
Zetagyne Ridley. Orchid. (II. 3). 1 Annam.
Zeylanidium Tul. Podostem. 2 S. India, Ceylon.
Zygocactus K. Schum. Cact. (III. 1). 3 Brazil.
Zygotritonia Mildbraed (*Tritonia* p.p.). Irid. (III). 5 trop. Afr.

The following names given by Rafinesque have been published by Pennell in *Bull. Torr. Bot. Club*, 48, 1921, p. 92: Actartife, Adenola, Aldinia, Alifiola, Allosandra, Aniketon, Anistelma, Antimion, Antrizon, Artorhiza, Atevala, Atirbesia, Banalia, Bazina, Braxilia, Bucranion, Cargila, Codomale, Dasiphora, Dematra, Dilax, Diplandra, Dipleina, Ebraxis, Eudemis, Evactoma, Exemix, Fenixanthes, Festania, Fuisa, Genlisa, Icmane, Idanthisia, Iondra, Iposues, Ixoca, Junia, Kobiosis, Knoxikas, Kumaria, Lepiphaia, Levana, Lomake, Luronium, Marzaria, Merleta, Misopates, Monastes, Monosemeion, Nemelaia, Nevrolis, Odostima, Orthilia, Ozandra, Parmentiera, Pelotris, Perxo, Pleconax, Pleopadium, Plethyrsis, Probatea, Reggeria, Rhizakenia, Rittera, Rodatia, Ronconia, Saliunca, Scubulon, Semetum, Shortia, Smidetia, Streblina, Streptilon, Tartona, Tatina, Termontis, Trimista, Troxilanthes, Tulista, Tursitis, Vandera, Xamilenis, Zeliauros.

The following names have been published without description, so far as we have traced, by N. E. Brown in *Gard. Chron.* 78, 1925, key on 411 (all Aizoaceae): Argyroderma, Cephalophyllum, Conicosia, Conophytum, Cryophytum, Dactylopsis, Delosperma, Didymaotus, Disphyma, Ectotropis, Erepsia, Fenestraria, Frithia, Gibbaeum, Glottiphyllum, Hydrodea, Hymenogyna, Lithops, Macrocaulon, Malephora, Nananthus, Odontophorus, Oophytum, Opophytum, Phyllobolus, Platythyra, Pleiospilos, Prenia, Psilocaulon, Punctillaria, Rimaria, Sceletium, Semnanthe, Sphalmanthus, Synaptophyllum, Thyrasperma, Trichocyclus, Zeuktophyllum.

KEY

TO THE FAMILIES OF

FLOWERING PLANTS

BASED ON ENGLER'S CLASSIFICATION AS GIVEN IN *DIE NATÜRLICHEN PFLANZENFAMILIEN*, AND REVISED IN HIS *SYLLABUS*, ED. 7.

MONOCOTYLEDONEAE

[Embryo with one cot.; stem with closed bundles; l. usu. ||-veined; fl. usu. 3-merous.]

A. Orders with predominant variability in number of floral parts (Orders 1—7):

a. *Typically achlamydeous fls. appear* (*Orders* 1—4).

α. Fls. usu. naked. Great variability in number of sta. and cpls.

1. PANDANALES. Marsh herbs, or trees, with linear l., and cpd. heads or spikes of naked, haplo- or homo-chlamydeous ♂ ♀ fls. P bractlike, A ∞—1, G ∞—1. Endosp.

β. Naked fls. occur, but also all stages from achlam. to heterochlam. fls., and from hypog. to epig. Number of essential organs definite or not (Orders 2, 3).

2. HELOBIAE. Water or marsh pl. with scales in axils, and cyclic or hemicyclic fls. P in 0, 1, or 2 whorls, homo- or hetero-chlam., hypog. or epig. A ∞—1, G ∞—1, free or united. Endosp. little or none.

1. *Potamogetonineae:* fl. hypog., achlam., haplo-, or homochlam. (fams. 1—4).

2. *Alismatineae:* fl. hypog., usu. heterochlam.; ov. on ventral suture (fam. 5).

3. *Butomineae:* fl. hypog. or epig., usu. heterochlam.; ov. on inner surface of cpls. (fams. 6, 7).

3. TRIURIDALES. Saprophytes with scale l. and small long-stalked homochlam. ☿ or ♂ ♀ fls. P 3—8, valv., petaloid; ♂ A 3, 4, or 6; ♀, 2 stds. G̲ ∞ each with 1 basal ov.; ∞ styles. Pericarp thick. Endosp.

MONOCOTYLEDONEAE

I

1. Typhaceae: rhiz. herbs with linear 2-ranked l. and cylindrical spikes of naked fls., ♀ below, ♂ above; A 2—5, G 1 on hairy axis with 1 pend. ov.; nutlet, with album. seed.
2. Pandanaceae: woody pl., sometimes climbing, with 3-ranked l. and term. or racemed spikes of ♂ ♀ fls., ♂ of ∞ sta. racemed or umbelled on short or long axis, ♀ of (∞—1) cpls. with sessile stigs. and ∞—1 ov.; heads of berries or drupes; endosp. oily.
3. Sparganiaceae: rhiz. herbs with 2-ranked l. and fls. in ♂ ♀ heads, ♀ heads lower. P 3—6, sepaloid, A 3—6, G (1—2), each with 1 pend. ov.; fr. drupaceous; endosp. floury.

2

1. Potamogetonaceae: submerged or floating herbs of fresh or salt water, with usu. 2-ranked l. and sol. or spiked ☿ or ♀ ♂ reg. fls. P usually 0, A 4—1, G 4—1 each with 1 pend. ov.; fr. 1-seeded.
2. Najadaceae: submerged herbs with opp. linear toothed l. and ♂ ♀ fls., ♂ P 2, A 1 term.; ♀ P 1 or 0, G 1, with 1 basal anatr. ov.
3. Aponogetonaceae: tuber-rhiz. water herbs with submerged or floating l. and spikes (in caducous spathes) of ☿ reg. fls. P 3—1 petaloid, A 3 + 3 or more, G 3—6; fr. leathery, seeds 2 or ∞, exalb.
4. Scheuchzeriaceae: marsh herbs with narrow l. and racemes or spikes of ☿ or ♂ ♀ reg. fls.; P usu. 3 + 3, homochlam., bractlike, A 3 + 3, G 3 + 3 sometimes united, outer often absent, 1 or 2 anatr. ov. in each. [*Lilaea* ☿ ♂ ♀, A 1, G 1.]
5. Alismaceae: water or marsh herbs with rad. l., latex, and much branched infl. of reg. heterochlam. ☿ or ♂ ♀ fls.; K 3, C 3, A 6—∞ or 3, G 6—∞ with 1—∞ anatr. ov. and 6—∞ styles; no endosp.
6. Butomaceae: water and marsh herbs; latex; usu. ± umbel-like cymose infl. of reg. usu. heterochlam. ☿ fls.; K 3, C 3, A 9—∞. G 6—∞, often united below, with ∞ ov. on inner surface; follicles.
7. Hydrocharitaceae: salt or fresh water pl. with alt. or whorled l. and sol. or cymose-paniculate fls. enclosed in 1 or 2 bracts, usu. heterochlam., reg., 3-merous, usu. ♂ ♀; A in 1—5 whorls, inner often stds., G (2—15), 1-loc. with parietal plac. and ∞ ov.; fr. irreg. dehisc. with ∞ seeds. Exalb.

3

1. Triuridaceae.

γ. Fls. usu. naked. Number of sta. rarely indefinite.

4. GLUMIFLORAE. Usu. herbs, with naked fls. (rarely with trichome-like or true P) covered by bracts (glumes). G 1-loc. with 1 ov.

b. *Fls. rarely naked, and then usu. by reduction, and accompanied by spathes of bracts; A and G commonly definite, but also frequently ∞ sta. and > 3 cpls.*

5. PRINCIPES. Tree-like or woody pl., sometimes climbing, with fan or feather l., and reg. usu. ♂ ♀ fls. in spikes (usu. compound) or spike-like racemes, usu. in spathe; P 3 + 3, A 3 + 3, or 3, 9, or ∞, G 3 or (3), usu. with 1 ov. each; berry or drupe; endosp. rich.

6. SYNANTHAE. Often palm-like pl., climbers, or large herbs with ♂ ♀ fls. alternating over surface of spike, ♂ naked or with thick short P and 6—∞ sta.; ♀ naked or with 4 fleshy scaly P and long thread-like std. in front of each, G (2) or (4) with 2 or 4 plac. and ∞ ov.; the 1-loc. ovaries sunk in spike and united; multiple fr. with ∞ seeds; endosp.

7. SPATHIFLORAE. Herbs, or woody, sometimes climbing, rarely forming erect stem, usu. sympodial; fls. cyclic, haplo- or homochlam. or naked by abortion, 3—2-merous, ☿ or ♂ ♀ often reduced to 1 sta. or cpl., in simple spikes (spadix), ± enclosed in bract (spathe).

B. Fls. typically 5-cyclic, whorls typically iso-, usu. 3-merous, rarely more or 2-merous (Orders 8—11).

a. *Fls. homo- to hetero-chlam., rarely naked; P still often bract-like; hypogyny and actinomorphy the rule* (*Orders* 8, 9).

8. FARINOSAE. Usu. herbs, rarely with stout stem; fls. cyclic, homo- or hetero-chlam, 3—2-merous, usu. P 3 + 3, A 3 + 3, G (3), one whorl of A sometimes wanting, or all reduced to 1; ov. usu. orthotr.; endosp. mealy.

1. *Flagellariineae:* P homochlam., bracteoid, hypog.; ov. anatr. (fam. 1).
2. *Enantioblastae:* P various, hypog.; ov. orthotr. (fams. 2—6).

4

1. Gramineae: herbs, rarely woody, with jointed stem and alt. 2-ranked l. with split sheath and ligule, and panicle or spike-like infls. of small ☿ rarely ♂ ♀ naked fls. in spikelets, each beginning with 1 or more empty glumes, then paleae with axillary fls.; A usu. 3, $\underline{G}$ with 1 ov., micropyle facing down; stigs. 2, 3, or 1; caryopsis with rich endosp.
2. Cyperaceae: herbs with usu. 3-angled stem and 3-ranked l. with closed sheath; fls. in spikelets or cymes united to large infls., naked, ☿ or ♂ ♀; A usu. 3—1, $\underline{G}$ (3—2), styles 3—2, 1-loc. with 1 basal anatr. ov.; nut; endosp.

5

1. Palmae.

6

1. Cyclanthaceae.

7

1. Araceae: tuberous herbs, sometimes woody, or lianes, with ☿ or ♂ ♀ fls. in same spike, often with spathe; fl. 2—3-merous or reduced to 1 sta. or cpl.; fr. usu. berry; outer seed-coat fleshy.
2. Lemnaceae: free swimming water pl. usu. with no l. and naked ♂ ♀ fls., ♂ of 1 sta., ♀ of 1 cpl. with 1—6 basal erect ov.; endosp. thin.

8

1. Flagellariaceae: pl. sometimes climbing, with long many-veined l. and small, ☿ or ♂ ♀, 3-merous, reg. fls. in cpd. term. panicles; P bractlike, $\underline{G}$ (3) 3-loc. each with 1 ov.; fr. 3-loc. or with 3—1 stones; endosp.
2. Restionaceae: rush-like xero. or marsh herbs with creeping rhiz. and 2-ranked bracts or scale l. on stem; fls. in spikes in axils of bracts, usu. ♂ ♀ reg.; P 3—2 + 3—2 sepaloid, A 3—2, $\underline{G}$ (3—1) with 3—1 styles, 3—1-loc. with 1 ov. in each; caps. or nut; endosp.
3. Centrolepidaceae: usu. marsh pl. with ☿ or ♂ ♀ fls., naked or with 1—3 hair-like br.; A 1—2, $\underline{G}$ (1—∞) each with 1 pend ov.

B; a

3. *Bromeliineae:* P usu. heterochlam., hypog. to epig.; ov. anatr. (fams. 7—9).

4. *Commelinineae:* P heterochlam.; part of A often stds. or wanting (fam. 10).

5. *Pontederiineae:* P homochlam., petaloid, united (fams. 11, 12).

6. *Philydrineae:* P petaloid, the outer l. larger than inner, the 2 post. of outer whorl united, the post. of inner whorl aborted (fam. 13).

9. LILIIFLORAE. As last, but endosp. fleshy or oily; ov. usu. anatr.; fls. usu. 3-merous, rarely 2, 4, or more.

1. *Juncineae:* P homochlam., bracteoid; endosp. mealy with starch (fam. 1).

2. *Liliineae:* P homochlam, rarely bracteoid, usu. petaloid, rarely heterochlam.; endosp. without starch; inner whorl of A present (fams. 2—8).

4. Mayacaceae: marsh pl. with alt. linear l. and sol. or umbelled ☿ reg. heterochlam. 3-merous fls.; K 3, C 3, A 3, $\underline{G}$ (3), style 1 with 3 stigs., 1-loc. with parietal plac. and few ov.: caps. 3-valved.
5. Xyridaceae: perenn. herbs with long narrow l. and axill. spikes of ☿ heterochlam. 3-merous fls.; K ·|· with 2 smaller lat. l., C (3) with tube, A 3 epipet., with sometimes 3 outer stds., $\underline{G}$ (3), 1-loc. with ∞ ov.; caps. 3-valved; endosp.
6. Eriocaulaceae: perenn. herbs with long linear l. and involucrate heads of fls. on long stalks, ♂ ♀, reg. or ·|·, heterochlam., 2—3-merous, sta. usu. in 1 whorl, $\underline{G}$ (2—3), 2—3-loc. with 1 pend. ov. in each: caps.; endosp.
7. Thurniaceae: perenn. herbs with narrow l. and heads of ☿, reg. homochlam. 3-merous fls. on △ stalks; P 3+3, A 6, $\underline{G}$ (3), 3-loc. with 1—∞ ov. in each; caps.; endosp.
8. Rapateaceae: perenn. herbs with 2-ranked narrow l.; infl. term. with 2 large spathes encl. head of spikelets, each of ∞ br. and term. ☿ reg. 3-merous heterochlam. fl.; K (3), C (3), A 3+3, $\underline{G}$ (3), 3-loc. with ∞—1 ov. in each; caps.; endosp.
9. Bromeliaceae: herbs, often epiph., with alt. usu. rad. l. and spikes or panicles of usu. ☿ reg. heterochlam. 3-merous fls.; K 3, C or (C) 3, A 3+3, G (3), sup. to inf., 3-loc. with ∞ ov.; berry or caps.; endosp.
10. Commelinaceae: herbs with jointed stems, alt. sheathing l. and cymes of blue or violet, ☿ reg. or ·|· heterochlam. 3-merous fls.; K 3, C 3, rarely united, A 3+3, $\underline{G}$ (3—2), style 1, 3—2-loc. with few ov.; caps.; endosp.
11. Pontederiaceae: water pl. often with 2-ranked l. and spicate ☿ ·|· fls.; P 3+3 with long tube, A 3+3, 3, or 1, on tube, $\underline{G}$ (3) with 1 style, 3-loc. with ∞ ov. or 1-loc. with 1; caps. or nut; endosp.
12. Cyanastraceae: herbs with tuber or rhiz. and raceme or panicle of ☿ reg. 3-merous fls.; (P) with short tube, $\overline{A}$ (6), $\overline{G}$ (3), with 1 style, 3-loc. with 2 ov. in each; caps. 1-seeded; perisp.
13. Philydraceae: herbs with 2-ranked narrow l. and spikes of homochlam. 3-merous ☿ ·|· fls.; sta. 1 ant., $\underline{G}$ (3) with 1 style, 3- or 1-loc. with ∞ ov.; caps.; endosp.

9

1. Juncaceae: perenn. herbs with narrow usu. rad. l. and many-fld. infl. of homochlam. 3-merous ☿ reg. fls.; P sepaloid, A 6 or 3, $\underline{G}$ (3), style 1 with 3 stigs., 1—3-loc. each with 1—∞ ov.; caps.; endosp.
2. Stemonaceae: perenn. herbs with rhiz. and often climbing stem and axillary infls. of homochlam. ☿ reg. 2-merous fls.; P sepaloid, $\underline{G}$ (2), 1-loc.; caps.; endosp.
3. Liliaceae: herbs with rhiz. or bulbs, shrubs, or trees with infl. of usu. racemose type, of usu. homochlam. ☿ reg. usu. 3-merous fls.; P or (P) 3+3, petaloid, A 3+3, $\underline{G}$ to $\overline{G}$ 3—(2—5)-loc.; fr. various; endosp. fleshy or cartilaginous.
4. Haemodoraceae: perenn. herbs with 2-ranked l. and simple or cpd. infl. of ☿ reg. or ·|· fls.; P 3+3, A 3, $\underline{G}$ to $\overline{G}$, 3-loc. with few ov.; caps.

B; a; b

3. *Iridineae:* as last, but inner sta. aborted (fam. 9).

b. *Fls. homo-(petaloid) or heterochlam., epig., usu.* ·|· (*Orders* 10, 11).

10. SCITAMINEAE. Trop. herbs, sometimes very large or woody, with cyclic, homo- or hetero-chlam. usu. ·|· 3-merous fls.; A typically 3 + 3, but often with great reduction, even to 1 sta., $\bar{G}$ usu. 3-loc. with large ov.; usu. aril, peri- and endosp.

11. MICROSPERMAE. Fls. cyclic, homo- or hetero-chlam., 3-merous, typically diplostemonous, but commonly with great reduction in A, $\bar{G}$ 3- or 1-loc. with ∞ small ov.; endosp. or 0.

1. *Burmanniineae:* fls. usu. reg.; endosp.
2. *Gynandrae:* fls. always ·|·; no endosp.

5. Amaryllidaceae: herbs or shrubs of various habit and cymose infl. on scape, of ☿ reg. or ·|· fls.; P 3+3 petaloid, A 3+3 usu. intr., often with stipular corona, $\overline{G}$ (3), rarely $\frac{1}{2}$-inf., 3-loc. with ∞ ov.; caps. or berry.
6. Velloziaceae: herbs or shrubs with linear crowded l. and term. sol. ☿ reg. 3-merous fls. on long stalks; P petaloid, A 6 or 6 bundles, $\overline{G}$ (3), 3-loc. with ∞ ov. on lamellar plac.; caps.; endosp.
7. Taccaceae: perenn. herbs with tubers and large entire or cymosely branched l., and cymose umbels of ☿ reg. fls. with long thread-like br.; P 3+3, petaloid, A 3+3, $\overline{G}$ (3), 1-loc. with parietal plac., 6 petaloid stigs. and ∞ ov.; caps. or berry; endosp.
8. Dioscoreaceae: climbing herbs with usu. tuberous rhiz. and alt. or opp. often sagittate l.; fls. in racemes, homochlam., ☿ or ♂ ♀, reg.; P sepaloid, usu. united, with tube, A 3+3, inner sometimes stds., $\overline{G}$ (3), 3- or 1-loc., usu. with 2 ov. to each, styles 3 or 6; caps. or berry; endosp.
9. Iridaceae: perenn. herbs or undershrubs with equitant l. and term. cymose infl. of ☿ reg. or ·|· fls.; P 3+3 homo- or hetero-chlam., A 3 extr., $\overline{G}$ (3), 3-loc. with 3 styles sometimes divided and leafy, ov. ∞, rarely 1-loc.; caps.; endosp.

10

1. Musaceae: very large herbs with 'false' stem, or trees, with cpd. infl. with large often petaloid br. and ☿ or ♂ ♀, ·|· homo- or hetero-chlam. fls.; P 3+3, petaloid, often united, A 3+2 and std., $\overline{G}$ (3), 3-loc. with 1—∞ ov. in each; berry or caps.; endosp. and perisp.
2. Zingiberaceae: perenn. herbs with tuberous rhiz. and lanc. petiolate l., with ligule and simple or cpd. infls. of usu. ☿ ·|· fls.; K (3), C (3) forming tube below, A 1 (of inner whorl, with labellum opp. to it of 2 inner stds., and sometimes 2 outer stds.) $\overline{G}$ (3), usu. 3-loc. with ∞ ov.; caps.; usu. aril; endosp. and perisp.
3. Cannaceae: perenn. herbs with large l. and cpd. infl. of showy heterochlam. ☿ asymmetric fls.; K 3, C (3), A 1—5, only half of 1 inner sta. fertile, the other half, and rest, petaloid stds., $\overline{G}$ (3), 3-loc. with ∞ ov.; caps.; endosp. and perisp.
4. Marantaceae: perenn. herbs with 2-ranked l. with pulvinus at end of stalk, and heterochlam. ☿ asymmetric fls.; P 3+3, A 4—5, only 1 inner half fertile, as in last, the 2 other inner and 1—2 outer petaloid (1 inner usu. hoodlike), $\overline{G}$ (3), 3-loc. or 1-loc. by suppression, with 1 ov. in each; aril; caps.; endosp. and perisp.

11

1. Burmanniaceae: green or saproph. herbs with sol. or cymose fls.; P (3+3) or 3+3, A 3+3 or 3, $\overline{G}$ (3), 3- or 1-loc.; caps., ∞ seeds; endosp.
2. Orchidaceae: perenn. herbs of various form, often epiph. with pseudobulbs, and ☿, ·|·, usu. resupinated, homo- or hetero-chlam. fls.; P 3+3, A 1 or 2, united with style of $\overline{G}$ (3) 1-loc. to form a column; pollen in tetrads usu. united to pollinia, stigmas 3, the third usu. rudimentary or forming a rostellum, ovules ∞; caps.; no endosp.

DICOTYLEDONEAE

[Embryo with two cots.; stem with open bundles; l. usu. net-veined; fl. usu. not 3-merous.]

Archichlamydeae (Orders 1—30)

(Fl. achlam., haplochlam., or diplochlam., usu. polypet., rarely sympet. or apet.)

A. Ov. with 20 or more embryo sacs, and chalazogamic fert. (Order 1).

1. VERTICILLATAE. Woody pl. of Equisetum habit; ♂ fls. in catkin-like spikes, ♀ in heads, at end of twigs; ♂ with 2 median bractlike P and a central sta., ♀ naked, G (2) with 2 threadlike stigmas, 2-loc., the post. sterile, the other with 2—4 erect orthotr. ov.; fr. indeh.; no endosp.

B. Ov. usu. with only 1 embryo sac (Orders 2—30).

a. *Fls. naked or with haplochlam. bract-like P (Orders 2—12).*

2. PIPERALES. L. simple, stip. or not, and spikes of small achlam. or haplochlam. ☿ or ♂ ♀ fls.; A 1—10, G 1—4, free or united.

3. SALICALES. Woody with simple alt. stip. l. and spikes of dioec. achlam. fls., disc cup-like or reduced to scales; A 2—∞, $\underline{G}$ (2), 1-loc. with parietal plac. and ∞ anatr. ov.; caps. with ∞ seeds, seeds small with basal tuft of hairs and no endosp.

4. GARRYALES. Woody pl. with opp. evergr. l. and fls. in catkin-like panicles, ♂ ♀; ♂ P 4, A 4, ♀ naked, $\underline{G}$ (2—3), 1-loc. with 2 ov.; endosp.

5. MYRICALES. Woody, usu. with simple l. and fls. in simple, rarely cpd. spikes, ♂ ♀ achlam., sometimes with bracts at base; A 2—16, usu. 4, $\underline{G}$ (2), 1-loc. with 1 basal orthotr. ov. and 2 stigs.; porogamous; drupe with waxy exocarp; no endosp.

6. BALANOPSIDALES. Woody with simple l.; ♂ fls. in spikes, haplochlam, ♀ sol. surrounded by ∞ scaly bracts; $\underline{G}$ (2), imperfectly 2-loc. each with 2 ascending ov.; drupe.

7. LEITNERIALES. Woody with alt. entire l. and spikes of dioec. fls.; ♂ achlam., A 3—12, ♀ haplochlam., P of small scaly united l., $\underline{G}$ 1 with long style and 1 amphitr. ov.; drupe; thin endosp.

8. JUGLANDALES. Woody with alt. usu. pinnate exstip. l. and spikes of achlam. or haplochlam. ♂ ♀ fls.; A 3—40, $\overline{G}$ (2), 1-loc. with 1 basal orthotr. ov.; chalazogamic; fr. drupe or nut-like; no endosp.

DICOTYLEDONEAE

Archichlamydeae

1

1 Casuarinaceae.

2

1. Saururaceae: herbs with alt. l. and spikes of achlam. ☿ fls.; A 6 or less, G̲ (3—4) or 3—4, plac. parietal, ov. 2—∞; endo- and peri-sp.

2. Piperaceae: herbs and shrubs with alt. l. of biting taste, and spikes, &c. of ☿ or ♂ ♀ achlam. fls.; A 1—10, G̲ (1—4), 1-loc. with 1 basal ov.; endo- and perisp.
3. Chloranthaceae: herbs or woody pl. with opp. stip. l. and spikes or cymes of ☿ or ♂ ♀ fls., sometimes with sepaloid P; A (1 or 3) united to ovary, G̲ 1 with 1 pend. ov.; peri- and endosp.
4. Lacistemaceae: shrubs with 2-ranked lanc. exstip. l. and spikes of minute ☿ fls., naked or with sepaloid P; A 1, G̲ (2—3) plac. parietal, with 1—2 pend. ov. on each; caps. 1-seeded; endosp.

3

1. Salicaceae:

4

1. Garryaceae:

5

1. Myricaceae:

6

1. Balanopsidaceae:

7

1. Leitneriaceae:

8

1. Juglandaceae:

9. BATIDALES. Coast shrub with opp. fleshy l. and panicles of spikes; fls. ♂ ♀, ♂ with cup-like P and A 4, ♀ naked, originally 2-loc. with 2 ov. in each, divided by false septum, all ♀ fls. in spike concrescent; aggregate fr.; no endosp.

10. JULIANIALES. Woody with alt. usu. pinnate exstip. l. and dioec. fls.; ♂ ∞ in ± dense panicle, P, A, 6—8, ♀ in fours at end of downward directed spike, naked, G 1-loc. with 1 ov. on broad hollowed funicle; no endosp.

11. FAGALES. Woody with alt. stip. l. and fls. in simple or cymose spikes, cyclic, homochlam., rarely naked, usu. monoec.; A opp. P, $\overline{G}$ (2—6) each with 1—2 ov.; fr. nut-like, seed 1; no endosp.

12. URTICALES. Herbs, shrubs, trees with alt. or opp. stip. l. and cymose infls. of cyclic homochlam. rarely haplochlam. or naked usu. reg. ☿ or ♂ ♀ fls., usu. 2+2 rarely 2+3-merous; sta. before P, $\underline{G}$ (2—1) with 1 ov.; drupe or nut.

b. *Usu. with sepaloid or petaloid P, rarely heterochlam.* (*Orders* 13—16).

13. PROTEALES. Woody with alt. exstip. l. and spikes or racemes of cyclic homo- (apparently haplo-)chlam. 2+2-merous ☿ or ♂ ♀ reg. or ·|· fls.; P petaloid; sta. anteposed and usu. adherent to P, $\underline{G}$ 1; fr. various, no endosp.

14. SANTALALES. Herbs, shrubs, trees, often paras., with cyclic, usu. homochlam. fls.; A anteposed, in 1 or 2 whorls, $\overline{G}$, rarely $\underline{G}$ (2—3), rarely 1, each with 1 pend. ov. (or ov. not differentiated).

1. *Santalineae:* ov. differentiated from plac., often without integ. (fams. 1—6).

9

1. Batidaceae:

10

1. Julianiaceae:

11

1. Betulaceae: shrubs and trees with alt. simple l. with caducous stips. and monoec. anemoph. fls. in catkins, typically 3 fls. per axil; P sepaloid or 0, A 2—10, $\overline{G}$ (2), 2-loc. each with 1 pend. ov.; nut; no endosp.
2. Fagaceae: trees, rarely shrubs, with simple l. and caducous scaly stips., and usu. catkins or small spikes of ♂ ♀ fls.; P sepaloid (4—7), A 4—7 or 8—14, $\overline{G}$ usu. (3), 3-loc., 3-styled, each with 2 pend. ov.; nut; no endosp.

12

1. Ulmaceae: trees and shrubs with 2-ranked simple stip. l. and axill. cymes of homochlam. ☿ or ♂ ♀ fls.; P 4—5, sepaloid, A 4—5 or 8—10, $\underline{G}$ (2), styles 2, usu. 1-loc. with 1 pend. ov.; nut or drupe; usu. no endosp.
2. Moraceae: usu. trees and shrubs with stip. l., latex, and cymes of small ♂ ♀ fls., often head-like; P usu. 4 or (4), persistent, rarely 0, A as many, opp. P, $\underline{G}$ (2), 1-loc. with usu. 1 pend. ov.; nut or drupe; endosp. or not.
3. Urticaceae: usu. herbs with opp. or alt. stip. l., no latex, and cymose infls. of small homochlam. usu. ♂ ♀ fls.; P usu. 4—5, A 4—5 opp. P, bent inwards in bud and exploding, $\underline{G}$ 1-loc. with 1 basal ov. and 1 style; nut or drupe; endosp.

13

1. Proteaceae:

14

1. Myzodendraceae: semiparas. undershrubs with alt. l. and minute naked ♂ ♀ fls.; A 2—3—1 with monothecous anthers, $\overline{G}$ (3) with axile plac. and 3 ov.; fr. with 3 feathery bristles in angles.
2. Santalaceae: semiparas. herbs, shrubs, trees with opp. or alt. l. and small ☿ or ♂ ♀ homochlam. fls. with perig. or epig. disc; P usu. 2+2 or 2+3, A as many, inserted on P, $\overline{G}$ 1-loc. with axile plac. and 1—3 ov.; nut or drupe, 1-seeded; endosp.

2. *Loranthineae:* ov. usu. not differentiated (fam. 7).

3. *Balanophorineae:* plac. central with pend. ov. with no integ.; chlorophyll-less paras. (fam. 8).

15. ARISTOLOCHIALES. Fls. cyclic, homo- or haplo-chlam, reg. or ·|·; P petaloid, G usu. inf. 3—6-loc. with axile plac., or 1-loc. with parietal, and ∞ ov.

16. POLYGONALES. L. usu. ochreate, fls. haplo- to hetero-chlam., ☿ reg.; G 1-loc. with usu. 1 basal erect ov.; nut; endosp.

c. *P haplochlam., sepaloid or petaloid, sometimes heterochlam.* (*Order* 17).

17. CENTROSPERMAE. Usu. herbs with spiral or cyclic homo- or hetero-chlam. fls.; A usu. = and opp. P, but also ∞—1, G (∞—1) or free, rarely Ḡ, usu. 1-loc. with ∞—1 campylotr. ov.; perisperm.

1. *Chenopodiineae:* P bracteoid, not > 5, A anteposed; ovule usu. 1 (fams. 1, 2).

3. Opiliaceae: fls. ☿ heterochlam. with slight seam-like K; $\overline{G}$ with 1 ov. with no integument.
4. Grubbiaceae: trees or shrubs with opp. leathery l. and small ☿ reg. fls.; P 4 sepaloid, A 4+4, $\overline{G}$ (2), 2-loc. below when young, later 1-loc. with 2 pend ov. on central plac.; drupe; oily endosp.
5. Olacaceae: trees and shrubs with usu. alt. entire l. and small ☿ reg. fls.; K 4—6, very small, C 4—6, A as many or 2—3 times as many, $\underline{G}$ (2—5), 2—5-loc. at base, 1-loc. above, with 1 ov. pend. into each loc.; 1-seeded drupe or nut; endosp.
6. Octoknemataceae: woody with alt. l. and ☿ fls.; P 2+3, A 2+3, anteposed, $\overline{G}$ 1-loc. with 3 pend. ov.; drupe 1-seeded.
7. Loranthaceae: woody semiparas., usu. on trees, with usu. reg. 2—3-merous, usu. homochlam. ☿ or ♂ ♀ fls.; P in two whorls, A as many, $\overline{G}$ 1-loc. usu. without differentiation of ov. and plac.; layer of viscin round seed; endosp.
8. Balanophoraceae: fleshy root paras. with tuberous rhiz. from which stems rise endog., and small fls. in spikes or heads, homochlam. or naked, usu. ♂ ♀; P in ♂ 3—4 (2—8), united below, A as many or 1—2; P in ♀ usu. 0; $\underline{G}$ (1—2), rarely (3—5); nut or drupe; endosp.

15

1. Aristolochiaceae: herbs or climbing shrubs with alt. exstip. l. and homochlam. ☿ reg. or ·|· fls.; P usu. (3), petaloid, A 6—36, free or united with style, $\overline{G}$, rarely $\underline{G}$, 4—6-loc. with ∞ ov.; caps.; endosp.
2. Rafflesiaceae: thalloid parasites, shoots very short with term. fl. or raceme, usu. ♂ ♀, reg. haplochlam.; P (4—5), A ∞ on column, $\overline{G}$ (4—6—8) with parietal plac. or ∞ twisted loc.; berry with ∞ seeds; endosp.
3. Hydnoraceae: thalloid paras. with ☿ reg. fls.; P (3—4), fleshy, A 3—4, epiphyllous, $\overline{G}$ (3) with parietal. plac. and ∞ ov.; berry; endo- and perisp.

16

1. Polygonaceae:

17

1. Chenopodiaceae: usu. herbs with alt. often fleshy l. and cymose infls. of small reg. homochlam. ☿ or ♂ ♀ fls.; P (5) or less, imbr. sepaloid, A as many, anteposed, bent inwards in bud, $\underline{G}$ (2) 1-loc. with 1 basal ov.; nut; endosp.
2. Amarantaceae: herbs or shrubs with opp. or alt. exstip. l. and small haplochlam. usu. ☿ reg. fls. in cymose or cpd. infls.; P 4—5 or (4—5) usu. sepaloid, A 1—5 anteposed and ± united below, $\underline{G}$ (2—3), 1-loc. with ∞—1 ov.; nut; endosp.

2. *Phytolaccineae:* P haplo- to hetero-chlam., tending to cyclic; A sometimes ∞, G sometimes little united (fams. 3—6).

3. *Portulacineae*: P heterochlam.; K 2, C 4—5 (fams. 7, 8).

4. *Caryophyllineae:* P heterochlam., K=C; fl. cyclic, sometimes with no C (fam. 9).

d. *Fls. usu. heterochlam.* (*Orders* 18—30).

a. **Apocarpy and hypogyny the rule; perig. and epig. fls. only in Lauraceae and Hernandiaceae (Order 18).**

18. RANALES. Herbs or woody pl. with spiral, spirocyclic, or cyclic, usu. haplo- or hetero-chlam. rarely achlam. reg. or ·|· fls.; A usu. ∞, G ∞—1, rarely united.

1. *Nymphaeineae:* fls. various, usu. spiral; ov. (exc. in 2) usu. ∞ on inner surface of cpls.; mostly water plants (fams. 1, 2).

2. *Trochodendrineae:* fls. naked, spirocyclic; ov. on ventral suture; no oil cells (fams. 3, 4).

3. *Ranunculineae:* fls. with P, spiral to cyclic; ov. on ventral suture; no oil cells (fams. 5—8).

3. Nyctaginaceae: herbs or woody, with opp. exstip. l. and cymose ☿ or ♂ ♀ reg. fls. with bracts, sometimes united or petaloid, at base; P (5) petaloid, lower part persistent on fr.; A typically 5 (1—30), $\underline{G}$ 1 with 1 basal erect ov.; achene; perisp.
4. Cynocrambaceae: herbs with fleshy stip. l., the lower opp., and ♂ ♀ fls., ♂ P 2—5, A 10—30, ♀ P (3—4), $\underline{G}$ 1, 1 ov.; drupe; endosp.
5. Phytolaccaceae: herbs or woody, with racemes or cymes of reg. usu. ☿ fls.; P usu. 4—5, A 4—5 or ∞, $\underline{G}$ (rarely $\overline{G}$) 1—∞, free or united, 1 ov. in each; drupe or nut, rarely caps.; perisp.
6. Aizoaceae: herbs or undershrubs with threadlike or fleshy opp. or alt. exstip. l. and cymose infls. of ☿ reg. fls.; P 4—5 or (4—5), A 5 (3—∞), the outer petaloid stds., $\underline{G}$ or $\overline{G}$ (2—∞) with ∞ ov., usu. 2—∞-loc.; caps.; perisp.
7. Portulacaceae: herbs or undershrubs with fleshy l. and often hair-like stips., and cymes of reg. ☿ fls.; K usu. 2, C 4—5, A 5 or 5+5, or fewer or ∞, $\underline{G}$ or semi-inf. (3—5) 1-loc. with 2—∞ ov. on basal plac.; caps.; endosp.
8. Basellaceae: twining herbs with ☿ reg. fls.; K 2, C 5 united below, A 5 anteposed, $\underline{G}$ (3), 1-loc. with 1 basal ov.; nut; endosp.
9. Caryophyllaceae: herbs or undershrubs with entire usu. opp. l. and cymose panicles of usu. reg. ☿ fls.; K 5 or (5), C 5 or 0, A 5 or 10, $\underline{G}$ (5—2), 1-loc. usu. with free-central plac., ov. 1—∞; caps. or berry; endosp.

18

1. Nymphaeaceae: water or marsh pl. with usu. submerged or swimming l. and sol. reg. ☿ fls.; axis often hollowed; P 6—∞, A 6—∞, $\underline{G}$ or $\overline{G}$ 3—∞ or (3—∞), each with 1—∞ ov.; endosp. or 0.
2. Ceratophyllaceae: submerged water pl. with whorls of 4 l. and sol. ♂ ♀ axillary reg. fls.; P 9—12 sepaloid, A 12—16, $\underline{G}$ 1 with 1 pend. ov.; nut; endosp.
3. Trochodendraceae: woody with alt. exstip. l. and sol. or racemed naked ☿ or ♂ ♀ fls.; A ∞, $\underline{G}$ 5—∞ with ∞—1 ov.; endosp.
4. Cercidiphyllaceae: woody with opp. stip. l. and sol. dioec. fls.; A ∞ spiral, $\underline{G}$ 2—5, stalked, with ∞ ov.; follicles; endosp.
5. Ranunculaceae: usu. herbs, often with divided l. and usu. ☿ reg. rarely ·|· or fully cyclic fls.; P often haplochlam., usu. petaloid, rarely K, C, A usu. ∞, $\underline{G}$ ∞—1 rarely united, with ∞—1 ov.; follicle or caps., rarely berry; endosp. oily.
6. Lardizabalaceae: climbing shrubs with cpd. l. and sol. or racemed ☿ or ♂ ♀ reg. fls.; P 3+3 usu. with two whorls of honey-l., A 3+3, $\underline{G}$ 3 or more with ∞ ov.; berry; endosp.
7. Berberidaceae: herbs or shrubs with simple or cpd. l. and ☿ reg. homo- or hetero-chlam. 3—2-merous fls.; P in 2—4 whorls, often with 2 whorls of honey-l., A in two, $\underline{G}$ 1, rarely more, with ∞—1 ov.; berry; endosp.

B; d; α; β

4. *Magnoliineae:* fls. with P, spiral to cyclic; ov. on ventral suture; oil cells (fams. 9—18).

β. Syncarpy and hypogyny the rule (Orders 19, 20).

19. RHOEADALES. Usu. herbs with racemes of fls., cyclic (exc. sometimes the A), heterochlam., rarely homochlam. or apet., hypog., reg. or ·|·; G (∞—2), ov. with 2 integ.

1. *Rhoeadineae:* fl. heterochlam, K usu. 2 (fam. 1).
2. *Capparidineae:* fls. heterochlam., K usu. 4 or more (fams. 2—4).

3. *Resedineae:* fls. heterochlam, spirocyclic (fam. 5).

8. Menispermaceae: climbing shrubs with usu. alt. simple l. and small usu. reg. ♂ ♀ fls.; K, C, A usu. each 2 whorls, $\underline{G}$ ∞—3—1 each with 1 ov.; drupe; endosp. or 0.
9. Magnoliaceae: woody pl. with alt. simple l. and usu. sol. reg. heterochlam. ☿ or ♂ ♀ fls.; P usu. petaloid; A ∞; $\underline{G}$ usu. ∞, rarely united; endosp.
10. Calycanthaceae: shrubs with opp. simple l. and ☿ fls. with hollowed recept.; P ∞, petaloid, A 10—30, $\underline{G}$ ∞ each with 2 ov.; achenes enclosed in axis; endosp. little.
11. Lactoridaceae: shrub with haplochlam. cyclic fls.; P 3, A 3+3, $\underline{G}$ 3.
12. Anonaceae: woody pl. with entire exstip. l. and showy usu. ☿ reg. heterochlam. fls.; P 3+3+3, A ∞ spiral, G ∞—1; berry; endosp. ruminate.
13. Eupomatiaceae: fl. deeply perig., naked; A ∞, G ∞.
14. Myristicaceae: woody pl. with evergr. simple l. and axill. racemes of ♂ ♀ reg. cyclic fls.; P (3), A (3—18) extr., $\underline{G}$ 1 with 1 basal ov.; fr. fleshy dehisc.; aril; endosp. ruminate.
15. Gomortegaceae: shrub with opp. evergr. l. and racemes of ☿ fls.; P 7, A 2—3, G (2—3), with 1 pend. ov. in each; drupe; endosp.
16. Monimiaceae: woody pl. with usu. opp. exstip. l. and sol. or cymose infls. of ☿ or ♂ ♀ reg. or ·|· fls.; P often perig. or epig., 4—∞ or 0, A ∞ or few, $\underline{G}$ ∞ each with 1 ov.; achene; endosp.
17. Lauraceae: woody with leathery alt. exstip. l., and oil cavities in tissues; infl. various, of 3-merous reg. ☿ or ♂ ♀ fls. with ± concave axis; P homochlam. in 2 whorls, A in 3 or 4, one sometimes stds., anthers opening by valves, $\underline{G}$ (3), 1-loc. with 1 pend. ov.; berry usu. enclosed in fleshy axis; no endosp.
18. Hernandiaceae: woody with alt. exstip. l., and oil passages; and ☿ or ♂ ♀ reg. homochlam. fls.; P 4—10, A in whorl before outer P, $\overline{G}$ 1-loc. with 1 pend. anatr. ov.; fr. winged; no endosp.

19

1. Papaveraceae: usu. herbs with alt. l. and latex, and reg. or ·|· ☿ fls.; K 2, C 4, rarely 6 or more, or 0, A ∞—4—2 (branched), $\underline{G}$ (2—16) with parietal plac. and ∞ ov., or 1 basal; caps.; oily endosp.
2. Capparidaceae: herbs and shrubs with alt. l. and racemes (with br.) of ☿ reg. or ·|· fls., axis usu. elongated below A or G; K, C 4, A ∞—6—4, $\underline{G}$ (2—several), 1-loc. or more with ∞ ov.; caps., berry or drupe; no endosp.
3. Cruciferae: herbs with alt. exstip. l. and simple or branched hairs, and racemes (without br.) of ☿ reg. fls.; K 2+2, C 4 diagonal, A 2 (short) + 2 + 2 (long), $\underline{G}$ (2), 1-loc, with "spurious" partition; usu. siliqua; no endosp.
4. Tovariaceae: herbs with ternate l. and term. racemes of ☿ reg. fls.; K, C, A 8, $\underline{G}$ (6—8) with plac. reaching centre, and ∞ ov.; berry; endosp. thin.
5. Resedaceae: herbs with alt. stip. l. and racemes of ☿ ·|· fls., with post. disc; K 4—8, C 0—8, A 3—10, $\underline{G}$ (2—6) open above, 1-loc. with 1—∞ ov.; caps.; no endosp.

B; d; β; γ

4. *Moringineae:* fls. homochlam, cyclic (fam. 6).

20. SARRACENIALES. Herbs with usu. alt. insectivorous l. and spirocyclic to cyclic homo- or hetero-chlam. hypog. reg. fls.; $\underline{G}$ (3—5) with parietal or axile plac. and 3—∞ ov.; endosp.

γ. Apocarpy and hypogyny occur, but perigyny is commoner; syncarpy and epigyny also common (Order 21).

21. ROSALES. Fl. cyclic, rarely spirocyclic, heterochlam. rarely apet., hypog. to epig., reg. or ⫩; G or (G) sometimes with thick plac. and ∞ ov.

1. *Podostemonineae:* submerged trop. water pl. of alga or lichen-like form (fams. 1—3).

2. *Saxifragineae:* G=or fewer than C; endosp. usu. rich (fams. 4—13).

6. Moringaceae: trees with pinnate exstip. l. and panicles of ☿ ·|· fls.; K, C, A 5, and 5 stds., $\underline{G}$ (3) on short gynophore, with parietal plac. and ∞ ov.; caps.; no endosp.

20

1. Sarraceniaceae: herbs with pitcher l. and scapes with sol. or racemed ☿ reg. fls.; K 8—5, C 5, A ∞, $\underline{G}$ (5—3) 5 or 3-loc. with ∞ ov.; caps.; endosp.
2. Nepenthaceae: climbers with alt. l., the lower with pitchers, the upper tendrilled, and racemes or panicles of ♂ ♀ reg. fls., P 2 + 2 homochlam., A (4—16), $\underline{G}$ (4), 4-loc. with ∞ ov.; caps.; endosp.
3. Droseraceae: herbs usu. with alt. l., usu. rolled in in bud, and with sticky glands, and cymose ☿ reg. fls.; K, C 5—4, A 5—4—20, $\underline{G}$ (5—3), 1-loc. with ∞—3 ov.; caps.; endosp.

21

1. Podostemaceae: herbs (usu. trop.) of rushing water with reg. or ·|· ☿ achlam. fls.; A ∞—1 free or united, $\underline{G}$ (2), 2—1-loc. with thick central plac. and ∞ or few anatr. ov.; caps.
2. Tristichaceae: as last, with reg. or slightly ·|· homochlam. ☿ fls.; P 3—5 sepaloid, A as many, or 4—5 times as many, or 2—1, $\underline{G}$ (2—3), 2—3-loc. with ∞ ov. on thick central plac.; caps.
3. Hydrostachyaceae: herbs (S. Afr.) of running water with spikes of dioec. naked fls.; ♂ of 1 sta., ♀ of (2) cpls. with ∞ ov.; caps.
4. Crassulaceae: succulent exstip. herbs or undershrubs, usu. with cymose infl. of reg. ☿ 3—30-merous fls.; C or (C), A obdipl. or in one whorl, $\underline{G}$ sometimes slightly united, with ∞ ov.; follicles; endosp.
5. Cephalotaceae: perenn. herbs with some pitcher l. and panicles of ☿ reg. fls.; P 6, A 6, $\underline{G}$ 6 with 1—2 basal ov.; follicles; endosp.
6. Saxifragaceae: herbs, shrubs or trees with usu. alt. l. and various infl. of usu. ∞ ☿ reg. (rarely ·|·) fls. with convex, flat or concave axis; A usu. obdipl. or = C, G = C or less, with usu. free styles, 2—1-loc. (rarely 5) with swollen plac. and ∞ ov. in several ranks, sup. or inf.; caps. or berry; endosp.
7. Pittosporaceae: woody, sometimes climbing, with alt. l. and resin passages, and ☿ reg. 5-merous fls.; $\underline{G}$ (2 or more) 1—5-loc. with parietal or axile plac. and 2-ranked ∞ anatr. ov., and simple style; caps. or berry; endosp.
8. Brunelliaceae: woody with opp. or whorled l. and panicles of small ♂ ♀ 4—5—7-merous diplost. fls.; K. valv., C 0, $\underline{G}$ 5—2 each with 2 pend. ov.; follicle-caps.; endosp.
9. Cunoniaceae: woody with opp. or whorled stip. l.; like 6, but ov. in 2 ranks.
10. Myrothamnaceae: small shrubs with opp. fan-folded l. and spikes of ♂ ♀ reg. achlam. fls.; A 4—8, $\underline{G}$ (4—3); caps. septicidal; endosp.

3. *Rosineae:* G ∞—1; ov. with 2 integ.; endosp. little or 0 (fams. 14—18).

δ. Fls. usu. with 5 or 4 whorls; apocarpy and isomery appear, but syncarpy and oligomery of G̲ are the rule (Orders 22—26).

22. PANDALES. Fls. cyclic, heterochlam., dioec. G̲ (3), each with 1 pend. orthotr. ov.; drupe.

23. GERANIALES. Fls. cyclic, heterochlam., apet. or naked, usu. 5-merous; A various, G̲ (5—2), rarely more, often separating when ripe, usu. with 2—1 rarely ∞ ov., pend. with ventral raphe and micropyle up, or when > 1 present, some with dorsal raphe and micropyle down.

1. *Geraniineae:* fls. heterochlam. rarely apet., usu. reg. and obdipl., rarely haplostemonous and in ·|· fls. usu. abortion of some sta.; anthers opening longitud., G iso- or oligo-merous; ov. with 2 integ. (fams. 1—12).

A. No secretory cells or passages (fams. 1—7).

11. Bruniaceae: heath-like undershrubs with alt. exstip. l. and cpd. spikes, racemes and heads of usu. reg. and perig. ☿ fls.; K, C, A 5, G̲ (3—2) each with 3—4 ov. or 1 with 1; caps.; aril; endosp.
12. Hamamelidaceae: woody with usu. alt. stip. l. and spikes or heads of ☿ or ♂ ♀ reg., heterochlam. apet. or naked fls. surrounded by br.; K, C, A 4—5, G̲ (2) with 1—∞ pend. ov.; caps.; endosp.
13. Eucommiaceae: trees with alt. extip. l. and latex, and naked ♂ ♀ reg. fls.; A 6—10, G̲ (2), one aborting, with 2 pend. ov.; samara; endosp.
14. Platanaceae: woody with alt. 3—5-lobed stip. l. and pend. spherical heads of ♂ ♀ reg. fls.; K, C, A 3—8, G̲ usu. 1, free, with 1—2 ov.; caryopsis; endosp.
15. Crossosomataceae: shrubs with small stiff grey-green l. and sol. fls.; like Rosaceae-Spiraeoideae, but seeds kidney-shaped; aril; endosp.
16. Rosaceae: herbs, shrubs, or trees with usu. alt. stip. l. and reg. (rarely ·|·) 5 (3—8 or more)-merous fls.; axis flat or hollowed; K 5, C 5 or 0, A 2—4 or more times as many, bent inwards in bud, G=K or 2—3 times as many, or ∞, rarely 1—4, free or united to hollow axis, usu. 1-loc. with 2 ov. per cpl.; follicle, achene, drupe or pome; endosp. thin or 0.
17. Connaraceae: usu. climbing shrubs, rarely trees, with alt. exstip. l. and panicles of reg. ☿ or ♂ ♀ fls.; K 5 or (5) persistent, C 5, A 5+5, G̲ usu. 5, rarely 4 or 1, each with 2 ov.; one follicle with 1 seed; aril; endosp. or none.
18. Leguminosae: trees, shrubs, or herbs, usu. with alt. stip. l. and racemes of reg. or ·|· usu. ☿ fls.; K, C 5, A 5+5 or more, G usu. 1, rarely 2—5—15, with ∞ ov.; pod or indeh. fr.; endosp. usu. none.

22

1. Pandaceae.

23

1. Geraniaceae: herbs with lobed or divided l., stip. or not, and ☿ usu. reg. 5-merous fls.; A 10—15, sometimes only 5 fertile, G̲ (5—2) usu. with 1—2, rarely 2—∞ ov. per cpl.; schizocarp, rarely caps.; endosp.
2. Oxalidaceae: usu. herbs with alt. cpd. stip. or exstip. l. and ☿ reg. 5-merous fls. with no disc; A 10 obdiplost., united at base, G̲ (5) with ∞—1 ov.; caps. or berry; endosp.

B; d; δ

B. Secretory cells or passages (in 10 sometimes only in pith and bark) (fams. 8—12).

2. *Malpighiineae:* as last, but fls. obliquely ∤, at least in G; l. often opp. (fams. 13—15).

3. Tropaeolaceae: usu. climbers with sensitive petiole, stip. or not, and ☿ 5-merous ·|· fls., with axis prolonged into post. spur; A 8, G̲ 3-loc. with 1 ov. in each; schizocarp; no endosp.
4. Linaceae: herbs or woody with alt. l., stip. or not, and ☿ reg. 5—4-merous fls. with no disc; A 5—20 united below, G̲ 5—4 (or less)-loc. with 1—2 ov. in each and often with extra partitions; caps. or drupe; endosp.
5. Humiriaceae: woody with alt. stip. l. and reg. ☿ 5-merous fls. with cup-shaped disc; A 10—∞, G̲ (5) each with 1—2 ov.; drupe.; endosp.
6. Erythroxylaceae: woody with alt. simple stip. l. and 5-merous ☿ reg. fls., heterostyled with no disc; C with appendages on inner side, A 10, united in tube at base, G̲ (3—4), 3—4-loc, but only 1 fertile, with 1—2 ov.; drupe; endosp.
7. Zygophyllaceae: usu. shrubby with opp. often pinnate stip. l. and cymes or cpd. infls. of reg. ☿ 5—4-merous fls. with disc or gynophore; A 10—8, rarely 15, often with united basal appendages, G̲ (5—4) or more with 1—∞ ov.; usu. caps. or schizocarp; endosp. or o.
8. Cneoraceae: shrubs with alt. narrow leathery exstip. l., oil cells, and single or cymose reg. ☿ 3—4-merous fls. with disc; A 3—4, G̲ (3—4), lobed, each with 2 ov.; style 1; schizocarp.
9. Rutaceae: usu. woody with alt. or opp. simple or cpd. exstip. l. and reg. or ·|· usu. ☿ 5—4-merous fls. with disc; A obdipl. or 5—4—3—2, rarely ∞, G̲ (5—4) rarely (3—1 or ∞) with ∞—2 ov.; fr. various; endosp. or none.
10. Simarubaceae: woody pl. with bitter bark, alt. or opp. usu. pinnate exstip. l. and reg. usu. ♂ ♀ 5—4-merous fls. with disc; A 10, 5, or ∞, G̲ (5) or less; fr. various; endosp. thin or none.
11. Burseraceae: woody pl. with alt. usu. cpd. l., resin-passages and small reg. usu. ♂ ♀ 5—4-merous fls. with disc; A obdipl. or 5, G̲ (5—3) each usu. with 2 ov.; style 1; drupe or caps.; no endosp.
12. Meliaceae: woody pl. usu. with pinnate exstip. l. and usu. ☿ reg. fls. in cymose panicles; axis rounded or with effigurations; K, C sometimes united, A usu. in tube, obdipl. or 5, G̲ (5) or less, multi-loc. with 1—2 rarely more ov. in each, and 1 style; fr. various; endosp. or o.
13. Malpighiaceae: woody usu. climbing pl. with opp. stip. l. and ☿ obdipl. 5-merous fls. with convex or flat axis, sometimes with gynophore; K (5), often with nectaries, C 5 usu. clawed, A 5 + 5, often some aborted, G̲ usu. (3), each with 1 ov.; schizocarp, nut or drupe; no endosp.
14. Trigoniaceae: woody often climbing pl. with alt. or opp. l. stip. or not and ☿ obliquely ·|· 5-merous fls.; K (5), C 5—3 often very unequal, A 5—6—10, ± united in tube at base, G̲ (3) with ∞—2 ov. each; caps.; endosp. or not.
15. Vochysiaceae: woody, rarely herbs, with opp. or whorled simple l., stip. or not, and ☿ obliquely ·|· fls.; K (5), one often spurred, C usu. 3—1, perig. or epig., A 1 and stds., G̲ or Ḡ (3) each with ∞—2 ov.; fr. indeh. or caps.; no endosp.

B; d; δ

3. *Polygalineae:* fls. reg. or ·|· with two whorls of sta.; anthers opening by pores, G (2), median (fams. 16, 17).

4. *Dichapetalineae:* fls. reg. or ·|· with 1 whorl of sta.; C or (C), ov. with 1 integ., seed sometimes with caruncle (fam. 18).

5. *Tricoccae:* fls. reg. ♂ ♀ often much reduced; G (3) each with 2—1 ov. with 2 integ.; usu. caruncle (fam. 19).

6. *Callitrichineae:* herbs, often submerged, with crowded l. and small axillary monoec. naked fls.; ♂ with term. sta., ♀ with 2 transv. cpls. divided into 4, with 1 ov. in each section; fr. of 4 nutlets; endosp. (fam. 20).

24. SAPINDALES. Usu. woody; as last, but ov. in reversed position, pend. with dorsal raphe and micropyle up, or erect with ventral raphe and micropyle down.

1. *Buxineae:* haplochlam.; ov. with 2 integs. (fam. 1).

2. *Empetrineae:* heterochlam., cpls. each with 1 erect ov. with 1 integ., united till ripe; shrubs (fam. 2).

3. *Coriariineae:* heterochlam., cpls. each with 1 pend. ov. with 2 integ., finally free; shrubs (fam. 3).

4. *Limnanthineae:* heterochlam., cpls. each with 1 erect ov. with 1 integ., finally free; herbs (fam. 4).

5. *Anacardiineae:* heterochlam., rarely apet., reg.; G usu. oligomerous; woody with resin passages (fam. 5).

6. *Celastrineae:* fls. heterochlam., reg., with 2 or 1 whorls of A; G most often oligomerous (fams. 6—14).

16. Tremandraceae: shrubs with entire or toothed l. and sol. axillary 4—5 (rarely 3)-merous ☿ reg. fls.; K free, C valv., A in 2 whorls, G̲ (2) with 1—2 ov. each; caps.; endosp.
17. Polygalaceae: herbs, shrubs, or trees with sim le entire usu. alt. exstip. l. and racemes, spikes, or panicles of ☿ ·|· fls.; K usu. 5, 2 larger and petaloid, C 3, 1 often keel-like, A (4+4) or fewer, usu. united below, G̲ usu. (2), 2-loc. with 1 ov. in each; caps. nut or drupe; endosp. or o.
18. Dichapetalaceae: woody, often lianes, with entire stip. l. and small ☿ or ♂ ♀ usu. reg. fls. with disc or scales; K 5 or (5), C 5 or (5), often forked, A 5, sometimes united to C, G̲ (2—3) each with 2 ov.; drupe; no endosp.
19. Euphorbiaceae: herbs, shrubs, and trees, usu. with alt. often stip. l., often latex, and cpd. infls. of ♂ ♀ reg. usu. 5-merous fls.; P usu. in 1 whorl, or o, A 1—∞ free or united or branched, G̲ usu. (3), 3-loc. with 2-lobed styles, and 1—2 pend. anatr. ov. in each, with ventral raphe and micropyle usu. with caruncle; usu. schizocarp-caps.; endosp.
20. Callitrichaceae:

24

1. Buxaceae: woody pl. with entire evergr. exstip. l. and reg. ♂ ♀ apet. or naked fls., sol. or in racemose infls.; A 4—∞, G̲ (3) or (2—4) each with 2—1 ov.; caps. or drupe; endosp.
2. Empetraceae: ericoid shrubs with linear exstip. grooved l. and heads of small ♂ ♀ reg. fls.; K, C, A 2—3, G̲ (2—9): drupe; no caruncle.
3. Coriariaceae: woody pl. with opp. or whorled exstip. l. and axillary or racemed ☿ or ♂ ♀ reg. fls.; K, C 5, A 5 + 5, G̲ 5—8; schizocarp, endosp.
4. Limnanthaceae: annuals with alt. exstip. l. and sol. axillary ☿ reg. 5—3-merous fls.; K, C, 5—3, A 10—6, G̲ (5—3), with 1 ov. in each, separating when ripe; no endosp.
5. Anacardiaceae: woody pl. with alt. exstip. not gland-dotted l. and ∞ fls. in panicles, typically 5-merous, hypog. to epig.; A 10—5 or other number, G (3—1) rarely (5), each with 1 anatr. ov., often only one fertile; drupe, no endosp.
6. Cyrillaceae: woody pl. with evergr. l., and racemes of small ☿ reg. 5-merous fls.; K, C sometimes united, A in 2 whorls, G̲ (5—2)-loc. each with 1 ov.; endosp.
7. Pentaphylacaceae: woody pl. with alt. leathery l. and small ☿ reg. fls. in racemes below l.; K, C, A 5, G̲ (5) each with 2 pend. ov.; caps.; endosp.
8. Corynocarpaceae: woody pl. with alt. leathery l. and small ☿ fls. in panicles; inner sta. stds., G̲ (2), 1 fertile with 1 pend. ov.; drupe; no endosp.

B; d; δ

7. *Icacinineae:* fls. heterochlam. reg. with 1 whorl of sta. before K; G usu. 1, integ. 1, fr. 1-seeded (fam. 15).

8. *Sapindineae:* fls. heterochlam., typically with 2 whorls of sta, but with aborted sta. and cpls., reg. or obliquely ·|·; ov. with 2 integs. (fams. 16—18).

9. *Sabiineae:* fls. heterochlam., sta. before pets. (fam. 19).

10. *Melianthineae:* fls. heterochlam., ·|·, with 1, rarely 2, whorls of sta. with free anthers (fam. 20).

11. *Balsaminineae:* as last, but anthers united (fam. 21).

9. Aquifoliaceae: woody pl. with alt. evergr. simple l., stips. small or none, and dioec., reg., 4—more-merous ♂ ♀ fls. in cymose umbels; K, C 4, A 4 often epipet., $\underline{G}$ (4—6) or more, each with 1—2 pend. ov.; drupe with several stones; endosp.

10. Celastraceae: woody pl. with simple opp. or alt. l., sometimes stip., and small ☿ reg. 4—5-merous fls. in cymose umbels; A 4—5 on edge of disc, $\underline{G}$ (2—5) each with ∞—1 ov.; caps. or berry; often aril; endosp. or not.

11. Hippocrateaceae: woody pl., often climbing, with opp. or alt. simple l., stips. small or none, and small, ☿ reg. fls. in cymose umbels; K, C 5, A 3, rarely 5, $\underline{G}$ (3) each with ∞—2 ov.; berry or 3-winged fr.; no endosp.

12. Salvadoraceae: woody pl. with opp. simple l. and sometimes bristle-like stips., and panicles of ☿ or ♂ ♀ reg. fls.; K (4—2), C 4—5 or (4—5), A 4—5, $\underline{G}$ (2), 1—2-loc. with 1—2 basal ov. in each; berry or drupe, usu. 1-seeded; no endosp.

13. Stackhousiaceae: herbs with alt. exstip. l. and spikes or cymes of fl.; K, C, A 5, $\underline{G}$ (2—5)-loc. each with 1 erect ov.; schizocarp; endosp.

14 Staphyleaceae: woody pl. with opp. lobed stip. l. and panicles or racemes of fls.; K, C 5, A 5, outside disc, $\underline{G}$ (2—3), free above with ∞—few pend. ov.; caps.; endosp.

15. Icacinaceae: woody pl. some climbing, usu. with alt. exstip. l. and small ☿ or ♂ ♀ reg. fls.; K, C, A 5—4, $\underline{G}$ (3), usu. 1 only with 2 pend. ov.; drupe; endosp.

16. Aceraceae: trees with opp. exstip. l. and small reg. ☿ ♂ ♀ fls. in spikes, racemes or panicles; axis disc-like or concave; K, C, A 4—10, $\underline{G}$ (2) each with 2 ov.; fr. with 1-seeded samaras; no endosp.

17. Hippocastanaceae: trees with opp. palmate exstip. l. and cymose racemes of ·|· ☿ ♂ ♀ fls.; K (5), C 4—5, A 5—8, $\underline{G}$ (3)-loc. each with 2 ov.; caps. 3—1-loc. usu. 1-seeded; no endosp.

18. Sapindaceae: woody pl. with alt. l. and usu. ·|· ☿ ♂ ♀ fls. with extrastaminal disc; K 5, C 5—3 or 0, often with scales, A usu. 8, rarely 10, 5, or ∞, $\underline{G}$ (2—3) each usu. with 1 ov.; caps., drupe, nut, or schizocarp; no endosp.

19. Sabiaceae: woody pl., often climbers, with alt. exstip. l. and small ☿ or ☿ ♂ ♀ fls. in racemes or cymose racemes; K (2—5), C 4—5, A 5 antepetalous, $\underline{G}$ (2—3) each with 2 ov.; fr. 1-loc., 1-seeded; no endosp.

20. Melianthaceae: woody pl. with alt. usu. pinnate l., stip. or not, and racemes of ☿ ·|· fls.; K, C 5, A 5—4, rarely 10, unequal or partly united, $\underline{G}$ (4—5) each with ∞—1 ov.; caps.; aril or not; endosp.

21. Balsaminaceae: herbs with watery translucent stems and alt. usu. exstip. l., and ☿ ·|· fls.; K 5, the 2 ant. often small or aborted, C 5, the lat. ones united in pairs, A (5), $\underline{G}$ (5)-loc. each with ∞ ov.; caps. usu. explosive; no endosp.

B; d; δ; ε

25. RHAMNALES. Fl. cyclic, diplochlam., sometimes apet., with 1 whorl of sta. before pets., reg.; G (5—2) each with 1—2 ascending ov. with dorsal, lat., or ventral raphe and 2 integs.

26. MALVALES. Fl. cyclic, exc. sometimes the A, heterochlam., rarely apet., usu. ☿ and reg.; K, C usu. 5-merous, K usu. valv., A ∞ or in 2 whorls, the inner branched, G (2—∞) each with 1—∞ anatr. ov. with 2 integs.

1. *Elaeocarpineae:* K ± free, anthers dithecous with pores; no mucilage cells (fam. 1).
2. *Chlaenineae:* K free, imbr., A enclosed by a cup, anthers dithecous with slits; mucilage cells often present (fam. 2).
3. *Malvineae:* K rarely imbr., usu. valv.; mucilage cells (fams. 3—7).
4. *Scytopetalineae:* seps. united into dish-like K (fam. 8).

ε. **Fls. spirocyclic or in 5—4 whorls; apocarpy only in lower forms, syncarpy the rule, often with a sinking of G in axis (Orders 27, 28).**

27. PARIETALES. Fl. spirocyclic or cyclic, often A and G ∞, heterochlam., rarely apet., hypog. to epig.; G ± united, often with parietal plac. which may touch in centre, very rarely with basal ov.

1. *Theineae:* G free on convex or flat axis; endosp. oily (fams. 1—9).

25

1. Rhamnaceae: woody pl., rarely herbs, often climbing, with simple stip. l. and small greenish or yellowish fls. often in axillary cymose infls.; K 5—4, C 5—4 small, or o, A 5—4, $\underline{G}$ to $\bar{G}$ (5—2) with 1 ov. in each; dry fr. or drupe; endosp. little or none.
2. Vitaceae: climbing shrubs often with tendrils opp. l.; like preceding, but berry: C valv., often united above and falling as a whole, $\underline{G}$ (2—8); endosp.

26

1. Elaeocarpaceae: woody pl. with simple stip. l. and ☿ 5—4-merous fls.; A ∞, $\underline{G}$ (2—∞) with ∞ ov. and 1 style, 2—∞-loc., rarely 1-loc.; caps., rarely drupe; sometimes aril; endosp.
2. Chlaenaceae: woody pl. with alt. stip. l. and ☿ reg. fls.; K 5, C 5—6, A 10—∞, $\underline{G}$ (3) each with 2 ov.; caps.; endosp.
3. Gonystilaceae: shrubs with alt. entire exstip. l. and cymose panicles of ☿ reg. fls.; K 5—4, C 5—4, usu. divided, A ∞, anthers dithecous, $\underline{G}$ (5—3), each with 1 pend. ov.; berry; no endosp.
4. Tiliaceae: usu. woody pl. with alt. stip. l. and ☿ reg. fls.; K 5, C 5 or o, A ∞ rarely to 10, free or in bundles, anthers dithecous, $\underline{G}$ (2—∞), each with 1—∞ ov., 2—∞-loc.; endosp.
5. Malvaceae: herbs, shrubs, or trees with simple or lobed stip. l. and ☿ usu. conspic. fls., sol., or in infls.; K 5, often with epicalyx, C 5, conv., A usu. ∞ in 2 whorls, united in a tube below, monothecous, with thorny pollen, $\underline{G}$ (5—∞), each with 1—∞ ov.; styles as many or twice; caps. or schizocarp; endosp.
6. Bombacaceae: woody pl. with entire or palmate stip. l. and often conspic. fls.; like last, but anthers with 1, 2 or more loc. and smooth pollen; $\underline{G}$ (2—5) with 2—∞ ov., seeds sometimes enclosed in hairs from pericarp; endosp. thin or o.
7. Sterculiaceae: trees, shrubs and herbs with alt. simple or cpd. stip. l. and complex infls. of ☿ or ♂ ♀ fls.; (K), C conv. or o, A in 2 whorls, the outer stds., the inner often branched, all ± united; anthers 2-loc., often andro-gynophore; $\underline{G}$ usu. (5), antepet., each with 2—∞ ov.; usu. schizocarp; endosp.
8. Scytopetalaceae: woody pl. with alt. leathery l. and bunches or racemes of long-stalked fls.; K dish-like, C 3—7 valv., A ∞, G (4—6), each with 2—6 pend. ov.; fr. woody or drupe, 1-seeded.

27

1. Dilleniaceae: woody, sometimes climbing, rarely herbs, with usu. entire alt. evergr. l., stip. or not, and usu. ☿ reg. yellow or white fls.; K 3—∞, C 5—3, A ∞, rarely 10 or less, $\underline{G}$ ∞—1, each with 1—∞ ov.; fr. dehisc. or not; aril; endosp.

B; d; ε

2. *Tamaricineae:* G free on flat axis; endosp. starchy or none, C free, A in whorls, or if ∞ in bundles (fams. 10—12).

3. *Fouquierineae:* as last, but endosp. oily, and (C) (fam. 13).

4. *Cistineae:* G free on flat or convex axis; endosp. starchy, C free, A ∞ not in bundles (fams. 14, 15).

2. Eucryphiaceae: woody with evergr. opp. stip. l. and sol. axillary ☿ reg. white fls.; K, C 4, A ∞, $\underline{G}$ (5—18) each with ∞ pend. ov., becoming free on ripening; seed winged; endosp.
3. Ochnaceae: woody, or undershrubs with evergr. stip. l., usu. with ‖ lat. nerves, and panicles of showy usu. yellow ☿ reg. (rarely ·|·) fls., axis often enlarging after flg.; K 4—10, C 5, rarely 4—10, A 5—10—∞, sometimes stds., $\underline{G}$ (2—5—10) with one style, often free below, with ∞—1 erect or pend. ov.; endosp or 0.
4. Caryocaraceae: woody with ternate evergr. stip. l. and term. racemes of ☿ reg. fls.; K (5), C (5), A ∞, $\underline{G}$ (4—8—20) rarely (1—3) each loc. with 1 pend. ov.; schizocarp; endosp. thin or 0.
5. Marcgraviaceae: woody, often climbing and epiph., with simple exstip. l. and racemes of ☿ reg. fls., the br. metam. into hollow nectaries; K 4—5, C (4—5), A 3—6—∞, $\underline{G}$ (5) or (2—8—∞) with ∞ ov. on originally parietal plac. afterwards meeting in centre; caps.; no endosp.
6. Quiinaceae: woody with shining evergr. stip. l. and racemes or panicles of ☿ ♂ ♀ reg. fls.; K, C 4—5, A 15—30, $\underline{G}$ (2—3) or (7), each with 2 axile ov.; berry, seeds felted.
7. Theaceae: woody with simple usu. alt. exstip. l. and ☿ reg. fls.; K 5—7, C 5—9, sometimes united below, A ∞—5, sometimes in bundles, $\underline{G}$ (3—5) or (2—∞) with ∞—1 ov. in each on axile plac.; caps.; endosp. or 0.
8. Guttiferae: woody, rarely herbs, with simple usu. opp. rarely stip. l., resin passages, and ☿ or ♂ ♀ reg. fls.; A ∞—4, often partly stds. and united in groups, $\underline{G}$ (3—5) or (1—15) with ∞—1 ov.; caps., berry, or drupe; no endosp.
9. Dipterocarpaceae: trees with alt. evergr. stip. l., resin passages, and panicles of ☿ reg. fls.; K 5 (2, 3 or all lengthening to wings on the fr.), C 5 free or united, A ∞ or 15—10—5, $\underline{G}$ (3—1) each with ∞—2 ov.; fr. usu. 1-seeded indeh.; no endosp.
10. Elatinaceae: undershrubs or herbs, often water pl. with opp. or whorled stip. l. and small ☿ reg. fls., axillary or in cymes, K, C 2—5, A 2—5 or 4—10, $\underline{G}$ (2—5) with ∞ axill. ov.; caps.; endosp. thin or 0.
11. Frankeniaceae: undershrubs or herbs with small opp. exstip. l. and term. or cymed ☿ reg. 4—6-merous fls.; (K), C with ligule, A usu. 6, sometimes ∞, free or united below, $\underline{G}$ (4—2) with ∞ erect ov. on parietal plac.; caps.; endosp.
12. Tamaricaceae: shrubs or herbs with small alt. exstip. l. and ☿ reg. 4—6-merous fls.; A as many or twice as many as C, or ∞ in groups, $\underline{G}$ (5—2) with ∞ ascending ov. on basal plac.; style divided; caps.; seed hairy; endosperm or none.
13. Fouquieriaceae: shrubs with decid. l. and thorny midrib, and racemes or panicles of showy ☿ reg. fls.; K 5, C (5), A 10—15, $\underline{G}$ (3), each with 4—6 ov.; seeds hairy or winged; endosp.
14. Cistaceae: herbs and shrubs with usu. opp. l. with glandular hairs and ethereal oil, and ☿ reg. fls.; K 5—3, C 5—3—0, A ∞, $\underline{G}$ (3—10) with ∞ or 2 ov. on parietal plac.; caps.; endosp.
15. Bixaceae: woody pl. with alt. simple l. and showy ☿ reg. fls. in panicles; K, C 5, A ∞, $\underline{G}$ (2) each with ∞ ov. on parietal plac.; style 1; caps.; endosp.

B; d; ε

5. *Cochlospermineae:* as last, but endosp. of kidney-shaped seed oily (fam. 16).

6. *Flacourtiineae:* G free on convex axis, or in tubular axis rarely united at sides to G; endosp. oily (fams. 17—24).

7. *Papayineae:* G free in tubular or bell-shaped axis; endosp. oily; latex (fam. 25).

8. *Loasineae:* G sunk in and united to axis; endosp. oily, rarely none (fam. 26).

9. *Datiscineae:* G sunk in and united to axis; endosp. thin, embryo oily; fls. in racemes (fam. 27).

10. *Begoniineae:* as last, but no endosp.; fls. in dichasia or scorpioid cymes (fam. 28).

16. Cochlospermaceae: woody, usu. with lobed or cpd. l. and showy ☿ reg. or ·|· fls. in racemes or panicles; K, C 4—5, A ∞, $\underline{G}$ (3—5) each with ∞ ov. on parietal or almost central plac.; caps.; endosp.
17. Winteranaceae: woody pl. with alt. exstip. l. and cymose umbels of ☿ reg. fls.; K 4—5, C 4—5 or o, A (20 or less), $\underline{G}$ (2—5) with 2—∞ ov. on parietal plac.; berry; endosp.
18. Violaceae: herbs, or woody, with alt. stip. l. and ☿ reg. or ·|· fls.; K, C, A 5, $\underline{G}$ (3), each with 1—∞ ov. on parietal plac.; caps. or berry; endosp.
19. Flacourtiaceae: usu. woody pl. with alt. stip. simple l., and ☿ or ♂ ♀ reg. fls.; K 2—15, C 15—o, A usu. ∞, $\underline{G}$ or semi-inf. (2—10) usu. with ∞ ov. on parietal plac.; berry or caps.; often aril; endosp.
20. Stachyuraceae: small shrubs with alt. l. and racemes of small ☿ or polyg. reg. fls.; K, C 4, A 8, $\underline{G}$ (4) with ∞ ov.; berry; aril; endosp.
21. Turneraceae: herbs, trees or shrubs with alt. l., stip. or not, and axillary or racemed or cymed ☿ reg. fls. with tubular axis; K, C, A 5, $\underline{G}$ (3), each with 3—∞ ov. on parietal plac.; style divided; caps.; aril; endosp.
22. Malesherbiaceae: herbs or undershrubs with alt. exstip. usu. very hairy l. and racemes or cymes of ☿ reg. 5-merous fls. with tubular axis and gynophore; A 5, concrescent with gynophore, $\underline{G}$ (3) with ∞ ov. on parietal plac.; caps.; no aril.
23. Passifloraceae: herbs or shrubs often climbing by tendrils with simple usu. palmately lobed l., stip. or not, and fls. sol. or in racemes or cymes, reg., ☿ or ♂ ♀, with axis often ± tubular ending in effigurations; K, C 5, rarely 3—8, A usu. 5 or 4—8, rarely ∞, united to prolongation of axis, $\underline{G}$ (3—5) usu. with ∞ ov. on parietal plac.; caps. or berry; usu. aril and endosp.
24. Achariaceae: herbs or undershrubs with simple or lobed l. and single fls. or few in an axil, ♂ ♀ reg., 3—5-merous; K, C, A 3—5, $\underline{G}$ as last; caps.; endosp.
25. Caricaceae: woody pl. with simple or cpd. exstip. l. and axillary infls. of ♂ ♀ reg. fls. with hollow axis; K 5, C (5) in long tube in ♂, short in ♀; A 5 + 5, $\underline{G}$ (3—5) with ∞ ov. on parietal plac.; berry; endosp.
26. Loasaceae: herbs, rarely shrubs, sometimes twining, with alt. or opp. exstip. l. and often stinging hairs, and ☿ fls.; K 5 (rarely 4—7), C 5, rarely united, often boat-shaped, A ∞, those before K often transformed to nectaries, $\overline{G}$ (3—7) each with 1—∞ ov., usu. on parietal plac.; caps. sometimes spirally twisted; endosp.
27. Datiscaceae: herbs or shrubs with exstip. l. and racemes of small usu. ♂ ♀ fls.; ♂ K 3—9, C o—4—9, A 4—25, ☿ and ♀ P 3—8, $\overline{G}$ (3—8) with parietal plac. and ∞ ov.; caps.; endosp. slight.
28. Begoniaceae: herbs or undershrubs with alt. asymmetric stip. l. and dichasia or cymes of ♂ ♀ fls.; ♂ K 2, rarely 5, C 2—6 or o, A ∞, ♀ P 5—2 or 3 + 3 or 8, $\overline{G}$ (3), rarely (4—5) with ∞ ov. on parietal plac. often united in middle; caps.; no endosp.

B; d; ε; ζ

11. *Ancistrocladineae:* G sunk in and united to axis, 1-loc. with 1 basal ov.; endosp. ruminate, starchy (fam. 29).

28. OPUNTIALES. Succulents, usu. without l., often thorny, with hemicyclic, heterochlam., ☿ reg., or rarely ·|·, fls.; K, C, A ∞, on tubular axis, and $\bar{G}$ (4—∞), 1-loc. with ∞ ov. on parietal plac.; berry-like fr. with ∞ seeds; endosp. little or none.

ζ. **Fls. cyclic; G usu. sunk in hollow axis, and usu. united thereto (Orders 29, 30).**

29. MYRTIFLORAE. Herbs or woody pl., with cyclic heterochlam., rarely apet. or ·|· fls. with concave axis; A in 1 or 2 whorls, sometimes branched and in bundles, G (2—∞) usu. united to axis, rarely 1 free.

1. *Thymelaeineae:* woody pl. rarely herbs, with simple l.; fls. with dish or tubular axis (at least in ☿ and ♀), reg. with (2—4) cpls. free of axis (fams. 1—5).

2. *Myrtineae:* herbs or woody pl. with alt. or opp. l. and fls. with tubular axis and (2—∞) cpls. usu. united to axis; ov. with 1 integ. (fams. 6—17).

29. Ancistrocladaceae: lianes with lanc. l. and racemes or panicles of ☿ reg. fls.; K 5, C 5, slightly united below, A 5—10, $\overline{G}$ (3), only 1 loc. with 1 basal ov.; nut; endosp.

28

1. Cactaceae:

29

1. Geissolomataceae: shrub with opp. evergr. l. and sol. axillary ☿ fls.; K 4, imbr., C o, A 4+4, $\underline{G}$ (4), each with 2 pend. ov.; 1 style; caps; endosp.
2. Penaeaceae: shrubs with small opp. l. and sol. axillary ☿ reg. fls., K 4, valv., C o, A 4, $\underline{G}$ (4), each with 2—4 erect ov.; 1 style; caps.; no endosp.
3. Oliniaceae: shrubs with opp. leathery l. and small ☿ fls. in cymose umbels at ends of twigs; K 4—5, petaloid, C 4—5, smaller, A 4—5, anteposed, $\overline{G}$ (3—5) each with 2—3 axile ov.; 1 style; drupe; no endosp.
4. Thymelaeaceae: shrubs and trees, rarely herbs, with entire alt. or opp. exstip. l. and sol. or racemed or spiked ☿ fls. with cup-like or tubular axis; K 5—4, C 5—4—o, A 5—4 or 10—8, $\underline{G}$ (5—2) or 1, each with 1 pend. ov.; 1 style; endosp. or o.
5. Elaeagnaceae: woody with alt. or opp. entire l. and fls. as last, ☿ or ♂ ♀ with flat or cup-shaped axis; K 4, C usu. o, A 4 or 8, $\underline{G}$ 1 with 1 ascending ov.; nut; endosp. little or none.
6. Lythraceae: herbs and shrubs with simple entire usu. opp. stip. l. and racemes, panicles, or dichasia of ☿, reg. or ·|·, 3—16- usu. 4—6-merous fls. with hollow or tubular axis; K valv., C sometimes o, A twice as many or 1—∞, $\underline{G}$ (2—6), 2—6 rarely 1-loc. each with ∞—2 ov.; caps.; no endosp.
7. Sonneratiaceae: woody pl. with opp. exstip. l. and ☿ or ♂ ♀ reg. fls. with bell-shaped axis; K 4—8, C 4—8 or o, A ∞, $\overline{G}$ (4—15) united to hollow axis, with 1 style, 4—15-loc. with ∞ ov.; caps. or berry-like fr.; no endosp.
8. Punicaceae: woody pl. with entire l. and showy axillary ☿ reg. fls. with top-shaped axis; K, C 5—7, A ∞, G (∞) in superposed whorls with ∞ ov. united to axis, 1 style; berry-like fr.; no endosp.
9. Lecythidaceae: woody pl. with alt. entire exstip. l. and ☿ fls. with hollow axis; K usu. 4—6, C 4—6, rarely more or o, A ∞, ± united at base, bent inwards in bud, $\overline{G}$ (2—6) each with ∞—1 ov.; style 1; fleshy or woody fr.; no endosp.
10. Rhizophoraceae: woody pl. usu. with opp. stip. l. and usu. ☿ reg. fls., sol. or in cymose infls., hypog. to epig.; K 3—16, usu. 4—8, C as many or o, A 8—∞, G usu. (2—5), rarely 6, each with 2—4—∞ pend. axile ov.; fr. usu. with 1 seed per loc.; sometimes viviparous, endosp. or o.

3. *Hippuridineae:* fls. epig. with 1 sta.; 1 cpl. with 1 ov. and no integ. (fam. 18).
4. *Cynomoriineae:* root paras. with epig. fls. with 1 sta., cpl. with 1 ov. with 1 integ. (fam. 19).

30. UMBELLIFLORAE. Fls. usu. in umbels, cyclic, heterochlam.; usu. with 1 whorl of sta., epig., 4—5-, rarely ∞-merous, ☿ reg.; $\overline{G}$ (5—1) or (∞) each with 1 (rarely 2) pend. ov. with 1 integ., rich endosp.

11. Nyssaceae: shrubs with alt. exstip. l. and small ☿ or ♂ ♀ fls. usu. with hollow axis, the ♂ in racemes, the ♀ sol., K 5 or more, C usu. 5, valv., or 0, A twice as many, $\overline{G}$ usu. 1-loc. rarely 6—10-loc. with 1 ov. in each; drupe; endosp.
12. Alangiaceae: shrubs with alt. l. and umbels of ☿ fls.; K $\overline{(4—10)}$, C 4—10, narrow, valv., A 4—10 or 2—4 times as many, $\overline{G}$ 1—2-loc. with 1 pend. ov. in each; fr. drupaceous with 1 seed; endosp.
13. Combretaceae: woody, often climbing, with opp. entire exstip. l. and racemes of ☿ or ♂ ☿ reg. fls.; K, C, 4—3, rarely 6—8 (C may be 0), A 4—5—8—10, rarely ∞, $\overline{G}$ 1-loc. with 2—6 pend. ov.; fr. leathery or drupaceous, often winged; no endosp.
14. Myrtaceae: woody with opp. or alt. entire exstip. l. and ☿ reg. fls.; K, C usu. 4—5, A ∞ sometimes in bundles, $\overline{G}$ (2—5—∞)-loc., each with ∞—1 ov.; style 1; fr. various; no endosp.
15. Melastomaceae: herbs or woody pl. with opp. or whorled exstip. l. with often 3—9 equal nerves, and showy ☿ reg. 3—∞-merous fls. with hollow axis; K=C, A twice as many, anthers usu. opening by pores, connective usu. with appendages, (G) usu.=K, free or united to axis, 1 style; seeds ∞ in caps. or berry; no endosp.
16. Onagraceae: usu. herbs with opp. or alt. exstip. l. and axillary or racemed ☿ usu. reg. fls. with tubular axis; K 2—4, rarely more, C 2—4 or more or 0, A usu. 4—8, $\overline{G}$ usu. (4), each with 1—∞ ov.; 1 style; caps., nut, or berry; endosp. little or 0.
17. Haloragidaceae: herbs often of marsh or water, with inconspic. reg. 4—1-merous ☿ or ♂ ♀ fls.; C often 0, A twice or less, $\overline{G}$ (4), rarely 1; fr. nut- or drupe-like; endosp.
18. Hippuridaceae: water pl. with whorled l. and inconspic. apet. fls., $\overline{G}$ 1 with 1 style and 1 pend. ov.
19. Cynomoriaceae: paras. with rhiz. and ☿ or ♂ ♀ fls.; ♂ with 1 epig. sta., ☿ with 1 pend. ov.

30

1. Araliaceae: woody pl., rarely herbs, with usu. alt. often much divided l., commonly stip., and oil passages, and usu. 5 (3—∞)-merous fls. in heads, umbels, or spikes, often in cpd. infls.; K sometimes indistinct, A=C, $\overline{G}$ (∞—1); fr. berry- or drupe-like with ∞—1 stones; endosp.
2. Umbelliferae: herbs with tap root or rhiz., hollow stem, and alt. usu. much divided, sheathing exstip. l., and usu. ☿ reg. small 5-merous fls. in umbels, simple or cpd.; K often indistinguishable, A=K, $\overline{G}$ (2) with two styles on swollen style base; schizocarp, the mericarps on a carpophore, each usu. with 5 ribs, often with vittae between; oily endosp.
3. Cornaceae: trees or shrubs with opp. or alt. usu. entire exstip. l. and umbels, panicles or heads of small, sometimes ♂ ♀, reg. 4—5—∞-merous fls.; A= or 2—4 times as many as C, $\overline{G}$ (4—1) with epig. disc and usu. 1 ov. each; fr. 1—4-loc. with 1—4 seeds.

A; B

Sympetalae (fl. usu. sympetalous)

A. Fls. sometimes polypetalous; 2 or 1 whorls of sta.; usu. hypog., rarely epig. (Orders 1—3).

1. ERICALES. Woody pl. or herbs with simple l. and ☿ usu. reg. 5—4-merous fls.; C usu. united, A hypog. or epig., rarely united to pets. at base, obdipl., or whorl before C not developed, G 2—∞, usu. before C when equal in number, sup. to inf., ov. with 1 integ.

2. PRIMULALES. Fls. ☿ or ♂ ♀, reg., rarely ·|·, 5—(rarely 4—∞)-merous, usu. with 1 whorl of epipet. sta., rarely also 5 opp. K.; C usu. united, G apparently as many as C, sup. to inf., 1-loc. with ∞—1 ov. on basal or free-central plac.

3. PLUMBAGINALES. Shrubs, undershrubs or herbs with simple l., often with water- or chalk-secreting glands and cpd. infl. of ☿ fls.; C or (C), A in 1 whorl, $\underline{G}$ (5) with 5 stigs., 1-loc. with 1 ov.; endosp. starchy.

B. Fls. sympet. only; sta. sometimes ∞, usu. in 3—2 whorls; fl. usu. hypog. (Order 4).

Sympetalae

1

1. Clethraceae: woody with alt. l. and racemes of ☿ reg., 5-merous obdipl. fls.; C free, A 10 hypog., G̲ (3) each with ∞ ov.; style long with 3 stigs.; caps. 3-valved; endosp.
2. Pyrolaceae: evergr. or saprophytic herbs with alt. l. and ☿ reg. 5-merous obdipl. fls., sol. or in racemes; C free or united, A hypog., G̲ (5—4) with ∞ ov. in each; caps. loculic.; endosp. fleshy.
3. Lennoaceae: root paras. with ∞ ☿ reg. 5—∞-merous fls.; A=C, G̲ (6—14) each with 2 ov. and false partition; drupe with 12—28 stones; endosp.
4. Ericaceae: usu. undershrubs or shrubs with alt. opp. or whorled usu. evergr. l. and single or racemed ☿ 5—4-merous obdipl. fls.; C rarely free, inserted with sta. on disc, anther loc. often with projections, pollen in tetrads, (G) sup. or inf. with axile plac. each with 1—∞ ov., style 1 with capitate stig.; berry, drupe, caps.; endosp.
5. Epacridaceae: shrubs or undershrubs with stiff entire sess. alt. l. and usu. racemes of ☿ reg. 5—4-merous fls.; (C), A=C, epipet. or at base of hypog. disc, thecae with common slit, G̲ usu. (5) each with 1—∞ ov. on axile plac., style 1 with capitate stig.; caps. or drupe; endosp.
6. Diapensiaceae: undershrubs or woody herbs with ☿ reg. fls.; K 5 or (5), C (5), A 10 obdipl., or 5, G̲ (3) each with ∞ ov. on axile plac., style 1; caps.; endosp.

2

1. Theophrastaceae: woody with alt. exstip. l. often crowded at ends of stem or branches, and ☿ or ♂ ♀ reg. rarely ·|· fls.; K 5, C (5), A 5+5 stds., G̲ 1-loc. with ∞ ov. on free-central or basal plac.; drupe with ∞—2 seeds; endosp.
2. Myrsinaceae: woody with often evergr. entire alt. exstip. l., and ☿ or ♂ ♀ reg. fls.; K 5, C (5), A 5 rarely with 5 stds., G̲ to Ḡ, 1-loc. with ∞ ov. on basal or free-central plac.; style 1; drupe with 1 or few seeds; endosp.
3. Primulaceae: herbs with usu. alt. exstip. l. and ☿ reg. rarely ·|· fls.; K (5), C (5), A 5, epipet., anteposed, and rarely 5 stds., G̲ rarely ½-inf., 1-loc. with ∞ ov. on free-central plac.; caps.; endosp.

3

1. Plumbaginaceae:

4. EBENALES. Woody pl. with simple l.; (C), A in 2—3 whorls, or in 1 by abortion, rarely ∞, G with axile plac. and several loc. with 1 or few ov. in each.

1. *Sapotineae:* G̲ completely divided into loc., each with 1 ascending ov. with 1 integ. (fam. 1).

2. *Diospyrineae:* G̲ or ½-inf. not chambered above; ov. with 2 integs. (fams. 2—4).

C. Sympetaly the rule; sta. always in 1 whorl; union of cpls. sometimes small; usu. hypogyny (Order 5).

5. CONTORTAE. Woody pl. or herbs with usu. opp. simple exstip. l. and usu. 5 (rarely 2—6)-merous fls.; usu. (C), rarely C or none, usu. conv., with as many or fewer sta. usu. epipet. at base of C, and G (2).

1. *Oleineae:* sta. 2, ov. with 1 integ. (fam. 1).

2. *Gentianineae:* A = C, G̲ 1—2-loc. usu. with ∞ ov. on axile or parietal plac. with each 1 integ. (fams. 2—5).

4

1. Sapotaceae: woody with simple alt. l., secretory passages, and usu. ☿ fls.; K 4—8 in two whorls, (C) as many in 1 whorl, or twice in 2, sometimes with lat. or dorsal appendages, A in 2 or 3 whorls, outer sometimes stds., (G̲) as many (or twice) as 1 whorl of sta., each with 1 basal or axile ov.; style 1; berry; endosp. or o.
2. Ebenaceae: trees with entire alt. rarely opp. exstip. l., and usu. ♂ ♀ fls., sol. or in few-fld. umbels, 3—more-merous; K persistent, C usu. conv., A as many, or 2-more times as many, free or united in bundles, G̲ (2—16) each with 1—2 pend. ov.; berry with 1 or few seeds; endosp. often ruminate.
3. Symplocaceae: woody pl. with alt. exstip. l. and ☿ 5-merous fls.; C=or twice K, ± united, A epipet. in 1—3 whorls, Ḡ sometimes ½-inf. (5—2) each with 2—4 pend. ov.; style 1; drupe; endosp.
4. Styracaceae: woody pl. with simple alt. l. with stellate or scaly hairs, and small or smallish ☿ fls.; K, C (5—4), A 10—8 united at base or rarely into tube, G̲, rarely ½-inf. (5—3) each with 1 or few ov., 3—5-loc. below, 1-loc. above; drupe, indeh. fr. or caps., with 1 or few seeds; endosp.

5

1. Oleaceae: woody, sometimes climbing, rarely herbs, with opp. or whorled simple or pinnate exstip. l., and cpd. infls. of ☿ or ♂ ♀ reg. 2—6-merous fls.; C 4—5—6 or o, free or united, imbr. or valv., A 2 epipet. or hypog., G̲ (2) each usu. with 2, rarely 1 or 4—8 axile ov.; caps., berry or drupe; endosp. or o.
2. Loganiaceae: woody, rarely herbs, with opp. or whorled often stip. l. and cymose umbels of ☿ or ♂ ♀ reg. fls.; K usu. imbr., C (4—5—∞), valv., imbr., or conv., A=C or 1, G̲ (2) rarely more with ∞—1 axile ov. and 1 style; caps.; endosp.
3. Gentianaceae: herbs, rarely shrubs with opp. entire exstip. l. and cymose infls. of usu. ☿ reg. 4—5-merous fls.; K or (K), (C) usu. conv., A as many, G̲ (2) usu. with ∞ ov. in 1-loc. ovary; caps.; endosp.
4. Apocynaceae: woody or herbs with simple usu. opp. entire l., and latex, and cymose infls. of ☿ reg. 5—4-merous fls.; (C) usu. conv., A epipet., G̲ (2) often only united by style; fr. various, endosperm thin or o.
5. Asclepiadaceae: herbs or shrubby, often climbing, some succulent, with opp. or whorled, rarely alt. exstip. l., and ☿ reg. fls. sol. or in cymose umbels; K 5, C (5), usu. conv., sometimes with appendages forming a corona, A 5 usu. united below, usu. with appendages forming a corona, pollen usu. in pollinia with translators, G̲ (2) enclosed in sta. tube, with ∞ rarely few or 1 pend. ov., united by style above; fr. 2 follicles, seeds usu. hairy; endosp.

D; a

D. Fls. always sympetalous, with 1 whorl of sta., often ·|·, with usu. 2 median cpls. fully united (Orders 6—10).

a. *K, C hypogynous,* with few exceptions (*Orders* 6, 7).

6. TUBIFLORAE. Usu. herbs, fls. typically with 4 isomerous whorls or usu. with oligomerous G, and if ·|· also oligomerous A; sta. epipet., ov. with 1 integ.

1. *Convolvulineae:* l. usu. alt., fls. usu. reg.; cpls. with few or 2 ov. with micropyle downwards; fr. rarely 4 nutlets (fams. 1, 2).

2. *Boragininеae:* as last, but micropyle facing upwards; caps. or drupe, or 4 nutlets (fams. 3, 4).

3. *Verbenineae:* l. usu. opp. or whorled, fls. usu. ·|·; cpls. with 2, rarely 1, ov.; fr. drupe or drupe-like, or 4 nutlets (fams. 5, 6).

4. *Solanineae:* fls. ·|· or reg. usu. 5-merous; A 5—4—2, G rarely (5), usu. (2) with usu. ∞, rarely 2—1 ov.; fr. usu. caps., never splitting to base, rarely berry or drupe (fams. 7—17).

A. Fr. splitting into 5 or many mericarps (fam. 7).

B. Fr. 2-, rarely 5—∞-loc., or 1-loc. (fams. 8—17).

1. Vascular bundles bicollateral (fam. 8).

2. Vascular bundles collateral (fams. 9—17).

i. G 2-loc. with ∞ to few ov. (fams. 9—11).

6

1. Convolvulaceae: usu. herbs with alt. l., often twining, usu. with large ☿ reg. 5—4-merous fls.; A epipet., $\underline{G}$ (2) rarely (3—5) each with 2 basal erect ov. on axile plac.; caps.; endosp.
2. Polemoniaceae: usu. herbs with alt. or opp. exstip. l. and ☿ usu. reg. 5-merous fls.; C usu. conv., $\underline{G}$ (3) rarely (2) or (5) each with ∞—1 erect ov.; caps.; endosp.
3. Hydrophyllaceae: herbs with alt. rarely opp. l. and scorpioid cymes of ☿ reg. 5-merous fls.; A 5, $\underline{G}$ (2) each with ∞—2 sessile or pend. ov.; caps.; endosp.
4. Boraginaceae: herbs or woody pl., often roughly hairy, with usu. alt. simple l., and scorpioid cymes of ☿ reg. 5 (rarely more)-merous fls.; $\underline{G}$ (2) each with 2 ov., 2-loc., usu. with false septum; fr. drupaceous or of 4 nutlets; endosp. or none.
5. Verbenaceae: herbs or woody pl. with usu. opp. or whorled entire or divided l. and cymose umbels of ☿ usu. ·|· 5—4 (rarely more)-merous fls.; (K), (C) often 2-lipped, A usu. 4 didynamous, or 2, $\underline{G}$ (2) rarely more, each with 2 ov., usu. 4-loc. by formation of secondary septa, style 1; drupe or schizocarp; usu. no endosp.
6. Labiatae: herbs or shrubs with decussate or whorled exstip. l. and cymose infls. often condensed in the axils into seeming whorls of ☿ ·|· 5-merous fls.; K (5), C usu. 2-lipped, A 4 didynamous or 2 with or without 2 stds., $\underline{G}$ (2) each with 2 erect ov., infolded between them; fr. of 4 nutlets; endosp. little or none.
7. Nolanaceae: herbs or undershrubs with alt. l. and sol. or racemed ☿ reg. fls.; K, C (5), A 5, $\underline{G}$ 5 with ∞ ov., divided by long. or transv. constrictions into 1—7-ovuled sections; endosp.

8. Solanaceae: herbs or shrubs with alt. l. and term. sol. or cymosely umbelled ☿ usu. reg. 5-merous fls.; A 5, $\underline{G}$ (2) obliquely placed, each with ∞—1 ov. on axile plac., style 1; berry or caps.; endosp.
9. Scrophulariaceae: herbs or shrubs, rarely trees, with alt. opp. or whorled l., and variously arranged fls., never term., ☿, ± ·|·, 5-merous fls.; A usu. 4 or 2, $\underline{G}$ (2) median with each ∞ or few ov. on axile plac., and 1 style; caps. or berry; endosp.
10. Bignoniaceae: woody pl. often climbing, with usu. opp. often cpd. l. and showy ☿ ·|· 5-merous fls., often in cpd. infls.; A 4 or 2, sometimes with 3—1 stds., $\underline{G}$ (2) median with ∞ ov., 2- or 1-loc., style 1; caps. or fleshy fr.; no endosp.

D; a; b; *α*

ii. G 1-loc. with ± parietal plac. and ∞ ov. (fams. 12—15).

iii. G rarely 2-loc., usu. 1-loc. with basal central plac. and ∞ ov. (fam. 16).

iv. G 2- or 1-loc., in each 1 pend. ov., or 1 pend. ov. only (fam. 17).

5. *Acanthineae:* fls. usu. ·|·, typically 5-merous; A 4 or 2, G̲ (2) with usu. ∞ ov.; caps. loculicidal to very base (fam. 18).

6. *Myoporineae:* woody with alt. or opp. l. and fls. reg. or ·|·, 5-merous; G̲ (2) later 4-loc., each with 2—4—∞ ov., or (2—∞) each with 1 pend. ov. with micropyle upwards; drupe; endosp. thin or none (fam. 19).

7. *Phrymineae:* herbs, fls. ·|·; G̲ 1 with 1 orthotr. ascending ov. (fam. 20).

7. PLANTAGINALES. Usu. herbs, rarely shrubby, with usu. alt. l.; fls. ☿ or ♂ ♀, reg., 4-merous; K (4), C (4), membranous, A 4, epipet., G̲ (2) or 1, 4—1-loc. with few or 1 anatr. ov.; caps. or nut; endosp.

b. *P epigynous* (*Orders* 8—10).

α. **Sta. free (Order 8).**

8. RUBIALES. Woody pl. or herbs with opp. usu. simple l. and usu. reg. 5—4-merous fls.; Ḡ 1-(or more)-loc., each with ∞—1 anatr. ov.

A. Sta. = C segments (fams. 1—3).

11. Pedaliaceae: herbs with glandular hairs and opp. l. (sometimes alt. above) and axillary or racemed ☿ ·|· 5-merous fls.; A 4 or 2, $\underline{G}$ (2) rarely (3—4) or $\overline{G}$, each with ∞ ov., 2—4-loc. transv. divided with axile plac.; caps. or nut; thin endosp.
12. Martyniaceae: as last, but anther thecae spurred; $\underline{G}$ with 2 bilobed parietal plac.; caps.; racemes; thin endosp.
13. Orobanchaceae: paras. herbs with scaly l. and term. or racemed ☿ ·|· 5-merous fls.; C 2-lipped, A 4 didynamous, $\underline{G}$ (2), rarely (3), each with 2 parietal plac. sometimes united in middle, and ∞ ov., 1 style; caps.; endosp.
14. Gesneriaceae: herbs or woody pl. with opp. simple l. and showy sol. or cymosely umbelled ☿ ·|· 5-merous fls.; C 2-lipped, A 4 or 2 with sometimes 1—3 stds., $\underline{G}$ to $\overline{G}$ (2), 1-loc. with parietal plac. and ∞ ov.; caps. or berry; endosp. or not.
15. Columelliaceae: woody pl. with opp. entire l. and cymose umbels of ☿ nearly reg. 5—8-merous fls.; A 2, $\underline{G}$ (2) with ∞ ov. on 2 parietal bilobed plac.; caps. 4-valved; endosp.
16. Lentibulariaceae: herbs, usu. of water or damp ground, with ☿ ·|· 5-merous fls.; C 2-lipped, A usu. 2, $\underline{G}$ (2) usu. 1-loc. with basal free plac. and ∞ ov.; caps. 2—4-valved, ∞ or 1-seeded; no endosp.
17. Globulariaceae: herbs with rad. l. and spherical heads or spikes of ☿ 5-merous ·|· fls.; A 4 or 2, $\underline{G}$ (2) 1-loc. each with 1 ov., or 1 ov. only, 1 style; 1-seeded nut; endosp.
18. Acanthaceae: herbs or shrubs with opp. l. and spikes, racemes or cymose umbels of ☿ ·|· 5-merous fls.; K free or united, C reg. or ·|·, A 4 or 2, sometimes with 1—3 stds., $\underline{G}$ (2) median, each with ∞—2 ov.; caps. loculicidal to very base; seeds usu. with no endosp. and with jaculators.
19. Myoporaceae:

20. Phrymaceae:

7

1. Plantaginaceae:

8

1. Rubiaceae: herbs or woody pl. with decussate entire l. and inter-petiolar stips. sometimes = l., and usu. ☿ reg. fls. in cymes often condensed to heads, 5—4 (rarely more)-merous; K usu. open, C valv. or conv., $\overline{G}$ (2) each with 1—∞ ov., style 1; fr. various; endosp. or 0.

B. Sta. fewer than C segments, $\overline{G}$ always with only 1 fertile loc. and 1 pend. ov. (fams. 4, 5).

β. Sta. close together or partly united (Orders 9, 10).

9. CUCURBITALES. Fls. typically 5-merous, usu. ♂ ♀ reg., with cup-like axis; A 5 free, at edge of axis, or each 2 united, or all 5 in a central synandrium, $\overline{G}$ usu. (3), 3-loc. usu. with ∞ ov. and usu. forked stigs.; fr. berry-like, no endosp.

10. CAMPANULATAE. Usu. herbs, rarely woody, with typically 5-merous fls. with 1 whorl of sta. and usu. fewer cpls.; anthers with 2-loc. thecae, often united, $\overline{G}$ or $\underline{G}$ with several loc. and ∞—1 ov. in each, or 1-loc. with 1 ov.

2. Caprifoliaceae: woody with opp. usu. exstip. l. and ☿ reg. or ·|· 5-merous fls.; (C), $\overline{G}$ (2—5) each with 1—∞ axile pend. ov.; fr. usu. berry- or drupe-like; endosp.
3. Adoxaceae: rhiz. herb; stems with 2 opp. l. and 5—7-fld. cyme of ☿ homochlam. fls. (or with aborted K); term. fl. 4 (5)-, lat. 5 (6)-merous, all with 2 bracteoles; A 4—5—6 split to base, G (3—4—5) ½-inf. each with 1 pend. ov.; drupe; endosp.
4. Valerianaceae: herbs, rarely shrubby, with opp. exstip. l. and cymose umbels or heads of ☿ or ♂ ♀ fls. without plane of symmetry; K indistinct in fl., later enlarging to pappus, C (5) or (3—4), often spurred at base, A 1—4, $\overline{G}$ (3), 1 developed with 1 pend. ov.; style 1; no endosp.
5. Dipsacaceae: herbs or undershrubs with opp. exstip. l. and cymose heads or umbels of ☿ usu. ·|· fls. with epicalyx; A 4 or less, $\overline{G}$ (2), 1-loc. with 1 pend. ov. and 1 style; endosp.

9

1. Cucurbitaceae:

10

1. Campanulaceae: herbs or woody pl. usu. with alt. exstip. l., latex, and often showy ☿ reg. or ·|· 5-merous fls.; C usu. united, A free or united with intr. anthers, $\overline{G}$ usu. (2—5) with ∞ ov., style 1, rarely 1-loc.; fr. caps. or berry-like; endosp.
2. Goodeniaceae: herbs or shrubs with simple l. and ☿ usu. ·|· 5-merous fls.; A free or epipet., G usu. inf., 2- rarely 1-loc. with 1—2 or many ov. in each; style with pollen cup; fr. caps.-like; endosp.
3. Brunoniaceae: herb with rad. entire exstip. l., and blue ☿ reg. 5-merous fls. in heads; C cylindrical, A 5 with united anthers, $\underline{G}$ 1, 1-loc., style simple with pollen cup; no endosp.
4. Stylidiaceae: herbs with simple exstip. l. and ☿ or ♂ ♀ usu. ·|· 5-merous fls.; C usu. united, A 3—2 free or united to style, with extr. anthers, $\overline{G}$ (2) 2- or 1-loc.; fr. septicidal or indeh.; endosp.
5. Calyceraceae: herbs or undershrubs with alt. exstip. l. and ☿ or ♂ ♀ reg. or ·|· 4—6-merous fls. in heads surrounded by bracts; A united but anthers free, $\overline{G}$ 1-loc. with 1 pend. ov.; style 1; little endosp.
6. Compositae: herbs, shrubs or rarely trees with usu. alt., rarely opp. l. and ☿ or ♂ ♀ reg. or ·|· 5-merous fls. in heads or short spikes, with invol.; K usu. repres. by hairs of pappus, C often ·|·, 2-lipped or strap-shaped, A at base epipet., anthers intr. united, $\overline{G}$ (2) median, 1-loc. with 1 erect ov., and 1 style with 2 stigs.; achene; no endosp.

SYSTEM OF BENTHAM AND HOOKER, 1862—93.

I. Dicotyledones (as above).

I. **Polypetalae** (fl. usually with two whorls of perianth, the inner polyphyllous: exceptions as in Engler's system):

SERIES I. THALAMIFLORAE. Sepals usu. distinct and separate, free from ovary; petals 1-, 2- to ∞-seriate, hypog.; sta. hypog., rarely inserted on a short or long torus or on a disc; ovary superior.

Order 1. *Ranales* (sta. rarely definite; cpls. free or immersed in torus, very rarely united; micropyle usu. inferior; embryo minute in fleshy albumen:

1. Ranunculaceae. 2. Dilleniaceae. 3. Calycanthaceae. 4. Magnoliaceae. 5. Anonaceae. 6. Menispermaceae. 7. Berberideae. 8. Nymphaeaceae.

Order 2. *Parietales* (sta. definite or ∞; cpls. united into a 1-loc. ovary with parietal placentae, rarely spuriously 2- or more-loc. by prolongation of placentae):

9. Sarraceniaceae. 10. Papaveraceae. 11. Cruciferae. 12. Capparideae. 13. Resedaceae. 14. Cistineae. 15. Violarieae. 16. Canellaceae. 17. Bixineae.

Order 3. *Polygalinae* (K and C 5, rarely 4 or 3; sta. as many or twice as many as petals; ovary 2-, rarely 1- or more-loc.; endosperm fleshy, rarely absent; herbs or shrubs with exstip. l.):

18. Pittosporeae. 19. Tremandreae. 20. Polygaleae. 21. Vochysiaceae.

Order 4. *Caryophyllinae* (fl. regular; K 2—5, rarely 6; petals usu. as many; sta. as many or twice as many, rarely more or fewer; ovary 1-loc. or imperfectly 2—5-loc.; placenta free-central, rarely parietal; embryo usu. curved in floury albumen):

22. Frankeniaceae. 23. Caryophylleae. 24. Portulaceae. 25. Tamariscineae.

Order 5. *Guttiferales* (fl. regular; K and C usu. 4—5, imbr.; sta. usu. ∞; ovary 3—∞-loc., rarely 2-loc. or of 1 cpl.; placentae on inner angles of loculi):

26. Elatineae. 27. Hypericineae. 28. Guttiferae. 29. Ternstroemiaceae. 30. Dipterocarpeae. 31. Chlaenaceae.

Order 6. *Malvales* (fl. rarely irregular; K 5, rarely 2—4, free or united, valvate or imbr.; petals as many or 0; sta. usu. ∞, monadelphous; ovary 3—∞-loc., rarely of 1 cpl.; ovules in inner angles of loculi):

32. Malvaceae. 33. Sterculiaceae. 34. Tiliaceae.

SERIES II. DISCIFLORAE. Sepals distinct or united, free or adnate to ovary; disc usu. conspicuous as a ring or cushion, or spread over the base of the calyx-tube, or confluent with the base of the ovary, or broken up into glands; sta. usu. definite, inserted upon or at the outer or inner base of the disc; ovary superior.

Order 7. *Geraniales* (fls. often irregular; disc usu. annular, adnate to the sta. or reduced to glands, rarely o; ovary of several cpls., syncarpous or sub-apocarpous; ovules 1—2, rarely ∞, ascending or pendulous; raphe usu. ventral):

35. Lineae. 36. Humiriaceae. 37. Malpighiaceae. 38. Zygophylleae. 39. Geraniaceae. 40. Rutaceae. 41. Simarubeae. 42. Ochnaceae. 43. Burseraceae. 44. Meliaceae. 45. Chailletiaceae.

Order 8. *Olacales* (fl. regular, ☿ or unisex.; calyx small; disc free, cupular or annular, rarely glandular or o; ovary entire, 1—∞-loc.; ovules 1—3 in each loc., pend.; raphe dorsal, integ. confluent with the nucellus; endosp. usu. copious, fleshy; embryo small; shrubs or trees; leaves alt., simple, exstip.):

46. Olacineae. 47. Ilicineae. 48. Cyrilleae.

Order 9. *Celastrales* (fl. regular, ☿; corolla hypo- or peri-gynous; disc tumid, adnate to base of calyx-tube or lining it; sta. = petals or fewer, rarely twice as many, perig. or inserted outside the disc or on its edge; ovary usu. entire; ovules 1—2 in each loc., erect with ventral raphe; leaves simple, except in fam. 52):

49. Celastrineae. 50. Stackhousieae. 51. Rhamneae. 52. Ampelideae.

Order 10. *Sapindales* (fl. often irregular and unisex.; disc tumid, adnate to base of calyx or lining its tube; sta. perig. or inserted upon the disc or between it and the ovary, usu. definite; ovary entire, lobed or apocarpous; ovules 1—2 in each loc. usu. ascending with a ventral raphe, or reversed, or pend. from a basal funicle, rarely ∞ horizontal; seed usu. exalb.; embryo often curved or crumpled; shrubs or trees, l. usu. compound):

53. Sapindaceae. 54. Sabiaceae. 55. Anacardiaceae.

Anomalous fams. or rather genera:

56. Coriarieae. 57. Moringeae.

SERIES III. CALYCIFLORAE. Sepals united, rarely free, often adnate to ovary; petals 1-seriate, peri- or epi-gynous; disc adnate to base of calyx, rarely tumid or raised into a torus or gynophore; sta. perig., usu. inserted on or beneath the outer margin of the disc: ovary often inferior.

Order 11. *Rosales* (fl. usu. ☿, regular or irregular; cpls. 1 or more, usu. quite free in bud, sometimes variously united afterwards with the calyx-tube or enclosed in the swollen top of the peduncle; styles usu. distinct):

58. Connaraceae. 59. Leguminosae. 60. Rosaceae. 61. Saxifrageae. 62. Crassulaceae. 65. Droseraceae. 64. Hamamelideae. 65. Bruniaceae. 66. Halorageae.

Order 12. *Myrtales* (fl. regular or sub-regular, usu. ☿; ovary syncarpous, usu. inferior; style undivided, or very rarely styles free; placentae axile or apical, rarely basal; l. simple, usu. quite entire, rarely 3-foliolate in fam. 68):

67. Rhizophoraceae. 68. Combretaceae. 69. Myrtaceae. 70. Melastomaceae. 71. Lythrarieae. 72. Onagrarieae.

Order 13. *Passiflorales* (fl. usu. regular, ☿ or unisex.; ovary usu. inferior, syncarpous, 1-loc. with parietal placentae, sometimes 3- or more-loc. by the produced placentae; styles free or connate):

73. Samydaceae. 74. Loaseae. 75. Turneraceae. 76. Passifloreae. 77. Cucurbitaceae. 78. Begoniaceae. 79. Datisceae.

Order 14. *Ficoidales* (fl. regular or sub-regular; ovary syncarpous, inferior to superior, 1-loc. with parietal, or 2—∞-loc. with axile or basal placentae; embryo curved, with endosp., or cyclical, or oblique with no endosp.):

80. Cacteae. 81. Ficoideae.

Order 15. *Umbellales* (fl. regular, usu. ☿; sta. usu. definite; ovary inferior, 1—2—∞-loc.; ovules solitary, pend. in each loc. from its apex; styles free or united at base; seeds with endosp.; embryo usu. minute):

82. Umbelliferae. 83. Araliaceae. 84. Cornaceae.

II. **Gamopetalae** (fl. usu. with two whorls of perianth, the inner gamophyllous; exceptions as in Engler's system):

SERIES I. INFERAE. Ovary inferior; sta. usu. as many as corolla-lobes.

Order 1. *Rubiales* (fl. regular or irregular; sta. epipet.; ovary 2—∞-loc., with 1—∞ ovules in each loc.):

85. Caprifoliaceae. 86. Rubiaceae.

Order 2. *Asterales* (fl. regular or irregular; sta. epipet.; ovary 1-loc., 1-ovuled, sometimes > 1-loc. but with only 1 ovule):

87. Valerianeae. 88. Dipsaceae. 89. Calycereae. 90. Compositae.

Order 3. *Campanales* (fl. usu. irregular; sta. usu. epig.; ovary 2—6-loc., with usu. ∞ ovules in each loc.):

91. Stylidieae. 92. Goodenovieae. 93. Campanulaceae.

SERIES II. HETEROMERAE. Ovary usu. superior; sta. epipet. or free from corolla, opp. or alt. to its segments, or twice as many, or ∞; cpls. > 2.

Order 4. *Ericales* (fl. usu. regular and hypog.; sta. as many or twice as many as petals; ovary 1—∞-loc. with 1—∞ ovules in each loc.; seeds minute):

94. Ericaceae. 95. Vaccinieae. 96. Monotropeae. 97. Epacrideae. 98. Diapensiaceae. 99. Lennoaceae.

Order 5. *Primulales* (corolla usu. regular and hypog., sta. usu. = and opp. to corolla-lobes; ovary 1-loc. with free-central or basal placenta and 1—∞ ovules):

100. Plumbagineae. 101. Primulaceae. 102. Myrsineae.

Order 6. *Ebenales* (corolla usu. hypog.; sta. usu. more than corolla-lobes, or if as many, then opposite to them, except in 103, often ∞; ovary 2—∞-loc.; ovules usu. few; trees or shrubs):

103. Sapotaceae. 104. Ebenaceae. 105. Styraceae.

SERIES III. BICARPELLATAE. Ovary usu. superior; sta. as many as or fewer than corolla-lobes, alt. to them; cpls. 2, rarely 1 or 3.

Order 7. *Gentianales* (corolla regular, hypog.; sta. epipet.; l. generally opp.):

106. Oleaceae. 107. Salvadoraceae. 108. Apocynaceae. 109. Asclepiadaceae. 110. Loganiaceae. 111. Gentianaceae.

Order 8. *Polemoniales* (corolla regular, hypog.; sta. = corolla-lobes, epipet.; ovary 1—5-loc.; l. generally alt.):

112. Polemoniaceae. 113. Hydrophyllaceae. 114. Boragineae. 115. Convolvulaceae. 116. Solanaceae.

Order 9. *Personales* (fl. usu. very irregular; corolla hypog., often 2-lipped; sta. generally fewer than corolla-lobes, usu. 4, didynamous, or 2; ovary 1—2- or rarely 4-loc.; ovules usu. ∞):

117. Scrophularineae. 118. Orobanchaceae. 119. Lentibularieae. 120. Columelliaceae. 121. Gesneraceae. 122. Bignoniaceae. 123. Pedalineae. 124. Acanthaceae.

Order 10. *Lamiales* (corolla usu. 2-lipped, hypog., rarely regular; sta. as in preceding; ovary 2—4-loc.; ovules solitary in loc., or rarely > 1 in fams. 125 and 127; fruit a drupe or nutlets):

125. Myoporineae. 126. Selagineae. 127. Verbenaceae. 128. Labiatae.

Anomalous Fam.

129. Plantagineae.

III. **Monochlamydeae or Incompletae** (fl. usu. with one whorl of perianth, commonly sepaloid, or none):

SERIES I. CURVEMBRYAE. Terrestrial plants with usu. ☿ fls.; sta. generally = perianth-segments; ovule usu. solitary; embryo curved in floury endosp.

130. Nyctagineae. 131. Illecebraceae. 132. Amarantaceae. 133. Chenopodiaceae. 134. Phytolaccaceae. 135. Batideae. 136. Polygonaceae.

SERIES II. MULTIOVULATAE AQUATICAE. Aquatic plants with syncarpous ovary and ∞ ovules.

137. Podostemaceae.

SERIES III. MULTIOVULATAE TERRESTRES. Terrestrial plants with syncarpous ovary and ∞ ovules.

138. Nepenthaceae. 139. Cytinaceae. 140. Aristolochieae.

SERIES IV. MICREMBRYAE. Ovary syn- or apo-carpous; ovules usu. solitary; embryo very small, surrounded by endosp.

141. Piperaceae. 142. Chloranthaceae. 143. Myristiceae. 144. Monimiaceae.

SERIES V. DAPHNALES. Ovary usu. of 1 cpl.; ovules solitary or few; perianth perfect, sepaloid, in 1 or 2 whorls; sta. perig.

145. Laurineae. 146. Proteaceae. 147. Thymelaeaceae. 148. Penaeaceae. 149. Elaeagnaceae.

SERIES VI. ACHLAMYDOSPOREAE. Ovary 1-loc., 1—3-ovuled; ovules not apparent till after fert.; seed with endosp., but no testa, adnate to receptacle or pericarp.

150. Loranthaceae. 151. Santalaceae. 152. Balanophoreae.

SERIES VII. UNISEXUALES. Fls. unisex.; ovary syncarpous or of 1 cpl.; ovules solitary or 2 per cpl.; endosp. or none; perianth sepaloid or much reduced or absent.

153. Euphorbiaceae. 154. Balanopseae. 155. Urticaceae. 156. Platanaceae. 157. Leitnerieae. 158. Juglandeae. 159. Myricaceae. 160. Casuarineae. 161. Cupuliferae.

SERIES VIII. ANOMALOUS FAMILIES. Unisex. fams. of doubtful or unknown affinities.

162. Salicaceae. 163. Lacistemaceae. 164. Empetraceae. 165. Ceratophylleae.

II. Monocotyledones (as in Engler).

SERIES I. MICROSPERMAE. Inner perianth petaloid; ovary inferior with 3 parietal or rarely axile placentae; seeds minute, exalb.

169. Hydrocharideae. 170. Burmanniaceae. 171. Orchideae.

SERIES II. EPIGYNAE. Perianth partly petaloid; ovary usu. inferior; endosp. abundant.

172. Scitamineae. 173. Bromeliaceae. 174. Haemodoraceae. 175. Irideae. 176. Amaryllideae. 177. Taccaceae. 178. Dioscoreaceae.

SERIES III. CORONARIEAE. Inner perianth petaloid; ovary usu. free, superior; endosp. abundant.

179. Roxburghiaceae. 180. Liliaceae. 181. Pontederiaceae. 182. Philydraceae. 183. Xyrideae. 184. Mayacaceae. 185. Commelinaceae. 186. Rapateaceae.

SERIES IV. CALYCINAE. Perianth sepaloid, herbaceous or membranous; ovary &c. as in III.

187. Flagellarieae. 188. Juncaceae. 189. Palmae.

SERIES V. NUDIFLORAE. Perianth none, or represented by hairs or scales; cpl. 1 or several syncarpous; ovary superior; ovules 1—∞; endosp. usu. present.

190. Pandaneae. 191. Cyclanthaceae. 192. Typhaceae. 193. Aroideae. 194. Lemnaceae.

SERIES VI. APOCARPAE. Perianth in 1 or 2 whorls, or none; ovary superior, apocarp.; no endosp.

195. Triurideae. 196. Alismaceae. 197. Naiadaceae.

SERIES VII. GLUMACEAE. Fls. solitary, sessile in the axils of bracts and arranged in heads or spikelets with bracts; perianth of scales, or none; ovary usu. 1-loc., 1-ovuled; endosp.

198. Eriocauleae. 199. Centrolepideae. 200. Restiaceae. 201. Cyperaceae. 202. Gramineae.

INDEX TO ORDERS AND GROUPS OF HIGHER RANK.